ANNUAL REVIEW
OF PHYSIOLOGY

ANNUAL REVIEW
OF PHYSIOLOGY

VOLUME 62, 2000

JOSEPH F. HOFFMAN, *Editor*
Yale University School of Medicine

PAUL De WEER, *Associate Editor*
University of Pennsylvania School of Medicine

www.AnnualReviews.org   science@annurev.org   650-493-4400

ANNUAL REVIEWS
4139 El Camino Way • P.O. Box 10139 • Palo Alto, California 94303-0139

ANNUAL REVIEWS
Palo Alto, California, USA

International Standard Serial Number: 0066-4278
International Standard Book Number: 0-8243-0362-8
Library of Congress Catalog Card Number: 39-15404

Annual Review and publication titles are registered trademarks of Annual Reviews.

⊛ The paper used in this publication meets the minimum requirements of American National Standards for Information Sciences—Permanence of Paper for Printed Library Materials. ANSI Z39.48-1992.

Annual Reviews and the Editors of its publications assume no responsibility for the statements expressed by the contributors to this *Annual Review*.

Typeset by Impressions Book and Journal Services, Inc., Madison, WI
Printed and Bound in the United States of America

PREFACE

As our readers will certainly take note, the *Annual Review of Physiology* enters the 21st century with the publication of this volume. As we begin the new century, I know that our editiorial board shares with all physiologists a genuine optimism for the future development of our field. To highlight this transition, members of our board were invited to write chapters that look retrospectively as well as prospectively about their respective fields. These are grouped together in the back of the book under the heading Views and Overviews of the 20th Century. The task turned out to be more daunting than anticipated and resulted in an interesting if not eclectic collection of articles, which I found both informative and stimulating to read. I encourage all of our readers to take a look.

Other than the above, this volume presents in its usual sectionalized thematic format, with recent advances in each of the respective fields of our discipline. We are also pleased to have our prefatory chapter written by Louis Sokoloff. In addition we have included two Special Topic sections. The first is on the Use of Transgenic Models in Cardiovascular Function, edited by Evangelia Kranias. The chapters presented here are meant to complement those contained in the regular section on Cardiovascular Physiology. A Commentary on this special topic is given at the end of the book.

The second Special Topic presents a breakaway subject not normally considered to fall within the corpus of physiology. This special topic is entitled Language Faculty as an Organ and is written by Stephen R. Anderson and David Lightfoot. Inclusion of this chapter emphasizes our aim to bring to our readers advances in areas they may infrequently encounter or with which they may not be familiar. In my view this chapter is a harbinger of future development of our field.

Readers are encouraged to send the editorial board comments about our published volumes as well as suggestions for articles/subjects that we should consider in the future. We can be reached at our web site AnnualReviews.org.

JOSEPH F. HOFFMAN
Editor

CONTENTS

RELATED ARTICLES

From the *Annual Review of Biochemistry*, Volume 68, 1999:

The Molecular Basis of Hypertension, David L. Garbers and Susan K. Dubois

Cellular and Molecular Biology of the Aquaporin Water Channels, Mario Borgnia, Søren Nielsen, Andreas Engel, and Peter Agre

Charting the Fate of the "Good Cholesterol:" Identification and Characterization of the High-Density Lipoprotein Receptor SR-B, Monty Krieger

Structural Mechanisms of Muscle Contraction, M. A. Geeves and K. C. Holmes

Functions of Cell Surface Heparan Sulfate Proteoglycans, Merton Bernfield, Martin Götte, Pyong Woo Park, Ofer Reizes, Marilyn L. Fitzgerald, John Lincecum, and Masahiro Zako

Membrane Fusion and Exocytosis, Reinhard Jahn and Thomas C. Südhof

From the *Annual Review of Cell Development Biology*, Volume 15, 1999:

Vacuolar Import of Proteins and Organelles from the Cytoplasm, Daniel J. Klionsky and Yoshinori Ohsumi

Cooperation Between Microtubule- and Actin-Based Motor Proteins, Susan S. Brown

Visual Transduction in Drosophila, Craig Montell

Regulation of Mammalian O_2 Homeostasis by Hypoxia-Inducible Factor, Gregg L. Semenza

Transport Between the Cell Nucleus and the Cytoplasm, Dirk Görlich and Ulrike Kutay

Synaptic Vesicle Biogenesis, Matthew J. Hannah, Anne A. Schmidt, and Wieland B. Huttner

The Translocan: A Dynamic Gateway at the ER Membrane, Arthur E. Johnson and Michael A. van Waes

From the *Annual Review of Medicine*, Volume 51, 2000:

Genetics of Psychiatric Disease, Wade H. Berrettini

Genetic Disorders of Iron Metabolism: Clinical Implications, Sujit Sheth and Gary M. Brittenham

Acupuncture: An Evidence-Based Review of the Clinical Literature, David J. Mayer

From the *Annual Review of Neuroscience*, Volume 23, 2000:

Microtubule-Based Transport Systems in Neurons: The Roles of Kinesins and Dyneins, Lawrence S. B. Goldstein and Zhaohuai Yang

Gain of Function Mutants: Ion Channels and G Protein-Coupled Receptors, Henry A. Lester and Andreas Karschin

Adaptation in Hair Cells, Ruth Anne Eatock

Guanylyl Cyclases as a Family of Putative Odorant Receptors, Angelia D. Gibson and David L. Garbers

Control of Cell Divisions in the Nervous System: Symmetry and Asymmetry, Bingwei Lu, Lily Jan, and Yuh-Nung Jan

Consciousness, John R. Searle

Molecular Genetics of Circadian Rhythms in Mammals, David P. King and Joseph S. Takahashi

Pain Genes?: Natural Variation and Transgenic Mutants, Jeffrey S. Mogil, Lei Yu, and Allan I. Basbaum

From the *Annual Review of Nutrition*, Volume 19, 1999:

Carrier-Mediated Membrane Transport of Folates in Mammalian Cells, F. M. Sirotnak and Berend Tolner

Energetics of Free-Ranging Mammals, Reptiles, and Birds, K. A. Nagy, I. A. Girard, and T. K. Brown

Regulation of Glucose Production by the Liver, Robert S. Nordlie, James D. Foster, and Alex J. Lange

Metabolic Engineering with Recombinant Adenoviruses, Peter A. Antinozzi, Hai K. Berman, Robert M. O'Doherty, and Christopher B. Newgard

From the *Annual Review of Pharmacology and Toxicology*, Volume 40, 2000:

Pharmacology of Cloned P2X Receptors, R. Alan North and Annmarie Surprenant

Targets of Drug Action, A. S. V. Burgen

Sequencing the Entire Genomes of Free-Living Organisms: The Foundation of Pharmacology in the New Millennium, Samuel Broder and J. Craig Venter

The Regulator of G Protein Signaling (RGS) Family, Luc de Vries, Bin Zheng, Thierry Fischer, Eric Elenko, and Marilyn Farquhar

Molecular Mechanisms and Regulation of Opiod Receptor Signaling, Ping Yee Law, Horace Loh, and Yung Wong

Louis Sokoloff

Annu. Rev. Physiol. 2000. 62:1–24

IN VIVO VERITAS: Probing Brain Function Through the Use of Quantitative In Vivo Biochemical Techniques[1]

Louis Sokoloff

Laboratory of Cerebral Metabolism, National Institute of Mental Health, Bethesda, Maryland 20892; e-mail: louis@shiloh.nimh.nih.gov

Key Words   local cerebral blood flow, local cerebral energy metabolism, functional brain imaging, deoxyglucose method, metabolic mapping of neural pathways

An invitation to write a Prefatory Chapter for the *Annual Review of Physiology* is an honor one cannot refuse, but I undertake it with uneasiness. For almost 50 years in biomedical research my writing has been in the traditional style of scientific articles that are supposed to be impersonal and concerned only with scientific content. According to this tradition, probably more idealistic than real, only accuracy and documentation and not people count. In this review of my life in science I must rely on memory, and recalled memory is often more imaginative than real. Nevertheless, I shall do my best to relate the events in my life that shaped my career with as little distortion of the truth and as much freedom from self-serving bias as I can achieve. The title of this chapter is slightly modified from one selected by my colleagues for a symposium held at the National Institutes of Health in recognition of my 75th birthday. They believed it summarized the course of my research career. I agree that it does reflect the major themes in my research life.

ORIGINS AND EARLY YEARS

Like most of my American colleagues of a "certain age," which I shall not define, I belong to the generation that Franklin Roosevelt labeled in his first inaugural address as one that had a "rendezvous with destiny." We were unquestionably influenced, indeed shaped, by momentous events during critical periods in our physical and intellectual development. In our childhood and adolescence we endured the Great Depression. Then as we were emerging from that crisis and entering young adulthood, we were confronted with World War II. It is fair to

---

[1]The US Government has the right to retain a nonexclusive, royalty-free license in and to any copyright covering this paper.

say that nothing in my personal, intellectual, and professional life was not directly or indirectly influenced from the impact of those cataclysmic events.

I was born in 1921 in a row-house in South Philadelphia, Pennsylvania, the younger of two sons of immigrant parents who had immigrated separately from Russia in 1912, met in Philadelphia soon after their arrival, and married. My brother was born in 1915. South Philadelphia was a notoriously tough neighborhood inhabited largely by poor and working-class immigrants or first generation Americans of a variety of national origins, e.g. Italian, Russian, Polish, Irish, Hungarian, and German. My parents' emphasis on education was a powerful influence in my childhood. Neither had had much formal education. My father's ended in Russia at age 12 when his father died and he had to work to support his mother and sister. It was then that he learned various tailoring skills that proved so useful during the depression years. My mother, as the oldest daughter, was brought up to keep house; she did this immaculately and acquired outstanding cooking skills of which she was very proud. Possibly because of their limited education, they valued that of their children's above all else. They could not help us directly but gently coerced my brother and me to study and do well in school. My grandfather once advised me to choose a profession, any one, so that all my significant possessions would reside within my mind. Thus when, inevitably, I would be persecuted, displaced, and deprived of all my material possessions, the contents of my mind would remain for use wherever I went. This attitude was probably derived from centuries of persecution.

THE DEPRESSION AND SECONDARY SCHOOL YEARS

One could not grow up in an industrialized city like Philadelphia during the Great Depression without developing misgivings about an economic system that could create and allow such severe injustices and hardships for a major portion of the population. Throughout childhood and adolescence I witnessed proud and capable men reduced to begging; masses of hungry people, professionals selling pencils, shoelaces, apples, anything to earn enough to feed themselves and their families. I remember the beggar at our door one evening who refused money and asked for food because he was hungry. Such experiences aroused in me intense inquisitiveness about politics, economics, and history. I zealously read newspapers, magazines, any periodicals that I could find in the public library and followed with trepidation the rise of Nazism in Germany, the Spanish civil war, the Italian invasion of Abyssinia, and the demise of the League of Nations.

Our family did not escape the ravages of the depression. My father had been employed as a fur finisher. Because fur coats were luxury items hardly in fashion during the depression, his employer was forced into bankruptcy, and my father became unemployed at a time when social security and unemployment insurance did not yet exist in the United States. When I was about 10, we lost our house because of arrears in real estate taxes and moved to a rented house a few blocks away. The move was traumatic. It meant leaving old friends with whom I had grown up, and making new friends was difficult for me because I was then quite shy. As it turned out, however, the move did lead eventually to very favorable consequences in my intellectual development.

The new home was a row-house located on a small side street. All the houses had open front porches where the residents usually congregated to escape the oppressive heat and humidity of Philadelphia summers. All the families knew one another and were often the friends who helped each other through financial and other crises so frequent during the depression. One of our neighbors was Israel Abrams, a mathematics teacher in the Philadelphia public school system, who, knowing that I was a serious student, took me under his wing. I had already developed an interest in biology, and he guided me in my reading and thinking about science. He also gave me one of his discarded tennis racquets, which introduced me to a sport that I once passionately pursued and still enjoy. Tennis lessons were unaffordable, but I tried to model my game after those of touring professionals and did develop some skill, at least enough to play Number 1 singles on my high school team. Our team, however, perpetually occupied last place in both the Public High School and Interscholastic Leagues, and I won only three matches during my three years on the team. One of my losses was to Victor Seixas, then the National Boys' champion and later winner of Wimbledon and USA National championships.

My interest in biology began when my brother set up a balanced aquarium. I was fascinated by it, and I avidly read about aquarium animals and plants and studied the anatomy, classifications, habitats, and diseases of fish and aquatic plants. My reading then expanded into biology and science in general. Like many at that time, I was influenced by Paul De Kruif s *Microbe Hunters,* Donald C Peattie's *Green Laurels,* and Eric Nordenskiöld's *History of Biology.* I spent hours studying *Chemistry in Medicine,* a free book distributed by the Chemical Rubber Company, in which each chapter described the history of specific medical or biological discoveries, e.g. discovery of vitamins and the cause and cure of pellagra; the development of germ theory and the work of Pasteur, Koch, and Metchnikoff, etc. A career in biological research seemed exciting, and this ambition was encouraged by Abrams.

The Depression had a salutary effect on the quality of my education. Jobs were scarce, and teaching positions in the Philadelphia public schools were eagerly sought. Consequently, we had excellent, dedicated teachers, and many of those in high school had doctoral degrees. Some had come from university faculties for better salaries and security. The educational environment also reflected the nature of the student body; most came from immigrant families strongly oriented toward education. I attended South Philadelphia High School for Boys, an all-boys school in a tough neighborhood known as Little Italy because it was largely populated by immigrants from Sicily and southern Italy. The student body, however, was multiethnic and multiracial, including Poles, Russians, Irish, Jews, Germans, blacks, and even some of Anglo-Saxon origin. It was an excellent school scholastically, second in academic standing only to Central High School, an elite school open only to specially qualified students. Many in our school, including myself, might have qualified but never applied because of the costs of transportation to central city where Central High School was located. School buses were then available only for handicapped children assigned to special schools.

Because South Philadelphia High was an all-boys school, discipline was strict, and misbehavior was dealt with quickly, firmly, and decisively. Students who violated accepted codes of behavior were summarily suspended or expelled. Smoking on school grounds and truancy could lead to suspension. Educational requirements were high, grading severe, and teachers routinely failed students who did not meet the standards. For example, Mr. Feick, the physics teacher, was uncompromisingly strict and demanding. On one of his examinations I received a grade of 98; two points were deducted because I had left out two commas in my examination paper. Mr. Wolf, who taught chemistry, recommended that we never believe anything unless we had positive evidence to believe it, good advice for a future scientist. Dr. Eilberg, a geometry teacher, would challenge us by betting pennies that we could not solve assigned geometry problems. My favorite teachers were Mr. Egnal, a history teacher, and Mr. Gregory, a biology teacher, because they served in sequential years as coach of the tennis team of which I was captain. In my senior year I was competing for an academic scholarship and considered foregoing tennis to concentrate on studies. Mr. Gregory, who was then coach, dissuaded me by telling me that he had faced the same dilemma and found that the diversions provided by athletic activities actually improved his academic performance.

During the depression my father was frequently unemployed or on strike, but because of his diverse tailoring skills, he could sometimes find employment in other branches of the garment trade when jobs in the fur trade were unavailable. Most of our neighbors were in similar straits. Because we could not afford material things, my friends and I found recreation in intellectual activities and spent many hours discussing literature, history, philosophy, science, and political and social issues. We also learned to construct items that our families could not afford, e.g. radios, from junk obtained in junk yards. For example, we wound our own radio coils with enamel-coated wire on cardboard cylinders from toilet tissue rolls. I learned a lot of physics that way.

Family finances could not possibly support college educations for my brother and me. Our only recourse was to obtain scholarships. The Philadelphia Board of Education provided two scholarships for each high school graduating class, one to the University of Pennsylvania for the top student and the other to Temple University for the second. My brother, who completed high school several years before me, was third in his class and missed out on these scholarships, but later won a Mayor's Scholarship to Penn, which was awarded on the basis of competitive examinations. I was more fortunate; I graduated first in my class and won the Board of Education scholarship to the University of Pennsylvania four years later.

THE COLLEGE YEARS

I entered college in September, 1939, just after World War II had begun in Europe. It was my intention to study zoology, a choice consistent with my previous interests but also influenced by the fact that my brother had majored in zoology before me. As we lived at home, I had access to his books, and, while still in high school, eagerly studied his zoology texts. Jobs for zoologists were scarce during the depression, and so I also considered medicine and veterinary medicine, thinking that these represented merely applied biology. Penn then had no special premedical curriculum. Premedical students pursued a standard liberal arts and sciences curriculum and chose, as electives, courses required for medical school admission. Prescribed courses in the first two years included English literature and composition, foreign language, mathematics, history, philosophy or social sciences, and natural sciences. I chose German for my foreign language requirement because German science was then predominant, and scientists often spent time studying in Germany. For natural sciences I chose a variety of courses in zoology, botany, and inorganic chemistry. Physics, physical and organic chemistry, and additional courses in zoology were added later.

English composition was divided into three successive semesters, one each on narration, description, and exposition. The course on exposition required us to write feature articles, and I wrote one on leprosy entitled "Unclean! Unclean!", a history of leprosy throughout the ages. Standards were high, grading rigorous, and mistakes in grammar unforgivable. Compositions harboring a run-on sentence automatically failed. During the narration course a student objected to writing weekly compositions and asked how that would help him earn a better living. The instructor replied, "You don't go to college to enrich your pocket book; you go to college to enrich your mind," an idea probably now lost in antiquity.

Between September 1940 and June 1941, I took a particularly memorable course on modern European history taught by William Lingelbach, an eminent historian and then Dean of the College of Arts and Sciences. The first semester covered the period from 1815 to the onset of World War 1, and the second from 1914 to the last day of the course. A listing of the titles of all the lectures was distributed in advance. The last one was entitled "Europe—Subject to change without notice," an amusingly ambiguous title because it was during World War II when Nazi armies were rampaging throughout Europe, and it was uncertain whether it was Europe or the subject of the lecture that was subject to change without notice. On the morning of this lecture, newspapers headlined the invasion of Crete by the Germans. The lecture that morning was on the battle of Crete, an extraordinarily scholarly and erudite review of the history of Crete and its strategic importance to the combatants.

Majors were chosen at the end of the sophomore year. This led to a family controversy. I preferred zoology, but my brother argued that employment opportunities for zoologists were limited, and admission to medical school was doubtful because most medical schools at that time restricted admission of some minorities. He wanted me to major in chemistry because of better prospects for employment. We compromised; I would choose zoology but would also take as electives all chemistry courses required of chemistry majors. This was a fortunate decision because not only did I enjoy chemistry, but the background in chemistry later proved to be critical in my research.

My first research experience was in my junior year at Penn. Lewis V. Heilbrunn in the Zoology Department taught a graduate/undergraduate course in general physiology. It was my experience with Heilbrunn that most influenced me toward a career in scientific research. Heilbrunn passionately sought to define biological phenomena in terms of physical and chemical mechanisms. He was rigidly analytical, rational, and impatient, even brutal, in his criticism of fuzzy thinking. He was readily accessible to students and reveled in their company. Heilbrunn and his wife, the artist Ellen Donovan, often held open house on Saturday nights, and his students tended to congregate at their home on such evenings. There were often other guests, friends and colleagues of the Heilbrunns, who broadened the flavor of the company. These were stimulating evenings with discussions about the arts, sciences, and humanities. The culture and life of the academic scientist seemed so full and rich that I felt drawn further to such a career.

Heilbrunn's course extended over two semesters and included lectures and laboratory work. His lectures, like his textbook (1), emphasized his ideas about the role of calcium in biological processes. Heilbrunn had earlier studied influences of calcium on cell membrane integrity and regulation of intracellular protoplasmic viscosity. His ideas about the effects of calcium were extended in part as a result of work of his students, D Mazia and JM Clark (2), who found that electrical, osmotic, mechanical, or ultraviolet stimulation of Elodea cells caused almost instant formation of calcium oxalate crystals in the vacuoles. The vacuoles were known to contain oxalic acid, and it was reasoned that the stimulations must have raised intracellular ionic Ca^{2+} concentrations, probably by release from bound sites. These and many other observations led Heilbrunn to propose that Ca^{2+} release was a critical component in the processes of excitation, conduction, muscular contraction, blood-clotting, secretion, etc, ideas that were certainly ahead of their time. He pushed these ideas in his lectures so forcefully that after the first semester's final examination a student led the class in a college cheer, "C-a-l-c-i-u-m! Calcium! Calcium! Calcium!"

The laboratory portion of the course consisted of some prescribed experiments followed by an original research project. My research in the first semester was to determine if protoplasmic flow in the pseudopod of the amoeba obeys Poiseuille's Law. The results showed that it does not. My project in the second semester was suggested by Dan Harris, an Instructor who had been a doctoral student with Heilbrunn. The project was to fractionate cells and localize enzymes to the subcellular components. This was 10 years before isolation of mitochondria by Hogeboom et al (3). The cell we chose was the unfertilized frog egg because of its ready availability and uniformity. The cells were homogenized and fractionated by centrifugation into plasmasol (the term then used for cytosol), lipids, yolk, and pigment fractions. We localized lipases to the lipid fraction, dipeptidases to the plasmasol, and a few other enzymes that I no longer remember. The results do not seem very interesting now, but the experience reinforced my taste for research.

In my final year, 1942, I chose as an elective, Zoology 50, Undergraduate Research in Zoology, a course that enabled me to continue research with Heilbrunn. The United States was now at war, and Heilbrunn had obtained a grant from the U.S. Army to study effects of heat on biological systems, allegedly because of concern about heat-related casualties suffered by the British 8th Army in North Africa. His entire group worked on various aspects of this problem. My assignment was to determine the heat sensitivities of nerve and muscle. Electrodes were applied to both the nerve and muscle of the rat sciatic nerve-gastrocnemius preparation, and muscle contractions were monitored by a lever and pen-writing assembly. Either the muscle, nerve, or both were immersed in Ringer's solution at 41°C, and the nerve and muscle were electrically. stimulated alternately until the muscle stopped contracting. When nerve alone was heated, the muscle responded to either nerve or muscle stimulation for relatively long periods. When only the muscle was heated, muscle contractions in response to nerve stimulation ceased quickly but could continue to be evoked by direct faradic stimulation of the muscle for longer periods. We concluded that it was the myoneural junction that was most susceptible to heat, and this observation was considered sufficiently interesting to publish. While I was in the process of drafting a manuscript, Paul LeFevre, one of Heilbrunn's graduate students later known for his work on red cells, called my attention to a publication by Claude Bernard in Charles Richet's *Dictionnaire de Physiologie* in 1870, describing essentially the same experiments and the same conclusions, except that he had used oil instead of Ringer's solution. Because similar experiments with the same conclusions had already been published, we decided not to publish, an attitude not in fashion today. Apropos differences in attitudes between then and now, Heilbrunn once remarked that "anyone publishing an average of more than two full papers per year is not doing good work or his own work." Today, such a publication rate would probably be insufficient to gain promotion, tenure, or a grant.

The experience with Heilbrunn led me to inquire whether he would accept me as a graduate student. He was willing but advised me to apply to medical school because he could not protect his graduate students from the military draft before they achieved their degrees, whereas medical students were being deferred. He also remarked that a medical degree did not necessarily spoil one for scientific research. I, therefore, applied to Penn's medical school, and Heilbrunn sent a letter of recommendation to the Admissions Committee, strong enough for them to admit me to the class beginning in March, 1943.

MEDICAL SCHOOL AND INTERNSHIP

Medical schools during the war adopted an accelerated program to speed up supplies of physicians to the armed forces. The semester system and vacations were abandoned, and the normal four-year curriculum was compressed into approximately three years. Three months after I entered, the military took over the medical, dental, and veterinary schools. Most of the students, including me, were inducted into the Army Specialized Training Program (ASTP) with the rank of Private First Class; some joined the Navy V-12 Program and were treated as Cadets. ASTP members at Penn were barracked and received military training, e.g. saluting, marching, etc. We assembled for reveille each morning and marched to breakfast at the university's basketball arena, which had been renovated into a huge mess hall. The university, however, retained control of curricular and educational affairs.

The military take-over had some benefits. First, it assumed the costs of the medical education and paid us $54 a month. I might not otherwise have been able to complete my medical education because of the family's limited financial resources. Secondly, it kept us out of combat. Our discomfort with this protected status at a time when our troops were engaged in bloody battles in Europe and the South Pacific was further aggravated by the easily recognizable shoulder patch on our uniforms that identified our organization.

Gross Anatomy was our first course and overlapped soon afterward by Histology and Neuroanatomy. At first, I found the atmosphere stifling. Compared with the excitement in Heilbrunn's laboratory, the rigidity of the curriculum and the treatment of the first-year students in medical school reminded me of grade school. I could not develop much interest, let alone enthusiasm, in subjects that required memorization of huge amounts of descriptive information. My mind did not work that way; dynamic processes that could be measured were much more stimulating. Nevertheless, I persisted, studied hard, and survived this dull period until eventually we progressed to Physiology, Biochemistry, and Pharmacology, subjects more to my liking. These courses were well taught by excellent teachers who emphasized the research that unearthed the facts being presented. Unlike present trends in medical schools, all these courses included hands-on laboratory experiments carried out by the students. In Physiology we learned cardiac physiology from H Bazett, who confessed that he had done experiments on himself in every branch of physiology except those involving female sex hormones. M Jacobs, known for his red cell research and the solution of diffusion equations for various boundary conditions, gave extraordinarily lucid lectures on the systemic circulation. Lectures in Biochemistry by D Drabkin, S Gurin, and J Buchanan were also excellent. Drabkin's lectures on the biochemistry of diabetes presented in great detail the procedures and experimental findings that documented the then existing concepts about the disease. My notes on the lectures on glycolysis given by the great German biochemist Otto Meyerhof, then a professor at Penn, is now one of my prized possessions. Pharmacology was probably the best taught course, mainly because of an outstanding trio of teachers, Carl Schmidt, Julius Comroe, and Seymour Kety. They emphasized physiological mechanisms, and the physiology of each system was comprehensively reviewed before the specific actions of drugs were examined. We probably learned as much physiology from them as in the physiology course. All their lectures emphasized mechanisms and rational approaches to diagnosis and therapy. Experimental methods and findings were described and critically interpreted and evaluated. Healthy skepticism permeated the course, an attitude forecast in Schmidt's opening lecture in which he cautioned us never to be seduced by the dictum, "Post hoc, ergo propter hoc." By the end of the course many of us had become therapeutic nihilists.

I found the clinical courses less interesting than the basic sciences. Neurology was fun because with knowledge of neuroanatomy and neuropathology one might deduce the location and nature of a lesion. Surgery, gynecology, and obstetrics were dull, and pediatrics required dealing with crying children who were difficult to examine. I enjoyed internal medicine, particularly metabolic and endocrine disorders which often involved physiological chemistry. In general, there was little in my medical school experience to divert my interest from basic science to the practice of medicine. My focus did change, however, from cellular to mammalian physiology and biochemistry.

The war ended in August 1945. I graduated from medical school in March 1946 and immediately entered internship at the Philadelphia General Hospital, a city hospital with 2500 beds. The army released us into the reserves to complete our internships and pass licensing board examinations after which we were to be recalled to active duty as medical officers. Pennsylvania then required rotating internships, and I rotated through internal medicine, tuberculosis service, surgery, orthopedic surgery, clinical laboratory medicine, neurology, psychiatry, obstetrics, and gynecology. My first service was in Psychiatry. Treatments in vogue at the time were insulin-shock or electroconvulsive therapy for schizophrenia and electroconvulsive therapy for reactive depression, involutional melancholia, and manic-depressive psychosis. Paresis was treated with fever therapy, induced by malaria in whites and intravenous typhoid vaccine administration in Afro-Americans. Penicillin was not yet routinely used for neurosyphilis. In addition, all patients received that esoteric, mystical, highly individualized "magic bullet" known as psychotherapy. We saw many patients with alcoholic hallucinosis, delirium tremens, hysterical paralyses, amnesia, and drug intoxications. A common drug problem at the time was chronic bromidism, which often bore a remarkable resemblance to schizophrenia. Brain tumors occasionally presented with psychosis. I found the incredible world of the mind intriguing. The strange and bizarre behaviors, irrational thoughts, delusions, and hallucinations were beyond scientific comprehension, yet were clearly real phenomena. Psychoanalysis, then popular in American psychiatry, ignored physical and chemical mechanisms and offered explanations based on early childhood experiences and abstract concepts, such as id, ego, superego, and unconscious mind, entities that lacked physical or biochemical structure or properties. Psychiatry was an unknown domain and a challenge to anyone who sought explanations on the basis of physical and chemical mechanisms.

Internships during the war were integrated into the accelerated program and reduced to nine months in duration. We were, therefore, obliged to complete all the required rotations within nine months. When our internship ended, however, the accelerated program was terminated, normal one-year internships were reinstituted, and our internship was extended to 15 months to implement transition to the prewar schedule. The extensions were limited, however, to a single service, and mine was in psychiatry. Thus, including my rotations in both neurology and psychiatry, I served during my internship a total of about nine months in neuropsychiatry, mostly psychiatry. Also, when the war ended, many physicians returning from military service sought specialty training under the G. I. Bill of Rights, and our hospital became a psychiatric training center. Classes and clinics organized to train them were open to us. When the new class of interns arrived, they overlapped us by three months and assumed our internship duties, leaving me free to attend these classes and clinics and to function as a resident in psychiatry. This experience enhanced my knowledge and competence in psychiatry and with it my interest in mental functions.

THE ARMY YEARS

During internship I married Betty, then a student at Ohio State University, who joined me in Philadelphia immediately after completing her first year. My internship ended in June, 1947. The Army allowed me two months to pass board examinations before ordering me to active duty at the Medical Field Services School, Fort Sam Houston, Texas, where we received four weeks of training in basic military medicine. During the training, a group of officers from Washington, DC arrived to interview us regarding our preferences for future assignment and promised to be accommodating in order to seduce us into permanent careers in the army. We were given three choices for both specialty and location. In orders of preference I chose physiological research, internal medicine, and neuropsychiatry for specialty; and Fort Knox, Tennessee, where there was a research program in environmental physiology, Europe, and the West Coast for location. Typical of the Army, they assigned me to my last choice of specialty and a location not on my list. Because of my experience in neuropsychiatry during internship, the Surgeon General of the Army ordained me a neuropsychiatrist and assigned me to Camp Lee, Virginia.

The medical facility at Camp Lee was a 150-bed hospital that provided a range of medical and surgical services to the military personnel and their dependents. No neuropsychiatrist had been there for several months before my arrival in September 1947; neuropsychiatry was being covered by the Medical Service. I was allowed to decide whether neuropsychiatry should become independent or remain within the Medical Service. Because I was then more interested in internal medicine than in neuropsychiatry, I chose the latter so that I could still participate in diagnosis and care of medical patients. Relatively few of my patients had neurological problems; mostly head, spine, and peripheral nerve injuries and subarachnoid hemorrhages due to cerebral aneurysms. Occasionally we saw brain tumors, strokes, multiple sclerosis, and a rare case of Thomsen's disease (myotonia congenita). Patients requiring neurosurgery were transferred to Walter Reed General Hospital, Washington, DC. Psychiatric patients, however, were many and varied. Conditions requiring hospitalization included schizophrenia, manic depressive disorders, psychotic depression, alcoholic hallucinosis, delirium tremens, etc. Patients requiring prolonged hospitalization were either transferred to Walter Reed or given medical discharges from the army. Most of them were outpatients suffering from alcoholism, personality disorders, anxiety neurosis, hypochondriasis, psychosomatic disease, and conversion reactions (e.g. hysterical paralyses and amnesia). A common diagnosis was acute situational maladjustment, a frequent condition in young recruits away from home for the first time. Character disorders were also common, particularly constitutional psychopathic inferior (nomenclature at that time now included in sociopathic personality). As a physician I was obligated to help my patients, but all I could offer was a type of psychotherapy that I considered consistent with the best teaching of the time and within my limits of competence. I studied psychiatric texts and journals, read the work of Freud and his disciples, and practiced a diluted version of psychoanalysis, which was then the most popular and dynamic approach to psychiatric treatment. Sometimes I prescribed sedatives and occasionally used amytal interviews (i.e. "twilight sleep"), mainly in conversion reactions. Results were probably no better nor worse than those obtained by fully qualified psychiatrists at that time. Some patients did improve, e.g. a soldier with a conversion reaction who regained the use of his paralyzed arm, an amnesic who recovered his memory, and a nymphomaniac who gave up sex for Lent. Another patient in her thirties had suffered from various systemic symptoms for years. The Medical Service, however, could find no organic basis, made the diagnosis of psychosomatic disease, and referred her to the neuropsychiatric clinic. After about six months of psychotherapy she declared that she was feeling better than she ever had in 11 years. I was astonished and wondered how her talking and my listening could have so altered her brain as to dispel the psychosomatic symptoms. For me mind and brain were inextricably linked, a linkage that was irrelevant to psychiatry at that time. This case and a few others aroused my interest in physiological and biochemical mechanisms in the brain in mental disease.

RETURN TO THE UNIVERSITY OF PENNSYLVANIA

In 1948 Kety & Schmidt (4), my former teachers at Penn, published their nitrous oxide method for measuring cerebral blood flow and metabolism in conscious human subjects. This method offered a means to examine brain functions in psychiatric disorders, and I considered trying to join them to learn the method. My army service ended in August, 1949. Betty and I returned to Philadelphia, and, as soon as possible, I dropped in on Kety and learned that he had transferred from Schmidt's department to a new Department of Physiology and Pharmacology, chaired by Julius Comroe, in the Graduate School of Medicine. I explained that I hoped to join him but was bringing nothing, no skills, no methods, no brilliant research ideas, only a desire to work with him and learn as much as I could. The timing was opportune; he had just learned that his National Institutes of Health grant, which included support for a still unnamed fellow, had been approved. Kety remembered me from medical school and was willing to take a chance on me, but he had planned on someone with more experience than mine. My stipend would necessarily have to be lower, and, besides, he noted, perhaps, the rest of the allocated salary could be used for an additional fellow at my level. Final approval had to be obtained from Comroe, who interviewed me two weeks later and approved the appointment, but immediately afterward asked about my plans for the future. I was puzzled; I thought that we had just agreed that I was joining his department.

"I mean your long-term professional goals," he explained. "Do you intend to work here for a year or two and then return to clinical medicine, or do you plan to make a career in physiology?"

I did not know. On the basis of my past experiences I guessed that I would like basic research but could not predict how suited I would be for it. He replied that he remembered me from medical school, was confident that I would do well, and hoped that I would choose a career in physiology. I was flattered, but then he immediately added, "But not here."

I was stunned and asked, "What did I say wrong? You just said that you thought that I would do well and hoped that I would stay in physiology."

"It's nothing personal," he explained. "This department has only three people on university salaries, myself, Dr. Kety, and Mrs. Sullivan, the department secretary. I am 38 years old and in good health and have no plans to leave. Kety is 35, and as far as I know, he is also in good health and does not plan to leave. And as for Mrs. Sullivan, I don't think you could do her job. Therefore, if you have any thoughts of replacing any of us, forget them. You are here to help us do our research. In return we will teach you how to do research, and if and when you learn it well enough to be able to do your own research, we will be glad to help you find a place to do it, but somewhere else."

He then continued, "I may as well tell you now because you will find out anyway. Your salary will be $2500 per year. Mrs. King, my chief technician, is paid $3300 per year. That is not a mistake; it is a reflection of the relative worth of the two of you to this department at this time."

That was putting it right on the line, but not unreasonable. I eventually came to appreciate that his forthrightness and honesty were reflections of his total commitment to physiology and good science. He was constantly challenging us to do our very best. Behind his gruff exterior there was actually a kind, considerate, and generous soul.

Although I had come specifically to study cerebral physiology, circulation, and metabolism, I acquired much broader experience in physiology. The grant providing my salary was on the use of Kety's $^{24}Na^+$ clearance method (5) to study peripheral circulation. My time was, therefore, divided between studies on cerebral and peripheral circulation. Working with the $^{24}Na^+$ clearance method introduced me to radioisotopic techniques and forced me to learn about radioactivity, which had been neglected in my college physics courses. Also, the clearance method was based on the design and mathematical analysis of a kinetic model. Physiological modeling was new and fascinating to me, but my mathematical skills were limited, and I was forced to extend my knowledge of mathematics. Once again, I was a student and studied every night until early morning hours. I did not feel deprived because with an annual income of $2500 other activities were very limited. My wife, who had been a Navy nurse during the war, was enrolled at Penn under the G. I. Bill of Rights and could not help financially. By 1952 my salary reached $4000, but then our son was born, further straining our financial resources.

Richard Wechsler was Kety's first postdoctoral fellow, and I was his second. We overlapped for about a year, and from him I learned the procedure of the N_2O method. Both of us learned the theory and principles of inert gas exchange between blood and tissues on which it was based directly from Kety, who was then writing his now classic review of the subject (6). Additional fellows arrived, including Renward Mangold from Switzerland, who worked on sleep, and Charles Kennedy, a pediatrician who came to adapt the N_2O method for use in children. We were joined later by a couple of anesthesiologists, Benton King and Eugene Conners. It was a highly interactive group that worked closely together, constantly argued about the rationale and interpretation of results of our experiments, and regularly discussed and exchanged information about publications in our fields of interest and in physiology in general. We worked together as a team in all the projects within the overall research program with no detectable rivalry among us and no prior decisions or concerns about authorship on publications. Authorship evolved by natural selection; each of us gravitated in our reading and thinking to specialized areas of interest, and it became obvious who was most expert in the literature and, therefore, probably best qualified to write the first draft of the manuscript. Whoever authored the first draft became first author. It came as a surprise when years later I became aware of rivalries and conflicts among coworkers with regard to authorship.

In addition to research-related discussions, there were also exchanges of broader scope among ourselves and with Kety. We usually met for lunch where we discussed news, politics, foreign affairs, political science, and scientific politics, as well as science. Kety and I often argued about psychiatry. Although I was skeptical about psychiatric theory and practice, my past responsibility to care for psychiatric patients had made me more tolerant. Kety was a critical hard-nosed physiologist with low regard for psychiatry, which he considered to be unscientific. I felt compelled to defend it and argued that it was not psychiatry but psychiatrists that were at fault. That was not an original idea. I had read an article by Iago Galdston (7) in which he compared Freud's impact on psychiatry with the inauguration of the Eiffel Tower at the Paris Exposition in 1889. At the opening, a powerful lantern at the top of the tower was turned on and directed downward, producing a giant circle of bright light on the ground below. It was night, and those outside the circle were in the dark and could see nothing, but those within the circle of light were so blinded by its brilliance that they also could see nothing. I too believed that many psychiatrists and disciples of Freud had interpreted and extrapolated too far beyond the bounds of logic and reason. Apparently, Kety and I were both very persuasive because I, subsequently, gravitated more deeply into basic science while Kety's interests drifted toward psychiatry in his studies on the genetics of schizophrenia.

The Department of Physiology and Pharmacology provided a superb environment for training in physiology. Contact between fellows and staff was continuous and close, and expectations and standards of performance were high. Seminars were held every Saturday morning, and professional staff members, including fellows, took turns presenting their work. No exceptions were allowed; if one had nothing to present, that itself might be revealing. Fellows compared these seminars to the Roman Coliseum because it was like being fed to the lions. There was little tolerance for pomposity or verbal gymnastics, and it was unwise to be glib. Every statement might be challenged, and every method or conclusion questioned or criticized. Presenters were stretched to the limits of their knowledge of the subject. One dared not make rash statements that could not be backed up by facts or reason. We learned to be just as critical of our own work as of that of others. In science it was more important never to be wrong than ever to be right. Scientific literature should never be polluted with bad or trivial science. How different it is today when publications often appear to be written more to contribute to one's bibliography than to scientific knowledge.

The first research project likely to lead to publications with me as first author was on the effects of hyperthyroidism on cerebral blood flow (CBF) and oxygen consumption ($CMRO_2$) in humans. The N_2O method had identified many clinical conditions with decreases in $CMRO_2$, but none yet with increased $CMRO_2$. It seemed that $CMRO_2$ should be increased in hyperthyroidism because it is generally accompanied by large increases in total body metabolic rate and marked anxiety. We, therefore, designed a long-term study in which patients with Graves' Disease would be studied before and after treatment and also compared with normal subjects of comparable age. The first few experiments showed that, contrary to expectations, $CMRO_2$ was normal in hyperthyroidism. While our study was still in progress, an abstract appeared reporting the same finding. We had been scooped. Kety's comment was "It must not have been such a great idea. Somebody else thought of it too." It reflected an attitude that valued uniqueness more than speed.

The study was eventually completed and published (8), but by then I had become intrigued with the question of why the brain failed to participate in the total body's increased metabolic rate in hyperthyroidism. What was different about the brain's metabolism? It was clear from the literature that the mechanisms underlying the stimulation of metabolic rate by thyroid hormones in responsive tissues, such as liver, muscle, and kidney, were still unknown. How could one then explain their lack of effect in brain? There was evidence in the literature that thyroid hormones might have actions specifically related to protein metabolism. Mature brain was known to derive almost all its energy from oxidative glucose metabolism, and the testis, the only organ other than brain known to have a respiratory quotient of one, indicating only carbohydrate oxidation, was also reported to have its rate of O_2 consumption unaffected by thyroid hormones. Perhaps, this was only a coincidence, but it also suggested that thyroid hormones might be acting primarily on protein metabolism and that effects on energy metabolism were only secondary. Effects on energy metabolism might, therefore, not be apparent in tissue in which protein turnover was low compared with that of carbohydrate. Also, if thyroid hormones acted on protein turnover, was it on protein synthesis, protein catabolism, or both? Thyroid hormones were essential for body growth and brain maturation and had been reported to stimulate O_2 consumption in developing brain when protein synthesis is undoubtedly active. Their lack of effect was in mature brain in which rates of protein synthesis were believed to be low. These considerations led us to speculate that the effects of thyroid hormones on energy metabolism were secondary to an effect on protein synthesis.

A test of this hypothesis required experiments on the effects of thyroid hormones on protein synthesis. There was then no practical method for studying protein synthesis in vivo, and in vitro biochemical experiments would have been required. Although I had a fair book knowledge of biochemistry, I had little experience in laboratory biochemical techniques and, instead, tried to persuade biochemical colleagues to undertake such studies. One such biochemist was B D Polis, one of the only two Ph.D. students Otto Meyerhof had had in America. He encouraged me to undertake the biochemical studies under his supervision, but I was then too busy with studies of peripheral blood flow and cerebral circulation and metabolism to undertake them.

THE YEARS AT THE NATIONAL INSTITUTE OF MENTAL HEALTH

In 1951, about two years after I arrived, Kety left Penn to become Scientific Director of the Intramural Research Programs of both the National Institute of Mental Health (NIMH) and the National Institute of Neurological Diseases and Blindness (NINDB). Because I was then his most senior fellow, I became responsible for maintaining his research projects, and he returned to Penn several times per month to discuss the work. The Department had two major research interests, pulmonary function and cerebral circulation and metabolism. After Kety's departure, the group working in the latter area shrank because the magnet was gone. We were reduced to a graduate student, technician, and me, and I began to feel quite isolated and started to explore opportunities elsewhere. I had been collaborating with the Aviation Medical Acceleration Laboratory of the U.S. Naval Air Development Center, Johnsville, Pennsylvania, to develop a method for rapid continuous measurement of CBF and metabolism in humans. The Navy wanted the method to study black-out in aviators pulling out of dives and offered me the position of Head of Physiology. Comroe thought it a bad choice for me, tried to dissuade me from accepting it, and invited me to join the group in respiratory physiology. When I explained that my interest was still in the brain and my reasons for wanting to leave his department, he called Kety and suggested that he recruit me for NIH. Kety then called me, offered me a position, and explained that he had not done so previously because he had not wished to raid the department at Penn. I accepted and arrived at the NIMH in December 1953. There were basic and clinical research programs in the Intramural Research Program of the NIMH. My past experience qualified me for appointment in either, the one in the clinical program at a higher grade and salary, but I chose basic research.

My appointment was in the Section on Cerebral Metabolism of the Laboratory of Neurochemistry. Kety was Section Chief and also acting Laboratory Chief until a permanent one was recruited. There were two other sections in the laboratory; Lipid Chemistry, under Roscoe Brady, and Physical Chemistry, under Alex Rich. The Intramural Research Program also contained the Laboratory of Cellular Pharmacology, under Giulio Cantoni, the discoverer of S-adenosylmethionine and its role in methylation reactions. Cantoni had recruited Seymour Kaufman, who had identified succinylCoA as an intermediate in the tricarboxylic acid cycle and its role in substrate phosphorylation. Biochemistry was, therefore, well represented, and a biochemical journal club was organized. In the first round of meetings, we each described our previous research before coming to NIH. I presented my work on hyperthyroidism and the hypothesis that many of the physiological effects of thyroid hormones could be explained by a stimulation of protein synthesis and/or turnover. It stimulated considerable discussion, and the session lasted well beyond its scheduled one hour. Shortly afterward, Kaufman visited me and told me that he liked the hypothesis and, in fact, had come to a similar opinion from an entirely different perspective. He asked what I intended to do about it, and I replied that the problem was biochemical and that, though I might have sounded like one, I was really not a biochemist. He then offered to collaborate with me, provide the biochemical expertise, and supervise and train me in biochemistry. I accepted, and thus began my career in biochemistry. With Kety's encouragement we initiated experiments in 1955 to develop and characterize an in vitro assay system for protein synthesis that could be used to examine the effects of thyroid hormones. Progress was slow because both of us were also involved in other projects, in my case studies of cerebral circulation and metabolism. We eventually established a satisfactory assay system and found that thyroid hormones did, indeed, stimulate protein synthesis (9, 10). Kaufman was an outstanding teacher, knowledgeable, scholarly, and rigorous with uncompromisingly high standards. His attitudes and mine meshed perfectly; we shared the same commitments to the traditional values of science. This experience and the capability to obtain definitive solutions that biochemistry seemed to offer seduced me away from physiology, and in 1959, when my projects on CBF were essentially completed, I turned my efforts fully to biochemical research. My main research project was still on mechanisms of thyroid hormone actions, but my interests broadened to include the relationships between biochemical processes and physiological functions in the nervous system.

When I arrived at NIMH, I planned to pursue studies of cerebral blood flow and metabolism in humans in conditions with normal and abnormal mental and neurological functions. Our initial studies were on normal aging and dementia (11) and the effects of LSD in normal subjects and schizophrenic patients (12). In these studies we used the N_2O method, which determines average blood flow and metabolism in the brain as a whole. This proved sufficient to show reductions in clinical conditions associated with depressed consciousness but failed to detect changes in cerebral energy metabolism associated with normal physiological alterations in mental function or psychiatric disorders. No changes in whole brain $CMRO_2$ were found during mental exercise, slow-wave sleep, sedation or tranquilization, schizophrenia, mild alcoholic inebriation, or LSD intoxication. One could conceive of at least three possible explanations for the negative results. (*a*) Mental functions not associated with altered levels of consciousness are unrelated to energy consuming processes in brain; (*b*) there are local increases and decreases in metabolic rates distributed throughout the brain without altering average metabolic rate in the brain as a whole; and (*c*) specific mental functions are localized to regions too small to be detectable in measurements of the total brain's metabolic rate. A method that determined local cerebral metabolic rates in conscious animals was clearly needed.

We had no idea how even to approach the issue of determination of local cerebral metabolic rates in unanesthetized, behaving animals, but Kety (6) in his analysis of the principles of inert gas exchange between blood and tissues had derived an equation that seemed applicable to the measurement of local CBF which, though not itself metabolic rate, was believed to be adjusted to energy metabolism. Kety and two neurophysiologists at the NIMH, William Landau and Walter Freygang, had already initiated development of such a method, and I joined them when I arrived. The outcome was the [^{131}I]trifluoroiodomethane ([^{131}I]CF$_3$1) method (13–16) for the determination of local CBF simultaneously in all regions of the brain in conscious animals. Localization was achieved by a unique quantitative autoradiographic technique that not only measured but also provided visual images of the local isotope concentrations and, therefore, also the relative rates of local CBF throughout the brain. Applications of this method proved that local CBF does indeed change with local functional activity; for example, retinal stimulation with light was shown to increase CBF in structures in the visual pathways of the cat (14, 16).

The changes in local CBF were believed to be secondary to changes in local energy metabolism, and CBF was known to be influenced also by systemic factors, such as arterial pCO_2, pO_2, and pH. One would, therefore, expect local energy metabolism to be more directly and specifically linked to local functional activity than blood flow. In 1955–1956 I considered a method to determine local cerebral glucose utilization ($lCMR_{glc}$) with [14C]glucose that took advantage of the spatial localization provided by quantitative autoradiography. It soon became apparent, however, that rapid loss of labeled products of [14C]glucose metabolism, e.g., $^{14}CO_2$ and possibly lactate and other metabolites, would necessitate extremely short experimental periods to minimize significant loss of product. Determination of $lCMR_{glc}$, required knowledge of the time-integrated specific activities of the precursor glucose pools at the local tissue sites, but these could not be measured directly in conscious animals and would have to be estimated from glucose specific activity measured in the plasma. Such estimations could not, however, be accurate with short experimental periods because of the lags in the tissue pools behind that of the plasma. Therefore, I abandoned the project.

In 1957, I was preparing a chapter on energy metabolism in the central nervous system for the *Handbook of Physiology*. While discussing it with Donald Tower of the NINDB, I learned from him about 2-deoxyglucose (2-DG), which in pharmacological doses produced a comatose state like that of hypoglycemic coma. Sols & Crane (17) had shown that hexokinase, the enzyme that phosphorylates glucose to glucose-6-phosphate (G-6-P), can also phosphorylate 2-DG to 2-DG-6-phosphate (DG-6-P). The next step in glycolysis is isomerization of G-6-P to fructose-6-phosphate (F-6-P), but (DG-6-P) cannot be isomerized and metabolized further in the glycolytic pathway because it lacks the hydroxyl group on its second carbon. The coma was caused by a block in glycolysis due to an accumulation of DG-6-P to concentrations that exceeded those of G-6-P and inhibited G-6-P isomerization to F-6-P. DG-6-P could accumulate to such high levels because it is a poor substrate for most enzymes in the brain that might metabolize it and also because glucose-6-phosphatase activity is negligible in the brain. When I learned that the product of 2-DG phosphorylation accumulated, it occurred to me that radioactive 2-DG in tracer amounts might be combined with the autoradiographic technique to measure $lCMR_{glc}$. I filed the idea away for future work but did make use of these properties of 2-DG in biochemical experiments in vitro. For example, in studies of oxidative phosphorylation by crude brain mitochondria, we had to use a combination of glucose and hexokinase to trap in G-6-P the inorganic phosphate incorporated into ATP because it was otherwise released back to the inorganic phosphate pool by the ATPase activity in contaminating synaptosomes. Crude brain mitochondrial preparations, however, also contained glycolytic enzymes that metabolized the G-6-P formed by the trap and generated additional ATP above that produced by oxidative phosphorylation. We, therefore, used 2-DG instead of glucose in the trapping system, and the DG-6-P formed was neither hydrolyzed to release inorganic phosphate nor metabolized further to generate additional ATP.

In 1964 Martin Reivich and Jane Jehle joined our laboratory and modified the quantitative autoradiographic technique and local CBF method for use with [14C]antipyrine (18), which we later replaced with the more diffusible tracer [14C]iodoantipyrine (19). Now that quantitative autoradiography with 14C was available, the idea of measuring lCMR$_{glc}$ with 2-[14C]DG was resurrected, and Kety, Reivich, and I often discussed it but left it for future research. After Reivich returned to Penn in 1966, he called me to inquire if I were still interested in 2-[14C]DG and would be willing to collaborate in the development of a method to measure lCMR$_{glc}$. I accepted on condition that my laboratory would temporarily not do any of the experimental work because of commitments to other projects. Initial experiments with brain slices incubated in vitro, which demonstrated proportionate uptakes of 2-[14C]DG and glucose from the medium, were done in his laboratory. These results encouraged us to design a kinetic model, essentially the same as the one for the local CBF method, except that it included a compartment for metabolized tracer. An equation to calculate lCMR$_{glc}$ was derived, but it required knowledge of local blood flow and other factors difficult to determine. This early attempt was reported in 1971 (20). The model and equation were not wrong but required information difficult if not impossible to obtain, and the project stagnated.

In 1968–1969 I spent a sabbatical year in Jean Roche's Laboratory of General and Comparative Biochemistry at the College de France, in Paris. There I worked with Jacques Nunez and Jacques Pommier studying horseradish peroxidase-catalyzed iodination of tyrosine residues in serum albumin, a model system for the peroxidase-catalyzed iodination of thyroglobulin in the pathway of thyroid hormone biosynthesis. The reaction exhibited complex non-Michaelian kinetics that intrigued me (21). While working on this problem, I became facile with enzyme kinetics and began to consider a new model for the 2-[14C]DG method that was based more on principles of enzyme kinetics than on blood flow and tissue-blood exchange. When I returned to my laboratory in late 1969, I found the project on actions of thyroid hormones in shambles. I could now turn my full attention to developing and evaluating such a model. The first animal experiment was done in February 1971, by Charles Kennedy, Michel Des Rosiers, Jane Jehle, and myself. We were later joined by Clifford Patlak, Karen Pettigrew, Osamu Sakurada, and Mami Shinohara, all of whom played unique and important roles. The method was fully developed for use in rats in 1974 and presented at the annual meeting of the American Society for Neurochemistry in New Orleans 1974. Detailed descriptions of the theory, procedure, and results of some of the applications of the method followed later (22–24).

Because we were not yet certain whether energy metabolism was linked to functional activity in neural as in other tissues, and, if so, whether the 2-DG method could localize changes in neuronal activity on the basis of altered metabolism, we first carried out so-called recovery experiments. Functional activation or depression in specific neural pathways was experimentally induced, and the 2-[^{14}C]DG method was used to look for changes in lCMR$_{glc}$ in appropriate stations of the pathways. The results were unequivocal; lCMR$_{glc}$ was clearly linked to local functional activity in neural tissues, and the effects on lCMR$_{glc}$ were often so pronounced that they could be visualized directly in the autoradiograms without the need for quantification. A particularly dramatic demonstration was the visualization of the nature, extent, and distribution of the ocular dominance columns and the loci of representation of the blind spots of the visual fields in the striate cortex of the monkey (25, 26).

The fully quantitative 2-[^{14}C]DG method yielded massive amounts of data derived from laborious and tedious manual densitometric analyses of the autoradiograms. Quantification was, therefore, limited to a relatively few selected structures, and valuable information in the autoradiograms was being lost. A more convenient means to combine the quantitative capability of the method with the spatial resolution of the autoradiography was needed. We, therefore, assembled a computerized image-processing system that scanned and digitized the autoradiograms, computed lCMR$_{glc}$ for each pixel, and reconstructed the autoradiographic images in pseudocolor on a monitor with the metabolic rates quantitatively encoded in a calibrated color-scale that was simultaneously displayed (27). This technique provided color-coded quantitative maps of the distribution of lCMR$_{glc}$ throughout the nervous system with often dramatic visual displays of the locations and magnitudes of the changes evoked by alterations in functional activity. This technique was first presented in 1978 at the meeting of the Society of Neuroscience in St. Louis Missouri, by Charlene Jarvis, who used it to identify structures in the monkey nervous system metabolically activated by visually cued unilateral arm movements contralateral to a visually deprived hemisphere. It produced a sensational response. The issue of *Chemical and Engineering News* reporting on the meeting featured on its cover a color-coded autoradiogram of the striate cortex showing the reduced metabolism in the deprived hemisphere with the caption, "Visualizing Brain Chemistry in Action." I must confess that, as a physiologist, I was disappointed that the images were more appreciated than the quantitative data.

After the 2-[^{14}C]DG method was completed and validated, Reivich raised the issue of adapting it for use in humans. Autoradiography was obviously impractical; a less invasive technique for measuring local isotope concentrations in brain was essential. David Kuhl at Penn had developed a section-scanner that measured local concentrations of γ-emitting isotopes in sections of human brain by external scintillation counting, and Reivich enlisted his collaboration. It was necessary, however, to insert a γ-emitting isotope into the deoxyglucose molecule, which contains only hydrogen, oxygen, and carbon. Hydrogen has no γ-emitting isotopes, and the half-lives of ^{15}O and ^{11}C are 2 and 20 min, respectively, at that time too short to synthesize deoxyglucose labeled with them. An alternative possibility was fluorinated deoxyglucose. Fluorine is so small an atom that when introduced into appropriate positions in the molecules of metabolic substrates, the biochemical properties of the natural compound are often retained. Furthermore, ^{18}F, a positron-emitting isotope, has a half-life of 110 minutes. Alfred Wolf, a radiochemist at Brookhaven National Laboratory, was brought into the project, and his team developed a synthesis for 2-[^{18}F]fluoro-2-deoxy-D-glucose (2-[^{18}F]FDG). Experiments were first carried out with 2-[^{14}C]FDG to establish that 2-FDG retained the biochemical properties of deoxyglucose. The 2-[^{18}F]FDG adaptation of the DG method was then developed and used for the first time in humans with Kuhl's Mark IV Section Scanner (28). Kuhl later moved to UCLA and brought along Michael Phelps and Edward Hoffman, pioneers in the development of positron-emission tomographic scanners. Positron-emission tomography (PET) offered better spatial resolution and accuracy than Kuhl's single photon scanner. They adapted the 2-[^{18}F]FDG technique for use with PET (29), and 2-[^{18}F]FDG is now widely used with PET in studies of the brain and heart in health and disease and for detecting neoplasms in the whole body.

It is gratifying that our basic physiological and biochemical research has become the basis of a new and useful field in neuroscience, i.e. metabolic mapping of brain function or functional brain imaging. We first developed methods to measure blood flow and metabolism in local regions of the conscious functioning brain and then used them to establish that blood flow and energy metabolism are linked to functional activity in neural tissues. Although these methods were designed for in vivo use, they were founded on fundamental physiological and biochemical knowledge, obtained from both in vivo and in vitro studies. Physiology is the physics and chemistry of living systems. Despite all the meandering, that is what has occupied me throughout my career.

REFLECTIONS ON THEN AND NOW

I would be remiss if from a perspective of 50 years in biomedical research I failed to comment on its state today. Certainly, the most striking changes have been in the tremendous expansions of knowledge and technology. Industry provides us with an ever-growing variety of equipment, materials, and supplies that facilitate experimentation. The pace has accelerated, information is accumulating at an overwhelming rate, and scientific literature grows explosively. Computerized techniques to access and manage all this information are becoming more sophisticated and available. It would seem to be a wonderful time for science, but is it equally good for scientists? It reminds me of the popular question after filtered cigarettes were introduced, "Are you smoking more and enjoying it less?" I fear that researchers in the biological sciences are not having as much fun as we once did in a more tranquil age.

When I began, biomedical research was mainly an academic pursuit, supported largely to advance knowledge for knowledge's sake and to educate future generations of scientists. It was like an ivory tower or monastery where one could leisurely ruminate, discuss, debate, and enjoy the processes of inquiry and learning. The process of research was itself as enjoyable as the discovery. Support in my postdoctoral fellowship came from an NIH grant to Kety, whose salary was provided by the university because it was then against NIH policy for principal investigators to receive salary from their own grants and for overhead to exceed 15 percent; fellows and support staff could be salaried. Principal investigators were then necessarily individuals who had already been evaluated and considered qualified for salaried positions by their institutions. The rationale was that it was to the nation's benefit to support research conceived and initiated by qualified scientists. This policy was later changed to one that was more as though the government wanted the work to be done and was, therefore, obligated to pay for all of it, including the principal investigator's salary and total overhead. Universities and research institutions were quick to take advantage of this golden egg. Faculties and departments expanded, every one possible was encouraged to apply for grants, and fellows were rushed through postdoctoral training to become independent as soon as possible. Independence now means having one's own grant and not necessarily being intellectually independent. Consequently, we now have multitudes of trained and not so well trained scientists competing for funds that constantly lag behind the number of grant applications. Many applications fail, and applicants, whose salaries and appointments depend on grants, spend more and more time preparing grant applications and less and less time on research and training of new scientists. Research proposals are often contrived more to get money than to advance knowledge. Corridor and dinner conversations at scientific meetings are now as much or more about grant seeking than about the substance of science. Such was not the case during my fellowship years. We could devote all of our time to research and study because we were supported by grants of senior investigators until we reached scientific maturity, and they, because they had assured salaries from their institutions, had the luxury of developing proposals based on sound scientific ideas rather than on criteria deemed most likely to gain grant support.

Also disturbing is the increasing bias toward so-called useful, goal-directed, disease-related research rather than idea-driven basic research. Researchers and their research are now often judged more on the basis of their area of research than on the uniqueness, originality, or quality of their work. Just working in a "hot" field receives more recognition than solid accomplishments in so-called lesser fields. New disciplines, such as molecular biology and genetics, have unquestionably revolutionized and deservedly assumed prominent roles in the biological sciences, but, unfortunately, it has also led to disparagement of other approaches, such as systems-based research, now often judged old-fashioned and, therefore, unworthy of support. These disciplines have also established close relationships with the biotechnology industry, and commercial interests with profit motives play an ever growing part in biomedical research. The net result, it seems to me, is that biomedical research has become less of an academic and scholarly endeavor that values ideas, fundamental conceptual thinking, and knowledge for knowledge's sake and more like a commercial or industrial enterprise that encourages advertisement, huckstering, and public relations. In short, the climate for biomedical research is now far less idyllic and appealing than it was when I chose to enter it.

Visit the Annual Reviews home page at www.AnnualReviews.org.

LITERATURE CITED

1. Heilbrunn LV. 1938. *An Outline of General Physiology.* Philadelphia: Saunders
2. Mazia D, Clark JM. 1936. Free calcium in the action of stimulating agents on Elodea cells. *Biol. Bull.* 71:306–23
3. Hogeboom GH, Schneider WC, Palade GH. 1948. Isolation of intact mitochondria from rat liver; some biochemical properties of mitochondria and submicroscopic particulate material. *J. Biol. Chem.* 172:619–35
4. Kety SS, Schmidt CF. 1948. The nitrous oxide method for the quantitative determination of cerebral blood flow in man: theory, procedure, and normal values. *J. Clin. Invest.* 27:476–83
5. Kety SS. 1951. The theory and applications of the exchange of inert gas at the lungs and tissues. *Pharmacol. Rev.* 3:1–41
6. Kety SS. 1949. The measurement of regional circulation by local clearance of radioactive sodium. *Am. Heart J.* 38:321–28
7. Galdston I. 1950. Psychiatry without Freud. *AMA Arch. Neurol. Psychiat.* 66:69–81
8. Sokoloff L, Wechsler RL, Mangold R, Balls K, Kety SS. 1953. Cerebral blood flow and oxygen consumption in hyperthyroidism before and after treatment. *J. Clin. Invest.* 32:202–8
9. Sokoloff L, Kaufman S. 1959. The effects of thyroxine on amino acid incorporation into protein. *Science* 129:569–70
10. Sokoloff L, Kaufman S. 1961. Thyroxine stimulation of amino acid incorporation into protein. *J. Biol. Chem.* 236:795–803
11. Dastur DK, Lane ME, Hansen DB, Kety SS, Butler RN, et al. 1963. Effects of aging on cerebral circulation and metabolism in man. In *Human Aging. A Biologic and Behavioral Study,* ed. JE Birren, RN Butler, SW Greenhouse, L Sokoloff, MR Yarrow, Public Health Service Publ. No. 986:59–76.Washington, DC: US GPO
12. Sokoloff L, Perlin S, Kornetsky C, Kety SS. 1957. The effects of D-lysergic acid diethylamide on cerebral circulation and over-all metabolism. *Ann. NY Acad. Sci.* 66:468–77
13. Landau WH, Freygang WH, Rowland LP, Sokoloff L, Kety SS. 1955. The local circulation of the living brain: values in the unanesthetized and anesthetized cat. *Trans. Am. Neurol. Assoc.* 80:125–29
14. Freygang WH, Sokoloff L. 1958. Quantitative measurements of regional circulation in the central nervous system by the use of radioactive inert gas. *Adv. Biol. Med. Physics* 6:263–79
15. Kety SS. 1960. Measurement of local blood flow by the exchange of an inert, diffusible substance. In *Methods in Medical Research,* ed. HD Bruner, VIII:228–36. Chicago: Year Book Publ.
16. Sokoloff L. 1961. Local cerebral circulation at rest and during altered cerebral activity induced by anesthesia or visual stimulation. In *The Regional Chemistry, Physiology, and Pharmacology of the Nervous System,* ed. SS Kety, J Elkes, pp. 107–17. Oxford, UK: Pergamon

17. Sols A, Crane RK. 1954. Substrate specificity of brain hexokinase. *J. Biol. Chem.* 210:581–95

18. Reivich M, Jehle J, Sokoloff L, Kety SS. 1969. Measurement of regional cerebral blood flow with antipyrine-^{14}C in awake cats. *J. Appl. Physiol.* 27:296–300

19. Sakurada O, Kennedy C, Jehle J, Brown JD, Carbin GL, Sokoloff L. 1978. Measurement of local cerebral blood flow with iodo[14]C]antipyrine. *Am. J. Physiol.* 234:H59–66

20. Reivich M, Sano N, Sokoloff L. 1971. Development of an autoradiographic method for the determination of regional glucose consumption. In *Brain and Blood Flow,* ed. RW Ross-Russell, pp. 397–400. London: Pitman

21. Pommier J, Sokoloff L, Nunez J. 1973. Enzymatic iodination of protein. Kinetics of iodine formation and protein iodination catalyzed by horse-radish peroxidase. *Eur. J. Biochem.* 3 8:497–506

22. Sokoloff L, Reivich M, Kennedy C, Des Rosiers MH, Patlak CS, et al. 1977. The ^{14}C]deoxyglucose method for the measurement of local cerebral glucose utilization: theory, procedure, and normal values in the conscious and anesthetized albino rat. *J. Neurochem.* 28:897–16

23. Sokoloff L. 1981. Localization of functional activity in the central nervous system by measurement of glucose utilization with radioactive deoxyglucose. *J. Cereb. Blood Flow Metab.* 1:7–36

24. Sokoloff L. 1982. The radioactive deoxyglucose method. Theory, procedure, and applications for the measurement of local glucose utilization in the central nervous system. In *Advances in Neurochemistry,* ed. BW Agranoff, MH Aprison MH, 4:1–82. New York: Plenum

25. Kennedy C, Des Rosiers MH, Jehle JW, Reivich M, Sharp F, Sokoloff L. 1975. Mapping of functional neural pathways by autoradiographic survey of local metabolic rate with ^{14}C]deoxyglucose. *Science* 187:850–53

26. Kennedy C, Des Rosiers MH, Sakurada O, Shinohara M, Reivich M, et al. 1976. Metabolic mapping of the primary visual system of the monkey by means of the autoradiographic ^{14}C]deoxyglucose technique. *Proc. Natl. Acad. Sci. USA* 73:4230–34

27. Goochee C, Rasband W, Sokoloff L. 1980. Computerized densitometry and color coding of ^{14}C]deoxyglucose autoradiographs. *Ann. Neurol.* 7:359–70

28. Reivich M, Kuhl D, Wolf A, Greenberg J, Phelps M, et al. 1979. The ^{18}F]fluorodeoxyglucose method for the measurement of local cerebral glucose utilization in man. *Circ. Res.* 44:127–37

29. Phelps ME, Huang SC, Hoffman EJ, Selin C, Sokoloff L, Kuhl DE. 1979. Tomographic measurement of local cerebral glucose metabolic rate in humans with (F-18)2–fluoro-2–deoxy-D-glucose: validation of method. *Ann. Neurol.* 6:371–88

Annu. Rev. Physiol. 2000. 62:25–50

VENTRICULAR FIBRILLATION:
Mechanisms of Initiation and Maintenance

José Jalife

*Department of Pharmacology, SUNY Health Science Center at Syracuse, Syracuse,
New York 13210; e-mail: jalifej@vax.cs.hscsyr.edu*

Key Words sudden death, cardiac turbulence, ventricles, phase singularities,
wavebreaks, vortex-like reentry, rotors, spiral waves, scroll waves,
fibrillatory conduction

■ **Abstract**   Ventricular fibrillation (VF) is the major immediate cause of sudden
cardiac death. Traditionally, VF has been defined as turbulent cardiac electrical activity, which implies a large amount of irregularity in the electrical waves that underlie
ventricular excitation. During VF, the heart rate is too high (> 550 excitations/minute)
to allow adequate pumping of blood. In the electrocardiogram (ECG), ventricular
complexes that are ever-changing in frequency, contour, and amplitude characterize
VF. This article reviews prevailing theories for the initiation and maintenance of VF,
as well as its spatio-temporal organization. Particular attention is given to recent
experiments and computer simulations suggesting that VF may be explained in terms
of highly periodic three-dimensional rotors that activate the ventricles at exceedingly
high frequency. Such rotors may show at least two different behaviors: (*a*) At one
extreme, they may drift throughout the heart at high speeds producing beat-to-beat
changes in the activation sequence. (*b*) At the other extreme, rotors may be relatively
stationary, activating the ventricles at such high frequencies that the wave fronts emanating from them breakup at varying distances, resulting in complex spatio-temporal
patterns of fibrillatory conduction. In either case, the recorded ECG patterns are indistinguishable from VF. The data discussed have paved the way for a better understanding of the mechanisms of VF in the normal, as well as the diseased, human heart.

> *When the heart is diseased, its work is imperfectly performed: the vessels*
> *proceeding from the heart become inactive, so that you cannot feel them . . .*
> *If the heart trembles, has little power and sinks, the disease is advancing and*
> *death is near.*
>
> Ebers Papyrus ~3500 BC

INTRODUCTION

Ventricular fibrillation (VF) is a major health problem in society and in clinical
practice. In the United States alone, approximately 300,000 patients die suddenly
each year because of VF (1, 2). During VF, the ventricular contraction is uncoor-

0066–4278/00/0315–0025$12.00

dinated and produces no effective systolic tension. Consequently, the arterial pressure suddenly drops to exceedingly low levels, and death usually ensues within less than ten minutes as a result of lack of oxygen delivery to vital organs. On the electrocardiogram (ECG), VF is diagnosed by the occurrence of completely aperiodic and irregular beat-to-beat changes in the ventricular electrical complexes. Thus from the ECG, VF brings to mind the idea that the activation of the three-dimensional ventricular muscle is extremely heterogeneous and complex (3), which has led to the general belief that VF is the result of totally random and disorganized activation. In fact, traditional concepts are based on the hypothesis that VF is the result of multiple wandering wave fronts of electrical excitation (4). Such wave fronts are thought to continually change in shape and direction, moving about independently at random across the ventricles and producing highly irregular patterns of local excitation (4, 5). Hence, the prevailing definition of VF as turbulent cardiac electrical activity (5, 6) from which one envisions a large amount of aperiodicity in the electrical waves that underlie ventricular excitation.

However, the recent application of nonlinear dynamics theory to the study of wave propagation in the heart (7–10), together with high resolution mapping techniques (11–20), has enabled investigators to think of ventricular fibrillation as a problem of self-organization of nonlinear electrical waves with both deterministic and stochastic components. This has led to the application of new experimental and numerical approaches to the study of the two-dimensional and three-dimensional spatio-temporal patterns of excitation that result in VF (21, 22). The purpose of this article is, first, to provide an historical perspective and review the most salient literature on the study of mechanisms of initiation and maintenance of VF. Second, to discuss recently published data that strongly support the hypothesis that VF in the structurally and electrophysiologically normal heart is not a totally random phenomenon.

HISTORICAL PERSPECTIVE

The passage quoted above from the Ebers Papyrus (23, 24) indicates that man has been aware of some of the key features of ventricular fibrillation since ancient times. In his classical anatomy book titled *De Humani Corporis Fabrica,* published in 1543, Andreas Vesalius referred to "worm-like" movements occurring just before death in the hearts he dissected from animals (24). Erichsen (25) published the first description of the onset of VF as a pathophysiological entity consequent to coronary artery ligation in 1842. Subsequently, in 1950, Hoffa & Ludwig (26) demonstrated that fibrillation can be induced by the application of faradic current. Yet Vulpian (27) appears to have been the first one to call the arrhythmia *mouvement fibrillaire* in an article published in 1874. In 1887, McWilliam (28) provided the first detailed visual description of VF, and subsequently (29) demonstrated how VF in man could be terminated by repetitive electric shocks applied through a large pair of electrodes, one located on the ventricular apex and the other over the sixth or seventh dorsal vertebra. Mc-William's brilliant observations on VF and defibrillation had to await the advent of the ECG to be fully appreciated. In 1911, Levy & Lewis (30) used the ECG to demonstrate that when VF occurred during chloroform anesthesia, it was often preceded by the appearance of multiform ventricular extrasystoles or ventricular tachycardia. However, it was Hoffman (31) who published in 1912 the first ECG of ventricular fibrillation in man. In the same year, Erlanger (32) brought attention to the fact that large beef hearts fibrillate with relative ease, and that once initiated, the arrhythmia seldom stops, as in other smaller hearts, by means of a bolus perfusion of KCl solution.

But it was Garrey (33) who, in 1914, published the first systematic study on the relationship between VF and the size of the heart. Previously, McWilliam observed that spontaneous recovery from VF may take place readily in the hearts of the cat, rabbit, rat, mouse, hedgehog, and fowl (29, 34). Based partly on McWilliam's observations and on his own experimental studies, Garrey (33) enunciated his well-known hypothesis of the "Critical Mass." As stated in his landmark article, "the ease with which the fibrillary process may be induced and with which spontaneous recovery from the fibrillary contractions takes place is inversely proportional to the mass of fibrillating tissue." Garrey (33) observed that any piece cut from any part of the mass of ventricular tissue obtained from mammals or turtles would cease fibrillating if its surface area was less than four square centimeters. In the same study he also found that rings cut from the base of the fibrillating ventricles of large turtles would not recover from the fibrillatory contractions. Moreover, if the ring was made thin enough, the uncoordinated fibrillatory contractions organized themselves into rotating waves that followed each other successively and repeatedly around the ring, in a manner similar to that described independently by Mines (35) for circus movement reentry. Lewis (36) also advocated the reentry mechanism. These seminal studies laid the foundation for our current understanding of the mechanisms and dynamics of VF. In fact, it was Garrey (33) who provided the first mechanistic description of the arrhythmia in terms of "intramuscular ringlike circuits, with resulting 'circus contractions' which are fundamentally essential to the fibrillary process." Garrey was also the first to report the possibility of setting up vortex-like reentrant circuits around a stimulated region without any anatomical obstacle, an idea that was later dismissed by theorists (37) but more recently confirmed by experimentalists (17, 38–40).

In 1930, Wiggers (41) conducted high-speed cinematographic studies on the evolution of VF produced by an electric shock in the dog heart and demonstrated that the uninterrupted arrhythmia goes through four different stages: (1) undulatory, lasting for a second or two; (2) convulsive incoordination, which lasts from 15 to 40 s; (3) tremulous incoordination, lasting 2 to 3 min; (4) atonic fibrillation, which usually develops 2 to 5 min after the onset of VF. During the undulatory and convulsive incoordination stages, the ventricular activation frequency is very high (about 10 Hz), whereas in the tremulous incoordination and atonic fibrillation stages, the activation rate gradually slows as a result of ischemia (3, 41, 42). Based on these and other observations (3, 41), Wiggers concluded that both formation of limited circuits and reentry occur throughout the evolution of fibrillation. Most important, he was first to bring attention to the fact that, "inasmuch as sequential reentrant excitations travel over a bulky mass of ventricular muscle, one must not think in terms of two-dimensional rings or circuits, but rather of massive wave fronts spreading in three dimensions" (43).

By the 1950s there seemed to be general agreement that atrial or ventricular tachycardias could certainly be produced either by repetitive discharges from an ectopic focus (44) or by the circulation of a wave front around an obstacle (37, 45). In either case, it was proposed that under certain conditions, the impulse initiated at the reentrant circuit or at the pacemaker source could occur so rapidly that neighboring tissues would be unable to respond regularly, thus giving rise to the apparently chaotic ECG pattern of fibrillation. In 1956, however, Moe (46) proposed that the mechanism of fibrillation was fundamentally different from that of tachycardia. His observations led him to contend that during fibrillation there was total disorganization of activity. He envisioned the arrhythmia as being the result of randomly wandering wave fronts, ever changing in number and direction. Subsequently, in 1959 Moe & Abildskov (47) demonstrated that atrial fibrillation could exist as a stable state, self-sustained and independent of its initiating agency, but also that such an independent survival of the arrhythmia was possible only in the presence of inhomogeneous repolarization. In 1962, Moe (4) postulated the "multiple wavelet" hypothesis of atrial fibrillation, in which randomness in the temporal and spatial distribution of membrane properties plays dominant roles. In 1964, Han & Moe (48) carried out a series of important experiments testing the effects of various agencies on the refractory period of the ventricular muscle and established the importance of heterogeneity in the relatively refractory period in the induction of cardiac fibrillation. The same year (5), the multiple wavelet hypothesis was crystallized by the development of the first computer model of cardiac fibrillation in two-dimensional myocardium. It demonstrated that without heterogeneous distribution of refractory periods reentrant activity remained periodic and the arrhythmia did not degenerate into fibrillation. Experimental support for the multiple wavelet hypothesis had to await about 20 years, until the development of high-resolution electrode mapping technology. In 1985, Allessie et al (49) mapped the spread of excitation in the atria of a dog heart during acetylcholine-induced atrial fibrillation and provided the first in vivo demonstration of multiple propagating wavelets giving rise to turbulent atrial activity.

Although Moe's computer model was intended to simulate atrial fibrillation, a large body of experimental literature has subsequently appeared in which it is assumed that the multiple wavelet hypothesis also applies to the mechanism of ventricular fibrillation (50–53). Thus, the traditional consensus is that, although focal activation may play a role in the initiation of the arrhythmia, maintenance of fibrillation in the three-dimensional ventricles involves multiple wandering wavelets of activation whose pathways usually change randomly from one cycle the next (4). However, in recent years, the use of computer modeling, together with newer and more advanced high-resolution mapping technology, has led to the reemergence of an old controversy: Are the complex dynamics of VF the result of the random occurrence and propagation of multiple independent wavelets (4, 5)? Or are multiple wavelets a consequence of the sustained activity of a single or a small number of dominant reentrant sources activating the ventricles at exceedingly high frequencies (21, 36, 54, 55)? Such questions are the subject of intense investigation in cardiac electrophysiology and nonlinear dynamics today.

INITIATION OF FIBRILLATION

Electrical Induction of VF and The Vulnerable Domain

In 1923, de Boer (56) first demonstrated that a single electric shock delivered late in systole to the frog's ventricle induced fibrillation. In 1940, Wiggers & Wégria (57) confirmed de Boer's results and further demonstrated that the application of very short electrical shocks to a small area on the ventricle induced VF when the shocks fell during late systole but never at any other phase of the heart cycle. This was termed the vulnerable phase of systole (57). A year later, Wégria et al (58) demonstrated that the vulnerable phase was of longer duration in premature ventricular complexes than in normal beats. Also, Moe et al (59) carried out detailed electrographic studies of the mechanism of reentry initiation by shocks applied during the vulnerable phase. Their results indicated that repetitive impulses induced by the shock were accompanied by a progressive decrease in refractory period combined with an increase in conduction time.

It is now well established that stimulating the ventricles during the vulnerable phase induces VF. However, despite intense investigation, no quantitative understanding of VF initiation has yet found widespread support. In a seminal paper published in 1946, Weiner & Rosenblueth (37), gave a theoretical description of the mechanisms of initiation of flutter and fibrillation in cardiac muscle in the presence and the absence of anatomical obstacles. They postulated that wave rotation around single or multiple obstacles was necessary to initiate and maintain both types of arrhythmia, which they assumed to be the result of a single reentrant mechanism. They also provided an explanation for how successive stimulation of two overlapping small regions in a two-dimensional excitable sheet, in the absence of an obstacle, gave rise to a single extra wave propagating in one direction. They considered this to be an unstable situation and dismissed the possibility that sustained rotating activity could be initiated in a homogeneous two-dimensional system (37) in this or any other manner in the absence of natural obstacles. Interestingly, in 1948, Selfridge (60) modified Weiner & Rosenblueth's model and showed a vortex in a two-dimensional medium.

An elegant theory of initiation of vortices in two dimensions that has been supported by experiments in a wide variety of excitable media appeared more than 30 years later. It is based on the "pinwheel experiment" protocol devised by Winfree (9, 61). In a two-dimensional sheet of excitable medium, this protocol involves the simultaneous establishment of a spatial gradient of momentary stimulus intensity with a spatial gradient of refractoriness by the prior passage of an activation front through the medium (62). According to this theory, when a stimulus of the right size is given at the right time, mirror image vortices begin to pivot around crossings of critical contours of transverse gradients of phase and stimulus intensity. The critical phase roughly corresponds to the vulnerable phase of Wiggers & Wégria (57) and falls near the end of the refractory period (63). On the basis of this theory, a vulnerable domain was described, whose temporal location happened to be just before complete recovery from a previous excitation. With its limits of timing and stimulus intensity, the idea of vulnerable domain complemented the empirical concept of the vulnerable phase. In 1988, Shibata et al (64) demonstrated the applicability of Winfree's theory (9, 61) to the induction of fibrillation in cardiac muscle. By pacing the ventricles of a dog and recording the sequence of activation after a strong shock during the vulnerable phase, they found that a pair of counter rotating waves could be formed at certain reproducible regions in the heart. As predicted by the theory, when the amplitude of the shock is large, the vortices can be induced even in completely uniform and healthy myocardium (62, 65). The key issue here is that a shock of appropriate amplitude applied at a critical phase within the vulnerable domain produces a transient discontinuity, called a phase singularity,which becomes the organizing center of a vortex (65, 66). Frazier et al (13) used an array of extracellular recording electrodes in combination with a variant of the pinwheel experiment, the so-called twin-pulse protocol, to demonstrate the mechanism of reentry and fibrillation in the canine ventricles. They used the term critical point to refer to a phase singularity and provided strong support to what is now universally known as the critical point hypothesis for the initiation of vortex-like reentry and fibrillation (13). They also demonstrated that there is an upper limit of vulnerability for VF, which establishes that, even when applied during the vulnerable phase, shocks whose strength is larger than a certain limit should not induce fibrillation. However, as discussed in depth by Roth & Krassowska (63), the precise mechanism by which the experimental approach of Frazier et al (13) leads to the initiation of vortices in cardiac muscle remains unexplained. The reason for this is that to date no experimental verification using transmembrane potential recordings has been published providing a complete demonstration of the details of activation sequence that follows the S_2 shock (63). Nevertheless, the critical point hypothesis has become one of the major explanations on which current understanding of the mechanisms of initiation of fibrillation as well as defibrillation is based (63, 67).

Another approach to initiating phase singularities and vortices is the cross-field stimulation protocol (17, 18). It differs from the pinwheel protocol described above in that the formation of vortices does not require a very large stimulus. In cross-field stimulation, a conditioning stimulus S_1 is used to initiate a plane wave propagating in one direction. Thereafter, a second stimulus, S_2, is applied perpendicularly to S_1 and timed to allow the interaction between a section of the S_2 wave front and a section of the recovery tail of the S_1 wave (for details see 18). Because the S_2 wave front cannot move on and invade refractory tissue at its site of interaction with the S_1 wave tail, it breaks, forming a phase singularity at the endpoint around which the S_2 wave begins to rotate. Computer simulations and experiments in thin sheets of ventricular epicardial muscle have demonstrated the ability of cross-field stimulation to induce sustained or drifting vortex-like reentry (68, 69).

The pinwheel and cross-field stimulation protocols require two different stimuli applied at different locations. However, both reentry and fibrillation can also be induced with relative ease by successive stimulation through a single unipolar (70) or bipolar (19) electrode. As suggested by Keener (71), the discrete nature of cardiac tissue and its structural anisotropy may play crucial roles here. Winfree (72) speculated that in the context of a bidomain model (73, 74) with anisotropies of the intracellular and extracellular spaces, application of two successive stimuli may result in four rather than two critical phase locations and induce four different rotors. More recently, it has been shown that in the presence of such unequal anisotropies, the transmembrane voltage contour of the S_2 wave front has a dogbone shape, which separates a region of depolarization under the cathode from regions of hyperpolarization 1 to 2 cm away along the fiber direction. In computer simulations, Saypol & Roth (75) and Roth (76) have shown that the mechanism of reentry following successive stimulation from a single unipolar electrode can be explained accurately by this model with unequal anisotropic ratios. A good agreement exists between the numerical studies using the bidomain model and experimental observation of reentry initiation using unipolar stimulation (77).

Phase Singularities and the Spontaneous Formation of Rotors in Two Dimensions

Current knowledge suggests that the most dangerous cardiac arrhythmias are the result of reentrant activity (1, 2, 53, 78), whereby electrical waves may rotate uninterruptedly and in a self-sustaining manner to give rise to high frequency electrical activity that propagates throughout the ventricles. It is generally believed that the initiating event in spontaneous reentrant arrhythmias may be the formation of circuits (79, 80), or of vortices (21, 22), brought about by the interaction of a propagating wave front with an obstacle in its path. Reentry may also be initiated by a spontaneous premature beat, which may be in the form of an early or delayed afterdepolarization (81, 82), the so-called triggered activity. Because of space limitations, the discussion here focuses exclusively on possible mechanisms of spontaneous reentry initiation by the interaction of waves with anatomical or functional obstacles. The interested reader is encouraged to consult articles by El-Sherif et al (83) and Asano et al (84) for excellent demonstrations of how triggered activity can initiate complex reentrant rhythms, including polymorphous ventricular tachycardia and VF.

Reentry is usually represented in two spatial dimensions (17, 18, 38–40). However, myocardial tissue is three-dimensional, and it is important to consider the full thickness of the ventricles when vortex-like reentry occurs. Surely, only experimental work can provide definite answers about three-dimensional vortex dynamics in the ventricles, but the technology available to date does not permit extensive recordings of waves moving through the ventricular myocardium to enable one to reach reliable conclusions about such dynamics. However, some qualitative features of three-dimensional vortex-like reentry can be predicted from theoretical and experimental analysis of two-dimensional myocardium (9, 78). As discussed elsewhere (78), the study of vortex dynamics in two-dimensions provides a good general qualitative understanding of vortex dynamics in three-dimensions, although there may be important differences when it comes to quantitative details.

The concept of phase singularity (65) has contributed substantially to our current understanding of the mechanisms of spontaneous initiation and maintenance of reentrant arrhythmias (8, 85–87). As previously shown in computer simulations and in the Ce-catalyzed Belousov-Zhabotinsky (BZ) reaction (88), under appropriate conditions of excitability, the interaction of a wave front with an obstacle can lead to fragmentation of that wave front and to vortex-like reentry. Hence, reentrant waves begin either as single vortices (17, 38, 40) or as pairs of counterrotating vortices (80). They may be initiated by the interaction of a propagating wave front with an appropriate obstacle in its path (18). In three-dimensional excitable media, the phase singularity is not a point but a filament (89), and the rotating vortex is a scroll (78, 90, 91).

Using a generic model of an excitable two-dimensional medium, Nagy-Ungvarai et al (92) and Pertsov et al (93) studied the conditions in which a propagating wave breaks after colliding with an obstacle. They concluded that a wavebreak leads to the formation of phase singularities at the broken endpoints whose dynamics depend on the existence of a critical curvature for propagation in the medium. When the curvature of the wave front in the area of the break was higher than critical, the wave would shrink, resulting in two-dimensional decremental conduction (92). If the curvature of the front was lower than critical, the wave would expand. If the expansion was slow and the size of the obstacle was large enough, the broken end would curve and give rise to vortex-like activity (92, 93). This concept of wavebreak is important not only for the understanding of reentry initiation, but also for the understanding of the interactions of wave fronts with anatomical as well as functional obstacles in their paths (88, 94, 95). Inhomogeneities in cardiac muscle may cause a break in a propagating wave, leading to phase singularities. In addition, changes in excitability may be used to fine tune such instabilities, in such a way that when excitability is low, a broken wave should contract and vanish (i.e. conduction block). However, at an intermediate level of excitability, a broken wave may either remain unchanged and propagate or curve and expand, resulting in initiation of vortex-like activity (95). As predicted by experiments in the BZ reaction and by simulations (92, 93), the dynamics of phase singularities should be determined by (*a*) the critical curvature of the wave front (i.e. the curvature at which propagation ceases), (*b*) the excitability of the medium, and (*c*) the frequency of wave succession. If frequency is excessively high, it would have the effect of decreasing the excitability; the obstacle must have sharp corners (88).

A two-dimensional representation of the initiation of reentry is illustrated in Figure 1, where one can observe the expected evolution of an electrical wave front that interacts with a relatively large anatomical obstacle (e.g. a scar) in a bounded sheet of cardiac muscle. Three different conditions of excitability are studied. In panel *A,* when the excitability of the sheet is high, upon circumnavi-

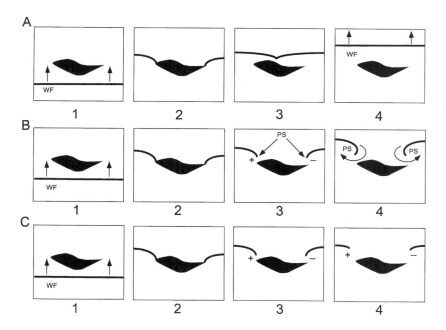

Figure 1   Formation of a wavebreak. In both panels, a wave front (WF) is seen moving upward to interact with an unexcitable obstacle, shown in black. (*A*) Normal excitability, Upon reaching the obstacle, the wave front splits in two. The two newly formed wave fronts circumnavigate the obstacle without detaching from it and then merge into a common wave front that continues moving upward, apparently undisturbed by its interaction with the discontinuity. (*B*) Lower excitability. The two broken wave fronts (wavelets) now detach from the obstacle, resulting in the formation of a singularity point (PS; also known as phase singularities) at the broken end of each wavelet. This leads to two counter rotating vortices. (*C*) When excitability is too low, the two broken waves are unable to rotate and instead undergo decremental conduction.

gating the obstacle, and without detaching from it, the two broken ends of the wave front (WF) come together and fuse; the wave front thus recovers its previous shape and moves on. No reentry is initiated in this case. However, in panel B, when the excitability is lower (or the excitation frequency is higher), upon detachment from the obstacle, the broken ends do not converge but move in opposite directions and the wave front fragments into two wavelets, each flanked by a phase singularity (PS) and a boundary. Curling of the two wave fronts around their respective phase singularities initiates functional reentry with two counter-rotating waves (figure-eight reentry). In panel C, when the excitability is too low, the wave front again breaks. However, after detaching from the obstacle, the two fragmented wavelets gradually shrink and die off (i.e. they undergo decremental conduction). Even though the broken ends of such wavelets do not progress laterally but shrink, forward propagation is similar to planar propagation. Eventually, as a result of the progressive shrinking of the broken ends, the excitation wave collapses.

The characteristics of the obstacle with which the wave front interacts also play a role in determining the formation of wavebreaks and vortex-like activity, including its shape and size. It has been shown in the BZ reaction that, for rotating waves to be initiated in the vicinity of an unexcitable barrier, the barrier must have sharp corners, as a wavebreak will not detach from a slowly curving barrier (88). In numerical simulations, Pertsov et al (96) demonstrated that a wave propagates much more readily through the distal end of a long channel than through a narrow slit in an unexcitable screen. In the former case, the distal end of the channel is equivalent to a slowly curving obstacle (90°), whereas in the latter, the slit corresponds to an obstacle with sharp curvature (180°). Hence, the necessary conditions for initiation of vortices by the interaction of a wave with an obstacle interposed in its path are a sufficiently short period of stimulation (i.e. sufficiently low excitability) and an obstacle of sufficient size and sufficiently sharp corners. As shown by Agladze et al (88), if the size of the obstacle is too small, or the stimulation period is too long, a planar wave initiated proximally to the obstacle will split at the obstacle into two waves with free ends, each of which will circumnavigate the obstacle (see Figure 1A). Subsequently, the two wave ends will meet again to form a single wave. However, when the size of the obstacle is large enough or the excitation period becomes shorter than some critical value, the wave splits and the ends remain separated from the obstacle and from each other (see Figure 1B). As discussed above, depending on the conditions of excitability, a pair of counter rotating waves may be formed beyond the obstacle.

As predicted by theory, the size of the obstacle must be equal to or greater than the width of the wave front for detachment to occur (97). At a propagation speed of about 0.5 cm/s, the wave front width in normal cardiac muscle is about 1 mm (98–100). It therefore follows that obstacles of 1 mm or larger have the potential for breaking wave fronts and generating phase singularities and vortex-like reentry.

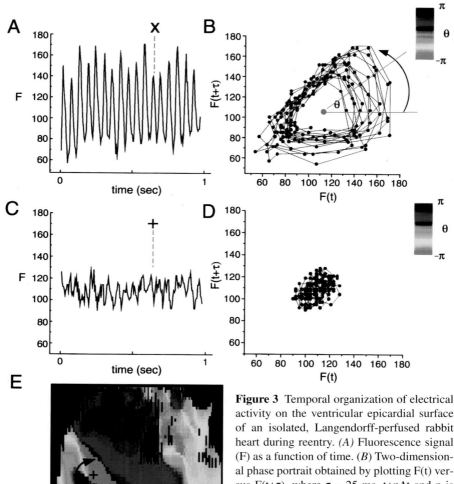

Figure 3 Temporal organization of electrical activity on the ventricular epicardial surface of an isolated, Langendorff-perfused rabbit heart during reentry. *(A)* Fluorescence signal (F) as a function of time. *(B)* Two-dimensional phase portrait obtained by plotting F(t) versus F(t+τ), where τ = 25 ms, t+nΔt and n is the video frame number (~8.3 ms/frame). Note trajectories circling around a center (F_{mean},F_{mean}) shown as a red dot. This allows the representation of the state of this recording site by its phase (θ) around the loop. *(C)* Fluorescence (F) changes at a single pixel showing very low amplitude oscillations, which suggests that the phase singularity was nearby. *(D)* Plot of F(t) versus F(t+τ) of the same signal shows how phase becomes undefined when the pixel is near the phase singularity. *(E)* Color isophase map, constructed by recording phase simultaneously from 20,000 pixels for one rotation during sustained clockwise vortex-like reentrant activity. The map corresponds to the times indicated by the broken vertical lines in A and C. Green represents wave front; red represents wave tail (see color codes for θ in B and D). Note that in E, all wave fronts converge toward the singularity (+). The x and + indicate the positions on the epicardium of pixels whose dynamics are represented in panels A-B and C-D, respectively.

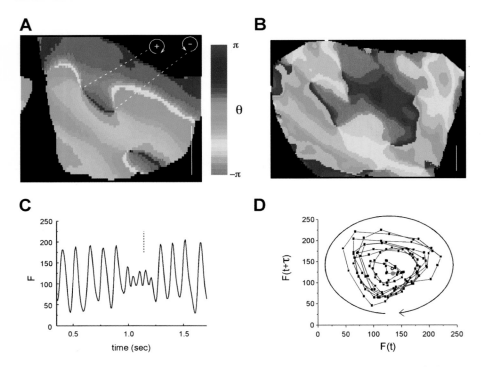

Figure 4 Snapshots of phase from the heart surface of the rabbit (*A*) and sheep (*B*) during sustained fibrillation showing coexisting phase singularities. Sense of rotation (chirality) is indicated by + for clockwise and - for counterclockwise rotation. (*A*) At this instant, three phase singularities (two clockwise and one counterclockwise) are observed. (*B*) In the larger sheep heart, nine singularities (five clockwise and four counterclockwise are seen). The variable phase, θ(t), was computed as Arc tan(F(t+τ)-F$_{mean}$,F(t)-F$_{mean}$). (*C*) Time series of fluorescence (F) from a single pixel showing low amplitude oscillations at the instant when the phase singularity is nearby. (*D*) When plotted as F(t) versus F(t+τ), the same signal remains near the center of the phase portrait; i.e. phase becomes undefined at the phase singularity. Dashed line and red dot indicate the time of the corresponding snapshot. Vertical line in *A* and *B* represents 1 cm. (Modified from Gray RA, Pertsov AM, Jalife J. 1998. *Nature* 392:75-78, by permission.)

The above phenomenon, termed vortex shedding, has been demonstrated in cardiac muscle (95) and is analogous to the formation of eddies in hydrodynamical systems (e.g. water waves interacting with physical obstacles in their paths). From the standpoint of cardiac electrophysiology, the concept of vortex shedding enables one to device testable quantitative predictions for the initiation and evolution of wavelets and vortices in VF. To illustrate the usefulness of such predictions, we start from the assumption that cardiac muscle represents an excellent substrate for the establishment of spatial gradients of refractory periods, as a result of a combination of structural and electrophysiological inhomogeneities (2, 79). In addition, we assume that, somewhere in the heart, conditions are established for the development of a dominant source of electrical waves. The source initiates such waves at very high frequency (e.g. a rapidly firing ectopic pacemaker), which sets the stage for interactions of the propagating wave fronts with the refractory tails of previously propagating waves. In Figure 2, theoretical predictions are illustrated for initiation of a wavelet by the interaction of a wave front with a functional barrier (e.g. a region of cells with relatively long and heterogeneous

Figure 2   Wave front-wave tail interactions lead to the formation of a pair of spatial phase singularities. The excitation wave front (gray line) cannot proceed into the refractory tail region (black line), and hence breaks, forming two phase singularities. Sustained rotation in the form of a pair of rotors occurs if the singularities are separated by a distance larger than the critical distance. (*A*) Sufficient space between the singularities allows the two excitation waves to rotate around them. (*B*) The singularities formed are too close to each other. The lack of enough elbow room leads to mutual annihilation of the two newly formed wave fronts before completion of a full rotation. (Modified from Gray RA, Pertsov AM, Jalife J. 1998. *Nature* 392:75–78, by permission.)

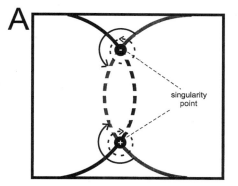

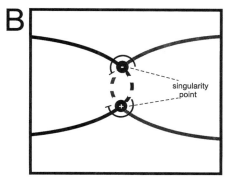

refractory periods). A pair of counter rotating waves forms when the local gradient becomes large; i.e. when the depolarization wave front (gray line) approaches a region that has not yet fully recovered (black line) from previous excitation. Similarly to what happens in vortex shedding, (see Figure 1), the depolarization wave cannot proceed into the incompletely repolarized barrier, so it breaks and wraps around the two break points (i.e. phase singularities; 65). If, as shown in panel *A* of Figure 2, the distance between the newly created phase singularities is sufficiently large, a pair of counter-rotating waves (figure-eight reentry) will emerge. However, as shown in panel *B,* if the distance between the singularities is too small, then neither of the two counter rotating waves would have enough "elbow room," such that their fronts would collide and mutually annihilate. Under these conditions the life span of the two wavelets will be extremely brief (95). As shown below, such predictions are borne out by experimental results. Recently, the appropriate tools have been developed to provide a more quantitative understanding of vortex and wavelet dynamics in VF.

MECHANISMS OF VF MAINTENANCE

Is Sustained VF Organized or Random?

From his early cinematographic studies, Wiggers (41) concluded that VF could not be adequately described as an asynchronous contraction of individual myocardial fibers. His observations suggested that the apparent lack of coordination and synchrony first involved relatively large areas of the myocardium, which seemed to gradually multiply and decrease in size as fibrillation evolved through its various stages. However, as Wiggers observed (41, 43), even during stage 3 (convulsive incoordination), in which all areas seemed to contract out of phase with each other, contraction of adjacent myocardial fibers within a give area seemed to occur with certain degree of synchrony. These observations are compatible with the idea that fibrillation is caused by wandering wavelets moving along randomly changing pathways that may change from one cycle to the next (4, 5). Thus, in the context of contemporary theory of the dynamics of wavebreaks and phase singularities (65, 88, 93, 95), one could conceive the unstable and fragmented activation that characterizes VF as being the result of waves that have been broken by interaction with the refractory tails of other waves (101) or with obstacles. As they break, some of these waves may shrink and undergo decremental conduction; other broken waves may propagate unchanged until annihilated by random collision with another wave or boundary; and still other waves will undergo curling around their phase singularities to create new vortices. The final result would be the fragmentation of the wave fronts into multiple daughter wavebreaks, giving rise to new wavebreaks that sometimes may lead to new vortices and more wavebreaks, and so on in a continuing self-perpetuating motion that is the hallmark of VF.

However, not infrequently during VF, excitation appears somewhat periodic, with sequentially occurring wave fronts that follow approximately the same pathway of activation (102). In addition, occasionally during VF, relatively stable vortices are observed to activate the ventricles for several cycles (21, 50). In 1981, Ideker et al (103) used an electrode mapping array to show that organized electrical activity occurred on the ventricular epicardium in the open-chest dog despite a disorganized pattern in the ECG during the transition to VF. More recently, Damle et al (104) demonstrated, also in the dog heart, spatial and temporal linking of successive epicardial activation patterns. Thus it appears that VF is not a totally random arrhythmia, which suggests the possibility of being able to quantify the spatial and temporal organization of the propagating waves. Nevertheless, it is clear that despite some lurking organization, VF is a complex process and its quantification is extremely difficult.

Standard techniques, such as spectral correlation and coherence analysis (105,106), as well as nontraditional nonlinear dynamics approaches have been used to study VF organization (106, 107). Ropella et al (105) studied the coherence of bipolar recordings of patients in sinus rhythm, tachycardia, and fibrillation. They found that the mean magnitude-squared value of the coherence was significantly lower during fibrillation compared with the other two rhythms. However, they did not state how far apart their electrodes were spaced, but it is reasonable to assume that even during fibrillation nearby regions were correlated, as suggested later by Bayly et al (106). The latter investigators used a rectangular array of 529 unipolar electrodes covering an area 2.35 x 2.46 cm to study spatial correlation during ventricular fibrillation in the open-chest pig heart. They condensed VF episodes into a single number, the correlation length, and found it to be approximately 4 to 11 mm, which is much smaller than the scale of the heart but larger than the inter-electrode spacing. On the basis of such measurements, Bayly et al (106, 108) estimated that at a given instant, there may exist up to 75 to 500 approximately independent areas of activity on the myocardium. It is important to note, however, that the field of view of unipolar electrodes is also 5 to 10 mm, so care must be taken in interpreting those results. Another attempt to make spatio-temporal correlations during VF was performed by Damle et al (104), who used the analysis of vector loops. This method involved calculating vectors that indicated the direction of waves at each site, either instantaneously or for each beat. They created a linear model to predict the wave direction at a given site using the activation directions of neighboring sites. They found that the degree of linking was correlated (r-value between 0.39 and 0.88) during VF. This indicated strong evidence for some degree of spatio-temporal organization during fibrillation.

Garfinkel et al (10) applied nonlinear dynamics theory to the study of fibrillation under stationary conditions. They used three different biological models and carried out computer simulations to test the idea that fibrillation is deterministic. In all four studies they found that fibrillation arose through an oscillatory process that was modulated by other oscillatory processes, resembling the quasiperiodic transition to chaos that has been shown in the development of fluid turbulence (109). They concluded that fibrillation is a form of spatio-temporal chaos. However, more recently, Bayly et al (108) used multiple electrode mapping in combination with several analytical techniques to quantify spatial organization and predictability of VF as it progresses from its onset in open-chest pigs. Although all measurements of organization and repeatability suggested that there was spatio-temporal reorganization after the initial breakdown of activity when VF was initiated, the results indicated that the arrhythmia was neither low-dimensional chaos nor random behavior. Bayly et al (108) concluded that VF is a highly dimensional activity in which the spatial coherence of the activation fronts change as the arrhythmia progresses.

Recently, the application of the theory of wave propagation in excitable media to the study of VF (8, 9), together with high resolution mapping techniques (17, 18, 21, 22), has enabled investigators to think of this arrhythmia as a problem of self-organization of nonlinear electrical waves with both deterministic and stochastic components (21, 22, 54, 55, 110). This has led to the hypothesis that there is both spatial and temporal organization during VF in the structurally normal heart, and to provide a quantification of its dynamics. In the following two sections, the two extremes in a wide spectrum of dynamic behaviors of the fibrillating heart (21, 54) are examined. On one extreme of that spectrum, it has been demonstrated in the structurally normal isolated rabbit heart that even a single three-dimensional electrical rotor (i.e. a scroll wave) that moves rapidly throughout the ventricles can give rise to complex patterns of cardiac muscle excitation that are indistinguishable from fibrillation. On the other extreme, a recently published algorithm (22) has been applied to analyze the most commonly observed mechanism of cardiac fibrillation; i.e. multiple electrical waves, by quantifying the dynamics of wavebreaks and phase singularities that are formed throughout the heart as a result of multiple wave front-wave tail interactions.

Drifting Vortices and VF in Small Hearts

Gray et al (21, 54) studied the applicability of spiral wave theory to VF using novel techniques of high-resolution video imaging of voltage dye fluorescence in the isolated Langendorff-perfused rabbit heart immersed in a warm oxygenated Tyrode's solution. Their study clearly and unequivocally demonstrated movement of a single vortex over the entire surface of the ventricles. Volume conductor ECG recordings obtained simultaneously with the optical recordings demonstrated that a nonstationary rotor could yield highly polymorphous QRS complexes that were indistinguishable from those recorded during VF in the in situ heart. Specifically, as the rotor drifted along intricate trajectories on the heart surface, the ECG displayed irregular periodicity and morphology. In complementary computer simulations incorporating a realistic heart geometry (21, 111), appropriate parameters allowed the formation of a single nonstationary rotor. The rotor moved rapidly through the heart, closely reproducing the experimental results. Spectral analysis of the irregular ECGs in both the experiments and simulations (21, 54) demonstrated narrow-band frequency spectra that were consistent with previous data obtained during fibrillation in humans and in animals (112–114). Moreover, the width of the frequency peaks in the spectra could be related to the frequency of rotation of the rotor, the speed of its drift, and the wave speed through the Doppler equation (21). The results suggest that the speed of the rotor determines the degree of irregularity of the ECG. In addition, the computer simulations support the idea that VF in these rabbit hearts most likely is the result of a rapidly drifting scroll wave with a straight filament that is oriented perpendicular to the epicardial wall (21, 54). Similar results have been recently obtained in mouse hearts (55), demonstrating that, contrary to what was predicted by the critical mass hypothesis (33), both sustained reentry and fibrillation are demonstrable in hearts whose mass is less than 200 mg.

Finding Phase Singularities During VF

Exploration of the significance of phase singularities in the context of propagation of electrical waves in cardiac muscle has just recently began. From studies in other excitable media (88, 89, 92, 95, 96), and knowledge that fibrillation usually does not occur spontaneously in healthy human hearts, it is reasonable to surmise that under normal conditions of excitability and cycle length, collision of an excitation wave with an obstacle in the cardiac muscle should not cause a wavebreak. It is only when the excitability of the tissue is relatively low that the broken wave front may detach and form a phase singularity after its interaction with an appropriate anatomical (see Figure 1) or functional (see Figure 2) obstacle. But what constitutes an appropriate obstacle?

The complicated anatomical structure of the normal atria and ventricles is probably an important substrate for the establishment of reentrant arrhythmias. For example, the natural orifices of the caval and pulmonary veins, the atrioventricular rings, and the highly heterogeneous tissue type distributions and geometrical arrangements of cardiac cells in the atrial and ventricular endocardium have all been implicated in the mechanisms of the arrhythmias. However, sustained arrhythmias do not occur under normal circumstances and can only be induced by high frequency or premature stimulation and facilitated by the presence of hormones or neurotransmitters. On the other hand, it is clear that the hearts of patients with congestive heart failure, myocardial ischemia, infarction (115), and cardiomyopathies have the appropriate histopathologic and electrophysiologic substrates for the spontaneous initiation of reentrant arrhythmias. Sclerotic patches, diffuse fibrotic displacement of the cardiac muscle, or both, are commonly found, particularly in elderly patients who are most vulnerable to these arrhythmias. In addition, in some of these patients, the onset of arrhythmias has been ascribed to increased dispersion of refractoriness; i.e. temporal differences in the duration of refractory periods between neighboring cells or tissues (115), secondary to uneven chamber enlargement (55). Such increased dispersion would set the stage for functionally determined obstacles that would interfere with the propagation of wave fronts. Phase singularities may result from such interference and may be one of the initiating causes of reentrant activation and fibrillation. In fact, it is well known that, in heart muscle and other excitable media, wave-breaks leading to rotating wave initiation may be a consequence of the interaction of a wave front with a wave tail (6, 18, 22). Upon initiation of vortex-like reentry, the broken wave front begins to rotate around its singularity at a high frequency and somehow leads to the cascade toward turbulent activity that characterizes VF.

Gray et al (22) have recently developed an analytical procedure to quantify VF dynamics. They began by representing in phase space (also known as phase-plane trajectory analysis) the signal obtained by a video camera pixel, viewing a small area of cardiac tissue that was previously stained with a fluorescent voltage-sensitive dye. Here the tissue may spend time either at a fixed point (resting membrane potential) or along a closed loop (repetitive spontaneous activity). In Figure 3 (see color insert), during repetitive activity (panel A), a limit cycle attractor in phase space may be observed when data of one pixel are plotted as F[t] versus F[t + τ] (panel B), where t is time and τ = 25 ms (i.e. about one fourth of the cycle length during VF). This simple procedure allows one to represent the fluorescent signal of each pixel in a movie by its phase (θ) around the loop. As shown in panels C and D (Figure 3), a pixel that remains at or near rest for some time represents a spatial phase singularity because its phase is arbitrary. It is close to a fixed point in phase space (e.g. the center of the loop) when neighboring points (e.g. panel A) exhibit a continuous progression of phase equal to $\pm \pi$ radians around this site. During reentry, loops in phase space are recorded by most pixels. Although trajectories from many consecutive cycles may not coincide in phase space, the trajectories circulate around a central region, allowing one to define the phase along the loop, θ, for each of 20,000 video camera pixels typically used in our VF experiments. The locations of the two pixels whose dynamics are analyzed in panels A-D are indicated in panel E, which shows a color snapshot of phase (an isophase map) from the ventricular epicardial surface, constructed by indicating the instantaneous phase of all pixels. This two-dimensional isophase map provides direct visualization of the complex, yet organized wave dynamics of VF. In the Langendorff-perfused heart (21), self-sustained vortex-like reentry can remain stationary for many rotations. In the example presented in Figure 3, a stationary vortex was seen on the lateral wall of the right ventricle, rotating clockwise around a singularity (+). Clearly, the singularity point is the location where all phases (colors) converge. Thus, by reducing each pixel value to a single variable (θ), the phase analysis approach provides definite proof to the theoretical prediction that spatial phase singularities exist and are a necessary factor in the spatio-temporal organization of complex reentrant arrhythmias such as VF.

Phase Singularities and VF Organization

Isophase maps from the ventricular epicardial surface of rabbit and sheep hearts during sustained VF analyzed by Gray et al (22) are reproduced, respectively, in panels *A* and *B* of Figure 4 (see color insert). The maps clearly reveal non-intersecting isophase lines in space (except at phase singularity points), indicating that cells are strongly coupled, and each site could be represented by its phase around a loop. Importantly, in both cases, the electrocardiogram is typical of VF (not shown), yet transmembrane signals at each site exhibit a strong periodic component centered near 8 Hz (22). The continuous spatial changes of phase reflect a high degree of organization of the electrical waves as a result of the fact that they are moving on the ventricular surface through excitation, recovery and diffusion (i.e. electrotonic propagation) processes.

In panel *C* of Figure 4, the phase space plot of one pixel's signal has been reproduced. This pixel was located at a point toward which one of the phase singularities had drifted at the instant of the phase map in panel *A* (+). As expected, the phase of that pixel had moved to the center of the loop at that instant in time (panel *D*). Spatial phase singularities can be classified depending on direction of wave rotation (also known as chirality; we chose + for clockwise; − for counter clockwise). As suggested by theory, isophase lines connect phase singularities with opposite chirality, or end on an anatomical barrier (88, 94, 95, 114).

Clearly, this novel method to represent spatio-temporal VF patterns by phase, θ [x,y,t], enables one to directly study the detailed dynamics of spatial phase singularities, wavelets and rotors, including their initiation, life span, and termination (22). Most importantly, the approach allows the study of the changes in VF dynamics in the course of global ischemia development as it occurs in the fibrillating heart in situ. As demonstrated elsewhere (22), such studies provide, for the first time, quantification of VF dynamics under steady state conditions in the well oxygenated, Langendorff-perfused heart.

IS THE RANDOM OCCURRENCE OF PHASE SINGULARITIES SUFFICIENT TO MAINTAIN VF?

The direct demonstration of phase singularities and of rotors (21, 22) in both large and small hearts during VF provides strong evidence that VF is not an entirely random phenomenon. Moreover, the ability to study the evolution of phase singularities in space and time throughout the ventricular surface allows quantification of VF in terms of rotor number and life span. From studies conducted thus far, it is clear that the formation of phase singularities is a necessary, although not sufficient condition for rotor formation (22). In addition to a phase singularity, a new excitation wave must be generated to form a rotor. Initial estimates indicate that, once formed, each rotor occupies an average area of ~ 12 cm^2. Hence, based on approximate measurements of heart surface area, Gray et al (22) estimated that the average number of rotors during a given instant in a 3-s episode of VF is approximately 1–2 for rabbits and mice, 5 for sheep, and 15 for humans. It is important to note, however, that measurements of life span for both sheep and rabbit hearts suggest that, in a given VF episode, close to 90% of phase singularities formed on the epicardial surface lasted less than 100 ms, which is less than one rotation. These results explain the inability of most authors to find organized reentry during Wiggers stage 2 VF (110). Termination of reentry occurred when counter rotating wave fronts around a pair of singularities merged or when a rotor collided with a boundary (22).

Thus strong evidence indicates that complex dynamics involving the formation of phase singularities that give rise to rotors and wavelets is an integral part of the fibrillatory process. Yet, if the life span of most formed wavelets is too short, then these wavelets will have a decreased chance to give rise to new wavelets. It would therefore be extremely difficult to achieve the critical number of wavelets that is thought to be responsible for the dynamic equilibrium that maintains fibrillation as originally postulated by Moe in 1964 (5). Consequently, based on these data, one cannot escape the conclusion that such ephemeral singularities and wavelets are probably not responsible for the maintenance of VF.

It is important to note once again that the video imaging experiments demonstrating phase singularities during VF reveal information only about the epicardial surface. Crucial data about the activity in the bulk of the myocardium and on the endocardium are missing, which greatly limits our ability to decide what mechanism is responsible for VF. Thus an alternative explanation for the maintenance of VF is that the formation of singularities and wavelets is a consequence of complex patterns of scroll wave formation in the bulk of the ventricular myocardium. Using plunge electrodes, Frazier et al (13), and Chen et al (67) demonstrated three-dimensional scroll waves (i.e. transmural reentry) during the initial stages of VF in the dog heart. In these experiments the organizing centers of pairs of counter rotating scroll waves (i.e. filaments) were aligned perpendicular to the ventricular epicardial surface and thus, on the epicardium, they manifested two wave fronts rotating in opposite directions around a pair of singularities (13). More recently, computer simulations have suggested that rotational anisotropy (116, 117) may play an important role in filament evolution and cause fibrillatory-like activity. In the studies of Fenton & Karma (117), fiber rotation of 120° from epicardium to endocardium in a simulated parallelepipidal slab of ventricular muscle, generated enough twist in the filament of a transmural scroll wave to destabilize it and cause a transition to wave turbulence analogous to VF.

Yet another explanation is that the formation of singularities and wavelets characterizing VF is the result of fibrillatory conduction (118); i.e. complex patterns of wave front propagation with spatially distributed regions of intermittent block. Such patterns would be established by the combination of heterogeneous distribution of refractoriness and the sustained activity of a single stationary rotor (a scroll wave) hidden from view and activating the ventricles at an exceedingly high frequency (118). The rapidly succeeding wave fronts emanating from such a rotor would result in wave front-wave tail interactions with the consequent formation of phase singularities and wavelets. Studies in sheep hearts (118, 119) have provided strong support that at least some cases of atrial fibrillation are the result of fibrillatory conduction caused by the interaction of wave fronts, generated at high frequency by localized reentrant sources, with the complex structure of the atria. Recent computer simulations by Berenfeld & Pertsov (120) suggest that the hypothesis is applicable to VF as well. Their studies suggest that one of the most stable positions for a vortex filament is to align intramurally along the fiber orientation. As such, it is therefore not difficult to perceive instances of VF whose mechanism is intramural reentry. Because the wave fronts generated by the vortex must propagate through a highly complex ventricular structure with rotational anisotropy (116), the stage would be set for the occurrence of multiple wave front-wave tail interactions with formation of phase singularities and rotors. On the epicardium, this would be manifest as multiple incomplete and nonsustained reentrant circuits. Thus viewed from the surface, the activity would appear highly disorganized and would be indistinguishable from the VF that is thought to be maintained by multiple randomly propagating independent wavelets (4). However, a closer look at the intramural activity would reveal a highly organized rotating wave front around a very thin filament. Proof for this hypothesis requires further investigation.

CONCLUSION

Is the Idea of Spatial and Temporal Periodicity Applicable to VF in the Human Heart?

Overall, the evidence discussed here demonstrates that there is indeed a high degree of temporal and spatial organization in cardiac fibrillation. The results may pave the way for a better understanding of the mechanisms of VF in the normal, as well as in the diseased human heart. In this regard, although it is traditionally believed that fibrillation in the human heart is the result of large numbers of wandering wavelets (4, 5, 52), the detailed mechanisms of fibrillation remain unclear (1, 2). Recent advances in optical mapping technology have made it possible to demonstrate that, in small hearts such as those of rabbits or mice (21, 22, 54), even a single drifting scroll can give rise to ECG patterns that resemble VF (21). However, in larger hearts more complex spatio-temporal organization usually prevails (22). Therefore, it seems feasible that self-organization in the case of the larger human heart occurs in the form of a relatively small number of drifting scroll waves that interact with each other giving rise to complex spatio-temporal patterns, with formation of multiple short-lived phase singularities with variable dynamics. Hence, video imaging and phase-mapping analysis of Langendorff-perfused human hearts (e.g. transplant rejects) should provide insight into the number of phase-singularities, their dynamics, and life span during fibrillation. Why is this important? Perhaps, the most immediate practical application involves incorporating phase singularity theory to reduce the energy of the electric field required to terminate fibrillation. Indeed, recent modeling and experimental work has focused on the study of how electrical shocks of high energy affect the dynamics of vortices, including their initiation and termination. For example, there is evidence to suggest that the timing of the stimuli and the position of the vortex with respect to the electrode applying the shock play crucial roles in defibrillation (121). Also, studies using numerical methods have shown that vortices drift in the direction of an applied electric field (122). It has also been shown in mathematical models that the application of a periodic uniform electric field at a rate similar to the vortex rotation period results in a resonant drift of the vortex (123). In fact a low-energy defibrillator has been suggested utilizing a feedback mechanism and the effect of resonant drift (124). Although it is not clear if resonant drift will occur in heart tissue, it has been shown to exist in chemical media (125). Finally, it has been recently demonstrated that formation of phase singularities in the myocardium, with reinduction of reentry, may explain the failure of certain strong monophasic shocks to effectively terminate VF when applied from an internal cardioverter defibrillator (126).

ACKNOWLEDGMENTS

The preparation of this article was supported in part by grants P01-HL39707 and R01-HL60843 from the National Heart, Lung and Blood Institute, National Institutes of Health. I thank Jay Chen for his invaluable help in preparing the figures and reading the manuscript.

Visit the Annual Reviews home page at www.AnnualReviews.org.

LITERATURE CITED

1. Myerburg RJ, Kessler KM, Interian Jr. A, et al. 1990. Clinical and experimental pathophysiology of sudden cardiac death. In *Cardiac Electrophysiology: From Cell to Bedside,* ed. DP Zipes, J Jalife, pp. 666–78. Philadelphia: Saunders. 1st ed.

2. Zipes DP, Wellens HJJ. 1998. Sudden cardiac death. *Circulation* 98: 2334–51

3. Wiggers CJ. 1940. The mechanism and nature of ventricular fibrillation. *Am. Heart J.* 20:399–412

4. Moe GK. 1962. On the multiple wavelet hypothesis of atrial fibrillation. *Arch. Int. Pharmacodyn.* CXL:183–88

5. Moe GK, Rheinbolt WC, Abildskov JA. 1964. A computer model of atrial fibrillation. *Am. Heart J.* 67:200–20

6. Winfree AT. 1994. Electrical turbulence in three-dimensional heart muscle. *Science* 266:1003–6

7. Gul'ko FB, Petrov AA. 1972. Mechanism of the formation of closed pathways of conduction in excitable media. *Biophysics* 17:271–81

8. Krinsky VI. 1978. Mathematical models of cardiac arrhythmias (spiral waves). *Pharmacol. Ther. B* 3:539–55

9. Winfree AT. 1987. *When Time Breaks Down.* Princeton: Princeton Univ. Press.

10. Garfinkel A, Chen PS, Walter DO, Karagueuzian HS, Kogan B, et al. 1997. Quasiperiodicity and chaos in cardiac fibrillation. *J. Clin. Invest.* 99:305–14

11. Ideker RE, Smith WM, Wallace AG, Kasell J, Harrison LA, et al. 1979. A computerized method for the rapid display of ventricular activation during the intraoperative study of arrhythmias. *Circulation* 59:449–58

12. Downar E, Parson ID, Mickelborough LL, Cameron DA, Yao LC, et al. 1984. On-line epicardial mapping of intraoperative ventricular arrhythmias: initial clinical experience. *J. Am. Coll. Cardiol.* 4:703–14

13. Frazier DW, Wolf PD, Wharton JM, Tang ASL, Smith WM, et al. 1989. Stimulus-induced critical point: mechanism for the electrical initiation of reentry in normal canine myocardium. *J. Clin. Invest.* 83:1039–52

14. Lee JJ, Kamjoo K, Hough D, Hwang C, Fan W, et al. 1996. Reentrant wave fronts in Wiggers' stage II ventricular fibrillation. *Circ. Res.* 78:660–75

15. Salama G, Morad M. 1976. Merocyanine 540 as an optical probe of transmembrane electrical activity in the heart. *Science* 191:485–87

16. Dillon SM. 1991. Optical recordings of the rabbit heart show that defibrillation strength shocks prolong the duration of depolarization and the refractory period. *Circ. Res.* 69:842–56

17. Davidenko J, Pertsov AM, Salomonsz R, Baxter WT, Jalife J. 1991. Stationary and drifting spiral waves of excitation in isolated cardiac muscle. *Nature* 355:349–51

18. Pertsov AM, Davidenko JM, Salomonsz R, Baxter WT, Jalife J. 1993. Spiral waves of excitation underlie reentrant activity in isolated cardiac muscle. *Circ. Res.* 72:631–50

19. Kavanagh KM, Kabas JS, Rollins DL, Melnick SB, Smith WM, et al. 1992. High current stimuli to the spared epicardium of a large infarct induce ventricular tachycardia. *Circulation* 85:680–98

20. Witkowski FX, Penkoske PA. 1990. Activation patterns during ventricular fibrillation. In *Mathematical Approaches to Cardiac Arrhythmias,* ed. J Jalife, 591:219–31. New York: NY Acad. Sci.

21. Gray RA, Jalife J, Panfilov AV, Baxter WT, Cabo C, et al. 1995. Mechanisms of cardiac fibrillation. *Science* 270:1222–25

22. Gray RA, Pertsov AM, Jalife J. 1998. Spatial and temporal organization during cardiac fibrillation. *Nature* 392:75–78

23. Brewer LA. 1983. Sphygmology through the centuries, Historical notes. *Am. J. Surg.* 145:696–702

24. Acierno LJ. 1994. *The History of Cardiology.* London: Pantheon

25. Erichsen JE. 1842. On the influence of the coronary circulation on the action of the heart. *London Med. Gaz.* 2:561–83

26. Hoffa M, Ludwig C. 1850. Einige neue Versuche über Herzbewegung. *Z. Rationelle Med.* 9:107–44

27. Vulpian A. 1874. Notes sur les éffets de la faradisation directe des ventricules du coeur chez le chien. *Arch. Physiol. Norm. Path.* 6:975–82

28. McWilliam JA. 1887. Fibrillar contraction of the heart. *J. Physiol.* 8:296–310

29. McWilliam JA. 1889. Electrical stimulation of the heart in man. *Br. Med. J.* 1:348

30. Levy AG, Lewis T. 1911. Heart irregularities, resulting from the inhalation of low percentages of chloroform vapour, and their relationship to ventricular fibrillation. *Heart* 3:99–112

31. Hoffman A. 1912. Fibrillation of ventricles at the end of an attack of paroxysmal tachycardia in man. *Heart* 3:213–18

32. Erlanger J. 1912. Observations on the physiology of Purkinje tissue. *Am. J. Physiol.* 30:395–419

33. Garrey WE. 1914. The nature of fibrillary contraction of the heart—Its relation to tissue mass and form. *Am. J. Physiol.* 33:397–414

34. McWilliam JA. 1887. On electrical stimulation of the mammalian heart.

Trans. Int. Med. Congress, 9th session. Washington, DC. vol. III. p. 253

35. Mines GR. 1913. On dynamic equilibrium in the heart. *J. Physiol.* 46:349–83

36. Lewis T. 1915. *Lectures on the Heart.* New York: Hoeber

37. Weiner N, Rosenblueth A. 1946. The mathematical formulation of the problem of conduction of impulses in a network of connected excitable elements, specifically in cardiac muscle. *Arch. Inst. Cardiol. Mex.* 16:205–65

38. Allessie MA, Bonke FIM, Schopman FJC. 1973. Circus movement in rabbit atrial muscle as a mechanism of tachycardia. *Circ. Res.* 33:54–62

39. Allessie MA, Bonke FIM, Schopman FJC. 1976. Circus movement in rabbit atrial muscle as a mechanism of tachycardia. II. The role of nonuniform recovery of excitability in the occurrence of unidirectional block as studied with multiple microelectrodes. *Circ. Res.* 39:168–77

40. Allessie MA, Bonke FIM, Schopman FJC.1977. Circus movement in rabbit atrial muscle as a mechanism of tachycardia. III. The "leading circle" concept: a new model of circus movement in cardiac tissue without the involvement of an anatomical obstacle. *Circ. Res.* 41:9–18

41. Wiggers CJ. 1930. Studies on ventricular fibrillation produced by electric shock. II. Cinematographic and electrocardiographic observations of the natural process in the dog's heart. *Am. Heart J.* 5:351–65

42. Mandapati R, Asano Y, Baxter WT, Gray R, Davidenko J, Jalife J. 1998. Quantification of effects of global ischemia on dynamics of ventricular fibrillation in isolated rabbit heart. *Circulation* 98:688–96

43. Wiggers CJ. 1940. Fibrillation. *Am. Heart J.* 20:399–422

44. Scherf D, Schott A. 1953. *Extrasystoles and Allied Arrhythmias.* New York: Grune & Stratton

45. Mines GR. 1914. On circulating excitation on heart muscles and their possible relation to tachycardia and fibrillation. *Trans. R. Soc. Can.* 4:43–53

46. Moe GK. 1956. Introductory remarks to part III of experimental methods for the evaluation of drugs in various disease states. *Ann. NY Acad. Sci.* 64:540–42

47. Moe GK, Abildskov JA. 1959. Atrial fibrillation as a self-sustaining arrhythmia independent of focal discharge. *Am. Heart J.* 58:59–70

48. Han J, Moe GK. 1964. Nonuniform recovery of excitability in ventricular muscle. *Circ Res.* 14:44–60

49. Allessie MA, Lammers WEJEP, Bonke FIM, Hollen J. 1985. Experimental evaluation of Moe's multiple wavelet hypothesis of atrial fibrillation. In *Cardiac Electrophysiology and Arrhythmias,* ed. DP Zipes, J Jalife, pp. 265–75. Orlando, FL: Grune & Stratton

50. Downar E, Harris L, Mickelbrough LL, Shaigh N, Parson I.. 1988. Endocardial mapping of ventricular tachycardia in the intact human ventricle: evidence for reentrant mechanisms. *J. Am. Col. Cardiol.* 11:703–14

51. Janse MJ, Wilms-Schopman FJG, Coronel R. 1995. Ventricular fibrillation is not always due to multiple wavelet reentry. *J. Cardiovasc. Electrophysiol.* 6: 512–21

52. Witkowski FX, Leon LJ, Penkoske PA, Giles WR, Spano ML, et al. 1998. Spatiotemporal evolution of ventricular fibrillation. *Nature* 392:78–82

53. Epstein AE, Ideker RE. 1995. Ventricular fibrillation. In *Cardiac Electrophysiology: From Cell to Bedside,* ed. DP Zipes, J Jalife, pp. 927–33. Philadelphia: Saunders. 2nd ed.

54. Jalife J, Gray RA. 1996. Drifting vortices of electrical waves underlie ventricular fibrillation in the rabbit heart. *Acta. Physiol. Scand.* 157:123–31

55. Jalife J, Gray RA, Morley GE, Davidenko JM. 1998. Self-organization and

the dynamical nature of ventricular fibrillation. *Chaos* 8:79–93

56. De Boer S. 1923. Die physiologie und pharmakologie des Flimmers. *Ergeb. Physiol.* 21:1

57. Wiggers CJ, Wégria R. 1940. Ventricular fibrillation due to single, localized induction and condenser shocks applied during the vulnerable phase of ventricular systole. *Am. J. Physiol.* 128:500–5

58. Wégria R, Moe GK, Wiggers CJ. 1941. Comparison of the vulnerable period and fibrillation thresholds of normal and idioventricular beats. *Am. J. Physiol.* 133:651–57

59. Moe GK, Harris AS, Wiggers CJ. 1941. Analysis of the initiation of fibrillation by electrographic studies. *Am. J. Physiol.* 134:473–92

60. Selfridge O. 1948. Studies on flutter and fibrillation. V. Some notes on the theory of flutter. *Arch. Inst. Cardiol. Mex.* 18:177–87

61. Winfree AT. 1990. The electrical thresholds of ventricular myocardium. *J. Cardiovasc. Electrophysiol.* 1:393–410

62. Winfree AT. 1990. Vortex action potentials in normal ventricular muscle. *Ann. NY Acad. Sci.* 591:190–207

63. Roth BJ, Krassowska W. 1998. The induction of reentry in cardiac tissue. The missing link: how electric fields alter transmembrane potential. *Chaos* 8:204–20

64. Shibata N, Chen P-S, Dixon EG, Wolf PD, Danieley ND, et al. RE. 1988. Influence of shock strength and timing on induction of ventricular arrhythmias in dogs. *Am. J. Physiol.* 255(24):H891–901

65. Winfree AT. 1989. Electrical instability in cardiac muscle: phase singularities and rotors. *J. Theor. Biol.* 138:353–405

66. Winfree AT. 1995. Theory of spirals. See Ref 53, pp. 379–89

67. Chen PS, Wolf PD, Dixon EG, Danieley ND, Frazier DW, et al. 1988. Mechanism of ventricular vulnerability to single premature stimuli in open chest dogs. *Circ. Res.* 62:1191–209

68. Davidenko JM. 1993. Spiral wave activity a common mechanism for polymorphic and monomorphic ventricular tachycardias. *J. Cardiovasc. Electrophysiol.* 4: 730–46

69. Davidenko JM. 1995. Spiral waves in the heart: experimental demonstration of a theory. See Ref. 53, pp. 478–88

70. Matta RJ, Verrier RL, Lown B. 1976. Repetitive extrasystole as an index of vulnerability to ventricular fibrillation. *Am. J. Physiol.* 230:1469–73

71. Keener JP. 1988. On the formation of circulating patterns of excitation in anisotropic excitable media. *J. Math. Biol.* 26:41–56

72. Winfree AT. 1990. Vetricular reentry in three dimensions. See Ref. 1, pp. 224–34

73. Miller WT III, Geselowitz DB. 1978. Simulation studies of the electrocardiogram. I. The normal heart. *Circ. Res.* 43:301–15

74. Tung L. 1978. *A bi-domain model for describing ischemic myocardial D-C potentials.* PhD thesis. MIT, Cambridge, MA

75. Saypol JM, Roth BJ. 1992. A mechanism for anisotropic reentry in electrically active tissue. *J. Cardiovasc. Electrophysiol.* 3:558–66

76. Roth BJ. 1997. Nonsustained reentry following successive stimulation of cardiac tissue through a unipolar electrode. *J. Cardiovasc. Electrophysiol.* 8:768–78

77. Lin S-F, Roth BJ, Echt DS, Wikswo JP Jr. 1996. Complex dynamics following unipolar stimulation during the vulnerable phase. *Circulation* 94:I-714 (Abstr.)

78. Pertsov AM, Jalife J. 1995. Three-dimensional vortex-like reentry. See Ref. 53, pp. 403–10

79. Dillon SM, Allessie MA, Ursell PC, Wit AL. 1988. Influence of anisotropic tissue

structure on reentrant circuit in the epicardial border zone of subacute canine infarcts. *Circ. Res.* 63:182–206

80. El-Sherif N, Smith A, Evans K. 1981. Canine ventricular arrhythmias in the late myocardial infarction period. 8. Epicardial mapping of reentrant circuits. *Circ. Res.* 49:255–65

81. Marban E, Robinson SW, Wier WG. 1986. Mechanisms of arrhythmogenic delayed and early afterdepolarizations in ferret ventricular muscle. *J. Clin. Invest.* 78(5):1185–92

82. Rosen MR, Gelband H, Hoffman BF. 1973. Correlation between the effects of ouabain in the canine electrocardiogram and transmembrane potential of isolated Purkinje fibers. *Circulation* 47:65–72

83. El-Sherif N, Caref EB, Yin H, Restivo M. 1996. The electrophysiological mechanism of ventricular arrhythmias in the long QT syndrome: Three-dimensional mapping of activation and recovery patterns. *Circ. Res.* 79:474–92

84. Asano Y, Davidenko JM, Baxter WT, Gray RA, Jalife J. 1997. Optical mapping of drug-induced polymorphic arrhythmias and torsades de pointes in the isolated rabbit heart. *J. Am. Coll. Cardiol.* 29: 831–84

85. Zykov VS. 1987. *Simulation of Wave Processes in Excitable Media.* Manchester, NY: University Press

86. Krinsky VI. 1984. Self-Organization: Autowaves and Structures far from Equilibrium. Berlin: Springer-Verlag

87. Winfree AT. 1972. Spiral waves of chemical activity. *Science* 175:634–36

88. Agladze K, Keener JP, Müller SC, Panfilov A. 1994. Rotating spiral waves created by geometry. *Science* 264:1746–48

89. Winfree AT, Strogatz SH. 1984. Organizing centers for three-dimensional chemical waves. *Nature* 311: 611–15

90. Winfree AT. 1973. Scroll-shaped waves in chemical activity in three dimensions. *Science* 181:937–39

91. Vinson M, Pertsov AM, Jalife J. 1993. Anchoring of vortex filaments in 3D excitable media. *Phys. D* 72:119–34

92. Nagy-Ungvarai Z, Pertsov AM, Hess B, Müller SC. 1992. Lateral instabilities of a wave front in the Ce-catalyzed Belousov-Zhabotinsky reaction. *Phys. D* 61:205–12

93. Pertsov AM, Panfilov AV, Medvedeva FU. 1983. Instability of autowaves in excitable media associated with the phenomenon of critical curvature. *Biofizica* 28:100–2

94. Starobin JM, Zilberter YI, Rusnak EM, Starmer CF. 1996. Wavelet formation in excitable cardiac tissue: the role of wavefront-obstacle intractions in initiating high-frequency fibrillatory-like arrhythmias. *Biophys. J.* 70:581–94

95. Cabo C, Pertsov AM, Davidenko JM, Baxter WT, Gray RA, et al. 1996. Vortex shedding as a precursor of turbulent electrical activity in cardiac muscle. *Biophys. J.* 70:1105–11

96. Pertsov AM, Emarkova EA, Shnol EE. 1990. On the diffraction of autowaves. *Phys. D* 44:178–99

97. Cabo C, Pertsov AM, Davidenko JM, Jalife J. 1998. Electrical turbulence as a result of the critical curvature for propagation in cardiac tissue. *Chaos* 8:116–26

98. Spach MS, Miller WT III, Dolber PC, Kootsey M, Sommer JR, et al. 1982. The functional role of structural complexities in the propagation of depolarization in the atrium of the dog. Cardiac conduction disturbances due to discontinuities of effective axial resistivity. *Circ. Res.* 50:175–91

99. Spach MS, Dolber PC, Anderson PAW. 1989. Multiple regional differences in cellular properties that regulate repolarization and contraction in the right atrium of adult and newborn dogs. *Circ. Res.* 65:1594–611

100. Spach MS, Dolber PC, Heidlage JF. 1989. Interaction of inhomogeneities of repolarization with anisotropic propagation in dog atria. A mechanism for both

preventing and initiating reentry. *Circ. Res.* 65:1612–31

101. Panfilov AV. 1998. Spiral breakup as a model of ventricular fibrillation. *Chaos* 8:57–64

102. Chen J, Mandapati R, Skanes A, Berenfeld O, Jalife J. 1998. Periodic epicardial breakthroughs and short-lived spiral waves during ventricular fibrillation in the isolated rabbit heart. *Circulation* 98:I-51 (Abstr.)

103. Ideker RE, Klein GJ, Harrison L, Smith WM, Kasell J, et al. 1981. The transition to ventricular fibrillation induced by reperfusion after acute ischemia in the dog: a period of organized epicardial activation. *Circulation* 63:1371–79

104. Damle RS, Kanaan NM, Robinson MS, Yu-Zhi G, Goldberger JJ, Kadish A. 1992. Spatial and temporal linking of epicardial activation directions during ventricular fibrillation in dogs. *Circulation* 86:1547–58

105. Ropella KM, Sahakian AV, Baerman JM, Swirin S. 1989. The coherence spectrum, a quantitative discriminator of fibrillatory and nonfibrillatory cardiac rhythms. *Circulation* 80:112–19

106. Bayly PV, Johnson EE, Wolf PD, Greenside HS, Smith WM, Ideker RE. 1993. A quantitative measurement of spatial order in ventricular fibrillation. *J. Cardiovasc. Electrophysiol.* 4:533–46

107. Goldberger AL, Bhargava V, West BJ, Mandell AJ. 1986. Some observations on the question: Is ventricular fibrillation "chaos"? *Phys. D* 19:282–89

108. Bayly PV, KenKnight BH, Rogers JM, Johnson EE, Ideker RE, et al. 1998. Spatial organization, predictability, and determinism in ventricular fibrillation. *Chaos* 8:103–15

109. Ruelle D, Takens F. 1971. On the nature of turbulence. *Commun. Math. Phys.* 20:167–92

110. Chen PS, Garfinkle A, Weiss JN, Karagueuzian HS. 1998. Computerized mapping of fibrillation in normal ventricular myocardium. *Chaos* 8:127–36

111. Panfilov AV, Keener JP. 1995. Reentry in an anatomical model of the heart. *Chaos, Solitons Fractals* 5:681–89

112. Herbshleb JN, Heethaar RM, van der Tweel I, Meijler FL. 1980. Frequency analysis of the ECG before and during ventricular fibrillation. *IEEE Comp. Cardiol.* pp. 365–68

113. Herbshleb JN, Heethaar RM, van der Tweel I, Zimmerman ANE, Meijler FL. 1979. Signal analysis of ventricular fibrillation. *IEEE Comp. Cardiol.* pp. 49–52

114. Wellner M, Pertsov AM, Jalife J. 1996. Spatial Doppler anomaly in an excitable medium. *Phys. Rev. E* 54:1120–25

115. Callans DJ, Josephson ME. 1995. Ventricular tachycardias in the setting of coronary artery disease. See Ref. 53, pp. 732–43

116. Streeter D. 1979. Gross morphology and fiber geometry in the heart. *In Handbook of Physiology,* ed. R Berne, 1:61–112, Bethesda, MD: Am. Physiol. Soc.

117. Fenton F, Karma A. 1998. Vortex dynamics in three-dimensional continuous myocardium with fiber rotation: filament instability and fibrillation. *Chaos* 8:20–47

118. Jalife J, Berenfeld O, Skanes A, Mandapati R. 1998. Mechanisms of atrial fibrillation. Mother rotors or multiple daughter wavelets, or both? *J. Cardiovasc. Electrophysiol.* 9:S2–12 (Suppl.)

119. Skanes AC, Mandapati R, Berenfeld O, Davidenko JM, Jalife J. 1998. Spatiotemporal periodicity during atrial fibrillation in the isolated sheep heart. *Circulation* 98(12):1236–48

120. Berenfeld O, Pertsov AM. 1999. Dynamics of intramural scroll waves in a 3-dimensional continuous myocardium with rotational anisotropy. *J. Theor. Biol.* In press

121. Krinsky VI, Biktashev VN, Pertsov AM. 1990. Autowave approaches to cessation

of reentrant arrhythmias. *Ann. NY Acad. Sci.* 591:232–46

122. Pumir A, Plaza F, Krinsky VI. 1994. Effect of an externally applied electric field on excitation in the cardiac muscle. *Chaos* 4(3):547–55

123. Biktashev VN, Holden AV. 1993. Resonant drift of an autowave vortex in a bounded medium. *Phys. Lett. A* 181:216–24

124. Biktashev VN, Holden AV. 1994. Design principles of a low voltage cardiac defib-rillator based on the effect of feedback resonant drift. *J. Theor. Biol.* 169:101–12

125. Muñizurri AP, Gomez-Gesteira M, Perez-Muñuzuri V, Krinsky VI, Perez-Villar V. 1994. Parametric resonance of a vortex in an active medium. *Phys. Rev. E* 50:4258–61

126. Efimov IR, Cheng Y, Van Wagoner DR, Mazgalev T, Tchou PJ. 1998. Virtual electrode-induced phase singularity. A basic mechanism of defibrillation failure. *Circ. Res.* 82:918–25

Annu. Rev. Physiol. 2000. 62:51–77

BASIC MECHANISMS OF ATRIAL FIBRILLATION—VERY NEW INSIGHTS INTO VERY OLD IDEAS

S. Nattel,[1,2,3,4] D. Li,[1] and L. Yue[1,4]

[1]*Research Center and* [2]*Department of Medicine, Montreal Heart Institute,* [3]*Department of Medicine, University of Montreal,* [4]*Department of Pharmacology and Therapeutics, McGill University, Montreal, Quebec, Canada H1T 1C8,* *e-mail: nattel@icm.umontreal.ca*

Key Words ion channels, remodeling, cardiac arrhythmias, reentry, antiarrhythmic drugs, action potential, molecular biology

■ **Abstract** Atrial fibrillation (AF) was recognized and studied extensively in the early twentieth century, but many fundamental aspects of the arrhythmia were poorly understood until quite recently. It is now recognized that AF can be initiated by a variety of mechanisms that share the ability to cause extremely rapid, irregular atrial electrical activity. Once initiated, AF causes alterations in atrial electrical properties (electrical remodeling), including both rapid functional changes and slower alterations in ion channel gene expression, which promote the maintenance of AF and facilitate reinitiation of the arrhythmia should it terminate. Electrical remodeling decreases the atrial refractory period in a heterogeneous way, thus decreasing the size and stability of potential functional atrial reentry waves and promoting multiple-circuit reentry. Whatever the initial cause of AF, electrical remodeling is likely to be a final common pathway that ultimately supervenes. Recent advances in understanding ion channel function, regulation, and remodeling at the molecular level have allowed for a much more detailed appreciation of the basic determinants of AF. Improvements in the clinical management of AF will inevitably follow the recent advances in our understanding of its detailed pathophysiology.

INTRODUCTION

Atrial fibrillation (AF) is currently the most common sustained clinical arrhythmia and is responsible for a substantial proportion of hospital costs incurred in the treatment of cardiac rhythm disorders (1). AF becomes increasingly common with age, having an incidence averaging $<0.5\%$ in patients <40 years of age and reaching a prevalence of $>5\%$ in patients >65 (2). Thus, AF is likely to become increasingly important with the aging of the population. The arrhythmia is defined by a very rapid atrial rate (generally $>400/min$ in humans) along with irregular

0066–4278/00/0315–0051$12.00

atrial activation and a lack of a repetitive pattern of coordinated atrial activity on the electrocardiogram (ECG). AF is associated with a variety of complications, including thromboemboli resulting from coagulation in the relatively static atrial blood pool, a loss of the fine adjustment of ventricular rate to the body's precise metabolic needs, potential impairment of cardiac function (particularly if the ventricular response is rapid), and subjective symptoms like palpitations, dizziness, breathlessness, and chest pain.

HISTORICAL OVERVIEW

Early Ideas About Atrial Fibrillation Mechanisms

In the latter half of the nineteenth century, Vulpian first described the induction of ventricular and atrial fibrillation by electrical shocks (3). At the turn of the century, Cushny suggested that AF might be the cause of highly disorganized rhythms (delirium cordis) in man (4). Fredericq demonstrated this experimentally by cutting the bundle of His and thereby regularizing the ventricular rhythm in the presence of AF (5). In 1913, Mines suggested that fibrillation was a type of reentrant process, requiring that the length of the excitation wave be shorter than the column of muscle on which it occurred (6). Both Mines (7) and Garrey (8) presented concepts of fibrillation as maintained by multiple-simultaneous-reentrant circuits. Garrey published a detailed review of the state of knowledge regarding AF in 1924 (9). Although he presented a consensus supporting the multiple-functional-reentry-circuit concept of AF, he pointed out alternative views of AF as caused by atrial hyperexcitability (one or more rapidly discharging atrial ectopic foci) or to a single, dominant mother wave with fibrillatory conduction. These notions of mechanisms underlying AF are portrayed schematically in Figure 1.

The Multiple Wavelet Hypothesis

In 1959, Moe & Abildskov (10) showed that AF could be produced by experimental paradigms of both multiple circuit reentry and rapid activity, and they suggested that either type of mechanism might cause clinical AF. Gordon Moe put forward the "multiple wavelet hypothesis" of AF in 1962 (11). This concept differed from previous multiple-circuit-reentry notions in that, rather than thinking of reentry waves that return to some initial starting point, Moe described propagation during AF as involving multiple independent wavelets circulating around functionally refractory tissue. In this concept, the trajectory of some wavelets leads them into paths of reduced excitability, causing them to extinguish, whereas other wavelets are able to propagate through tissues of adequate excitability and maintain themselves and/or spawn daughter wavelets. The maintenance of AF then depends on the probability that electrical activity can be

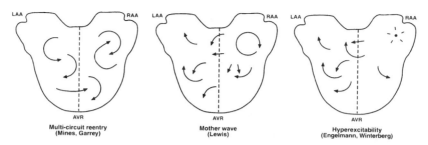

Figure 1   Schematic representations of concepts of atrial-fibrillation mechanisms held by various investigators in the early twentieth century. The atria are represented in an unfolded manner, with a dashed line indicating the position of the septum. Mines & Garrey believed that AF is caused by multiple, simultaneous functional reentry circuits. Lewis held that AF is maintained by a single, rapid atrial reentry circuit with variable conduction through atrial tissue (because some regions are unable to follow the very rapid primary frequency), producing rapid, irregular activation. Engelmann & Winterberg supported the notion that rapidly discharging ectopic foci maintain the arrhythmia. LAA, left atrial appendage; RAA, right atrial appendage; AVR, atrioventricular ring.

sustained by a sufficient number of active wavelets at any time. This idea is best understood as a more quantitative refinement of earlier ideas than as a truly novel conceptualization. The implications of the multiple-wavelet hypothesis were evaluated in 1964 with a simple two-dimensional cellular automaton-based computer model (12). Experimental support for Moe's ideas was obtained subsequently with the use of computerized mapping of AF maintained in the presence of acetylcholine in dog hearts (13).

Important Recent Developments

Two types of recent developments have had particularly important consequences for our understanding of AF mechanisms. The first was the demonstration in 1995 that AF itself alters atrial electrophysiology in ways that promote the occurrence and maintenance of AF (14). Subsequent work on this process of atrial remodeling has provided important insights into a wide range of mechanisms involved in AF at the organ, cell, and molecular levels. The second development was the emergence of evidence for rapidly discharging atrial foci in some clinical forms of AF (15) and for a mother wave form of mechanism in experimental AF (16, 17). These observations reflect back to ideas prevalent in the early twentieth century, as outlined above, and suggest that each of the competing theories of AF may accurately describe the mechanism of AF in particular circumstances. In addition, they point to a dynamic and potentially multifaceted perspective on the arrhythmia, as further discussed below.

Conceptual Models of Reentry and Relationship to Atrial Fibrillation

Closed-Circuit Reentry   Multiple-circuit reentry clearly plays an important role in AF. The precise mechanisms involved in multiple-circuit reentry and the underlying determinants have been the subject of considerable development. Mines considered that reentry occurs in "closed circuits in the myocardium" (6). The determinants of this form of closed-circuit reentry are illustrated in Figure 2 (left). The inexcitability of the core that underlies the substrate may be caused by the anatomical arrangement of potential conducting pathways, by anatomical obstacles like the venae cavae or pulmonary veins, or by a region of inexcitability caused by heart disease. Because the size of the circuit is fixed, reentry depends critically on a circuit time that is greater than the refractory period, and the circuit time equals the path length divided by conduction velocity. The refractory period determines whether reentry can be maintained (for reentry to occur, the refractory period must be less than circuit time), but does not directly affect circuit time or tachycardia rate.

Leading-Circle Reentry   A great limitation of the closed-circuit reentry concept is that it does not account for the dynamic nature of reentry in arrhythmias like AF, in which the reentry substrate appears functional rather than fixed, as pointed out by Garrey in 1924 (9). Allessie et al presented the first detailed conceptual model of functional reentry in 1977 (18). Reentry is maintained in a leading circle, which establishes itself in the smallest circuit that can maintain continuous activity

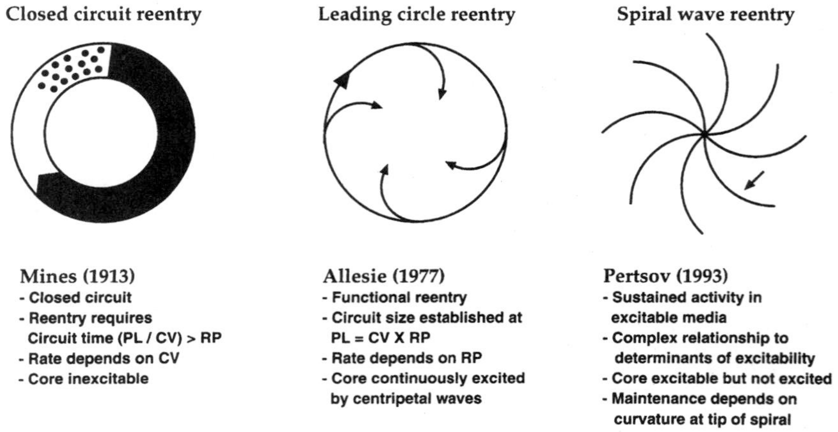

Closed circuit reentry	Leading circle reentry	Spiral wave reentry
Mines (1913)	**Allesie (1977)**	**Pertsov (1993)**
- Closed circuit	- Functional reentry	- Sustained activity in
- Reentry requires	- Circuit size established at	excitable media
Circuit time (PL / CV) > RP	PL = CV X RP	- Complex relationship to
- Rate depends on CV	- Rate depends on RP	determinants of excitability
- Core inexcitable	- Core continuously excited	- Core excitable but not excited
	by centripetal waves	- Maintenance depends on
		curvature at tip of spiral

Figure 2   Schematic diagrams of closed-circuit reentry (*left*), leading-circle reentry (*middle*), and spiral-wave reentry (*right*). PL, path length; CV, conduction velocity; RP, refractory period.

(Figure 2, *middle*). This minimum circuit size for reentry is given by the wavelength, a concept first presented by Mines (6) and later quantified by Wiener & Rosenblueth (19) as the product of conduction velocity and refractory period. The core of the reentry circuit is continuously invaded by centripetal impulses from the circulating reentrant wave and is thus continuously excited. A change in conduction velocity causes the reentrant impulse to move concentrically based on the path length traveled in one refractory period; increased conduction velocity moves the wave outwards, to travel in a larger orbit, whereas decreased conduction velocity allows the wave to move inwards to a smaller path. Because the circuit time equals the refractory period (by definition in a path equal to the wavelength), refractory period is the sole determinant of circuit time and tachycardia rate.

Spiral-Wave Reentry   More recently, Pertsov et al suggested that the concept of spiral wave activity, a generalized form of continuous activity in excitable media, may be applicable to cardiac reentry (20). As indicated in Figure 2 (right), spiral-wave reentry differs from the other models in that the core is fully excitable. Maintenance of spiral-wave reentry depends on the curvature of wavefronts at the tip of the spiral (21). A present limitation on the applicability of the spiral-wave concept is the difficulty of formulating predictions regarding the stability and rate of reentry based on simple electrophysiological properties like conduction velocity and refractory period.

Experimental Evidence   The experimental observations available in support of specific models of reentry are limited. The leading-circle concept suggests that the number of waves that the atria can accommodate should be related to the wavelength, which should give the size of functional reentry circuits. Rensma et al (22) noted that the ability to induce AF in dogs is related to the wavelength under various conditions, with wavelengths under ~7.5 cm associated with AF. Antiarrhythmic drugs that increase the wavelength at rapid atrial rates terminate vagotonic AF by reducing the number of functional circuits to the point that AF fails to sustain itself (23–25). The rate of functional reentry during AF (as indicated by the AF cycle length) appears related to the refractory period, rather than the wavelength, which is consistent with the predictions of the leading-circle model (26). On the other hand, high-density mapping data have been presented that provide direct evidence for the presence of spiral waves with an excitable core during atrial reentry (27). To complicate matters further, anatomical obstacles (28) and structures like pectinate muscles (29) can serve to stabilize and anchor spiral waves. It is questionable whether any form of stable reentry, as implied by the simplest interpretation of the models illustrated in Figure 2, can account for all of the complex activity associated with AF. Indeed, high-density optical mapping during AF in sheep hearts failed to show any complete reentry circuits (30). In this regard, Moe's notion of the maintenance of AF being a probabilistic function of the number of meandering wavelets that are able to propagate successfully

(11, 12) is appealing. Alternatively, Jalife et al (31) have argued that AF may be maintained by a dominant rotor, somewhat akin to Lewis's mother wave concept. In such a case, the failure to detect discrete reentry may simply be due to inadequate resolution of recording techniques in the region of the dominant reentry circuit.

ELECTROPHYSIOLOGICAL DETERMINANTS OF ATRIAL FIBRILLATION: IN VIVO OBSERVATIONS

Effects of the Autonomic Nervous System on Atrial Fibrillation Induction and Maintenance

Cholinergic mechanisms have long been know to play an important role in the occurrence and maintenance of AF. In 1914, Rothberger & Winterberg showed that vagal stimulation converted atrial flutter into fibrillation (32), and Garrey (9) cited the work of numerous investigators who established in the early twentieth century the AF-promoting role of vagal-nerve activation (9). Vagal stimulation or acetylcholine administration has been used in many studies evaluating basic mechanisms of AF and/or its response to antiarrhythmic drug therapy (13, 18, 24–26, 33). Vagal-nerve stimulation decreases the atrial refractory period in a spatially heterogeneous way (34, 35). The vagally mediated decrease in refractory period reduces the wavelength and the size of potential reentry circuits, resulting in multiple-circuit reentry (13, 24–26), although at least one study has suggested that, at very high acetylcholine concentrations, AF may be maintained in isolated canine right atrial preparations by a single rapid microreentry circuit (36). Increases in refractoriness heterogeneity appear to be particularly important in the AF-promoting effects of vagal stimulation (37, 38). The atrial repolarization heterogeneity-promoting effects of vagal stimulation may be caused by patchy distribution of vagal nerve terminals and acetylcholine receptors; however, unmasking of underlying cellular action potential heterogeneity by reducing the space constant may also play an important role (39). Vagal nerve stimulation increases the duration of induced AF, with moderate vagal stimulation often permitting AF to be sustained indefinitely. In addition, vagal stimulation greatly promotes the initiation of AF by single premature atrial activations. This action appears to depend both on refractoriness shortening at the site of premature impulse generation and on heterogeneous effects that cause the premature wave front to block in a region with a lesser degree of refractoriness abbreviation (37).

Role of the Sympathetic Nervous System

Whereas the role of vagal-nerve activation in promoting experimental (9, 24–26, 38) and clinical (40, 41) AF is clear, the role of sympathetic activation is much more murky (38, 40, 41). Sympathetic-nerve stimulation abbreviates atrial refractoriness, but, for a comparable degree of refractoriness and wavelength abbreviation, bilateral sympathetic outflow stimulation has a much smaller AF-promoting action than bilateral cervical vagal-nerve stimulation (38). This difference may be caused by a much more spatially heterogeneous effect of vagal stimulation. Nonetheless, sympathetic activation may be important in some types of AF, particularly in the early phases after cardiac surgery (42). There is evidence that patients with larger atrial L-type Ca^{2+} current ($I_{Ca,L}$) may be more prone to postoperative AF (43), suggesting a role for mechanisms (like arrhythmogenic afterdepolarizations) favored by cellular Ca^{2+} overload. If so, the role of sympathetic activation in postoperative AF might be explained by the I_{Ca}-enhancing effects of β-adrenoceptor stimulation.

Animal Models of Atrial Fibrillation Involving Atrial Dilation and/or Inflammation

Congestive heart failure (CHF) is the single strongest clinical predictor of AF, with even asymptomatic left-ventricular dysfunction significantly increasing the risk of the arrhythmia (44). Boyden et al (45, 46) studied the cellular electrophysiological properties of atrial preparations in animals with spontaneous atrial tachyarrhythmias, including AF, occurring in association with atrial dilatation caused by chronic mitral-valve disease (45) or cardiomyopathy (46). Action potential abnormalities were subtle, consisting of reduced resting potential, decreased phase-0 upstroke velocity, and increased action potential duration (APD) in the most affected cells (46). A striking finding was marked structural derangement, with large amounts of interstitial fibrosis and cellular hypertrophy (45, 46).

Experimentally induced chronic CHF promotes AF, the occurrence of which is related to plasma norepinephrine concentrations (47). Recent work suggests that CHF produces a substrate for AF by causing marked interstitial fibrosis, which results in localized conduction abnormalities and promotes macroreentry, which in many cases resembles mother-wave reentry (16, 48). Figure 3 shows an epicardial activation map during AF in one dog with experimental CHF. Note the presence of an apparent, relatively stable reentry circuit involving the right atrium, Bachmann's Bundle, and the septum. Although AF was clearly present on the surface ECG and electrogram activity was quite irregular in rate and morphology in some regions, electrograms from the zone of the apparent reentry circuit showed substantial regularity (Figure 3*A*). Furthermore, the overall activation pattern was basically similar over three consecutive cycles (Figure 3*B–D*), 10 cycles earlier (Figure 3*E*) or 10 cycles later (Figure 3*F*). These findings are consistent with mother-wave reentry as illustrated schematically in Figure 1 (*middle*).

The ability of interstitial fibrosis to interfere with anisotropic atrial conduction and promote atrial reentry is well documented (49). Interstitial fibrosis is commonly seen in clinical conditions associated with AF such as mitral valve disease,

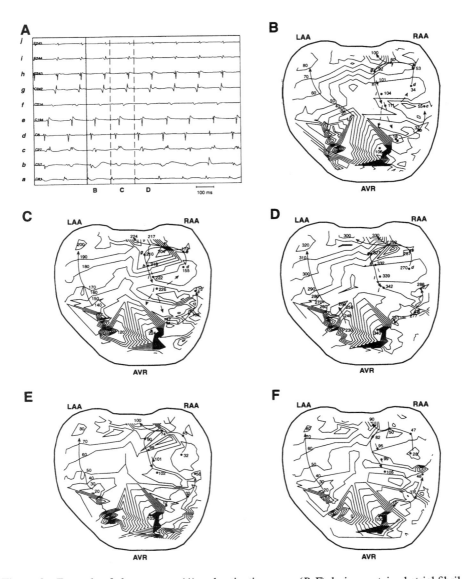

Figure 3 Example of electrograms (*A*) and activation maps (*B-F*) during sustained atrial fibrillation in a dog with CHF. Computerized mapping was used to create activation maps with the use of 243 bipolar electrodes covering the atrial epicardial surface. Five bipolar electrograms were also recorded form the septum. The lines on the activation maps are 10-s isochrones. The locations of electrodes *a* through *j* (of panel *A*), for which electrograms are shown, are indicated in panels *B-D*. Panels *B–D* are activation maps of consecutive cycles corresponding to the time frames indicated in *A*. Panel *E* is a map of a cycle 10 cycles before the window illustrated in *A*, and panel *F* shows activation 10 cycles after the window in *A*. Note the relative regularity of electrograms within the putative reentry circuit and the consistency of the overall activation pattern in *B-F*. Electrode sites *g* through *j* were in the septum, and their activation times were not used in isochrone construction (because they were out of the plane of the other electrode sites).

CHF, and senescence (50–53). Furthermore, interstitial fibrosis is also a common finding in patients with lone AF, unassociated with clinically evident heart disease (54). Thus, the substrate for AF in dogs with experimentally induced heart failure (16, 48) may also apply to many clinical forms of the arrhythmia.

Another animal model that has been used to study AF is sterile pericarditis in the dog (55, 56). AF in this model is caused by a limited number of unstable reentry circuits (55), which appear to involve the interatrial septum preferentially. More recently, evidence for mother-wave reentry has been obtained in the model (17). The precise electrophysiological alterations responsible for AF in association with sterile pericarditis are unclear, but a combination of subtle conduction changes and anatomically based factors may be involved (55, 56).

Atrial Remodeling Induced by Atrial Fibrillation and Atrial Tachycardia

A particularly important recent development in our understanding of the mechanisms of AF was the demonstration that AF alters the atrial electrophysiological milieu in a way that promotes its own maintenance. Wijffels et al (14) very elegantly demonstrated that, when AF is maintained in goats by electrical-burst stimulation whenever sinus rhythm supervenes, the interval between spontaneous reversions increases progressively from several seconds to hours or even days when AF is maintained for up to 2 weeks (Figure 4). Wijffels et al have very descriptively coined this phenomenon "AF begets AF." The AF-promoting effect

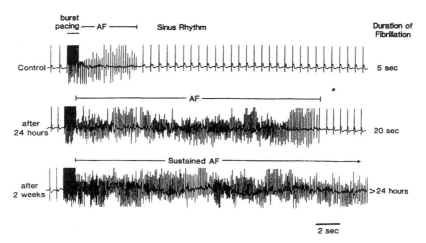

Figure 4 Duration of atrial fibrillation induced by electrical-burst pacing in a chronically instrumented goat after atrial fibrillation had been maintained for the durations indicated to the left of each panel (reproduced from reference 14, by Wijffels et al, with the permission of the American Heart Association, Inc).

of AF is associated with a progressive decrease in atrial effective refractory period (ERP) and in the AF cycle length, an indicator of ERP during AF. Similar changes are observed after either electrically maintained AF (14, 57) or atrial pacing at rates of $\geq$400 beats per minute (bpm) (58–60). Wijffels et al evaluated several potential mediators of the changes produced by AF and found that atrial tachycardia alone appears to be the primary factor, with no detectable contribution from I_{KATP} activation, changes in autonomic tone, atrial stretch, or atrial natriuretic peptide release (61). Atrial tachycardia causes atrial ultrastructural changes, including mitochondrial swelling, mild cellular hypertrophy, sarcoplasmic-reticulum degeneration, loss of myofibrils, and glycogen accumulation (58, 59, 62). Changes in intercellular junction proteins may occur, but the published findings are somewhat inconsistent, with one study showing that AF increases connexin43 expression (63) and another suggesting that connexin43 is unaltered, but connexin40 is decreased in a patchy fashion (64).

Recovery from the changes induced by 2 to 8 weeks of atrial tachycardia occurs within 24 to 48 h (14, 65). Tachycardia-induced changes in left atrial refractoriness may recover somewhat more slowly compared with ERP changes in Bachmann's Bundle or the right atrium, producing a transient exaggeration in atrial refractoriness heterogeneity (65). Progressive increases in atrial ERP and ERP rate adaptation have been observed within several days after cardioversion of longstanding AF in humans (mean duration >5 years), indicating substantial reversibility of remodeling-induced changes after even very long periods of atrial tachycardia (66).

In addition to decreasing atrial ERP, long-term atrial tachycardia appears to slow intra-atrial conduction (57, 58, 60), thus tending to decrease the wavelength for reentry. Furthermore, changes induced by remodeling are spatially heterogeneous, increasing the heterogeneity in atrial refractory properties (67). The combination of decreased wavelength and increased heterogeneity would be expected to promote multiple-circuit reentry. Epicardial mapping studies have provided evidence for a progressive increase in the number of apparent reentry waves during AF as atrial tachycardia-induced remodeling develops (60), consistent with increased stability of multiple-circuit reentry underlying AF promotion by atrial tachycardia.

Tachycardia-Induced Remodeling and Multiple-Circuit Reentry as a Final Common Pathway for Atrial Fibrillation

The evolving information regarding atrial tachycardia-induced remodeling has fundamental implications regarding the mechanisms of AF. Since all cases of AF involve very rapid atrial activation, tachycardia-induced remodeling will inevitably follow, irrespective of the mechanisms initially involved. Thus, even if AF begins as a result of other mechanisms, such as single reentrant circuits (mother waves) with fibrillatory conduction or rapid ectopic activity, tachycardia remodeling will act as a final common pathway to reduce the wavelength in a heterogeneous fashion and promote multiple-circuit reentry.

In Vivo Observations Regarding Atrial Fibrillation Mechanisms in Humans

Clinical studies point to an important role in AF for electrophysiological properties that form a substrate for reentry. Patients with AF tend to have shorter atrial refractory periods (68, 69) and greater dispersion in atrial refractoriness (68, 70, 71) and atrial repolarization times (72). The regional dispersion in atrial repolarization times increases with aging (73), consistent with the known age-related increase in AF prevalence. In addition, atrial conduction abnormalities are observed in patients with AF (69, 74, 75) and are exaggerated in response to atrial premature stimulation (75).

AF is frequently initiated by atrial premature beats (76, 77). Consistent with experimental observations (37, 67), sites at which AF can be initiated are characterized by shorter refractoriness compared with sites at which premature beats do not initiate AF (68). Variable trends in heart rate and ectopic activity have been observed before the onset of AF (77–79). Circadian periodicity has been noted (80) in the duration of AF episodes and the time of AF termination, both pointing to a minimum probability of AF maintenance around midday (11 AM). These observations suggest a role of autonomic and/or neurohumoral factors in AF maintenance, one possible candidate being vagal tone, which tends to be greatest at night and least at midday.

Activation mapping in patients points to different forms of atrial activation during AF (81, 82), which have been divided into three subtypes of AF based on the complexity of activation (81). Individual patients tend to have a predominance of activation subtypes, although individual activation sequences in any patient may fall into any subtype (81, 83). The mechanistic significance of AF subtyping is at present unknown. Local capture of atrial tissue is possible during AF (84), paralleling previous animal studies (85) and consistent with the presence of excitable gaps or regions outside the primary reentry circuit during AF. Signal processing points to a spatial organization of clinical AF (86, 87). Mapping during AF in some patients points to the presence of dominant macroreentry circuits (88, 89), consistent with the observations in dogs with CHF-related AF (16) as illustrated in Figure 3. Other studies point to the role of rapidly firing ectopic foci in patients with AF that tend to be younger and to have very frequent atrial ectopic activity (15, 90).

Clinical Manifestations of Atrial Fibrillation-Related Remodeling

Although the concept of AF-induced remodeling was first established by Wijffels et al in 1995 (14), earlier clinical observations are in agreement with the expected consequences of tachycardia-related atrial remodeling. Since the 1920s, it has been recognized that the greater the duration of persistent AF, the more resistant AF is to therapy (91), consistent with changes in the AF substrate caused by the arrhythmia itself. Attuel et al (92) noted, in 1982, that patients with high vulnerability to AF had a blunted response of atrial refractoriness to heart rate, consistent with changes typical of remodeling (14, 57, 60), although it should be noted that Attuel's patients may not have been in AF immediately prior to study. AF was also shown to cause progressive enlargement of the atria (93), pointing to an effect of AF on atrial mechanical properties.

Several studies have shown that short-term AF (5–15 min) decreases the atrial refractory period and facilitates subsequent AF reinduction (94–96). These phenomena are greatly attenuated by the L-type Ca^{2+} channel blocker verapamil (95, 96). Although the term remodeling has been applied to these short-term changes, they likely represent functional changes in ion channel behavior and action potential properties that are well known to cause action potential abbreviation with increased cardiac frequency (97). Patients with longstanding AF and atrial flutter show changes in atrial monophasic action potentials typical of remodeling after conversion to sinus rhythm (98), showing that typical remodeling occurs in humans and is a consequence of atrial tachycardia, not AF per se. A recent study shows that abnormalities in atrial refractoriness typical of AF-induced remodeling revert toward normal within 4 days of conversion of very longstanding AF (>5 years mean duration), pointing to the reversibility of remodeling even after long periods of the arrhythmia (66). After electrical cardioversion, recurrence of AF is most likely within the first 5 days (99), an interval consistent with the time required for remodeling to dissipate (14, 66). This observation is consistent with the notion that the changes caused by AF-induced remodeling increase the vulnerability to AF and that, if sinus rhythm can be maintained long enough for the reversal of remodeling, sinus rhythm will be more likely.

CHANGES IN ACTION POTENTIALS AND IONIC CURRENTS IN ATRIAL FIBRILLATION

Changes in Atrial Cellular Electrophysiology Caused by Tachycardia-Induced Remodeling

The prominent changes in atrial refractoriness caused by AF (and atrial tachycardias in general) point to important alterations in the atrial action potential and particularly APD, the principle cellular determinant of the refractory period. Boutdjdir et al showed marked action potential changes in atrial preparations from patients with AF compared with patients in sinus rhythm (100). These alterations, illustrated in Figure 5 (*right*), include a loss of the plateau and decreased APD, as well as increased APD heterogeneity (100). Very similar action potential alterations (Figures 6A,B) were subsequently observed (101) to develop progressively in dogs as a result of pacing-induced atrial tachycardia (400 bpm). Furthermore,

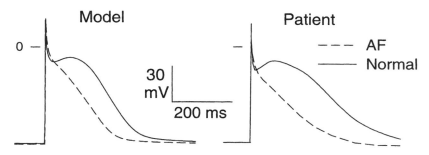

Figure 5 Action potentials from normal human atria (solid lines) and from atria with atrial fibrillation (dashed lines). Results at right are based on experimental data recorded by Boutjdir et al (100), and results at left were obtained with mathematical reconstructions of the human atrial-action potential based on formulations of directly measured ionic currents. The figure is reproduced from Courtemanche et al (108), with permission.

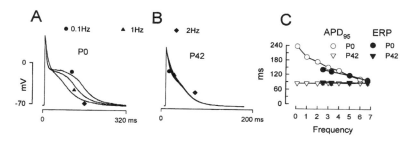

Figure 6 Action potentials recorded at 0.1, 1, and 2 Hz from (A) a normal canine atrial myocyte (P0) and from (B) a myocyte of a dog atrially paced at 400 bpm for 42 days (P42). (C) Mean ± SEM APD_{95} (in isolated cells) and refractory periods (ERP, measured in vivo) in sham (P0) and 42-day rapidly paced (P42) dogs.

pacing-induced APD alterations in isolated cells correspond closely to refractory period changes in vivo (Figure 6C), indicating that cellular action potential modifications likely account for the refractory period changes that promote AF. Sustained rapid atrial pacing in dogs was found to cause progressive reductions in L-type Ca^{2+} current ($I_{Ca,L}$) (Figures 7A,B) and in transient outward K^+ current (I_{to}), without altering delayed-rectifier, ultrarapid-delayed-rectifier (I_{Kur}), or inward-rectifier K^+ currents, Ca^{2+}-dependent Cl^- current, or T-type Ca^{2+} current (101). Current kinetics and voltage dependencies were not altered. The action potential changes caused by rapid pacing (Figures 7C,D) were mimicked in normal cells by blocking I_{Ca} (Figure 7E) and were reversed in cells from rapidly paced dogs by increasing I_{Ca} (Figure 7F), suggesting that $I_{Ca,L}$ changes are central to tachycardia-induced atrial action potential abnormalities. The response of the action potential to pharmacological inhibition of I_{to} suggested that I_{to} changes

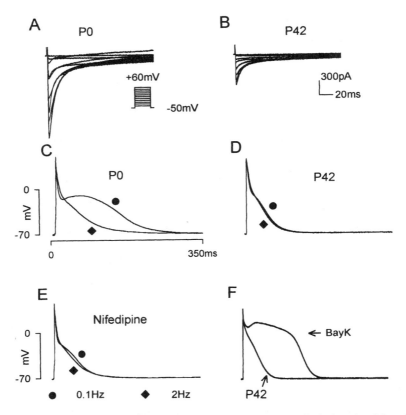

Figure 7 Role of L-type Ca^{2+} current alterations in tachycardia-induced atrial-action potential remodeling. L-type Ca^{2+} currents from representative sham (P0) and 42-day rapidly paced (P42) dog atrial myocytes are shown in *A* and *B*. Action potentials at 0.1 and 2 Hz are shown for P0 and P42 cells in *C* and *D*. Strong I_{CaL} inhibition in a P0 cell by 10 μM nifedipine produced action potential changes (*E*) strongly resembling those caused by atrial tachycardia. Increasing I_{Ca} in a P42 cell by exposure to Bay K8644 restored a more normal action potential morphology to a P42 cell.

play a relatively minor role in the action potential changes caused by remodeling (101). Atrial tachycardia also appears to reduce I_{Na} (102, 103), possibly accounting for conduction slowing after prolonged periods of atrial tachycardia (57, 58, 60, 102). In addition to alterations in the steady-state values of APD at different frequencies, AF also affects the dynamics of APD alterations associated with premature beats and with abrupt rate change (104). The modified APD dynamics produced by atrial tachycardia are related to important alterations in Ca^{2+} handling (104, 105), which likely contribute to the transient atrial contractile dysfunction observed after cardioversion of AF (105).

Studies of ionic currents in patients with AF are complicated by the potential effects of concurrent cardiac disease and drug therapy; however, the limited data available are in general agreement with results in animal studies. There is evidence that both I_{to} (106) and $I_{Ca,L}$ (107) are reduced in patients with AF. In addition, I_{Kur} also appears reduced in patients with AF (106). When the ionic current alterations reported in atrial myocytes from patients with AF (106, 107) are incorporated into a mathematical representation of the human atrial action potential based on detailed formulations of directly measured ionic currents (108), the results resemble recorded action potentials closely (Figure 5). Evaluation of the contributions of individual-ionic-current alterations to action potential alterations in the mathematical model suggests that reductions in $I_{Ca,L}$ account for most of the action potential abnormality associated with AF in humans (108), consistent with the data shown in Figure 7.

Observations in Cardiac Conditions that Predispose to Atrial Fibrillation

Studies in patients with conditions associated with AF may give insights into the cellular and ionic abnormalities that lead to the occurrence of the arrhythmia. Action potentials in multicellular atrial preparations from patients with severe atrial disease are depolarized (109) and show a reduced resting potential response to changed $[K^+_o]$ (110), compatible with decreased I_{K1}. Myocytes from dilated human atria show a reduction in APD and an attenuated APD accommodation to rate change (111). Transient outward K^+ current is decreased (111, 112), as is I_{Ca} (111, 113) and, to a lesser extent, the end-pulse outward current related to I_{Kur} (111, 112). The ionic changes seen in cells from patients with chronic AF are not observed in patients with sinus rhythm and a history of paroxysmal AF (106), suggesting that they are a result, and not the primary cause, of the arrhythmia.

Relatively little information is available in the literature about the properties of atrial myocytes in models of cardiac diseases associated with AF. Boyden & Hoffman showed that right-atrial action potential durations were not significantly altered in dogs with right-atrial enlargement from tricuspid insufficiency (114). Similarly, no major atrial action potential property changes were noted in dogs with chronic mitral-valve disease and atrial arrhythmias (45). Right-atrial action potentials were not altered in cats with cardiomyopathy and atrial arrhythmias, but slight APD prolongation was noted in tissue from the more severely dilated left atria (46). We have found that right-atrial APD is not altered at slow rates in dogs with CHF and a substrate for AF, but that APD is increased at rapid rates, consistent with refractoriness alterations (115). CHF decreased I_{to} strongly (by about 50%), and produced smaller but significant decreases in $I_{Ca,L}$ and in the slow component of the delayed rectifier (I_{Ks}) (115). The atrial ionic remodeling caused by CHF differs from tachycardia-induced remodeling in that the latter causes larger decreases in I_{Ca} and has no effect on I_{Ks}. These differences likely explain the different action potential remodeling under the two conditions. The atrial action potential changes caused by CHF do not obviously account for the substrate for AF produced by CHF, which appears rather to be caused by atrial structural remodeling (48). On the other hand, CHF-induced ionic remodeling has important effects on the electrophysiological milieu in which AF occurs and on the response to antiarrhythmic-drug therapy.

MOLECULAR MECHANISMS ASSOCIATED WITH ATRIAL FIBRILLATION

Molecular Mechanisms of Tachycardia-Related Remodeling

The molecular basis of the atrial electrophysiological remodeling induced by atrial tachycardia is beginning to be unraveled. Dogs subjected to rapid atrial pacing show a progressive reduction in the atrial concentrations of messenger RNA (mRNA) encoding the pore-containing α subunits of L-type Ca^{2+}, Na^+, and I_{to} channels (116). Corresponding reductions in Na^+ and I_{to} channel protein are apparent on immunoblots (116), and atrial dihydropyridine receptor binding (a reflection of the number of L-type Ca^{2+} channels) is also decreased in dogs subjected to atrial tachycardia (117). The mRNA concentrations of clones (DERG and Kir2.1) corresponding to currents (I_{Kr} and I_{K1}) that are unaltered by atrial tachycardia, are unchanged, and there is quantitative agreement between the extent of mRNA downregulation and directly measured changes in $I_{Ca,L}$, I_{to}, and I_{Na} (Figure 8). No change in Na^+-Ca^{2+}-exchanger mRNA or protein expression was observed (116). These observations point to decreases in mRNA levels, likely owing to transcriptional downregulation, as the molecular mechanism of tachycardia-induced changes in atrial ionic-current expression.

Recent clinical studies support the relevance to clinical AF of the results of experimental studies on the molecular basis of tachycardia-induced atrial ionic remodeling. Patients with persistent AF have significant decreases (average decrease ranging from 49 to 60%) in mRNA encoding L-type Ca^{2+} channel α_{1c} subunits, as measured by semiquantitative reverse transcriptase-polymerase chain reaction (118–120). Expression levels of Na^+-Ca^{2+}-exchanger, calsequestrin, phospholamban, and ryanodine receptor mRNA were unaltered (118–120), but a decrease in sarcoplasmic-reticulum Ca^{2+} ATPase mRNA of variable magnitude has been noted (118, 120). L-type Ca^{2+} channel protein levels were also reduced as measured by slot-blot analysis (120).

The signal transduction pathways responsible for changes in mRNA levels induced by atrial tachycardia are currently unknown. The histological appearance of atrial tissue subjected to several hours of rapid pacing is compatible with Ca^{2+} overload (59), and there is some evidence for a protective effect of Ca^{2+} channel blockers against the consequences of short-term (95, 96) and longer-term (121, 122) atrial tachycardia. Ca^{2+}_i-sensitive pathways may therefore be involved, but

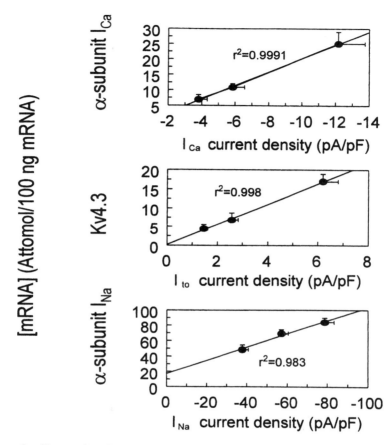

Figure 8 Changes in mRNA concentration as measured by competitive reverse transcriptase-polymerase chain reaction and corresponding ionic current densities measured in atrial tissue from sham dogs and dogs subjected to 7 and 42 days of atrial pacing at 400 bpm. Results are mean ± SEM and best-fit regression lines are shown.

the present evidence is limited, and the precise signaling pathways remain unknown.

Genetic Aspects and Possibility of Molecular Therapeutics

The description of a kindred with genetically based AF (123) has raised exciting new opportunities in the understanding and management of AF. The specific gene involved in familial AF is still unknown, but work is proceeding at a pace that suggests that the molecular basis of familial AF will be known within two years. Recent advances in molecular electrophysiology have provided for exciting new opportunities in arrhythmia management (124). The identification of ion channel clones that are functionally expressed in the human atrium and not the ventricle, along with the demonstration of specific knockdown of the corresponding current by exposure to antisense oligodeoxynucleotides (125), raises the possibility of chamber-specific antiarrhythmic therapy that would be effective against AF without collateral side effects like ventricular proarrhythmia. Recent demonstrations of the ability of adenoviral gene transfer to knock down cardiac ion channel expression (126) and to alter cellular excitability (127, 128) indicate that the therapy of cardiac arrhythmias by modifying gene expression may become a reality in the foreseeable future.

A PATHOPHYSIOLOGICAL ANALYSIS OF ATRIAL FIBRILLATION AND RELATIONSHIP TO NEW THERAPEUTIC OPPORTUNITIES

Recent advances in our understanding of the pathophysiology of AF provide potential new insights into AF mechanisms, as illustrated in Figure 9, with implications for novel approaches to AF therapy. Atrial ectopic activity can produce

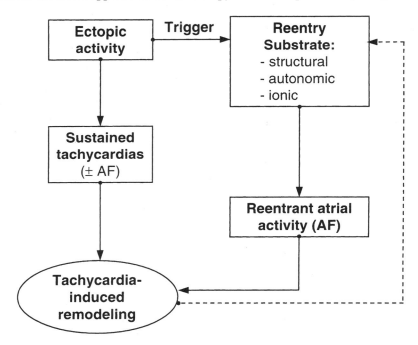

Figure 9   Schematic of mechanisms that can initiate atrial fibrillation and promote its maintenance. Tachycardia-induced remodeling is a final common pathway via which AF caused by any mechanism results in a substrate that favors multiple-circuit reentry and promotes the maintenance of AF.

atrial tachyarrhythmias, which may at times present as very rapid atrial tachycardias and at others as frank AF (15). Ectopic activity can also act as a trigger for a substrate that can maintain reentry, with potential primary substrates including important structural components, as in CHF-related AF (48), autonomic determinants as in vagal AF (37, 38, 40, 41), or ionic determinants (101) such as recurrence of AF in a patient with remodeled atria within 1 or 2 days after electrical cardioversion. Atrial tachycardia resulting either from rapid ectopic activity or from reentrant AF will cause tachycardia-induced remodeling, which will tend to promote the maintenance of AF by favoring multiple-circuit reentry. The pathophysiology associated with AF is thus a dynamic function of the underlying cause(s) and the changes resulting from maintenance of the arrhythmia itself.

This analysis points to potential therapeutic targets other than the traditional ionic currents involved in atrial repolarization. For example, it may be possible to intervene at the level of the signal transduction system that causes AF-promoting structural remodeling. Clinical results point to a beneficial effect of angiotensin-converting enzyme inhibitors in preventing AF after myocardial infarction (129), and we have obtained preliminary data suggesting that converting enzyme inhibitors may prevent AF-promoting structural remodeling in a dog model of CHF (130). If the structural basis for AF results in single-circuit reentry, a single ablation lesion at a critical point in the pathway may be sufficient to prevent the arrhythmia (89). The ablation of ectopic foci that trigger AF may cure AF caused by ectopic focal discharge (15). The development of tachycardia-induced remodeling may be amenable to pharmacological manipulation. For example, the T-type Ca^{2+} channel blocker mibefradil has been found to be highly effective in preventing development of the atrial tachycardia-induced AF substrate in dogs (122). Prevention of AF-induced remodeling could have a variety of beneficial effects (131), including decreasing the resistance of the arrhythmia to antiarrhythmic-drug therapy and decreasing the risks of recurrence following cardioversion. The prompt cardioversion of AF by an implanted device may result in a progressive increase in the interval to the next AF recurrence (132) by preventing remodeling from developing, exemplifying a concept that has become known as "sinus rhythm begets sinus rhythm." Many other innovative therapeutic approaches are likely to follow our recently improved understanding of fundamental AF mechanisms.

CONCLUSIONS

In retrospect, the insight of researchers in the early twentieth century into AF mechanisms is remarkable. Recent work confirms the accuracy of this early work, while providing deep and sophisticated insights into underlying mechanisms at levels ranging from the molecule to humans. A great deal was known about AF before 1925, but the explosion of new knowledge about the arrhythmia in the last five years has been impressive. This new knowledge will certainly be translated into important practical advances in arrhythmia management over the next five years.

Visit the Annual Reviews home page at www.AnnualReviews.org.

LITERATURE CITED

1. Waktare JEP, Camm AJ. 1998. Acute treatment of atrial fibrillation: why and when to maintain sinus rhythm. *Am. J. Cardiol.* 81:3C–15

2. The National Heart, Lung, and Blood Institute Working Group on Atrial Fibrillation. 1993. Atrial fibrillation: current understandings and research imperatives. *J. Am. Coll. Cardiol.* 22:1830–34

3. Vulpian A. 1874. Note sur les effets de la faradisation directe des ventricules du cœur chez le chien. *Arch. Physiol.* 1:975–80

4. Cushny AR. 1899. On the interpretation of pulse–tracings. *J. Exp. Med.* 4:327–47

5. Fredericq L. 1904. Rythme affolé des ventricules dû à la fibrillation des oreillettes: physiologie du faisceau auriculo–ventriculaire. *Arch. Int. Physiol.* 5:281–85

6. Mines GR. 1913. On dynamic equilibrium in the heart. *J. Physiol.* 46:349–82

7. Mines GR. 1914. On circulating excitations in heart muscles and their possible relation to tachycardia and fibrillation. *Proc. Trans. R. Soc. Can.* 8:43–53

8. Garrey WE. 1914. The nature of fibrillary contraction of the heart—its relation to tissue mass and form. *Am. J. Physiol.* 33:397–414

9. Garrey WE. 1924. Auricular fibrillation. *Physiol. Rev.* 4:215–50

10. Moe GK, Abildskov JA. 1959. Experimental and laboratory reports. Atrial fibrillation as a self–sustaining arrhythmia independent of focal discharge. *Am. Heart J.* 58:59–70

11. Moe GK. 1962. On the multiple wavelet hypothesis of atrial fibrillation. *Arch. Int. Pharmacodyn. Ther.* 140:183–88

12. Moe GK, Rheinboldt WC, Abildskov JA. 1964. A computer model of atrial fibrillation. *Am. Heart J.* 67:200–20

13. Allessie MA, Lammers WJEP, Bonke FIM, Hollen J. 1985. Experimental evaluation of Moe's multiple wavelet hypothesis of atrial fibrillation. In *Cardiac Arrhythmias,* ed. DP Zipes, J Jalife, pp. 265–76. New York: Grune & Stratton

14. Wijffels MC, Kirchhof CJ, Dorland R, Allessie MA. 1995. Atrial fibrillation begets atrial fibrillation: a study in awake chronically instrumented goats. *Circulation* 92:1954–68

15. Haissaguerre M, Jais P, Shah DC, Takahashi A, Hocini M, et al. 1998. Spontaneous initiation of atrial fibrillation by ectopic beats originating in the pulmonary veins. *N. Engl. J. Med.* 339:659–66

16. Li D, Leung TK, Nattel S. 1998. Mechanisms of atrial fibrillation in dogs with congestive heart failure: electrical remodeling of a different sort. *Circulation* 98(Suppl. I):I209–10 (Abstr.)

17. Matsuo K, Tomita Y, Uno K, Khrestian CM, Waldo AL. 1998. A new mechanism of sustained atrial fibrillation: studies in the canine sterile pericarditis model. *Circulation* 98(Suppl. I):I209 (Abstr.)

18. Allessie MA, Bonke FIM, Schopman FJG. 1977. Circus movement in rabbit atrial muscle as a mechanism of tachycardia. III. The "leading circle" concept: a new model of circus movement in cardiac tissue without the involvement of an anatomical obstacle. *Circ. Res.* 41:9–18

19. Wiener N, Rosenblueth A. 1946. The mathematical formulation of the problem of conduction of impulses in a network of connected excitable elements, specif-

ically in cardiac muscle. *Arch. Inst. Cardiol. Mex.* 16:205–65

20. Pertsov AM, Davidenko JM, Salomonsz R, Baxter WT, Jalife J. 1993. Spiral waves of excitation underlie reentrant activity in isolated cardiac muscle. *Circ. Res.* 72:631–50

21. Cabo C, Pertsov AM, Baxter WT, Davidenko JM, Gray RA, et al. 1994. Wavefront curvature as a cause of slow conduction and block in isolated cardiac muscle. *Circ. Res.* 75:1014–28

22. Rensma PL, Allessie MA, Lammers WJEP, Bonke FIM, Schalij MJ. 1988. Length of excitation wave and susceptibility to reentrant atrial arrhythmias in normal conscious dogs. *Circ. Res.* 62:395–410

23. Wang Z, Pagé P, Nattel S. 1992. The mechanism of flecainide's antiarrhythmic action in experimental atrial fibrillation. *Circ. Res.* 71:271–87

24. Wang J, Bourne GW, Wang Z, Villemaire C, Talajic M, Nattel S. 1993. Comparative mechanisms of antiarrhythmic drug action in experimental atrial fibrillation: importance of use–dependent effects on refractoriness. *Circulation* 88:1030–44

25. Wang J, Feng J, Nattel S. 1994. Class III antiarrhythmic drug action in experimental atrial fibrillation: differences in reverse use dependence and effectiveness between d–sotalol and the new antiarrhythmic drug ambasilide. *Circulation* 90:2032–40

26. Nattel S, Bourne G, Talajic M. 1997. Insights into mechanisms of antiarrhythmic drug action from experimental models of atrial fibrillation. *J. Cardiovasc. Electrophysiol.* 8:469–80

27. Ikeda T, Uchida T, Hough D, Lee JJ, Fishbein MC, et al. 1996. Mechanism of spontaneous termination of functional reentry in isolated canine right atrium. Evidence for the presence of an excitable but nonexcited core. *Circulation* 94:1962–73

28. Ikeda T, Yashima M, Uchida T, Hough D, Fishbein MC, et al. 1997. Attachment of meandering reentrant wave fronts to anatomic obstacles in the atrium. Role of the obstacle size. *Circ. Res.* 81:753–64

29. Wu TJ, Yashima M, Xie F, Athill CA, Kim YH, et al. 1998. Role of pectinate muscle bundles in the generation and maintenance of intra–atrial reentry. Potential implications for the mechanism of conversion between atrial fibrillation and atrial flutter. *Circ. Res.* 83:448–62

30. Gray RA, Pertsov AM, Jalife J. 1996. Incomplete reentry and epicardial breakthrough patterns during atrial fibrillation in the sheep heart. *Circulation* 94:2649–61

31. Jalife J, Berenfeld O, Skanes A, Mandapati R. 1998. Mechanisms of atrial fibrillation: mother rotors or multiple daughter wavelets, or both? *J. Cardiovasc. Electrophysiol.* 9:S2–12

32. Rothberger CJ, Winterberg H. 1914. Uber Vorhofflimmern and Vorhofflattern. *Pflügers Arch.* 160:42–90

33. Nattel S, Liu L, St–Georges D. 1998. Effects of the novel antiarrhythmic agent azimilide on experimental atrial fibrillation and atrial electrophysiologic properties. *Cardiovasc. Res.* 37:627–35

34. Ninomiya I. 1966. Direct evidence of nonuniform distribution of vagal effects on dog atria. *Circ. Res.* 19:576–83

35. Alessi R, Nusynowitz M, Abildskov JA, Moe GK. 1958. Nonuniform distribution of vagal effects on the atrial refractory period. *Am. J. Physiol.* 194:406–10

36. Schuessler RB, Grayson TM, Bromberg BI, Cox JL, Boineau JP. 1992. Cholinergically mediated tachyarrhythmias induced by a single extrastimulus in the isolated canine right atrium. *Circ. Res.* 71:1254–67

37. Wang J, Liu L, Feng J, Nattel S. 1996. Regional and functional factors determining induction and maintenance of atrial fibrillation in dogs. *Am. J. Physiol.* 271(40):H148–58

38. Liu L, Nattel S. 1997. Differing sympa-

thetic and vagal effects on atrial fibrillation in dogs: role of refractoriness heterogeneity. *Am. J. Physiol.* 273(42): H805–16

39. Feng J, Yue L, Wang Z, Nattel S. 1998. Ionic mechanisms of regional action potential heterogeneity in the canine right atrium. *Circ. Res.* 83:541–51

40. Murgatroyd FD, Camm AJ. 1992. Sinus rhythm, the autonomic nervous system, and quality of life. In *Atrial Fibrillation, a Treatable Disease?* ed. JH Kingman, HM van Hemel, KI Lie, pp. 195–210. Dordrecht, The Netherlands: Kluwer

41. Coumel P. 1994. Fibrillation auriculaire paroxystique; le rôle du système nerveux autonome. *Arch. Mal. Cœur* 87:55–62

42. Andrews TC, Reimold SC, Berlin JA, Antman EM. 1991. Prevention of supraventricular arrhythmias after coronary artery bypass surgery. A meta–analysis of randomized control trials. *Circ. Suppl.* 84:III236–44

43. Kirian MA, Lamorgese M, Van Wagoner DR. 1998. Calcium current density in human atrial myocytes is inversely correlated with the occurrence of post–operative atrial fibrillation. *Circ. Suppl.* 98:I–334 (Abstr.)

44. Vaziri SM, Larson MG, Benjamin EJ, Levy D. 1994. Echocardiographic predictors of nonrheumatic atrial fibrillation. The Framingham Heart Study. *Circulation* 89:724–30

45. Boyden PA, Tilley LP, Pham TD, Liu SK, Fenoglio JJ Jr, et al. 1982. Effects of left atrial enlargement on atrial transmembrane potentials and structure in dogs with mitral valve fibrosis. *Am. J. Cardiol.* 49:1896–908

46. Boyden PA, Tilley LP, Albala A, Liu SK, Fenoglio JJ Jr, et al. 1984. Mechanisms for atrial arrhythmias associated with cardiomyopathy: a study of feline hearts with primary myocardial disease. *Circulation* 69:1036–47

47. Borzak S, Goldstem S, Sabbah HN. 1993. Hemodynamic and neurohumoral predictors of the development of atrial fibrillation in dogs with chronic heart failure. *Circ. Suppl.* 88:I18 (Abstr.)

48. Li D, Fareh S, Leung TK, Nattel S. 1999. Promotion of atrial fibrillation by heart failure in dogs: atrial remodeling of a different sort. *Circulation* 100:87–95

49. Spach MS, Dolber PC, Heidlage JF. 1988. Influence of the passive anisotropic properties on directional differences in propagation following modification of the sodium conductance in human atrial muscle. A model of reentry based on anisotropic discontinuous propagation. *Circ. Res.* 62:811–32

50. Pham TD, Fenoglio JJ Jr. 1982. Right atrial ultrastructure in chronic rheumatic heart disease. *Int. J. Cardiol.* 1:289–304

51. Thiedemann KU, Ferrans VJ. 1997. Left atrial ultrastructure in mitral valvular disease. *Am. J. Pathol.* 89:575–604

52. Lie JT, Hammond PI. 1988. Pathology of the senescent heart: anatomic observation on 237 autopsy studies of patients of 90 to 105 years old. *Mayo Clin. Proc.* 63:552–64

53. Anderson KR, St. John–Sutton MG, Lie JT. 1979. Histological types of cardiac fibrosis in myocardial disease. *J. Pathol.* 128:79–85

54. Frustaci A, Caldarulo M, Buffon A, Bellocci F, Fenici R, et al. 1991. Cardiac biopsy in patients with "primary" atrial fibrillation. Histologic evidence of occult myocardial diseases. *Chest* 100:303–6

55. Kumagai K, Khrestian C, Waldo AL. 1997. Simultaneous multisite mapping studies during induced atrial fibrillation in the sterile pericarditis model. Insights into the mechanism of its maintenance. *Circulation* 95:511–21

56. Li H, Hare J, Mughal K, Krum D, Biehl M, et al. 1996. Distribution of atrial electrogram types during atrial fibrillation: effect of rapid atrial pacing and intercaval junction ablation. *J. Am. Coll. Cardiol.* 27:1713–21

57. Elvan A, Wylie K, Zipes DP. 1996. Pac-

ing–induced chronic atrial fibrillation impairs sinus node function in dogs. Electrophysiological remodeling. *Circulation* 94:2953–60

58. Morillo CA, Klein GJ, Jones DL, Guiraudon CM. 1995. Chronic rapid atrial pacing: structural, functional, and electrophysiological characteristics of a new model of sustained atrial fibrillation. *Circulation* 91:1588–95

59. Goette A, Honeycutt C, Langberg JL. 1996. Electrical remodeling in atrial fibrillation: time course and mechanisms. *Circulation* 94:2968–74

60. Gaspo R, Bosch RF, Talajic M, Nattel S. 1997. Functional mechanisms underlying tachycardia–induced sustained atrial fibrillation in a chronic dog model. *Circulation* 96:4027–35

61. Wijffels MC, Kirchhof CJ, Dorland R, Power J, Allessie MA. 1997. Electrical remodeling due to atrial fibrillation in chronically instrumented conscious goats: role of neurohumoral changes, ischemia, atrial stretch, and high rate of electrical activation. *Circulation* 96:3710–20

62. Ausma J, Wijffels M, Thoné F, Wouters L, Allessie M. 1997. Structural changes of atrial myocardium due to sustained atrial fibrillation in the goat. *Circulation* 96:3157–63

63. Elvan A, Huang XD, Pressler ML, Zipes DP. 1997. Radiofrequency catheter ablation of the atria eliminates pacing–induced sustained atrial fibrillation and reduces connexin43 in dogs. *Circulation* 96:1675–85

64. van der Velden HM, van Kempen MJ, Wijffels MC, van Zijverden M, Groenewegen WA, et al. 1998. Altered pattern of connexin40 distribution in persistent atrial fibrillation in the goat. *J. Cardiovasc. Electrophysiol.* 9:596–607

65. Lee SH, Lin FY, Yu WC, Cheng JJ, Kuan P, et al. 1999. Regional differences in the recovery course of tachycardia–induced

changes of atrial electrophysiological properties. *Circulation* 99:1255–64

66. Yu WC, Lee SH, Tai CT, Tsai CF, Hsieh MH, et al. 1999. Reversal of atrial electrical remodeling following cardioversion of long–standing atrial fibrillation in man. *Cardiovasc. Res.* 42:470–76

67. Fareh S, Villemaire C, Nattel S. 1998. Importance of refractoriness heterogeneity in the enhanced vulnerability to atrial fibrillation induction caused by tachycardia–induced atrial electrical remodeling. *Circulation* 98:2202–9

68. Hashiba K, Centurion OA, Shimizu A. 1996. Electrophysiologic characteristics of human atrial muscle in paroxysmal atrial fibrillation. *Am. Heart J.* 131:778–89

69. Kumagai K, Akimitsu S, Kawahira K, Kawanami F, Yamanouchi Y, et al. 1991. Electrophysiological properties in chronic lone atrial fibrillation. *Circulation* 84:1662–68

70. Ramanna H, Hauer RN, Wittkampf FH, de Bakker JM, van Capelle FJ, et al. 1997. Increased dispersion of refractoriness in patients with paroxysmal atrial fibrillation: a multielectrode endocardial approach. *PACE* 20:1063 (Abstr.)

71. Ramdat Misier AR, Opthof T, van Hemel NM, Vermeulen JT, de Bakker JM, et al. 1992. Increased dispersion of "refractoriness" in patients with idiopathic paroxysmal atrial fibrillation. *J. Am. Coll. Cardiol.* 19:1531–35

72. Cui G, Fonarow GC, Laks H. 1997. Exaggerated dispersion of P–Ta and Ta–T interval as a predictor of atrial fibrillation. *J. Am. Coll. Cardiol.* 29(Suppl. A):191A (Abstr.)

73. Diker E, Ozdemir M, Aydogdu S, Tezcan UK, Korkmaz S, et al. 1998. Dispersion of repolarization in paroxysmal atrial fibrillation. *Int. J. Cardiol.* 63:281–86

74. Steinberg JS, Zelenkofske S, Wong SC, Gelernt M, Sciacca R, Menchavez E. 1993. Value of the P–wave signal–averaged ECG for predicting atrial fibrillation

after cardiac surgery. *Circulation* 88: 2618–22

75. Hashiba K, Tanigawa M, Fukatani M, Shimizu A, Konoe A, et al. 1989. Electrophysiologic properties of atrial muscle in paroxysmal atrial fibrillation. *Am. J. Cardiol.* 64:20J–23J

76. Bennett MA, Pentecost BL. 1970. The pattern of onset and spontaneous cessation of atrial fibrillation in man. *Circulation* 41:981–88

77. Hnatkova K, Waktare JE, Murgatroyd FD, Guo X, Baiyan X, et al. 1998. Analysis of the cardiac rhythm preceding episodes of paroxysmal atrial fibrillation. *Am. Heart J.* 135:1010–19

78. Hogue CW, Domitrovich PP, Stein PK, Despotis GD, Re L, et al. 1998. RR interval dynamics before atrial fibrillation in patients after coronary artery bypass graft surgery. *Circulation* 98:429–34

79. Waktare JEP, Hnatkova K, Murgatroyd FD, Baiyan X, Camm AJ, et al. 1997. Atrial ectopic activity prior to the onset of paroxysmal atrial fibrillation. *J. Am. Coll. Cardiol.* 191A (Abstr.)

80. Yamashita T, Murakawa Y, Sezaki K, Inoue M, Hayami N, et al. 1997. Circadian variation of paroxysmal atrial fibrillation. *Circulation* 96:1537–41

81. Konings KTS, Kirchhof CJHJ, Smeets JRLM, Wellens HJJ, Pen OC, et al. 1994. High–density mapping of electrically induced atrial fibrillation in humans. *Circulation* 89:1665–80

82. Holm M, Johansson R, Brandt J, Lührs C, Olsson SB. 1997. Epicardial right atrial free wall mapping in chronic atrial fibrillation. Documentation of repetitive activation with a focal spread—a hitherto unrecognised phenomenon in man. *Eur. Heart J.* 18:290–310

83. Hoekstra BPT, Diks CGH, Allessie MA, DeGoede J. 1995. Nonlinear analysis of epicardial atrial electrograms of electrically induced atrial fibrillation in man. *J. Cardiovasc. Electrophysiol.* 6:419–40

84. Pandozi C, Bianconi L, Villani M, Castro

A, Altamura G, et al. 1997. Local capture by atrial pacing in spontaneous chronic atrial fibrillation. *Circulation* 95:2416–22

85. Kirchhof C, Chorro F, Scheffer GJ, Brugada J, Konings K, et al. 1993. Regional entrainment of atrial fibrillation studied by high–resolution mapping in open–chest dogs. *Circulation* 88:736–49

86. Gerstenfeld EP, Sahakian AV, Swiryn S. 1992. Evidence for transient linking of atrial excitation during atrial fibrillation in humans. *Circulation* 86:375–82

87. Botteron GW, Smith JM. 1996. Quantitative assessment of the spatial organization of atrial fibrillation in the intact human heart. *Circulation* 93:513–18

88. Giorgberidze I, Saksena S, Krol R, Prakash A, Munsif A, et al. 1997. Catheter endocardial mapping of spontaneous termination of atrial fibrillation. *PACE* 20:1065 (Abstr.)

89. Shoda M, Kajimoto K, Matsuda N, Umemura J, Ohnishi S, Kasanuki H. 1997. A novel mechanism of human atrial fibrillation: single macro–reentry with intra–atrial conduction block. *PACE* 20:1065 (Abstr.)

90. Jaïs P, Haïssaguerre M, Shah DC, Chouairi S, Gencel L, et al. 1997. A focal source of atrial fibrillation treated by discrete radiofrequency ablation. *Circulation* 95:572–76

91. Parkinson J, Campbell M. 1929. The quinidine treatment of auricular fibrillation. *Q. J. Med.* 22:281–303

92. Attuel P, Childers R, Cauchemez B, Poveda J, Mugica J, et al. 1982. Failure in the rate adaptation of the atrial refractory period: its relationship to vulnerability. *Int. J. Cardiol.* 2:179–97

93. Sanfilippo AJ, Abascal VM, Sheehan M, Oertel LB, Harrigan P, et al. 1990. Atrial enlargement as a consequence of atrial fibrillation. A prospective echocardiographic study. *Circulation* 82:792–97

94. Daoud EG, Bogun F, Goyal R, Harvey M, Man KC, et al. 1996. Effect of atrial

fibrillation on atrial refractoriness in humans. *Circulation* 94:1600–6

95. Daoud EG, Knight BP, Weiss R, Bahu M, Paladino W, et al. 1997. Effect of verapamil and procainamide on atrial fibrillation–induced electrical remodeling in humans. *Circulation* 96:1542–50

96. Yu WC, Chen SA, Lee SH, Tai CT, Feng AN, et al. 1998. Tachycardia–induced change of atrial refractory period in humans: rate–dependency and effects of antiarrhythmic drugs. *Circulation* 97: 2331–37

97. Boyett MR, Jewell BR. 1980. Analysis of the effects of changes in rate and rhythm upon electrical activity in the heart. *Prog. Biophys. Mol. Biol.* 36:1–52

98. Franz MR, Karasik PL, Li C, Moubarak J, Chavez M. 1997. Electrical remodeling of the human atrium: similar effects in patients with chronic atrial fibrillation and atrial flutter. *J. Am. Coll. Cardiol.* 30:1785–92

99. Tieleman RG, Van Gelder IC, Crijns HJGM, De Kam PJ, Van Den Berg MP, et al. 1998. Early recurrences of atrial fibrillation after electrical cardioversion: a result of fibrillation–induced electrical remodeling of the atria? *J. Am. Coll. Cardiol.* 31:167–73

100. Boutjdir M, Le Heuzey JY, Lavergne T, Chavaud S, Guize L. 1986. Inhomogeneity of cellular refractoriness in human atrium: factor of arrhythmia? *PACE* 9:1095–100

101. Yue L, Feng J, Gaspo R, Li GR, Wang Z, Nattel S. 1997. Ionic remodeling underlying action potential changes in a canine model of atrial fibrillation. *Circ. Res.* 81:512–25

102. Gaspo R, Bosch RF, Bou–Abboud E, Nattel S. 1997. Tachycardia–induced changes in Na^+ current in a chronic dog model of atrial fibrillation. *Circ. Res.* 97:1045–52

103. Pu J, Shvilkin A, Hara M, Danilo P Jr, Boyden PA.1997. Altered inward currents in myocytes from chronically fibril-lating canine atria. *Circ. Suppl.* 96:I–180 (Abstr.)

104. Hara M, Shvilkin A, Rosen MR, Danilo P Jr, Boyden PA. 1999. Steady–state and nonsteady–state action potentials in fibrillating canine atrium: abnormal rate adaptation and its possible mechanisms. *Cardiovasc. Res.* 42:455–69

105. Sun H, Gaspo R, Leblanc N, Nattel S. 1998. The cellular mechanisms of atrial contractile dysfunction caused by sustained atrial tachycardia. *Circulation* 98:719–27

106. van Wagoner DR, Pond AL, McCarthy PM, Trimmer JS, Nerbonne JM. 1997. Outward K^+ current densities and Kv1.5 expression are reduced in chronic human atrial fibrillation. *Circ. Res.* 80:772–81

107. van Wagoner DR, Lamorgese M, Kirian P, Cheng Y, Efimov IR, et al. 1997. Calcium current density is reduced in atrial myocytes isolated from patients in chronic atrial fibrillation. *Circ. Suppl.* 96:I–180 (Abstr.)

108. Courtemanche M, Ramirez RJ, Nattel S. 1999. Ionic targets for drug therapy and atrial fibrillation–induced electrical remodeling: insights from a mathematical model. *Cardiovasc. Res.* 42:477–89

109. Hordof AJ, Edie R, Malm JR, Hoffman BF, Rosen MR. 1976. Electrophysiologic properties and response to pharmacologic agents of fibers from diseased human atria. *Circulation* 54:774–79

110. Ten Eick RE, Singer DH. 1979. Electrophysiological properties of diseased human atrium. I. Low diastolic potential and altered cellular response to potassium. *Circ. Res.* 44:545–57

111. Le Grand B, Hatem S, Deroubaix E, Couétil JP, Coraboeuf E. 1994. Depressed transient outward and calcium currents in dilated human atria. *Cardiovasc. Res.* 28:548–56

112. Mansourati J, Le Grand B. 1993. Transient outward current in young and adult diseased human atria. *Am. J. Physiol.* 265(34):H1466–70

113. Ouadid H, Albat B, Nargeot J. 1995. Calcium currents in diseased human cardiac cells. *J. Cardiovasc. Pharmacol.* 25:282–91

114. Boyden PA, Hoffman BF. 1981. The effects on atrial electrophysiology and structure of surgically induced right atrial enlargement in dogs. *Circ. Res.* 49:1319–31

115. Li D, Feng J, Nattel S. 1998. Remodeling of atrial cellular and ionic electrophysiology by congestive heart failure. *Circ. Suppl.* 98:I–33 (Abstr.)

116. Yue L, Melnyk P, Gaspo R, Wang Z, Nattel S. 1999. Molecular mechanisms underlying ionic remodeling in a dog model of atrial fibrillation. *Circ. Res.* 84:776–84

117. Gaspo R, Sun H, Fareh S, Levi M, Yue L, et al. 1999. Dihydropyridine and beta adrenergic receptor binding in dogs with tachycardia–induced atrial fibrillation. *Cardiovasc. Res.* 42:434–42

118. Lai LP, Su MJ, Lin JL, Lin FY, Tsai CH, et al. 1999. Down–regulation of L–type calcium channel and sarcoplasmic reticular Ca^{2+}–ATPase mRNA in human atrial fibrillation without significant change in the mRNA of ryanodine receptor, calsequestrin and phospholamban. *J. Am. Coll. Cardiol.* 33:1231–37

119. Van Gelder IC, Brundel BJJM, Henning RH, Tuinenburg AE, Tieleman RG, et al. 1999. Alterations in gene expression of proteins involved in the calcium handling in patients with atrial fibrillation. *J. Cardiovasc. Electrophysiol.* 10:552–60

120. Brundel BJJM, Van Gelder IC, Henning RH, Tuinenburg AE, Deelman LE, et al. 1999. Gene expression of proteins influencing the calcium homeostatis in patients with persistent and paroxysmal atrial fibrillation. *Cardiovasc. Res.* 42:443–54

121. Tieleman RG, De Langen CDJ, Van Gelder IC, de Kam PJ, Grandjean J, et al. 1997. Verapamil reduces tachycardia–induced electrical remodeling of the atria. *Circulation* 95:1945–53

122. Fareh S, Thibault B, Nattel S. 1998. Treatment with a T–type calcium channel blocker prevents atrial fibrillation caused by tachycardia–induced atrial remodeling. *Circ. Suppl.* 98:I–210 (Abstr.)

123. Brugada R, Tapscott T, Grazyna Z, Czernuszewicz MS, Marian AJ, et al. 1997. Identification of a genetic locus for familial atrial fibrillation. *N. Engl. J. Med.* 336:905–11

124. Nattel S. 1999. The molecular and ionic specificity of antiarrhythmic drug actions. *J. Cardiovasc. Electrophysiol.* 10:272–82

125. Feng J, Wible B, Li GR, Wang Z, Nattel S. 1997. Antisense oligodexynucleotides directed against Kv1.5 mRNA specifically inhibit ultrarapid delayed rectifier K^+ current in cultured adult human atrial myocytes. *Circ. Res.* 80:572–79

126. Johns DC, Nuss HB, Marban E. 1997. Suppression of neuronal and cardiac transient outward currents by viral gene transfer of dominant–negative Kv4.2 constructs. *J. Biol. Chem.* 272:31598–603

127. Nuss HB, Marban E, Johns DC. 1999. Overexpression of a human potassium channel suppresses cardiac hyperexcitability in rabbit ventricular myocytes. *J. Clin. Invest.* 103:889–96

128. Hoppe UC, Johns DC, Marban E, O'Rourke B. 1999. Manipulation of cellular excitability by cell fusion: effects of rapid introduction of transient outward K^+ current on the guinea pig action potential. *Circ. Res.* 84:964–72

129. Pederson OD, Bagger H. 1997. Trandolapril reduces the incidence of atrial fibrillation following acute myocardial infarction. *Circ. Suppl.* 96:I–75 (Abstr.)

130. Li D, Shi YF, Levi M, Leung TK, Tardif JC, Nattel S. 1999. Prevention of atrial structural remodeling—a potential new approach to treating atrial fibrillation. *Circulation* (Abstr.) In press

131. Nattel S. 1999. Atrial electrophysiological remodeling caused by rapid atrial activation: underlying mechanisms and clinical relevance to atrial fibrillation. *Cardiovasc. Res.* 42:298–308

132. Timmermans C, Wellens HJJ. 1998. Effect of device–mediated therapy on symptomatic episodes of atrial fibrillation. *J. Am. Coll. Cardiol. Suppl.* 31:331A (Abstr.)

Annu. Rev. Physiol. 2000. 62:79–109

ISCHEMIC PRECONDITIONING: From Adenosine Receptor to K_{ATP} Channel

Michael V. Cohen, Christopher P. Baines, and James M. Downey

Departments of Medicine and Physiology, University of South Alabama, College of Medicine, Mobile, Alabama 36688; e-mail: mcohen@usamail.usouthal.edu, jdowney@usamail.usouthal.edu

Key Words protein kinase C, tyrosine kinase, p38 mitogen-activated protein kinase, MAPKAPK-2

■ **Abstract** Ischemic preconditioning is a phenomenon whereby exposure of the myocardium to a brief episode of ischemia and reperfusion markedly reduces tissue necrosis induced by a subsequent prolonged ischemia. It is hoped that elucidation of the mechanism for preconditioning will yield therapeutic strategies capable of reducing myocardial infarction. In the rabbit, the brief period of preconditioning ischemia and reperfusion releases adenosine, bradykinin, opioids, and oxygen radicals. The combined effect of the release of these substances on G proteins and the cell's phospholipases induces the translocation and activation of the ε isozyme of protein kinase C.

Protein kinase C appears to be the first element of a complex kinase cascade that is activated during the prolonged ischemia in preconditioned hearts. Current evidence indicates that this cascade contains at least one tyrosine kinase and ultimately leads to the activation of p38 mitogen-activated protein kinase. p38 Mitogen-activated protein kinase phosphorylates mitogen-activated protein kinase-activated protein kinase 2. Mitogen-activated protein kinase-activated protein kinase 2 phosphorylates HSP27, a 27-kDa heat shock protein that controls actin filament polymerization, and, therefore, affects the integrity of the cytoskeleton. Finally, mitochondrial adenosine 5'-triphosphate-sensitive K^+ channels open, and the latter may be the final mediator of protection for ischemic preconditioning. The protective pathway has many built-in redundancies, perhaps creating a safety factor. These redundancies may also explain some of the species-related differences seen in ischemic preconditioning in which one redundant pathway may predominate over another.

INTRODUCTION

Despite recent advances in the prevention and treatment of heart disease, cardiac ailments continue to rank as the most frequent cause of mortality in the United States. Furthermore morbidity causes untold suffering and results in a staggering economic burden. Prolonged occlusion of a coronary artery can have lethal effects

0066–4278/00/0315–0079$12.00

on the myocardium it supplies. Because infarcted tissue is no longer able to contract, global function of the heart can be severely impaired and may lead to heart failure. Many have searched for a means of protecting the heart from the consequences of coronary stenosis and occlusion. To date the only proven way of salvaging ischemic, jeopardized myocardium in patients with acute coronary occlusion is urgent revascularization with either a pharmacologic agent intended to lyse the occluding intracoronary thrombus, for example, tissue plasminogen activator, catheter-based interventions with angioplasty, stenting, and atherectomy intended to mechanically displace or remove the occluding atherosclerotic plaque, or surgical bypass procedures that reroute arterial blood around the obstruction. However, not all hospitals are able to supply these services, and, even when the services are available, the unavoidable period between patient presentation and successful revascularization is almost always too long to avoid considerable infarction. The extent of necrosis is proportional to the duration of the interval between coronary occlusion and reestablished flow, with little expected salvage if revascularization is not achieved within 6 h of clinical coronary occlusion. Therefore, a pharmacological agent capable of protecting the heart from infarction before revascularization has been the subject of intense research.

Early attempts at tissue salvage with calcium channel antagonists, β-adrenergic receptor antagonists, and oxygen radical scavengers (1) were disappointing. However, in 1986 an endogenous protective mechanism in the form of ischemic preconditioning was discovered (2). Ischemic preconditioning exerts a very powerful anti-infarct effect, and it is hoped that manipulation of the signaling pathway used for this phenomenon can lead to development of an effective anti-infarct therapy.

THE NATURAL HISTORY OF ISCHEMIC PRECONDITIONING

Ischemic preconditioning was first reported by Murry et al in 1986 (2). Anesthetized dogs were subjected to four sequential 5-min periods of regional ischemia, each followed by 5 min of reperfusion, before a sustained 40-min ischemic insult. Paradoxically, Murry et al found that the brief ischemic periods, which were too brief to cause necrosis themselves, greatly reduced the amount of infarction generated during the subsequent sustained occlusion, from an expected 30% of the affected region to only 7%. Although the cumulative ischemic time was increased, preconditioning had a salutary effect! Protection was also found to be unrelated to changes in collateral flow. This was the first intervention short of revascularization that unequivocally limited myocardial infarction and consequently has been the object of major clinical and scientific interest.

Ischemic preconditioning has since been shown to reduce infarct size in every other species tested including rats (3), rabbits (4) (Figure 1), and pigs (5). For ethical reasons it has not been possible to test directly whether preconditioning

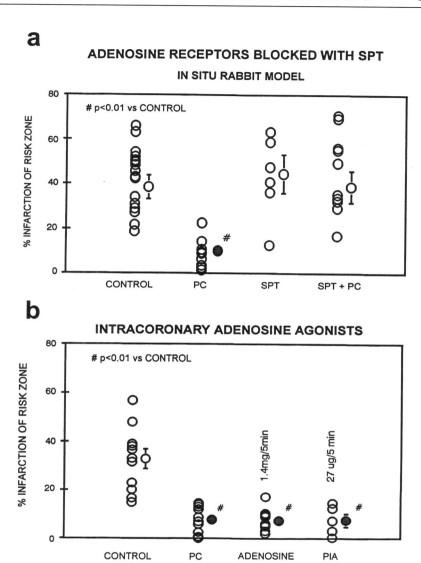

Figure 1 Infarct size as a percentage of the risk zone after a 30-min period of regional ischemia in rabbits. Open circles represent individual data points, and means and standard error bars are also shown for each group. (*a*) Preconditioning (PC) with a 5-min coronary occlusion/10-min reperfusion before the long occlusion reduced infarction from nearly 40% in the control group to 10% (*p* < 0.01). This protection was blocked by 8-(*p*-sulfophenyl) theophylline (SPT), a nonspecific adenosine receptor antagonist. (*b*) Conversely, protection could be mimicked in the isolated heart preparation by the addition of either adenosine or R(-)N⁶-(2-phenylisopropyl) adenosine (PIA), an adenosine analog, to the perfusate in lieu of brief ischemia. Hence, adenosine receptor stimulation is an important trigger of the preconditioning phenomenon.

can protect human hearts against infarction. However, Speechly-Dick et al (6) demonstrated that recovery of function in isolated human atrial trabeculae after an extended period of hypoxia was greatly enhanced by earlier hypoxic preconditioning. Preconditioning has also been shown to protect human ventricular myocytes against simulated ischemia (7). Although several approaches (e.g. percutaneous transluminal coronary angioplasty, intraoperative aortic cross-clamping, serial exercise tests, and preinfarction angina) have been developed to document the effect of preconditioning on the intact human heart, methodologic limitations and conflicting results make this area of research controversial.

Although the initial observations documented how preconditioning diminishes infarction, investigators have attempted to confirm that preconditioning is also protective in other settings. For example Shiki & Hearse (8) noted a lower incidence of ventricular arrhythmias in preconditioned rat hearts, and Veghet al made similar observations in anesthetized dogs (9, 10). Additionally preconditioning attenuates the postischemic decrease in left ventricular-developed pressure seen after reperfusion in isolated hearts (11) and accelerates resumption of effective left-ventricular function in intact, conscious animals (12).

Cardioprotection by ischemic preconditioning is relatively short-lived. In anesthetized animals, protection wanes when the interval between the brief preconditioning ischemia and the prolonged infarct-generating ischemia is extended beyond 1 h (13), although the interval may be as long as 2 to 4 h in conscious rabbits (14). A full 5 min of deep ischemia is required to put the heart into a preconditioned state in rats and rabbits (13). Shorter periods of ischemia can successfully precondition the heart if it is also metabolically challenged (15) or exposed to agents that increase local levels of selected agonists such as adenosine (16) or bradykinin (17).

Most recently a second window of protection has been reported to reappear 24 h after a preconditioning protocol. This protection is thought to be the result of induction of a protective protein. We have found this second window of protection to be much less potent than that of classical preconditioning (18). This review concentrates on the first window (classical) preconditioning, although many of the proposed mechanisms are similar for both.

ISCHEMIC PRECONDITIONING IS RECEPTOR MEDIATED

It is known that ischemic myocardium rapidly degrades ATP to adenosine, which then accumulates in this flow-deprived tissue. To determine whether this metabolite might have an effect on the preconditioning phenomenon, Liu et al (4) administered adenosine antagonists to preconditioned hearts. They found that pretreatment with either of the nonselective adenosine receptor antagonists PD-115199 or 8-(p-sulfophenyl) theophylline (SPT) (Figure 1a) blocked protection induced by a single cycle of 5 min of ischemia and 10 min of reperfusion before a 30-min occlusion in anesthetized rabbits (4). Conversely, a 5-min intracoronary infusion of adenosine in lieu of brief ischemia, followed by a 10-min washout, was just as protective as ischemic preconditioning (4) (Figure 1b). Thus, these observations demonstrated a central role of adenosine receptors in the induction of ischemic preconditioning.

Three adenosine receptor subtypes (A_1, A_2, and A_3) have been characterized and cloned (1). Infusion of an A_1 receptor–selective agonist [either R(-)N^6-(2-phenylisopropyl) adenosine (rPIA) (Figure 1b) or 2-chloro-N^6-cyclopentyladenosine], in lieu of the 5-min ischemia, mimicked ischemic preconditioning in the rabbit (19). The A_2-selective agonist CGS-21680 had no protective effect (19). These data suggest that the A_1 receptor is involved in preconditioning in the rabbit. However, administration of 8-cyclopentyl-1,3-dipropylxanthine, a highly selective A_1 receptor antagonist, failed to abort protection, suggesting that another subtype is involved (20). The A_3 agonist APNEA is able to induce protection, whereas the relatively potent A_3 receptor antagonist BW-A1433 attenuates the effects of ischemic preconditioning (20). Recently the highly selective A_3 agonist N^6-(3-iodobenzyl) adenosine-5'-N -methyluronamide (IB-MECA) has been shown to mimic preconditioning (21). Therefore, at least in the rabbit, both the A_1 and A_3 receptors are thought to be involved in triggering protection.

Activation of adenosine A_1 receptors is also a key step in triggering of ischemic preconditioning in other species. In dogs, both PD-115199 and 8-cyclopentyl-1,3-dipropylxanthine prevent any reduction in infarct size by preconditioning (22). Enhanced breakdown of endogenous adenosine abolishes protection (23), whereas rPIA is able to reduce infarct size in pigs (24). Protection in both human atrial trabeculae (25) and ventricular myocytes (7) can be blocked with SPT or mimicked with rPIA or adenosine. Although initially it was felt that adenosine was not involved in ischemic preconditioning in rat heart (3), more recent evidence reveals that an adenosine antagonist can at least blunt protection (26).

THE RECEPTOR SYSTEM IS HIGHLY REDUNDANT

In addition to adenosine, the ischemic heart releases many metabolites, by-products, and agonists such as bradykinin, endothelin, and free radicals. Although the above data documented that adenosine plays a critical role in triggering of the preconditioning response, it must be asked whether this triggering role is shared with other agonists and/or metabolites.

Parratt (27) proposed that bradykinin is a key trigger in the anti-arrhythmic effect of ischemic preconditioning. In a follow-up study, Goto et al (28) found that infusion of the selective bradykinin B_2 receptor antagonist HOE 140 before a single 5-min ischemic event completely blocked protection in anesthetized rabbits. Conversely, brief infusion of bradykinin reduced infarction. Thus the response to bradykinin is remarkably similar to that seen with adenosine. Was either bradykinin or adenosine the true trigger, or were both equally important? The explanation is readily apparent if it is understood that a single 5-min occlusion is just above the threshold to precondition the heart. Presumably the ischemic heart releases both adenosine and bradykinin in amounts that are ineffective alone, and which must be added together to reach that threshold required for protection (Figure 2). If both adenosine and bradykinin receptors are contributing to the activation of a common downstream signal pathway, then loss of either component would raise the threshold needed to trigger protection (Figure 2). Indeed, HOE 140 could not prevent protection from four preconditioning cycles that presumably produced enough cumulative adenosine (and other agonists) to reach the threshold for protection without bradykinin. Other triggers have since been

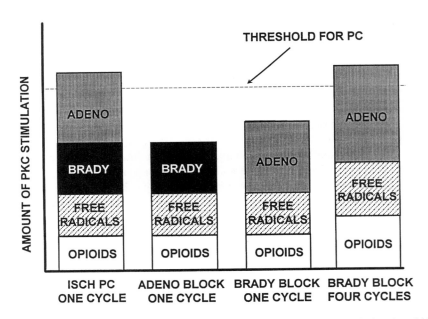

Figure 2 Each of the major agonists and metabolites released by the ischemic rabbit myocardium, that is, adenosine (ADENO), bradykinin (BRADY), opioids, and free radicals, stimulates protein kinase C (PKC). Whereas none alone can sufficiently activate PKC to trigger protection, their effects during one cycle of ischemic preconditioning (ISCH PC) can sum to exceed the threshold and initiate downstream signaling. But if any of the major contributors is eliminated by an antagonist, the hypothesized threshold can no longer be reached, and the ischemic-preconditioning protection is blocked. Increased production of other agonists can substitute for the blocked one to restore the likelihood that the PKC threshold can be reached. Thus with multiple cycles of brief ischemia, tissue adenosine, opioids, and free radicals can be increased sufficiently to make up for lack of a bradykinin effect in the face of bradykinin receptor blockade. Hence receptor triggering of preconditioning has built-in redundancy.

identified. Schultz et al (29) found that naloxone could block preconditioning's protection in rat hearts. Miki et al (30) showed that naloxone could block protection in rabbits from one but not multiple preconditioning cycles. It was concluded that opioids were acting in concert with adenosine and bradykinin, by now a familiar theme.

Oxygen radicals appear to act as a fourth, nonreceptor trigger in rabbit heart. N-2-mercaptopropionyl glycine, a cell-permeable radical scavenger, completely abolished protection by ischemic preconditioning in rabbit heart (31). Infusion of hypoxanthine and xanthine oxidase to form an oxygen radical-generating system was able to mimic preconditioning and reduce infarct size (31). But again, N-2-mercaptopropionyl glycine could not inhibit protection when four preconditioning cycles were used instead of one. Thus, again, interference with free-radical formation could momentarily interfere with preconditioning. But more frequent episodes of brief ischemia presumably permitted the other three triggers to further accumulate until the hypothesized cumulative threshold was exceeded, thus effectively triggering the preconditioning process.

Therefore, it would appear that simultaneous activation of adenosine, bradykinin and opioid receptors, as well as the release of oxygen radicals during the brief ischemia/reperfusion, all contribute to triggering ischemic preconditioning in rabbit heart. Such a scheme would of course require that all converge on a common distal pathway. That pathway appears to be protein kinase C (PKC), because protection from bradykinin (28), adenosine (32), opioids (30), and free radicals (31) can all be blocked by PKC inhibitors. These observations certainly suggest a central role for PKC.

If this were the case, one would assume that any activator of PKC should be able to initiate the triggering of preconditioning. Several other receptors in the heart are known to activate PKC, including α_1-adrenergic, angiotensin AT_1, and endothelin ET receptors. Indeed, all of these are capable of triggering preconditioning-like protection (33–35). However, inhibition of α_1, ET, or AT_1 receptors does not affect ischemic preconditioning in the rabbit (33–35), implying that these receptor systems do not participate in the rabbit's endogenous ischemic preconditioning response, presumably because of release of very small amounts of the receptor agonists by ischemic myocardium. In another species, however, they may well be more important because ischemia triggers the local release of all to some degree.

Hence, activation of surface receptors was proved to be an unequivocal early requirement for protection. But was this receptor activation critical during the preconditioning or long ischemia, or both? Thornton (36) addressed this issue by examining the importance of adenosine production during both phases of ischemia. He observed that adenosine production was necessary at both times. Therefore, selective blockade of adenosine receptors either during the preconditioning ischemia or during the long ischemia effectively aborted protection. But redundancy continued to be evident. As previously noted, infusions of many agonists including bradykinin, opioids, and endothelin could substitute for either brief ischemia or adenosine and be equally protective. Similarly adenosine receptor blockade at the beginning of the long ischemia could also block protection, but protection could be restored by simultaneous infusion of the α_1-adrenergic agonist phenylephrine (33). Therefore, there was nothing unique about adenosine. However, receptor activation was required at two different times, first to trigger and then to mediate the protection process. Because the receptor type itself did not confer any specificity to the signaling cascade, it was hypothesized that all receptor activations would lead to a single common event, most likely stimulation of PKC.

THE ROLE OF PROTEIN KINASE C AND THE TRANSLOCATION HYPOTHESIS

PKC is a family of at least 12 serine/threonine kinases, many of which are present in rabbit heart (37). The PKC isozymes can be split into three broad categories: conventional, novel, and atypical (38, 39). The conventional PKCs (α, β_I, β_{II}, and γ) require Ca^{2+}, diacylglycerol (DAG), and phospholipid for activation. The novel PKC isoforms (δ, ϵ, η, θ) lack the calcium-binding region, so these subtypes are not dependent on Ca^{2+} for activation. Activation of isozymes of the atypical PKC group (ζ, ι, λ, μ) is also independent of Ca^{2+}. However, atypical PKC isozymes lack the Zn^{2+} finger region required for binding of DAG or phorbol ester. Instead, 3'-phosphoinositides may be the activators of atypical PKCs.

Studies in the rabbit by Ytrehus et al (40) and in the rat by Mitchell et al (41) simultaneously concluded that PKC activation is central to protection by ischemic preconditioning. They showed that PKC inhibitors block the protection of ischemic preconditioning (Figure 3). Conversely, infusion of either phorbol 12-myristate 13-acetate (PMA) or the DAG 1-oleoyl-2-acetyl-*sn*-glycerol, two activators of PKC, in lieu of the brief ischemia, is just as protective as ischemic preconditioning (Figure 3). Preconditioning can be blocked by a variety of PKC inhibitors including polymyxin B (40) and the extremely selective chelerythrine (42). Speechly-Dick et al (43) mimicked preconditioning in the rat with a second analog of DAG, 1,2-dioctanoyl-*sn*-glycerol, and blocked preconditioning with chelerythrine. Identical results were obtained in isolated human atrial trabeculae (6). Furthermore, administration of PMA protected human cardiomyocytes against sustained ischemia (7). Therefore, preconditioning in human tissue also requires PKC activation. These data support a central role for PKC in the ischemic preconditioning signaling cascade and are consistent with observations that all PKC-coupled receptors are capable of triggering preconditioning.

These data confirm the involvement of PKC in preconditioning in rabbit, rat, and human tissue. However, studies of the role of PKC in dogs have produced conflicting results (44, 45), perhaps in part related to difficulties achieving sufficiently high plasma concentration of the very expensive, hemodynamically desta-

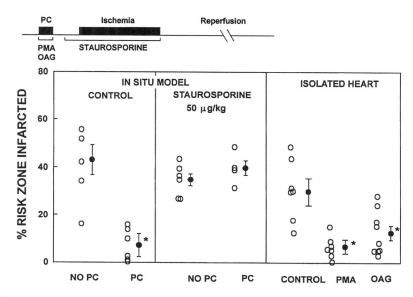

Figure 3   Infarct size expressed as a percentage of risk zone after 30 min of regional ischemia in rabbits. Open circles represent individual data points; closed circles and vertical bars indicate means and standard errors. Preconditioning (PC) with 5 min of ischemia caused marked protection with reduction of infarction from >40 to <10% of the risk zone. This protection was abolished when the PKC antagonist staurosporine was infused shortly before and during the 30-min ischemia. Furthermore, addition of either phorbol 12-myristate 13-acetate (PMA) or 1-oleoyl-2-acetyl-*sn*-glycerol (OAG), two direct activators of PKC, instead of brief ischemia, was equally as protective as ischemic preconditioning. These data strongly suggest that PKC plays an important role in preconditioning. *$p <$ 0.05 vs no PC or control.

bilizing PKC antagonists. Initial reports also showed that inhibition of PKC in pigs failed to block ischemic preconditioning (5). However, a more recent study found that, although inhibition of PKC alone does not prevent protection in porcine myocardium, simultaneous blockade of both PKC and tyrosine kinase (see below) reverses protection (46). This would suggest that in some species a pathway containing at least one tyrosine kinase acts in parallel to PKC. The high degree of redundancy at both the receptor and kinase level seems to ensure that protection will occur.

If PKC activation mediates the protection of preconditioning, then activation of PKC should be detectable in preconditioned hearts by biochemical methods. One of the prerequisites for activation of PKC is its translocation from the cytosolic to the particulate fraction, which includes membranes and cytoskeletal structures. Recent evidence indicates that translocation is dependent on PKC binding to a family of proteins called receptors of activated C kinase (RACKs) (38, 47).

These anchoring proteins are highly specific, and each PKC isozyme can bind to only one RACK. Different PKC isozymes may be linked to distinctive aspects of myocardial function, and this functional segregation may be mediated by the geographic localization of the isozyme-specific RACKs on given myocardial structures. Phosphorylation of substrates by PKC cannot occur until this trans-location from cytosol to membrane- or structure-bound RACK is accomplished. This led to experiments to determine whether translocation occurs in preconditioned myocardium.

One of the earliest studies reported no differences in subcellular distribution of total PKC between preconditioned and nonpreconditioned dog hearts (44). But we now know that a limitation in methodology may have contributed to this finding. Because of the multiple PKC isozymes identified in myocardial tissue, measurement of total PKC translocation or activity may not reflect the subtle alterations in the subcellular distribution of one crucial isozyme. More recent studies have documented isozyme-selective translocation of PKC in response to preconditioning stimuli. Using immunohistochemical staining, Banerjee's group showed that PKC-δ and -ε isozymes are translocated in ischemically preconditioned rat hearts and that PKC-δ and -ζ isozymes are translocated in rat hearts preconditioned with phenylephrine (41). Yoshida et al (48) reported that PKC-α, -δ, and -ε were translocated to the membrane fraction in rat hearts after ischemic preconditioning and that this movement is completely blocked by the PKC inhibitor chelerythrine. In a subsequent study in rat hearts, Kawamura et al (49) correlated the protection of ischemic preconditioning under various conditions with translocation of either PKC-δ or -ε. Miyawaki & Ashraf (50) demonstrated that calcium preconditioning in the rat heart causes translocation of only the α and δ isozymes. Finally, PKC-α, -δ, and -ε are translocated in isolated rat neonatal cardiomyocytes during hypoxic preconditioning (47, 51). However, these positive studies in rat myocardium were challenged by a comprehensive study in rabbit cardiomyocytes that was unable to document translocation of PKC-α, -ε, or -ζ after either ischemic preconditioning or adenosine treatment (52). A technical flaw may have contributed to these results because analysis was performed immediately after isolation of the myocytes, a process that we now know preconditions cells. Thus it is likely that all of the groups were, in fact, preconditioned at the time of study.

The issue of translocation of the isozymes during preconditioning has since been resolved. Using meticulous techniques in myocardium from conscious instrumented rabbits, Ping et al (37) showed that brief periods of ischemia and reperfusion cause selective translocation of only PKC-ε and -η isozymes without demonstrable change in total PKC activity in either membrane or cytosolic fractions. Furthermore they demonstrated that measurements of total PKC activities are not sufficiently sensitive to detect the activation of PKC in preconditioning.

One popular paradigm proposes that PKC activates 5′-nucleotidase that in turn releases adenosine, which subsequently protects the heart (45). However, in a recent experiment it was clearly shown that the adenosine receptor resides upstream of PKC in ischemic preconditioning. Isolated hearts were exposed to combinations of PMA (a PKC activator) and SPT (an adenosine receptor blocker), or chelerythrine (a PKC antagonist) and rPIA (an A_1-selective adenosine agonist). The chelerythrine-rPIA combination completely blocked protection; protection was preserved with the PMA-SPT combination. It seems obvious that in the signaling pathway activation of adenosine receptors must be an earlier step than stimulation of PKC. We suggest that PKC increases 5'-nucleotidase activity, which then probably acts as a positive feedback producing more adenosine to reinforce the preconditioning signal.

PKC activation during ischemic preconditioning exhibits temporal dependence. Infusion of staurosporine (a PKC antagonist that primarily inhibits PKC's kinase activity), which bracketed the 5-min preconditioning ischemia with subsequent washout before the prolonged ischemia, failed to prevent protection in isolated rabbit hearts (53). However, when the PKC inhibitor was present just before and during the prolonged ischemia, the reduction in infarct size was completely abolished (Figure 3). These data indicate that PKC's kinase activity is not required during the preconditioning period, but is essential only during the sustained ischemia.

This raises the question of how receptor activation during the preconditioning ischemia is linked to PKC activation in the subsequent ischemic period, that is, the so-called memory of preconditioning. Liu et al (54) proposed that translocation of PKC explains the temporal discrepancy between receptor stimulation and kinase activity and may represent the memory of ischemic preconditioning. Triggers released during the preconditioning ischemia would induce the relatively slow translocation of PKC to the target site. The kinase would now be poised so that, upon induction of the second period of ischemia, PKC could be rapidly reactivated to protect the cell, which would explain why adenosine and/or other receptors have to be reoccupied at the onset of the second ischemia. Consequently, as long as PKC remains translocated, the heart would be in a preconditioned state. Only when the enzyme reverted back to the cytosol would protection be lost.

The data supporting the translocation hypothesis are controversial. Disruption of microtubules with colchicine, which inhibits intracellular translocation, blocked ischemic preconditioning in rabbits (54). Although many studies have shown that PKC is translocated in preconditioned myocardium, few have correlated that translocation with the presence of a protected state. In support of the theory, Wilson et al (55) have reported that PKC-ε, once translocated, remains in the particulate fraction for up to 4 h after preconditioning in the dog heart. Whether translocation of PKC represents the memory of preconditioning has yet to be resolved.

It is now generally accepted that PKC isozyme translocation does occur during preconditioning. However, activation of an individual isozyme as evidenced by its translocation during a preconditioning protocol is not proof that the isozyme is mediating the protection. Isozyme-specific inhibitors would be required to identify which, if any, PKC isozyme mediates the protection of preconditioning.

Mochly-Rosen and co-workers (56) recently developed PKC isozyme-specific peptides that duplicate portions of the PKC-binding site contained in the first variable binding region of the PKC molecule (57). These peptides have high affinities for the RACKs. Each peptide will attach to only one type of RACK to block docking and activation of only that PKC isozyme from which it was derived. Thus specific PKC isozyme inhibitors are now available. A covalent disulfide linkage between the inhibitor peptides and a membrane-translocating sequence from the third helix of the *Drosophila* Antennapedia homeodomain (16-amino-acid peptide) was formed to introduce the peptides into cells (58, 59). This linkage results in avid internalization of the entire complex by the cell. Once inside the cell, the Cys-Cys bond is cleaved, which leaves the PKC peptide to migrate and bind to its RACK.

We have used these specific isozyme inhibitors in an isolated adult-rabbit cardiomyocyte model in which ischemia is simulated by gently centrifuging the cells into an oxygen-free pellet. When pelleted, the cells behave as an ischemic tissue in which cytokines and metabolites such as adenosine can concentrate in the extracellular space. These cells undergo a progressive increase in osmotic fragility (detected by trypan blue staining) when an aliquot of cells is incubated in hypo-osmotic buffer. Preconditioning delays this increase in osmotic fragility by ~30 min. The model has almost perfectly mimicked the whole-heart infarct model. Similar to the intact rabbit heart, preconditioning's protection in isolated cardiomyocytes is dependent on adenosine (60), PKC activation (61), and potassium channels (62) (see below).

Inhibitors of classical and three novel (-δ, -ε, and -η) PKC isozymes have been evaluated (63). The action of these peptides has been previously validated in rat cardiomyocytes (56) and in other cell types (57) by Mochly-Rosen's group. In the isolated cardiomyocyte model, the protection of preconditioning (delay in trypan blue staining of pelleted cells) was completely abolished by inhibition of the PKC-ε isozyme with ε V1-2 (a selective peptide inhibitor of PKC-ε), but not by a specific peptide inhibitor of any of the classical or novel δ or η PKC isozymes. The ε peptide inhibitor also blocked the protection mediated by 1-oleoyl-2-acetyl-*sn*-glycerol. These data strongly argue that protection subsequent to preconditioning in rabbit heart is solely the result of the activity of the ε isozyme of PKC.

TYROSINE KINASES AND THEIR POTENTIAL ROLE IN ISCHEMIC PRECONDITIONING

Events downstream of PKC activation are now the main focus of research. We recently tested for the presence of protein tyrosine kinases in this pathway. Tyrosine kinases, unlike PKC, which is a serine-threonine kinase, phosphorylate proteins at tyrosine residues. Tyrosine kinases play pivotal roles in many signal transduction events and can be divided into two major groups: receptor tyrosine kinases, such as the kinase which is part of the platelet-derived growth factor receptor, and the nonreceptor/cytosolic tyrosine kinases, such as the pp60[src] family of kinases (64).

A receptor tyrosine kinase could act to turn on PKC and hence induce protection. Platelet-derived growth factor and endothelial growth factor receptors possess tyrosine kinase activity that autophosphorylates tyrosine residues within the receptors' intracellular domains upon stimulation. These residues can bind and activate several key translocation proteins including PLCγ. Growth factor-induced activation of PLCγ (64) could liberate DAG and hence stimulate PKC. Consequently, receptor tyrosine kinases could conceivably act in parallel with other activators of PKC during preconditioning and induce cardioprotection. Horrigan et al (65) demonstrated that infusion of basic fibroblast growth factor during ischemia and reperfusion in dogs greatly reduced infarct size. Similarly, pretreatment of pigs with acidic fibroblast growth factor, insulin, or insulin-like growth factor-II was protective and dependent on tyrosine kinase (66, 67). Infarction in anesthetized rats could be attenuated by infusion of insulin-like growth factor-I (68). However, the signal transduction pathway evoked by the growth factors is at present largely unmapped. We have recently shown that insulin reduces infarct size in isolated rabbit hearts (69). Although the insulin receptor is also a tyrosine kinase, its protective pathway is through phosphatidylinositol 3-kinase, and it is independent of PKC or ATP-sensitive K^+ (K_{ATP}) channels. Hence, insulin's protection does not appear to be related to ischemic preconditioning mechanisms.

There is growing evidence that G protein–coupled receptors can induce tyrosine kinase activation. Sadoshima & Izumo (70) demonstrated that angiotensin II induces rapid tyrosine phosphorylation of the adapter protein Shc in rat ventricular myocytes. Similarly, activation of pp60[src] and tyrosine phosphorylation of Shc in response to thrombin or carbachol have been reported in fibroblasts (71, 72) and were not affected by phorbol-induced depletion of PKC (72). G_q-coupled receptors, such as adrenergic α_1 receptors in myocytes (73), endothelin ET receptors in both myocytes (73) and glomerular mesangial cells (74), and bradykinin receptors in fibroblasts (75), have been shown to induce tyrosine phosphorylation. Phospholipase D activation may involve a tyrosine kinase step (76). Phospholipase D has been shown to be an important part of the ischemic-preconditioning signal transduction cascade in rabbit cardiomyocytes and may be partly responsible for activation of PKC in this phenomenon (77). Thus a G protein–coupled receptor-tyrosine kinase-phospholipase D-PKC sequence could also account for preconditioning.

Tyrosine kinases can also be located downstream of PKC. Seger et al (78) showed that PMA induced tyrosine phosphorylation of several proteins in Chinese hamster ovary cells. Phorbol ester promoted tyrosine phosphorylation of p21[ras] GTPase-activating protein-associated protein, called p60, in rat hepatocytes (79) and mitogen-activated protein kinases (MAPKs) in neural cells (80). Furthermore, activation of G_q-coupled receptors by phenylephrine (81) or carbachol (80) elicits PKC-dependent tyrosine phosphorylation.

Maulik et al (82) were the first to demonstrate that the isoflavone genistein, a relatively selective tyrosine kinase antagonist owing to competitive inhibition of the enzyme's ATP-binding site, blocked the enhanced postischemic functional recovery seen in preconditioned rat hearts. We tested the ability of genistein and the more selective tyrosine kinase antagonist lavendustin A (a noncompetitive inhibitor at the ATP binding site, as well as an uncompetitive inhibitor at the substrate binding site) to block the preconditioning anti-infarct effect in the rabbit (83). When present during the brief ischemia the inhibitors failed to block protection. However, if the inhibitors were present during the prolonged ischemic period, protection was aborted (Figure 4). Consequently, activation of tyrosine kinase is required during the infarct-generating ischemia, which is reminiscent of the results described above for PKC (53). Of interest, in this same series of experiments, isolated rabbit hearts were perfused with one of two concentrations

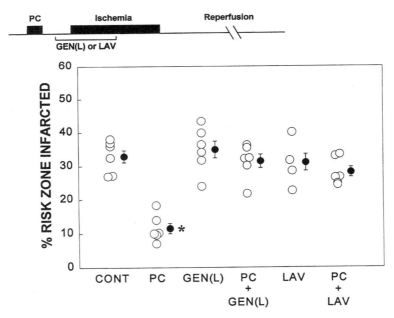

Figure 4 Infarct size expressed as a percentage of risk zone after 30 min of regional ischemia in rabbits. Preconditioning (PC) with 5 min of ischemia is very protective. Whereas neither genistein [GEN(L)] nor lavendustin A (LAV), two potent inhibitors of tyrosine kinase, infused shortly before and during the long occlusion alone had any effect on infarction, each could prevent the infarct-sparing property of PC. These data confirm that a tyrosine kinase is involved in PC's signal transduction pathway. *$p < 0.05$ versus control.

of lavendustin A, either 0.1 or 0.5 μM. At lower concentrations, lavendustin A is selective for receptor tyrosine kinases such as the endothelial growth factor receptor [50%-inhibitory concentration (IC_{50}), 0.011 μM], whereas at higher concentrations it will also inhibit nonreceptor tyrosine kinases such as $pp60^{src}$ (IC_{50}, 0.5 μM). However, it is important that lavendustin A at concentrations of <100 μM does not inhibit PKC. The lower concentration of this tyrosine kinase antagonist failed to prevent the reduction in infarct size elicited by preconditioning. Increasing the concentration fivefold, however, allowed lavendustin A to completely block protection, thus implicating a nonreceptor protein tyrosine kinase.

The relative positions of PKC and tyrosine kinase in this cascade were revealed by concomitant administration of the tyrosine kinase inhibitors and PMA, a direct activator of PKC. Although the magnitude of salvage of ischemic myocardium by PMA was similar to that of preconditioning, this protection was lost when either lavendustin A or genistein was present. This observation indicates that the involved tyrosine kinase is unlikely to be part of a surface receptor, but is rather downstream of PKC, at least in rabbit myocardium.

Despite the apparent involvement of tyrosine kinase in rabbits and rats, genistein failed to block ischemic preconditioning in dogs (84). Vahlhaus et al (46) found that genistein alone could not block the reduction in infarct size by ischemic preconditioning in pigs. This was similar to their previous results with the PKC inhibitor staurosporine (5). Yet combination of the two inhibitors completely blocked protection, implying that a redundant pathway exists in parallel to PKC in pigs and that this pathway contains at least one tyrosine kinase (46). Even in the rabbit, there is evidence of redundant, parallel pathways. Whereas PKC blockers can prevent protection from a single preconditioning cycle, that blockade can be overcome if the heart is instead preconditioned with multiple cycles of brief ischemia (85, 86). Moreover, in the rat as well, the combination of a PKC and tyrosine kinase inhibitor completely prevented protection from multiple cycles of ischemic preconditioning, whereas either alone could only attenuate the protective response (87).

MITOGEN-ACTIVATED PROTEIN KINASES

If both PKC and a tyrosine kinase are involved in ischemic preconditioning, then it is probable that they are two components of a much larger kinase cascade. One of the major cascades in the mammalian heart is the highly conserved MAPK family. These enzymes can be activated by receptor tyrosine kinases, PKC, G protein–coupled receptors, and diverse cellular stresses.

The three major MAPK pathways (Figure 5) identified in the heart are the 42 and 44-kDa extracellular signal-regulated kinases and the two stress-activated MAPK families– the 46- and 54-kDa c-Jun N-terminal kinases (JNK) and the 38-kDa p38/reactivating kinases (88). Each pathway follows the same conserved three-tier module. A MAPK kinase kinase (also known as MEKK) is activated

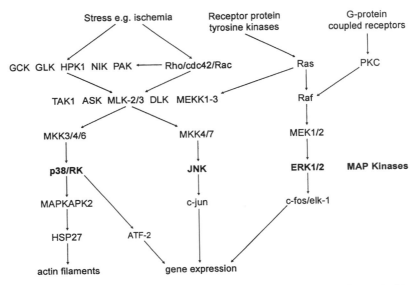

Figure 5 A simplified scheme of the three major mitogen-activated protein kinase (MAPK) cascades. The three MAPKs, p38/RK, JNK, and extracellular signal-regulated kinases 1/2, are indicated in bold-faced type. Activation of either of the two stress-activated protein kinases, p38 MAPK or JNK, has been implicated in ischemic preconditioning. Abbreviations: GCK, germinal center kinase; GLK, GCK-like kinase; HPK1, hematopoietic progenitor kinase-1; NIK, Nck-interacting kinase; PAK, p21-activated kinase. See text for other abbreviations.

and, in turn, phosphorylates a MAPK kinase (MKK or MEK) on serine/threonine residues (88). The MKK is a dual-specificity kinase that phosphorylates both a threonine and a tyrosine within the motif of Thr-X-Tyr (89) on the MAPK. Phosphorylation of both of these residues is essential for activation of the MAPK. The MAPK itself is a proline-directed serine/threonine kinase, preferentially phosphorylating serine and threonine residues within a Pro-X-Ser/Thr-Pro sequence (89).

The extracellular signal-regulated kinase pathway is the most well studied and is activated by growth factor and G protein–coupled receptors (89). However, there is no evidence that it is involved in ischemic preconditioning (90). Current evidence suggests that JNK and/or p38 MAPK may constitute the downstream pathway. These two cascades are activated in response to environmental stresses such as UV radiation, osmotic shock, cytokines, lipopolysaccharide, and ischemia (91, 92).

The JNK family consists of at least two isoforms: the 46-kDa JNK1 and the 54-kDa JNK2, both of which are present in the heart (93). These are activated by the upstream MKK4 and MKK7 (94, 95). MKK4 is unique in that it is capable of activating p38 MAPK as well as JNK in vitro (94), whereas MKK7 is specific for the JNK isoforms (95). Phosphorylation and hence activation of these MKKs is mediated by the MEKK isoforms (94). The primary substrate for JNK is the transcription factor *c*-Jun, which is rapidly phosphorylated within its N-terminal activation domain (92). Significantly, the JNK isoforms are activated during ischemia and reperfusion. Clerk et al (93) demonstrated that both JNK1 and JNK2 are strongly activated upon reperfusion, but are not affected by ischemia alone, although a recent preliminary report suggests that JNK1 can also be activated by simple coronary occlusion (96). Therefore, the brief periods of ischemia/reperfusion as seen with preconditioning could activate the JNK pathway. Furthermore, activation of G_q-coupled receptors and subsequently PKC (97) can also activate JNK. Ping et al (98) have recently demonstrated that transfection of rabbit cardiomyocytes with the wild-type cDNA of PKC-ϵ induced activation of p46/p54 JNK, whereas the activation of JNK by coronary occlusion and reperfusion in rabbit hearts is abolished by chelerythrine (96).

At least six isoforms (α_1, α_2, β_1, β_2, γ, δ) of p38 MAPK have been identified. However, it would appear that only the p38α and β isoforms are expressed to any degree within the heart (92). As already mentioned, MKK4 can phosphorylate both JNK and p38 MAPK in vitro. Two other kinases, MKK3 and MKK6, selectively activate p38 MAPK in several cell types and exhibit a degree of isoform specificity: MKK3 will activate only p38α and γ isoforms, whereas MKK6 can activate the α, β, and γ subtypes (92). Upstream activators of these MKKs include dual leucine zipper-bearing kinase, mixed-lineage kinases-2/3, apoptosis-stimulating kinase, and transforming growth factor-β–activated kinase-1 (99). However, controversy still exists as to whether PKC is capable of activating the p38 MAPK pathway (91, 100).

The primary substrate of p38 MAPK is MAPK-activated protein kinase 2 (MAPKAPK-2) (101). This enzyme phosphorylates the small (27-kDa) heat shock protein HSP27 (101), an important regulator of actin dynamics. The phosphorylated HSP27 promotes polymerization of actin filaments, thus increasing the stability of the cytoskeleton (102). Activation of the p38 MAPK/HSP27 pathway has been shown to prevent oxygen-radical- and cytochalasin D-induced (102, 103) fragmentation of actin filaments, thus preserving cell viability. Overexpression of HSP27 in isolated rat myocytes confers protection against simulated ischemia, whereas depletion exacerbates injury (104). Because prolonged ischemia is known to cause cytoskeletal disruption (105), activation of the p38 MAPK/HSP27 pathway could well contribute to the protective action of ischemic preconditioning by maintaining the integrity of the actin cytoskeleton. Indeed, brief exposure to adenosine increases p38 MAPK activity (106, 107) in cardiomyocytes, and Maulik & colleagues (82) have revealed that MAPKAPK-2 activity is increased in preconditioned rat hearts. Clerk et al (108) have made the important observation that activation of PKC elevates MAPKAPK-2 activity in neonatal rat ventricular cardiomyocytes. These observations and those previously described for JNK strongly suggest that there is a link between PKC and the stress-activated protein kinase cascades, although the intermediate steps have not yet been identified.

Our laboratory has examined phosphorylation of p38 MAPK's tyrosine-182 residue, which is required for its activation (109). Western blot analysis with either p38 MAPK or phosphospecific p38 MAPK (tyrosine-182) antibodies showed decreased phosphorylation during 30 min of global ischemia in nonpreconditioned, isolated rabbit hearts. But phosphorylation was enhanced after 10 and 20 min of ischemia in preconditioned hearts, with a peak increase of nearly threefold at 20 min. Furthermore, when protection from ischemic preconditioning was blocked by the nonspecific adenosine receptor blocker SPT, the expected increased phosphorylation of p38 MAPK during ischemia was not evident. Therefore, phosphorylation of p38 MAPK at tyrosine-182, which is required for the kinase's activation, occurs during ischemia but only when protection from preconditioning is present. Perhaps even more notable is the revelation that this increase in phosphorylation, which was observed only during the long ischemia in the preconditioned heart, coincided with the timing of PKC and tyrosine kinase activation.

We also tested whether direct activation of p38 MAPK or JNK could mimic preconditioning. The bacterial product anisomycin activates MKK3, 4, 6, and 7 (95, 100). Therefore, anisomycin will strongly activate p38 MAPK and JNK, but not extracellular signal-regulated kinase. Anisomycin reduced infarct size in both isolated rabbit hearts (83) and in the in situ rabbit model (110). Because anisomycin activates both p38 MAPK and JNK, it is impossible to distinguish which of these kinases mediates protection. SB203580 is a recently developed selective inhibitor of p38 MAPK (111). SB203580 was able to abort protection triggered by either ischemic preconditioning or anisomycin in isolated rabbit cardiomyocytes (109), which suggests that p38 MAPK had mediated protection. Although SB203580 could block the preconditioning protection in our model of isolated cardiomyocytes and had little effect in nonpreconditioned cells, Armstrong et al (112) reported that SB203580 promoted injury in nonpreconditioned cells, whereas other groups have concluded that SB203580 actually protected cardiomyocytes (113, 114). In support of our observations, D Yellon (personal communication) has shown that SB203580 can selectively block the anti-infarct effect of preconditioning in isolated rat hearts and that this blockade occurred only when the inhibitor was present during the prolonged ischemic period.

A recent study has reported that SB203580 will also inhibit JNK2 at the concentration used in rabbit myocytes (115). Therefore, a role for JNK in mediating cardioprotection in the rabbit heart cannot be ruled out. Barancik et al (116) found that ischemic preconditioning greatly enhanced JNK, rather than p38 MAPK, activity in pig myocardium. Furthermore, the reduction in infarct size in swine after anisomycin administration correlated with an increased JNK, but not p38 MAPK, activity (117).

To further explore the nature of the stress-activated protein kinase cascade involved in preconditioning, we examined the activity of MAPKAPK-2 in ventricular biopsies obtained before and after 20 min of global ischemia in control and preconditioned rabbit hearts (118). Tissue homogenates were fractionated by column, and each fraction was tested for its ability to phosphorylate a synthetic substrate peptide specific for MAPKAPK-2. Activity was not altered in hearts subjected to only 20 min of ischemia. By contrast a 3.8-fold increase of MAP-KAPK-2 activity during ischemia was evident in preconditioned hearts. This activation was blocked by SPT, but increased ~3.5-fold when hearts were treated with either rPIA or anisomycin in lieu of the brief preconditioning ischemia. Furthermore MAPKAPK-2 activation by anisomycin, as well as the latter's protective effect on infarcting myocardium, was blocked by genistein. Because p38 MAPK and MAPKAPK-2 are serine/threonine and not tyrosine kinases, the dual-specificity MKKs may represent the genistein-sensitive step in the signaling pathway of preconditioning.

Because HSP27 is the substrate for MAPKAPK-2, it seems obvious that a documented increase in activity of the latter should naturally lead to an increase in HSP27 phosphorylation. Attempts to document increases in HSP27 activity in ischemically preconditioned hearts or myocytes have not been successful (112). Further investigations are required to confirm expected involvement of HSP27 in the preconditioning signal transduction pathway.

Hence, it is clear that the stress-activated protein kinase cascade is part of the preconditioning-signal transduction pathway. As with other parts of the pathway, this section may also be redundant. A given species may be more dependent on p38 MAPK, whereas JNK may be more important in another. The activation sequence from PKC to MEKK is not clear. Perhaps identification of the more distal pathway and the end-effector are more important and clinically relevant.

MITOCHONDRIAL ATP-SENSITIVE K^+ CHANNELS MAY BE THE END EFFECTOR IN ISCHEMIC PRECONDITIONING

The nature of the end effector(s) ultimately activated by ischemic preconditioning has been very elusive. Considerable evidence suggests that opening of K_{ATP} channels represents the final step in this signal transduction process. The K_{ATP} channel has been described in many tissues including pancreatic β-cells, neurons, vascular smooth muscle, skeletal muscle, and cardiac myocytes. Reconstitution and cloning of the K_{ATP} channel have revealed that it is composed of two subunits: the channel protein itself, which belongs to the inward-rectifier K^+ channel family, and the sulfonylurea receptor, a member of the ATP-binding cassette superfamily, which is involved in the binding of ATP and sulfonylurea compounds (119, 120). Both subunits are absolutely required for channel activity and are associated with a 1:1 stoichiometry. K_{ATP} channels are inhibited by ATP in the low-micromolar-concentration range and open as ATP levels fall (119).

Much of the evidence supporting the K_{ATP} hypothesis is based on blockade of the protective effects of both ischemic and pharmacological preconditioning by inhibitors of K_{ATP} channels (121). There have always been discrepancies, however. Thornton et al (122) were unable to prevent the anti-infarct effect of preconditioning with glibenclamide in pentobarbital-anesthetized rabbits. However, with ketamine-xylazine anesthesia of rabbits, glibenclamide completely abolished protection (123). Glibenclamide also failed to block preconditioning's protection in isolated rat hearts (3). But most data confirm participation of K_{ATP} channels in preconditioning. 5-hydroxydecanoate (5-HD), another inhibitor of K_{ATP} channels, also blocks ischemic preconditioning in rabbits (124). Furthermore, protection induced by PMA in isolated rabbit hearts could be nullified with 5-HD (125). Ischemic preconditioning in dogs could be abolished by both glibenclamide (126) and 5-HD (127). Protection could be blocked when glibenclamide was given after preconditioning but before the 60-min occlusion, which suggests that opening of K_{ATP} channels is critical only during the lethal ischemic period (126). K_{ATP} channel inhibition blocked the reduction in infarct size by both ischemic preconditioning (128) and rPIA (24) in pigs. In one report 5-HD inhibited ischemic preconditioning in rat heart (129). Preconditioning in human tissue also appears to rely on K_{ATP} channels (6).

As expected, direct activation of K_{ATP} channels is cardioprotective. Administration of bimakalim (130) and cromakalim (131) before ischemia can reduce infarct size in dogs. Armstrong et al (62) showed that pinacidil could protect rabbit myocytes against simulated ischemia. In guinea pig hearts, post-ischemic recovery of function was greatly improved by either of the K_{ATP} openers BMS-180448 or cromakalim (132). These data further support a role for K_{ATP} channels in cardioprotection by ischemic preconditioning.

To explain the salutary effect of these K_{ATP} channels, it was originally proposed that opening sarcolemmal channels caused shortening of the myocardial action potential duration, which in turn would exert a cardioplegic action (121). However, Yao & Gross (130) demonstrated that bimakalim reduced infarct size at a dose that did not affect action potential duration. Additionally, the protective qualities of BMS-180448 (132) and cromakalim (131) were also independent of action potential duration shortening. Finally, opening of the K_{ATP} channels protected quiescent isolated cardiomyocytes that were not generating any action potential (62). These observations argue that a change in action potential duration is not a marker of protection and that the latter must not be the result of opening of sarcolemmal K_{ATP} channels. Further evidence refuting a role of the sarcolemmal K_{ATP} channel in cardioprotection is the failure of 5-HD to block the cromakalim-induced K_{ATP} currents in cardiomyocytes in the face of effective abrogation of the opener's cardioprotective action (133).

Instead, recent evidence suggests that mitochondrial K_{ATP} channels mediate protection. Garlid et al (134) demonstrated that diazoxide was 2000-fold more selective for opening mitochondrial channels than sarcolemmal K_{ATP} channels in the heart. It is interesting that 5-HD can reverse diazoxide-induced mitochondrial K^+ flux (134) yet have little effect on cardiac sarcolemmal channels (133). Therefore, 5-HD appears to selectively block mitochondrial K_{ATP} channels. A subsequent study by the same group in isolated rat hearts revealed that diazoxide preserves post-ischemic function as well as preconditioning or cromakalim and that this protection is independent of sarcolemmal K_{ATP} channels (134); in addition, this protection can be inhibited by 5-HD. Similar results have been obtained in isolated rabbit cardiomyocytes (135). We found that diazoxide significantly reduced infarct size in anesthetized rabbits and that the protection could be reversed with 5-HD (110). Furthermore, the protective effect of anisomycin could also be reversed by 5-HD (110), implying that the kinase cascade activated during preconditioning ultimately leads to the opening of mitochondrial K_{ATP} channels. It is unclear how p38 MAPK could effect opening of channels on the inner mitochondrial membrane, but at least one experiment implicates HSP27 and actin filaments. In isolated rabbit cardiomyocytes the protection afforded by ischemic preconditioning, the selective mitochondrial K_{ATP} channel opener diazoxide, or the nonselective channel opener pinacidil can be abolished by disruption of the cytoskeleton by cytochalasin D (110). Therefore, in at least rabbit heart, actin filament assembly may directly affect the mitochondrial K_{ATP} channel function required for cardioprotection.

Can the preconditioning signal transduction pathway involving agonists and kinases described above be linked to K_{ATP} channels? The K_{ATP} channel cloned from the heart contains three consensus sites for phosphorylation (136), and K_{ATP} channels are sensitive to PKC (137, 138). The nature of the effects of PKC on K_{ATP} channels is controversial, however. Light et al (139) have shown that PKC activation closes K_{ATP} channels. In contrast, Liu and colleagues (140) observed in isolated rabbit cardiomyocytes that the phorbal ester PMA potentiates the opening of K_{ATP} channels by pinacidil when ATP levels are reduced by metabolic inhibition with potassium cyanide. They also reported that adenosine has little effect on myocytes in the basal state, but it opens K_{ATP} channels after pretreatment with PMA, which suggests that PKC participates to open the channels. When Liu combined PMA and rPIA in the presence of 1 mM ATP, there was no effect on I_{KATP}. Only when cell ATP was lowered by potassium cyanide pretreatment did the combination open K_{ATP} channels. Therefore, opening of K_{ATP} channels during preconditioning may require phosphorylation by PKC or another kinase, as well as the presence of adenosine or another G protein–coupled agonist. Kirsch et al (141) reported that G_i released by stimulated adenosine A_1 receptors opens K_{ATP} channels directly. In that study, other G protein subunits also affected K_{ATP} channel conductance. The direct gating of a K_{ATP} channel has previously been demonstrated in heart tissue (142–144) and may contribute to the mechanism of protection.

It is not clear why opening of mitochondrial ATP-sensitive K^+ channels is cardioprotective. In steady-state conditions, K^+ influx into the mitochondrial matrix is balanced by K^+ efflux via a K^+/H^+-exchanger that likely maintains mitochondrial volume (145). However, opening of mitochondrial K_{ATP} channels would cause a net influx of K^+ ions and hence increase matrix volume (mitochondrial swelling). Alternatively, because of the K^+/H^+ exchanger, K^+ influx would tend to dissipate the potential across the inner membrane and uncouple electron transfer. This may be beneficial in ischemia as it may prevent wasteful ATP hydrolysis (134) or possibly reduce the electrical gradient favoring Ca^{2+} influx into the mitochondrion (146).

Of course, it is still not proven that the K_{ATP} channel is indeed the end effector. One must be receptive to other suggestions. A very different ion channel (147) or even an unidentified protein may still be that elusive protector. Investigation should continue not only until the end effector has been identified but also until it is understood why it is protective.

CONCLUSION

The mechanism of ischemic preconditioning is emerging as a complex series of receptors, protein kinases, and ion channels (Figure 6). Consequently, there are a whole host of sites within this cascade that can be targeted in the search for a therapeutic anti-infarct agent. Although we already can mimic preconditioning

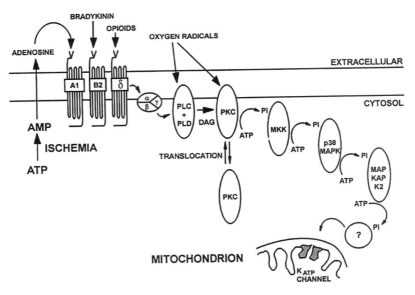

Figure 6   Schematic representation of the proposed mechanism of preconditioning in rabbit heart. Ischemia leads to release of adenosine, bradykinin, opioids, and free radicals that together produce enough stimulation of phospholipase C and/or D that sufficient PKC is activated to translocate and initiate a complex kinase cascade that involves a downstream tyrosine kinase (possibly one of the MKKs), p38 MAPK, and MAPKAPK-2. These kinases eventually open mitochondrial K_{ATP} channels that may be the end effectors. Many steps in this sequence remain unknown.

with a number of agents, their clinical application has been limited in that, like ischemic preconditioning itself, all require pretreatment. In the setting of acute myocardial infarction, however, pretreatment is seldom an option. If the preconditioning mechanism can be understood, it is likely that tools for initiating its protection after ischemia has already begun or even prophylactically will be developed. If successful, such an intervention will lead to a salutary effect on morbidity and mortality from ischemic heart disease.

ACKNOWLEDGMENTS

This review was supported by grants HL-20648 and HL-50688 from the National Institutes of Health, National Heart, Lung, and Blood Institute.

Visit the Annual Reviews home page at www.AnnualReviews.org.

LITERATURE CITED

1. Downey JM, Cohen MV. 1995. Signal transduction in ischemic preconditioning. *Z. Kardiol.* 84 (Suppl. 4):77–86
2. Murry CE, Jennings RB, Reimer KA. 1986. Preconditioning with ischemia: a delay of lethal cell injury in ischemic myocardium. *Circulation* 74:1124–36
3. Liu Y, Downey JM. 1992. Ischemic preconditioning protects against infarction in rat heart. *Am. J. Physiol.* 263:H1107–12
4. Liu GS, Thornton J, Van Winkle DM, Stanley AWH, Olsson RA, Downey JM. 1991. Protection against infarction afforded by preconditioning is mediated by A_1 adenosine receptors in rabbit heart. *Circulation* 84:350–56
5. Vahlhaus C, Schulz R, Post H, Onallah R, Heusch G. 1996. No prevention of ischemic preconditioning by the protein kinase C inhibitor staurosporine in swine. *Circ. Res.* 79:407–14
6. Speechly-Dick ME, Grover GJ, Yellon DM. 1995. Does ischemic preconditioning in the human involve protein kinase C and the ATP-dependent K^+ channel? Studies of contractile function after simulated ischemia in an atrial in vitro model. *Circ. Res.* 77:1030–35
7. Ikonomidis JS, Shirai T, Weisel RD, Derylo B, Rao V, et al. 1997. Preconditioning cultured human pediatric myocytes requires adenosine and protein kinase C. *Am. J. Physiol.* 272:H1220–30
8. Shiki K, Hearse DJ. 1987. Preconditioning of ischemic myocardium: reperfusion-induced arrhythmias. *Am. J. Physiol.* 253:H1470–76
9. Vegh A, Szekeres L, Parratt J. 1992. Preconditioning of the ischaemic myocardium; involvement of the *L*-arginine nitric oxide pathway. *Br. J. Pharmacol.* 107:648–52
10. Vegh A, Papp JG, Szekeres L, Parratt J. 1992. The local intracoronary administration of methylene blue prevents the pronounced antiarrhythmic effect of ischaemic preconditioning. *Br. J. Pharmacol.* 107:910–11
11. Asimakis GK, Inners-McBride K, Medellin G, Conti VR. 1992. Ischemic preconditioning attenuates acidosis and postischemic dysfunction in isolated rat heart. *Am. J. Physiol.* 263:H887–94
12. Cohen MV, Yang X-M, Downey JM. 1999. Reduction in infarct size after preconditioning does not predict the extent of early functional improvement of

reperfused myocardium. *Am. J. Physiol.* 277:In press

13. Van Winkle DM, Thornton JD, Downey DM, Downey JM. 1991. The natural history of preconditioning: Cardioprotection depends on duration of transient ischemia and time to subsequent ischemia. *Coron. Art. Dis.* 2:613–19

14. Burckhartt B, Yang X-M, Tsuchida A, Mullane KM, Downey JM, Cohen MV. 1995. Acadesine extends the window of protection afforded by ischaemic preconditioning in conscious rabbits. *Cardiovasc. Res.* 29:653–57

15. Goto M, Miura T, Itoya M, Sakamoto J, Iimura O. 1992. Infarct size limitation by preconditioning occurs in the absence of myocardial stunning. *Circulation* 86:I–31 (Suppl. I) (Abstr.)

16. Itoya M, Miura T, Sakamoto J, Urabe K, Iimura O. 1994. Nucleoside transport inhibitors enhance the infarct size-limiting effect of ischemic preconditioning. *J. Cardiovasc. Pharmacol.* 24:846–52

17. Miki T, Miura T, Ura N, Ogawa T, Suzuki K, et al. 1996. Captopril potentiates the myocardial infarct size-limiting effect of ischemic preconditioning through bradykinin B_2 receptor activation. *J. Am. Coll. Cardiol.* 28:1616–22

18. Yang X-M, Baxter GF, Heads RJ, Yellon DM, Downey JM, Cohen MV. 1996. Infarct limitation of the second window of protection in a conscious rabbit model. *Cardiovasc. Res.* 31:777–83

19. Thornton JD, Liu GS, Olsson RA, Downey JM. 1992. Intravenous pretreatment with A_1-selective adenosine analogues protects the heart against infarction. *Circulation* 85:659–65

20. Liu GS, Richards SC, Olsson RA, Mullane K, Walsh RS, Downey JM. 1994. Evidence that the adenosine A_3 receptor may mediate the protection afforded by preconditioning in the isolated rabbit heart. *Cardiovasc. Res.* 28:1057–61

21. Auchampach JA, Rizvi A, Qiu Y, Tang X-L, Maldonado C, et al. 1997. Selective activation of A_3 adenosine receptors with N^6-(3-iodobenzyl) adenosine-5′-N-methyluronamide protects against myocardial stunning and infarction without hemodynamic changes in conscious rabbits. *Circ. Res.* 80:800–9

22. Auchampach JA, Gross GJ. 1993. Adenosine A_1 receptors, K_{ATP} channels, and ischemic preconditioning in dogs. *Am. J. Physiol.* 264:H1327–36

23. Schulz R, Rose J, Post H, Heusch G. 1995. Involvement of endogenous adenosine in ischaemic preconditioning in swine. *Pflügers Arch.* 430:273–82

24. Van Winkle DM, Chien GL, Wolff RA, Soifer BE, Kuzume K, Davis RF. 1994. Cardioprotection provided by adenosine receptor activation is abolished by blockade of the K_{ATP} channel. *Am. J. Physiol.* 266:H829–39

25. Walker DM, Walker JM, Pugsley WB, Pattison CW, Yellon DM. 1995. Preconditioning in isolated superfused human muscle. *J. Mol. Cell. Cardiol.* 27:1349–57

26. Headrick JP. 1996. Ischemic preconditioning: bioenergetic and metabolic changes and the role of endogenous adenosine. *J. Mol. Cell. Cardiol.* 28:1227–40

27. Parratt JR. 1994. Protection of the heart by ischaemic preconditioning: mechanisms and possibilities for pharmacological exploitation. *Trends Pharmacol. Sci.* 15:19–25

28. Goto M, Liu Y, Yang X-M, Ardell JL, Cohen MV, Downey JM. 1995. Role of bradykinin in protection of ischemic preconditioning in rabbit hearts. *Circ. Res.* 77:611–21

29. Schultz JEJ, Hsu AK, Gross GJ. 1996. Morphine mimics the cardioprotective effect of ischemic preconditioning via a glibenclamide-sensitive mechanism in the rat heart. *Circ. Res.* 78:1100–4

30. Miki T, Cohen MV, Downey JM. 1998. Opioid receptor contributes to ischemic preconditioning through protein kinase C

activation in rabbits. *Mol. Cell. Biochem.* 186:3–12

31. Baines CP, Goto M, Downey JM. 1997. Oxygen radicals released during ischemic preconditioning contribute to cardioprotection in the rabbit myocardium. *J. Mol. Cell. Cardiol.* 29:207–16

32. Sakamoto J, Miura T, Goto M, Iimura O. 1995. Limitation of myocardial infarct size by adenosine A_1 receptor activation is abolished by protein kinase C inhibitors in the rabbit. *Cardiovasc. Res.* 29:682–88

33. Tsuchida A, Liu Y, Liu GS, Cohen MV, Downey JM. 1994. α_1-Adrenergic agonists precondition rabbit ischemic myocardium independent of adenosine by direct activation of protein kinase C. *Circ. Res.* 75:576–85

34. Wang P, Gallagher KP, Downey JM, Cohen MV. 1996. Pretreatment with endothelin-1 mimics ischemic preconditioning against infarction in isolated rabbit heart. *J. Mol. Cell. Cardiol.* 28:579–88

35. Liu Y, Tsuchida A, Cohen MV, Downey JM. 1995. Pretreatment with angiotensin II activates protein kinase C and limits myocardial infarction in isolated rabbit hearts. *J. Mol. Cell. Cardiol.* 27:883–92

36. Thornton JD, Thornton CS, Downey JM. 1993. Effect of adenosine receptor blockade: Preventing protective preconditioning depends on time of initiation. *Am. J. Physiol.* 265:H504–8

37. Ping P, Zhang J, Qiu Y, Tang X-L, Manchikalapudi S, et al. 1997. Ischemic preconditioning induces selective translocation of protein kinase C isoforms ε and η in the heart of conscious rabbits without subcellular redistribution of total protein kinase C activity. *Circ. Res.* 81:404–14

38. Mochly-Rosen D, Gordon AS. 1998. Anchoring proteins for protein kinase C: a means for isozyme selectivity. *FASEB J.* 12:35–42

39. Jaken S. 1996. Protein kinase C isozymes and substrates. *Curr. Opin. Cell Biol.* 8:168–73

40. Ytrehus K, Liu Y, Downey JM. 1994. Preconditioning protects ischemic rabbit heart by protein kinase C activation. *Am. J. Physiol.* 266:H1145–52

41. Mitchell MB, Meng X, Ao L, Brown JM, Harken AH, Banerjee A. 1995. Preconditioning of isolated rat heart is mediated by protein kinase C. *Circ. Res.* 76:73–81

42. Liu Y, Cohen MV, Downey JM. 1994. Chelerythrine, a highly selective protein kinase C inhibitor, blocks the antiinfarct effect of ischemic preconditioning in rabbit hearts. *Cardiovasc. Drugs Ther.* 8:881–82

43. Speechly-Dick ME, Mocanu MM, Yellon DM. 1994. Protein kinase C: its role in ischemic preconditioning in the rat. *Circ. Res.* 75:586–90

44. Przyklenk K, Sussman MA, Simkhovich BZ, Kloner RA. 1995. Does ischemic preconditioning trigger translocation of protein kinase C in the canine model? *Circulation* 92:1546–57

45. Kitakaze M, Node K, Minamino T, Komamura K, Funaya H, et al. 1996. Role of activation of protein kinase C in the infarct size-limiting effect of ischemic preconditioning through activation of ecto-5′-nucleotidase. *Circulation* 93:781–91

46. Vahlhaus C, Schulz R, Post H, Rose J, Heusch G. 1998. Prevention of ischemic preconditioning only by combined inhibition of protein kinase C and protein tyrosine kinase in pigs. *J. Mol. Cell. Cardiol.* 30:197–209

47. Gray MO, Karliner JS, Mochly-Rosen D. 1997. A selective ε-protein kinase C antagonist inhibits protection of cardiac myocytes from hypoxia-induced cell death. *J. Biol. Chem.* 272:30945–51

48. Yoshida K-i, Kawamura S, Mizukami Y, Kitakaze M. 1997. Implication of protein kinase C-α, δ, and ε isoforms in ischemic

preconditioning in perfused rat hearts. *J. Biochem.* 122:506–11

49. Kawamura S, Yoshida K-I, Miura T, Mizukami Y, Matsuzaki M. 1998. Ischemic preconditioning translocates PKC-δ and -ε, which mediate functional protection in isolated rat heart. *Am. J. Physiol.* 275:H2266–71

50. Miyawaki H, Ashraf M. 1997. Ca^{2+} as a mediator of ischemic preconditioning. *Circ. Res.* 80:790–99

51. Goldberg M, Zhang HL, Steinberg SF. 1997. Hypoxia alters the subcellular distribution of protein kinase C isoforms in neonatal rat ventricular myocytes. *J. Clin. Invest.* 99:55–61

52. Armstrong SC, Hoover DB, Delacey MH, Ganote CE. 1996. Translocation of PKC, protein phosphatase inhibition and preconditioning of rabbit cardiomyocytes. *J. Mol. Cell. Cardiol.* 28:1479–92

53. Yang X-M, Sato H, Downey JM, Cohen MV. 1997. Protection of ischemic preconditioning is dependent upon a critical timing sequence of protein kinase C activation. *J. Mol. Cell. Cardiol.* 29:991–99

54. Liu Y, Ytrehus K, Downey JM. 1994. Evidence that translocation of protein kinase C is a key event during ischemic preconditioning of rabbit myocardium. *J. Mol. Cell. Cardiol.* 26:661–68

55. Wilson S, Song W, Karoly K, Ravingerova T, Vegh A, et al. 1996. Delayed cardioprotection is associated with the sub-cellular relocalisation of ventricular protein kinase C ε, but not p42/44MAPK. *Mol. Cell. Biochem.* 160/161:225–30

56. Johnson JA, Gray MO, Chen C-H, Mochly-Rosen D. 1996. A protein kinase C translocation inhibitor as an isozyme-selective antagonist of cardiac function. *J. Biol. Chem.* 271:24962–66

57. Souroujon MC, Mochly-Rosen D. 1998. Peptide modulators of protein-protein interactions in intracellular signaling. *Nat. Biotechnol.* 16:919–24

58. Derossi D, Joliot AH, Chassaing G, Prochiantz A. 1994. The third helix of the Antennapedia homeodomain translocates through biological membranes. *J. Biol. Chem.* 269:10444–50

59. Théodore L, Derossi D, Chassaing G, Llirbat B, Kubes M, et al. 1995. Intraneuronal delivery of protein kinase C pseudosubstrate leads to growth cone collapse. *J. Neurosci.* 15:7158–67

60. Armstrong S, Ganote CE. 1994. Adenosine receptor specificity in preconditioning of isolated rabbit cardiomyocytes: evidence of A_3 receptor involvement. *Cardiovasc. Res.* 28:1049–56

61. Armstrong S, Downey JM, Ganote CE. 1994. Preconditioning of isolated rabbit cardiomyocytes: induction by metabolic stress and blockade by the adenosine antagonist SPT and calphostin C, a protein kinase C inhibitor. *Cardiovasc. Res.* 28:72–77

62. Armstrong SC, Liu GS, Downey JM, Ganote CE. 1995. Potassium channels and preconditioning of isolated rabbit cardiomyocytes: effects of glyburide and pinacidil. *J. Mol. Cell. Cardiol.* 27:1765–74

63. Liu GS, Cohen MV, Mochly-Rosen D, Downey JM. 1999. Protein kinase C-ε is responsible for the protection of preconditioning in rabbit cardiomyocytes. *J. Mol. Cell. Cardiol.* 31:In press

64. Cantley LC, Auger KR, Carpenter C, Duckworth B, Graziani A, et al. 1991. Oncogenes and signal transduction. *Cell* 64:281–302

65. Horrigan MCG, MacIsaac AI, Nicolini FA, Vince DG, Lee P, et al. 1996. Reduction in myocardial infarct size by basic fibroblast growth factor after temporary coronary occlusion in a canine model. *Circulation* 94:1927–33

66. Htun P, Ito W, Kirsch K-P, Schaper W. 1996. aFGF induced cardioprotection in ischemic myocardium can be antagonized by Suramin. *Circulation* 94:I–607 (Suppl. I) (Abstr.)

67. Vogt AM, Htun P, Kluge A, Zimmer-

mann R, Schaper W. 1997. Insulin-like growth factor-II delays myocardial infarction in experimental coronary artery occlusion. *Cardiovasc. Res.* 33: 469–77

68. Buerke M, Murohara T, Skurk C, Nuss C, Tomaselli K, Lefer AM. 1995. Cardioprotective effect of insulin-like growth factor I in myocardial ischemia followed by reperfusion. *Proc. Natl. Acad. Sci. USA* 92:8031–35

69. Baines CP, Wang L, Cohen MV, Downey JM. 1999. Myocardial protection by insulin is dependent on phosphatidyl-inositol 3-kinase but not protein kinase C or K_{ATP} channels in the isolated rabbit heart. *Basic Res. Cardiol.* 94:188–98

70. Sadoshima J-i, Izumo S. 1996. The heterotrimeric G_q protein-coupled angiotensin II receptor activates $p21^{ras}$ via the tyrosine kinase-Shc-Grb2-Sos pathway in cardiac myocytes. *EMBO J.* 15:775–87

71. Chen Y-h, Pouysségur J, Courtneidge SA, Van Obberghen-Schilling E. 1994. Activation of Src family kinase activity by the G protein-coupled thrombin receptor in growth-responsive fibroblasts. *J. Biol. Chem.* 269:27372–77

72. Chen Y-h, Grall D, Salcini AE, Pelicci PG, Pouysségur J, Van Obberghen-Schilling E. 1996. Shc adaptor proteins are key transducers of mitogenic signaling mediated by the G protein-coupled thrombin receptor. *EMBO J.* 15:1037–44

73. Sadoshima J, Qiu Z, Morgan JP, Izumo S. 1995. Angiotensin II and other hypertrophic stimuli mediated by G protein-coupled receptors activate tyrosine kinase, mitogen-activated protein kinase, and 90-kD S6 kinase in cardiac myocytes: the critical role of Ca^{2+}-dependent signaling. *Circ. Res.* 76:1–15

74. Simonson MS, Herman WH. 1993. Protein kinase C and protein tyrosine kinase activity contribute to mitogenic signaling by endothelin-1: cross-talk between G

protein-coupled receptors and $pp60^{c-src}$. *J. Biol. Chem.* 268:9347–57

75. Lee K-M, Toscas K, Villereal ML. 1993. Inhibition of bradykinin- and thapsigargin-induced Ca^{2+} entry by tyrosine kinase inhibitors. *J. Biol. Chem.* 268: 9945–48

76. Maulik N, Watanabe M, Engelman R, Zu Y-L, Huang C-K, et al. 1996. Preconditioning triggers tyrosine kinase-phospholipase D signaling leading to activation of multiple protein kinases in heart. *J. Mol. Cell. Cardiol.* 28:A187 (Abstr.)

77. Cohen MV, Liu Y, Liu GS, Wang P, Weinbrenner C, et al. 1996. Phospholipase D plays a role in ischemic preconditioning in rabbit heart. *Circulation* 94:1713–18

78. Seger R, Biener Y, Feinstein R, Hanoch T, Gazit A, Zick Y. 1995. Differential activation of mitogen-activated protein kinase and S6 kinase signaling pathways by 12-*O*-tetradecanoylphorbol-13-acetate (TPA) and insulin: evidence for involvement of a TPA-stimulated protein-tyrosine kinase. *J. Biol. Chem.* 270:28325–30

79. Ogawa W, Hosomi Y, Roth RA. 1995. Activation of protein kinase C stimulates the tyrosine phosphorylation and guanosine triphosphatase-activating protein association of p60 in rat hepatoma cells. *Endocrinology* 136:476–81

80. Offermanns S, Bombien E, Schultz G. 1993. Stimulation of tyrosine phosphorylation and mitogen-activated-protein (MAP) kinase activity in human SH-SY5Y neuroblastoma cells by carbachol. *Biochem. J.* 294:545–50

81. Khalil RA, Menice CB, Wang C-LA, Morgan KG. 1995. Phosphotyrosine-dependent targeting of mitogen-activated protein kinase in differentiated contractile vascular cells. *Circ. Res.* 76:1101–8

82. Maulik N, Watanabe M, Zu Y-L, Huang C-K, Cordis GA, et al. 1996. Ischemic preconditioning triggers the activation of

MAP kinases and MAPKAP kinase 2 in rat hearts. *FEBS Lett.* 396:233–37

83. Baines CP, Wang L, Cohen MV, Downey JM. 1998. Protein tyrosine kinase is downstream of protein kinase C for ischemic preconditioning's anti-infarct effect in the rabbit heart. *J. Mol. Cell. Cardiol.* 30:383–92

84. Kitakaze M, Node K, Funaya H, Mizu-kami Y-i, Yoshida K-i. 1997. Tyrosine kinase is not involved in the infarct size-limiting effect of ischemic precondition-ing in the canine heart. *Circulation* 96:I–574 (Suppl. I) (Abstr.)

85. Sandhu R, Diaz RJ, Mao GD, Wilson GJ. 1997. Ischemic preconditioning: differ-ences in protection and susceptibility to blockade with single-cycle versus mul-ticycle transient ischemia. *Circulation* 96:984–95

86. Miura T, Miura T, Kawamura S, Goto M, Sakamoto J, et al. 1998. Effect of protein kinase C inhibitors on cardioprotection by ischemic preconditioning depends on the number of preconditioning episodes. *Cardiovasc. Res.* 37:700–9

87. Tanno M, Tsuchida A, Hasegawa T, Miura T, Shimamoto K. 1998. Both pro-tein kinase C (PKC) and tyrosine kinase contribute to cardioprotection by repeti-tive preconditioning in rats. *J. Mol. Cell. Cardiol.* 30:A312 (Abstr.)

88. Robinson MJ, Cobb MH. 1997. Mito-gen-activated protein kinase pathways. *Curr. Opin. Cell Biol.* 9:180–86

89. Sugden PH, Bogoyevitch MA. 1995. Intracellular signalling through protein kinases in the heart. *Cardiovasc. Res.* 30:478–92

90. Maulik N, Yoshida T, Das DK. 1998. p38 MAP kinase and not MEK 1 kinase is involved in ischemic preconditioning. *J. Mol. Cell. Cardiol.* 30:A264 (Abstr.)

91. Raingeaud J, Gupta S, Rogers JS, Dick-ens M, Han J, et al. 1995. Pro-inflam-matory cytokines and environmental stress cause p38 mitogen-activated pro-tein kinase activation by dual phosphory-lation on tyrosine and threonine. *J. Biol. Chem.* 270:7420–26

92. Sugden PH, Clerk A. 1998. "Stress-responsive" mitogen-activated protein kinases (c-Jun N-terminal kinases and p38 mitogen-activated protein kinases) in the myocardium. *Circ. Res.* 83:345–52

93. Clerk A, Fuller SJ, Michael A, Sugden PH. 1998. Stimulation of "stress-regu-lated" mitogen-activated protein kinases (stress-activated protein kinases/c-Jun N-terminal kinases and p38-mitogen-acti-vated protein kinases) in perfused rat hearts by oxidative and other stresses. *J. Biol. Chem.* 273:7228–34

94. Deacon K, Blank JL. 1997. Characteriza-tion of the mitogen-activated protein kinase kinase 4 (MKK4)/c-Jun NH$_2$-ter-minal kinase 1 and MKK3/p38 pathways regulated by MEK kinases 2 and 3: MEK kinase 3 activates MKK3 but does not cause activation of p38 kinase in vivo. *J. Biol. Chem.* 272:14489–96

95. Foltz IN, Gerl RE, Wieler JS, Luckach M, Salmon RA, Schrader JW. 1998. Human mitogen-activated protein kinase kinase 7 (MKK7) is a highly conserved c-Jun N-terminal kinase/stress-activated protein kinase (JNK/SAPK) activated by environmental stresses and physiological stimuli. *J. Biol. Chem.* 273:9344–51

96. Ping P, Zhang J, Cao X, Qiu Y, Tang X-L, et al. 1998. Activation of the p38 MAPK and the p46/p54 JNKs after brief episodes of ischemia/reperfusion in the heart of conscious rabbits. *J. Mol. Cell. Cardiol.* 30:A263 (Abstr.)

97. Nagao M, Yamauchi J, Kaziro Y, Itoh H. 1998. Involvement of protein kinase C and Src family tyrosine kinase in Gα$_{q/11}$-induced activation of c-Jun N-terminal kinase and p38 mitogen-activated protein kinase. *J. Biol. Chem.* 273:22892–98

98. Ping P, Cao X, Kong D, Zhang J, Li RCX, et al. 1998. PKC ε isoform induces activation of the p42/p44 MAPKs and the p46/p54 JNKs in adult rabbit cardiac

myocytes. *J. Mol. Cell. Cardiol.* 30:A263 (Abstr.)

99. Widmann C, Gibson S, Jarpe MB, Johnson GL. 1999. Mitogen-activated protein kinase: conservation of a three-kinase module from yeast to human. *Physiol. Rev.* 79:143–80

100. Zanke BW, Rubie EA, Winnett E, Chan J, Randall S, et al. 1996. Mammalian mitogen-activated protein kinase pathways are regulated through formation of specific kinase-activator complexes. *J. Biol. Chem.* 271:29876–81

101. Freshney NW, Rawlinson L, Guesdon F, Jones E, Cowley S, et al. 1994. Interleukin-1 activates a novel protein kinase cascade that results in the phosphorylation of hsp27. *Cell* 78:1039–49

102. Guay J, Lambert H, Gingras-Breton G, Lavoie JN, Huot J, Landry J. 1997. Regulation of actin filament dynamics by p38 map kinase-mediated phosphorylation of heat shock protein 27. *J. Cell Sci.* 110:357–68

103. Huot J, Houle F, Spitz DR, Landry J. 1996. HSP27 phosphorylation-mediated resistance against actin fragmentation and cell death induced by oxidative stress. *Cancer Res.* 56:273–79

104. Martin JL, Mestril R, Hilal-Dandan R, Brunton LL, Dillmann WH. 1997. Small heat shock proteins and protection against ischemic injury in cardiac myocytes. *Circulation* 96:4343–48

105. Ganote C, Armstrong S. 1993. Ischaemia and the myocyte cytoskeleton: review and speculation. *Cardiovasc. Res.* 27:1387–403

106. Kim SO, Salh B, Pelech SL, Wong G, Katz S. 1997. Activation of MAPKAP kinase-2 by adenosine in rat heart. *J. NIH Res.* 9(1):54

107. Haq SEA, Clerk A, Sugden PH. 1998. Activation of mitogen-activated protein kinases (p38-MAPKs, SAPKs/JNKs and ERKs) by adenosine in the perfused rat heart. *FEBS Lett.* 434:305–8

108. Clerk A, Michael A, Sugden PH. 1998. Stimulation of the p38 mitogen-activated protein kinase pathway in neonatal rat ventricular myocytes by the G protein-coupled receptor agonists, endothelin-1 and phenylephrine: a role in cardiac myocyte hypertrophy? *J. Cell Biol.* 142:523–35

109. Weinbrenner C, Liu G-S, Cohen MV, Downey JM. 1997. Phosphorylation of tyrosine 182 of p38 mitogen-activated protein kinase correlates with the protection of preconditioning in the rabbit heart. *J. Mol. Cell. Cardiol.* 29:2383–91

110. Baines CP, Liu GS, Birincioglu M, Critz SD, Cohen MV, Downey JM. 1999. Ischemic preconditioning depends on interaction between mitochondrial K_{ATP} channels and actin cytoskeleton. *Am. J. Physiol.* 276:H1361–68

111. Cuenda A, Rouse J, Doza YN, Meier R, Cohen P, et al. 1995. SB 203580 is a specific inhibitor of a MAP kinase homologue which is stimulated by cellular stresses and interleukin-1. *FEBS Lett.* 364:229–33

112. Armstrong SC, Delacey M, Ganote CE. 1999. Phosphorylation state of hsp27 and p38 MAPK during preconditioning and protein phosphatase inhibitor protection of rabbit cardiomyocytes. *J. Mol. Cell. Cardiol.* 31:555–67

113. Nagarkatti DS, Sha'afi RI. 1998. Role of p38 MAP kinase in myocardial stress. *J. Mol. Cell. Cardiol.* 30:1651–64

114. Mackay K, Mochly-Rosen D. 1999. An inhibitor of p38-mitogen-activated protein kinase protects neonatal cardiac myocytes from ischemia. *J. Biol. Chem.* 274:6272–79

115. Clerk A, Sugden PH. 1998. The p38-MAPK inhibitor, SB203580, inhibits cardiac stress-activated protein kinases/c-Jun N-terminal kinases (SAPKs/JNKs). *FEBS Lett.* 426:93–96

116. Barancik M, Htun P, Maeno Y, Zimmermann R, Schaper W. 1997. Differential regulation of distinct protein kinase cascades by ischemia and ischemia/

reperfusion in porcine myocardium. *Circulation* 96:I–252 (Suppl. I) (Abstr.)

117. Htun P, Barancik M, Maeno Y, Zimmermann R, Schaper W. 1997. Stimulation of stress activated protein kinases by anisomycin protects ischemic myocardium. *Circulation* 96:I–252 (Suppl. I) (Abstr.)

118. Nakano A, Kim SO, Pelech SL, Downey JM, Cohen MV, Critz SD. 1999. Activation of MAPKAPK2 is involved in preconditioned rabbit heart. *J. Mol. Cell. Cardiol.* 31:A43 (Abstr.)

119. Trapp S, Ashcroft FM. 1997. A metabolic sensor in action: news from the ATP-sensitive K^+-channel. *News Physiol. Sci.* 12:255–63

120. Aguilar-Bryan L, Clement JP IV, Gonzalez G, Kunjilwar K, Babenko A, Bryan J. 1998. Toward understanding the assembly and structure of K_{ATP} channels. *Physiol. Rev.* 78:227–45

121. Grover GJ. 1997. Pharmacology of ATP-sensitive potassium channel (K_{ATP}) openers in models of myocardial ischemia and reperfusion. *Can. J. Physiol. Pharmacol.* 75:309–15

122. Thornton JD, Thornton CS, Sterling DL, Downey JM. 1993. Blockade of ATP-sensitive potassium channels increases infarct size but does not prevent preconditioning in rabbit hearts. *Circ. Res.* 72:44–49

123. Walsh RS, Tsuchida A, Daly JJF, Thornton JD, Cohen MV, Downey JM. 1994. Ketamine-xylazine anaesthesia permits a K_{ATP} channel antagonist to attenuate preconditioning in rabbit myocardium. *Cardiovasc. Res.* 28:1337–41

124. Hide EJ, Thiemermann C. 1996. Limitation of myocardial infarct size in the rabbit by ischaemic preconditioning is abolished by sodium 5-hydroxydecanoate. *Cardiovasc. Res.* 31:941–46

125. Van Winkle DM, Kuzume K, Dote K, Wolff RA. 1995. Infarct limitation by protein kinase C (PKC) is attenuated by blockade of ATP-sensitive potassium

(K_{ATP}) channels. *J. Mol. Cell. Cardiol.* 27:A142 (Abstr.)

126. Gross GJ, Auchampach JA. 1992. Blockade of ATP-sensitive potassium channels prevents myocardial preconditioning in dogs. *Circ. Res.* 70:223–33

127. Auchampach JA, Grover GJ, Gross GJ. 1992. Blockade of ischaemic preconditioning in dogs by the novel ATP dependent potassium channel antagonist sodium 5-hydroxydecanoate. *Cardiovasc. Res.* 26:1054–62

128. Schulz R, Rose J, Heusch G. 1994. Involvement of activation of ATP-dependent potassium channels in ischemic preconditioning in swine. *Am. J. Physiol.* 267:H1341–52

129. Schultz JEJ, Qian YZ, Gross GJ, Kukreja RC. 1997. The ischemia-selective K_{ATP} channel antagonist, 5-hydroxydecanoate, blocks ischemic preconditioning in the rat heart. *J. Mol. Cell. Cardiol.* 29:1055–60

130. Yao Z, Gross GJ. 1994. Effects of the K_{ATP} channel opener bimakalim on coronary blood flow, monophasic action potential duration, and infarct size in dogs. *Circulation* 89:1769–75

131. Grover GJ, D'Alonzo AJ, Parham CS, Darbenzio RB. 1995. Cardioprotection with the K_{ATP} opener cromakalim is not correlated with ischemic myocardial action potential duration. *J. Cardiovasc. Pharmacol.* 26:145–52

132. Grover GJ, D'Alonzo AJ, Hess T, Sleph PG, Darbenzio RB. 1995. Glyburide-reversible cardioprotective effect of BMS-180448 is independent of action potential shortening. *Cardiovasc. Res.* 30:731–38

133. McCullough JR, Normandin DE, Conder ML, Sleph PG, Dzwonczyk S, Grover GJ. 1991. Specific block of the anti-ischemic actions of cromakalim by sodium 5-hydroxydecanoate. *Circ. Res.* 69:949–58

134. Garlid KD, Paucek P, Yarov-Yarovoy V, Murray HN, Darbenzio RB, et al. 1997.

Cardioprotective effect of diazoxide and its interaction with mitochondrial ATP-sensitive K^+ channels: possible mechanism of cardioprotection. *Circ. Res.* 81: 1072–82

135. Liu Y, Sato T, O'Rourke B, Marban E. 1998. Mitochondrial ATP-dependent potassium channels: novel effectors of cardioprotection? *Circulation* 97:2463–69

136. Ashford MLJ, Bond CT, Blair TA, Adelman JP. 1994. Cloning and functional expression of a rat heart K_{ATP} channel. *Nature* 370:456–59

137. de Weille JR, Schmid-Antomarchi H, Fosset M, Lazdunski M. 1989. Regulation of ATP-sensitive K^+ channels in insulinoma cells: activation by somatostatin and protein kinase C and the role of cAMP. *Proc. Natl. Acad. Sci. USA* 86:2971–75

138. Harding EA, Jaggar JH, Squires PE, Dunne MJ. 1994. Polymyxin B has multiple blocking actions on the ATP-sensitive potassium channel in insulin-secreting cells. *Pflügers Arch.* 426:31–39

139. Light PE, Allen BG, Walsh MP, French RJ. 1995. Regulation of adenosine triphosphate-sensitive potassium channels from rabbit ventricular myocytes by protein kinase C and type 2A protein phosphatase. *Biochemistry* 34:7252–57

140. Liu Y, Gao WD, O'Rourke B, Marban E. 1996. Synergistic modulation of ATP-sensitive K^+ currents by protein kinase C and adenosine: implications for ischemic preconditioning. *Circ. Res.* 78:443–54

141. Kirsch GE, Codina J. Birnbaumer L, Brown AM. 1990. Coupling of ATP-sensitive K^+ channels to A_1 receptors by G proteins in rat ventricular myocytes. *Am. J. Physiol.* 259:H820–26

142. Kurachi Y, Ito H, Sugimoto T, Shimizu T, Miki I, Ui M. 1989. α-Adrenergic activation of the muscarinic K^+ channel is mediated by arachidonic acid metabolites. *Pflügers Arch.* 414:102–4

143. Yatani A, Codina J, Brown AM, Birnbaumer L. 1987. Direct activation of mammalian atrial muscarinic potassium channels by GTP regulatory protein G_k. *Science* 235:207–11

144. Ito H, Tung RT, Sugimoto T, Kobayashi I, Takahashi K, et al. 1992. On the mechanism of G protein by $\beta\gamma$ subunit activation of the muscarinic K^+ channel in guinea pig atrial cell membrane: comparison with the ATP-sensitive K^+ channel. *J. Gen. Physiol.* 99:961–83

145. Garlid KD. 1996. Cation transport in mitochondria—the potassium cycle. *Biochim. Biophys. Acta* 1275:123–26

146. Holmuhamedov EL, Wang L. Terzic A. 1999. Openers of ATP-sensitive K^+ channels protect cardiac mitochondria from Ca^{2+} overload. *FASEB J.* 13: A1079 (Abstr.)

147. Diaz RJ, Losito VA, Mao GD, Ford MK, Backx PH, Wilson GJ. 1999. Chloride channel inhibition blocks the protection of ischemic preconditioning and hypoosmotic stress in rabbit ventricular myocardium. *Circ. Res.* 84:763–75

Annu. Rev. Physiol. 2000. 62:111–133

SODIUM-CALCIUM EXCHANGE:
A Molecular Perspective

Kenneth D. Philipson and Debora A. Nicoll

Departments of Physiology and Medicine and the Cardiovascular Research Laboratories, UCLA School of Medicine, Los Angeles, California 90095–1760; e-mail: kphilipson@mednet.ucla.edu

Key Words   sodium transport, calcium transport, antiporter, excitation-contraction coupling, calcium signaling

■ **Abstract**   Plasma membrane Na^+-Ca^{2+} exchange is an essential component of Ca^{2+} signaling pathways in several tissues. Activity is especially high in the heart where the exchanger is an important regulator of contractility. An expanding exchanger superfamily includes three mammalian Na^+-Ca^{2+} exchanger genes and a number of alternative splicing products. New information indicates that the exchanger protein has nine transmembrane segments. The exchanger, which transports Na^+ and Ca^{2+}, is also regulated by these substrates. Some molecular information is available on regulation by Na^+ and Ca^{2+} and by PIP_2 and phosphorylation. Altered expression of the exchanger in pathophysiological states may contribute to various cardiac phenotypes. Use of transgenic approaches is beginning to improve our knowledge of exchanger function.

INTRODUCTION

Ca^{2+} is a major intracellular messenger, and nature has evolved multiple mechanisms to regulate Ca^{2+} levels. One of these mechanisms is Na^+-Ca^{2+} exchange. The Na^+-Ca^{2+} exchanger is a transporter catalyzing the countertransport of three Na^+ for one Ca^{2+} and is present in the plasma membrane of most cells. The exchanger is primarily a Ca^{2+} extrusion mechanism and, as such, requires the energy of the Na^+ gradient produced by the Na^+ pump. Cells have several regulated pathways to handle Ca^{2+}, and Na^+-Ca^{2+} exchange competes with these other pathways. The relative abundance of the various Ca^{2+} transporters determines the importance of Na^+-Ca^{2+} exchange in a particular cell type. In some tissues the importance of the exchanger is apparently low, e.g. liver. In other tissues, however, Na^+-Ca^{2+} exchange is clearly a major player in regulating the physiological response to Ca^{2+}. These tissues include kidney, smooth muscle, and brain. It is cardiac muscle, however, in which Na^+-Ca^{2+} exchange has received the most attention. Exchange activity is especially high in cardiomyocytes and plays a key role in contractile events (see below).

0066–4278/00/0315–0111$12.00

111

The Na^+-Ca^{2+} exchanger was cloned in 1990 (1), and in the ensuing decade many investigators have taken advantage of the molecular tools that are now available. Detailed analysis of exchanger function has also been aided by the giant excised patch technique developed by Hilgemann (2). Advances have been made in understanding the Na^+-Ca^{2+} exchange protein itself, and molecular tools have now been applied to physiological problems. These are the primary topics reviewed here. There are now at least 1500 articles in the literature addressing the topic of Na^+-Ca^{2+} exchange, and a comprehensive review will not be attempted. Only selected topics are covered based on the biases of the authors. Readers interested in other aspects of Na^+-Ca^{2+} exchange can find several excellent reviews (3–6).

PHYSIOLOGICAL RELEVANCE: THE HEART

We do not review the significance of Na^+-Ca^{2+} exchange in all tissues but use cardiac muscle as the paradigm of an exchanger-dependent tissue. The process of Na^+-Ca^{2+} exchange was first described in guinea pig atria by Reuter & Seitz in 1968 (7) and physiological implications were immediately apparent. Shortly thereafter, Na^+-Ca^{2+} exchange was also demonstrated in the squid giant axon by Baker et al (8). It is in cardiac tissue that a major role for the exchanger is most unequivocal and where most attention is focused. In a survey of 100 recent Na^+-Ca^{2+} exchange keyword listings in Medline, 65 of the articles involved the use of myocardial tissue.

The Ca^{2+} signal inducing contraction in cardiac muscle originates from two sources: Ca^{2+} enters the cell through voltage-dependent Ca^{2+} channels. This Ca^{2+} binds to and activates Ca^{2+} release channels (ryanodine receptors) of the sarcoplasmic reticulum (SR) through a Ca^{2+}-induced Ca^{2+} release (CICR) process. Ca^{2+} from both sources can then induce contraction. Estimates indicate that 20% of the Ca^{2+} inducing contraction comes from extracellular sources and that 80% of the Ca^{2+} is released from the SR (9). (These estimates can vary considerably with species and with developmental stage.) Entry of Ca^{2+} with each contraction requires an equal amount of Ca^{2+} extrusion within a single heartbeat to maintain Ca^{2+} homeostasis and to ensure relaxation. The principal cardiac extrusion mechanism is Na^+-Ca^{2+} exchange. In this role, the exchanger is an important determinant of intracellular Ca^{2+} and hence contractility. A plasma membrane ATP-dependent Ca^{2+} pump is also present in cardiac sarcolemma. It has been difficult to demonstrate a physiological role for this extrusion pathway although recent studies have delineated a minor role for the Ca^{2+} pump (10).

The ability of the Na^+-Ca^{2+} exchanger to rapidly remove Ca^{2+} from cardiac myocytes is readily demonstrated (e.g. 11–13). For example, Bridge et al (12) showed that in the presence of caffeine, which disables SR function, ventricular myocytes would not relax following stimulation in the absence of external Na^+. Upon re-application of Na^+, relaxation rapidly occurred. If 80% of coupling Ca^{2+}

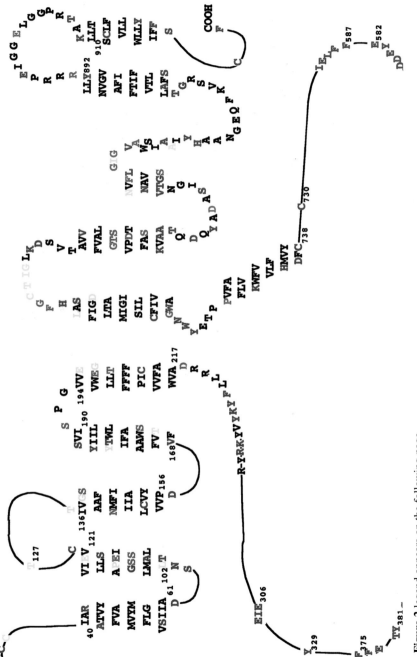

Figure 2 legend appears on the following page.

Figure 2 Summary of the results of single-site mutations of Na^+-Ca^{2+} exchange activity. In the "traffic light" model, mutation of residues shown in green did not have a substantial effect on activity. Mutation of residues shown in yellow resulted in activities between 20 and 50%. Mutation of residues shown in red resulted in substantial inhibition to a level less than 20%. Hot spots of sensitivity to mutations include the α repeats. In some but not all cases, immuno-fluorescence confirmed that exchanger protein reaches the plasma membrane. In most cases, residues have been mutated to only one other amino acid. For those residues that have been mutated to several amino acids (e.g. C730A and C730S), the figure reflects the mutant with the best activity. Data are primarily from References 29, 57, 63, 73, 77, and unpublished data from KD Philipson & DA Nicoll.

THE Na$^+$-Ca^{2+} EXCHANGER MOLECULE: AN OVERVIEW

The first Na$^+$-Ca^{2+} exchanger to be isolated (26) and cloned (1) was that from cardiac sarcolemma. This is the exchanger that has been studied in most molecular detail and is referred to as NCX1. The exchanger was initially modeled to have 12 transmembrane segments based on hydropathy analysis. Subsequently, it was found that the initial hydrophobic segment of 32 amino acids is a signal peptide that is cleaved from the protein during initial processing in the endoplasmic reticulum (27, 28). The full-length mature cardiac exchanger is 938 amino acids long. As described in more detail below, the exchanger is now modeled to contain 9 transmembrane segments (29; Figure 1). The N terminus of the mature protein is glycosylated at position 9 and is thus extracellular. Neither glycosylation (28) nor cleavage of the signal peptide is functionally important (30–32).

The exchanger consists of two sets of hydrophobic domains containing transmembrane segments separated by a large intracellular loop of about 550 amino

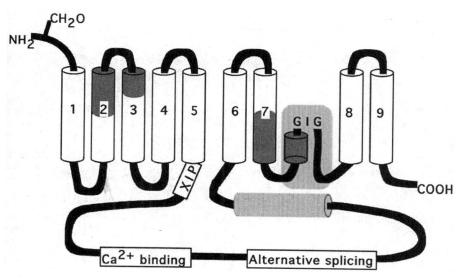

Figure 1 Model of the Na$^+$-Ca^{2+} exchanger. The exchanger is now modeled to have 9 transmembrane segments as shown (29). The N terminus is glycosylated and extracellular. Earlier models predicted 11 transmembrane segments. Former transmembrane segment 6 is likely to be a portion of the large intracellular loop (light shaded cylinder). Hydrophobic segment 9 does not span the membrane and is speculatively modeled to form a P loop-like structure (light shading). The α-repeat regions in transmembrane segments 2, 3, and 7 are shaded. Shown on the large intracellular loop are the endogenous XIP region, the binding site for regulatory Ca^{2+}, and the region where extensive alternative splicing occurs. The large intracellular loop is not drawn to scale but encompasses almost 550 amino acids—more than half the length of the protein.

acids (Figure 1). The N-terminal hydrophobic domain has 5 transmembrane segments and the C-terminal hydrophobic domain is modeled to have 4 transmembrane segments. (In initial models, this domain had 6 transmembrane segments.) Deletion experiments (33) indicate that the large intracellular loop (loop f) is not essential for transport. Rather, it is the transmembrane segments that catalyze the ion translocation reaction. As detailed below, however, the loop has important regulatory functions.

Of interest are regions of NCX1 displaying intramolecular homology as first noted by Schwarz & Benzer (34). The sequence spanning transmembrane segments 2 and 3 is similar to the sequence spanning hydrophobic segments 8 and 9 (Figure 1). These regions are the α repeats: α-1 and α-2. Their presence suggests that the evolution of the exchanger protein involved a gene duplication event. The α repeats appear to have an important role in ion transport (see below). The large intracellular loop also contains a repeat region: the β repeats. The β-1 and β-2 repeats are similar regions of about 60 amino acids. Interestingly, the β repeats are also similar to a portion of the cytoplasmic domain of the integrin β4 subunit. No functional role for the β repeats has been proposed.

THE EXCHANGER SUPERFAMILY

An ever increasing number of proteins are members of the exchanger superfamily. These proteins are defined by the presence of α repeats and similar hydrophobicity plots, indicating multiple transmembrane segments. We have performed BLAST (35) searches of the GenBank database to find proteins that may belong to this superfamily. The existence of many of these proteins is inferred only from large-scale sequencing projects. We propose that these proteins are membrane transporters. The superfamily members were aligned using ClustalW (36). Based on this analysis, members of the exchanger superfamily fall into roughly four different families (Table 1).

The first is the NCX, Na^+-Ca^{2+} exchanger, family. All members of the NCX family share a striking degree of sequence identity, especially in the transmembrane domains. They all have a pair of α repeats. Five of the 8 members, which include three known mammalian exchangers, NCX1 (1), NCX2 (37), and NCX3 (38), have been shown to function as Na^+-Ca^{2+} exchangers. The functional properties of NCX1, NCX2, and NCX3 do not show striking differences (39, 40). The clones isolated from *Caenorhabditis elegans* are similar enough to the other members that they most likely are also Na^+-Ca^{2+} exchangers. The clone from *Arabidopsis* shows considerable sequence variability and may have some other function.

The second family is designated NCKX because it consists of proteins similar to the Na^+-Ca^{2+} + K^+ exchanger initially cloned from retinal tissue. Besides the mammalian NCKX1 (41) and NCKX2 (42) exchangers, which have been cloned and expressed, there are six members from *C. elegans* and one each from *Ara-*

TABLE 1 Exchanger superfamily

Species	Gene	GenBank access number	Ions exchanged
NCX Family			
Canis sp.	NCX1	164073	Na^+-Ca^{2+}
Rattus norvegicus	NCX2	1346653	Na^+-Ca^{2+}
Rattus norvegicus	NCX3	2498054	Na^+-Ca^{2+}
Drosophila melanogaster	Calx	2266953	Na^+-Ca^{2+}
Loligo opalescens	NCX-SQ1	1947092	Na^+-Ca^{2+}
Caenorhabditis elegans	CEJ001181	2826835	
Caenorhabditis elegans	CENACAEX	2826759	
Arabidopsis thaliana	ATAC002535	3522931	
NCKX Family			
Bos taurus	NCKX1	108825	Na^+-Ca^{2+} + K^+
Rattus norvegicus	NCKX2	2662461	Na^+-Ca^{2+} + K^+
Caenorhabditis elegans	CEF35C12	3876734	
Caenorhabditis elegans	CEC35A5	3874763	
Schizosaccharomyces pombe	SPAC3A12.06c	2104422	
Arabidopsis thaliana	AC0001061	1922938	
Caenorhabditis elegans	C13D9.7	2291174	
Caenorhabditis elegans	C13D9.8	2291175	
Caenorhabditis elegans	C07A9.11	465776	
Caenorhabditis elegans	C07A9.4	465770	
Bacterial Family			
Escherichia coli	YRBG ECOLI	1176841	
Treponema pallidum	TP1034	3323364	
Synechocystis sp.		1652037	
Aquifex aeolicus	aq 066	2982830	
Borrelia burgdorferi	BB0164	2688049	
Pyrococcus horikoshii	PH0473	3256878	
Methanococcus jannaschii	MJ0091	2495791	
M. thermoautotrophicum	MTH1155	2622261	
M. thermoautotrophicum	MTH1073	2622172	
CHX Family			
Saccharomyces cerevisiae	VCX1	2131201	Ca^{2+}-H^+
Arabidopsis thaliana	AF049236	3068713	

bidopsis thaliana and *Schizosaccharomyces pombe*. Again, the members of this family show sequence identity primarily in the transmembrane domains and contain a pair of α repeats. There is very little sequence similarity between the proteins in the N terminal and cytoplasmic loop domains. The NCKX1 protein exchanges four Na^+ for one Ca^{2+} plus one K^+ (43).

The third family consists entirely of bacterial proteins all of unknown function. The proteins in this group are much smaller (350–450 residues) than those in the NCX and NCKX groups. The smaller size is due to the absence of any large hydrophilic segments. For the bacterial members of the exchanger superfamily, homology between the two halves of the protein extends beyond the α-repeat regions. That is, intramolecular similarities are much more extensive than for the NCX proteins. Thus evidence for a gene duplication event is more apparent.

The fourth family contains just two proteins, one of which has been shown to function as a yeast vacuolar Ca^{2+}-H^+ exchanger (44, 45). The other member of this group, from *A. thaliana,* is twice as long as the yeast member and is obviously the product of a second gene duplication event (i.e. four α repeats are present). These two proteins are also members of a different large family of proteins, which includes two other gene products from *A. thaliania* (46) and one from *Escherichia coli* (47), both functional Ca^{2+}-H^+ exchangers.

GENE STRUCTURE

The chromosomal locations of the NCX1, NCX2, and NCX3 genes have all been determined (38). The intron-exon organization of the NCX1 gene has also been characterized (48) and some features are of note. The gene is organized into 12 exons, although most of the protein is coded within a single exon of 1.8 kb. Also, there are three alternative 5' exons under the control of separate tissue-specific promoters (49–51). The cardiac-specific promoter has been analyzed and is primarily controlled by a minimum promoter region of about 200 base pairs. Mutation of a GATA 4 transcriptional element within the minimum promoter eliminates over 90% of transcriptional activity (52).

Alternative Splicing

A variety of splice variants of NCX1 have been described (49, 53, 54). These variants arise from a region of the large intracellular loop of the exchanger encoded by six small exons (labeled A through F) used in different combinations in a tissue-specific manner (Figure 1). To maintain an open reading frame, all splice variants must include either exon A or B, which are mutually exclusive. At least 12 splice variants have been detected. Excitable tissues usually have exchangers with exon A, whereas exon B predominates in other tissues. A single combination of exons (ACDEF) predominates in cardiac muscle.

The physiological and functional significance of alternative splicing remains unclear. A tissue-specific pattern of alternative splicing suggests that the properties of each splice variant are tailored to meet the specific needs of particular tissues or cell types. For example, Omelchenko et al (55) found that two splice variants of the *Drosophila* Na^+-Ca^{2+} exchanger were regulated quite differently by Na^+ and Ca^{2+}. Also, He et al (56) report that a splice variant containing exons AD could be stimulated in *Xenopus* oocytes by activation of a PKA pathway, whereas splice variant BD could not. Much work on the importance of alternative splicing of the Na^+-Ca^{2+} exchanger remains to be done.

TOPOLOGY

As mentioned above, the exchanger is now considered to have 9 transmembrane segments (29). Two hydrophobic segments, initially determined to be transmembrane, are no longer thought to span the membrane (Figure 1). The most recent detailed data on topology have come from the use of cysteine substitution mutagenesis (29, 57). The accessibility of cysteines to either intra- or extracellular sulfhydryl reagents has helped to map the topology of almost the entire exchanger molecule. Epitope mapping has also provided some useful information (58). The new model has some features of interest. First there is an extracellular disulfide bond connecting Cys792 with either Cys14 or Cys20 (59). Second, the ninth hydrophobic segment (formerly transmembrane segment 9) is speculatively modeled to be a reentrant membrane loop similar to the pore-forming region of ion channels. The center of this hydrophobic segment has a GIG sequence, conducive to a turn, and is also reminiscent of the GYG motif characteristic of K^+ channel P loops. Third, the regions of intramolecular homology, the α repeats, are now modeled to be on opposite sides of the membrane (Figure 1). This arrangement is similar to that of the aquaporin water channels, which have also been found to have intramolecular repeats on opposite membrane surfaces (60).

Two studies have reported that expression of the N-terminal half of the exchanger by itself can induce a low level of Na^+-Ca^{2+} exchange activity (61, 62). In each case, it was proposed that the truncated exchanger dimerized to form a functional exchanger. Such an event, however, is inconsistent with the proposed topology. Dimerization would form a structure with both α repeats facing the extracellular surface. In contrast, the topological data indicate that the α repeats of a functional exchanger are on opposite sides of the membrane. This apparent discrepancy needs to be resolved. We have been unable to detect exchange activity after expression of half exchangers (KD Philipson & DA Nicoll, unpublished observations).

STRUCTURE AND FUNCTION: TRANSPORT

Molecular understanding of the transport process requires identification of amino acid residues involved in ion binding and identification of those transmembrane segments that line the translocation pathway. Such information is difficult to obtain for ion transporters in general, but some initial information is available for the exchanger. Nicoll et al (63) examined the effects of a large number of transmembrane segment mutations. A striking finding was that exchange activity was extremely sensitive to mutations, including conservative mutations, within the α-repeat regions (Figure 2, see color insert). For example, mutation of serine at position 110 to alanine, cysteine, or threonine eliminated exchange activity. Likewise, mutation of glutamate 113 to either aspartate or glutamine produced nonfunctional exchangers. The two halves of the exchanger are the result of a gene duplication event (see above). The fact that sequence similarity has been retained only in the α-repeat regions through evolution implies special functional importance for the α repeats. This contention is supported by the mutagenesis data (63).

Some mutations near the intracellular membrane surface of transmembrane segment 2 alter ion selectivity (57). Normally, the exchanger has a rigorous requirement for Na^+ as the transported monovalent cation. A mutated exchanger with a valine instead of a threonine at position 103 can catalyze Li^+-Ca^{2+} as well as Na^+-Ca^{2+} exchange.

The results from a series of mutagenesis studies from our laboratory are summarized in a "traffic light" model in Figure 2 (see color insert). As described above, exchange activity is sensitive to mutations at specific sites within the transmembrane segments. Exchange activity is generally impervious to mutations within the large intracellular loop, although many of these mutations affect regulatory properties (see below).

The Na^+-Ca^{2+} exchanger uses a consecutive reaction mechanism with ion binding sites alternatively accessible from each side of the membrane (64, 65). For example, Ca^{2+} might first bind at the intracellular surface of the exchanger and be translocated across the plasma membrane for release. The binding sites are then available to bind three extracellular Na^+ ions for translocation into the cell. A consecutive reaction mechanism involving multiple ions is, by necessity, complex. Nevertheless, high resolution electrophysiological techniques have resolved "half reaction cycles" of the exchanger (Figure 3). It appears that the major electrogenic step for NCX1 involves Na^+ translocation, whereas Ca^{2+} movement is largely electroneutral. The implication is that two negative charges on the exchanger protein cross the membrane electric field with the conformational changes that accompany ion translocation (65–67). The exchanger protein has a high turnover rate for a transporter ($5000\ s^{-1}$) as determined by noise analysis and voltage-induced charge movements (66).

An interesting feature of the electrogenicity of the exchanger reaction cycle is species variability. In the squid neuronal Na^+-Ca^{2+} exchanger NCX-SQ1 (68), charge movement accompanies Ca^{2+} translocation but not Na^+ translocation, the opposite of what is observed in the mammalian cardiac exchanger NCX1. Charge movements associated with half reaction cycles of these two exchangers are displayed in Figure 3. In these experiments, Na^+ (panels *A* and *B*) or Ca^{2+} (panels *C* and *D*) is rapidly applied to excised patches of oocyte membrane expressing either NCX1 or NCX-SQ1. Within the pipette is either Na^+ or Ca^{2+}, respectively.

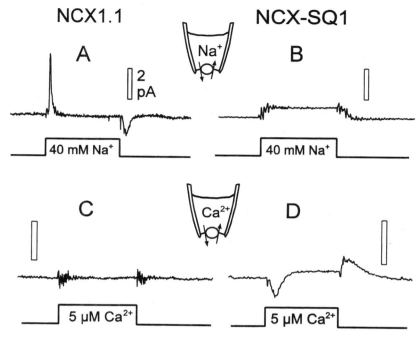

Figure 3 Charge movements associated with half reaction cycles of the Na^+-Ca^{2+} exchanger. In the *top panels* (*A,B*), Na^+ is present in the pipette and Na^+ is applied to the bath as indicated; no Ca^{2+} is present. In the *bottom panels* (*C,D*), Ca^{2+} is present in the pipette and is applied to the bath; no Na^+ is present. That is, at no time will steady-state Na^+-Ca^{2+} exchange currents be activated. With Na^+ or Ca^{2+} in the pipette at the beginning of the experiment, exchanger binding sites will all be empty and facing internally. When Na^+ or Ca^{2+}, respectively, is then rapidly applied to the intracellular surface, binding and translocation will occur. If the initial translocation is electrogenic, a current transient will be observed. Note that for the cardiac exchanger NCX1, current transients are associated with Na^+ translocation (panel *A*) but not with Ca^{2+} translocation (panel *C*). Strikingly, the opposite is true of the squid exchanger NCX-SQ1. In this case, the electrogenic step is Ca^{2+} translocation (panel *D*) and not Na^+ translocation (panel *B*). For further details see References 65 and 68.

Before the application of intracellular cation, all ion binding sites on the exchanger face the intracellular surface. Application of Na^+ or Ca^{2+} allows translocation of ions and reorientation of binding sites to the extracellular surface. This half reaction cycle produces a transient current if the reaction is electrogenic. For NCX1, current is produced by Na^+ and not by Ca^{2+}. Strikingly, the opposite is true for NCX-SQ1. For more details see References 65 and 68.

STRUCTURE AND FUNCTION: REGULATION

The Na^+-Ca^{2+} exchanger is dynamically regulated by a variety of factors. We discuss four that have been investigated, to varying degrees, at the molecular level. These factors are Ca^{2+}, Na^+, phosphatidylinositol-4,5-bisphosphate (PIP$_2$), and phosphorylation. Ca^{2+} and Na^+, besides being substrates for the exchanger, also exert separate regulatory influences on exchange activity.

Ca^{2+} Regulation

Regulatory Ca^{2+} interacts with the exchanger at a high-affinity binding site located on the large intracellular loop (Figure 1) and is required for exchange activity. The influence of regulatory Ca^{2+} is most readily apparent during reverse exchange measurements using the giant excised patch technique, as shown in Figure 4. With Ca^{2+} in the pipette at the extracellular surface, the addition of Na^+ to the intracellular surface does not elicit an exchange current in the absence of a submicromolar level of intracellular Ca^{2+}. The regulatory Ca^{2+} is not transported but serves only to activate the exchanger. This effect was first observed in flux studies using the squid giant axon (69). Despite having such a dominant influence on exchange activity, the physiological significance of Ca^{2+} regulation is unclear. An important unresolved issue is the Ca^{2+} affinity of the site. In excised patches, the apparent Ca^{2+} affinity for regulation is about 0.1–0.3 μM. Indirect measurements using intact cells, however, suggest a higher affinity of 20–50 nM (70, 71). If the latter measurements reflect the in situ value for Ca^{2+} regulation, then the Ca^{2+} regulatory sites would always be saturated and perhaps have little relevance. If the lower affinity applies, then the exchanger would be activated to extrude Ca^{2+} upon elevation of cytoplasmic Ca^{2+} levels such as occurs during cardiac contraction.

Levitsky et al (72) identified a high-affinity Ca^{2+}-binding site on the exchanger through the use of fusion proteins and the $^{45}Ca^{2+}$ overlay technique. The site is located in the center of loop f and is about 130 amino acids in length. The site does not resemble other known Ca^{2+} binding sites. The binding of Ca^{2+} induces a substantial conformational change, as indicated by electrophoretic mobility shifts. Mutational analysis identified two groups of aspartate residues involved in the binding of Ca^{2+}. Subsequently, it was found that any mutation that affects the binding of $^{45}Ca^{2+}$ to the protein also disrupts normal Ca^{2+} regulation (73). Thus the binding site for regulatory Ca^{2+} has been unequivocally identified.

An interesting anomaly occurs with the *Drosophila* Na^+-Ca^{2+} exchanger, Calx (74). In this case, regulatory Ca^{2+} decreases activity. Full activity is seen only in the absence of regulatory Ca^{2+}. Interestingly, identical mutations affect Ca^{2+} regulation in both Calx and NCX1 (75). Apparently, Ca^{2+} binding to the same site produces opposite results in the two exchangers.

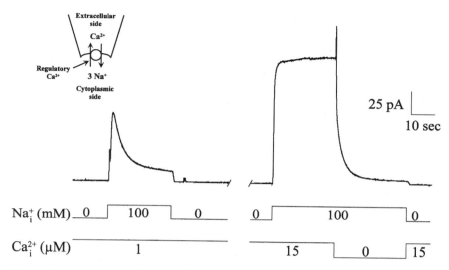

Figure 4 Secondary Na$^+$ and Ca^{2+} regulation of the cardiac Na$^+$-Ca^{2+} exchanger, NCX1. A giant patch was excised from a *Xenopus* oocyte expressing NCX1. Ca^{2+} was constantly present within the pipette, and outward exchange currents were initiated by applying Na$^+$ into the bath at the intracellular surface. Regulatory Ca^{2+} was also present as shown. The *left* panel demonstrates Na$^+$-dependent inactivation. Upon application of internal Na$^+$, outward exchange current peaks and then inactivates to a new steady-state level. The *right* panel demonstrates Ca^{2+} regulation. In this case, the level of regulatory Ca^{2+} in the bath was 15 µM instead of 1 µM. Two phenomena are evident. First, the Na$^+$-dependent inactivation is eliminated in the presence of high regulatory Ca^{2+}. Ca^{2+} modulates Na$^+$ regulation. Second, upon removal of regulatory Ca^{2+}, exchange activity declines to zero. Ca^{2+} is transported by the exchanger but also exerts a separate modulatory effect.

Na$^+$ Regulation

When Na$^+$ is applied to the intracellular surface of an excised patch, the outward Na$^+$-Ca^{2+} exchange current rapidly peaks and then partially inactivates to a steady-state level (Figure 4). The inactivation process is analogous to that commonly observed in ion channels and has been referred to as Na$^+$-dependent inactivation (2). The Na$^+$-dependent inactivation does not appear to result from binding of Na$^+$ to a distinct regulatory site. Detailed analysis and modeling indicate that the inactive state arises when Na$^+$ binds to transport sites at the intracellular surface of the exchanger (76). That is, Na$^+$ binding initiates two possible responses: The Na$^+$ can be translocated across the membrane or the exchanger can undergo a transition into an inactive state. The amount of inactivation that occurs is dependent on both the Na$^+$ concentration and the level of regulatory Ca^{2+}. As with Ca^{2+} regulation, the physiological significance of Na$^+$ regulation is unknown. Intracellular Na^+ levels are unlikely to undergo the large fluctuations needed to effect Na^+-dependent inactivation. However, a possible role for Na^+-dependent inactivation is presented below.

We have found that a 20-amino acid segment of the exchanger, referred to as the endogenous XIP region (Figure 1), is involved in Na^+-dependent inactivation (77). Based on sequence analysis, it was postulated that the XIP region might have an autoregulatory function. A peptide with a sequence the same as the XIP region was synthesized and found to be a relatively potent inhibitor of exchange activity (78). The name XIP derives from Exchanger Inhibitory Peptide. The peptide acts at the intracellular surface of the exchanger and is noncompetitive with both Na^+ and Ca^{2+}. Thus a peptide with the sequence of the XIP region affects activity, but this does not prove that the endogenous XIP region of the exchanger protein is involved in exchanger function. Subsequently, the endogenous XIP region was subjected to mutational analysis (77). Strikingly, mutations within the XIP region altered the inactivation process. Some mutations increased the rate of inactivation, whereas others completely eliminated Na^+-dependent inactivation. Overall, the data strongly support the involvement of the endogenous XIP region in Na^+-dependent inactivation.

PIP$_2$

Hilgemann (2) noted that Na^+-Ca^{2+} exchange currents were stimulated by the application of ATP to the intracellular surface of a patch excised from a cardiac myocyte. The stimulation is due to the ATP-induced production of the signaling lipid PIP_2 from phosphatidylinositol (PI; 79). Several observations are consistent with this interpretation. For example, the ATP effect could be abolished by pretreatment of the membrane with PI-specific phospholipase C but could be recovered by re-incorporation of PI into the patch. The mechanism of the stimulation is primarily an elimination of the Na^+-dependent inactivation process. That is, inactivation is regulated by PIP_2.

Because the endogenous XIP region of the exchanger is involved in inactivation, it is natural to speculate that PIP_2 directly interacts with the XIP region. XIP is a basic peptide and may bind to the acidic PIP_2. Also, the XIP region is modeled to be at a site on the protein near the membrane interface and therefore is potentially accessible to PIP_2. Indeed, we have found that iodinated XIP peptide does bind to PIP_2 (Z He & KD Philipson, unpublished observation), but there is no direct evidence that this interaction occurs in the intact exchanger protein.

PIP_2 may be a physiologically relevant regulator of Na^+-Ca^{2+} exchange activity. This possibility also suggests a role for Na^+-dependent inactivation. The existence of inactivation may provide the flexibility for the exchanger to be regulated by messengers such as PIP_2. Signals that activate phospholipase C will decrease membrane PIP_2 and inhibit the exchanger by increasing inactivation. This in turn can lead to decreased Ca^{2+} extrusion and a positive inotropic effect. Work is needed to test this hypothesis.

Phosphorylation

Stimulation of Na^+-Ca^{2+} exchange activity by phosphorylation was first described in the squid giant axon and has been elegantly analyzed by DiPolo & Beaugé (for a review, see Reference 80). The mechanism involves a Ca^{2+}-dependent kinase reaction that activates an increase in the affinity for Ca^{2+}_i and Na^+_o. A 13-kDa cytoplasmic protein has been isolated that is required for stimulation of the squid exchanger by ATP (81). Interestingly, the squid axonal exchanger is also stimulated by phosphoarginine by a mechanism apparently involving phosphorylation but distinct from the ATP effect (82).

Somewhat disappointingly, the findings in squid axon have been difficult to reproduce in other tissues. However, recent positive results using myocytes have attracted interest. First, Iwamoto et al (83, 84) directly detected phosphorylation of the cardiac and aortic smooth muscle exchangers by immunoprecipitation and autoradiography. The levels of exchange activity and phosphorylation were modulated by agents acting via protein kinase C. Although the effects on activity were relatively modest, the results appeared promising. Subsequently, Iwamoto et al (85) determined that the effects of PKC on exchanger activity did not require direct phosphorylation of the exchanger protein. Second, frog heart Na^+-Ca^{2+} exchange activity is substantially downregulated by isoproterenol via activation of the protein kinase A pathway (86). This effect fits in nicely with known amphibian physiology and does not occur with mammalian cardiac exchangers. It has been speculated that the unique sensitivity of the frog heart exchanger to cAMP is due to the presence of a novel exon that generates a potential nucleotide-binding site on the exchanger (87).

ALTERED PHYSIOLOGY

Pathophysiology

The literature abounds with descriptions of alterations (usually modest) in levels of exchanger activity, protein, or RNA after various interventions. One of the more impressive examples is provided by Kent et al (88) who found a two- to threefold increase in exchanger mRNA after only one hour of right ventricular pressure overload in a feline model of hypertrophy. Oxygen-derived free radicals arising during cardiac reperfusion may also stimulate Na^+-Ca^{2+} exchange activity (89). Much recent attention has focused on the role of the Na^+-Ca^{2+} exchanger during heart failure, with most studies finding augmented exchanger protein, RNA, and activity (90–95). Even a modest alteration of exchange activity could potentially have a substantial effect on cardiac contractility (96).

Development

The sarcoplasmic reticulum is poorly developed in the hearts of many neonatal mammals, and these hearts are more heavily dependent on transsarcolemmal Ca^{2+} fluxes for excitation-contraction coupling. That is, fluxes carried by the sarcolemmal Ca^{2+} channel and by Na^+-Ca^{2+} exchange are more essential. Consistent with this model, cardiac Na^+-Ca^{2+} exchange is highest in newborns and decreases rapidly with age. The decrease in exchange activity is concomitant with the development of the sarcoplasmic reticulum and the transverse tubules. Thus the cardiac Na^+-Ca^{2+} exchanger is even more important in neonates than in adults (97–101).

Apoptosis

The mature exchanger protein (120 kDa) copurifies with an active proteolytic fragment of 70 kDa (26). Iwata et al (102) found that the 70-kDa fragment arises from proteolytic cleavage at either of two nearby sites in the large intracellular loop of the exchanger. Although not recognized at the time, these locations are consensus sites for caspases, the proteases activated during apoptosis. We have found that the exchanger protein is indeed a substrate for caspases but have not yet detected functional effects of caspase digestion (KD Philipson, unpublished observation).

Antisense Inhibition

Antisense oligonucleotides have been used to inhibit exchanger synthesis and function in myocytes (103–105) and other cell types (106, 107). Various studies have focused primarily on development of the technique. In general, the results have confirmed information available from other approaches, but further application of antisense oligonucleotides may prove to be even more useful in the future.

Transgenic Mice

Genetic manipulations provide another tool for studying the physiological function of Na^+-Ca^{2+} exchange. Cardiac-specific overexpression of the exchanger has been achieved in transgenic mice through the use of the α-myosin heavy chain promoter (108–110). The level of NCX1 overexpression was about 200%, whereas the levels of other Ca^{2+} transporters were unchanged. Both exchanger-mediated Ca^{2+} influx and efflux across the sarcolemma were accelerated. Reverse exchange was able to trigger Ca^{2+}-induced Ca^{2+} release from the SR of transgenic hearts, however, not as effectively as release triggered by influx through Ca^{2+} channels. Interestingly, overexpression of exchange activity increased susceptibility to ischemia/reperfusion injury in male, but not female, transgenic mice (111). When the level of overexpression was further increased by generating homozygous transgenic mice, some animals developed cardiac hypertrophy (R Ross & KD Philipson, unpublished observations).

PERSPECTIVE

Much remains to be understood regarding the Na^+-Ca^{2+} exchanger. Advances in the next few years should occur in at least three areas: (*a*) Structure. Combinations of biochemical and molecular biological techniques should be productive in this area; (*b*) Regulation. Various forms of regulation have been elucidated. A challenge is to now determine the physiological roles of regulation; (*c*) Physiology and pathophysiology. Genetic manipulations using adenoviruses and transgenic models, including tissue-specific knockouts, should provide insights.

Visit the Annual Reviews home page at www.AnnualReviews.org.

LITERATURE CITED

1. Nicoll DA, Longoni S, Philipson KD. 1990. Molecular cloning and functional expression of the cardiac sarcolemmal Na^+-Ca^{2+} exchanger. *Science* 250:562–65

2. Hilgemann DW. 1990. Regulation and deregulation of cardiac Na^+-Ca^{2+} exchange in giant excised sarcolemmal membrane patches. *Nature* 344:242–45

3. Khananshvili D. 1998. Structure, mechanism, and regulation of the cardiac Na^+-Ca^{2+} exchanger. *Adv. Mol. Cell Biol.* 23B:311–58

4. Reeves JP. 1998. Na^+/Ca^{2+} exchange and cellular Ca^{2+} homeostasis. *J. Bioenerg. Biomembr.* 30:151–60

5. Blaustein MP, Lederer WJ. 1999. Sodium-calcium exchange: its physiological implications. *Physiol. Rev.* 79:763–854

6. Philipson KD. 1999. Sodium-calcium exchange. In *Calcium as a Cellular Regulator*, ed. E Carafoli, C Klee, pp. 279–94. New York: Oxford Univ. Press

7. Reuter H, Seitz N. 1968. The dependence of calcium efflux from cardiac muscle on temperature and external ion composition. *J. Physiol.* 195:451–70

8. Baker PF, Blaustein MP, Hodgkin AL, Steinhardt RA. 1969. The influence of calcium on sodium efflux in squid axons. *J. Physiol.* 200:431–58

9. Delbridge LM, Bassani JW, Bers DM. 1996. Steady-state twitch Ca^{2+} fluxes and cytosolic Ca^{2+} buffering in rabbit ventricular myocytes. *Am. J. Physiol.* 270:C192–99

10. Choi HS, Eisner DA. 1999. The role of sarcolemmal Ca^{2+}-ATPase in the regulation of resting calcium concentration in rat ventricular myocytes. *J. Physiol.* 515:109–18

11. Bers DM, Bridge JHB, Spitzer KW. 1989. Intracellular Ca^{2+} transients during rapid cooling contractures in guinea-pig ventricular myocytes. *J. Physiol.* 417:537–53

12. Bridge JHB, Smolley JR, Spitzer KW. 1990. The relationship between charge movements associated with I_{Ca} and $I_{Na\text{-}Ca}$ in cardiac myocytes. *Science* 248:376–78

13. Crespo LM, Grantham CJ, Cannell MB. 1990. Kinetics, stoichiometry and role of the Na-Ca exchange mechanism in isolated cardiac myocytes. *Nature* 345:618–21

14. Leblanc N, Hume JR. 1990. Sodium current-induced release of calcium from cardiac sarcoplasmic reticulum. *Science* 248:372–76

15. Sham JSK, Cleemann L, Morad M. 1992. Gating of the cardiac Ca^{2+} release channel–the role of Na^+ current and Na^+-Ca^{2+} exchange. *Science* 255:850–53

16. Lipp P, Niggli E. 1994. Sodium current-induced calcium signals in isolated guinea-pig ventricular myocytes. *J. Physiol.* 474:439–46

17. Wasserstrom JA, Vites AM. 1996. The role of Na^+-Ca^{2+} exchange in activation of excitation-contraction coupling in rat ventricular myocytes. *J. Physiol.* 493:529–42

18. Litwin S, Kohmoto O, Levi AJ, Spitzer KW, Bridge JH. 1996. Evidence that reverse Na-Ca exchange can trigger SR calcium release. *Ann. NY Acad. Sci.* 779:451–63

19. Sipido KR, Maes M, Van de Werf F. 1997. Low efficiency of Ca^{2+} entry through the Na^+-Ca^{2+} exchanger as trigger for Ca^{2+} release from the sarcoplasmic reticulum. A comparison between L-type Ca^{2+} current and reverse-mode Na^+-Ca^{2+} exchange. *Circ. Res.* 81:1034–44

20. Litwin SE, Li J, Bridge JH. 1998. Na-Ca exchange and the trigger for sarcoplasmic reticulum Ca release: studies in adult rabbit ventricular myocytes. *Biophys. J.* 75:359–71

21. Fujioka Y, Matsuoka S, Ban T, Noma A. 1998. Interaction of the Na^+-K^+ pump and Na^+-Ca^{2+} exchange via $[Na^+]_i$ in a restricted space of guinea-pig ventricular cells. *J. Physiol.* 509:457–70

22. Su Z, Zou A, Nonaka A, Zubair I, Sanguinetti MC, et al. 1998. Influence of prior Na^+ pump activity on pump and Na^+/Ca^{2+} exchange currents in mouse ventricular myocytes. *Am. J. Physiol.* 275:H1808–17

23. Juhaszova M, Blaustein MP. 1997. Na^+ pump low and high ouabain affinity alpha subunit isoforms are differently distributed in cells. *Proc. Natl. Acad. Sci. USA* 94:1800–5

24. Blaustein MP, Juhaszova M, Golovina VA. 1998. The cellular mechanism of action of cardiotonic steroids: a new hypothesis. *Clin. Exp. Hypert.* 20:691–703

25. Santana LF, Gómez AM, Lederer WJ. 1998. Ca^{2+} flux through promiscuous cardiac Na^+ channels: slip-mode conductance. *Science* 279:1027–33

26. Philipson KD, Longoni S, Ward R. 1988. Purification of the cardiac Na^+-Ca^{2+} exchange protein. *Biochim. Biophys. Acta* 945:298–306

27. Durkin JT, Ahrens DC, Pan YCE, Reeves JP. 1991. Purification and amino-terminal sequence of the bovine cardiac sodium calcium exchanger–evidence for the presence of a signal sequence. *Arch. Biochem. Biophys.* 290:369–75

28. Hryshko LV, Nicoll DA, Weiss JN, Philipson KD. 1993. Biosynthesis and initial processing of the cardiac sarcolemmal Na^+-Ca^{2+} exchanger. *Biochim. Biophys. Acta* 1151:35–42

29. Nicoll DA, Ottolia M, Lu L, Lu Y, Philipson KD. 1999. A new topological model of the cardiac sarcolemmal Na^+-Ca^{2+} exchanger. *J. Biol. Chem.* 274:910–17

30. Furman I, Cook O, Kasir J, Low W, Rahamimoff H. 1995. The putative amino-terminal signal peptide of the cloned rat brain Na^+-Ca^{2+} exchanger gene (Rbe-1) is not mandatory for functional expression. *J. Biol. Chem.* 270:19120–27

31. Loo TW, Ho C, Clarke DM. 1995. Expression of a functionally active human renal sodium-calcium exchanger lacking a signal sequence. *J. Biol. Chem.* 270:19345–50

32. Sahin-Tóth M, Nicoll DA, Frank JS, Philipson KD, Friedlander M. 1995. The cleaved N-terminal signal sequence of the cardiac Na^+-Ca^{2+} exchanger is not required for functional membrane integration. *Biochem. Biophys. Res. Commun.* 212:968–74

33. Matsuoka S, Nicoll DA, Reilly RF, Hilgemann DW, Philipson KD. 1993. Initial localization of regulatory regions of the cardiac sarcolemmal Na^+-Ca^{2+}

exchanger. *Proc. Natl. Acad. Sci. USA* 90:3870–74

34. Schwarz EM, Benzer S. 1997. *Calx*, a Na-Ca exchanger gene of *Drosophila melanogaster. Proc. Natl. Acad. Sci. USA* 94:10249–54

35. Altschul SF, Madden TL, Schaffer AA, Zhang J, Zhang Z, et al. 1997. Gapped BLAST and PSI-BLAST: a new generation of protein database search programs. *Nucleic Acids Res.* 25:3389–402

36. Thompson JD, Higgins DG, Gibson TJ. 1994. CLUSTAL W: improving the sensitivity of progressive multiple sequence alignment through sequence weighting, position-specific gap penalties and weight matrix choice. *Nucleic Acids Res.* 22:4673–80

37. Li Z, Matsuoka S, Hryshko LV, Nicoll DA, Bersohn MM, et al. 1994. Cloning of the NCX2 isoform of the plasma membrane Na^+-Ca^{2+} exchanger. *J. Biol. Chem.* 269:17434–39

38. Nicoll DA, Quednau BD, Qui Z, Xia YR, Lusis AJ, et al. 1996. Cloning of a third mammalian Na^+-Ca^{2+} exchanger, NCX3. *J. Biol. Chem.* 271:24914–21

39. Iwamoto T, Shigekawa M. 1998. Differential inhibition of Na^+-Ca^{2+} exchanger isoforms by divalent cations and isothiourea derivative. *Am. J. Physiol.* 275:C423–30

40. Linck B, Qiu Z, He Z, Tong Q, Hilgemann DW, et al. 1998. Functional comparison of the three isoforms of the Na^+-Ca^{2+} exchanger (NCX1, NCX2, NCX3). *Am. J. Physiol.* 274:C415–23

41. Reiländer H, Achilles A, Friedel U, Maul G, Lottspeich F, et al. 1992. Primary structure and functional expression of the Na/Ca,K-exchanger from bovine rod photoreceptors. *EMBO J.* 11:1689–95

42. Tsoi M, Rhee KH, Bungard D, Li XF, Lee SL, et al. 1998. Molecular cloning of a novel potassium-dependent sodium-calcium exchanger from rat brain. *J. Biol. Chem.* 273:4155–62

43. Schnetkamp PP, Basu DK, Szerencsei RT. 1989. Na^+-Ca^{2+} exchange in bovine rod outer segments requires and transports K^+. *Am. J. Physiol.* 257:C153–57

44. Cunningham KW, Fink GR. 1996. Calcineurin inhibits VCX1-dependent H^+/Ca^{2+} exchange and induces Ca^{2+} ATPases in *Saccharomyces cerevisiae. Mol. Cell Biol.* 16:2226–37

45. Pozos TC, Sekler I, Cyert MS. 1996. The product of HUM1, a novel yeast gene, is required for vacuolar Ca^{2+}/H^+ exchange and is related to mammalian Na^+/Ca^{2+} exchangers. *Mol. Cell Biol.* 16:3730–41

46. Hirschi KD, Zhen RG, Cunningham KW, Rea PA, Fink GR. 1996. CAX1, an H^+/Ca^{2+} antiporter from Arabidopsis. *Proc. Natl. Acad. Sci. USA* 93:8782–86

47. Ivey DM, Guffanti AA, Zemsky J, Pinner E, Karpel R, et al. 1993. Cloning and characterization of a putative Ca^{2+}/H^+ antiporter gene from *Escherichia coli* upon functional complementation of Na^+/H^+ antiporter- deficient strains by the overexpressed gene. *J. Biol. Chem.* 268:11296–303

48. Kraev A, Chumakov I, Carafoli E. 1996. The organization of the human gene NCX1 encoding the sodium-calcium exchanger. *Genomics* 37:105–12

49. Lee SL, Yu ASL, Lytton J. 1994. Tissue-specific expression of Na^+-Ca^{2+} exchanger isoforms. *J. Biol. Chem.* 269:14849–52

50. Barnes KV, Cheng G, Dawson MM, Menick DR. 1997. Cloning of cardiac, kidney, and brain promoters of the feline ncx1 gene. *J. Biol. Chem.* 272:11510–17

51. Nicholas SB, Yang W, Lee SL, Zhu H, Philipson KD, et al. 1998. Alternative promoters and cardiac muscle cell-specific expression of the Na^+/Ca^{2+} exchanger gene. *Am. J. Physiol.* 274:H217–32

52. Nicholas SB, Philipson KD. 1999. Cardiac expression of the Na^+-Ca^{2+} exchanger (NCX1) is GATA factor dependent. *Am. J. Physiol.* 277:H324–30

53. Kofuji P, Lederer WJ, Schulze DH. 1994.

Mutually exclusive and cassette exons underlie alternatively spliced isoforms of the Na/Ca exchanger. *J. Biol. Chem.* 269:5145–49

54. Quednau BD, Nicoll DA, Philipson KD. 1997. Tissue specificity and alternative splicing of the Na$^+$/Ca^{2+} exchanger isoforms NCX1, NCX2, and NCX3 in rat. *Am. J. Physiol.* 272:C1250–61

55. Omelchenko A, Dyck C, Hnatowich M, Buchko J, Nicoll DA, et al. 1998. Functional differences in ionic regulation between alternatively spliced isoforms of the Na$^+$-Ca^{2+} exchanger from *Drosophila melanogaster. J. Gen. Physiol.* 111:691–702

56. He S, Ruknudin A, Bambrick LL, Lederer WJ, Schulze DH. 1998. Isoform-specific regulation of the Na$^+$/Ca^{2+} exchanger in rat astrocytes and neurons by PKA. *J. Neurosci.* 18:4833–41

57. Doering AE, Nicoll DA, Lu Y, Lu L, Weiss JN, et al. 1998. Topology of a functionally important region of the cardiac Na$^+$/Ca^{2+} exchanger. *J. Biol. Chem.* 273:778–83

58. Cook O, Low W, Rahamimoff H. 1998. Membrane topology of the rat brain Na$^+$-Ca^{2+} exchanger. *Biochim. Biophys. Acta* 1371:40–52

59. Santacruz-Toloza LK, Nicoll DA, Philipson KD. 1998. Cys14 or cys20 forms an intramolecular disulfide bond with cys792 in the Na$^+$/Ca^{2+} exchanger NCX1. *Biophys. J.* 74:A197 (Abstr.)

60. Walz T, Hirai T, Murata K, Heymann JB, Mitsuoka K, et al. 1997. The three-dimensional structure of aquaporin-1. *Nature* 387:624–27

61. Gabellini N, Zatti A, Rispoli G, Navangione A, Carafoli E. 1996. Expression of an active Na$^+$/Ca^{2+} exchanger isoform lacking the six C-terminal transmembrane segments. *Eur. J. Biochem.* 239:897–904

62. Li XF, Lytton J. 1999. A circularized sodium-calcium exchanger exon 2 transcript. *J. Biol. Chem.* 274:8153–60

63. Nicoll DA, Hryshko LV, Matsuoka S, Frank JS, Philipson KD. 1996. Mutation of amino acid residues in the putative transmembrane segments of the cardiac sarcolemmal Na$^+$-Ca^{2+} exchanger. *J. Biol. Chem.* 271:13385–91

64. Khananshvili D. 1990. Distinction between the 2 basic mechanisms of cation transport in the cardiac Na$^+$-Ca^{2+} exchange system. *Biochemistry* 29:2437–42

65. Hilgemann DW, Nicoll DA, Philipson KD. 1991. Charge movement during Na$^+$ translocation by native and cloned cardiac Na$^+$-Ca^{2+} exchanger. *Nature* 352:715–18

66. Hilgemann DW. 1996. Unitary cardiac Na$^+$,Ca^{2+} exchange current magnitudes determined from channel-like noise and charge movements of ion transport. *Biophys. J.* 71:759–68

67. Kappl M, Hartung K. 1996. Rapid charge translocation by the cardiac Na$^+$-Ca^{2+} exchanger after a Ca^{2+} concentration jump. *Biophys. J.* 71:2473–85

68. He Z, Tong Q, Quednau BD, Philipson KD, Hilgemann DW. 1998. Cloning, expression, and characterization of the squid Na$^+$-Ca^{2+} exchanger (NCX-SQ1). *J. Gen. Physiol.* 111:857–73

69. DiPolo R. 1979. Calcium influx in internally dialyzed squid giant axons. *J. Gen. Physiol.* 73:91–113

70. Miura Y, Kimura J. 1989. Sodium-calcium exchange current. Dependence on internal Ca and Na and competitive binding of external Na and Ca. *J. Gen. Physiol.* 93:1129–45

71. Fang Y, Condrescu M, Reeves JP. 1998. Regulation of Na$^+$/Ca^{2+} exchange activity by cytosolic Ca^{2+} in transfected Chinese hamster ovary cells. *Am. J. Physiol.* 275:C50–55

72. Levitsky DO, Nicoll DA, Philipson KD. 1994. Identification of the high affinity Ca^{2+}-binding domain of the cardiac Na$^+$-Ca^{2+} exchanger. *J. Biol. Chem.* 269:22847–52

73. Matsuoka S, Nicoll DA, Hryshko LV, Levitsky DO, Weiss JN, et al. 1995. Regulation of the cardiac Na^+-Ca^{2+} exchanger by Ca^{2+}-mutational analysis of the Ca^{2+}-binding domain. *J. Gen. Physiol.* 105:403–20

74. Hryshko LV, Matsuoka S, Nicoll DA, Weiss JN, Schwarz EM, et al. 1996. Anomalous regulation of the *Drosophila* Na^+-Ca^{2+} exchanger by Ca^{2+}. *J. Gen. Physiol.* 108:67–74

75. Dyck C, Maxwell K, Buchko J, Trac M, Omelchenko A, et al. 1998. Structure-function analysis of CALX1.1, a Na^+-Ca^{2+} exchanger from Drosophila. Mutagenesis of ionic regulatory sites *J. Biol. Chem.* 273:12981–87

76. Hilgemann DW, Matsuoka S, Nagel GA, Collins A. 1992. Steady-state and dynamic properties of cardiac sodium-calcium exchange—sodium-dependent inactivation. *J. Gen. Physiol.* 100:905–32

77. Matsuoka S, Nicoll DA, He Z, Philipson KD. 1997. Regulation of cardiac Na^+-Ca^{2+} exchanger by the endogenous XIP region. *J. Gen. Physiol.* 109:273–86

78. Li ZP, Nicoll DA, Collins A, Hilgemann DW, Filoteo AG, et al. 1991. Identification of a peptide inhibitor of the cardiac sarcolemmal Na^+-Ca^{2+} exchanger. *J. Biol. Chem.* 266:1014–20

79. Hilgemann DW, Ball R. 1996. Regulation of cardiac Na^+, Ca^{2+} exchange and K_{ATP} potassium channels by PIP_2. *Science* 273:956–59

80. DiPolo R, Beaugé L. 1991. Regulation of Na-Ca exchange. An overview. *Ann. NY Acad. Sci.* 639:100–11

81. DiPolo R, Berberian G, Delgado D, Rojas H, Beaugé L. 1997. A novel 13 kDa cytoplasmic soluble protein is required for the nucleotide (MgATP) modulation of the Na/Ca exchange in squid nerve fibers. *FEBS Lett.* 401:6–10

82. DiPolo R, Beaugé L. 1998. Differential up-regulation of Na^+-Ca^{2+} exchange by phosphoarginine and ATP in dialysed squid axons. *J. Physiol.* 507:737–47

83. Iwamoto T, Wakabayashi S, Shigekawa M. 1995. Growth factor-induced phosphorylation and activation of aortic smooth muscle Na^+/Ca^{2+} exchanger. *J. Biol. Chem.* 270:8996–9001

84. Iwamoto T, Pan Y, Wakabayashi S, Imagawa T, Yamanaka HI, et al. 1996. Phosphorylation-dependent regulation of cardiac Na^+/Ca^{2+} exchanger via protein kinase C. *J. Biol. Chem.* 271:13609–15

85. Iwamoto T, Pan Y, Nakamura TY, Wakabayashi S, Shigekawa M. 1998. Protein kinase C-dependent regulation of Na^+/Ca^{2+} exchanger isoforms NCX1 and NCX3 does not require their direct phosphorylation. *Biochemistry* 37:17230–38

86. Fan J, Shuba YM, Morad M. 1996. Regulation of cardiac sodium-calcium exchanger by beta-adrenergic agonists. *Proc. Natl. Acad. Sci. USA* 93:5527–32

87. Shuba YM, Iwata T, Naidenov VG, Oz M, Sandberg K, et al. 1998. A novel molecular determinant for cAMP-dependent regulation of the frog heart Na^+-Ca^{2+} exchanger. *J. Biol. Chem.* 273:18819–25

88. Kent RL, Rozich JD, McCollam PL, McDermott DE, Thacker UF, et al. 1993. Rapid expression of the Na^+-Ca^{2+} exchanger in response to cardiac pressure overload. *Am. J. Physiol.* 265:H1024–29

89. Goldhaber JI. 1996. Free radicals enhance Na^+/Ca^{2+} exchange in ventricular myocytes. *Am. J. Physiol.* 271: H823–33

90. Studer R, Reinecke H, Bilger J, Eschenhagen T, Bohm M, et al. 1994. Gene expression of the cardiac Na^+-Ca^{2+} exchanger in end-stage human heart failure. *Circ. Res.* 75:443–53

91. Flesch M, Schwinger RH, Schiffer F, Frank K, Sudkamp M, et al. 1996. Evidence for functional relevance of an enhanced expression of the Na^+-Ca^{2+} exchanger in failing human myocardium. *Circulation* 94:992–1002

92. Reinecke H, Studer R, Vetter R, Holtz J, Drexler H. 1996. Cardiac Na^+/Ca^{2+} exchange activity in patients with end-stage heart failure. *Cardiovasc. Res.* 31:48–54

93. Dipla K, Mattiello JA, Margulies KB, Jeevanandam V, Houser SR. 1999. The sarcoplasmic reticulum and the Na^+/Ca^{2+} exchanger both contribute to the Ca^{2+} transient of failing human ventricular myocytes. *Circ. Res.* 84:435–44

94. O'Rourke B, Kass DA, Tomaselli GF, Kaab S, Tunin R, et al. 1999. Mechanisms of altered excitation-contraction coupling in canine tachycardia-induced heart failure, I: experimental studies. *Circ. Res.* 84:562–70

95. Pogwizd SM, Qi M, Yuan W, Samarel AM, Bers DM. 1999. Upregulation of Na/Ca exchanger expression and function in an arrhythmogenic rabbit model of heart failure. *Circ. Res.* In press

96. Winslow RL, Rice J, Jafri S, Marban E, O'Rourke B. 1999. Mechanisms of altered excitation-contraction coupling in canine tachycardia-induced heart failure, II: model studies. *Circ. Res.* 84:571–86

97. Artman M, Ichikawa H, Avkiran M, Coetzee WA. 1995. Na^+/Ca^{2+} exchange current density in cardiac myocytes from rabbits and guinea pigs during postnatal development. *Am. J. Physiol.* 37:H1714–22

98. Vetter R, Studer R, Reinecke H, Kolar F, Ostadalova I, et al. 1995. Reciprocal changes in the postnatal expression of the sarcolemmal Na^+-Ca^{2+} exchanger and SERCA2 in rat heart. *J. Mol. Cell Cardiol.* 27:1689–701

99. Chen F, Mottino G, Shin VY, Frank JS. 1997. Subcellular distribution of ankyrin in developing rabbit heart–relationship to the Na^+-Ca^{2+} exchanger. *J. Mol. Cell Cardiol.* 29:2621–29

100. Haddock PS, Coetzee WA, Artman M. 1997. Na^+/Ca^{2+} exchange current and contractions measured under Cl^- free conditions in developing rabbit hearts. *Am. J. Physiol.* 273:H837–46

101. Koban MU, Moorman AF, Holtz J, Yacoub MH, Boheler KR. 1998. Expressional analysis of the cardiac Na-Ca exchanger in rat development and senescence. *Cardiovasc. Res.* 37:405–23

102. Iwata T, Galli C, Dainese P, Guerini D, Carafoli E. 1995. The 70 Kd component of the heart sarcolemmal Na^+/Ca^{2+}-exchanger preparation is the C-terminal portion of the protein. *Cell Calcium* 17:263–69

103. Lipp P, Schwaller B, Niggli E. 1995. Specific inhibition of Na-Ca exchange function by antisense oligodeoxynucleotides. *FEBS Lett.* 364:198–202

104. Slodzinski MK, Blaustein MP. 1998. Na^+/Ca^{2+} exchange in neonatal rat heart cells: antisense inhibition and protein half-life. *Am. J. Physiol.* 275:C459–67

105. Slodzinski MK, Blaustein MP. 1998. Physiological effects of Na^+/Ca^{2+} exchanger knockdown by antisense oligodeoxynucleotides in arterial myocytes. *Am. J. Physiol.* 275:C251–59

106. Van Eylen F, Lebeau C, Albuquerque-Silva J, Herchuelz A. 1998. Contribution of Na/Ca exchange to Ca^{2+} outflow and entry in the rat pancreatic beta-cell: studies with antisense oligonucleotides. *Diabetes* 47:1873–80

107. White KE, Gesek FA, Reilly RF, Friedman PA. 1998. NCX1 Na/Ca exchanger inhibition by antisense oligonucleotides in mouse distal convoluted tubule cells. *Kidney Int.* 54:897–906

108. Adachi-Akahane S, Lu L, Li Z, Frank JS, Philipson KD, et al. 1997. Calcium signaling in transgenic mice overexpressing cardiac Na^+-Ca^{2+} exchanger. *J. Gen. Physiol.* 109:717–29

109. Terracciano CM, Souza AI, Philipson KD, MacLeod KT. 1998. Na^+-Ca^{2+} exchange and sarcoplasmic reticular Ca^{2+} regulation in ventricular myocytes from transgenic mice overexpressing the

Na$^+$-Ca^{2+} exchanger. *J. Physiol.* 512: 651–67

110. Yao A, Su Z, Nonaka A, Zubair I, Lu L, et al. 1998. Effects of overexpression of the Na$^+$-Ca^{2+} exchanger on [Ca^{2+}]$_i$ transients in murine ventricular myocytes. *Circ. Res.* 82:657–65

111. Cross HR, Lu L, Steenbergen C, Philipson KD, Murphy E. 1998. Overexpression of the cardiac Na$^+$/Ca^{2+} exchanger increases susceptibility to ischemia/reperfusion injury in male, but not female, transgenic mice. *Circ. Res.* 83:1215–23

Annu. Rev. Physiol. 2000. 62:135–55

THE EVOLUTIONARY PHYSIOLOGY OF ANIMAL FLIGHT: Paleobiological and Present Perspectives

Robert Dudley

Section of Integrative Biology, University of Texas, Austin, Texas, 78712 and Smithsonian Tropical Research Institute, P.O. Box 2072, Balboa, Republic of Panama; e-mail: r_dudley@utxvms.cc.utexas.edu

Key Words   evolution, gigantism, hyperoxia, insect, oxygen

■ **Abstract**   Recent geophysical analyses suggest the presence of a late Paleozoic oxygen pulse beginning in the late Devonian and continuing through to the late Carboniferous. During this period, plant terrestrialization and global carbon deposition resulted in a dramatic increase in atmospheric oxygen levels, ultimately yielding concentrations potentially as high as 35% relative to the contemporary value of 21%. Such hyperoxia of the late Paleozoic atmosphere may have physiologically facilitated the initial evolution of insect flight metabolism. Widespread gigantism in late Paleozoic insects and other arthropods is also consistent with enhanced oxygen flux within diffusion-limited tracheal systems. Because total atmospheric pressure increases with increased oxygen partial pressure, concurrently hyperdense conditions would have augmented aerodynamic force production in early forms of flying insects. By the late Permian, evolution of decompositional microbial and fungal communities, together with disequilibrium in rates of carbon deposition, gradually reduced oxygen concentrations to values possibly as low as 15%. The disappearance of giant insects by the end of the Permian is consistent with extinction of these taxa for reasons of asphyxiation on a geological time scale. As with winged insects, the multiple historical origins of vertebrate flight in the late Jurassic and Cretaceous correlate temporally with periods of elevated atmospheric oxygen. Much discussion of flight performance in *Archaeopteryx* assumes a contemporary atmospheric composition. Elevated oxygen levels in the mid- to late Mesozoic would, however, have facilitated aerodynamic force production and enhanced muscle power output for ancestral birds, as well as for precursors to bats and pterosaurs.

INTRODUCTION

Today's oxidizing atmosphere, with an oxygen concentration of about 21%, derives in part from the metabolic activity of photosynthetic organisms. Starting with the anoxic conditions and reducing atmosphere of the Archean and early Proterozoic eons, evolution of cyanobacteria, sulfide-oxidizing bacteria, and algae contributed to buildup of oxygen partial pressures by the beginning of the Cambrian (570 MYa) to values likely comparable to those of the present day (1–6). Increased atmospheric oxygen, in turn, may have been an important factor underlying radiations of metazoan taxa in the late Proterozoic and at the base of the Cambrian (7–14). The paleobiological significance of Proterozoic oxygen levels for animal evolution in aquatic habitats has long been recognized, as has been the role of gradual oxygen buildup for subsequent evolution of plant and animal terrestrial communities (6, 8, 9). Less well-studied, however, are potential fluctuations in atmospheric constituents through the course of the Phanerozoic.

In particular, variation in oxygen partial pressure and concomitant variation in air density potentially influence the physiology and biomechanics, respectively, of animal flight performance. Geophysical analyses suggest the presence of a late Paleozoic oxygen pulse beginning in the late Devonian and continuing through to the late Carboniferous. Oxygen concentrations ranged possibly as high as 35% during the initial period of insect flight evolution (late Devonian or early Carboniferous). Atmospheric hyperoxia may thus have physiologically facilitated the initial evolution of insect flight metabolism. Because total atmospheric pressure increases with an increased oxygen partial pressure, concurrently hyperdense conditions would have augmented aerodynamic force production in ancestral winged insects. The multiple historical origins of vertebrate flight similarly appear to correlate temporally with periods of hyperoxia. In particular, elevated oxygen levels in the mid- to late Mesozoic may have facilitated aerodynamic force production and enhanced muscle metabolism for ancestral birds, as well as for precursors to bats and pterosaurs. Because of such implications for the evolution of animal flight performance, discussion of the mechanisms underlying substantial variation in composition of the earth's atmosphere is warranted.

PHANEROZOIC VARIATION IN THE EARTH'S ATMOSPHERE

The physical properties of the earth's atmosphere are determined almost exclusively by two major constituents, namely diatomic oxygen and diatomic nitrogen. Nitrogen content of the atmosphere is thought to have been approximately constant through geological time (15–17), although some variation in this constituent may derive through biotic linkages with the atmospheric pool (CD Nevison, unpublished data). Various models for oxygen content of the atmosphere in Phanerozoic times have suggested major fluctuations that are driven biotically (6, 8, 13, 16, 19, 20). In particular, geochemical modeling (21, 22) suggests a late Paleozoic disequilibrium between the rate of carbon fixation by terrestrial plants and the rate at which this fixed material was decomposed and recycled. Through the mid- to end-Devonian (390–362 MYa), this disequilibrium led to a moderate increase in oxygen concentration from 18 to 20%, followed by a more substantial rise by the end of the Carboniferous (290 MYa) to remarkable values as high as 35% (see Figure 1). Thereafter, an equally pronounced decline resulted in end-Permian and early Triassic values as low as 15%. Relative to the present atmospheric level of 21% (PAL), such hyperoxic and subsequently hypoxic conditions must have had major biological effects during the Paleozoic (23–26). Moreover, atmospheric hyperoxia may also have characterized portions of the Mesozoic. According to the aforementioned geochemical model (21), a secondary rise in oxygen levels characterized the the mid-Jurassic and the Cretaceous (170–65 MYa), with oxygen concentration increasing to 25 to 30% and then declining to PAL only by the end-Tertiary (Figure 1). Such postulated changes in oxygen concentration are at sharp odds with any uniformitarian perspective of atmospheric composition.

The various assumptions underlying reconstruction of ancient atmospheric composition obviously require examination. Current models for Phanerozoic oxygen and carbon dioxide concentrations (21, 27–29) are based on estimates of the exchange rates of fixed and reduced carbon among atmospheric, oceanic, and sedimentary reservoirs. Variation in rates of carbon exchange is driven primarily by the effects of plant terrestrialization, variable rates of organic carbon deposition and decomposition, and changes in continental weathering (20, 22, 30–32). An additional feedback loop potentially influencing atmospheric oxygen levels involves marine phosphorus (33, 34). Because the relative importance of these different mechanisms can be, in many cases, only broadly constrained, considerable uncertainty must be associated with such efforts that model global geochemical cycles. Of particular relevance to the late Paleozoic atmosphere,

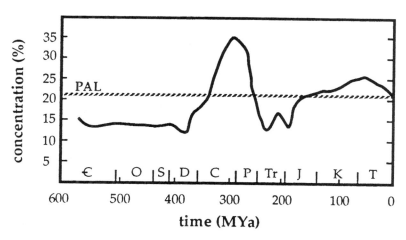

Figure 1   Estimate of atmospheric oxygen concentrations through the Phanerozoic (21). PAL: present atmospheric level (20.95%).

however, are the changes necessarily associated with the global phenomenon of terrestrialization by plants. During this process, photosynthetic production of oxygen became decoupled from breakdown of fixed carbon. An ensuing decompositional bottleneck, due apparently to the absence of biotic processes leading to rapid breakdown, resulted in extensive deposition of coal and other carbonates. Subsequent evolution by the mid-Permian of microbial decomposers, in particular fungi, then depleted atmospheric oxygen via decay processes and inhibited further carbon accumulation (20, 31, 35). Biological underpinnings to a late Paleozoic oxygen pulse are thus well-grounded, although more precise estimates of excursions in atmospheric carbon dioxide and oxygen await further investigation.

Constraints on fire processes can be used to evaluate the validity of geophysical reconstructions of ancient atmospheres. The models of atmospheric oxygen considered here suggest concentrations approaching but not exceeding 35%, a value that represents an approximate threshold for sustained combustion of the terrestrial biosphere (36, 37). Proliferation of terrestrial ecosystems would clearly be precluded under such circumstances, and analysis of charcoal deposits and of the vegetational fossil record demonstrates that atmospheric oxygen concentrations have not exceeded this upper bound (38). At the lower extreme, the minimum oxygen concentration required for contemporary natural fuels to ignite is about 13% (36, 39); the regular presence of charcoal in the fossil record suggests that atmospheric oxygen never fell below this level (40–42). Methodologically, it is important to realize that ignition of homogeneous woody or paper materials in modern laboratory contexts is not functionally equivalent to the propagation of fire in natural ecosystems. Extrapolation of experimental results with contemporary fuels to the prediction of fire regimes in Paleozoic vegetation is necessarily imprecise, although some inference is possible (34). In sum, these considerations suggest that atmospheric oxygen levels have been historically constrained between 13 and 35%; the best estimate derived from atmospheric modeling (15–35%; Reference 21) is nominally congruent with this range.

No direct indicator is available to test empirically these predictions for ancient levels of atmospheric oxygen. However, diverse geochemical and isotopic evidence is consistent with substantial late Permian declines in both marine and atmospheric oxygen concentrations, declines that likely contributed to the end-Permian extinction event (43–51). Furthermore, atmospheric models incorporating effects of plant terrestrialization suggest substantial changes in the concentration of carbon dioxide. Both modeling and empirical observations demonstrate an approximate 10-fold reduction in carbon dioxide from the mid- to late Paleozoic (22, 27–29, 53–56). For plants, the physiological effects of this drawdown in carbon dioxide are evident in paleontological analyses of stomatal density and other proxies of photosynthetic activity (56–58). Shortcomings of atmospheric modeling notwithstanding, a diversity of empirical evidence is consistent both with carbon dioxide drawdown and with an oxygen pulse in the mid- to late Paleozoic, and with enhanced levels of oxygen in the mid- to late Mesozoic and in much of the Cenozoic.

THE ORIGINS OF ANIMAL FLIGHT

Powered flapping flight evolved independently four times during the Phanerozoic, once in the insects and three times among vertebrates. Evolutionary origins of all volant taxa remain controversial, but both insects and the three taxa of flying vertebrates may have originated during periods of atmospheric hyperoxia. Flight is both biomechanically and physiologically demanding, and the evolution of flight requires dramatic up-regulation of metabolic capacity in addition to the expression of flapping structures that generate useful aerodynamic forces. Although wings are not homologous between insects and volant vertebrates, common physical mechanisms of flight suggest that historically elevated concentrations of atmospheric oxygen have yielded similar aerodynamic consequences during flight evolution.

Wings and Aerodynamic Force Production

Fundamental to force generation by flapping animal wings is the physical nature of the medium to which the wings transfer momentum (59). Air density, the mass of air per unit volume, is a principal determinant of force production by airfoils, biological and otherwise; aerodynamic forces on structures tend to increase linearly with air density. Also, air responds to applied forces by resisting not deformation but rather the rate of deformation, as determined by the viscosity or the internal resistance to flow. For an object such as a wing moving in a fluid, the ensuing reaction force acting parallel to the direction of movement is termed drag. Presence of the wing removes momentum and thus kinetic energy from the moving fluid system, and acts to slow the wing relative to flow. This pressure drag, also known as inertial drag, derives from disruption of the inertial characteristics of the moving flow field and varies with fluid density, relative fluid velocity, and the wing's shape.

Viscous drag, by contrast, emerges from boundary interactions between the wing and the surrounding fluid. Viscosity ensures resistance to flow between adjacent layers of fluid, engendering shear forces within the boundary layer over the wing and imposing a reaction force throughout the fluid that terminates at the wing's surface. Viscous drag thus varies not with density but with fluid viscosity, the relative fluid velocity, and the total wetted surface area of the wing. Pressure and viscous drag have in common a dependence on relative fluid velocity and on object dimensions, but differ fundamentally in their dependence on fluid density and viscosity, respectively. The ratio of inertial to viscous forces on an object moving within a fluid will therefore vary with the ratio of density and viscosity, and must additionally change with object dimensions and its relative velocity. The simplest dimensionless formulation of these four parameters is the Reynolds number (Re), which is proportional to the ratio of inertial to viscous forces that act on objects moving within fluids. Different situations of fluid flow are physically equivalent if the corresponding Res are approximately the same. In contrast, variation in either the density or viscosity of a fluid alters the relative magnitude of inertial and viscous forces.

Just as drag is the force parallel to flow around an object, lift is defined as the component of force orthogonal to flow and thus perpendicular to drag in a two-dimensional perspective. For wings at low angles of attack, air flows smoothly over both dorsal and ventral wing surfaces. Because pressure drag of well-designed airfoils is low, momentum extraction from the flow field is minimized. The positive camber of the wing and the downward deflection of air near the trailing wing edge yield slightly different translational velocities for the dorsal and ventral airstreams–airflow is slightly faster above and slower beneath the airfoil. Bernoulli's Principle indicates that this difference in dorsal and ventral airstream velocities results in a pressure gradient; a net force (i.e. lift) acts dorsally upon the wing. In a cross-sectional perspective, air appears to move anteriorly from the ventral to dorsal wing surface and to yield a net rotational movement of air around the wing. This motion of air is equivalent to a rotating flow field or vortex that circulates around the wing and that is centered about the wing itself. For every bound wing vortex, a starting vortex of comparable magnitude but of opposite sense is shed into the wake, ensuring conservation of angular momentum in the fluid.

The physical origin of lift thus lies within the creation of net air circulation about a translating wing. As a wing translates in space, the pressure gradient underlying lift production yields airflow not only around spanwise wing sections (the bound circulation), but also around the wing tip, creating the so-called tip vortex. The tip vortex is linked to the starting and the bound wing vortices and creates a closed vortex loop that exerts a momentum flux on the surrounding air. The downward momentum induced by the presence of the vortex loop is accordingly proportional to the mass of the air moved ventrally (i.e. to the air density) and to the velocity at which the air moves (i.e. the circulation). Lift production thus increases with increased air density (59). The Re at which a wing is operating also exerts a strong influence on lift production. Under highly viscous circumstances, vortex generation becomes more difficult as intermolecular stickiness progressively impedes rotational motions of airflow. Circulatory lift becomes increasingly more difficult to maintain at low Re, whereas the effects of viscous drag also become more pronounced. The lift:drag ratio must then decrease at lower Re, as confirmed empirically for insect and vertebrate wings (60, 61).

Lifting characteristics of wings are thus strongly dependent on both air density and the Re at which they operate. Concomitant with large-scale changes in oxygen concentration during the Phanerozoic, numerous physical characteristics of air must vary if, as suggested previously, nitrogen content of the atmosphere remains constant (23). Parameters such as heat capacity of air, thermal conductivity, diffusivity, and the speed of sound would all have substantially changed under hyperoxic conditions. Of particular interest for the evolution of animal flight is the possibility of density-mediated increases in aerodynamic performance during initial periods of wing evolution (23, 25). The predicted value of air density at the peak of the late Paleozoic oxygen pulse (285 MYa) is about 1.56 kg/m^3, an increase of 29% relative to the present sea-level value of 1.21 kg/m^3. The relative changes in the viscosity of air are, by contrast, much smaller (23). Winglets or proto-wings moving in hyperoxic atmospheres would thus experience a higher air density and would be moving at a comparably increased *Re*. Both conditions would have facilitated lift production in early flying forms, although the magnitude of these aerodynamic effects would have varied both with morphological features and with the particular wing and body motions of the taxon concerned. Because insect and vertebrate wings are so distinct both ontogenetically and anatomically, origins of flight in the two groups are considered separately.

Origins of Flight in Insects

The evolution of insect flight, a major event in biotic history, can be correlationally linked to atmospheric hyperoxia. The origins of winged (pterygote) insects are indeterminate but probably lie in the Upper Devonian or early Lower Carboniferous. Wingless hexapods are known from 395–390 MYa (62–65), whereas fossils of pterygote hexapods (i.e. winged insects) date from approximately 325 MYa (66, 67). By the Upper Carboniferous, pterygotes are impressively diversified into about fifteen orders (68–71). Although pterygote insects are likely monophyletic (72–78), the morphological origins of wings remain obscure. Wings have been proposed to derive either from fixed paranotal outgrowths of thoracic and abdominal segments in terrestrial taxa (79–86), or from ancestrally mobile gills, gill covers, leg structures, or styli in aquatic forms (87–95). Unfortunately, no transitional forms are known between the wingless apterygotes and the winged pterygote insects, and the biology of early protopterygote forms remains speculative and contentious. Of particular interest to the origins of flight is ancestral habitat association of protopterygotes—were these animals terrestrial or aquatic?

Most evidence, particularly that relating to the physiology and origins of the insect tracheal system, indicates that winged insects are derived from terrestrial apterygote ancestors (61, 96–99). Aquatic larvae, particularly those of the extant and phylogenetically basal Odonata and Ephemeroptera, appear to be secondarily derived (73, 99, 100). Independent of habitat association, however, both larvae and adults of ancestral winged insects probably expressed lateral lobed structures on the abdominal as well as the thoracic segments (68, 90, 101–103). If winglets or wings derived initially from fixed paranotal lobes, flapping motions might have emerged indirectly through action of dorsoventral leg muscles that insert on the thorax, as characterizes so-called bifunctional muscles in many extant insects (104–108). A general question relating to wing origins concerns the possible evolution of novel wing-like structures, as opposed to modification of pre-existing morphological features (85). Acquisition of wings from ancestrally mobile structures might seem more parsimonious than the derivation of flapping wings from stationary paranotal lobes, although the neontological and paleontological data available at present are insufficient to decide unequivocally between these two hypotheses (61).

A variety of possible functional roles have been attributed to winglets or wings of protopterygotes, including aerodynamic utility, epigamic display during courtship, and thermoregulation (109–115). Hydrodynamic use for what ultimately became aerodynamic structures has been proposed for ancestrally aquatic protopterygotes, as have been possibly amphibious lifestyles (116, 117). Protopterygotes could also have used wing-like structures in air either to drift passively or to skim actively along water surfaces, as do many extant insect taxa (118–122). This behavior is probably a derived rather than a retained ancestral trait of winged insects (61, 123, 124). Although improbable for reasons outlined above, biomechanical considerations suggest that aquatic protopterygotes would have been unlikely to evolve wings that served aerodynamic functions. Water and air differ by almost three orders of magnitude in density, with a corresponding difference in the Re and in the nature of forces generated by oscillating structures. The functionality of wing designs intermediate to either hydrodynamic or aerodynamic force generation is correspondingly unclear (61). Forces of surface tension would present a formidable physical barrier to partial body emergence as well as to projection and oscillation of flattened structures, particularly for the body sizes (2–4 cm) likely characteristic of ancestral pterygotes (64, 125, 126).

Given the assumption of terrestrial pterygote ancestors, a standard explanation for the evolution of wings has been that these structures aerodynamically facilitate jumping escapes from predators on land. Suggestively, a suite of morphological and behavioral protoadaptations for jump-mediated glides are evident among extant apterygote hexapods, the terrestrial sister taxon of the winged insects. Thoracic paranotal lobes as well as styli on the legs and abdominal segments of extant apterygotes could potentially have served in ancestral taxa to generate lift and to facilitate saltatorial escape (61). Neurobiological studies also support the ancestral presence of dedicated sensorimotor pathways underlying escape behavior in both apterygotes and pterygotes (127–129). The startle response of ancestral apterygote insects was then apparently co-opted during pterygote evolution to stimulate jumping, wing flapping, and even evasive flight once airborne (130–137). The historical context of early pterygote evolution was appropriate for imposition of intense predatory pressure by both invertebrates and vertebrates, with a diversity of insectivorous arthropods (particularly arachnids), amphibians, and reptiles found in Devonian and Carboniferous terrestrial ecosystems (138–142). Various morphological characteristics evident among the early Upper Carboniferous entomofauna are also consistent with the hypothesis of predatory defense (141, 143, 144).

Furthermore, the increasing arborescence and geometrical complexity of terrestrial vegetation through the Devonian and into the Carboniferous would have provided a three-dimensional substrate suitable for jumping escapes and ultimately the evolution of flight in protopterygotes (145). Terrestrial vegetation during the period of pterygote origins was composed of fern-like lycopsids and psilopsids, together with arborescent lycopods, sphenopsids, and progymnosperms (146–150). Lateral jumps from branches or leaves, and particularly jumps directed downward, would have yielded the increased translational velocities necessary for substantial buildup of lift on both thoracic and abdominal projections. Access to nutritional resources, appropriate microhabitats, and suitable oviposition sites would have been facilitated by such an increased capacity for three-dimensional movements. Increased feeding on plants would have been one outcome of enhanced mobility. For example, non-insect hexapods (e.g. Collembola) that feed on living plant tissue are rare, whereas approximately 85% of extant insect species are phytophagous at some stage in their life cycle (151). Most tellingly, the fossil record confirms feeding on plants by insects in the Upper Carboniferous and early Permian (152–154).

Given this paleobiological background to wing evolution in insects, it is instructive to consider two distinct features of atmospheric hyperoxia that may have contributed to the evolution of flight. Biomechanically, the greater density of a hyperoxic atmosphere would yield enhanced aerodynamic characteristics of both winglets and the bodies of protopterygotes. Alternatively phrased, less winglet area would be necessary to generate comparable forces if air density were higher, although the magnitude of this effect is strongly dependent on the nature of vortex production around the body and winglets and on the relative air velocity and/or acceleration during takeoffs. Aerodynamic forces on both the body and winglets of protopterygotes would enhance aerial escape during either jumping or steady-state glides (115, 125, 155). The de facto increase in Re associated with increased air density may furthermore have contributed to greater lift production by winglets, particularly for the low aspect ratio wings and Re relevant to pterygote evolution (61, 156). In contrast to theories of wing evolution that require aquatic protopterygotes and a discontinuous selection regime across the air-water interface, escape jumping in terrestrial protopterygotes would from the outset favor gradual and continuous improvement in lift generation. Winglet mobility would then enhance force production, and additionally could be used to control body orientation during flight and while landing (109, 125, 157, 158). Increased air density and higher Re would have been advantageous in any evolutionary scenario involving lift production by winglets or wings. Greater air densities may also have facilitated flight in progressively larger taxa, leading to the giant pterygotes of the late Paleozoic, as discussed below (61, 159).

Physiologically, an increased oxygen content of the late Paleozoic atmosphere would have favored higher and ever more sustained levels of the oxidative metabolism required for flight. As wing flapping became more rapid and of greater amplitude, the energetic costs of flight would have increased substantially; thoracic muscles of extant insects in flight exhibit the highest mass-specific rates of oxygen consumption known for any locomotor tissue (61, 160, 161). This demand for oxygen is met by the air-filled tracheal system, a branching network of cuticular tubes that functions primarily through gaseous diffusion rather than by convective air movement (162–165). Both diffusion and tracheal convection represent potentially rate-limiting steps in insect respiration, although the much reduced thoracic diameters of small insects (e.g. *Drosophila*) probably alleviate any metabolically based need for active ventilation of the tracheal system. In larger insects, however, diffusional limits on oxygen supply likely constrain maximum body size. For example, flight metabolic rates in an extant dragonfly species vary directly with ambient oxygen concentration (166), a result consistent with diffusion-limited oxygen delivery by the tracheal system. In the late Paleozoic, diffusion of oxygen to the respiring flight muscles would obviously have been enhanced by greater partial pressures of this gas, as well as by the increased diffusion constants associated with an increased total pressure of the atmosphere (25).

Moreover, a spectacular bioindicator of atmospheric hyperoxia is provided by gigantism among late Paleozoic terrestrial arthropods (23, 25, 26). Gigantism in the Carboniferous and Permian was characteristic of many arthropod taxa, including a number of phylogenetically unrelated pterygote orders (141, 167, 168) as well as apterygote insects (169) and other arthropods, including diplopods, arthropleurids, and arachnids (138, 141, 170–172). Although a number of non-mutually exclusive selective forces may have contributed to the evolution of gigantism (90, 141, 173), relaxation of diffusional constraints on maximum body size through atmospheric hyperoxia seems to be the most parsimonious explanation for this phenomenon (19, 23, 25, 174, 175). Necessarily global effects of hyperoxia on animal physiology were thus manifested in the form of dramatically increased body size in diverse arthropod lineages. Furthermore, all giant arthropod taxa of the late Paleozoic went extinct by mid- to end-Permian (23, 25, 168), as would be predicted by the concomitant decline in atmospheric oxygen concentration. Also consistent with the hypothesis linking atmospheric oxygen and diffusional constraints on insect body size is a secondary peak of gigantism (e.g. among mayflies) in the Cretaceous at a time of elevated oxygen concentrations (25, 168). Systematic analysis of Paleozoic gigantism has been precluded to date because of generally poor fossil preservation and incomplete knowledge of interspecific body size distributions. However, detailed analysis of phyletic size change within diffusion-limited taxa does represent an important bioassay for possible effects of atmospheric hyperoxia in the late Paleozoic and the Cretaceous/Tertiary.

Origins of Vertebrate Flight

As with winged insects, the historical origins of flying vertebrates are known only imprecisely. Nonetheless, circumstantial evidence is at least consistent with origins of bats, birds, and pterosaurs during times of hyperdense and hyperoxic atmospheres. The most recent of volant vertebrates are the bats, with a modern morphology apparent in a microchiropteran fossil from 50 MYa. Given this date, chiropteran origins would appear to lie within the early Paleocene or late Cretaceous (176, 177). A similar appearance during hyperoxic times seems likely for birds in the mid- to late Jurassic (178–180). The timing of pterosaur origination and early diversification is unknown but possibly lies within the Permian given well-developed pterosaur morphologies by the mid- to late Triassic (181, 182). Because a detailed fossil record is unavailable for any of these three taxa, biomechanical analysis of the transitional forms of flight is seriously constrained. Independent of the behavioral or ecological context of flight, however, greater atmospheric density would facilitate aerodynamic force production, whereas increased oxygen partial pressures would similarly enhance oxygen transport to and within the muscles powering flight. Aforementioned discussions of vertebrate flight origins generally assume atmospheric composition of the present day, although the implications of flight evolution in physically variable atmospheres clearly deserve further attention. In a similar vein, reconstructions of ancestral flight physiology that are based on comparisons with extant taxa (183–185) may not fully reflect aerial performance of now extinct taxa in hyperoxic and hyperdense atmospheres.

Most scenarios of vertebrate flight evolution presume jumping takeoffs (directed either with or against gravity), whereas jump-initiated gliding origins of flight are biomechanically more parsimonious than "ground-up" hypotheses for both volant vertebrates and insects (60, 61, 186–188). Jumping via a startle response is widespread among animals (189), and one potential commonality among volant vertebrates and pterygote insects is acquisition of active flight via the pathway of jumping and subsequent gliding to escape predation. Also, unsteady aerodynamic performance during the accelerating portion of a jump may be of greater relevance to escape success than steady-state glides (61). Jump-initiated glides that increased survivorship during predation attempts would potentially select for greater aerodynamic performance, an effect likely to be enhanced at the higher *Re* of hyperdense air. That predation is a major factor underlying the evolution of aerial locomotion is suggested by the increased longevity of flying animals relative to their non-volant counterparts. For example, volant endotherms have mortality rates significantly lower than those for non-volant endotherms of equivalent body mass (190–193). Paleophysiological simulations of jumping performance can be carried out in extant gliding and flying taxa using variable-density gas mixtures (194), and potentially can be used to investigate the ancestral role of jumping and takeoff aerodynamics in flight evolution.

CONCLUSIONS AND IMPLICATIONS

Modeling, isotopic and geochemical data, and indirect biological indicators suggest major historical changes in atmospheric composition, particularly during the late Paleozoic but also in the late Mesozoic and Tertiary. Periods of atmospheric hyperoxia can be correlationally linked with the late Paleozoic origin of flight in insects and with contemporaneous arthropod gigantism and can be more tentatively associated with the origin of flight in three vertebrate lineages. Causal association between periods of hyperoxia and the appearance of flight resides at two levels: biomechanical enhancement of aerodynamic force production through increases in air density and the *Re,* and physiological facilitation of the oxygen flux required to sustain high rates of flight metabolism. In and of themselves, increased oxygen concentrations did not act directly on particular phenotypes or behaviors. Instead, a new selective background of slowly increasing oxygen concentrations provided the opportunity (but not necessity) for the evolution and progressive enhancement of a novel locomotor capacity (26).

Falsification of such historical hypotheses is necessarily challenging, but neontological investigations of animal flight performance provide a useful perspective on paleobiological reconstructions. Postulated air densities and oxygen concentrations of ancient atmospheres can be mimicked experimentally using different combinations of oxygen and nonreactive gases (194). Similar gas mixtures can be used to investigate the effects of atmospheric hyperoxia on the biomechanics and physiology of flight in extant volant forms. Phenotypic plasticity in the respiratory system of insects (195–197) and vertebrates (198–204) suggests widespread occurrence of ontogenetic as well as short-term and chronic physiological flexibility in response to variable oxygen availability. Over evolutionary time scales, artificial selection for enhanced flight performance in *Drosophila* (205) can be imposed in different gas mixtures that decouple the effects of hyperoxia from those associated with a hyperdense flight medium (25, 194).

In modern ecological contexts, variation in altitude provides the closest analogue to historic variation in atmospheric composition. Covariance in air density and oxygen partial pressure characterizes altitudinal gradients, as would similarly characterize atmospheres with varying oxygen content and a constant quantity of nitrogen. Modern volant taxa display remarkable flight abilities under both hypoxic and hypodense conditions (61, 206–209). In natural montane contexts, wing length of birds and insects varies directly with altitude, suggesting morphological compensation for the greater power expenditure during flight at lower air densities (194, 210–213). The wide range of extant adaptations to variation in air density and oxygen availability suggests substantial evolutionary capacity to respond to variable atmospheric composition. Although considerable uncertainty still surrounds paleoatmospheric reconstructions, further study of animal flight performance in simulated ancient atmospheres is likely to prove rewarding.

ACKNOWLEDGMENTS

I thank Doug Altshuler, Bob Berner, Carl Gans, and Tim Lenton for useful comments, and acknowledge grants from the National Science Foundation for research support.

Visit the Annual Reviews home page at www.AnnualReviews.org.

LITERATURE CITED

1. Hudson JD. 1989. Palaeoatmospheres in the Phanerozoic. *J. Geol. Soc. London* 146:155–60
2. Lambert IB, Donnelly TH. 1991. Atmospheric oxygen levels in the Precambrian: a review of isotopic and geological evidence. *Palaeogeogr. Palaeoclimatol. Palaeoecol.* 97:83–91
3. Des Marais DJ, Strauss H, Summons RE, Hayes, JM. 1992. Carbon isotope evidence for the stepwise oxidation of the Proterozoic environment. *Nature* 359:605–9
4. Knoll AH. 1992. The early evolution of eukaryotes: a geological perspective. *Science* 256:622–27
5. Canfield DE, Teske A. 1996. Late Proterozoic rise in atmospheric oxygen concentration inferred from phylogenetic and sulphur-isotope studies. *Nature* 382:127–32
6. Gilbert DL. 1996. Evolutionary aspects of atmospheric oxygen and organisms. In *Environmental Physiology,* ed. MJ Fregly, CM Blatteis, 2:1059–94. New York: Oxford Univ. Press
7. Nursall JR. 1959. Oxygen as a prerequisite to the origin of Metazoa. *Nature* 183:1170–72
8. Berkner LV, Marshall LC. 1965. On the origin and rise of oxygen concentration in the Earth's atmosphere. *J. Atmos. Sci.* 22:225–61
9. Berkner LV, Marshall LC. 1967. The rise of oxygen in the earth's atmosphere with notes on the martian atmosphere. *Adv. Geophys.* 12:309–31
10. Knoll AH, Hayes JM, Kaufman AJ, Swett K, Lambert, IB. 1986. Secular variation in carbon isotope ratios from Upper Proterozoic successions of Svalbard and East Greenland. *Nature* 321:832–38
11. Conway Morris S. 1993. The fossil record and the early evolution of the Metazoa. *Nature* 361:219–25
12. Kasting JF, Holland HD, Kump LR. 1992. Atmospheric evolution: the rise of oxygen. In *The Proterozoic Biosphere. A Multidisciplinary Study,* ed. JW Schopf, C Klein, pp. 159–63. New York: Cambridge Univ. Press
13. Kasting JF. 1993. Earth's early atmosphere. *Science* 259:920–26
14. Logan GA, Hayes JM, Hieshima GB, Summons RE. 1995. Terminal Proterozoic reorganization of biogeochemical cycles. *Nature* 376:53–56
15. Holland HD. 1984. *The Chemical Evolution of the Atmosphere and Oceans.* Princeton, NJ: Princeton Univ. Press
16. Budyko MI, Ronov AB, Yanshin AL. 1985. *History of the Earth's Atmosphere.* Berlin: Springer-Verlag
17. Schlesinger WH. 1991. *Biogeochemistry: An Analysis of Global Change.* San Diego: Academic
18. Deleted in proof
19. Tappan H. 1974. Molecular oxygen and evolution. In *Molecular Oxygen in Biology,* ed. O. Hayaishi, pp. 81–135. Amsterdam: North Holland
20. Robinson JM. 1991. Phanerozoic atmospheric reconstructions: a terrestrial perspective. *Palaeogeogr. Palaeoclimatol. Palaeoecol.* 97:51–62
21. Berner RA, Canfield DE. 1989. A new model for atmospheric oxygen over Phanerozoic time. *Am. J. Sci.* 289:333–61
22. Berner RA. 1998. The carbon cycle and CO_2 over Phanerozoic time: the role of land plants. *Philos. Trans. R. Soc. London Ser. B* 353:75–82
23. Graham JB, Dudley R, Aguilar N, Gans C. 1995. Implications of the late Palaeozoic oxygen pulse for physiology and evolution. *Nature* 375:117–20

24. Graham JB, Aguilar N, Dudley R, Gans, C. 1997. The late Paleozoic atmosphere and the ecological and evolutionary physiology of tetrapods. In *Amniote Origins: Completing the Transition to Land,* ed. SS Sumida, KLM Martin, pp. 141–67. New York: Academic

25. Dudley R. 1998. Atmospheric oxygen, giant Paleozoic insects and the evolution of aerial locomotor performance. *J. Exp. Biol.* 201:1043–50

26. Gans C, Dudley, R, Aguilar NM, Graham JB. 1999. Late Paleozoic atmospheres and biotic evolution. *Hist. Biol.* 13:199–219

27. Berner RA. 1990. Atmospheric carbon dioxide levels over Phanerozoic time. *Science* 249:1382–85

28. Berner RA. 1994. GEOCARB II: a revised model of atmospheric CO_2 over Phanerozoic time. *Am. J. Sci.* 294:56–91

29. Berner RA. 1997. The rise of plants and their effect on weathering and atmospheric CO_2. *Science* 276:544–46

30. Mackenzie FT, Morse JW. 1992. Sedimentary carbonates through Phanerozoic time. *Geochim. Cosmochim. Acta* 56:3281–95

31. Visscher H, Brinkhuis H, Dilcher DL, Elsik WC, Eshet Y, et al. 1996. The terminal Paleozoic fungal event: evidence of terrestrial ecosystem destabilization and collapse. *Proc. Natl. Acad. Sci. USA* 93:2155–58

32. Algeo TJ, Scheckler SE. 1998. Terrestrial-marine teleconnections in the Devonian: links between the evolution of land plants, weathering processes, and marine anoxic events. *Philos. Trans. R. Soc. London Ser. B* 353:113–30

33. Van Cappellen P, Ingall ED. 1996. Redox stabilization of the atmosphere and oceans by phosphorus-limited marine productivity. *Science* 271:493–96

34. Lenton TM, Watson AJ. 1999. Redfield revisited: 2. What regulates the oxygen content of the atmosphere? *Global Biogeochem. Cycles.* In press

35. Robinson JM. 1990. Lignin, land plants, and fungi: biological evolution affecting Phanerozoic oxygen balance. *Geology* 15:607–10

36. Watson A, Lovelock JE, Margulis L. 1978. Methanogenesis, fires and the regulation of atmospheric oxygen. *BioSystems* 10:293–98

37. Kump LR. 1989. Chemical stability of the atmosphere and ocean. *Global Planet. Change* 1:12 3–26

38. Jones TP, Chaloner WG. 1991. Fossil charcoal, its recognition and palaeoatmospheric significance. *Palaeogeogr. Palaeoclimatol. Palaeoecol.* 97:39–50

39. Rasbash DJ, Langford B. 1968. Burning of wood in atmospheres of reduced oxygen concentrations. *Combust. Flame* 12:33–40

40. Cope MJ, Chaloner WG. 1980. Fossil charcoal as evidence of past atmospheric composition. *Nature* 283:647–49

41. Clark FRS, Russell DA. 1981. Fossil charcoal and the palaeoatmosphere. *Nature* 290:428

42. Chaloner WG. 1989. Fossil charcoal as an indicator of palaeoatmospheric oxygen level. *J. Geol. Soc. London* 146:171–74

43. Berner RA. 1989. Drying, O_2 and mass extinction. *Nature* 340:603–4

44. Holser WT, Schönlaub HP, Attrep M Jr, Boeckelmann K, Klein P, et al. 1989. A unique geochemical record at the Permian/Triassic boundary. *Nature* 337:39–44

45. Małkowski K, Gruszczyński M, Hoffman A, Halas S. 1989. Oceanic stable isotope composition and a scenario for the Permo-Triassic crisis. *Hist. Biol.* 2:289–309

46. Hallam A. 1991. Why was there a delayed radiation after the end-Palaeozoic extinctions? *Hist. Biol.* 5:257–62

47. Wignall PB, Hallam A. 1992. Anoxia as a cause of the Permian/Triassic mass extinction: facies evidence from northern Italy and the western United States.

Palaeogeogr. Palaeoclimatol. Palaeoecol. 93:21–46

48. Erwin DH. 1993. *The Great Paleozoic Crisis: Life and Death in the Permian.* New York: Columbia Univ. Press

49. Wignall PB, Hallam A. 1993. Griesbachian (Earliest Triassic) palaeoenvironmental changes in the Salt Range, Pakistan and southeast China and their bearing on the Permo-Triassic mass extinction. *Palaeogeogr. Palaeoclimatol. Palaeoecol.* 102:215–37

50. Wignall PB, Twitchett RJ. 1996. Oceanic anoxia and the End Permian mass extinction. *Science* 272:1155–58

51. Isozaki Y. 1997. Permo-Triassic boundary superanoxia and stratified superocean: records from lost deep sea. *Science* 276:235–38

52. Deleted in proof

53. Berner RA. 1991. A model for atmospheric CO_2 over Phanerozoic time. *Am. J. Sci.* 291:339–76

54. Mora CI, Driese SG, Colarusso LA. 1996. Middle to late Paleozoic atmospheric CO_2 levels from soil carbonate and organic matter. *Science* 271:1105–7

55. Retallack GJ. 1997. Early forest soils and their role in Devonian global change. *Science* 276:583–85

56. McElwain JC. 1998. Do fossil plants signal palaeoatmospheric CO_2 concentration in the geological past? *Philos. Trans. R. Soc. London Ser. B* 353:83–96

57. Beerling DJ, Woodward FI, Lomas MR, Wills MA, Quick WP, Valdes PJ. 1998. The influence of Carboniferous palaeo-atmospheres on plant function: an experimental and modelling assessment. *Philos. Trans. R. Soc. London Ser. B* 353:131–40

58. Edwards D. 1998. Climate signals in Palaeozoic land plants. *Philos. Trans. R. Soc. London Ser. B* 353:141–57

59. Vogel S. 1994. *Life in Moving Fluids: The Physical Biology of Flow.* Princeton, NJ: Princeton Univ. Press

60. Norberg UM. 1990. *Vertebrate Flight.* Berlin: Springer-Verlag

61. Dudley R. 2000. *The Biomechanics of Insect Flight: Form, Function, Evolution.* Princeton, NJ: Princeton Univ. Press

62. Whalley P, Jarzembowski EA. 1981. A new assessment of *Rhyniella*, the earliest known insect, from the Devonian of Rhynie, Scotland. *Nature* 291:317

63. Shear WA, Grierson JD, Rolfe WDI, Smith EL, Norton RA. 1984. Early land animals in North America: evidence from Devonian age arthropods from Gilboa, New York. *Science* 224:492–94

64. Labandeira CC, Beall BS, Hueber FM. 1988. Early insect diversification: evidence from a Lower Devonian bristletail from Québec. *Science* 242:913–16

65. Jeram AJ, Selden PA, Edwards D. 1990. Land animals in the Silurian: arachnids and myriapods from Shropshire, England. *Science* 250:658–61

66. Nelson CR, Tidwell WD. 1987. *Brodioptera stricklani* n.sp. (Megasecoptera: Brodiopteridae), a new fossil insect from the Upper Manning Canyon Shale Formation, Utah (lowermost Namurian B). *Psyche* 94:309–16

67. Brauckmann C, Zessin W. 1989. Neue Meganeuridae aus dem Namurian von Hagen-Vorhalle (BRD) und die Phylogenie der Meganisoptera. *Dtsch. Entomol. Z. N.F* 36:177–215

68. Wootton RJ. 1981. Palaeozoic insects. *Annu. Rev. Entomol.* 26:319–44

69. Wootton RJ. 1990. Major insect radiations. In *Major Evolutionary Radiations,* ed. PD Taylor, GP Larwood, Systematics Assoc. Special Volume 42:187–208. Oxford, UK: Clarendon

70. Kukalová-Peck J. 1991. Fossil history and the evolution of hexapod structures. In *The Insects of Australia,* ed. CSIRO, 1:141–79. Ithaca, NY: Cornell Univ. Press. 2nd ed.

71. Labandeira CC, Sepkoski JJ. 1993. Insect diversity in the fossil record. *Science* 261:310–15

72. Boudreaux BH. 1979. *Arthropod Phylogeny with Special Reference to Insects.* New York: Wiley & Sons

73. Hennig W. 1981. *Insect Phylogeny.* Chichester, UK: Wiley & Sons

74. Kristensen NP. 1981. Phylogeny of insect orders. *Annu. Rev. Entomol.* 26:135–57

75. Kristensen NP. 1989. Insect phylogeny based on morphological evidence. In *The Hierarchy of Life,* ed. B Fernholm, K Bremer, H. Jörnvall, pp. 295–306. Amsterdam: Elsevier Sci.

76. Kristensen NP. 1991. Phylogeny of extant hexapods. See Ref. 70, pp. 125–40

77. Kristensen NP. 1997. The groundplan and basal diversification of the hexapods. In *Arthropod Relationships,* ed. RA Fortey, RH Thomas, pp. 281–93. London: Chapman & Hall

78. Brodsky AK. 1994. *The Evolution of Insect Flight.* Oxford, UK: Oxford Univ. Press

79. Crampton GC. 1916. The phylogenetic origin and the nature of the wings of insects according to the paranotal theory. *J. NY Entomol. Soc.* 24:1–39

80. Forbes WTM. 1943. The origin of wings and venational types in insects. *Am. Midl. Nat.* 29:381–405

81. Hamilton KGA. 1971. The insect wing, Part I. Origin and development of wings from notal lobes. *J. Kans. Entomol. Soc.* 44:421–33

82. Rasnitsyn AP. 1981. A modified paranotal theory of insect wing origin. *J. Morphol.* 168:331–38

83. Quartau JA. 1985. On some objections to the paranotal theory on the origin of insect wings. *Bol. Soc. Port. Entomol. Suppl.* 1:359–71

84. Quartau JA. 1986. An overview of the paranotal theory on the origin of the insect wings. *Publ. Inst. Zool. Dr. Augusto Nobre, Fac. Cienc. Porto* 194:1–42

85. Wootton RJ. 1986. The origin of insect flight: Where are we now? *Antenna* 10:82–86

86. Bitsch J. 1994. The morphological groundplan of Hexapoda: critical review of recent concepts. *Ann. Soc. Entomol. Fr.* 30:103–29

87. Woodworth CW. 1906. The wing veins of insects. *Univ. Calif. Bull. Entomol.* 1:1–52

88. Wigglesworth VB. 1973. Evolution of insect wings and flight. *Nature* 246:127–29

89. Wigglesworth VB. 1976. The evolution of insect flight. In *Insect Flight,* ed. RC Rainey, pp. 255–69. Oxford, UK: Blackwell

90. Kukalová-Peck J. 1978. Origin and evolution of insect wings and their relation to metamorphosis, as documented by the fossil record. *J. Morphol.* 156:53–126

91. Kukalová-Peck J. 1983. Origin of the insect wing and wing articulation from the arthropodan leg. *Can. J. Zool.* 61:1618–69

92. Kukalová-Peck J. 1992. The "Uniramia" do not exist: the ground plan of the Pterygota as revealed by Permian Diaphanopterodea from Russia (Insecta: Paleodictyopteroidea). *Can. J. Zool.* 70:236–55

93. Kukalová-Peck J. 1997. Arthropod phylogeny and 'basal' morphological structures. See Ref. 77, pp. 249–68

94. Kukalová-Peck J. 1997. Mazon Creek insect fossils: the origin of insect wings and clues about the origin of insect metamorphosis. In *Richardson's Guide to the Fossil Fauna of Mazon Creek,* ed. CW Shabic, AA Hay, pp. 194–207. Chicago: Northeastern Illinois Univ. Press

95. Averof M, Cohen, SM. 1997. Evolutionary origin of insect wings from ancestral gills. *Nature* 385:627–30

96. Little C. 1983. *The Colonisation of Land. Origins and Adaptations of Terrestrial Animals.* Cambridge, UK: Cambridge Univ. Press

97. Resh VH, Solem JO. 1984. Phylogenetic

relationships and evolutionary adaptations of aquatic insects. In *An Introduction to the Aquatic Insects of North America,* ed. RW Merrit, KW Cummins, pp. 66–75. Dubuque, IA: Kendall/Hunt. 2nd ed.

98. Messner B. 1988. Sind die Insekten primäre oder sekundäre Wasserbewohner? *Dtsch. Entomol. Z. N.F* 35:355–60

99. Pritchard G, McKee MH, Pike EM, Scrimgeour GJ, Zloty J. 1993. Did the first insects live in water or in air? *Biol. J. Linn. Soc.* 49:31–44

100. Hinton HE. 1968. Spiracular gills. *Adv. Insect Physiol.* 5:65–161

101. Carpenter FM. 1966. The Lower Permian insects of Kansas. Part 11. The orders Protorthoptera and Orthoptera. *Psyche* 73:46–88

102. Kukalová J. 1968. Permian mayfly nymphs. *Psyche* 75:310–27

103. Carroll SB, Weatherbee SD, Langeland JA. 1995. Homeotic genes and the regulation and evolution of insect wing number. *Nature* 375:58–61

104. Becker EG. 1952. The problem of the origin and development of the wing in insects. Chapter 1. Precursors of the insect wing. *Vestn. Mosk. Univ. Ser. Phys. Math. Nat. Sci.* 9:59–68

105. Wilson DM. 1962. Bifunctional muscles in the thorax of grasshoppers. *J. Exp. Biol.* 39:669–77

106. Ewer DW. 1963. On insect flight. *J. Entomol. Soc. S. Afr.* 26:3–13

107. Ewer DW, Nayler LS. 1967. The pterothoracic musculature of *Deropeltis erythrocephala,* a cockroach with a wingless female, and the origin of wing movements in insects. *J. Entomol. Soc. S. Afr.* 30:18–33

108. Fourtner CR, Randall JB. 1982. Studies on cockroach flight: the role of continuous neural activation of non-flight muscles. *J. Exp. Zool.* 221:143–54

109. Wigglesworth VB. 1963. The origin of flight in insects. *Proc. R. Entomol. Soc. London* 28:23–32

110. Alexander RD, Brown WL. 1963. Mating behavior and the origin of insect wings. *Occas. Pap. Mus. Zool. Univ. Mich.* 628:1–19

111. Alexander RD. 1964. The evolution of mating behaviour in arthropods. *Symp. R. Entomol. Soc. London* 2:78–94

112. Whalley PS. 1979. New species of Protorthoptera and Protodonata (Insecta) from the Upper Carboniferous of Britain, with a comment on the origin of wings. *Bull. Br. Mus. Nat. Hist.* 32:85–90

113. Douglas MM. 1981. Thermoregulatory significance of thoracic lobes in the evolution of insect wings. *Science* 211:84–86

114. Kingsolver JG, Koehl MAR. 1985. Aerodynamics, thermoregulation, and the evolution of insect wings: differential scaling and evolutionary change. *Evolution* 39:488–504

115. Kingsolver JG, Koehl MAR. 1994. Selective factors in the evolution of insect wings. *Annu. Rev. Entomol.* 39: 425–51

116. Bradley, JC. 1942. The origin and significance of metamorphosis and wings among insects. In *Proc. 8th Am. Sci. Congr.* pp. 303–9. Washington DC: Dept. State

117. Mamayev BM. 1977. The gravitational hypothesis of the origin of insects. *Entomol. Rev.* 54:13–17

118. Marden JH, Kramer MG. 1994. Surface-skimming stoneflies: a possible intermediate stage in insect flight evolution. *Science* 266:427–30

119. Marden JH, Kramer MG. 1995. Locomotor performance of insects with rudimentary wings. *Nature* 377:332–34

120. Thomas ALR, Norberg RÅ. 1996. Skimming the surface–the origin of flight in insects? *Trends Ecol. Evol.* 11:187–88

121. Samways MJ. 1994. 'Sailing' on the water surface by adult male *Enallagma nigridorsum* Selys (Zygoptera: Coenagrionidae). *Odonatologica* 23:175–78

122. Kramer MG, Marden JH. 1997. Almost airborne. *Nature* 385:403–4
123. Will KW. 1995. Plecopteran surface-skimming and insect flight evolution. *Science* 270:1684–85
124. Ruffieux L, Elouard J-M, Sartori M. 1998. Flightlessness in mayflies and its relevance to hypotheses on the origin of insect flight. *Proc. R. Soc. London Ser. B* 265:2135–40
125. Flower JW. 1964. On the origin of flight in insects. *J. Insect Physiol.* 10:81–88
126. Wootton RJ. 1976. The fossil record and insect flight. See Ref. 89, pp. 235–54
127. Ritzmann RE, Fourtner CR. 1980. Flight activity initiated via giant interneurons of the cockroach: evidence for bifunctional trigger interneurons. *Science* 210:443–45
128. Ritzmann RE. 1984. The cockroach escape response. In *Neural Mechanisms of Startle Behavior,* ed. RC Eaton, pp. 93–131. New York: Plenum
129. Edwards JS, Reddy GR. 1986. Mechanosensory appendages in the firebrat (*Thermobia domestica,* Thysanura): a prototype system for terrestrial predator invasion. *J. Comp. Neurol.* 243:535–46
130. Bristowe WS. 1958. *The World of Spiders.* London: Collins
131. Edwards JS. 1985. Predator evasion and the origin of insect flight: an exercise in evolutionary neuroethology. *Soc. Neurosci. Abstr.* 11:497
132. Edwards JS, Palka J. 1991. Insect neural evolution–a fugue or an opera*? Semin. Neurosci.* 3:391–98
133. Edwards JS. 1992. Giant interneurons and the origin of insect flight. In *Nervous Systems: Principles of Design and Function,* ed. RN Singh, pp. 485–95. Bombay: Wiley Eastern
134. Edwards JS. 1997. The evolution of insect flight: implications for the evolution of the nervous system. *Brain Behav. Evol.* 50:8–12
135. Ganihar D, Libersat F, Wendler G, Camhi, JM. 1994. Wind-evoked evasive responses in flying cockroaches. *J. Comp. Physiol. A* 175:49–65
136. Kutsch W, Breidbach O. 1994. Homologous structures in the nervous systems of Arthropoda. *Adv. Insect Physiol.* 24:1–11
137. Libersat F. 1994. The dorsal giant interneurons mediate evasive behavior in flying cockroaches. *J. Exp. Biol.* 197:405–11
138. Rolfe WD. 1980. Early invertebrate terrestrial fossils. In *The Terrestrial Environment and the Origin of Land Vertebrates,* ed. AL Panchen, Systematics Assoc. Special Vol. No. 15, pp. 117–57. London: Academic
139. Rolfe WD. 1985. Early terrestrial arthropods: a fragmentary record. *Philos. Trans. R. Soc. London Ser. B* 309:207–18
140. Carroll RL. 1988. *Vertebrate Paleontology and Evolution.* New York: Freeman
141. Shear WA, Kukalová-Peck J. 1990. The ecology of Paleozoic terrestrial arthropods: the fossil evidence. *Can. J. Zool.* 68:1807–34
142. Behrensmeyer AK, Damuth JD, DiMichele WA, Sues H-D, Wing SL. 1992. *Terrestrial Ecosystems through Time: Evolutionary Paleoecology of Terrestrial Plants and Animals.* Chicago: Univ. Chicago Press
143. Carpenter FM. 1971. Adaptations among Paleozoic insects. *Proc. N. Am. Paleontol. Conv.* 1969:1236–51
144. Burnham L. 1983. Studies on Upper Carboniferous insects: 1. The Geraridae (Order Protorthoptera). *Psyche* 90:1–57
145. Kevan PG, Chaloner WG, Savile DBO. 1975. Interrelationships of early terrestrial arthropods and plants. *Paleontology* 18:391–417
146. Chaloner WG, Sheerin A. 1979. Devonian macrofloras. *Spec. Pap. Palaeontol.* 23:145–61
147. Gensel PG, Andrews HN. 1984. *Plant Life in the Devonian.* New York: Praeger
148. Stewart WN. 1983. *Paleobotany and the Evolution of Plants.* Cambridge, UK: Cambridge Univ. Press
149. Raven JA. 1986. Evolution of plant life forms. In *On the Economy of Plant Form*

and Function, ed. TJ Givnish, pp. 421–92. Cambridge, UK: Cambridge Univ. Press

150. Kenrick P, Crane PR. 1997. The origin and early evolution of plants on land. *Nature* 389:33–39

151. Strong DR, Lawton JH, Southwood R. 1984. *Insects on Plants.* Oxford, UK: Blackwell

152. Rasnitsyn AP, Krassilov VA. 1996. First find of pollen grains in the gut of Permian insects. *Paleontol. J.* 30:484–90

153. Labandeira CC, Phillips TL. 1996. A Carboniferous insect gall: insight into early ecologic history of the Holometabola. *Proc. Natl. Acad. Sci. USA* 93:8470–74

154. Labandeira CC, Phillips TL. 1996. Insect fluid-feeding on Upper Pennsylvanian tree ferns (Palaeodictyoptera, Marattiales) and the early history of the piercing-and-sucking functional feeding group. *Ann. Entomol. Soc. Am.* 89:157–83

155. Ellington CP. 1991. Aerodynamics and the origin of insect flight. *Adv. Insect Physiol.* 23:171–210

156. Ennos AR. 1989. The effect of size on the optimal shapes of gliding insects and seeds. *J. Zool. London* 219:61–69

157. Haupt H. 1941. Die ältesten geflügelten Insekten und ihre Beziehungen zur Fauna der Jetztzeit. *Z. Naturwiss.* (Halle) 94:60–121

158. Smart J. 1971. Palaeoecological factors affecting the origin of winged insects. *Proc. 13th Int. Congr. Entomol.* I:304–6

159. Harlé É, Harlé A. 1911. Le vol de grands reptiles et insectes disparus semble indiquer une pression atmosphérique élevée. *Bull. Soc. Geol. Fr. Ser. 4* 11:18–21

160. Kammer AE, Heinrich B. 1978. Insect flight metabolism. *Adv. Insect Physiol.* 13:133–228

161. Casey TM. 1989. Oxygen consumption during flight. In *Insect Flight,* ed. GJ Goldsworthy, CH Wheeler, pp. 257–72. Boca Raton, FL: CRC Press

162. Weis-Fogh T. 1964. Diffusion in insect wing muscle, the most active tissue known. *J. Exp. Biol.* 41:229–56

163. Weis-Fogh T. 1964. Functional design of the tracheal system of flying insects as compared with the avian lung. *J. Exp. Biol.* 41:207–27

164. Kestler P. 1984. Respiration and respiratory water loss. In *Environmental Physiology and Biochemistry of Insects,* ed. KH Hoffman, pp. 137–83. Berlin: Springer-Verlag

165. Mill PJ. 1985. Structure and physiology of the respiratory system. In *Comprehensive Insect Physiology, Biochemistry, and Pharmacology,* ed. GA Kerkut, LI Gilbert, 3:517–93. Oxford, UK: Pergamon

166. Harrison JF, Lighton JRB. 1998. Oxygen-sensitive flight metabolism in the dragonfly *Erythemis simplicicollis. J. Exp. Biol.* 201:1739–44

167. Kukalová-Peck J. 1985. Ephemeroid wing venation based upon new gigantic Carboniferous mayflies and basic morphology, phylogeny, and metamorphosis of pterygote insects (Insecta, Ephemerida). *Can. J. Zool.* 63:933–55

168. Carpenter FM. 1992. *Treatise on Invertebrate Paleontology. Part R, Arthropoda 4, Volumes 3 and 4 (Hexapoda).* Lawrence, KS: Univ. Kansas Press

169. Kukalová-Peck J. 1987. New Carboniferous Diplura, Monura, and Thysanura, the hexapod ground plan, and the role of thoracic lobes in the origin of wings (Insecta). *Can. J. Zool.* 65:2327–45

170. Rolfe WDI. 1969. Arthropleurida. In *Treatise on Invertebrate Paleontology. Arthropoda 4: Crustacea (Except Ostracoda): Myriapoda,* ed. RC Moore, C Teichert, pp. 607–20. Lawrence, KS: Univ. Kansas Press

171. Kraus O. 1974. On the morphology of Paleozoic diplopods. *Symp. Zool. Soc. London* 32:13–22

172. Briggs, DEG. 1985. Gigantism in Palaeozoic arthropods. *Spec. Pap. Paleontol.* 33:157

173. Vermeij GJ. 1987. *Evolution and Escalation.* Princeton, NJ: Princeton Univ. Press

174. Rutten MG. 1966. Geologic data on atmospheric history. *Paleogeogr. Palaeoclimatol. Palaeoecol.* 2:47–57

175. Schidlowski M. 1971. Probleme der atmosphärischen Evolution im Präkambrium. *Geol. Rundsch.* 60:1351–84

176. Jepsen GL. 1970. Bat origins and evolution. In *Biology of Bats,* ed. WA Wimsatt, 1:1–64. London: Academic

177. Altringham JD. 1996. *Bats: Biology and Behaviour.* Oxford, UK: Oxford Univ. Press

178. Chiappe LM. 1995. The first 85 million years of avian evolution. *Nature* 378:349–55

179. Qiang J, Currie PJ, Norell MA, Shu-An J. 1998. Two feathered dinosaurs from northeastern China. *Nature* 393:753–61

180. Padian K, Chiappe LM. 1998. The origin and early evolution of birds. *Biol. Rev.* 73:1–42

181. Wild R. 1984. Flugsaurier aus der Obertrias von Italien. *Naturwissenschaften* 71:1–11

182. Wellnhofer P. 1991. *The Illustrated Encyclopedia of Pterosaurs.* London: Salamander

183. Ruben J. 1991. Reptilian physiology and the flight capacity of *Archaeopteryx. Evolution* 45:1–17

184. Ruben J. 1993. Powered flight in *Archaeopteryx:* response to Speakman. *Evolution* 47:935–38

185. Speakman JR. 1993. Flight capabilities in *Archaeopteryx. Evolution* 41:336–40

186. Norberg UM. 1985. Evolution of vertebrate flight: an aerodynamic model for the transition from gliding to active flight. *Am. Nat.* 126:303–27

187. Rayner JMV. 1988. The evolution of vertebrate flight. *Biol. J. Linn. Soc.* 34:269–87

188. Bennett SC. 1997. The arboreal leaping theory of the origin of pterosaur flight. *Hist. Biol.* 12:265–90

189. Eaton RC, ed. 1984. *Neural Mechanisms of Startle Behavior.* New York: Plenum

190. Tuttle MD, Stevenson D. 1982. Growth and survival of bats. In *Ecology of Bats,* ed. TH Kunz, pp. 105–50. New York: Plenum

191. Pomeroy D. 1990. Why fly? The possible benefits for lower mortality. *Biol. J. Linn. Soc.* 40:53–65

192. Rose MR. 1991. *Evolutionary Biology of Aging.* New York: Oxford Univ. Press

193. Holmes DJ, Austad SN. 1995. The evolution of avian senescence patterns: implications for understanding primary aging processes. *Am. Zool.* 35:307–17

194. Dudley R, Chai P. 1996. Animal flight mechanics in physically variable gas mixtures. *J. Exp. Biol.* 199:1881–85

195. Loudon C. 1988. Development of *Tenebrio molitor* in low oxygen levels. *J. Insect Physiol.* 34:97–103

196. Loudon C. 1989. Tracheal hypertrophy in mealworms: design and plasticity in oxygen supply systems. *J. Exp. Biol.* 147:217–35

197. Greenberg S, Ar A. 1996. Effects of chronic hypoxia, normoxia and hyperoxia on larval development in the beetle *Tenebrio molitor. J. Insect Physiol.* 42:991–96

198. Temple GF, Metcalfe J. 1970. The effects of increased incubator oxygen tension on capillary development in the chick chorioallantois. *Condor* 90:187–92

199. McGrath JJ. 1971. Acclimation response of pigeons to simulated high altitude. *J. Appl. Physiol.* 31:274–76

200. Pionetti J-M, Bouverot P. 1977. Effects of acclimation to altitude on oxygen affinity and organic phosphate concentrations in pigeon blood. *Life Sci.* 20:1207–12

201. Metcalfe J, McCutcheon, IE, Francisco DL, Metzenberg AB, Welch JE. 1981. Oxygen availability and growth of the chick embryo. *Respir. Physiol.* 46:81–88

202. Williams JB, Swift K. 1988. Oxygen consumption and growth of Northern

Bobwhite embryos under normoxic and hyperoxic conditions. *Condor* 90:187–92

203. Bigard AX, Brunet A, Guezennec C-Y, Monod H. 1991. Effects of chronic hypoxia and endurance training on muscle capillarity in rats. *Pflügers Arch.* 419: 225–29

204. Hoppeler H, Desplanches D. 1992. Muscle structural modifications in hypoxia. *Int. J. Sports Med.* 13(Suppl. 1):S166–68

205. Weber KE. 1996. Large genetic change at small fitness cost in large populations of *Drosophila melanogaster* selected for wind tunnel flight: rethinking fitness surfaces. *Genetics* 144:205–13

206. Galun R, Fraenkel G. 1961. The effect of low atmospheric pressure on adult *Aedes aegyptii* and on housefly pupae. *J. Insect Physiol.* 7:161–76

207. Dudley R. 1995. Extraordinary flight performance of orchid bees (Apidae: Euglossini) hovering in heliox (80% He/20% O$_2$). *J. Exp. Biol.* 198:1065–70

208. Chai P, Dudley R. 1995. Limits to vertebrate locomotor energetics suggested by hummingbirds hovering in heliox. *Nature* 377:722–25

209. Chai P, Dudley R. 1996. Limits to flight energetics of hummingbirds hovering in hypodense and hypoxic gas mixtures. *J. Exp. Biol.* 199:2285–95

210. Stalker HD, Carson HL. 1948. An altitudinal transect of *Drosophila robusta* Sturtevant. *Evolution* 2:295–305

211. Hamilton TH. 1961. The adaptive significances of intraspecific trends of variation in wing length and body size among bird species. *Evolution* 15:180–95

212. Feinsinger P, Colwell RK, Terborgh J, Chaplin SB. 1979. Elevation and the morphology, flight energetics, and foraging ecology of tropical hummingbirds. *Am. Nat.* 113:481–97

213. Epting RJ. 1980. Functional dependence of the power for hovering on wing disc loading in hummingbirds. *Physiol. Zool.* 53:347–57

Annu. Rev. Physiol. 2000. 62:157–78

VARIABILITY IN THE SIZE, COMPOSITION, AND FUNCTION OF INSECT FLIGHT MUSCLES

James H. Marden

Department of Biology, Pennsylvania State University, University Park, Pennsylvania 16802; e-mail: jhm10@psu.edu

Key Words   maturation, hypertrophy, histolysis, contraction, performance

■ **Abstract**   In order to fly, insects require flight muscles that constitute at least 12 to 16% of their total mass, and flight performance increases as this percentage increases. However, flight muscles are energetically and materially expensive to build and maintain, and investment in flight muscles constrains other aspects of function, particularly female fecundity. This review examines ways in which insects vary the size of their flight muscles, and how variation in the relative size and composition of flight muscles affects flight performance. Sources of variability in flight muscle size and composition include genetic differences within and between species, individual phenotypic responses to environmental stimuli, and maturational changes that occur before and during the adult stage. Insects have evolved a wide variety of ways to adjust flight muscle size and contractile performance in order to meet demands imposed by variation in life history and ecology.

INTRODUCTION

Insect flight muscles operate at high contraction rates and produce the highest known rates of mechanical power output and metabolic power input. These characteristics, along with the activation of certain insect flight muscles by mechanical rather than neural stimuli (stretch activation), have long attracted the attention of physiologists interested in the mechanical and biochemical bases of flight muscle contraction and metabolism (1–4). The same characteristics have also attracted the attention of comparative physiologists interested in determining the causes and consequences of variation in muscle function within this exceedingly diverse group of organisms. Among the topics examined by comparative physiologists, interspecific variation in flight-related thermoregulatory mechanisms and thermal ecology has been fairly well explored and summarized (5). Other aspects of variability in insect flight muscle function have been more sparsely studied and less frequently reviewed. Here I present an overview of what is known about variation in the size, composition, and contractile physiology of insect flight muscles, focusing particularly on how that variation affects whole-organism function.

0066–4278/00/0315–0157$12.00

VARIATION IN OVERALL SIZE OF THE
FLIGHT MUSCULATURE

The flight muscles of insects represent a major allocation of energy and material. Flight muscles constitute as much as 55 to 65% of body mass (6–8), with the percentage dropping to nearly zero in species that temporarily or permanently break down their flight muscles and lose the ability to fly. The variation is not continuous, since total flight muscle mass must be at least 12 to 16% of body mass for weight-supported flight in still air (7). Thus insects are forced to either make a substantial investment in flight muscle or forego the benefits of aerial travel.

Nearly every order of insects contains species that are either flightless or polymorphic in the extent of flight muscle development (9–15). In some cases polymorphisms are caused by simple Mendelian genetic differences. For example, flight muscle development in female *Heptophylla picea* beetles (Scarabaeidae) is a homozygous recessive trait (16). Muscle suppression occurs in heterozygous as well as homozygous dominant females, and the frequency of flight-capable females varies from 0 to 100% at different geographic locations (17). Males in this species are always flight capable. These data suggest that a single copy of an uncharacterized flightless allele gives rise to a threshold level of a flight muscle repressor in females, but two copies of this allele fail to produce a threshold level of the repressor in males.

In a wide variety of insects, flight muscle size responds in a flexible manner to environmental factors such as local population density and food availability (9–15). For example, both sexes of bark beetles (*Ips pini*; Scolytidae) undergo degeneration of their flight muscles within five days of entering a tree that is a suitable breeding site (18). Males mate with females and remain paired in order to assist in initiating the construction of a tunnel system in which the young will develop. Within about one month, males gradually regenerate their flight muscles and become capable of emigrating to another breeding site. Males that have located a tree and undergone muscle degeneration, but are unable to locate a mate, regenerate their flight muscles to emigration-phase levels within only five days.

Many insect taxa undergo fairly predictable changes in flight muscle size and ultrastructure during the course of adult maturation. The flight muscles of tsetse flies (*Glossina* spp., Diptera) are not fully mature until after they have consumed a number of blood meals, undergoing a total increase in mass of about 75% (19). Nearly all taxa of dragonflies (Odonata) undergo substantial growth of their flight muscles during adult maturation (20), with dragonflies of the genus *Libellula* showing as much as a doubling or tripling of muscle size (8). The exoskeletal size of insects is fixed shortly after adult eclosion when the cuticle hardens, so maturational increases in muscle size occur by displacement of air sacs and perhaps by some compression of the expandable volume of the foregut. Because of this, maturational and other changes in flight muscle size are difficult or impossible to detect externally.

It has long been assumed that material and energy costs of building and maintaining flight muscles limit reproductive output, and indeed, it is generally true in polymorphic species that flightless morphs reach sexual maturity more rapidly and attain higher fecundity (9–15). This is particularly true for females, which in many taxa display the well-characterized oogenesis-flight syndrome, which involves a seasonal or ontogenetic transition between high flight capability and ovarian development (9). The costs of developing a flight motor are less clear for males, but some evidence exists that male reproduction is also enhanced in flightless morphs that lack or have histolyzed their flight muscles (21, 22).

EFFECTS OF RELATIVE FLIGHT MUSCLE SIZE ON AERIAL PERFORMANCE

Effects of flight muscle development on aerial performance have frequently been assessed by examining flight endurance, which is typically measured as the number of revolutions accomplished while an insect is tethered to a rotary flight mill (23–28). Flight endurance tends to show a strong positive correlation with relative muscle size and a negative correlation with female ovarian development, although in some species there are seasons when females show high flight capacity even when their ovaries are highly developed (23, 24, 29). More fully developed flight muscles tend to possess higher levels of aerobic enzyme activity, mitochondrial density, tracheation, energy stores, and proteins involved in the translocation of fatty acids from storage depots (30–36). For example, a fatty acid binding protein that is undetectable in migratory locusts at adult emergence becomes the most abundant soluble protein in flight muscle by 10 days of age, comprising 18% of total soluble protein in the sarcoplasm (31). During adult maturation in *Libellula* dragonflies, the fractional cross-sectional area of mitochondria increases from 0.15 to 0.46 (8) over a period when the percentage of time spent flying by free-living dragonflies increases from 2 to 32% (38). These observations indicate that many of the gross changes in composition that occur during flight muscle hypertrophy involve an up-scaling of aerobic metabolic capacity, which allows greater endurance.

In addition to the need to periodically remain airborne for long periods of time, insects frequently need to achieve high levels of aerial performance in order to evade predators, compete for mates, lift loads, or overcome low muscle temperature. Thus it is also important to consider how variation in flight muscle development affects maximal short-burst flight performance. Load-lifting experiments using a wide variety of taxa (7) indicate that insects at warm muscle temperatures achieve a fairly consistent amount of short-burst lift per unit muscle mass (60–80 N/kg). The relationship between lift force and flight muscle mass scales isometrically and is not affected by variation in the relative size or shape of the wings, within the naturally occurring extremes exhibited by flight-capable insects. The minimum amount of flight muscle required for weight support is 12 to 16% of total body mass, and increases in the flight muscle ratio (the ratio of flight muscle mass to total body mass) above the marginal level bring about a linearly increasing ability to lift loads and to accelerate.

Consequences of the relationship between flight muscle ratio (FMR) and aerial performance have been explored by comparing FMRs of butterflies that vary in their susceptibility to aerial predation by birds. Due to variability in the chemical composition of host plants eaten during the caterpillar stage, butterflies vary in a highly dichotomous fashion in the degree to which they are preyed upon by birds (39, 40). This stimulated the prediction that palatable species should be more reliant on short bursts of high-performance flight to evade birds and thus they should have higher FMRs than do unpalatable species. In a comparison of 122 species of neotropical butterflies, FMRs of females of unpalatable, mimetic species averaged 0.24, whereas females of palatable, non-mimetic species averaged 0.35 (41). Unpalatable female butterflies have significantly larger abdomens (42) and ovaries (41), thus demonstrating that unpalatability not only reduces predation but also allows greater reproductive effort. Phylogenetically based statistical analyses show that these associations between FMR and palatability have evolved independently in numerous lineages.

Male butterflies also show differences in mean FMR between unpalatable (0.31) and palatable species (0.42), although less of the variation in male FMR is explained by palatability status (41). This suggests that other aspects of male function, such as aerial pursuit of mates, might affect the evolution of FMR in males. This prediction was tested in a study that compared mean FMRs of a broad taxonomic selection of male butterflies that employ different mating tactics (43). Species in which males fly continuously in search of females showed lower FMRs and different wing shapes than did males that perch and use short-burst flight to rapidly overtake passing females. The importance of burst performance for aerially mating male insects has also been shown by experiments that reduced the FMR of territorial male dragonflies. Small weight loads (6–13 % of body mass) attached to the bodies of territorial males reduced their territorial and mating success (8).

An alternative hypothesis for the observed variability in butterfly body design is that a smaller abdomen places the center of rotation closer to the thorax and wingbase, thereby allowing more rapid body rotation and greater aerial maneuverability (44). According to this hypothesis, differences in FMR are a secondary result of selection acting on the relative size of the abdomen. There is statistical evidence against this (41), as the relative mass of flight muscle among species that differ in palatability and mimicry status varies independently of relative abdomen mass, but not vice versa. This pattern argues for a primary effect of FMR rather than abdomen size. Experiments presently underway (45) are further exploring this issue by attaching weight loads to butterflies at different distances from the body center of rotation, then releasing the marked butterflies and determining mortality rates in nature. Results of this experiment will show whether the effect of weight alone or both weight and location are important.

A high FMR is also beneficial in ecological contexts that require lifting large external loads. For example, male Empidid flies (Diptera, Empididae) capture small insects and present them to females as "nuptial gifts." Females permit males to copulate while they consume these prey items, and while doing so they are carried in flight by the male. In order to mate, a male Empidid fly must support his own weight along with that of the female and the prey item. The overall size and FMR of males is positively related to the total load that they can support during aerial copulation (46). Female cicada killer wasps (*Sphecius speciosus*) are another example of extraordinary load lifting. Female cicada killers are unusual in that their FMR is as high as that of conspecific males. A relatively high FMR allows them to carry prey that average 88% heavier than their own weight (47). Even so, carrying such heavy prey causes a threefold reduction in FMR compared with the unloaded state, which drops them below the marginal flight muscle ratio. Female cicada killers lack sufficient force production to take off with an average-sized cicada, but they compensate behaviorally by repeatedly climbing trees and descending under power in the direction of their burrows.

In ectothermic insects, variation in the relative size of flight muscles also affects the thermal breadth for flight (i.e. the range of ambient and muscle temperature over which flight is possible). Insects with higher FMRs should be capable of maintaining flight at lower thoracic temperatures, and this appears to be part of the suite of adaptations that allow male winter-flying Geometrid moths (*Operophtera bruceata*) to fly at ambient and thoracic temperatures ranging from approximately 0 to 28°C (48). *Operophtera* females are flightless and their thoracic cavity is filled with eggs rather than muscle. Based on the thermal sensitivity of power output in male flight muscles, *Operophtera* females would require a 17% reduction in egg number to fly over a fairly narrow range of temperatures (13 to 22°C), whereas an 82% reduction in egg number would be required to fly over the broad temperature range accomplished by males.

CONTROL OF FLIGHT MUSCLE HYPERTROPHY

Hypertrophy of the flight muscles of insects begins during the nymph or pupal stages prior to adult emergence and in some taxa continues during adult maturation. This hypertrophy is controlled by the same hormones that orchestrate the insect molting process, juvenile hormone (JH), and ecdysteroids. The time course of the relative concentration of these hormones regulates muscle and wing development, including morph determination in species that are polymorphic for flight capability (14).

A long-standing hypothesis is that an elevated JH titer at a critical stage of development suppresses morphogenesis of flight muscles and wings. Experimental evaluation of this hypothesis has progressed the farthest in studies of Orthopterans (crickets and locusts). Treatment of final instar nymphs of the monomorphic, flight-capable cricket *Teleogryllus oceanicus* with the JH-analog methoprene slows the 30-fold increase in muscle mass that normally occurs during the first few days of adult life and blocks the growth of mitochondria and tracheoblasts (49). The flight motor neural pattern in *Teleogryllus* crickets is detectable well before the final nymphal instar and therefore might also play a role in stimulating muscle growth and differentiation. Denervated muscles of *T. oceanicus* show a reduced muscle growth rate, but no change in mitochondrial or tracheoblast proliferation. These results indicate that both neural and endocrine factors contribute to flight muscle hypertrophy in *T. oceanicus* but that endocrine factors alone appear to determine ultrastructural differentiation of mitochondria and tracheoblasts. In *Schistocerca gregaria* locusts, methoprene treatment has a curiously different effect on muscle development (50). Methoprene-treated final instar nymphs molt to a supernumerary nymph stage rather than to the adult stage. Thoracic muscles within these supernumerary nymphs show a fairly normal increase in the size and distribution of mitochondria, but little growth of myofibrils, i.e. a pattern that is opposite that produced by JH treatment in *T. oceanicus* crickets. These contrasting effects in two Orthopterans indicate that there is likely to be wide diversity in the details of JH inhibition of muscle hypertrophy among species.

The most detailed studies of endocrine effects on flight muscle development have been performed using the cricket *Gryllus rubens*. In this species, experimental application of JH during the penultimate or ultimate nymph stage redirects the development of a flight-destined morph to a flight-incapable morph (51). Native levels of JH are higher in final instar nymphs of the flight-incapable morph, and newly emerged adults of the flight-capable morph have higher activity of the degradative enzyme, JH esterase (52). Regulation of JH and its degradative enzymes may not be the only endocrine mechanism at work in *G. rubens,* for there are also differences in the level and timing of the ecdysteroid peak during the last stages of nymphal development and early adult maturation (53). Thus morph determination in this species is likely to be regulated by covariation in both JH and ecdysteroid titers (15, 53).

To date there is little understanding of the molecular details of regulatory processes controlling flight muscle hypertrophy, but evidence obtained from other types of insect muscles suggests an important role for ecdysteroids and ecdysteroid receptors. In an abdominal body wall muscle present in pupae of *Manduca sexta,* temporal and spatial patterning of different isoforms of the ecdysone receptor (EcR) match the developmental response of the muscle to changing steroid titers and to the pattern of innervation (54). Only one fiber of this muscle participates in the regrowth of the muscle during the adult stage, and only this fiber shows an upregulation of a particular EcR isoform (EcR-B1). Denervation of the muscle prevents both the upregulation of EcR-B1 and myoblast proliferation. Thus growth of this muscle appears to be regulated by the pattern of expression of hormone receptor isoforms, rising and falling ecdysteroid titers, and local interactions with nerve cells (54).

CONTROL OF FLIGHT MUSCLE DEGENERATION

Certain insects are capable of degenerating their flight muscles in response to environmental stimuli that signal a temporary or permanent end to the need to fly. Numerous aspects of the degeneration process indicate that it is not a passive process resulting from muscle disuse, but rather an active process of programmed cell death, triggered by specific environmental and social signals (55). Post-migratory muscle degeneration is blocked by environmental stimuli that signal habitat unsuitability (i.e. food shortage) (9, 56), by antibiotics that inhibit RNA and protein synthesis (56), and by chemicals that inhibit secretion of JH from the corpus allatum (56). Muscle degeneration is stimulated by treatment with a JH analog (55, 57) and by transplantation of brain tissue from reproductive females into pre-reproductive females (58).

One of the species in which the degeneration process has been best characterized is the fire ant, *Solenopsis* spp. (Hymenoptera). After performing a mating flight and initiating a terrestrial search for a colony founding site, fire ant queens shed their wings and undergo flight muscle histolysis. When hemolymph from mated females is injected into virgin females, within 24 h there is a marked breakdown of the flight musculature, but no such breakdown occurs in control females injected with hemolymph from virgin females, or those injected with male seminal fluids or heat-degraded (70°C) hemolymph from mated females (59). Lysis of the flight muscles begins within 2 h after mating, appearing first as lesions in the membranes of the sarcotubular system and mitochondria, followed by breakage and dissolution of the myofilaments, and lastly by the disappearance of sarcomeric Z-lines (60–62). The initial membrane disruption is thought to cause mitochondria and SR to release calcium into the sarcoplasm (62), thereby activating the calcium-dependent proteases that are constitutively present in striated muscle (63). As this is occurring, there is also a sharp rise in ubiquitination of the myofilaments, Z-lines, and mitochondria (64), thus indicating that muscle proteins are tagged for ultimate degradation by the ATP/ubiquitin-dependent proteolytic pathway (65). In fire ants, this process is apparently all-or-none; once triggered, the flight muscles are rapidly and completely degraded.

It is interesting to note that a similar process of muscle degeneration, featuring both calcium-dependent proteases and the ubiquitin pathway, occurs in crustaceans. Lobsters undergo a specific regional atrophy of the distal portion of their claw muscles that allows withdrawal of the large distal portion of the muscle through narrow proximal joints during molting (66). The ubiquitin pathway has also been shown to function during a muscle-specific and hormonally regulated adult-stage atrophy of abdominal intersegmental muscles in *Manduca* moths (67–

69). These muscles are used to free the nascent adult from the pupal exoskeleton during molting and then disappear during early adult life. The process is hormonally regulated by falling ectdysteroid titers, and features selective repression of actin and myosin heavy chain genes (70). Flight muscle histolysis in insects is likely to be derived evolutionarily from these processes that arthropods use to remodel muscle before, during, and after molting.

Flight muscle degeneration is thought to allow a large re-allocation of energy and protein, which females may subsequently use for ovarian development and oocyte provision (14, 15). Direct evidence for this is rare, although protein transfer from degenerating flight muscles to developing oocytes has been demonstrated in *Dystdercus cingulatus* bugs (Heteroptera) (71). Surgical removal of the wings of female *Velarifictorus parvus* crickets (Orthoptera) stimulates flight muscle histolysis and ovarian development (72), and when denied access to food, wing-intact females produce no eggs during the first 5 days after adult emergence, whereas de-alated females under the same conditions break down their flight muscles and produce an average of 23 eggs.

Recent studies of *Gryllus* crickets have shown that simply maintaining the flight muscles has negative impacts on female fecundity (73–75). A flight-capable morph in *G. firmus* has pink-colored thoracic muscles that contain higher lipid and triglyceride energy reserves, three- to sevenfold higher mass-specific metabolic enzyme activities, and a higher resting metabolic rate than white-colored thoracic muscles from a flight-incapable morph. The mass-specific resting metabolic rate of pink-colored flight muscles is ninefold higher than that of ovarian tissue (75). Flight-capable and flight-incapable crickets do not differ in the amount of food consumed or assimilated, but the high maintenance costs and disproportionate energy consumption by their flight muscles causes flight-capable crickets to have lower efficiencies of energy assimilation, which is manifested ultimately as a decrease in fecundity. These patterns of muscle physiology, energetics, and fecundity were first observed in the naturally polymorphic species *G. firmus* and *G. rubens* (73, 74) and subsequently reproduced experimentally by hormonally manipulating the monomorphic species *G. assimilis* by using a JH analog (methoprene) to stimulate flight muscle histolysis and increased ovarian development (75).

VARIABILITY IN METABOLIC ENZYMES AND THEIR EFFECTS ON FLIGHT

In addition to varying in size, insect flight muscles show functionally important variation in their molecular composition, ultrastructure, and biochemistry. One such category of variability involves the effects of polymorphism at gene loci that encode enzymes which participate in energy metabolism. A detailed review of older literature is available (76), and here I discuss primarily the few recent studies that have specifically addressed the effects of allozyme variation on flight performance.

One of the main motivations for studying allozymes is to help distinguish between neutrality versus selection as causative factors for the unexpectedly high levels of heterozygosity found in most populations. The predominant approach in this field has been to analyze gene sequence data for patterns of nucleotide diversity indicative of selection, and this approach has been highly successful in providing evidence for natural selection acting on polymorphic loci (77). However, statistical analyses of nucleotide data reveal little about organismal physiology and function. In this regard, studies of the effects of polymorphic loci on insect flight metabolism and performance have the potential to provide particularly clear insights. Flying insects possess the highest known mass-specific metabolic rates, and therefore they may be particularly sensitive to the effects of allozymes on metabolic performance.

A prominent set of studies in this area has been the work of Watt and colleagues (78–85), who examined the impact of different phosphoglucose isomerase (PGI) allozymes on *Colias* butterflies. Purified PGI allozymes differ in reaction kinetics and thermostability, and genotypes differ in the flux rate of radiolabeled carbon in muscle. Field studies show temperature-dependent variation among genotypes in survivorship, flight activity, male mating success, and female fecundity. These results have been interpreted as an indication that kinetic differences among PGI allozymes affect glycolytic metabolite flux, thereby limiting ATP production rate and ultimately the power output of the flight muscles. The specific effects of PGI genotype on flight physiology remain to be determined, as there are no data showing genotype or genotype x temperature effects on muscle contraction, wingbeat kinematics, energetics, or other such measures of flight motor function.

An interesting recent development in the biology of PGI polymorphism in insects comes from a study of two species of crickets (*Gryllus veletis, G. pennsylvanicus*) that each show clinal variation in PGI allozyme frequency (86). Each species possesses six distinct PGI bands on starch electrophoresis gels; however, nucleotide sequence data show that amino acid substitutions have occurred at different sites in the two species, thus indicating independent evolution of a similar level of allozyme diversity. Moreover, the variable sites in both species have undergone predominately radical, as opposed to conservative, amino acid substitutions (i.e. substitutions that change the size, charge, or hydrophobicity at a site). The authors of the study suggest that there may be balancing selection occurring on gross physical characteristics such as overall charge of the PGI molecule. Rapid accumulation of radical amino acid substitutions in a metabolic enzyme is an unusual observation and warrants an examination of physiological effects.

In *Drosophila melanogaster* (Diptera), there is clinal and seasonal variation in alleles at the glycerol-3-phosphate dehydrogenase (GPDH) locus that has been shown to have subtle effects on flight performance. GPDH enzyme activity is highest for the SS genotype, intermediate for FS, and lowest for FF (87). The SS genotype shows an approximately 2 to 4% greater aerodynamic power output during tethered flight than the FF genotype among flies raised at 15°C and flown at 15°C, whereas the reverse is true for flies raised at 30°C and flown at 30°C. These temperature effects on power output are consistent with the geographical and seasonal variation observed at the GPDH locus in nature. Larval development rate also varies subtly among GPDH genotypes (88), and here again the S allele slightly outperforms the F allele at cooler temperatures, in a manner consistent with clinal variation in allele frequency.

In the moth *Epiphyas postvittana* (Lepidoptera), polymorphism at the phosphoglucomutase (PGM) locus is associated with significant variation in tethered flight duration (89). Artificial selection on flight capacity resulted in significant genotypic differentiation.

Polymorphism at the malate dehydrogenase allele (MDH-1) in honeybees (*Apis mellifera,* Hymenoptera) shows clinal variation on three continents and has been shown to affect the metabolic rate of honeybees during free flight (90, 91). A 20% difference between FF and SS MDH-1 genotypes was found in the original study (90), but since each genotype came from a different colony, it could not be determined what portion of this variation was attributable to genotypic as opposed to colony-level effects. A subsequent study (91) solved this problem by using sister queens (MF heterozygotes) to establish two adjacently located colonies. Both queens were artificially inseminated with sperm from a single S genotype drone (male Hymenoptera are haploid). This established replicate colonies of highly related worker bees having either the SM or the SF MDH-1 genotype. Flight metabolic rates of SF genotype worker bees significantly exceeded those of SM genotype bees by an average of 3%, with a significant colony effect of about the same magnitude. This effect of malate dehydrogenase genotype on honeybee flight metabolism is puzzling because the malate-aspartate shuttle, which is the main cytosol-to-mitochondria redox shuttle in mammalian muscles, is not known to operate in insect flight muscles. There may be some as-yet undetected activity of this shuttle in bee flight muscle, or perhaps the known gluconeogenic role of the malate-aspartate shuttle in the fat body affects the rate of metabolite supply to the working muscles during prolonged flights (91).

It was recently shown that a flight muscle-specific isoform of GPDH in *Drosophila* is located at specific locations on the sarcomere (the Z-lines and M-line), and imposes spatial organization on the two enzymes (GAPDH and aldolase) that catalyze adjacent reactions in glycolysis (92). The flight muscle-specific isoform contains three C-terminal amino acids not present in other GPDH isoforms. A mutant line that expresses a non-muscle isoform in flight muscle shows no spatial organization of GPDH or adjacent glycolytic enzymes, and the flies are flightless. This finding indicates that spatial organization of glycolytic enzymes has powerful functional consequences for insect flight muscles. No studies have yet examined the effects of naturally occurring allozyme variation on spatial organization of glycolytic enzymes in flight muscle or the age- or morph-related differences in GPDH isoform expression within individuals, but this may be an important source of functional differences. Furthermore, these results indicate that catalytic properties measured from purified enzymes or tissue homogenates may not always be an accurate indication of catalytic properties that exist in the spatially defined setting of the intact flight muscle sarcomere, thus reiterating the need for detailed in vivo studies.

VARIABILITY IN FLIGHT MUSCLE CONTRACTION

Insect flight muscles operate over a broad and unusually high range of contraction frequencies, from a low of about 5 Hz, up to values in excess of 500 Hz. Individual insects vary their muscle power output by changing both the frequency and amplitude of muscle contraction, and we have some knowledge of how variability in the composition of insect flight muscles affects these processes. As a starting point to understanding variability in the contractile function of insect flight muscles, it is instructive to consider how vertebrate striated muscles adjust to different contraction frequencies. A general trend in vertebrates is that striated muscles operating at higher contraction frequencies have faster shortening velocities and higher myosin ATPase rates (93, 94). Vertebrate muscles adjust to changes in contractile regimes that arise from growth, training, or environmental temperature variation (ectotherms) by qualitative and quantitative changes in expression of myosin heavy chain genes (95, 96), thereby changing the composition and contractile characteristics of their myosin cross bridges.

Insects also vary myosin expression, but not within their flight muscles. Insects use alternative splicing to generate myosin heavy chain isoforms in an age- and tissue-specific manner (97–99). These different myosins are likely to have functional differences, but flight muscles appear to express only one isoform. Furthermore, insect flight muscles show fairly uniform unloaded shortening velocities (V_{max}) across species that vary widely in wingbeat frequency. V_{max} measurements from katydids (100), sphinx moths (48), and dragonflies (101) show values ranging from 10 to16 muscle lengths per s, with no correlation between V_{max} and contraction frequency (range = 20–200 Hz). Tetanic tension per muscle cross-sectional area also shows little variation among species (generally about 10–13 N/cm^2). Thus the common vertebrate mechanism of adjusting myosin heavy chain composition and cross-bridge cycling rates in order to accommodate different contraction frequencies does not appear to be used by insect flight muscles.

Rather than adapt to different contractile regimes by varying the nature of the molecular motor itself, insect flight muscles vary the regulatory processes that turn muscle contraction on and off. The most radical such change is that between synchronous and asynchronous muscle activation. Synchronous muscles have a 1:1 relationship between neural stimuli and contractions, with contraction initiated by intracellular calcium release and terminated by calcium uptake by the SR. This is the typical regulatory mechanism for striated muscle. Asynchronous muscles are divergent; they show an approximately 1:10 ratio of neural stimuli to contractions. Neural stimulation in asynchronous muscles releases intracellular calcium that removes thin filament inhibition, but the cross bridges themselves are activated by stretch and deactivated by sarcomere shortening. Asynchronous flight muscles are stretched by thoracic deformation caused by contraction of antagonistic muscles, and this mechanical feedback keeps asynchronous muscles contracting over many cycles (1, 2). The large power-producing asynchronous muscles are controlled by a set of small synchronous muscles that produce little power (some in fact absorb power) but are capable of rapid and finely graded responses to neural stimuli (4, 102). This dichotomy of muscle size and function has led to the colorful characterization of "big dumb power-producing muscles" versus "small smart steering muscles."

In synchronous insect flight muscles, as well as in the synchronous sound-producing tymbal muscles of cicadas (Homoptera), there is a strong positive relationship between the relative density of SR and twitch contraction kinetics and operating frequency of the muscles (103). Similarly, there is an inverse relationship between the diameter of myofibrils and operating frequency. Having a higher density of SR and more narrow myofibrils reduces diffusion distances and increases calcium pumping capacity, which presumably results in more rapid calcium cycling within the sarcoplasm, and thus shorter response times for both activation and deactivation of the cross bridges. The drawback of adapting synchronous muscles to function at high frequencies is that elaboration of SR can occur only at the cost of reductions in the relative volume of the force-generating myofibrils, and/or the energy-supplying mitochondria. An extreme example of this tradeoff is a sound-producing muscle in the cicada, *Okanagana vanduzeei,* which has the highest known contraction frequency of any synchronous muscle (500 Hz). SR comprises nearly a third of this muscle's cross-sectional area, whereas myofibrils constitute only 22% (104). Flight muscles are more constrained than sound-producing muscles because they have an absolute requirement to generate sufficient force to counteract body weight, and there are no such extreme examples of ultrastructural specializations in synchronous insect flight muscles. The highest contraction frequencies of any synchronous flight muscles are probably those of sphingid moths, of which the smallest species have wingbeat frequencies in the range of 50–100 Hz (105).

The relationship described above between ultrastructure and contraction kinetics also occurs between muscles that perform different functions within an individual insect (100, 106). In a katydid that uses its metathoracic muscles strictly for flying (20 Hz) and its mesothoracic muscles for sound production (200 Hz) in addition to flying, the metathoracic muscles have a much briefer twitch duration (6–8 versus 12–15 ms from onset to 50% relaxation), narrower myofibrils, and a smaller ratio of myofibril volume to SR volume. One curious result is that the increase in SR and reduction of myofibrillar diameter, thought to allow faster twitch kinetics, develop prior to the attainment of faster twitch kinetics, thus suggesting that additional factors with a different developmental time course must also be affecting twitch kinetics. Densities and/or activities of Ca^{2+} ATPase pumps and Ca^{2+} gates in the SR are likely candidates, but this possibility remains unexplored.

In addition to ultrastructural changes that affect the rate of calcium diffusion, recent studies indicate that variability in calcium regulatory processes also affects cross-bridge recruitment and force production. In flight muscles of the dragonfly *Libellula pulchella,* the mixture of isoforms of the alternatively spliced calcium regulatory protein troponin-t changes during adult maturation, with correlated changes in calcium sensitivity of muscle activation and twitch force (101). The same muscles show no maturational changes in V_{max} or tetanic tension, thus indicating that variation in twitch tension is the result of changes in the way the muscle responds to a transient pulse of calcium rather than a difference in cross-bridge kinetics. The mechanisms by which increased calcium sensitivity affect twitch force remain to be determined, although it is quite likely that higher calcium sensitivity increases the probability or duration of activation of any given cross-bridge binding site during a single calcium transient, particularly at myofilament locations that are relatively distant from the SR membrane. A spatially explicit model for calcium movement and troponin binding during single SR release events in frog muscle (107) indicates that there is spatial variation in the rate and extent of force development and that differences in calcium sensitivity of troponin units can alter these effects.

It is interesting to consider why Libellulid dragonflies, which have the highest known investment in flight muscle (FMR reaches as high as 0.63 at maturity), have a mechanism that allows them to modulate the force and power production of those muscles. Mark-recapture studies of newly emerged free-living *Libellula* dragonflies indicate that a large proportion of individuals fail to gain mass and apparently starve during the first few days of adult maturation (108). It has been suggested that power output, and therefore energy consumption during flight, is downregulated during the early adult stage when the only function of flight in these dragonflies is for capturing small, non-evasive prey. Muscle power output and energy consumption are then upregulated at maturity when high-performance flight is used during intense aerial competition for mating territories. Interestingly, the protein whose isoform expression appears to mediate this functional switch, troponin-t, has recently been suggested to perform a similar role in modulating power output and energy consumption in mammalian heart muscle during severe stress and impending failure (109). Thus troponin-t isoform variation may be generally involved in modulating performance versus economy in striated muscles.

In addition to regulation by troponin-tropomyosin, contraction of insect flight muscles is also regulated, or at least modulated, by phosphorylation of myosin light chains (MLCs). In *D. melanogaster* flight muscles, myosin light chain kinase (MLCK) and other phosphorylases appear to become active during the first few hours following adult emergence, since only dephosphorylated MLC is present in late pupae, and phosphorylated MLC accumulates in the hours following adult emergence (110, 111). MLC phosphorylation increases the ATPase activity of purified *D. melanogaster* myosin (110, 112). These observations, along with the similar time course of MLC phosphorylation and flight acquisition in newly emerged adults, suggest that MLC phosphorylation upregulates muscle activation.

Genetic manipulations of *D. melanogaster* have been used to characterize the in vivo functional effects of variability in MLC phosphorylation (113, 114). Flightless heterozygotes of homozygous-lethal MLC null mutants have been rescued to normal muscle ultrastructure and flight ability by P-element transformation with the wild-type allele. Site-directed mutagenesis was subsequently used to create cDNA constructs in which two serine residues, the sites of MLC2 phosphorylation by MLCK, were replaced by unphosphorylatable alanines. These constructs were transposed into MLC2 null mutants, resulting in lines of flies in which the only full-length, functional copy of MLC2 lacked either one or both of the sites that can be phosphorylated by MLCK. The resulting flies were examined for flight muscle ultrastructure, skinned fiber mechanical characteristics, and aerodynamic power output and metabolic power input during tethered flight (114). Muscles from the flies transformed with MLC2 lacking one or both MLCK phosphorylation sites showed no apparent changes in myofibrillar ultrastructure during rest, maximal activation, or rigor, nor did they show significantly altered calcium sensitivity, cross-bridge kinetics, or maximum steady state isometric tension. Mutant muscles did show mechanical features indicative of a reduced recruitment of force-producing cross bridges during stretch activation. Mechanical power output of mutant lines during tethered flight was reduced by 19 to 28% compared with wild-type transformants, along with a similar decrease in metabolic power input, with no change in efficiency. Mutant flies could generally produce sufficient vertical net aerodynamic force to support their body weight, but significantly less than the 1.35 force/weight ratio produced by wild-type rescued and unmanipulated control flies.

These results demonstrate that phosphorylation of MLC2 has a modulatory effect on stretch-activated flight muscle force and power production in *Drosophila*, although the significance of the naturally occurring changes in phosphorylation that occur during maturation remains to be determined. One possibility is that the delay in MLC2 phosphorylation during the first few hours following adult emergence allows the thoracic exoskeleton and wings to harden prior to full force and power production. This would be analogous to the neural suppression of muscle tension that prevents damage to the legs of grasshoppers during the period following molting, when the cuticle is not yet structurally mature (115).

Flightin, a novel protein found to date only in insect flight muscle, also shows a change in phosphorylation during adult maturation in *Drosophila* (116). Flies that are heterozygous for a chromosomal mutation that deletes the flightin gene are flightless, and their isolated muscles show patterns of stretch activation that suggest altered cross-bridge kinetics (117). How phosphorylation of flightin affects cross bridges and the functional significance of maturational changes in flightin phosphorylation have yet to be determined.

Different strains of *D. melanogaster* are polymorphic for a flight muscle–specific form of tropomyosin (the misnamed troponin-H), but different forms of this protein show no qualitative effects on flight performance (118). Like many other studies examining *Drosophila* flight ability, this study used a fairly crude and qualitative performance assay (94–99.5% of the flies are reported to have gone "up"), so subtle differences would not have been revealed. Recent development of methods for obtaining quantitative assays of *Drosophila* performance during tethered (114, 119) and free flight (120) will allow in future studies a more sensitive resolution of in vivo consequences of variability in motor performance.

A large number of studies have examined the effects on flight and/or muscle contractile function of mutant muscle contractile proteins or altered tissue specificity of protein isoform expression in *Drosophila*. Because these alterations have no known role in natural variation, I forgo reviewing them here.

SUMMARY

Like other forms of striated muscle, insect flight muscles are highly labile. In order to provide sufficient aerodynamic power output for weight-supported flight, insect flight muscles must be very large and metabolically active, and thus they constitute a considerable expense to synthesize and maintain. Materials and energy consumed by flight muscle growth and maintenance have a large negative impact on reproductive output. However, in ecological settings where flight is important, relatively larger flight muscles are clearly beneficial. Thus relative size of the flight musculature presumably evolves to a level that balances selective forces favoring different and often conflicting aspects of organismal performance. Because the balance of selective forces shifts in different habitats, at different life stages, and in specific ecological and social contexts, many insects have evolved the ability to rapidly build up, break down, or alter the composition of their flight muscles.

Our current understanding of the physiological details underlying these processes are, in general, fairly rudimentary. Endocrine studies have revealed the gross patterns of hormonal regulation of flight muscle size and composition, but the molecular details are poorly known. Metabolic biochemistry in insects shows ample intraspecific variation, but there is little understanding of how allozymes affect specific metabolic pathways or whole-organism performance. Ultrastructural variation that affects twitch kinetics and contraction frequency in synchronous flight muscles is well documented, but recent studies show that contractile mechanics are also strongly affected by molecular variation in regulatory proteins associated with both the thin and thick filaments. Naturally occurring molecular variation affecting contractile regulation has been examined in only two taxa, so it is impossible to make generalizations regarding the prevalence of these mechanisms. The emergence of *Drosophila* as a genetically malleable model organism has allowed powerful manipulative experiments, but the predominant focus has been on determining the effects of experimentally induced mutations rather than naturally occurring variation. Variability in insect flight muscle size and function has been much more extensively studied by researchers interested in ecology, evolution, and biomechanics than by comparative physiologists whose main interests lie in determining the mechanistic bases and root causes of naturally occurring variability. It is abundantly clear that insect flight physiology constitutes a relatively untapped source for future exploration and discovery by comparative physiologists, and a fertile ground for integrative studies that combine mechanistic approaches with ecology, evolution, and behavior.

Visit the Annual Reviews home page at www.AnnualReviews.org.

LITERATURE CITED

1. Pringle JWS. 1957. *Insect Flight.* Cambridge, UK: Cambridge Univ. Press
2. Tregear RT. 1977. *Insect Flight Muscle.* Amsterdam: North-Holland
3. Beenakkers AMT, van der Horst DJ, van Marrewijk WJA. 1985. Biochemical processes directed to flight muscle metabolism. In *Comprehensive Insect Biochemistry and Pharmacology,* ed. GA Kerlat, LI Gilbert, 10:451–86. New York: Permagon
4. Dickinson MH, Tu MS. 1997. The function of Dipteran flight muscle. *Comp. Biochem. Physiol.* 116A:223–38
5. Heinrich B. 1993. *The Hot-Blooded Insects, Strategies and Mechanisms of Thermoregulation.* Cambridge, MA: Harvard Univ. Press
6. Morgan KR, Shelly TE, Kimsey LS. 1985. Body temperature regulation, energy metabolism, and foraging in light-seeking and shage seeking robber flies. *J. Comp. Physiol. B* 155:561–70
7. Marden JH. 1987. Maximum lift production during takeoff in flying animals. *J. Exp. Biol.* 130:235–58
8. Marden JH. 1989. Bodybuilding dragonflies: costs and benefits of maximizing flight muscle. *Physiol. Zool.* 62:505–21
9. Johnson CG. 1969. *Migration and Dispersal of Insects by Flight.* London: Methuen

10. Harrison RG. 1980. Dispersal polymorphism in insects. *Annu. Rev. Ecol. Syst.* 11:95–118
11. Roff DA. 1986. The evolution of wing dimorphism in insects. *Evolution* 40: 1009–20
12. Roff DA. 1990. The evolution of flightlessness in insects. *Ecol. Monogr.* 60: 389–421
13. Roff DA. 1994. Habitat persistence and the evolution of wing dimorphism in insects. *Am. Nat.* 144:772–98
14. Dingle H, Winchell R. 1997. Juvenile hormone as a mediator of plasticity in insect life histories. *Arch. Insect Biochem. Physiol.* 35:359–73
15. Zera AJ, Denno RF. 1997. Physiology and ecology of dispersal polymorphism in insects. *Annu. Rev. Entomol.* 42:207–31
16. Tada S, Honma K, Kakizaki M, Fujisaki K. 1994. Genetic mode of flight muscle dimorphism in a Scarabaeid, *Heptophylla picea* Motschulsky. *Appl. Entomol. Zool.* 29:303–5
17. Tada S, Honma K, Kakizaki M, Fujisaki K. 1995. Geographic variation of flight muscle dimorphism in adult females of a scarabacid, *Heptophylla picea. Appl. Entomol. Zool.* 30:501–7
18. Robertson IC. 1998. Flight muscle changes in male pine engraver beetles

during reproduction: the effects of body size, mating status and breeding failure. *Physiol. Entomol.* 23:75–80

19. Bursell, E. 1961. The behaviour of tsetse flies (*Glossina swynnertoni* Austen) in relation to problems of sampling. *Proc. R. Ent. Soc. London Ser.* A 36:9–20

20. Anholt BR, Marden JH, Jenkins DM. 1991. Patterns of mass gain in adult odonates. *Can. J. Zool.* 69:1156–63

21. Crnokrak P, Roff DA. 1995. Fitness differences associated with calling behavior in the two wing morphs of the sand cricket, *Gryllus firmus. Anim. Behav.* 50:1475–81

22. Fujisaki K. 1992. A male fitness advantage to wing reduction in the oriental chinch bug, *Cavelerius saccharivorus* Okajima (Heteroptera: Lygaeidae). *Res. Popul. Ecol. Kyoto* 34:171–81

23. Rankin MA, Rankin SM. 1980. Some factors affecting presumed migratory flight activity of the convergent ladybeetle, *Hippodamia convergens* (Coccinellidae: Coleoptera) *Biol. Bull.* 158: 336–69

24. Rankin MA, Rankin SM. 1980. The hormonal control of migratory flight behavior in the convergent ladybeetle, *Hippodamia convergens* (Coccinellidae: Coleoptera). *Physiol. Entomol.* 5:175–82

25. McAnelly, ML. 1985. Migration in the grasshopper *Melanoplus sanguinipes* (Fab.). I. The capacity for flight in nonswarming populations. *Biol. Bull.* 170:368–77

26. McAnelly ML, Rankin MA. 1986. Migration in the grasshopper *Melanoplus sanguinipes* (Fab.). II. Interactions between flight and reproduction. *Biol. Bull.* 170:378–92

27. Weber, DC, Ferro DN, Stoffolano J. 1993. Quantifying flight of Colorado potato beetles (Coleoptera: Chrysomelidae) with a microcomputer-based flight mill system. *Ann. Entomol. Soc. Am.* 86:66–71

28. Yee WL, Anderson JR. 1995. Tethered flight capabilities and survival of *Lambornella clarki*-infected, blood-fed, and gravid *Aedes sierrensis* (Diptera: Culicidae). *J. Med. Entomol.* 32:153–60

29. Dingle H. 1996. *Migration: The Biology of Life on the Move.* Oxford, UK: Oxford Univ. Press

30. Swanson MS, Zieminn SM, Miller DD, Garber EA, Margoliash E. 1985. Developmental expression of nuclear genes that encode mitochondrial proteins: insect cytochromes c. *Proc. Natl. Acad. Sci.USA* 82:1964–68

31. Haunerland NH, Chen X, Andolfatto P, Chisholm JM, Wang Z. 1993. Developmental changes of FABP concentration, expression, and intracellular distribution in locust flight muscle. *Mol. Cell. Biochem.* 123:153–58

32. van der Horst DJ, van Doorn JM, Passier PC, Vork MM, Glatz JF. 1993. Role of fatty acid-binding protein in lipid metabolism of insect flight muscle. *Mol. Cell. Biochem.* 123:145–52

33. Zera AJ, Mole S, Rokke K. 1994. Lipid, carbohydrate and nitrogen content of long-winged and short-winged *G. firmus:* implications for the physiological cost of flight capability. *J. Insect Physiol.* 40:1037–44

34. Wegener G. 1996. Flying insects: model systems in exercise physiology. *Experientia* 52:404–12

35. Ramirez JM. 1998. Reconfiguration of the respiratory network at the onset of locust flight. *J. Neurophysiol.* 80:3137–47

36. Vroemen SF, van der Horst DJ, van Marrewijk WJ. 1998. New insights into adipokinetic hormone signaling. *Mol. Cell. Endocrinol.* 141:7–12

37. Deleted in proof

38. Marden JH, Kramer MG, Frisch J. 1996. Age-related variation in body temperature, thermoregulation and activity in a thermally polymorphic dragonfly. *J. Exp. Biol.* 199:529–35

39. Chai P. 1986. Field observations and

feeding experiments on the responses of rufous-tailed jacamars (*Galbula ruficauda*) to free-flying butterflies in a tropical rainforest. *Biol. J. Linn. Soc.* 29:161–89

40. Chai, P. 1988. Wing coloration of free-flying Neotropical butterflies as a signal learned by a specialized avian predator. *Biotropica* 20:20–30

41. Marden JH, Chai P. 1991. Aerial predation and butterfly design: how palatability, mimicry, and the need for evasive flight constrain mass allocation. *Am. Nat.* 138:15–36

42. Srygley RB, Chai P. 1990. Flight morphology of Neotropical butterflies: palatability and distribution of mass to the thorax and abdomen. *Oecologia* 84:491–99

43. Wickman PO. 1992. Sexual selection and butterfly design-a comparative study. *Evolution* 46:1525–36

44. Srygley RB, Dudley R. 1993. Correlations of the position of center of body mass with butterfly escape tactics. *J. Exp. Biol.* 174: 155–66

45. Srygley RB, Kingsolver JGH. 1997. Effects of weight loading on flight performance and survival of palatable butterflies. *Am. Zool.* 37:107A (Abstr.)

46. Marden JH. 1989. Effects of load-lifting constraints on the mating system of a dance fly (Empididae: Hilara). *Ecology* 70:496–502

47. Coelho JR. 1997. Sexual size dimorphism and flight behavior in cicada killers, *Sphecius speciosus. Oikos* 79: 371–75

48. Marden JH. 1995. Evolutionary adaptation of contractile performance in muscle of ectothermic winter-flying moths. *J. Exp. Biol.* 198:2087–94

49. Novicki A 1989. Control of growth and ultrastructural maturation of a cricket flight muscle. *J. Exp. Zool.* 250:263–72

50. Wang Z, Chen X, Haunerland NH. 1993. Flight muscle development in juvenile and adult forms of the desert locust,

Schistocerca gregaria. J. Insect Physiol. 39:325–33

51. Zera AJ, Tiebel KC. 1988. Brachypterizing effect of group rearing, juvenile hormone-IIII, and methoprene on winglength development in the wing-dimorphic cricket, *Gryllus rubens. J. Insect Physiol.* 34:489–98

52. Zera AJ, Tiebel KC. 1989. Differences in juvenile hormone esterase activity between presumptive macropterous and brachypterous *Gryllus rubens:* implications for the hormonal control of wing polymorphism. *J. Insect Physiol.* 35:7–17

53. Zera AF, Strambi C, Tieble KC, Strambi A, Rankin MA. 1989. Juvenile hormone and ecdysteroid titers during critical periods of wing morph determination in *Gryllus rubens. J. Insect Physiol.* 35:501–11

54. Hegstrom CD, Riddiford LM, Truman JW. 1998. Steroid and neuronal regulation of ecdysone receptor expression during metamorphosis of muscle in the moth, *Manduca sexta. J. Neurosci.* 18: 1786–94

55. Kobayashi M, Ishikawa H. 1994. Mechanisms of histolysis in indirect flight muscles of altate aphid (*Acyrthosiphon pisum). J. Insect. Physiol.* 40:33–38

56. Kobayashi M, Ishikawa H. 1993. Involvement of juvenile hormone and ubiquitin-dependent proteolysis in flight muscle breakdown of altae aphid (*Acyrthosiphon pisum). J. Insect. Physiol.* 40:107–11

57. Tanaka S. 1994. Endocrine control of ovarian development and flight muscle histolysis in a wing dimorphic cricket, *Modicogryllus confirmatus. J. Insect Physiol.* 40: 483–90

58. Edwards FJ. 1970. Endocrine control of flight muscle histolysis in *Dysdercus intermedius. J. Insect Physiol.* 16:2027–31

59. Davis WL, Jones RG, Framer GR. 1989. Insect hemolymph factor promotes mus-

cle histolysis in *Solenopsis. Anat. Rec.* 224:473–78

60. Jones RG, Davis WL, Hung AC, Vinson SB. 1978. Insemination-induced histolysis of the flight musculature in fire ants (*Solenopsis,* spp.): an ultrastructural study. *Am. J. Anat.* 151:603–10

61. Jones RG, Davis WL, Vinson SB. 1982. A histochemical and X-ray microanalysis study of calcium changes in insect flight muscle degeneration in *Solenopsis,* the queen fire ant. *J. Histochem. Cytochem.* 30:293–304

62. Davis WL, Jacoby BH, Jones RG, Goodman DB. 1993. Superoxide formation preceding flight muscle histolysis in *Solenopsis:* fine structural cytochemistry and biochemistry. *Histochem. J.* 25:478–90

63. Mykles DL, Skinner DM. 1990. Calcium-dependent proteinases in Crustaceans. In *Intracellular Calcium-Dependent Proteolysis,* ed. RL Mellgren, T Murachi, pp. 139–54. Boca Raton, FL: CRC Press

64. Davis WL, Jacoby BH, Goodman DB. 1994. Immunolocalization of ubiquitin in degenerating insect flight muscle. *Histochem. J.* 26:298–305

65. Hochstrasser M. 1996. Ubiquitin-dependent protein degradation. *Annu. Rev. Genet.* 30:405–39

66. Shean BS, Mykles DL. 1995. Polyubiquitin in crustacean striated muscle: increased expression and conjugation during molt-induced claw muscle atrophy. *Biochem. Biophys. Acta* 1264:312–22

67. Schwartz LM. 1992. Insect muscle as a model for programmed cell death. *J. Neurobiol.* 23:1312–26

68. Myer A, Schwartz LM. 1996. Allelic variation of the polyubiquitin gene in the tobacco hawkmoth, *Manduca sexta,* and its regulation by heat shock and programmed cell death. *Insect. Biochem. Mol. Biol.* 26:1037–46

69. Haas AL, Baboshina O, Williams B,

Schwartz LM. 1995. Coordinated induction of the ubiquitin conjugation pathway accompanies the developmentally programmed death of insect skeletal muscle. *J. Biol. Chem.* 270:9407–12

70. Schwartz LM, Jones ME, Kosz L, Kuah K. 1993. Selective repression of actin and myosin heavy chain expression during the programmed cell death of insect skeletal muscle. *Dev. Biol.* 158:448–55

71. Nair CRM, Prabhu VKK. 1985. Entry of proteins from degenerating flight muscles into oocytes in *Dystdercus cingulatus* (Heteroptera: Pyrrhocoridae). *J. Insect Physiol.* 31:383–88

72. Tanaka S. 1991. De-alation and its influence on egg production and flight muscle histolysis in a cricket (*Velarifictorus parvus)* that undergoes inter-reproductive migration. *J. Insect Physiol.* 37:517–23

73. Zera AJ, Mole S. 1994. The physiological costs of flight capability in wing-dimorphic crickets. *Res. Popul. Ecol. Kyoto* 36:151–56

74. Zera AJ, Sall J, Grudzinski K. 1997. Flight-muscle polymorphism in the cricket *Gryllus firmus*: muscle characteristics and their influence on the evolution of flightlessness. *Physiol. Zool.* 70:519–29

75. Zera AJ, Potts J, Kobus K. 1998. The physiology of life-history tradeoffs: experimental analysis of a hormonally induced life-history tradeoff in *Gryllus assimilis. Am. Nat.* 152:7–23

76. Zera AJ, Koehn RK, Hall JG. 1985. Allozymes and biochemical adaptation. In *Comprehensive Insect Biochemistry and Pharmacology,* ed. GA Kerlat, LI Gilbert, 10:633–74. New York: Permagon

77. Kreitman M, Akashi H. 1995. Molecular evidence for natural selection. *Annu. Rev. Ecol. Syst.* 26:403–22

78. Watt WB. 1977. Adaptation at specific loci. I. Natural selection on phosphoglucose isomerase of *Colias* butterflies: biochemical and population aspects. *Genetics* 87:177–94

79. Watt WB. 1983. Adaptation at specific loci. II. Demographic and biochemical elements in the maintenance of the *Colias* PGI polymorphism. *Genetics* 103:691–724

80. Watt WB, Cassin RC, Swan MS. 1983. Adaptation at specific loci. III. Field behavior and survivorship differences among *Colias* PGI genotypes are predictable from in vitro biochemistry. *Genetics* 103:725–39

81. Watt WB, Carter PA, Blower SM. 1985. Adaptation at specific loci. Differential mating success among glycolytic allozyme genotypes of *Colias* butterflies. *Genetics* 109:157–75

82. Watt WB, Carter PA, Donohue K. 1986. Females' choice of "good genotypes" as mates is promoted by an insect mating system. *Science* 233:1187–90

83. Watt WB, Boggs CL. 1987. Allelic isozymes as probes of the evolution of metabolic organization. *Isozymes Curr. Top. Biol. Med. Res.* 15:27–47

84. Carter PA, Watt WB. 1988. Adaptation at specific loci: metabolically adjacent enzyme loci may have very distinct experiences of selective pressures. *Genetics* 119:913–24

85. Watt WB. 1992. Eggs, enzymes, and evolution: natural genetic variants change insect fecundity. *Proc. Natl. Acad. Sci. USA* 89:10608–12

86. Katz LA, Harrison RG. 1997. Balancing selection on electrophoretic variation of phosphoglucose isomerase in two species of field crickets: *Gryllus veletis* and *G. pennsylvanicus*. *Genetics* 147:609–21

87. Barnes PT, Laurie-Ahlberg CC. 1986. Genetic variability of flight metabolism in *Drosophila melanogaster*. III. Effects of Gpdh allozymes and environmental temperature on power output. *Genetics* 112:267–94

88. Barnes PT, Holland B, Courreges V. 1989. Genotype-by-environment and epistatic interactions in *Drosophila melanogaster:* the effects of Gpdh allozymes, genetic background and rearing temperature on larval developmental time and viability. *Genetics* 122:859–68

89. Gu HN. 1991. Electrophoretic variation at flight-related enzyme loci and its possible association with flight capacity in *Epiphyas postvittana*. *Biochem. Genet.* 29:345–54

90. Coelho JR, Mitton JB. 1988. Oxygen consumption during hovering is associated with genetic variation of enzymes in honeybees. *Func. Ecol.* 2:141–46

91. Harrison JF, Nielsen DI, Page RE Jr. 1996. Malate dehydrogenase phenotype, temperature and colony effects on flight metabolic rate in the honey-bee, *Apis mellifera.. Func. Ecol.* 10:81–88

92. Wojtas K, Slepecky N, von Kalm L, Sullivan D. 1997. Flight muscle function in Drosophila requires colocalization of glycolytic enzymes. *Mol. Biol. Cell* 8:1665–75

93. Close RI. 1965. The relation between intrinsic speed of shortening and duration of the active state of the muscle. *J. Physiol.* 180:542–59

94. Close RI. 1972. Dynamic properties of mammalian skeletal muscles. *Physiol. Rev.* 52:129–97

95. Pette D, Staron RS. 1997. Mammalian skeletal muscle fiber type transitions. *Int. Rev. Cytol.* 170:143–223

96. Goldspink G. 1998. Selective gene expression during adaptation of muscle in response to different physiological demands. *Comp. Biochem. Physiol. B* 120B:5–15

97. Standiford DM, Davis MB, Sun W, Emerson CP Jr. 1997. Splice-junction elements and intronic sequences regulate alternative splicing of the *Drosophila* myosin heavy chain gene transcript. *Genetics* 147:725–41

98. Bernstein SI, Milligan RA. 1997. Fine

tuning a molecular motor: the location of alternative domains in the *Drosophila* myosin head. *J. Mol. Biol.* 271:1–6

99. Davis MB, Dietz J, Standiford DM, Emerson CP Jr. 1998. Transposable element insertions respecify alternative exon splicing in three *Drosophila* myosin heavy chain mutants. *Genetics* 150:1105–14

100. Josephson RK. 1984. Contraction dynamics of flight and stridulatory muscles of tettigonid insects. *J. Exp. Biol.* 108:77–96

101. Fitzhugh GH, Marden JH. 1997. Maturational changes in troponin-t expression, Ca^{2+} sensitivity and twitch contraction kinetics in dragonfly flight muscle. *J. Exp. Biol.* 200:1473–82

102. Dickinson MH, Lehman F-O, Chan WP. 1998. The control of mechanical power in insect flight. *Am. Zool.* 38:718–28

103. Josephson RK, Young D. 1987. Fiber ultrastructure and contraction kinetics in insect fast muscles. *Am. Zool.* 27:991–1000

104. Josephson RK, Young D. 1985. A synchronous insect muscle with an operating frequency greater than 500Hz. *J. Exp. Biol.* 118:185–208

105. Casey TM. 1976. Flight energetics of sphinx moths: power input during hovering flight. *J. Exp. Biol.* 64:529–43

106. Ready, N.E. 1986. Development of fast singing muscles in a katydid. *J. Exp. Zool.* 238: 43–54

107. Baylor SM, Hollingworth S. 1998. Model of sarcomeric Ca^{2+} movements, including ATP Ca^{2+} binding and diffusion, during activation of frog skeletal muscle. *J. Gen. Physiol.* 112:297–316

108. Marden JH, Fitzhugh GH, Wolf MR. 1998. From molecules to mating success: integrative biology of muscle maturation in a dragonfly. *Am. Zool.* 38:528–44

109. Kameyama T, Chen Z, Bell SP, VanBuren P, Maughan D, LeWinter MM.

1998. Mechanoenergetic alterations during the transition from cardiac hypertrophy to failure in Dahl salt-sensitive rats. *Circulation* 98:2919–29

110. Takahashi S, Maruyama K. 1987. Activity changes in myosin ATPase during metamorphosis of fruitfly. *Zool. Sci.* 4:833–38

111. Takahashi S, Takano-Ohmuro H, Maruyama K. 1990. Regulation of Drosophila myosin ATPase activity by phosphorylation of myosin light chains–I. Wild-type fly. *Comp. Biochem. Physiol.* 95B:179–81

112. Takahashi S, Takano-Ohmuro H, Maruyama K, Hotta Y. 1990. Regulation of *Drosophila* myosin ATPase activity by phosphorylation of myosin light chains–II. Flightless and mfd- fly. *Comp. Biochem. Physiol.* 95B:183–85

113. Tohtong R, Yamashita H, Graham M, Haeberle J, Simcox A, Maughan D. 1995. Impairment of muscle function caused by mutations of phosphorylation sites in myosin regulatory light chain. *Nature* 374:650–53

114. Dickinson MH, Hyatt CJ, Lehmann F-O, Moore JR, Reedy MC, et al. 1997. Phosphorylation-dependent power output of transgenic flies: an integrated study. *Biophys. J.* 73:3122–34

115. Norman A. 1995. Adaptive changes in locust kicking and jumping behaviour during development. *J. Exp. Biol.* 198:1341–50

116. Vigoreaux JO, Perry LM. 1994. Multiple isoelectric variants of flightin in *Drosophila* stretch-activated muscles are generated by temporally regulated phosphorylations. *J. Muscle Res. Cell Motil.* 15:607–16

117. Vigoreaux JO, Hernandez C, Moore J, Ayer G, Maughan D. 1998. A genetic deficiency that spans the flightin gene of *Drosophila melanogaster* affects the ultrastructure and function of the flight muscles. *J. Exp. Biol.* 201:2033–44

118. Cripps RM, Sparrow JC. 1992. Polymorphism in a Drosophila indirect flight muscle-specific tropomyosin isozyme does not affect flight ability. *Biochem. Genet.* 30:159–68

119. Dickinson MH, Lighton JR. 1995. Muscle efficiency and elastic storage in the flight motor of *Drosophila*. *Science* 268:87–90

120. Marden JH, Wolf MR, Weber KE. 1997. Aerial performance of *Drosophila melanogaster* from populations selected for upwind flight ability. *J. Exp. Biol.* 200:2747–55

Annu. Rev. Physiol. 2000. 62:179–205

FLIGHT RESPIRATION AND ENERGETICS

Jon F. Harrison[1] and Stephen P. Roberts[2]

[1]*Department of Biology, Arizona State University, Tempe, Arizona 85287–1501;
e-mail: j.harrison@asu.edu;* [2]*Department of Biological Sciences, University of Nevada,
Las Vegas, Nevada 89154–4004*

Key Words   flight, metabolism, gas exchange, muscle, temperature

■ **Abstract**   We use a comparative approach to examine some of the physiological traits that make flight possible. Comparisons of related fliers and runners suggest that fliers generally have higher aerobic metabolic capacities than runners but that the difference is highly dependent on the taxa studied. The high metabolic rates of fliers relative to runners, especially in insects, are correlated with high locomotory muscle cycle frequencies and low efficiences of conversion of metabolic power to mechanical power. We examine some factors that produce variation in flight respiration and energetics. Air temperature strongly affects the flight metabolic rate of some insects and birds. Flight speed interacts with flier mass, so that small fliers tend to exhibit a J-shaped power curve and larger fliers a U-shaped power curve. As body size increases, mass-specific aerobic flight metabolism decreases in most studies, but mass-specific power output is constant or increases, leading to an increase in efficiency with size. Intraspecific studies have revealed specific genetically based effects on flight metabolism and power output and multiple ecological correlates of flight capabilities.

INTRODUCTION

Flight ability is considered a key trait responsible for the tremendous success and diversity of the insects, birds, and bats. This paper reviews recent advances in our understanding of flight respiration and energetics and the physiological mechanisms that underlie flight ability in these diverse taxa. This is a broad topic, and the interested reader should refer to recent reviews focused on avian flight energetics and biomechanics (1), related reviews in this volume (2, 3), reviews of vertebrate and invertebrate locomotory physiology (4, 5), books on comparative exercise physiology (6), and recent and forthcoming books on animal flight (7, 8). Herein we identify and suggest explanations for comparative patterns in flight energetics and respiration and point attention to serious gaps in our understanding of these topics.

This review is divided broadly into two sections. In the first section, we review physiological correlates of flight, including aerobic and anaerobic metabolism, gas exchange structure and function, and flight muscle biomechanics and biochemistry. In the second section we examine factors that are associated with variation in flight respiration and energetics of volant animals, including temperature, flight speed, flier body mass, and intraspecific genetic variation.

A recurring theme of flight energetics is a comparison of the mechanical power output of flight to the metabolic power input. The mechanical power output of flying animals has been estimated using various physical and kinematic measurements, combined with biomechanical theory. For example, power output of fliers can be estimated from measures of wing beat frequency, wing stroke amplitude, and body and stroke plane angles, combined with measures of wing and body morphology (9–11). Power outputs can also be estimated from the force outputs of flying or running muscles or bodies in vivo or in vitro (12–14). The metabolic power input is the rate of energy production by metabolic processes that supply ATP to the flight muscles. Metabolic power input has most commonly been estimated using respirometric measures of gas exchange, although other methods such as mass balance (15) and doubly labeled water (16) have been used.

PHYSIOLOGICAL CORRELATES OF FLIGHT

What are the physiological mechanisms that make flight possible? One approach to answering this question is to compare the physiological systems of flying and nonvolant organisms. The evolutionary relationships of the insect orders are poorly known, so we compare the characteristics of insects fliers and runners across many orders and within single orders. Birds are usually compared to mammals by physiologists because they are the two major homeothermic groups, but given their reptilian ancestory, it is perhaps more interesting to compare bird and reptile locomotory physiology. However, since there are so many dramatic differences between birds and extant reptiles, the best comparison for understanding the physiological correlates of avian flight may be to contrast running and flying birds. We compare bat physiological systems to runners of many mammalian orders. These comparisons all imperfectly control for possible historical effects on physiology, which emphasizes the need for future physiological studies of flight that are performed in a phylogenetic context. An approach that may hold particular promise is a study of physiological systems of insect groups such as the stoneflies, which have species ranging from flightless through various degrees of flight capability (17).

Aerobic Flight Metabolism

Fliers are considered paradigms of aerobic performance, and the assertion that they have higher aerobic metabolic rates than do runners or swimmers is common in the literature. Is this paradigm justified? We address this question by considering the mass-specific oxygen consumption rates (V_{O2}) of flying and running insects, birds, mammals, and reptiles. Our analysis focuses on the size range of

1 to 7 g, where these taxa nearly overlap in body size (Table 1). These comparisons can also be made using allometric relationships of aerobic locomotory metabolism for these groups (Figure 1).

Insects   Flying insects have mass-specific oxygen consumption rates at least 3-fold greater and often over 30-fold greater than reported for terrestrially locomoting insects at the same body temperature (Table 1, Figure 1). Allometric comparisons of 118 invertebrate flying and running species from diverse orders suggest that the aerobic capacity of a 1-g flier is 28 times that of a 1-g runner, with this factorial difference little affected by body size (Figure 1) (5). Thus the higher V_{O_2} of fliers relative to runners seems independent of phylogeny (although a careful study of this question is lacking).

Allometric comparisons (18) and a perusal of Table 1 suggest that flight metabolic rates of insects with asynchronous muscle overlap those of insects with synchronous flight muscle, despite the much higher wing beat frequencies

TABLE 1   Rates of oxygen consumption (ml g^{-1} h^{-1}) of active 1- to 7-g animals

Animal	Mass (g)	Reference	V_{O_2}(ml g^{-1} h^{-1})
Flying insects			
"Euglossine bee"	1	(157)	66
"Sphingid moth"	2	(172)	62
Fig beetle	1.3	(173)	61
Cicada	2.8	(49)	39
Tabanid fly	1	(174)	18
Locust	1.7	(175)	13
Running insects			
"Running insect"	2	(5)	2.4
Jumping grasshopper	1.7	(176)	1.3
"Running endothermic beetle"	1.3	(32)	4.5
Hovering hummingbirds			
V_{O_2} max, heliox	3.5	(177)	55
"Hummingbird"	2	(25)	45
"Hovering bird"	2	(178)	42
"Running reptile" (30°C)	2	(179)	1.2
Hovering Glossophagine bat	7	(25)	25
Running mammals			
Etruscan shrew	2.4	(180)	24
"Mammal V_{O_2} max"	2	(26)	16

Values for animals in quotations are calculated from published allometric regressions between body mass and oxygen consumption or metabolic rate, with 1 ml O_2 (STP) s^{-1} (20.1 W), and a Q_{10} of 2 applied if necessary for temperature correction.

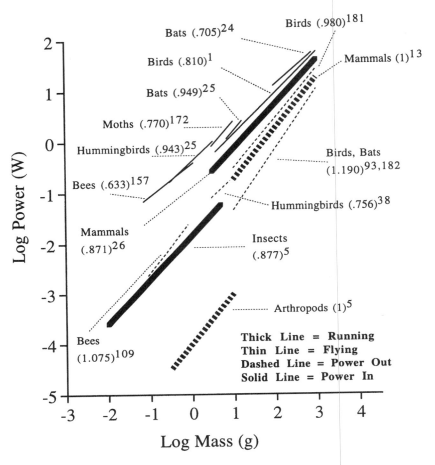

Figure 1 Log power (watts) versus log body mass (grams). The values shown represent either the metabolic power input of locomotion, calculated from respiratory measures of aerobic metabolism, or the mechanical power output of locomotion, calculated from measurements of animal force outputs and/or locomotory kinematics. The value in parentheses is the scaling exponent, and the superscript indicates the reference.

observed in the former group. Comparisons within orders of species that can both fly and run provide similar conclusions. For example, flying locusts and beetles have V_{O_2}s at least 10-fold higher than terrestrially locomoting animals at similar body temperatures (Table 1). Thus the data for insects clearly support the notion that flight is correlated with much higher aerobic metabolic rates than running is.

Birds The most dramatic example of evolutionary change in aerobic capacity appears in the comparison of birds and reptiles. Hovering birds have V_{O_2}s during flight that exceed those of running reptiles by at least 40-fold and exceed those of resting birds by 5- to 14-fold (19). However, studies of ostriches and emus running on treadmills suggest that running birds can attain V_{O_2}s at least 11-fold above rest (20). Running and flying birds exhibit similar scaling of locomotory oxygen consumption rates (21). Thus it appears that the high metabolic rates of exercising birds are not specifically associated with flight.

An alternate explanation is that the high V_{O_2} of flying birds relative to ancestral running reptiles is associated with the evolution of endothermic homeothermy (22). However, since the maximal V_{O_2} associated with cold exposure is approximately half that associated with flight (23), development of endothermic capacity seems unlikely to completely explain the high exercise V_{O_2} of birds. The high V_{O_2} of exercising birds may be best correlated with the evolution of the efficient parabronchial lung.

Bats There is good evidence that aerobic locomotory metabolism is higher in bats than in other mammals, but the degree of difference is much smaller than for insects. Some small active insectivores (shrews) have V_{O_2}s in the same range as those of bats (Table 1). Thomas (24) estimated that bat flight metabolic rates were about twice that of running mammals. Comparison of allometric data for bats of (25) with those for nonvolant mammals would suggest that 7-g bats have aerobic capacities approximately 50% higher than running mammals (Figure 1, Table 1). The mass-scaling coefficient of V_{O_2} in hovering bats is 1 (Figure 1) (25) and only 0.87 for mammals running at maximum aerobic speed (26), so the difference between flight and runner V_{O_2} in mammals may increase with size.

Comparison Among Taxa These comparisons of V_{O_2} have several important caveats. First, for technical reasons, physiologists attempting to measure gas exchange in fliers generally choose species that hover well in containers and that produce large, easily measurable gas exchange. These sampling biases may cause the available measures of locomotory V_{O_2} for fliers to be higher than the distribution of actual values. Within the insects, there is a paucity of gas exchange data for small weak-flying groups such as butterflies and neuropterans. In birds, gas exchange data are particularly difficult to obtain for large species, which depend heavily on gliding. However, for these animals, estimates of metabolic rates from mass balance or doubly labeled water studies suggest that flight metabolic rates are well below predicted metabolic rates from aerodynamic equations (9, 27–29) and well below maximal treadmill V_{O_2} for a similarly sized runner.

A second concern is that the data for runners represent primarily maximal V_{O_2} measured with treadmill studies, whereas the data for most fliers are obtained during hovering when V_{O2} is often not maximal. For fliers, the best (but not perfect) data on maximal V_{O2} come from studies that manipulate air density to increase work load. In hummingbirds, decreasing air density by replacing nitrogen with helium (heliox) leads to increases in V_{O2} 24% higher than during hovering in normal air (30, 31). It is not even clear that these values are representative of the maximal possible V_{O2}, since flight failure in hummingbirds at low air densities appears to be due to mechanical constraints (limits on stroke amplitude) rather than oxygen delivery. Similar studies with carpenter bees flying in heliox indicate that maximal V_{O2}, can be increased to values about 30% higher than those occurring during hovering in normal air (S Roberts, J Harrison & R Dudley, unpublished observations).

An important conclusion drawn from these comparisons is that the difference between flight and running V_{O2} depends on taxa, i.e. large (30-fold) in insects, small (2- to 1.5-fold) in mammals, and perhaps nonexistant in birds (Table 1, Figure 1). These differences are consistent with published measures of power output during locomotion. Insect fliers have mechanical power outputs about 30-fold higher than that of insect runners (Figure 1) (5), whereas maximal aerobic mechanical power output for birds is about double the power output of running mammals (Figure 1). We suggest two mechanisms that might partially explain this observation. First, efficiency (power output divided by power input) increases with size (Figure 1), and insect body masses are lower than those of birds and bats. Although insect, avian, and bat mechanical power outputs and metabolic power inputs show similar scaling relationships (Figure 1), at the small body masses typical of insects, the power output and power input regression lines increasingly diverge. This causes flight metabolic rates to rise relative to flight power requirements and running metabolism in small animals.

A second mechanism that may contribute to the large flight-runner V_{O2} differences among insects, birds, and mammals is a correlation between V_{O2} and the thermal biology of these groups. Both volant and nonvolant birds and mammals are endothermic homeotherms. In contrast, insect fliers are often endothermic homeotherms, whereas insect runners are mostly ectothermic poikilotherms. Insect flier V_{O2}s overlap with those of birds and mammals, whereas insect runners have V_{O2}s well below those of bird and mammalian runners and V_{O2}s similar to those of running reptiles (Table 1; allometric plot of reptilian runners not shown in Figure 1). Many large insect fliers thermoregulate, in part because of the high aerobic metabolic rates associated with flight and perhaps because the flight muscles are centrally located within the insulatable thorax. Most insects do not thermoregulate during terrestrial locomotion probably because of low metabolic rates and peripherally placed locomotory muscles. Therefore, insect leg muscles must function at a range of temperatures often well below the temperature of flight muscle. Among insect runners, the highest V_{O2}s occur for animals that use their flight muscles to warm up during activity (5, 32). Regulation of a high, relatively constant body temperature has been hypothesized to allow the evolution of high-power output systems in insects, birds, and mammals (33).

Anaerobic Flight Metabolism and Non-Sustainable Performance

The use of anaerobic metabolism during flight has received remarkably little attention perhaps because of the dominant view equating flight and aerobic metabolism. This is unfortunate because estimates of power output during loaded take-off suggest that short-term, maximal power outputs are approximately double those during sustainable flight (34–37). In hummingbirds, maximal, short-term (< 1 s) power outputs measured with string-lifting protocols are even higher (up to fourfold) than those sustainable aerobically (38, 39). These short, high-power output flights are likely to be of considerable importance during behaviors such as predation, predator avoidance, mating, and surviving extreme weather.

At present, the mechanisms of ATP production during these short-term, high-power output flights remain unclear. Insect flight muscle generally has very low levels of lactate dehydrogenase (40), and other possible mechanisms of anaerobic metabolism in insects remain unexplored. The flight muscles of some large birds are known to contain high levels of lactate dehydrogenase (41), and anaerobic metabolism is presumed to be critical for flight in all large flying birds (36). However, to our knowledge there are no quantitative data on the kinetics of lactate accumulation during flight in any flying animal.

High-energy phosphate depletion (creatine phosphate in birds and bats; arginine phosphate in insects) is a potential mechanism of rapid ATP production, but arginine phosphate levels have been shown to remain constant at the onset of flight in locusts (42). While it is known that hummingbird flight muscle contains high levels of creatine kinase (43), the kinetics of high-energy phosphagen utilization and how this might vary among flying species is unknown.

Aerobic metabolism in excess of that sustainable is also a possible mechanism of short-term high ATP production. Over the short-term, animals might deplete internal muscle and blood oxygen stores at rates greater than those sustainable by gas exchange systems.

Gas Exchange

Gas exchange in fliers can be modeled as multistep processes, with convective ventilation of the gas exchange organ in series with diffusion of oxygen and carbon dioxide across a membrane (44). In the following section, we focus on the gas phase components of gas exchange in fliers, to facilitate comparisons among insects, birds, and mammals. Unfortunately, except in the case of mammals, there are insufficient data to compare the gas exchange structures of volant and nonvolant groups. Therefore, we compare the mechanisms of gas exchange during flight across the flying taxa and review evidence for variation among fliers within a taxa.

Insects   In all the flying insects studied to date, flight is associated with large increases in convective ventilation through the spiracles relative to resting (45–

47). This convection is due to the compression of air sacs or soft elliptical trachea by the body walls or hemolymph (46, 47). Convective gas exchange during flight can occur via (a) abdominal pumping, in which rhythmical abdominal contractions synchronized with spiracular openings drive air flow through the spiracles; (b) autoventilation of the thorax, in which wing movements cause changes in thoracic volume thus driving convection; or (c) draught ventilation, in which air pressure generated by the forward speed of the insect forces air flow in through open thoracic spiracles.

Abdominal pumping appears to be the predominant mechanism of convective ventilation in the hymenopterans (46, 48). Thoracic autoventilation is the primary mechanism of convective ventilation in locust (46), dragonfly (46), and cicada (49). Draught ventilation and thoracic ventilation predominate in Cerambicid, Elaterid, and Anthribid beetles, and a combination of thoracic autoventilation and abdominal pumping produces convection in Scarabid and Buprestid beetles (47). Comparative explanations for these differences are lacking. Unfortunately, there are no quantitative data on convective ventilation in insect runners for comparison, nor are there data for comparison of different insect fliers with varying flight ability and V_{O2}.

Final delivery of oxygen from the trachea to to the mitochondria occurs via the tracheoles, small (< 1 μm diameter) air passageways formed by a single layer of cells. Theoretical calculations suggest that diffusion could suffice for oxygen transport through the tracheolar step (45), although this hypothesis has not been tested. The fractional volume of tracheoles relative to the fractional volume of mitochondria should provide a quantitative measure of the capacity of the tracheoles to perform this final step in oxygen delivery. Unfortunately, no data exist on the morphology of the tracheal system that allow us to address quantitative differences in tracheal structure associated with flight. Electron microscopic studies demonstrate that flight muscle has a high density of tracheoles (45), but to our knowledge there have been no systematic studies of the tracheole supply to nonflight locomotory muscles in insects.

Wigglesworth & Lee (50) have compared the tracheoles of the flight muscles of nine insect species of six orders. In all these insects, tracheoles enter into the flight muscle within invaginated plasma membrane and T-tubular systems (50). In all these species, very small tracheole branches (40–200 nm diameter) penetrate the sarcomeres and contact or even encircle virtually every mitochondrion. Observations of the tracheoles to the flight muscles of a fly and a butterfly suggest that these tubes are fluid-filled at rest and air-filled during activity (50). Together these data suggest that gas exchange to the mitochondria of the active flight muscle should occur primarily in the gas phase.

Muscle P_{O2} varies little between resting and flight (8–10 kPa) (51), which suggests that increases in oxygen conductance closely match the need for oxygen delivery during flight. This finding is consistent with the high safety margin for oxygen delivery observed for honey bees. Flight metabolic rate and performance do not decrease until atmospheric P_{O2} drops below 10 kPa (52). In contrast, flight metabolic rate increases with hyperoxia and decreases with moderate hypoxia in a dragonfly (53), which suggests a small safety margin for oxygen delivery in these animals. It is possible that insects using abdominal pumping to drive convection are less sensitive to atmospheric hypoxia and altitudinal variation because they are able to decouple ventilation from flight muscle activity. This might not be possible in animals in which flight muscle movements simultaneously drive wing movements and ventilation (53). In honey bees, there is also evidence for increases in ventilation during flight at higher temperatures (in honey bees), which may increase respiratory water loss and aid thermoregulation (54).

Birds In birds, the onset of flight is accompanied by strong (17-fold) increases in ventilation (19, 55). As in insects, ventilation occurs via compression of air sacs (56). Increases in ventilation occur primarily due to increases in breathing frequency (55). Ventilation (liters per minute) during flight scales similarly to V_{O2} in birds, suggesting that ventilatory response to flight is size independent (55). In contrast to current data for insects, avian flight studies have found that rises in ventilatory air flow exceed elevations in V_{O2} (57–59) and that blood P_{CO2} falls while blood P_{O2} rises (57). This hyperventilation has been attributed to hyperthermia (and the need for increased evaporative cooling) and/or lactate acidosis (55). The increased ventilation during flight is driven by a combination of mechano-receptive feedback and feed-forward locomotor inputs (60, 61).

The ratio of wing beat frequency to ventilation frequency is highly variable in birds, and the importance of such locomotory-ventilatory coupling has been controversial. However, recent studies support the hypothesis that coordinating wing beat and respiratory rhythm produces energetic savings in birds (62–64).

The high aerobic metabolism achieved by birds is associated with the evolution of the parabronchial lung (56). Its cross-current gas exchange structure leads to greater efficiency of oxygen transfer than the mammalian lung (56). The diffusing barrier of the bird lung has a mean harmonic thickness approximately 40% of mammals (19), and a gas exchange surface area two to four times greater than in mammals (65). This may partially explain the hypoxia tolerance of birds, although other factors such as the insensitivity of cerebral blood flow to hypocapnia may be more important (19).

Bats Like insects and birds, bats demonstrate strong increases in both tidal volume and ventilation frequency during flight (66, 67). As for insects and birds, contractions of the flight muscles are integrated with ventilation. Wing beat frequencies and breathing rates are identical during flight, with this coupling apparently aiding inspiration (66, 68, 69). Unlike insects, but similarly to birds, bats hyperventilate during flight, with increases in pulmonary ventilation exceeding increases in V_{O2} by 20 to 40% (66, 67). This hyperventilation has been hypothesized to be due to thermoregulation, a means to increase oxygen delivery, or an acid-base regulatory response (24).

Mammals provide the best data for the comparison of gas exchange structure and function between volant and nonvolant species. Bats in the small (<10 g) size range have lung volumes and surface areas about two to three times that of nonvolant mammals, about a 10% shorter blood-gas diffusion barrier, and an approximately threefold greater lung diffusing capacity (70). Bat lung variables increase less with size than they do in running mammals and have lower scaling exponents than V_{O_2} during hovering (25), which may partly explain the poor endurance and lack of hovering ability in larger bats (70).

Comparisons Across the Flying Taxa   Flight is accompanied by strong increases in ventilation in all taxa. In birds and bats, data suggest that ventilation changes exceed increases in V_{O_2}, while the limited data for insects suggest close matches between V_{O_2} and ventilation during flight. In all taxa, there is a tendency for wing beats to be coupled with and aid in the driving of ventilation. Throughout the fliers there is some evidence that ventilation and respiratory water loss can vary with air temperature, providing thermoregulatory benefits.

The high capacity of the insect tracheal system to deliver oxygen may be the reason why some flying insects achieve higher mass-specific oxygen consumption rates than do any birds or mammals (71). The tracheal systems of insects do have very small liquid diffusion distances (< 1 µm) (50) relative to normal 10- to 20-µm capillary-to-mitochondria diffusion distances in birds. This may allow greater oxygen flux in the critical terminal step of oxygen delivery, which may be why some insects have evolved oxygen and ATP utilization capacities beyond any found in other animals. Another possible, but apparently slight, advantage for tracheated relative to capillary-supplied muscles is that the volume of the insect muscle occupied by the trachea (1–7%) (45) may be smaller than the volume of the vertebrate muscle occupied by capillaries (9% in hummingbirds) (72). However, the general hypothesis of the superiority of the insect tracheal oxygen delivery system has not been well tested and seems to be contradicted by the hypoxia insensitivity of avian flight metabolism (31, 58, 59).

Muscle

The available information for flight muscle physiology differs greatly among taxa. There is a growing body of information on the in vitro contractile performance of insect flight muscle, but a dearth of similar information in birds and bats. However, there are more in vivo flight muscle power output and fiber type data for birds. Therefore, in the following section we consider all the flying taxa together and attempt to relate what is known about flight muscle properties to flight energetics.

Muscle Fiber Types   The high aerobic metabolism of flight is generally supported by highly aerobic flight muscle. Insect and hummingbird flight muscle have particularly high Krebs cycle enzyme and mitochondrial content and low activities of lactate dehydrogenase (40, 41, 71, 72). The high oxidative capacity in insect and bird flight muscles appears to be due in part to high oxidative enzyme content and to utilization of a high fraction of the enzyme capacity (73, 74). Comparisons of the flight and leg muscles of insects and birds are rare but generally support the contention that leg muscles are more heterogeneous in fiber type, have lower capillary densities, and generally contain lower levels of oxidative enzymes and higher levels of lactate dehydrogenase compared to flight muscles (75–79). An exception is the leg muscle of the highly cursial emus, which is similar to avian flight muscle in fiber type composition and enzyme activities, correlating with their similar scope for aerobic activity (80).

Evidence in both birds and insects also supports the hypothesis that different fiber types within the flight muscle maintain sustainable and nonsustainable flight. Avian flight muscle contains primarily fast oxidative glycolytic (FOG) fibers with a smaller percentage of fast glycolytic (FG) fibers (21). The FOG fibers of birds have very high mitochondrial and Krebs cycle enzyme content and high capillarity densities relative to most vertebrate skeletal muscle (43, 81, 82). The FG fibers are relatively large, metabolize glycogen anaerobically, and are believed to be used during burst performance such as take-off and acceleratory flight (83, 84).

Most insect flight muscle is composed of relatively homogeneous, highly oxidative fibers (85). However, at least some species contain distinctly smaller and more oxidative pink fibers and larger, less-oxidative white fibers (dragonflies, hemipterans, cockroaches) (86, 87). It is not known whether burst performance in insects requires recruitment of the less-oxidative-fiber types, as is believed to occur in birds.

Variation in muscle fiber types appears to be associated with flight capabilities in birds. The flight muscle of large birds, which are primarily short-burst flyers, consists of primarily FG fibers, whereas the flight muscle of birds capable of continuous flapping flight have primarily FOG fibers (88). There is also evidence that birds that primarily use flapping flight have smaller oxidative fibers and greater capillary density than birds that glide, whereas gliders have more or larger slow oxidative fibers (78). Similarly, passerine birds, which migrate longer distances, have smaller fibers and higher capillary densities (82).

Muscle Cycle Frequencies   A general pattern among animals is that muscle metabolism and power output increase with the frequency of contraction (89, 90). To what extent is the relatively high cost of insect flight associated with high muscle cycle frequencies? Available data suggest that this frequency is a central factor. Most insect fliers have substantially higher muscle cycle frequencies than do insect runners (5). Insects with asynchronous muscle have the highest frequencies (bees have cycle frequencies 11 times greater than similarly sized 1-g runners). Fliers with synchronous flight muscle have similar to fivefold higher values than do insect runners, with frequency explaining most but not all of the differences in energetic cost (5). Among insect clades (Saturniid moths, Sphinx moths, bumblebees, euglossine bees), variation in flight metabolic rate with size is largely explained by variation in wing beat frequency, with mass-specific metabolic rate per wing stroke being independent of size in most of these groups (5, 18).

High locomotory cycle frequencies occur in flying birds and bats relative to runners. Ten-gram birds and bats have wing beat frequencies 1.5- to 1.8-fold greater than the predicted cycle frequency of a 10-g mammalian runner at maximum galloping speed (91–93). These frequency differences are similar to the difference in flight metabolic rates for these groups (Table 1, Figure 1).

The high cycle frequency of fliers, and the higher wing beat frequencies of smaller fliers, may partly explain the higher V_{O_2} of these groups. Muscle efficiency tends to decrease in smaller animals with higher cycle frequencies. Calculated efficiencies for endothermic runners decrease with size, from 70% in humans to 7% in 44-g quail (94). Estimated efficiencies for moderately sized avian flight muscle are 10 to 13% (95). Values for muscle efficiency of insect fliers range from 5 to 16%, and decrease as size decreases and wing beat frequency increases within a clade (11, 96–98).

What flight muscle characteristics are responsible for the generation of high wing beat frequencies? Synchronous flight muscle is similar to other fast muscles, possessing a well-developed sarcoplasmic reticulum and fast contraction kinetics (99, 100). Some insect fliers have asynchronous flight muscle, in which the muscle can oscillate at a frequency much higher than motoneuron activity (101). Asynchronous flight muscle has slow, weak isometric contractions but maximal velocities among the fastest measured for muscle (102). The high frequencies of asynchronous muscle are attributable to specialized characteristics, including stretch-activation, reduction of the sarcoplasmic reticulum, high stiffness, and low strain (101–103).

Muscle Power Output   Flight muscles can produce high power output. Power output of synchronous insect flight muscle ranged from 60 to 90 W kg^{-1}, as determined with workloop techniques at normal operating temperatures (35–40°C) (96). These values are within the range of the aerodynamically calculated required power outputs, assuming substantial elastic energy storage (96). Power outputs of in vitro muscle preparations have yielded maximal power outputs up to approximately 100 W kg^{-1} using workloop techniques, but this value is thought to underestimate maximal power output in vivo for technical reasons (104, 105).

The mechanical power output of bird muscle has been estimated using in vivo bone-strain measurements of pectoralis muscle force and filming of wing kinematics. These measurements indicate that muscle-mass-specific power output ranges from 40 to 104 W kg^{-1}, consistent with respirometric measures of power input and efficiencies of about 12% (12, 95, 106). Similar estimations of muscle power output have been made for hummingbirds from aerodynamic models (107).

Modulating the Flight Muscle   Very little is known about how muscle power output is modulated within individuals. During load carriage or flight at high speeds, power output in bumblebees is increased by increasing wing beat frequency and lift coefficient (108). Variation in power output in euglossine bees or hummingbirds exposed to low air density increases primarily from increases in stroke amplitude (30, 109). Both wing beat frequency and stroke amplitude modulation contribute to variation in power output for *Drosophila melanogaster* steering in a virtual flight arena (110).

The mechanisms responsible for such flexibility are poorly known but have been best studied in insects. Octopamine increases twitch tension and rate of flight muscle contraction and is released during flight in locusts (111–115). Frequency of neuronal activation may be important for synchronous flight muscle, as increasing the frequency of electrical stimulation of muscle activation can increase power output (116) . Interestingly, in some cases, large variations in speed occur without any changes in wing beat frequency or stroke amplitude. In these cases, variation in flight performance is due to variation in stroke plane angle or lift coefficient (117, 118).

FACTORS ASSOCIATED WITH VARIATION IN FLIGHT RESPIRATION AND ENERGETICS

Temperature

The contractile properties of muscle, particularly rate parameters (i.e. shortening velocity and relaxation time), are strongly temperature dependent (116, 119). Accordingly, power production of isolated flight muscle generally increases with muscle temperature to a point [insects (96, 103, 104, 119–121), bats (122)], then decreases as muscle temperature continues to rise (123).

The muscle temperature for optimal power production varies among species and apparently has been influenced by natural selection. For example, the optimal temperature for muscle power production and flight ability in the heterothermic bat *Murina leucogaster* spans 30 to 40°C (122), which is a much broader and generally lower optimal temperature range than that of muscles from homeothermic mammals and birds. Moreover, the optimal muscle temperature in the ectothermic, winter-flying geometrid moth *Operophtera bruceata* (15–20°C) (124) is much lower than in the sphingid moth *Manduca sexta* (40–44°C) (124) and bumblebees (38–41°C) (104), which fly at elevated, well-regulated muscle temperatures. Interestingly, the temperature sensitivities of the metabolic enzymes citrate synthase and pyruvate kinase do not differ between *O. bruceata* and *M. sexta* (125), suggesting that at least some of the thermal characteristics of these enzymes are conserved.

The body temperatures of extremely small flying insects (i.e. *Drosophila*, midges, stingless bees) conform to air temperatures despite any heat gain from metabolism or solar radiation. Their thermal conformance is due to extremely high rates of convective cooling caused by their high surface area-to-volume ratios and wing movements. In turn, metabolism, wing beat frequency, and aerodynamic power production of small insects flying at moderate air temperatures are positively correlated with air temperature (126–130). However, it has not yet been demonstrated in small, ectothermic insects that flight metabolism and kinematic performance decrease when air temperature exceeds optimal muscle temperature.

There is some evidence that insects may exhibit morphological variation that compensates for thermal effects on muscle power output. *Drosophila* developing in cool climates or laboratory conditions have relatively larger wings (lower wing loading) than conspecifics developing in a warmer environment, and it has been proposed that this morphological variation is an adaptive response to enhance power production and flight ability at low air temperatures, when wing beat frequency is low (131). However, whether this is a general developmental response in small ectothermic flyers and whether this morphological variation affects power production during free flight at different air temperatures remain unknown.

Birds, bats, and many large insects regulate muscle temperature close to the optimal muscle temperature during flight, which allows them to fly and remain active over a wide range of ambient thermal conditions. The functional importance of such thermoregulation is illustrated by honey bee (132) and dragonfly (123, 133) vertical force production during tethered flight, which decreases at muscle temperatures above or below optimal temperatures. Although insect flight thermoregulation has received considerable attention, the mechanisms by which birds and bats thermoregulate during flight are still unknown, since heat exchange (metabolic heat gain, radiation, convection and evaporation) has not been measured as a function of temperature during flight for these groups. Some insect groups, particularly sphingid moths and certain bumblebee species, maintain flight metabolic rates independent of air temperature (18, 134–137) and thus thermoregulate by varying convective and radiative heat loss (134, 135). However, other endothermic insects strongly decrease wing beat frequency (138–142) and metabolic heat production (54, 138, 139, 143) during flight in hot conditions, which helps maintain muscle temperature near optimal values. Hummingbirds also decrease wing beat frequency and metabolic rates as air temperature rises, although to a lesser degree than the insects cited above (144–146).

What behavioral, physiological, or biomechanical explanations can be offered for the decrease in metabolic rate and wing beat frequency with air temperature? The decrease in flight metabolism and wing beat frequency at high air temperatures is probably not due to varying aerodynamic requirements, since the decrease in air density and the increase in kinematic viscosity with rising air temperature (147) predict a very slight increase in aerodynamic power requirements (148). The decrease in flight metabolism as air temperature rises could result from increasing mechanochemical efficiency (perhaps due to an increase in elastic energy storage at high muscle temperatures) and/or decreasing mechanical power output at higher air temperatures, as suggested by the similar thermal sensitivity of wing beat frequency. Indeed, the hummingbird *Archilochus colubris,* which lowers flight metabolism at high air temperatures, increases the mechanochemical efficiency of hovering flight as air temperature rises by decreasing wing beat frequency and increasing stroke amplitude. As a result, mechanical power output is independent of air temperatures (145). Thermal variation in muscle efficiency and power input could also be due to temperature-specific variation of an unsteady aerodynamic mechanism (149), such as varying the wing's angle of attack. Thus it is not clear whether the decrease in flight metabolism and wing beat frequency at higher temperatures in some flying insects is due to active thermoregulation or some passive consequence of temperature on the flight system.

Speed

All volant taxa are capable of varying flight speed, and the aerodynamic mechanisms and energetic consequences of this variation have been the subjects of numerous theoretical and empirical investigations. Animal flight theory predicts that total mechanical power requirements for steady-state flapping flight should vary with flight speed, with the greatest power required at the slowest and fastest speeds, and the minimum at some intermediate speed (9). The resultant U-shaped curve for total mechanical power is a composite of four distinct power components: the induced, the profile and parasite powers (collectively termed the aerodynamic power requirements), and the inertial power. Induced power is the power required to impart sufficient momentum on the air to generate lift and thrust. Induced power is inversely proportional to flight speed and is a major power requirement during hovering and at low-speed flight. Profile power is the power required to overcome drag on the wings and is directly proportional to flight speed. Parasite power, which is proportional to the cube of flight speed, is the power required to overcome drag forces on all body parts exclusive of the wings. Inertial power is the power required to accelerate the wings during each stroke. Importantly, if the kinetic energy of the oscillating wings can be stored as elastic strain energy in the flight muscles or other structures of the flight motor (as is thought to be true for most flyers), then inertial power requirements can be significantly reduced.

The power requirements during forward flight have been predicted for a variety of animals based on their morphology and flight kinematics. However, only one study has measured in vivo mechanical force production and mechanical power output by flight muscles at a range of airspeeds. In a major technological advance, Dial et al (95) recently measured wing kinematics and in vivo pectoralis muscle force to determine the mechanical power output for a magpie (*Pica pica*) flying at airspeeds of 0 to 14 m s^{-1}. At low speeds, their results closely agreed with the predictions of aerodynamic theory, with mechanical power output highest during hovering (~21 W kg^{-1}) and decreasing to 9 W kg^{-1} at an airspeed of 4 m s^{-1}. However, mechanical power output remained relatively constant at speeds between 4 and 12 m s^{-1} and increased only marginally at the maximum speed of 14 m s^{-1}. The coefficient of variation for power output and wing kinematics was lowest at the slowest (0–2 m s^{-1}) and fastest (12–14 m s^{-1}) flight speeds, suggesting that performance was at or near maximal. In contrast, at intermediate speeds, increased variability of wing beat patterns and power output suggests an ability to alter wing and tail configurations to maintain constant power requirements (150).

Metabolic power input has been measured during hovering and forward flight only in bumblebees and hummingbirds (151, 152). The speed-dependence of oxygen consumption in these groups is very different from the power output versus speed relationship for the much larger magpie. In bumblebees and hummingbirds, which generate lift and thrust during both the upstroke and downstroke of the wing cycle, metabolic rates do not vary between hovering and flight speeds up to 4 and 7 m s^{-1}, respectively. Although no kinematic data are available for hummingbirds at various airspeeds, the independence of bumblebee metabolism and flight speed between 0 and 4 m s^{-1} is consistent with the constant wing beat frequency and amplitude of bumblebees flying across a similar range of flight speeds (152). In these animals, flight speed across this range is increased by decreasing the body angle and increasing the stroke plane angle relative to the horizon such that forward thrust is produced (152).

During flight at very high airspeeds, parasite power requirements apparently become very high. For hummingbirds, metabolism increases by roughly 35% as flight speeds increase from 7 to 11 m s^{-1}. Although bumblebee metabolism has not been measured at flight speeds exceeding 4 m s^{-1}, wing beat frequency in this group significantly increases by approximately 7% as airspeed increases from 4 to 7 m s^{-1} (108). Thus the power curve for these species is not U-shaped, but rather J-shaped, with power requirements changing little from hovering to intermediate flight speeds and increasing only at high speeds. A J-shaped power curve may be applicable to most small flyers, particularly those with low advance ratios (the ratio of flight velocity to wing velocity) (25). However, more data on the interactive effect of body size and speed on flight energetics are necessary to test these models.

Body Mass

The effect of body mass on burst flight performance has received much attention (34–39), so here we focus instead on the effects of body mass on sustainable aerobic flight metabolism and mechanical power requirements. Within several broad taxonomic groups (bees, moths, birds, and bats), interspecific mass-scaling coefficients of metabolic rate (or available power) during forward and hovering flight are generally lower than 1, ranging from 0.63 to 0.94 (Figure 1). In contrast, the scaling coefficients of mechanical power requirements, when calculated from contemporary aerodynamic theory during sustained flapping flight, are usually near or slightly greater than 1 (Figure 1). Thus as flyers get bigger, mechanical power requirements increase at a greater rate than metabolic power production. This results in a higher calculated mechanochemical efficiency in larger flyers. Moreover, flight at high and low speeds becomes increasingly limited with increasing mass because mechanical power requirements appear to increase at these speeds in larger fliers.

In response to such limitations, aerobic hovering is found only in insects, hummingbirds, and the smallest bats, whereas many large birds must rely on unsustainable anaerobic power reserves to provide the energy needed for short bursts of hovering or very fast flight. In some instances, very large birds, such as condors and albatrosses, must taxi against headwinds or drop from elevated perches to achieve sufficient lift and momentum to reach minimal power speeds. Ultimately, a mass is reached at which power requirements for all speeds exceed available metabolic power and flight is not possible. However, there is some debate as to whether the maximal size of extant birds is purely a result of this limitation because larger fliers are found in the fossil record.

Despite the reasonable congruence between aerodynamic theory, measured metabolic data, and observed flight performance, there are notable exceptions regarding the allometry of flight energetics and kinematics. For example, Chai & Millard (38) examined hovering in hummingbirds ranging in body mass from 3 to 8.4 g (11 individuals representing 4 species), and a scaling coefficient of 0.76 for mechanical power output can be calculated from their results. However, a scaling coefficient of 0.95 has been calculated for metabolic power input for 10 hovering hummingbird species spanning a similar size range (25). This comparison suffers from small sample sizes (particularly for mechanical power output), phylogenetic bias, and different methodologies for measuring gas exchange. However, it begs a comprehensive scaling study of hummingbird flight metabolism and mechanical power output to determine whether the allometry of hummingbird flight energetics truly deviates from aerodynamic theory and the patterns generally observed in other fliers.

The intraspecific mass scaling of flight performance of some insects, particularly dipterans, also often disagrees with predictions from aerodynamic theory. In hovering tachinid flies (*Nowickia* sp.), the scaling coefficient of flight metabolic rate is 1 (153). A possible explanation for these results is that the larger body masses of some flies were due to food ingestion, which increases flight metabolic requirements in bees (154). In robber flies (Diptera: Asilidae), the interspecific mass-scaling coefficient of flight metabolism is 1.06 (155). In this case, however, the disproportionately high rates of metabolism in larger species were due to the fact that their body temperatures exceed ambient temperature by 3 to 6°C, whereas smaller species are strict thermoconformers.

Perhaps the most unusual recent finding is the significant positive relationship between wing beat frequency and wing length during hovering in the mosquitos *Anopheles gambiae* and *A. arabiensis* (156). For geometrically similar fliers, wing beat frequency should theoretically scale with length to the power of -0.5 (9), and interspecific mass-scaling coefficients in this range are reported for other small insects such as bees (157, 158) and homopterans (159). In these mosquitoes, however, wing length might be largely fixed relative to the variation in body mass, with a mass-scaling of wing length much lower than that predicted for isometry (0.33). As a result, higher wing beat frequencies (and perhaps metabolic rates) may be required in larger individuals to compensate for the relatively smaller wing areas. These examples suggest that extreme caution is needed when predicting the intraspecific mass dependence of flight parameters from interspecific allometric relationships.

Intraspecific Variation in Flight Respiration and Energetics

Although broad-scale comparisons of taxa and mode of locomotion provide insight into general patterns of organismal design, understanding the evolution of variation in flight-related physiological parameters seems most tractable for intraspecific studies. With such studies it is possible to link individual behavior to variation in physiological or morphological traits. Several interesting patterns of intraspecific variation have been observed. Male *Plathemis lydia* dragonflies with greater ratios of flight muscle to body mass have greater mating success but reduced fat reserves (160). African races of the honey bee *Apis mellifera* have greater flight metabolic rates (161), higher thorax/body mass ratios, and lower wing-loading than do European honey bees (162), suggesting a greater flight capacity in African bees that may correlate with their greater attack vigor and high colonial growth rates. High-altitude honey bees have larger thoraxes and larger wings (163), which should enhance their flight performance at low air densities.

Allozymic variation of metabolic enzymes can also affect organismal flight performance. *Colias* butterfly populations from different altitudes vary in the frequency of several allozymes, and the different forms of these allelic isozymes affect flight ability and the temperature of optimal flight performance (164). In honey bees, the proportion of the electrophoretically fast and medium alleles of cytoplasmic malate dehydrogenase (MDH) exhibit clines on three continents (165). Bees with the fast and medium alleles differ in their flight metabolic rates in hives with naturally mated queens (166) and in hives with singly inseminated queens in which all genes not tightly linked to to the MDH locus were randomly distributed between workers with different MDH phenotypes (167). Similarly, in *D. melanogaster,* there are latitudinal clines in the frequency of allozymes of glycerophosphate dehydrogenase (GPDH) on three continents, with the electrophoretically fast form of GPDH found in higher proportions at low latitudes (168). These allozymes may differ in their kinetics and temperature dependence (169). Flies with different GPDH allozymes differ in their power output during tethered flight and in the temperature dependence of flight, with phenotypes with the fast GPDH allozymes having higher power outputs at higher rearing and flight temperatures (128). Together, these studies support the hypothesis that metabolic allozymes produce small but measurable genetic effects and that variation in these allozymes might be important in understanding why genotypes perform differently in different environments.

Intraspecific studies allow us to directly link variation in flight physiology to its genetic and/or environmental bases. Direct evidence for genetic effects on intraspecific variation in tethered flight performance has been presented for iso-genetic lines of *D. melanogaster.* These lines show heritabilities of wing beat frequencies and aerodynamic power outputs ranging from 0.24 to 0.42 (170). Selection for upwind flight ability of *D. melanogaster* increases the flight effort of fruitfly populations, although it does not change the population-level maximal performance (171). Future studies that incorporate traditional and modern molec-ular genetic experimental designs may eventually allow us to understand some of the genetic bases to the tremendous diversity observed in flight respiration and energetics of animals.

Visit the Annual Reviews home page at www.AnnualReviews.org.

LITERATURE CITED

1. Norberg UM. 1996. Energetics of flight. In *Avian Energetics and Nutritional Ecology,* ed. C Carey, pp. 199–249. New York: Chapman & Hall

2. Dudley R. 2000. The evolutionary phys-iology of animal flight: paleobiological and present perspectives. *Annu. Rev. Physiol.* 62:135–55

3. Marden JH. 2000. Ontogenetic patterns of insect flight muscle: function and composition. *Annu. Rev. Physiol.* 62:157–78

4. Gans C, Gaunt AS, Webb PW. 1997. Ver-tebrate locomotion. In *Handbook of Physiology. Section 13: Comparative Physiology,* ed. WH Dantzler, I:55–214. New York: Oxford Univ. Press

5. Full RJ. 1997. Invertebrate locomotor systems. In *Handbook of Physiology Sec-tion 13: Comparative Physiology,* ed. WH Dantzler, II:853–930. New York: Oxford Univ. Press

6. Jones JH. 1994. *Comparative Vertebrate Exercise Physiology: Phyletic Adapta-tions,* Vol. 38B. San Diego: Academic

7. Brodsky AK. 1994. *The Evolution of Insect Flight.* New York: Oxford Univ. Press.

8. Dudley R. 2000. *The Biomechanics of Insect Flight: Form, Function, Evolution.* Princeton, NJ: Princeton Univ. Press. In press

9. Pennycuick CJ. 1975. Mechanics of flight. In *Avian Biology,* ed. DS Farner, JR King, 5:1–75. New York: Academic

10. Rayner JMV. 1982. Avian flight energet-ics. *Annu. Rev. Physiol.* 44:109–19

11. Ellington CP. 1984. The aerodynamics of hovering insect flight. IV. Aerodynamic mechanisms. *Proc. R. Soc. London Ser. B* 305:79–113

12. Dial KP, Biewener AA. 1993. Pectoralis muscle force and power output during different modes of flight in pigeons (*Columba livia*). *J. Exp. Biol.* 176:31–54

13. Heglund NC, Fedak MA, Taylor CR, Cavagna GA. 1982. Energetics and mechanics of terrestrial locomotion. *J. Exp. Biol.* 97:57–66

14. Full RJ, Tu MS. 1990. Mechanics of six-legged runners. *J. Exp. Biol.* 148:129–46

15. Winter Y, von Helversen O. 1998. The energy cost of flight: Do small bats fly more cheaply than birds? *J. Comp. Phys-iol. B* 168:105–11

16. Wolf TJ, Ellington CP, Davis S, Feltham MJ. 1996. Validation of the doubly labelled water technique for bumblebees *Bombus terrestris* (L.). *J. Exp. Biol.* 199:959–72

17. Marden JH, Kramer MG. 1994. Surface-skimming stoneflies: a possible interme-diate stage in insect flight evolution. *Science* 266:427–30

18. Casey TM. 1989. Oxygen consumption during flight. In *Insect Flight*, ed. GJ Goldsworthy, CH Wheeler, pp. 257–72. Boca Raton, FL: CRC Press

19. Saunders DK, Fedde MR. 1994. Exercise performance of birds. In *Comparative Vertebrate Exercise Physiology: Phyletic Adaptations*, ed. JH Jones, 38B:139–90

20. Fedak MA, Seeherman JH. 1979. Reappraisal of energetics of locomotion shows identical costs in bipeds and quadrapeds including ostrich and horse. *Nature* 282:713–16

21. Butler PJ. 1991. Exercise in birds. *J. Exp. Biol.* 160:233–62

22. Bennett AF. 1991. The evolution of activity capacity. *J. Exp. Biol.* 160:1–23

23. Dutenhoffer MS, Swanson DL. 1996. Relationship of basal to summit metabolic rate in passerine birds and the aerobic capacity model for the evolution of endothermy. *Physiol. Zool.* 69:1232–54

24. Thomas SP. 1987. The physiology of bat flight. In *Recent Advances in the Study of Bats*, ed. MB Fenton, P Racey, JMV Rayner, pp. 75–99. Cambridge, UK: Cambridge Univ. Press

25. Voigt CC, Winter W. 1999. Energetic cost of hovering flight in nectar feeding bats (Phyllostomidae: Glossophaginae) and its scaling in moths, birds and bats. *J. Comp. Physiol. B* 169:38–48

26. Jones JH, Lindstedt SL. 1993. Limits to maximal performance. *Annu. Rev. Physiol.* 55:547–69

27. Flint EN, Nagy KA. 1984. Flight energetics of free-living sooty terns. *Auk* 101:288–94

28. Adams NJ, Brown CR, Nagy KA. 1986. Energy expenditure of free-ranging wandering albatrosses *Diomedea exulans*. *Physiol. Zool.* 59:583–91

29. Ballance LT. 1995. Flight energetics of free-ranging red-footed boobies (*Sula sula*). *Physiol. Zool.* 68:887–914

30. Chai P, Dudley R. 1995. Limits to vertebrate locomotor energetics suggested by hummingbirds hovering in heliox. *Nature* 377:722–25

31. Chai P, Dudley R. 1996. Limits to flight energetics of hummingbirds hovering in hypodense and hypoxic gas mixtures. *J. Exp. Biol.* 199:2285–95

32. Bartholomew GA, Casey TM. 1977. Endothermy during terrestrial activity in large beetles. *Science* 195:882–83

33. Heinrich B. 1977. Why have some animals evolved to regulate a high body temperature? *Am. Nat.* 623–40

34. Marden JH. 1987. Maximum lift production during takeoff in flying animals. *J. Exp. Biol.* 130:235–58

35. Marden JH. 1990. Maximum load-lifting and induced power output of Harris' hawks are general functions of flight muscle mass. *J. Exp. Biol.* 149:511–14

36. Marden JH. 1994. From damselflies to pterosaurs: how burst and sustainable flight performance scale with size. *Am. J. Physiol.* 266:R1077–84

37. Ellington CP. 1991. Limitations on animal flight performance. *J. Exp. Biol.* 160:71–91

38. Chai P, Millard D. 1997. Flight and size constraints: hovering performance of large hummingbirds under maximal loading. *J. Exp. Biol.* 200:2757–63

39. Chai P, Chen JSC, Dudley R. 1997. Transient hovering performance of hummingbirds under conditions of maximal loading. *J. Exp. Biol.* 200:921–29

40. Beenakkers AMT, Van der Horst DJ, Van Marrewijk WJA. 1984. Insect flight metabolism. *Ins. Biochem.* 14:243–60

41. Crabtree B, Newsholme EA. 1972. The activities of phosphorylase, hexokinase, phosphofructokinase, LDH, G 3-P Dh in muscles from vertebrates and invertebrates. *Biochem. J.* 126:49–58

42. Schneider A, Wiesner RJ, Grieshaber MK. 1989. On the role of arginine kinase in insect flight muscle. *Ins. Biochem.* 19:471–80

43. Suarez RK, Brown GS, Hochachka PW. 1986. Metabolic sources of energy for

hummingbird flight. *Am. J. Physiol.* 251:R537–42

44. Piiper J, Scheid P. 1982. Models for a comparative functional analysis of gas exchange organs in vertebrates. *J. Appl. Physiol.* 53:1321–29

45. Weis-Fogh T. 1964. Diffusion in insect wing muscle, the most active tissue known. *J. Exp. Biol.* 41:229–56

46. Weis-Fogh T. 1967. Respiration and tracheal ventilation in locusts and other flying insects. *J. Exp. Biol.* 47:561–87

47. Miller PL. 1966. The supply of oxygen to the active flight muscles of some large beetles. *J. Exp. Biol.* 45:285–304

48. Bailey L. 1954. The respiratory currents of the tracheal system of the adult honeybee. *J. Exp. Biol.* 31:589–93

49. Bartholomew GA, Barnhart CM. 1984. Tracheal gases, respiratory gas exchange, body temperature and flight in some tropical cicadas. *J. Exp. Biol.* 111:131–44

50. Wigglesworth VB, Lee WM. 1982. The supply of oxygen to the flight muscles of insects: a theory of tracheole physiology. *Tissue Cell* 14:501–18

51. Komai Y. 1998. Augmented respiration in a flying insect. *J. Exp. Biol.* 201:2359–66

52. Joos B, Lighton JRB, Harrison JF, Suarez RK, Roberts SP. 1997. Effects of ambient oxygen tension on flight performance, metabolism and water loss of the honeybee. *Physiol. Zool.* 70:167–74

53. Harrison JF, Lighton JRB. 1998. Oxygen-sensitive flight metabolism in the dragonfly *Erythemis simplicicollis*. *J. Exp. Biol.* 201:1739–44

54. Roberts SP, Harrison JF. 1999 Mechanisms of thermal stability during flight in the honey bee *Apis mellifera*. *J. Exp. Biol.* 202:1523–33

55. Bernstein MH. 1987. Respiration in flying birds. In *Bird Respiration,* ed. TJ Seller, 2:44–73. Boca Raton, FL: CRC Press

56. Scheid P. 1979. Mechanisms of gas exchange in bird lungs. *Rev. Physiol. Biochem. Pharm.* 86:138–86

57. Butler PJ, West NH, Jones DR. 1977. Respiratory and cardiovascular responses of the pigeon to sustained, level flight in wind-tunnel. *J. Exp. Biol.* 71:7–26

58. Kiley JP, Faraci FM, Fedde MR. 1985. Gas exchange during exercise in hypoxic ducks. *Resp. Physiol.* 59:105–15

59. Fedde MR, Orr JA, Shams H, Scheid P. 1989. Cardiopulmonary function in exercising bar-headed geese during normoxia and hypoxia. *Resp. Physiol.* 77:239–62

60. Funk GD, Milsom WK, Steeves JD. 1992. Coordination of wingbeat and respiration in the Canada goose. I. Passive wing flapping. *J. Appl Physiol.* 73:1014–24

61. Funk GD, Steeves JD, Milsom WK. 1992. Coordination of wingbeat and respiration in birds. II. "Fictive" flight. *J. Appl. Physiol.* 73:1025–33

62. Funk GD, Valenzuela IJ, Milsom WK. 1997. Energetic consequences of coordinating wingbeat and respiratory rhythms in birds. *J. Exp. Biol.* 200:915–20

63. Boggs DF, Jenkins FA, Dial KP. 1997. The effects of the wingbeat cycle on respiration in black-billed magpies (*Pica pica*). *J. Exp. Biol.* 200:1403–12

64. Boggs DF, Seveyka JJ, Kilgore DL, Dial KP. 1997. Coordination of respiratory cycles with wingbeat cycles in the black-billed magpie (*Pica pica*). *J. Exp. Biol.* 200:1413–20

65. Dubach M. 1981. Quantitative analysis of the respiratory system of the house sparrow, budgerigar and violet-eared hummingbird. *Resp. Physiol.* 46:43–60

66. Thomas SP. 1981. Ventilation and oxygen extraction in the bat *Phyllostomus hastatus* during rest and steady flight. *J. Exp. Biol.* 94:231–50

67. Thomas SP, Lust MR, Van Riper HJ. 1984. Ventilation and oxygen extraction in the bat *Phyllostomus hastatus* during

rest and steady flight. *Physiol. Zool.* 57:237–50

68. Carpenter RE. 1986. Flight physiology of intermediate-sized fruit bats (Pteropodidae). *J. Exp. Biol.* 120:79–103

69. Rayner JMV. 1991. The cost of being a bat. *Nature* 350:383–84

70. Maina JN, Thomas SP, Hyde DM. 1991. A morphometric study of the lungs of different sized bats: correlations between structure and function of the chiropteran lung. *Philos. Trans. R. Soc. London Ser. B* 333:31–50

71. Suarez RK. 1996. Upper limits to mass-specific metabolic rates. *Annu. Rev. Physiol.* 58:583–605

72. Suarez RK, Lighton JRB, Brown GS, Mathieu-Costello O. 1991. Mitochondrial respiration in hummingbird flight muscles. *Proc. Natl. Acad. Sci. USA* 88:4870–73

73. Suarez RK, Moyes CD. 1992. Mitochondrial respiration in locust flight muscles. *J. Exp. Zool.* 263:351–55

74. Staples JF, Suarez RK. 1997. Honeybee flight muscle phosphoglucose isomerase: matching enzyme capacities to flux requirements at a near-equilibrium reaction. *J. Exp. Biol.* 200:1247–54

75. Marsh RL, Dawson WR. 1982. Substrate metabolism in seasonally acclimatized American goldfinches. *Am. J. Physiol.* 242:R563–69

76. Leon-Velarde F, Sanchez J, Bigard AX, Brunet A, Lesty C, et al. 1993. High altitude tissue adaptation in Andean coots: capillarity, fibre area, fibre type and enzymatic activities of skeletal muscle. *J. Comp. Physiol. B* 163:52–58

77. Torrella JR, Fouces V, Palomeque J, Viscor G. 1998. Capillarity and fibre types in locomotory muscles of wild yellow-legged gulls (*Larus cachinnans*). *Physiol. Zool.* 71:425–34

78. Torrella JR, Fouces V, Palomeque J, Viscor G. 1998. Comparative skeletal muscle fibre morphometry among wild birds

with different locomotor behaviour. *J. Anat.* 192:211–22

79. Gade G. 1984. Anaerobic energy metabolism. In *Environmental Physiology and Biochemistry of Insects,* ed. KH Hoffman, pp. 119–36. Berlin/Heidelberg: Springer Verlag

80. Patak A, Baldwin J. 1993. Structural and metabolic chatacterization of the muscles used to power running in the emu (*Dromaius novaehollandiae*), a giant flightless bird. *J. Exp. Biol.* 175:233–49

81. Marsh RL. 1981. Catabolic enzyme activities in relation to premigratory fattening and muscle hypertrophy in the gray catbird (*Dumetella carolinensis*). *J. Comp. Physiol. B* 141:417–23

82. Lundgren BO, Kiessling K. 1988. Comparative aspects of fibre types, areas, and capillary supply in the pectoralis muscle of some passerine birds with differing migratory behavior. *J. Comp. Physiol.* 158:165–73

83. Parker GH, George JC. 1975. Effects of short and long-term exercise on intracellular glycogen and fat in pigeon pectoralis. *Jpn. J. Physiol.* 25:175–84

84. Dial KP, Kaplan SR, Goslow JE Jr, Jenkins FA Jr. 1987. Structure and neural control of the pectoralis in pigeons: implications for flight mechanics. *Anat. Rec.* 218:284–87

85. Elder HY. 1975. Muscle structure. In *Insect Muscle,* ed. PNR Usherwood, pp. 1–74. London: Academic

86. Bhat UKM. 1970. Heterogeneity in the fibre composition in the flight muscles of *Periplaneta americana* and *Belostoma* sp. *Experientia* 26:995–97

87. Downer RGH, Matthews JR. 1976. Glycogen depletion of thoracic musculature during flight in the american cockroach, *Periplaneta americana* L. *Comp. Biochem. Physiol.* 55B:501–2

88. Talesara GL, Goldspink G. 1978. A combined histochemical and biochemical study of myofibrillar ATPase in pectoral,

leg and cardiac muscle of several species of bird. *Histochem. J.* 10:695–710

89. Taylor CR, Heglund NC, McMahon TA, Looney TR. 1980. Energetic cost of generating muscular force during running. *J. Exp. Biol.* 86:109–18

90. Rome LC. 1992. Scaling of muscle fibres and locomotion. *J. Exp. Biol.* 168:243–52

91. Heglund NC, Taylor CR. 1988. Speed, stride frequency and energy cost per stride: How do they change with body size and gait? *J. Exp. Biol.* 138:301–18

92. Norberg UM, Kunz TH, Steffensen JF, Winter Y, von Helversen O. 1993. The cost of hovering and forward flight in a nectar-feeding bat, *Glossophaga soricina,* estimated from aerodynamic theory. *J. Exp. Biol.* 182:207–27

93. Rayner JMV. 1988. Form and function in avian flight. In *Current Ornithology,* ed. RF Johnston, 5:1–66. New York: Plenum

94. Taylor CR, Heglund NC. 1982. Energetics and mechanics of terrestrial locomotion. *Annu. Rev. Physiol.* 44:97–107

95. Dial KP, Biewener AA, Tobalske BW, Warrick DR. 1997. Mechanical power output of bird flight. *Nature* 390:67–70

96. Stevenson RD, Josephson RK. 1990. Effects of operating frequency and temperature on mechanical power output from moth flight muscle. *J. Exp. Biol.* 149:61–78

97. Dickinson MH, Lighton JRB. 1995. Muscle efficiency and elastic storage in the flight motor of *Drosophila. Science* 268:87–90

98. Wakeling JM, Ellington CP. 1997. Dragonfly flight. III. Lift and power requirements. *J. Exp. Biol.* 200:583–600

99. Josephson RK. 1984. Contraction dynamics of flight and stridulatory muscles of tettigonid insects. *J. Exp. Biol.* 108:77–96

100. Mizisin AP, Ready NE. 1986. Growth and development of flight muscle in the locust (*Schistocerca nitens,* Thunberg). *J. Exp. Zool.* 237:45–55

101. Usherwood PNR. 1975. *Insect Muscle.* London: Academic

102. Josephson RK, Ellington CP. 1997. Power output from a flight muscle of the bumblebee *Bombus terrestris.* I. Some features of the dorso-ventral flight muscle. *J. Exp. Biol.* 200:1215–26

103. Gilmour KM, Ellington CP. 1993. In vivo muscle length changes in bumblebees and the in vitro effects on work and power. *J. Exp. Biol.* 183:101–13

104. Gilmour KM, Ellington CP. 1993. Power output of glycerinated bumblebee flight. *J. Exp. Biol.* 183:77–100

105. Josephson RK. 1997. Power output from a flight muscle of the bumblebee *Bombus terrestris.* II. Characterization of the parameters affecting power output. *J. Exp. Biol.* 200:1227–39

106. Biewener AA, Dial KP, Goslow GE. 1992. Pectoralis muscle force and power output during flight in the starling. *J. Exp. Biol.* 164:1–18

107. Wells DJ. 1993. Muscle performance in hovering hummingbirds. *J. Exp. Biol.* 178:39–57

108. Cooper AJ. 1993. *Limitations of bumblebee flight performance.* PhD thesis. Univ. Cambridge, UK. 205 pp.

109. Dudley R. 1995. Extraordinary flight performance of orchid bees (Apidae: Euglossini) hovering in heliox (80% He/20% O_2). *J. Exp. Biol.* 198:1065–70

110. Lehmann FO, Dickinson MH. 1997. The changes in power requirements and muscle efficiency during elevated force production in the fruit fly *Drosophila melanogaster. J. Exp. Biol.* 200:1133–43

111. Goosey MW, Candy DJ. 1982. The release and removal of octopamine by tissues of the locust *Schistocerca americana gregaria. Insect Biochem.* 12:681–85

112. Bailey BA, Martin RJ, Downer RGH. 1983. Haemolymph octopamine levels during and following flight in the American cockroach, *Periplaneta americana* L. *Can. J. Zool.* 62:19–22

113. Whim MD, Evans PD. 1988. Octopaminergic modulations of flight muscle in the locust. *J. Exp. Biol.* 134:247–66

114. Orchard I, Ramirez J-M, Lange AB. 1993. A multifunctional role of octopamine in locust flight. *Annu. Rev. Entomol.* 38:227–49

115. Stevenson PA, Meuser S. 1997. Octopaminergic innervation and modulation of a locust flight steering muscle. *J. Exp. Biol.* 200:633–42

116. Josephson RK. 1993. Contraction dynamics and power output of skeletal muscle. *Annu. Rev. Physiol.* 55:527–46

117. Dudley R, Ellington CP. 1990. Mechanics of forward flight in bumblebees I. Kinematics and morphology. *J. Exp. Biol.* 148:19–52

118. Wakeling JM, Ellington CP. 1997. Dragonfly flight. II. Velocities, accelerations and kinematics of flapping flight. *J. Exp. Biol.* 200:557–82

119. Josephson RK. 1981. Temperature and the mechanical performance of insect muscle. In *Insect Thermoregulation,* ed. B Heinrich, pp. 19–44. New York: Wiley

120. Machin KE, Pringle JWS, Tamsige M. 1962. The physiology of insect flight muscle. IV. *Proc. R. Soc. London Ser. B* 155:493–99

121. Steiger GJ, Ruegg JC. 1969. Energetics and efficiency in the isolated contractile machinery of an insect fibrillar muscle at various frequencies of oscillation. *Pflügers Arch.* 307:1–21

122. Choi I-H, Cho Y, Oh YK, Jung N-P, Shin H-C. 1998. Behavior and muscle performance in heterothermic bats. *Physiol. Zool.* 71:257–66

123. Marden JH. 1995. Large-scale changes in thermal sensitivity of flight performance during adult maturation in a dragonfly. *J. Exp. Biol.* 198:2095–102

124. Marden JH. 1995. Evolutionary adaptation of contractile performance in muscle of ectothermic winter-flying moths. *J. Exp. Biol.* 198:2087–94

125. Heinrich R, Mommsen TP. 1985. Flight of winter moths near 0°C. *Science* 228:177–79

126. May ML. 1981. Wingstroke frequency of dragonflies (Odonata: Anisoptera) in relation of temperature and body size. *J. Comp. Physiol. B* 144:229–40

127. Unwin DM, Corbet SA. 1984. Wingbeat frequency, temperature and body size in bees and flies. *Physiol. Entomol.* 9:115–21

128. Barnes PT, Laurie-Ahlberg CC. 1986. Genetic variability of flight metabolism in *Drosophila melanogaster.* III. Effects of Gpdh allozymes and environmental temperature on power output. *Genetics* 112:267–94

129. Sotavalta O. 1947. The flight tone of insects. *Acta Entomol. Fenn.* 4:1–117

130. Yurkiewicz WJ, Smyth T Jr. 1966. Effects of temperature on oxygen consumption and fuel utilization by the sheep blowfly. *J. Ins. Physiol.* 12:403–8

131. Azevedo RBR, James AC, McCabe J, Partidge L. 1998. Latitudinal variation of wing: thorax size ratio and wing-aspect ratio in *Drosophila melanogaster. Evolution* 52:1353–62

132. Coelho JR. 1991. The effect of thorax temperature on force production during tethered flight in honeybee (*Apis mellifera*) drones, workers, and queens. *Physiol. Zool.* 64:823–35

133. Marden JH, Dramer MG, Frisch J. 1996. Age-related variation in body temperature, thermoregulation and activity in a thermally polymorphic dragonfly. *J. Exp. Biol.* 199:529–35

134. Heinrich B. 1971. Temperature regulation of the sphinx moth, *Manduca sexta. J. Exp. Biol.* 54:141–52

135. Heinrich B. 1975. Thermoregulation in bumblebees. *J. Comp. Physiol.* 96:155–66

136. Heinrich B, Casey TM. 1973. Metabolic rate and endothermy in sphinx moths. *J. Comp. Physiol. B* 82:195–206

137. Casey TM. 1981. Energetics and thermoregulation of *Malacosoma americanum* (Lepidoptera: Lasiocampidae) during hovering flight. *Physiol. Zool.* 54:362–71

138. Harrison JF, Fewell JH, Roberts SP, Hall HG. 1996. Achievement of thermal stability by varying metabolic heat production in flying honeybees. *Science* 274:88–90

139. Roberts SP, Harrison JF, Hadley NF. 1998. Mechanisms of thermal balance in flying *Centris pallida* (Hymenoptera: Anthophoridae). *J. Exp. Biol.* 201:2321–31

140. Spangler HG. 1992. The influence of temperature on the wingbeat frequencies of free-flying honey bees, *Apis mellifera* L. (Hymenoptera: Apidae). *Bee Sci.* 2:181–86

141. Spangler HG, Buchmann SL. 1991. Effects of temperature on wingbeat frequency in the solitary bee *Centris caesalpiniae* (Anthophoridae: Hymenoptera). *J. Kans. Entomol. Soc.* 64:107–9

142. May ML. 1995. Simultaneous control of head and thoracic temperature by the green darner dragonfly *Anax junius* (Odonata: Aeshnidae). *J. Exp. Biol.* 198:2373–84

143. May ML. 1995. Dependence of flight behavior and heat production on air temperature in the green darner dragonfly *Anax junius* (Odonata: Aeshnidae). *J. Exp. Biol.* 198:2385–92

144. Schuchmann KL. 1979. Metabolism of flying hummingbirds. *Ibis* 121:85–86

145. Chai P, Chang AC, Dudley R. 1998. Flight thermogenesis and energy conservation in hovering hummingbirds. *J. Exp. Biol.* 201:963–68

146. Berger M, Hart JS. 1972. Die Atmung beim Kolibri *Amazilia fimbriata* wahrend des Schwirrfluges bei verschiedenen Umgebungstemperaturen. *J. Comp. Physiol. B* 81:363–80

147. Lide DR, ed. 1991. *CRC Handbook of Chemistry and Physics.* 72nd ed. Boca Raton, FL: CRC Press

148. Ellington CP. 1984. The aerodynamics of hovering insect flight. VI. Lift and power requirements. *Philos. Trans. R. Soc. London Ser. B* 305:145–81

149. Ellington CP, van den Berg C, Willmott AP, Thomas ALR. 1996. Leading-edge vortices in insect flight. *Nature* 384:626–30

150. Tobalske BW, Dial KP. 1996. Flight kinematics of black-billed magpies and pigeons over a wide range of speeds. *J. Exp. Biol.* 199:263–80

151. Berger M. 1985. Sauerstoffverauch von kolibris (*Colibri coruscans* und *C. thalassinus*) beim horizontalflug. In *BIONA Report 3*, ed. W Nachtigall, pp. 307–14. Stuttgart: Fischer

152. Dudley R, Ellington CP. 1990. Mechanics of forward flight in bumblebees. *J. Exp. Biol.* 148:53–88

153. Chappell MA, Morgan KR. 1987. Temperature regulation, endothermy, resting metabolism, and flight energetics of tachinid flies (*Nowickia,* sp.). *Physiol. Zool.* 60:550–59

154. Wolf TJ, Schmid-Hempel P, Ellington CP, Stevenson RD. 1989. Physiological correlates of foraging efforts in honeybees: oxygen consumption and nectar load. *Func. Ecol.* 3:417–24

155. Morgan KR, Shelley TE, Kimsey LS. 1985. Body temperature regulation, energy metabolism and foraging in light-seeking and shade-seeking robber flies. *J. Comp. Physiol. B* 155:561–70

156. Waseka JW, Brogdon WG, Hawley WA, Besansky NJ. 1998. Flight time of field collected populations of *Anopheles gambiae* and *A. arabiensis* (Diptera: Culicidae). *Physiol. Entomol.* 23:289–94

157. Casey TM, May ML. 1985. Flight energetics of euglossine bees in relation to morphology and wing stroke frequency. *J. Exp. Biol.* 116:271–89

158. Joos B, Young PA, Casey TM. 1991. Wingstroke frequency of foraging and

hovering bumblebees in relation to morphology and temperature. *Physiol. Entomol.* 16:191–200

159. Byrne DN, Buchmann SL, Spangler HG. 1988. Relationship between wing loading, wingbeat frequency and body mass in homopterous insects. *J. Exp. Biol.* 135:9–23

160. Marden JH. 1989. Bodybuilding dragonflies: costs and benefits of maximizing flight muscle. *Physiol. Zool.* 62:505–21

161. Harrison JF, Hall HG. 1993. African-European honeybee hybrids have low nonintermediate metabolic capacities. *Nature* 363:258–60

162. Hepburn HR, Radloff SE, Fuchs S. 1999. Flight machinery dimensions of honeybees, *Apis mellifera. J. Comp. Physiol. B* 169:107–12

163. Hepburn HR, Youthed C, Illgner P, Radloff SE, Brown RE. 1999. Production of aerodynamic power in mountain honeybees (*Apis mellifera*). *Naturwissenschaften* 85:389–90

164. Watt WB. 1985. Allelic isozymes and the mechanistic study of evolution. In *Isozymes: Current Topics in Biological and Medical Research,* ed. MC Ratazzi, JG Scandalios, GS Whitt, 12:89–132. New York: Liss

165. Nielsen DI, Page RE, Crosland MWJ. 1994. Clinal variation and selection of malate dehydrogenase allozymes in honey bee populations. *Experientia* 50:867–71

166. Coelho JR, Mitton JB. 1988. Oxygen consumption during hovering is associated with genetic variation of enzymes in honey-bees. *Func. Ecol.* 2:141–46

167. Harrison JF, Nielsen DI, Page REJ. 1996. Malate dehydrogenase phenotype, temperature and colony effects on flight metabolic rate in the honey-bee, *Apis mellifera. Func. Ecol.* 10:81–88

168. Oakeshott J, McKechnie S, Chambers G. 1984. Population genetics of the metabolically related Adh, Gpdh and Tpi polymorphisms in *Drosophila melanogaster.* I. Geographic variation in Gpdh and Tpi allele frequencies in different continents. *Genetica* 63:21–29

169. Bewley G, Niesel D, Wilkins J. 1984. Purification and characterization of the naturally occurring allelic variants of *sn*-glycerol-3–phosphate dehydrogenase in *Drosophila melanogaster. Comp. Biochem. Physiol.* 79B:23–32

170. Laurie-Ahlberg CC, Barnes PT, Curtsinger JW, Emigh TH, Karlin B, et al. 1985. Genetic variability of flight metabolism in *Drosophila melanogaster.* II Relationship between power output and enzyme activity levels. *Genetics* 111:845–68

171. Marden JH, Wolf MR, Weber KE. 1997. Aerial performance of *Drosophila melanogaster* from populations selected for upwind flight ability. *J. Exp. Biol.* 200:2747–55

172. Bartholomew GA, Casey TM. 1978. Oxygen consumption of moths during rest, pre-flight warm-up, and flight in relation to body size and wing morphology. *J. Exp. Biol.* 76:11–25

173. Chappell MA. 1984. Thermoregulation and energetics of the green fig beetle (*Cotinus texana*) during flight and foraging behavior. *Physiol. Zool.* 57:581–89

174. Bartholomew GA, Lighton JRB. 1986. Endothermy and energy metabolism of a giant tropical fly, *Pantophthalmus tabaninus Thumberg. J. Comp. Physiol. B* 156:461–67

175. Armstrong G, Mordue W. 1985 Oxygen consumption of flying locusts. *Physiol. Entomol.* 10:353–58

176. Harrison JF, Phillips JE, Gleeson TT. 1991. Activity physiology of the two-striped grasshopper, *Melanoplus bivittatus:* gas exchange, hemolymph acid-base status, lactate production, and the effect of temperature. *Physiol. Zool.* 64:451–72

177. Chai P, Harrykissoon R, Dudley R. 1996. Hummingbird hovering performance in hyperoxic heliox: effects of body mass and sex. *J. Exp. Biol.* 199:2745–55

178. Calder WA. 1974. Consequences of body

size for avian energetics. In *Avian Energetics,* ed. RA Paynter, pp. 86–151. Cambridge, UK: Nuttall Ornithological Club

179. Bennett AF, Dawson WR. 1976. Metabolism. In *Biology of the Reptilia,* ed. C Gans, WR Dawson, pp. 127–223. New York: Academic

180. Fons R, Sicart R. 1976. Contribution a la connaissance du metabolisme energetique chez deuz crocidurinae: *Suncus etruscus* (Savi, 1822) et *Crocidura russala* (Hermann, 1780) (Insectivora, Soricidae). *Mammalia* 40:299–311

181. Hedenstrom A, Alerstam T. 1992. Climbing performance of migrating birds as a basis for estimating limits for fuel-carrying capacity and muscle work. *J. Exp. Biol.* 164:19–38

182. Norberg UM, Rayner JMV. 1987. Ecological morphology and flight in bats (Mammalia: Chiroptera): wing adaptations, flight performance, foraging strategies and echolocation. *Philos. Trans. R. Soc. London Ser. B* 316:337–419

Annu. Rev. Physiol. 2000. 62:207–35

MECHANISMS UNDERLYING THE COST OF LIVING IN ANIMALS

A. J. Hulbert[1] and Paul Lewis Else[2]

[1,2]*Metabolic Research Centre,* [1]*Departments of Biological Science, and*
[2]*Biomedical Science, University of Wollongong, Wollongong, NSW, Australia 2522;*
e-mail: hulbert@uow.edu.au, paul_else@uow.edu.au

Key Words metabolism, membranes, polyunsaturation, active transport, allometry

■ **Abstract** The cost of living can be measured as an animal's metabolic rate. Basal metabolic rate (BMR) is factorially related to other metabolic rates. Analysis of BMR variation suggests that metabolism is a series of linked processes varying in unison. Membrane processes, such as maintenance of ion gradients, are important costs and components of BMR. Membrane bilayers in metabolically active systems are more polyunsaturated and less monounsaturated than metabolically less-active systems. Such polyunsaturated membranes have been proposed to result in an increased molecular activity of membrane proteins, and in this manner the amount of membrane and its composition can act as a pacemaker for metabolism. The potential importance of membrane acyl composition in metabolic depression, hormonal control of metabolism, the evolution of endothermy, as well as its implications for lifespan and human health, are briefly discussed.

INTRODUCTION

To measure the metabolic rate (MR) of an animal is to quantify its cost of living. The MR most often measured is basal/standard MR (BMR/SMR), which is the MR of a fasted adult at rest in a thermo-neutral environment. In endotherms, BMR is the energy turnover at normal body temperature, whereas in ectotherms, the temperature at which SMR is measured should be specified. BMR is to some extent an artificial construct and does not include the cost of growing, feeding, processing food, nor the cost of activity, all of which are normal processes of free-living animals. In endotherms it also does not include the costs associated with thermoregulation.

Over several decades, the SMRs of many animal species have been measured and catalogued. Although it can vary extensively between different species, in general, the SMR of a vertebrate species is surprisingly predictable, requiring only knowledge of the body mass and the phylogenetic group to which the species belongs. Despite this mathematical predictability, the mechanistic determinants of SMR are not known. The group for which the most complete set of information on MR exists is the mammals, and this review relies heavily on the data for this group. Considerable insight has come from comparison of different-sized mammals and also from comparison of similar-sized endothermic and ectothermic vertebrates. The conclusions from these comparisons appear to be more generally applicable to vertebrates but may also apply to the MR of invertebrates.

THE NATURE OF THE COST OF LIVING

BMR and Other Metabolic Rates

In the nineteenth century, it was proposed that MR was proportional to the body surface area of mammals (1, 2). Early this century, the distinguished zoophysiologist, August Krogh (3) suggested that BMR of mammals was related to a power function of their body mass (i.e. M^n) and that the allometric exponent 'n' should be empirically determined. In 1932, both Kleiber (4) and Brody & Procter (5) determined n for mammalian BMR to be 0.739 and 0.734, respectively. Since then, many studies have determined allometric equations relating the MRs of different animal groups to body mass. A compilation by Withers (6) concluded that the average exponent from interspecific comparisons was 0.76 (range 0.42–0.98), whereas that from intraspecific comparisons was 0.72 (range 0.32–1.08). An exponent of 0.75 means that for a 100% increase in body mass, BMR increases only 68%. Expressed on a mass-specific basis, the mass-specific MR of a species with a 10 g body mass is ten times that of a species from the same phylogenetic group weighing 100 kg. Such allometric exponents appear to be general for multicellular animals, and although they have been known for over half a century, there is still no generally agreed theoretical basis for them being approximately 0.75.

Probably the best explanation was proposed by Hemmingsen (7) in his classic contribution, who suggested that as species change size over evolutionary time, there is a tendency for metabolic activity to increase in direct proportion to body mass (i.e. n = 1.0), larger species being copies of smaller species, but the geometry of structures meant that surface areas change only with the two third power of size (i.e. n = 0.67), and this produced a fundamental conflict. In animals, absorption of food and respiratory gases and waste elimination are surface area-related functions, and thus would limit the ability to serve a metabolism directly proportional to body mass. Species would be selected for decreases in their mass-specific MR or for increases in the areas of surfaces that service metabolism as they increased in body size. Both evolutionary strategies were followed and the measured exponents represent a compromise between these two tendencies. The fact that exponents are ~0.75 suggests that, overall, surface limitations were approximately three times stronger than the tendency for MR to increase in direct proportion to mass. Hemmingsen gave the memorable example that if a rhinoceros had the same mass-specific MR as a mouse, it would need a surface temperature of boiling water to rid itself of the heat produced by its BMR! Such an evolutionary explanation suggests there is no overarching physical theory to precisely explain the allometry of MR and also suggests that, especially over small size ranges, there will be considerable variation in exponents, depending on the evolutionary history of the group being studied.

Although in allometric plots, body mass is placed on the x-axis and MR on the y-axis, this should not be taken that body mass determines MR as is sometimes implied. Mathematical determination of MR does not necessarily mean physiological determination. Indeed, a possible cause-effect relationship is the inverse; that a species' metabolic intensity (i.e. its mass-specific MR) in some broad and largely unknown way influences, in combination with other factors, the adult body size that a species will reach. In mammals, mass-specific MR changes relatively little throughout the course of development. For example, a single-celled rat zygote has the same mass-specific MR as the adult, but the embryo's MR rapidly increases to approximately three to four times the adult level and generally remains at this level until after birth when it starts to decline to the adult level (8). If mass-specific MR is relatively constant during early development, the allometric exponent for whole animal MR will be ~ 1.0, and as mass-specific MR decreases after this period it will be < 1.0. Brody (9) reported such developmental profiles for the MR of cattle, rats and humans. Similarly, in the marsupial *Macropus eugenii,* for both SMR and mitochondrial membrane surface area, n is ~ 1.0 until 20 to 30% of adult body mass is reached and thereafter n is ~ 0.75 (10).

As well as suggesting that MR was related to mass^n, Krogh (3) also recognized "that the oxidative energy of tissues is greater in the warm-blooded than in a cold-blooded organism." Although they have the same allometric exponents, the SMR of mammals and birds is four to ten times that of ectotherms of the same size and same body temperature (7, 11).

BMR represents the cost of living while doing nothing but maintaining the thermodynamic non-equilibrium state of living. The cost of living during normal activity is represented by the field MR (FMR) or daily energy expenditure (DEE). The development of the doubly-labeled water turnover technique (12) has allowed calculation of CO_2 excretion rates of a large number of free-ranging animals. Nagy (13) showed that FMR of mammals, birds, and iguanid lizards was allometrically related to body mass. His recent update (14) gave n = 0.72 for mammalian FMR. Variation in log body mass accounted for 96% of the variation in log FMR with the remaining variation related to seasonal differences but not to taxonomic order, diet, or habitat (except for desert-dwelling eutherian mammals). His earlier review gave exponents of 0.75 for passerine birds, 0.75 for all other birds, and 0.80 for iguanid lizards (13). The fact that FMR and SMR have approximately the same exponents, means that overall, SMR is a relatively constant fraction of FMR irrespective of the species size. Comparing the allometric equations for FMR (13, 14) and SMR (6), it can be concluded that on average the FMR of mammals is about three to four times their SMR, whereas for passerine and nonpasserine birds FMR is about two to three times SMR, and for iguanid lizards FMR is about five times SMR at 20°C and about equal to their SMR at 38°C.

The relationship between BMR and DEE has been analyzed for mammals and birds by examining whether there are correlations between the deviations (residuals) of log BMR and log DEE from their respective allometric equations, using the techniques of phylogenetically independent contrasts (15). The variation in these residuals is considerably greater for mammals than for birds (approximately sixfold greater), and these authors found a strong statistical relationship between the BMR and DEE residuals for mammals but not for birds. The lack of a statistical relationship between BMR and DEE residuals of birds does not imply there is no relationship between BMR and DEE in birds but rather reflects tighter allometric relationships for birds. Both BMR and DEE were strongly allometrically related to body mass in birds and mammals in this study (15). Measurement of BMR and summit MR (cold-induced maximal MR) in ten species of passerine birds has shown a strong correlation between BMR and summit MR, which remained when the effects of both body mass and phylogeny were removed by appropriate statistical techniques (16).

Although FMR and DEE are greater than BMR, they do not represent the maximal MR capable of being sustained aerobically, which is known as $V_{O_{2}max}$. Taylor and coworkers measured (using a treadmill to produce maximal activity) the $V_{O_{2}max}$ of a large number of wild and domestic mammals, ranging in size from the shrew to the horse, and calculated an exponent of 0.85 (17). A more complete compilation of the data yielded n = 0.87 (18). The maximal MR of reptiles (at body temperature of 30°C) has an exponent of 0.82 (19).

The higher exponent for $V_{O_{2}max}$ compared with BMR and FMR of mammals means that smaller mammals are operating closer to their maximal aerobic capacity than larger mammals during normal daily activities. The fact that n < 1.0, however, also shows that smaller mammals, in general, have a higher mass-specific $V_{O_{2}max}$ than do larger mammals. The greater exponent for $V_{O_{2}max}$ is related to the fact that skeletal muscle mass (the predominant tissue metabolizing during maximal activity) has an exponent of ~1.0 in mammals, whereas the size of internal organs (the predominant tissues metabolizing during BMR) all have exponents of < 1.0 (see below for values; also Reference 20). This difference in body composition allometry also exists in reptiles (21).

For a given body mass there is often still significant variation in $V_{O_{2}max}$ of mammals. In a series of studies, Taylor and colleagues compared the oxygen and substrate pathways used to fuel exercise in two similar-sized species (dog and goat) that differed twofold in their $V_{O_{2}max}$. Despite this, these two species showed almost identical patterns of substrate use when these were expressed relative to their $V_{O_{2}max}$ (22). This suggests some form of constant stoichiometry related to overall metabolic activity.

While it was not known when the conditions of BMR were first devised and early measurements made, BMR has turned out to be a reasonable parameter to compare the cost of living of different species, in that it is a relatively consistent and substantial proportion (about 25–40%) of the MR of free-living individuals. Although BMR is not quantitatively the same as the cost of living, it appears to be factorially related to it. Another advantage is that BMR can also be relatively easily related to many sub-organismal parameters and is helpful in analyzing the mechanistic basis of cost of living in animals. These conclusions are based largely on the accumulated data for mammals but they also appear to be reasonably true for other groups of animals when factors such as temperature (for ectotherms) are taken into account. Because of the paucity of data, we can be less sure for groups distant from mammals (e.g. invertebrates).

Composition of BMR at the Cellular Level

Although BMR varies considerably, an intriguing finding is that the percentage contribution of various processes to BMR appears to be relatively constant irrespective of the actual level of BMR. This is deduced from the fact that many physiological processes have the same exponents as BMR. Once again, the data are most complete for mammals. It has long been known that urinary excretion of endogenous nitrogen and neutral sulfur by mammals has exponents of 0.72 and 0.74, respectively (9). Similarly, numerous studies have shown many other rates of respiratory, circulatory, and renal activity (such as cardiac output, glomerular filtration rate, etc) are allometrically related to body mass in the same manner as BMR. The reader is referred to two excellent books for specific information (23, 24).

The whole body turnover rates of proteins in mammals have an exponent of 0.72 (25), and whole body turnover rates of r-RNA, t-RNA, and m-RNA in mammals are similar (26). These latter measurements come from the non-invasive method of measuring urinary excretion rates of modified catabolites of these macromolecules. The principle is described in Schoch et al (26) and is likely to have interesting applications in future comparative studies. Most macromolecules are modified, after their synthesis, in specific positions, and several such modified building blocks are not reused during macromolecular synthesis, nor further metabolized, but are quantitatively excreted in urine following breakdown of the parent macromolecule. Knowledge of the stoichiometry of these modified building blocks in their parent macromolecules, allows calculation of the rate of breakdown of the parent macromolecule which, in steady-state conditions, will equal their turnover rate. For example, N^2,N^2-dimethylguanosine occurs exclusively in t-RNA, whereas pseudouridine occurs in both t-RNA and r-RNA, and 7-methylguanine is found in all three RNA classes. Thus measurement of urinary excretion of all three modified RNA catabolites allows calculation of whole body turnover of all three RNA classes (26). Recently, ethane exhalation by rats and humans has been measured and shown to have an exponent of 0.72 (27). Ethane originates as a product of the peroxidation of omega-3 polyunsaturated acyl chains (PUFA) by reactive oxygen species and is a useful marker of lipid peroxidation (for a review see 28). These findings support the proposition that there is a relatively constant stoichiometry associated with the energy processes of life, irrespective of the total overall activity of these processes in different species.

Whole organism MRs such as BMR are the sum of MRs of individual tissues. During BMR, most of the metabolic activity is associated with the internal organs (such as liver, kidney, heart, brain, etc) that constitute only a small proportion of body mass. Their contribution to BMR is the product of their size and metabolic intensity. Part of the exponent for BMR is due to changes in relative size of tissues. In mammals, tissues vary in their relationship to body mass. Brain mass has an exponent of ~0.7, liver and kidney have exponents of 0.87 and 0.85, gut mass a value of 0.94, and the heart, lung, and skeletal muscle mass remain a relatively constant proportion of total body mass with exponents of 0.98, 0.99, and 1.0, respectively. Relative skeleton mass increases with body size having an exponent of ~1.1 (24). The same tissues have almost identical exponents in birds.

Thus part of BMR variation in mammals is due to relative mass of tissues, and the remainder is due to differences in mass-specific tissue MR. Krebs (29) showed that the in vitro mass-specific MR of mammalian tissue slices differed with body size. This was confirmed in a recent study that showed that sodium pump activity also varied allometrically in mammals. For example, the mass-specific MR varied with exponents of -0.21 and -0.11 for liver and kidney slices, respectively, whereas in vitro sodium pump activity in the same tissues had exponents of -0.14 and -0.13 (30). Similarly, intact hepatocytes isolated from mammals ranging from mice to horses show mass-specific MRs with an exponent of -0.20 (31).

In these hepatocytes the oxygen consumption rate by (*a*) non-mitochondrial processes, (*b*) mitochondria to counteract their proton leak, and (*c*) mitochondria to support phosphorylation of ADP all had exponents almost identical to that for total oxygen consumption. This means that the relative importance of these processes remains the same irrespective of differences in total hepatocyte MR. Non-mitochondrial processes, mitochondrial proton leak, and mitochondrial phosphorylation were respectively responsible for an average, 13, 19, and 68% of hepatocyte resting MR (31).

Although the rate of cellular metabolism varies with body size, tissue composition (water, protein, potassium, and sodium content) is relatively constant in the different-sized mammals (30). Total liver DNA, protein, and phospholipid have exponents of 0.88, 0.84, and 0.84, respectively in mammals (32), values almost identical to the exponent for liver mass (0.87), which means irrespective of body size, mammalian liver has an almost constant composition of these three macromolecules. Interestingly, liver RNA has an exponent of 0.76 (32).

The approximately eightfold difference in SMR of mammals compared with ectothermic reptiles is due in part to differences in tissue size and to differences in the mass-specific tissue MR (33–36). Because cell diameter is relatively constant in different-sized endotherms and ectotherms (respective exponents of 0.03

and 0.05) (37) tissue size differences will be largely due to differences in cell number. Tissue size in organisms appears to be controlled by largely unknown feedback mechanisms related to tissue workload. The physiological implications of such changes have been elegantly discussed by Diamond and colleagues with respect to safety margins (38). Since safety margins will be related to the tissue's ability to perform the required work, it may be that tissue size (i.e. number of cells) is determined as an emergent property of the inherited MR of the individual cells that make up the tissue. If this is the case, then the large differences in whole organism MR can be explained as an emergent consequence of smaller differences at the level of cellular MR.

In cells, energy can be stored in three forms: (*a*) as high-energy phosphate compounds, (*b*) as transmembrane ion gradients, and (*c*) as metabolic substrates. All three forms are interconnected in that energy enters cells as substrates that are catabolized to yield high-energy phosphate compounds either directly or indirectly via an ion gradient (the mitochondrial proton gradient). The high-energy ATP is used for anabolic reactions (e.g. protein synthesis), mechanical movement (e.g. actinomyosin shortening), or for creating the *trans*-plasmalemma Na^+ gradient, which in turn is used as the immediate energy source for other cellular activities (e.g. action potentials, intracellular ion homeostasis, and substrate uptake). Although the linkage of these forms of cellular energy appears constant between cells, their quantitative importance varies between cell types. The relative static size of these compartments does not represent their cost of maintenance. It has become obvious over the last few decades that the maintenance of transmembrane ion gradients is a significant source of energy consumption in living systems. The *trans*-plasmalemma gradients of several ions, intracellular ion homeostasis, appear linked to the Na gradient in a self-regulatory Gibbs-Donnan near-equilibrium system (e.g. 39).

Each cell must make its own ATP, and because most ATP is formed from aerobic metabolism, then the amount of mitochondrial inner membrane can be used as an indicator of the cell's overall MR. This does not apply to anaerobic ATP production where each cell that makes ATP anaerobically can either process the end-product (e.g. lactate) itself or export it to another cell for further processing. Because most animals are aerobic at the whole organism level, this is only a temporary form of internal book-keeping to pass through periods of either high-energy requirements (such as intense muscular exercise) or periods of hypoxia and does not effect the cost of living. In this light, it is of interest that anaerobic metabolism appears much more adaptable to the individual circumstances of specific species, whereas aerobic metabolism often appears to lack this flexibility. For example, although aerobic metabolism enzymes often exhibit allometric exponents similar to BMR, glycolytic enzymes in specific tissues need not (e.g. 40). A comparison of different vertebrates showed that cardiac cytochrome oxidase (CO) reflected the aerobic capacity of species, cardiac content of phosphorylated adenylates varied considerably less than cardiac total creatine content (including creatine phosphate), and the ratios of creatine kinase/CO and pyruvate kinase/CO were high in those species whose myocardia frequently experience hypoxia, but relatively constant in all other species (41).

The quantitative importance of various processes in BMR of mammals has been recently reviewed (42) as has the significance of cation transport in MR (43). When the contributions from various tissues are summed, it is estimated that ~10% of mammalian BMR is non-mitochondrial oxygen consumption. Approximately 20% is oxygen consumed to maintain the mitochondrial membrane potential against a leak of protons. The remaining 70% of oxygen consumed is used for mitochondrial ATP manufacture to provide energy for protein synthesis (~20–25%), maintenance of transmembrane Na^+ gradients (~20–25%), maintenance of transmembrane Ca^{2+} gradients (~5%), gluconeogenesis (~7%), ureagenesis (~2.5%), actinomyosin ATPase (~5%), with activities such as nucleic acid synthesis and substrate cycling accounting for the remainder of ATP turnover (42). A substantial portion of BMR is energy used by membrane-linked processes (i.e. mitochondrial proton leak and maintenance of transmembrane ion gradients, as well as parts of protein synthesis and non-mitochondrial oxygen consumption). From the available information these values appear to be relatively constant fractions of total energy turnover in different mammals.

Similarly, despite a large endotherm-ectotherm difference in SMR, the percentage composition of MR appears similar. For example, the sodium pump uses the same proportion of tissue metabolism in mammals and reptiles (34, 35), and this proportion appears also to be similar in fish, amphibian, and bird liver and kidney slices (44). Hepatocytes from lizards devote approximately the same proportion of MR to mitochondrial proton leak as in the rat (45). In the liver of rats, protein synthesis accounts for ~24% of total MR (42), whereas measurements in toad liver slices give a value of 12% (46) and in turtle hepatocytes a value of 36% (47).

The response of these subcellular processes to energy shortage in rat thymocytes has revealed a hierarchy of responses. Proton leak was responsible for 39% of total MR, the sodium pump consumed 10%, calcium pumping another 10%, nucleotide synthesis 15%, protein synthesis 20%, and unidentified ATP consumers the remaining 6% of total MR. When respiration was inhibited, macromolecular synthesis (protein synthesis and nucleotide synthesis) was the most sensitive, followed by sodium pumping, then calcium pumping. Mitochondrial proton leak was the least sensitive process to changes in energy supply (48). Membrane-linked processes were both the major contributors to total MR and the most resistant to changes in energy supply.

Comparison of the allometry of the different processes that make up the BMR in mammals, together with the limited comparative data for endotherm-ectotherm difference, strongly suggests that metabolism is a series of linked processes. That is, when variation occurs in BMR, it is not the result of change in a single (or only a few) process, but to all processes varying to a similar degree. This suggests there is likely a common factor that has a large influence (either direct or indirect) on all these processes. Such a factor might be thought of as a pacemaker, and in view of the redundancy often found in biological systems, there may be more than one. We have proposed that membranes, specifically the amount and composition of the membrane bilayer, may be such a pacemaker for metabolism (49).

MEMBRANES AND THE COST OF LIVING

Membrane Acyl Composition Varies with BMR

Twenty-two years ago Gudbjarnason (50) demonstrated that the docosahexanoic acid content of cardiac phospholipids from mammals ranging from mice to whales was strongly correlated with their heart rate. Docosahexanoic acid is an omega-3 PUFA that is 22 carbons long and highly polyunsaturated with 6 double bonds (thus called 22:6). This intriguing finding stimulated us to examine the fatty acyl composition of phospholipids from similar-sized reptiles and mammals with the same body temperature (36, 45) and from mammals of different body size (51). We confirmed Gudbjarnason's observation concerning cardiac phospholipids and found it was a more general trend. Those tissues with high mass-specific MRs had membranes that were more polyunsaturated, whereas those that were less metabolically active were more monounsaturated. Because the biochemistry and nomenclature of fatty acyl chains is complex, only general terms are used here. For a discussion of membrane acyl chains see Reference 49.

The phospholipids of small mammals, and thus their membrane bilayers in all tissues examined had a relatively high PUFA content (especially omega-3 PUFAs) and low monounsaturated acyl (MUFA) content. With increasing body size in mammals, there was a relative decrease in polyunsaturation and an increase in monounsaturation of phospholipids. The exception was the brain, which retained high polyunsaturation/low monounsaturation irrespective of body size. This trend was especially manifest in the omega-3 PUFAs, with 22:6 being the predominant omega-3 PUFA in small mammals, with shorter chain, less polyunsaturated omega-3 PUFAs being more common in the larger species (51). Interestingly, the tissue phospholipids of shrews are reported to have exceptionally high polyunsaturation (especially 22:6) and very low monounsaturation, with the smaller common shrew *Sorex araneus* more so than the larger water shrew *Neomys fodiens* (52). In keeping with this trend, tissues from the metabolically inactive bearded-dragon lizard have phospholipids that are less polyunsaturated/more monounsaturated than those from the metabolically active rat (36).

How Is Membrane Acyl Composition Regulated?

Biological membranes often contain hundreds of molecular species of phospholipid (53). It has become evident that membrane bilayers are regulated in a homeostatic manner to maintain a relatively constant physical state. This regulation has been called homeoviscous adaptation and has been recently reviewed (54, 55). In bacteria, phospholipid head group composition is generally resistant to changes in growth conditions, whereas the fatty acyl composition is very adaptive to such changes (53). To some extent the acyl chain composition of membrane bilayers can be regarded separately from head group composition.

In rat hepatocytes, only four phospholipid molecular species are synthesized de novo, and all other molecular species result from remodeling of these four phospholipid species (56). Such remodeling is achieved by deacylation-reacylation from the combined actions of phospholipases and acyltransferases, and transacylases (e.g. 57, 58). In vivo incorporation of labeled acyl chains has shown that saturated fatty acyl chains are largely incorporated via de novo synthesis, whereas polyunsaturated acyl chains are also introduced into phospholipids via deacylation-reacylation (59). During phospholipid remodeling, incorporation of labeled acyl chains is greater in microsomes than in plasma membranes, and changes are rapid, with labels appearing in plasmalemma phospholipids within 2 to 10 min (60). That these enzymes participate in a self-regulatory system is illustrated by the finding in rat liver microsomes that changes in lipid environment can influence acyltransferase affinity for its acyl-CoA substrate (61).

Changes in membrane acyl composition also occur via de novo synthesis and direct desaturation of acyl chains. Vertebrates are able to synthesize de novo only saturated and MUFA chains and must obtain their PUFAs from their diet or intestinal biota. These PUFAs are appropriately modified by desaturases, which introduce double bonds at specific locations in the acyl chain. The desaturases are membrane-bound multi-enzyme complexes that consume oxygen (62). They prefer omega-3 PUFAs over omega-6 PUFAs and MUFAs as substrates. Their activities are inversely affected by membrane fluidity and thus are also involved in membrane homeoviscous adaptation (63–65). Oxygen consumption by desaturases is part of non-mitochondrial consumption by cells. It is thus of interest that in hepatocytes, non-mitochondrial oxygen consumption is allometrically related to body size, being highest in the small mammals (31) that have the most polyunsaturated phospholipids (51).

The genome establishes membrane acyl composition by determining the characteristics of these various enzymes, which constitute a self-regulatory system for maintaining appropriate physical characteristics of membrane bilayers. The genomically determined characteristics of these enzymes are not just involved in homeoviscous adaptation but, we propose, are also a mechanism whereby cellular metabolic activity can be influenced. These enzyme characteristics possibly also influence the final body size of a species by determining its cellular metabolic intensity. Because they can only modify PUFAs obtained by the animal, there will be genome-diet interactions that modify membrane composition that sometimes will have, in humans, medical implications (discussed below). Such a self-regulatory system also explains why, although it is possible to modify the relative acyl composition of membranes by dietary manipulation, it is very difficult to alter overall levels of unsaturation of membranes (e.g. 66). Membrane acyl composition is not fixed and has been shown to be influenced by other conditions such as neonatal development, old age, and catecholamine-mediated stress (e.g. 67).

The Mitochondrial Proton Leak and Membranes

Although ignored by most biochemistry texts, it has long been known that mitochondria consume oxygen when not manufacturing ATP. This oxygen consumption is used to pump protons across the mitochondrial membrane to counteract a proton leak in the opposite direction. It has been most examined in liver mitochondria but has similar characteristics in other tissues (68) and has been recently reviewed (69, 70). Mitochondrial proton leak is greatest when mitochondria are not phosphorylating ADP and rapidly decreases as ATP manufacture increases. In many ways it is analogous to the governor of a steam engine.

The identity of proton leak is unknown, and the possible role of "uncoupling proteins" (UCPs) is discussed by Brand et al (69). Measurement of proton flux across liposomes made from rat liver mitochondrial phospholipids shows the mitochondrial bilayer itself accounts for <5% of total proton leak (71). Proton flux is constant in liposomes, differing widely in fatty acyl composition (72). Thus any influence the membrane acyl chains have on proton leak is likely via their influence on membrane proteins.

The proton leakiness of mitochondria varies allometrically with body size of mammals in both hepatocytes (73) and isolated mitochondria (31). Mitochondrial membrane surface area varies allometrically in mammals (20, 74), as does the acyl composition of mitochondrial phospholipids (74). Hence greater mitochondrial proton leakiness in smaller mammals could arise from either increased membrane surface area and/or difference in mitochondrial acyl composition. A comparison of allometric exponents suggests that about two thirds of the allometric variation in the proton leakiness of liver mitochondria is due to differences in the relative amount of mitochondrial membrane, whereas approximately one third is due to variation in mitochondrial membrane composition (74). Rat liver mitochondria have a proton leakiness that is approximately five times that of liver mitochondria from a similar-sized lizard with the same body temperature. Mitochondrial phospholipids are more polyunsaturated/less monounsaturated (with greater 22:6 content) in the rat than the lizard (45).

Isolated liver mitochondria from a wide range of vertebrates show a relationship between mitochondrial acyl composition and proton leakiness (75). There were large differences in the resting mitochondrial proton leak (measured as state 4 respiration rate) between ectothermic and endothermic vertebrates but considerably smaller differences in resting mitochondrial membrane potential. Relative proton leakiness of mitochondria can be assessed by comparison of the curve relating proton leak to membrane potential. Mammalian and avian liver mitochondria have a similar leakiness, which is several times that of reptilian mitochondria (three lizard species). Proton leakiness of amphibian mitochondria (two species) is similar to the endothermic vertebrates, while that of a single fish species shows a leakier pattern. Proton leakiness of isolated liver mitochondria is consistent within but varied between vertebrate classes. When mitochondrial proton leakiness was compared with phospholipid fatty acyl composition (72), it was noted that reptile mitochondrial membranes were least polyunsaturated/most monounsaturated, fish were most polyunsaturated/least monounsaturated, and amphibian, avian, and mammalian mitochondria had intermediate compositions. When combined with literature data for other species, there are significant correlations between mitochondrial phospholipid acyl composition and SMR (75). Although this study refutes a general endotherm-ectotherm difference in the proton leakiness of isolated liver mitochondria, it reinforces a correlation between membrane acyl polyunsaturation and mitochondrial proton leakiness. A key indicator is 22:6 content, which appears to be related to the average body temperature experienced by the ectotherm species, being very high in the fish species. In some cold-water fish mitochondria, 22:6 can constitute 59% of phospholipid acyl chains (76).

Thus in both mammalian allometric comparisons and phylogenetic comparisons, there are correlations between the polyunsaturation/monounsaturation of a mitochondrial membrane and its proton leakiness.

The Sodium Pump and Membranes

When the sodium pump is inhibited with ouabain, tissue slice MRs of mammals and reptiles decrease by approximately the same proportion even though the total tissue slice MR differs considerably (34, 35). This is associated with a lower sodium leak into cells of the ectotherm tissues (34). This finding was later extended to an avian and a fish species, and a correlation was established between sodium leak into liver cells and energy turnover of the sodium pump (44). When sodium pump densities were measured in tissues from endothermic and ectothermic vertebrates, there were expected differences between tissues but no difference between endothermic and ectothermic species (77). However, when enzymatic activity of Na^+-K^+-ATPase was measured, differences between tissues and endotherm-ectotherm differences were observed. This anomaly was resolved when enzymatic activity of an average sodium pump (its molecular activity) was calculated. The difference between tissues largely disappeared, but a consistent endotherm-ectotherm difference in sodium pump molecular activity became apparent. Sodium pumps from any tissue of the endotherms had molecular activities of ~8000 ATP/min, whereas those from tissues of ectotherms operated at ~2500 ATP/min (77). These values are in vitro enzymatic activities and likely represent maximal activities. The activities of sodium pumps in liver slices from rats and toads (at the same temperature) are ~10% of their respective molecular activities in both species (Z-X Du & AJ Hulbert, unpublished results).

In experiments (78) designed to investigate this endotherm-ectotherm difference in molecular activity, microsomes were prepared from both brain and kidney of rat and cane toad (*Bufo marinus*) and sodium pump molecular activity was measured. Delipidation resulted in a decrease in sodium pump molecular activity (dependent on the degree of delipidation) until molecular activities were the same for both species. Relipidation with heat-inactivated microsomes (which does not alter acyl composition) resulted in increased sodium pump molecular activity. Delipidated rat pumps relipidated with rat microsomes returned to normal rat molecular activity, and toad pumps relipidated with toad microsomes similarly returned to toad molecular activity. However, when rat pumps were relipidated with toad microsomes, they had decreased molecular activities, and when toad pumps were relipidated with rat microsomes, they showed an increased molecular activity. These results were identical for brain and kidney pumps. Similar membrane cross-over studies between cattle and crocodile tissues have produced the same results, and a double relipidation technique further accentuated the effects (BJ Wu & PL Else, unpublished results). These results suggest the membrane lipid environment is important in determining sodium pump molecular activity. The precise role of membranes has yet to be determined, but microsomes from the endotherm tissues were more polyunsaturated/less monounsaturated than the ectotherm microsomes. These cross-over experiments represent the first experimental support of the role of membrane lipids in the endotherm-ectotherm metabolism difference in that most of the other evidence is largely correlative. These cross-over studies are reminiscent of some results from homeoviscous-related research in fish where cold acclimation in trout resulted in increased molecular activity of sodium pumps (79). Similarly, mitochondrial membrane lipids extracted from cold-acclimated goldfish exhibit a greater reactivation of delipidated succinic dehydrogenase than do those from warm-acclimated goldfish (80).

It is not yet known if the sodium leakiness of vertebrate cells is also affected by membrane acyl composition. The ionophore, valinomycin (a cyclic peptide) mediates a faster Rb^+ flux in polyunsaturated membranes compared with monounsaturated lipid bilayers (81), and its ability to transport protons is positively related to liposome polyunsaturation and negatively related to liposome monounsaturation (82). These results are suggestive that sodium leak is also influenced by membrane acyl composition.

Influence of Membrane Lipids on Membrane Proteins

The influence of membrane lipids on the activities of membrane-bound proteins is becoming more apparent. Focus has previously been on specific lipid requirements (see 83) and specific lipid-protein interactions (e.g. 84–86). It now appears that effects due to specific lipid requirements of membrane proteins are either rare or weak (83, 85–87), with bulk physical bilayer characteristics a more important influence on protein activity (e.g. 88). The bilayer physical characteristics are influenced by lipid molecular species and membrane leaflet distribution, as well as by phospholipid head group and acyl composition (89). Changes in protein activity may occur by variation in a number of these characters within the heterogeneous lipid mixture of a membrane. The task is to see within such lipid diversity any general principles that affect membrane protein activities and hence the cost of living in animals.

Direct manipulation of natural membranes allows for examination of lipid effects. In one such study, membrane acyl composition was modified using lyso-phosphatidylcholine and various CoA fatty acid derivatives to change membrane phosphatidylcholines by the endogenous acyltransferase. At an equivalent level of incorporation (12%), the saturated fatty acid (16:0) had no effect, the mono-unsaturate (18:1) caused a 10–20% increase in Na^+-K^+ATPase and lysolecithin-acyltransferase activities and 5–10% decrease in γ-glutamyltransferase and Mg^{2+}ATPase activities. The two polyunsaturates (18:2 and 20:4) increased Na^+-K^+ATPase by 75% and lysolecithin-acyltransferase activity by 150%, while γ-glutamyltransferase and Mg^{2+}ATPase decreased by 75% and 40%, respectively (90). These results show a differential effect on different enzymes, but polyun-saturates had a greater effect than monounsaturates and in the case of lysolecithin-acyltransferase, its activity can be self-modulated by changes in membrane composition.

Direct in vitro increase of lipid unsaturation resulted in an increased activity of protein kinase C when phosphatidylcholine was modified and decreased activity if associated with phosphatidylserine (91). Likewise the G protein of the visual system, found in membranes with high 22:6 content, showed increased rates of product formation in phospholipid vesicles of increased unsaturation (92). Reconstitution of the hexose transporter in pure lecithins showed a decreased transporter activity with both short acyl chains and decreased unsaturation, with transporter molecular activity varying by orders of magnitude and governed by bulk membrane properties (93).

Dietary manipulation is also used to change membrane lipid composition and investigate effects on membrane enzyme activities. Increasing membrane polyun-saturation of cells has been shown to modify the activity of various membrane enzymes (94, 95). A review of major membrane proteins concluded that 5′ nucleotidase activity increased with greater membrane unsaturation, adenylate cyclase varied between tissues, and Na^+-K^+ATPase activity decreased with increasing polyunsaturation (96).

Direct and dietary manipulation of membrane lipids sometimes appears to result in different effects for some enzymes (e.g. Na^+-K^+ATPase). Unlike direct in vitro modification, dietary manipulations occur over time and involve adaptive changes associated with maintenance of homeostasis. Changes in enzyme activity may involve either a change in enzyme molecular activity or changes in enzyme concentration or both. Such changes may be in opposite directions. Since gross enzyme activities are normally measured, changes in molecular activity versus changes in enzyme concentration cannot be separated. Such differences in response may account for some of the different results on enzyme activities between direct and dietary-induced changes in membrane composition.

CHANGES IN THE COST OF LIVING DURING LIFE HISTORY

The cost of living during ontogeny of different species produces varying patterns of energy use (8, 97, 98). Studies of the cellular mechanisms underlying these changes have primarily focused on mammals and on protein synthesis and active transport. In mammals, mass-specific MR is constant from fertilization to the morula. During blastocyst formation it increases (up to fourfold) (99), and mass-specific MR remains relatively high and constant from implantation through to later fetal stages where a slight decline may occur (8). In human fetus (weeks 7–12), mass-specific MR varies between organs, with liver (an organ with average mass-specific MR in adults) having twice the MR of most other organs (100). An increase in MR (1.2–2 times) usually follows birth, and thereafter a gradual decline in mass-specific MR to adult levels ensues (8, 9, 101–103).

Early Development

Protein synthesis is a significant but variable contributor to BMR throughout development. During blastocyst formation, protein synthesis has been calculated to account for 28% of MR (8), and ouabain treatment drastically reduces MR, which suggests that electrolyte movement during blastocoele formation is another major energy-requiring process (104, 105). During fetal development, protein synthesis may represent a constant proportion of MR as mid- and late-fetal sheep show exponents of 0.74 and 0.73, respectively (106). During the same period, concentrations of active transporters increase (1.2–2.3 times) in skeletal and cardiac muscles, suggesting an increased energy use by active transport (107).

The postnatal peak in MR is associated with increases in sodium pump concentrations in skeletal muscles (2–6 times), heart (1.25 times), and brain (10 times) during the first few weeks following birth (52, 108, 109). These concentrations are either maintained or decreased during maturation. In humans, an increase in active transporter concentrations has been found in cardiac tissues, where sodium pump concentrations are twofold higher in 0.5–3-year old infants than in older children and adults (110).

Increases in organ Na^+-K^+-ATPase activity support the notion of increased energy use by active transport in early postnatal life (111–113). Additionally, mass-specific MR of rat liver increases 60% within hours after birth with a postnatal peak MR that is 3.5-fold that of adult liver, with most of this increase being ouabain inhibitable (114). In heart, active rubidium uptake (115) and sodium pump concentration (109) in guinea pig pups is twice that of adult animals. In rats, renal proximal tubules increase their Na^+ influx by 32% between 10 and 12 days, followed by a steady fivefold increase in Na^+-K^+-ATPase activity between days 16 to 40 (111). Similar changes also occur for another active transporter. The membrane-bound calcium pump increases in cardiac (1.8 times) and skeletal muscles (3–5 times) of pigs during the first few weeks of postnatal life (107).

Jejunal enterocytes from juvenile rats have increased Na^+-K^+- and Na^+-ATPase activity and protein content compared with older animals (116).

Increased intracellular ion concentrations seem a likely stimulus for increases in the concentration and activity of active transporters. Changed ion concentrations may occur by changes in number or activity of ion channels and secondary active transporters. During development of the rat, the early postnatal increase in Na^+-K^+ ATPase activity of renal proximal tubular cells is preceded by an increased Na^+ influx through increased amiloride-sensitive Na^+/H^+ exchanger activity (111). Voltage-gated sodium channel density in rat brain increases tenfold and affinity decreases fourfold from birth to day 120 (117). Similarly, in skeletal muscle, Na^+-channel density is greater in younger than older animals (118).

At the same time as activities of energy-utilizing membrane-linked processes are changing during ontogeny, the nature of membrane lipids is also changing. For example, in rat brain between late embryonic to early postnatal life, membrane phospholipids double their omega-3 PUFA (mostly 22:6) content at the expense of MUFAs (119). In rat heart, PUFA content (especially 18:2, 20:4, and 22:6) of the two major phospholipids phosphatidylcholine and phosphatidylethanolamine change two- to threefold (67).

Changes in the molecular activity of membrane proteins also occur during ontogeny. Sodium pumps from rat kidney and brain show an approximately fourfold increase in molecular activity from fetus to adult (BJ Wu & PL Else, unpublished results).

The potential importance of bilayer acyl composition in determining the molecular activity of membrane proteins may also be gleaned from a completely different tissue, the chick jejunum. Glucose transporter activity of the brush border membranes of these cells increases twofold during early postnatal life (2 days to 14 weeks). This increase is matched by a twofold increase in transporter density, and thus there is no change in molecular activity. During the same period there are substantial changes in cholesterol and phospholipid content and phospholipid head group composition. In contrast, membrane fatty acyl composition remains remarkably constant (120). Therefore the molecular activity of these glucose transporters remains constant, as does membrane acyl composition, despite major changes in other aspects of membrane composition.

Changes during ontogeny in expression of different transporter isozymes often occur. For example, in both rat skeletal muscle and heart, major changes in types and abundance of sodium pump isozymes occur (121, 122). Similar changes also occur for the calcium pump where isozymes are developmentally regulated in both mammalian skeletal (123) and cardiac muscle (124). Currently, there is no understanding as to whether different isozymes have different molecular activities. Organs of adult mammals with different sodium pump isozymes have similar molecular activities (114), which suggests no major differences in molecular activity of different isozymes. For the sodium pump, the currently accepted roles for different isoforms include differential sensitivity to endogenous inhibitors, Na^+/K^+ affinity, and ability to regulate expression pathways (125). However, there remains the possibility that energy utilization by active transporters may be influenced by changes in isozymal composition of membranes during development.

The cellular mechanisms underpinning changes in energy utilization during ontogeny include protein synthesis and active transport as major energy consumers. The role of proton leak in energy use during ontogeny is unstudied. Active transporters implicate themselves in MR changes by similar changes in their tissue concentrations and enzyme activity, as well as by developmental changes in the degree of inhibition of MR. Changes in the molecular activity of active transporters also appear to be involved in changing energy requirements during ontogeny. In determining the relative contributions of different cellular processes during ontogeny, consideration of the highly variable and changing relationships between protein and water content and wet to dry mass ratios of tissues is important.

Older Age

In older age BMR declines. In humans, MR decreases slowly at first then at about 4% per decade after 50 years of age (126, 127). A recent study of mice showed a 15% reduction in hepatocyte MR with age, with mitochondrial proton leak being 13% and ATP-demanding processes 56% of total MR (versus, respectively, 7% and 67% in young mice), with no quantitative change in non-mitochondrial oxygen consumption (128). These results show that the age-associated decrease in liver MR is primarily derived from a decrease in ATP-consuming processes.

ATP-demanding processes known to decrease with age include protein synthesis and sodium pumping. Humans studies show whole-body protein synthesis decreases 20% with age, with muscle accounting for most of this decline (129, 130). Similar declines occur in rat skeletal muscles, yet liver protein levels remain unaffected by age (131). The decline in muscle protein is primarily associated with reduced synthesis of contractile proteins (130) that appears not to be due to disuse (129). Protein synthesis in older age accounts for ~15–16% of BMR (127). Age effects on active transporters have not been extensively studied. Red blood cell Na^+ efflux rate of young men is 20% higher than in older men (132), and active rubidium influx in lymphocytes decreases sixfold between age 20 and 90 (133). In rats, liver mass-specific MR declines with age, but the ouabain-inhibitable proportion (30%) remains constant (114), suggesting active transporter activity may decline in proportion to the overall reduction in energy use with age. Changes in molecular activity may occur, but at the present time this can only be implied. For example, brain synaptic membranes from 6-month-old mice show a 20% decrease in Na^+-K^+-ATPase activity, but sodium pump concentration does not decrease until 20 months of age, suggesting a decreased pump molecular activity with age (134).

The specific activity of $\Delta 5$ and $\Delta 6$ desaturase activity associated with omega-3 long chain PUFA formation in rat liver declines rapidly with age, whereas $\Delta 6$

desaturase activity specific for omega-6 linoleic acid appears to remain stable with age (135).

MODIFICATIONS TO THE COST OF LIVING

Metabolic Depression

Food, water, and oxygen are essential requirements for normal living processes in most animals. Some animals are able to tolerate conditions and times when one or all of these requirements are limited, by depressing their costs of living. Only brief discussion of this ability is given, as a current extensive review is now available (136). Often such conditions are associated with low temperatures. In ectotherms low temperature will depress MR, as normal. Some endotherms will abandon homeothermy and its associated energy costs and reap large benefits due to the physical effects of low body temperature on MR. Several species also depress their MR independently of changes in body temperature.

Some freshwater turtles tolerate several months of anoxia submerged. The heart of the turtle *Chrysemys picta* is able to continue to work in vivo under such conditions, and although all its energy must be obtained by anaerobic metabolism, it shows no greater glycolytic ability than hypoxia-sensitive mammals or fish. Its exceptional ability to tolerate anoxia appears due to its ability to depress its MR (137). The ATP demand of turtle hepatocytes is decreased by 94% during anoxia (138). These hepatocytes cease gluconeogenesis and decrease protein turnover by 94%, whereas the ATP requirements of the sodium pump decrease by only 74% and urea synthesis by 70% (138). Although sodium pump activity is dramatically decreased, cell membrane potentials are maintained presumably because sodium leak is also reduced to a similar extent (139). Because they are ectotherms, normoxic turtles have a low cell leakiness to sodium. For example, turtle neurons have an ionic leakiness that is about 25% of that of rat neurons at the same temperature (140). During anoxia, turtle neurons decrease their firing rates and thus ionic leakiness (141). The degree of MR depression of turtle hepatocytes (~94%) is considerably greater than that of their brain (~50%), and they achieve this by further reducing their low ionic leakiness by a process described as channel arrest; however, the precise mechanisms remain unknown (138).

Although oxygen sensing pathways have been implicated in the hypoxia/anoxia depression of MR (138), they may not be essential, as substantial MR depression occurs in many species under normoxic conditions. For example, several frog species and snail species can depress their MRs by ~80% during water and food deprivation (estivation) but with access to oxygen. A common finding is that during metabolic depression intracellular ATP levels and cell energy charge are maintained as are normal transmembrane ion gradients. Protein synthesis is relatively more depressed than sodium pump activity (142–146). During MR depression in the snail, whole snail MR is decreased by 84%, tissue MR of mantle is decreased by 50%, and a degree of dehydration occurs together with decreases in both the pO_2 and pH of the hemolymph. Experiments suggest that the decreases in hemolymph pO_2 and pH could account for about 70% of the decrease in mantle MR, the remainder being due to some unknown mechanism (143).

Stuart et al (147) recently found that although there was no change in the total phospholipid content of the hepatopancreas of estivating snails, there was a 72% decrease in mitochondrial phospholipids, with a 83–84% decrease in both cardiolipin content and cytochrome oxidase activity. They also found a 49% decrease in polyunsaturated acyl content and a 37% increase in monounsaturated acyl content of mitochondrial phospholipids. These results are fascinating and implicate changes in membrane amount and composition in MR depression. They should stimulate further examination of this aspect of metabolic depression in this and other species.

Although most cases of metabolic depression have been described in ectotherms, food restriction (50% normal intake) has been demonstrated to result in a dramatic decline (by ~50%) in the resting MR of the spiny mouse, *Acomys russatus,* but not in the laboratory mouse. The resting MR returned to normal within one day of ad libitum access to food (148). Similarly, the Bedouin goat reduces its resting MR by ~40% during food restriction (149). Although resting MR is reduced, activity MR is unaffected. The depression of MR does not involve either the catecholamines or the thyroid hormones and does not involve the gut, but it appears that skeletal muscle is one of the primary tissues involved (149). The mechanism(s) of metabolic depression in these two mammalian examples is unknown, but it is of interest in the rat that starvation resulted in no change in the intracellular ATP content of erythrocytes, but a lower intracellular Na content, coupled with substantial decreases in both active and passive fluxes of ions (150).

Thyroid Hormones

The thyroid hormones have long been known as modulators of metabolic activity of vertebrates. Their physical chemistry and their effects in vertebrates have been recently reviewed (151). Although their mode of action is often assumed to be via nuclear receptors, thyroid hormones also inact changes in membrane acyl composition, specifically in increased polyunsaturation of omega-6 fatty acyl chains, and it is suggested that this effect is the main pathway whereby they exert their MR effects (151). In rat hepatocytes, top-down elasticity analysis has shown in the hypothyroid-euthyroid comparison, half of the increased oxygen consumption is from an increase in non-mitochondrial oxygen consumption and half from an increased mitochondrial proton leak, whereas in the euthyroid-hyperthyroid comparison, just under half the increase is from a greater mitochondrial proton leak, and the remainder is due to an enhanced ATP turnover (152). It is of current interest that the thyroid hormone-induced change in membrane acyl composition is also associated with an increased V_{max} of many mitochondrial membrane transporters yet no change in their number (153–158), which implies that thyroid hormones result in an increase in their molecular activities.

Metabolic Syndrome

It has become obvious over the last few decades that the human conditions of obesity, hypertension, and hyperinsulinemia are part of a disease syndrome (called the metabolic syndrome) that includes tissue insulin-resistance and is related to diet. In rats, diets deficient of omega-3 PUFAs result in the same syndrome: First insulin-resistance and hyperinsulinemia develop, followed by hypertension and obesity (159). Insulin resistance is correlated with diminished omega-3 PUFA content of skeletal muscle in rats and humans, and their provision in the diet both diminishes insulin-resistance and results in an increased MR in rats and humans (160). The average western diet would appear to result in omega-3 PUFA deficiency in a substantial part of population with significant metabolic and health consequences.

Evolution of Endothermy

An important event during vertebrate evolution was the evolution of homeothermic endothermy, separately in two major groups, the birds and mammals. This evolutionary change consists of two separate aspects: (*a*) the evolution of the neural regulatory system used to increase heat production in the cold (homeothermy) and (*b*) the evolution of an enhanced cellular furnace (endothermy). Elsewhere (49) we have suggested that this second change was possibly due to changes in the enzyme systems regulating membrane acyl composition, with the consequence of an increase in membrane polyunsaturation in early mammals and an increase in cellular MR. If cellular metabolic activity consists of a series of linked processes, as it thus appears, then such an increase in MR not only allowed a broader thermal niche over which homeothermy could be maintained, but was also associated with greater aerobic capacity, and faster growth rates and shorter generation times, as well as greater food requirements. Each of these effects will have its own variety of ecological and evolutionary advantages and disadvantages on which natural selection could operate. Likely, the balance of selective pressures and evolutionary reasons for retention of the high MR of endothermy differed between various groups and times (11, 161), even though the mechanistic basis may be common.

LIFE SPAN, MEMBRANES, AND METABOLISM

It has long been known that there is a connection between metabolic intensity and lifespan. Various theories have been put forward, including one that proposes that the rate of aging is determined by the rate of free radical production. This has been recently reviewed, from a comparative approach, where it has been suggested that no antioxidant defense can be perfect and where the inevitable production of reactive oxygen species during mitochondrial respiration results in lipid peroxide production and consequent damage to mitochondrial DNA (162). Since only unsaturated acyl chains produce lipid peroxides (with PUFAs being especially susceptible), the specific acyl composition of membranes is an important determinant of the maximum longevity of a species. In this scenario, membrane unsaturates are more important determinants of maximum life span than antioxidant defenses, which surprisingly are often low in long-living species. If this proposal is correct, then membrane acyl composition not only acts as a pacemaker for metabolism but also as its timer-stop watch, being a key link between the pace of life and its duration.

ACKNOWLEDGMENTS

Our own work has at various times been supported by grants from the Australian Research Committee. We thank our many colleagues for input over the years into the ideas expressed in this review.

Visit the Annual Reviews home page at www.AnnualReviews.org.

LITERATURE CITED

1. Sarrus R. 1838. Rapport sur un memoire adresse a l'Academic royale de medecine. *Bull. Acad. Nat. Med. Paris* 3:1094–100
2. Rubner M. 1883. Uber den Einfluss der Korpergrosse auf stoff- und kraft-wechsel. *Z. Biol.* 19:535–62
3. Krogh A. 1916. *The Respiratory Exchange of Animals and Man.* London: Longmans Green
4. Kleiber M. 1932. Body size and metabolism. *Hilgardia* 6:315–53
5. Brody S, Procter RC. 1932. Relation between basal metabolism and mature body weight in different species of mammals and birds. *Univ. Miss. Agric. Exp. Sta. Res. Bull.* 115 pp.
6. Withers PC. 1992. *Comparative Animal Physiology.* Sydney: Saunders. 949 pp.
7. Hemmingsen AM. 1960. Energy metabolism as related to body size and respiratory surfaces and its evolution. *Rep. Steno. Mem. Hosp. Nord. Insulinab.* 9:1–110

8. Adolph EF. 1983. Uptakes and uses of oxygen, from gametes to maturity: an overview. *Resp. Physiol.* 53:135–60
9. Brody S. 1945. *Bioenergetics and Growth.* Canada: Hafner. 1023 pp.
10. Hulbert AJ, Mantaj W, Janssens PA. 1991. Development of mammalian endothermic metabolism: quantitative changes in tissue mitochondria. *Am. J. Physiol.* 261(30):R561–68
11. Hulbert AJ. 1980. The evolution of energy metabolism in mammals. In *Comparative Physiology: Primitive Mammals,* ed. K Schmidt-Nielsen, L Bolis, CR Taylor, pp. 129–39. Cambridge, UK: Cambridge Univ. Press.
12. Lifson N, McClintock R. 1966. Theory of use of the turnover rates of body water for measuring energy and material balance. *J. Theor. Biol.* 12:46–74
13. Nagy KA. 1987. Field metabolic rate and food requirement scaling in mammals and birds. *Ecol. Mono.* 57(2):111–28

14. Nagy KA. 1994. Field bioenergetics of mammals: what determines field metabolic rates. *Aust. J. Zool.* 42:43–53

15. Ricklefs RE, Konarzewski M, Daan S. 1996. The relationship between basal metabolic rate and daily energy expenditure in birds and mammals. *Am. Nat.* 147(6):1047–71

16. Dutenhoffer MS, Swanson DL. 1996. Relationship of basal and summit metabolic rate in passerine birds and the aerobic capacity model for the evolution of endothermy. *Physiol. Zool.* 69(5):1232–54

17. Taylor CR, Maloiy MO, Weibel ER, Langmon VA, Kamau VMZ, et al. 1981. Design of the mammalian respiratory system. III. Scaling maximum aerobic capacity to body mass: wild and domestic mammals. *Resp. Physiol.* 44:25–37

18. Jones JH, Lindstedt SL. 1993. Limits to maximal performance. *Annu. Rev. Physiol.* 55:547–69

19. Bennett AF, Dawson WR. 1976. Metabolism. In *Biology of the Reptilia,* ed. C Gans, WR Dawson, pp. 127–23. New York: Academic

20. Else PL, Hulbert AJ. 1985. Mammals: an allometric study of metabolism at the tissue and mitochondrial level. *Am. J. Physiol.* 248(22):R1–7

21. Else PL, Hulbert AJ. 1985. An allometric comparison of the mitochondria of mammalian and reptilian tissues: the implications for the evolution of endothermy. *J. Comp. Physiol. B* 156:3–11

22. Roberts TJ, Weber J-M, Hoppeler H, Weibel ER, Taylor RC. 1996. Design of the oxygen and substrate pathways. II. Defining the upper limits of carbohydrate and fat oxidation. *J. Exp. Biol.* 199:1651–58

23. Calder WA. 1984. *Size, Function and Life History.* London: Harvard Univ. Press. 431 pp.

24. Peters RH. 1983. *The Ecological Implications of Body Size.* Cambridge, UK: Cambridge Univ. Press. 329 pp.

25. Waterlow JC. 1984. Protein turnover with special reference to man. *Q. J. Exp. Physiol.* 69:409–38

26. Schoch G, Topp H, Held A, Heller-Schoch G, Ballauff A, et al. 1990. Interrelation between whole-body turnover rates of RNA and protein. *Eur. J. Clin. Nutr.* 44:647–58

27. Topp H, Vangala M, Kritzler K, Schoch G. 1995. Assessment of lipid peroxidation in rats of different body weight by determining expired ethane. *Biol. Chem. Hoppe-Seyler* 376:691–94

28. Kneepkins C, Lepage G, Roy CC. 1994. The potential of the hydrocarbon breath test as a measure of lipid peroxidation. *Free Rad. Biol. Med.* 17(2):127–60

29. Krebs HA. 1950. Body size and tissue respiration. *Biochim. Biophys. Acta* 4:249–69

30. Couture P, Hulbert AJ. 1995. Relationship between body mass, tissue metabolic rate and sodium pump activity in mammalian liver and kidney. *Am. J. Physiol.* 268:R641–50

31. Porter RK, Brand MD. 1995. Causes of differences in respiration rate of hepatocytes from mammals of different body mass. *Am. J. Physiol.* 269(38):R1213–24

32. Munro HN. 1969. Evolution of protein metabolism in mammals. *In Mammalian Protein Metabolism,* ed. HN Munro, III:133–82. New York: Academic

33. Else PL, Hulbert AJ. 1981. Comparison of the "mammal machine" and the "reptile machine": energy production. *Am. J. Physiol.* 240(9):R3–9

34. Else PL, Hulbert AJ. 1987. Evolution of mammalian endothermic metabolism: "Leaky" membranes as a source of heat. *Am. J. Physiol.* 253(1):R1–7

35. Hulbert AJ, Else PL. 1981. Comparison of the "mammal machine" and the "reptile machine": energy use and thyroid activity. *Am. J. Physiol.* 241(10):R350–56

36. Hulbert AJ, Else PL. 1989. The evolution of endothermic metabolism: mitochon-

drial activity and changes in cellular composition. *Am. J. Physiol.* 256(25): R1200–8

37. Maldonado R, San Jose H, Martinoya C, Günther B. 1974. Cell size and body weight in some homeotherms and poikilotherms. *Acta Phyiol. Latino Am.* 24:328–35

38. Diamond J. 1993. Enzymes and elevator cables: the evolutionary basis of physiological design. In *The Logic of Life,* ed. CAR Boyd, D Noble. New York: Oxford Univ. Press

39. Masuda T, Dobson GP, Veech RL. 1990. The Gibbs-Donnan near-equilibrium system of heart. *J. Biol. Chem.* 265(33): 20321–34

40. Somero GN, Childress JJ. 1980. A violation of the metabolism-size scaling paradigm: activities of glycolytic enzymes in muscle increase in larger-size fish. *Physiol. Zool.* 53(3):322–37

41. Christensen M, Hartmund T, Gesser H. 1994. Creatine kinase, energy-rich phosphates and energy metabolism in heart muscle of different vertebrates. *J. Comp. Physiol.* 164:118–23

42. Rolfe DFS, Brown GC. 1997. Cellular energy utilization and molecular origin of standard metabolic rate in mammals. *Physiol. Rev.* 77(3):731–58

43. Clausen TC, Hardeveld CV, Everts ME. 1991. Significance of cation transport in control of energy metabolism and thermogenesis. *Physiol. Rev.* 71(3):733–75

44. Hulbert AJ, Else PL. 1990. The cellular basis of endothermic metabolism: a role for "leaky" membranes? *NIPS* 5:25–28

45. Brand MD, Couture P, Else PL, Withers KW, Hulbert AJ. 1991. Evolution of energy metabolism: proton permeability of the inner membrane of liver mitochondria is greater in a mammal than in a reptile. *Biochem. J.* 275:81–86

46. Fuery CJ, Withers PC, Guppy M. 1998. Protein synthesis in the liver of Bufo marinus: cost and contribution to oxygen consumption. *Comp. Biochem. Physiol.* 119A(2):459–67

47. Land SC, Buck LT, Hochachka PW. 1993. Response of protein synthesis to anoxia and recovery in anoxia-tolerant hepatocytes. *Am. J. Physiol.* 265:R41–48

48. Buttgereit F, Brand MD. 1995. A hierarchy of ATP-consuming processes in mammalian cells. *Biochem. J.* 312:163–67

49. Hulbert AJ, Else PL. 1999. Membranes as possible pacemakers of metabolism. *J. Theor. Biol.* 199: 257–74

50. Gudbjarnason S, Doell B, Oskardottir G, Hallgrimsson J. 1978. Modification of cardiac phospholipids and catecholamine stress tolerance. In *Tocopherol, Oxygen and Biomembranes,* ed. C de Duve, O Hayaishi pp. 297–310 Amsterdam: Elsevier

51. Couture P, Hulbert AJ. 1995. Membrane fatty acid composition of tissues is related to body mass of mammals. *J. Membr. Biol.* 148:27–39

52. Kakela R, Hyvarinen H. 1995. Fatty acids in the triglycerides and phospholipids of common shrew (*Sorex araneus*) and the water shrew (*Neomys fodiens*). *Comp. Biochem. Physiol.* 112B(1):71–81

53. Dowhan W. 1997. Molecular basis for membrane phospholipid diversity: Why are there so many lipids? *Annu. Rev. Biochem.* 66:199–32

54. Hazel JR, Williams EE. 1990. The role of alterations in membrane lipid composition in enabling physiological adaptation of organisms to their physical environment. *Prog. Lipid Res.* 29(3): 167–77

55. Hazel JR. 1995. Thermal adaptation in biological membranes: Is homeoviscous adaptation the explanation? *Annu. Rev. Physiol.* 57:19–42

56. Schmid PC, Deli E, Schmid HHO. 1995. Generation and remodeling of phospholipid molecular species in rat hepatocytes. *Arch. Biochem. Biophys.* 319(1): 168–76

57. Balsinde J, Bianco ID, Ackermann EJ, Conde-Frieboes K, Dennis EA. 1995. Inhibition of calcium-independent phospholipase A2 prevents arachidonic acid incorporation and phospholipid remodeling in P388D1 macrophages. *Proc. Natl. Acad. Sci. USA* 92:8527–31

58. Yamashita A, Sugiura T, Waku K. 1997. Acyltransferases and transacylases involved in fatty acid remodeling of phospholipids and metabolism of bioactive lipids in mammalian cells. *J. Biochem.* 122:1–16

59. Valtersson C, Filipsson L, Dallner G. 1986. Localization of phosphatidylethanolamine in microsomal membranes and regulation of its distribution by the fatty acid composition. *J. Lipid Res.* 27:731–41

60. Chakravarthy BR, Spence MW, Cook HW. 1986. Turnover of phospholipid fatty acyl chains in cultured neuroblastoma cells: involvement of deacylation-reacylation and de novo synthesis in plasma membranes. *Biochim. Biophys. Acta* 879:264–77

61. Fyrst H, Pham DV, Lubin BH, Kuypers FA. 1996. Formation of vesicles by the action of acyl-CoA:1–acyllysophosphatidylcholine acyltransferase from rat liver microsomes: optimal solubilization conditions and analysis of lipid composition and enzyme activity. *Biochemistry* 35:2644–50

62. Pugh EL, Kates M. 1979. Membrane-bound phospholipid desaturases. *Lipids* 14:159–65

63. Thompson GA, Nozawa Y. 1984. The regulation of membrane fluidity in Tetrahymena. In *Biomembranes: Membrane Fluidity,* ed. M Kates, LA Manson, 12:397–432. New York: Plenum

64. Kates M, Pugh EL, Ferrante G. 1984. Regulation of membrane fluidity by lipid desaturases. In *Biomembranes: Membrane Fluidity,* ed. M Kates, LA Manson, 12:379–95. New York: Plenum

65. Brenner RR. 1981. Nutritional and hormonal factors influencing desaturation of essential fatty acids. *Prog. Lipid Res.* 19:155–86

66. Withers KW, Hulbert AJ. 1987. The influence of dietary fatty acids and hypothyroidism on mitochondrial fatty acid composition. *Nutr. Res.* 7:1139–50

67. Gudbjarnason S. 1989. Dynamics of *n*-3 and *n*-6 fatty acids in phospholipids of heart muscle. *J. Int. Med.* 225(1):117–28

68. Rolfe DFS, Hulbert AJ, Brand MD. 1994. Characteristics of mitochondrial proton leak and control of oxidative phosphorylation in the major oxygen consuming tissues of the rat. *Biochim. Biophys. Acta* 1118:405–16

69. Brand MD, Brindle KM, Buckingham JA, Harper JA, Rolfe DFS, Stuart JA. 1999. The significance and mechanism of mitochondrial proton conductance. *Int. J. Obesity* 23(Suppl. 6):S4–11

70. Brand MD, Chien L, Ainscow EK, Rolfe DFS, Porter RK. 1994. The causes and functions of mitochondrial proton leak. *Biochim. Biophys. Acta* 1187:132–39

71. Brookes PS, Rolfe DFS, Brand MD. 1997. The proton permeability of liposomes made from mitochondrial inner membrane phospholipids: comparison with intact mitochondria. *J. Membr. Biol.* 155:167–74

72. Brookes PS, Hulbert AJ, Brand MD. 1997. The proton permeability of liposomes made from mitochondrial inner membrane phospholipids: no effect of fatty acid composition. *Biochim. Biophys. Acta* 1330:157–64

73. Porter RK, Brand MD. 1993. Body mass dependence of proton leak in mitochondria and its relevance to metabolic rate. *Nature* 362:628–30

74. Porter RK, Hulbert AJ, Brand MD. 1996. Allometry of mitochondrial proton leak: influence of membrane surface area and fatty acid composition. *Am. J. Physiol.* 271(40):R1550–60

75. Brookes PS, Buckingham JA, Tenreiro AM, Hulbert AJ, Brand MD. 1998. The

proton permeability of the inner membrane of liver mitochondria from ectothermic and endothermic vertebrates and from obese rats: correlations with standard metabolic rate and phospholipid composition. *Comp. Biochem. Physiol.* 119B:325–34

76. Guderley H, St Pierre J, Couture P, Hulbert AJ. 1997. Plasticity of the properties of mitochondria from rainbow trout red muscle with seasonal acclimatization. *Fish Physiol. Biochem.* 16:531–41

77. Else PL, Windmill DJ, Markus V. 1996. Molecular activity of sodium pumps in endotherms and ectotherms. *Am. J. Physiol.* 271(40):R1287–94

78. Else PL, Wu BJ. 1999. Improved performance of the sodium pump: role of membranes and implications for the evolution of endothermy. *J. Comp. Physiol. B* 169:296–302

79. Raynard RS, Cossins AR. 1991. Homeoviscous adaptation and thermal compensation of sodium pump of trout erythrocytes. *Am. J. Physiol.* 260(29):R916–24

80. Hazel JR. 1972. The effect of temperature acclimation upon succinic dehydrogenase activity from the epaxial muscle of the common goldfish (*Carassius auratus* L.) II. Lipid reactivation of the soluable enzyme. *Comp. Biochem. Physiol.* 43B:863–82

81. Benz R. 1985. Black lipid membranes from polymerizable *Lipids Angew. Chem. Int. Engl.* 24:905–23

82. Brand MD, Coutre P, Hulbert AJ. 1994. Liposomes from mammalian liver mitochondria are both more polyunsaturated and leakier to protons than those from reptiles. *Comp. Biochem. Physiol.* 108B:181–86

83. Devaux PF, Seigneuret M. 1985. Specificity of lipid-protein interactions as determined by spectroscopic techniques. *Biochim. Biophys. Acta* 822:63–125

84. Lands WE. 1992. Biochemistry and physiology of n-3 fatty acids. *FASEB J.* 6:2530–36

85. Ordway RW, Walsh JV, Singer JJ. 1989. Arachidonic acid and other fatty acids directly activate potassium channels in smooth muscle cells. *Science* 244:1177–79

86. Bendahhou S, Cummins TR, Agnew WS. 1997. Mechanism of modulation of the voltage-gated skeletal and cardiac muscle sodium channels by fatty acids. *Am. J. Physiol.* 272(41):C592–600

87. Marsh D. 1987. Selectivity of protein-lipid interactions. *J. Bioenerg. Biomemb.* 19(6):677–89

88. In't Veld G, Driessen AJM, Konings WN. 1993. Bacterial solute transport proteins in their lipid environment. *FEMS Microbiol. Rev.* 12:293–314

89. Stubbs CD, Smith AD. 1984. The modification of mammalian membrane polyunsaturated fatty acid composition in relation to membrane fluidity and function. *Biochim. Biophys. Acta* 779:89–97

90. Szamel M, Resch K. 1981. Modulation of enzyme activities in isolated lymphocyte plasma membranes by enzymatic modification of phospholipid fatty acids. *J. Biol. Chem.* 256(22):11618–23

91. Slater SJ, Kelly M, Yeager MD, Larkin J, Ho C, et al. 1996. Polyunsaturation in cell membranes and lipid bilayers and its effects on membrane proteins. *Lipids* 31(Suppl.):S189–92

92. Litman B, Mitchell DC. 1996. A role for phospholipid polyunsaturation in modulating membrane protein function. *Lipids* 31(Suppl.):S193–97

93. Carruthers A, Melchior DL. 1984. Human erythrocyte hexose transporter activity is governed by lipid composition in reconstituted vesicles. *Biochemistry* 23:6901–11

94. Niot I, Gresti J, Boichot J, Sempore G, Durand G, et al. 1994. Effect of dietary n-3 and n-6 polyunsaturated fatty acids on lipid-metabolizing enzymes in obese rat liver. *Lipids* 29(7):481–89

95. Vajreswari A, Narayanareddy K. 1992. Effects of dietary fats on some membrane-bound enzyme activities, membrane lipid composition and fatty acid profiles of heart sarcolemma. *Lipids* 27(5):339–43

96. Murphy MG. 1990. Dietary fatty acids and membrane function. *J. Nutr. Biochem.* 1:68–79

97. Whitehead PJ, Seymour RS. 1990. Patterns of metabolic rate in embryonic crocodilians *Crocodylus johnstoni* and *Crocodylus porosus*. *Physiol. Zool.* 63(2):334–52

98. Visser G. 1998. Development of temperature regulation. In *Avian Growth and Development*, ed. JM Sterck, RE Ricklefs, 5:117–56. New York: Oxford Univ. Press

99. Houghton FD, Thompson JG, Leese HJ. 1996. Oxygen consumption and energy metabolism of the early mouse embryo. *Mol. Reprod. Dev.* 44(4):476–85

100. Pruzkova V, Jirasek J, Mourek J, Zwinger A, Capkova A. 1972. Oxygen consumption in some human fetal tissues. *Biol. Neonate* 20:170–74

101. Piekarzewska AB. 1977. Changes in thermogenesis and its hormonal regulators during the postnatal development of rabbits and guinea pigs. *Acta Theriol.* 22(9):159–80

102. Hill JR, Rahimtulla KA. 1965. Heat balance and the metabolic rate of new-born babies in relation to environmental temperature; and the effect of age and weight on basal metabolic rate. *J. Physiol.* 180:239–65

103. Spiers DE, Adair ER. 1986. Ontogeny of homeothermy in the immature rat: metabolic and thermal responses. *J. Appl. Physiol.* 60(4):1190–97

104. Benos DJ, Balaban RS. 1980. Energy requirements of the developing blastocyst for active transport. *Biol. Reprod.* 23:941–47

105. Brison DR, Leese HJ. 1994. The role of exogenous energy substrates in blasto-coele fluid accumulation in the rat. *Zygote* 2(1):69–77

106. Kennaugh JM, Bell AW, Teng C, Meschia G, Battaglia FC. 1987. Ontogenetic changes in the rates of protein synthesis and leucine oxidation during fetal life. *Pediatr. Res.* 22(6):688–92

107. Dauncey MJ, Harrison AP. 1996. Developmental regulation of cation pumps in skeletal and cardiac muscle. *Acta Physiol. Scand.* 156:313–23

108. Kjeldsen K, Nørgaard A, Clausen T. 1984. The age-dependent changes in the number of ^{3}H-ouabain binding sites in mammalian skeletal muscle. *Pflügers Arch.* 402:100–8

109. Khatter CJ. 1985. Mechanisms of age-related differences in the cardiotoxic action of digitalis. *J. Cardiovas. Pharmacol.* 7:258–61

110. Kjeldsen K, Grøn P. 1990. Age-dependent changes in myocardial cardiac glycoside receptor (Na, K-pump) concentration in children. *J. Cardiovas. Pharmacol.* 15:332–37

111. Larsson SH, Rane S, Fukuda Y, Aperia A, Lechene C. 1990. Changes in Na influx precede post-natal increase in Na,K-ATPase activity in rat renal proximal tubular cells. *Acta Physiol. Scand.* 138:99–100

112. Matsuda T, Shimizu I, Baba A. 1992. Postnatal changes in a Ca^{2+}-mediated decrease in $(Na^+ + K^+)$-ATPase activity in brain slices. *Brain Res.* 572:349–51

113. Valcana T, Timiras PS. 1969. Effect of hypothyroidism on ionic metabolism and Na-K activated ATP phosphohydrolase activity in the developing rat brain. *J. Neurochem.* 16:935–43

114. Else PL. 1991. Oxygen consumption and sodium pump thermogenesis in a developing mammal. *Am. J. Physiol.* 261(30):R1575–78

115. Marsh JA, Lloyd BL, Taylor RR. 1981. Age dependence of myocardial Na^+-K^+ATPase activity and digitalis intoxi-

cation in the dog guinea pig. *Circ. Res.* 48(3):329–33

116. Tosco M, Orsenigo MN, Zoppi S, Faelli A. 1990. Aging and ATPase activities in rat jejunum. *Mech. Age. Dev.* 56:265–74

117. Xia Y, Haddad GG. 1994. Postnatal development of voltage sensitive Na$^+$ channels in rat brain. *J. Comp. Neurol.* 345:279–87

118. Harrison AP, Nielsen OB, Clausen T. 1997. Role of Na$^+$-K$^+$ pump and Na$^+$ channel concentrations in contractility of rat soleus muscle. *Am. J. Physiol.* 271(41):R1402–8

119. Green P, Yavin E. 1996. Fatty acid composition of late embryonic and early postnatal rat brain. *Lipids* 31(8):859–65

120. Vasquez CM, Rovira N, Ruiz-Gutierrez V, Planas JM. 1997. Developmental changes in glucose transport, lipid composition and fluidity of jejunal BBM. *Am. J. Physiol.* 273(42):R1086–97

121. Orlowski J, Lingrel JB. 1988. Tissue-specific and developmental regulation of rat Na, K-ATPase catalytic α isoform and β subunit mRNAs. *J. Biol. Chem.* 263:10436–42

122. Orlowski J, Lingrel JB. 1988. Differential expression of the Na,K-ATPase α1 and α2 subunit genes in a murine myogenic cell line. Induction of the α2 isozyme during myocyte differentiation. *J. Biol. Chem.* 263:17817–21

123. Brandl DH. 1987. Adult forms of the Ca^{2+} ATPase of sarcoplasmic reticulum. Expression in developing skeletal muscle. *J. Biol. Chem.* 262:3768–74

124. Moorman AFM, Vermeulen VJL, Koban MU, Schwartz MU, Lamers WH, Boheler KR. 1995. Patterns of expression of sarcoplasmic reticulum Ca^{2+}-ATPase and phospholamban mRNAs during rat heart development. *Circ. Res.* 76:616–25

125. Horisberger JD. 1994. *The Na,K-ATPase: Structure-Function Relationship,* Boca Raton, FL: CRC Press. 120 pp.

126. Poehlman ET, Goran MI, Gardner AW, Ades PA, Arciero PJ, et al. 1993. Deter-minants of decline in aging females. *Am. J. Physiol.* 264(27):E450–55

127. Benedek C, Berclaz PY, Jequier E, Schutz Y. 1995. Resting metabolic rate and protein turnover in apparently healthy elderly Gambian men. *Am. J. Physiol.* 268(38):E1083–88

128. Harper M-E, Monemdjou S, Ramsey JJ, Weindruch R. 1998. Age-related increase in mitochondrial proton leak and decrease in ATP turnover reactions in mouse hepatocytes. *Am. J. Physiol.* 275(38):E197–206

129. Welle S, Thornton C, Statt M. 1995. Myofibrillar protein synthesis in young and old human subjects after three months of resistance training. *Am. J. Physiol.* 268(31):E422–27

130. Balagopal P, Rooyackers OE, Adey DB, Ades PA, Nair KS. 1997. Effects of aging on in vivo synthesis of skeletal muscle myosin heavy-chain sarcoplasmic protein in humans. *Am. J. Physiol.* 273(36):E790–800

131. Mosoni L, Valluy MC, Serrurier B, Prugnaud J, Obled C, et al. 1995. Altered response of protein synthesis to nutritional state and endurance training in old rats. *Am. J. Physiol.* 268(31):E328–35

132. Poehlman ET, Toth MJ, Webb GD. 1993. Sodium-potassium pump activity contributes to age-related decline in resting metabolic rate. *J. Clin. Endocrin. Metab.* 76(4):1054–57

133. Witkowski JM, Mysliwski A, Mysliwski J. 1985. Decrease of lymphocyte (Na$^+$,K$^+$)ATP-ase activity in aged people. *Mech. Aging Dev.* 33:11–17

134. Tanaka Y, Ando S. 1992. Age-related changes in [^{3}H] ouabain binding to synaptic plasma membranes isolated from mouse brains. *J. Biochem.* 112:117–21

135. Maniongui C, Blond JP, Ulmann L, Durand G, Poisson JP, et al. 1993. Age-related changes in D6 and D5 desaturase activities in rat liver microsomes. *Lipids* 28(4):291–97

136. Guppy M, Withers P. 1999. Metabolic

depression in animals: physiological perspectives and biochemical generalizations. *Biol. Rev.* 74(1):1–40

137. Arthur PG, Franklin CE, Cousins KL, Thorarensen H, Hochachka PW, et al. 1997. Energy turnover in the normoxic and anoxic turtle heart. *Comp. Biochem. Physiol.* 117A(1):121–26

138. Hochachka PW, Land SC, Buck LT. 1997. Oxygen sensing and signal transduction in metabolic defense against hypoxia: lessons from vertebrate facultative anaerobes. *Comp. Biochem. Physiol.* 118A(1):23–29

139. Buck LT, Hochachka PW. 1993. Anoxic suppression of Na$^+$ K$^+$ ATPase and constant membrane potential in hepatocytes: support for channel arrest. *Am. J. Physiol.* 265:R1020–25

140. Doll CJ, Hochachka PW, Reiner PB. 1993. Reduced ionic conductance in turtle brain. *Am. J. Physiol.* 265:R929–33

141. Lutz PL. 1992. Mechanisms for anoxic survival in the anoxic vertebrate brain. *Annu. Rev. Physiol.* 54:619–37

142. West TG, Boutilier RG. 1998. Metabolic suppression in anoxic frog muscle. *J. Comp. Physiol. B* 168:273–80

143. Pedler S, Fuery CJ, Withers PC, Flanigan J, Guppy M. 1996. Effectors of metabolic depression in an estivating pulmonate snail (*Helix aspersa*): whole animal and in vitro tissue studies. *J. Comp. Physiol. B* 166:375–81

144. Flanigan JE, Guppy M. 1997. Metabolic depression and sodium-potassium ATPase in the aestivating frog, *Neobatrachus kunapalari*. *J. Comp. Physiol. B* 167:135–45

145. Flanigan JE, Withers PC, Fuery CJ, Guppy M. 1993. Metabolic depression and Na$^+$/K$^+$ gradients in aestivating Australian goldfields frog, *Neobatrachus wilsmorei*. *J. Comp. Physiol. B* 163:587–93

146. Fuery CJ, Withers PC, Hobbs AA, Guppy M. 1998. The role of protein synthesis during metabolic depression in the Australian desert frog, *Neobatrachus centralis*. *Comp. Biochem. Physiol.* 119A(2):469–76

147. Stuart JA, Gillis TE, Ballantyne JS. 1998. Compositional correlates of metabolic depression in the mitochondrial membranes of estivating snails. *Am. J. Physiol.* 275(44):R1977–82

148. Merkt JR, Taylor CR. 1994. "Metabolic switch" for desert survival. *Proc. Natl. Acad. Sci. USA* 91:12313–16

149. Choshniak I, Ben-Kohav N, Taylor CR, Robertshaw D, Barnes et al. 1995. Metabolic adaptations for desert survival in the Bedouin goat. *Am. J. Physiol.* 268(37):R1101–10

150. Zhao MJ, Willis JS. 1988. Reduced ion transport in erythrocytes of male Sprague-Dawley rats during starvation. *J. Nutr.* 118:1120–27

151. Hulbert AJ. 1999. Thyroid hormones and their effects. *Biol. Rev.* In press

152. Harper M-E, Brand MD. 1993. The quantitative contributions of mitochondrial proton leak and ATP turnover reactions to the changed respiration rates of hepatocytes from rats of different thyroid hormone status. *J. Biol. Chem.* 268:14850–60

153. Paradies G, Ruggiero FM, Petrosillo G, Quagliariello E. 1994. Enhanced cytochrome oxidase activity and modification of lipids in heart mitochondria from hyperthyroid rats. *Biochim. Biophys. Acta* 1225:165–70

154. Paradies G, Ruggiero FM. 1989. Decreased activity of pyruvate translocator and changes in the lipid composition in heart from hypothyroid rats. *Arch. Biochem. Biophys.* 269:595–602

155. Paradies G, Ruggiero FM. 1990. Enhanced activity of the tricarbocylic acid carrier and modification of lipids in hepatic mitochondria from hyperthyroid rats. *Arch. Biochem. Biophys.* 278:425–30

156. Paradies G, Ruggiero FM. 1990. Stimulation of phosphate transport in rat liver

mitochondria by thyroid hormones. *Biochim. Biophys. Acta* 1019:133–36

157. Paradies G, Ruggiero FM, Dinoi P. 1991. The influence of hypothyroidism on the transport of phosphate and on the lipid composition in rat-liver mitochondria. *Biochim. Biophys. Acta* 1070:180–86

158. Paradies G, Ruggiero FM, Dinoi P, Petrosillo G, Quagliariello E. 1993. Decreased cytochrome oxidase activity and changes in phospholipids in heart mitochondria from hypothyroid rats. *Arch. Biochem. Biophys.* 307:91–95

159. Barnard RJ, Roberts CK, Varon SM, Berger JJ. 1998. Diet-induced insulin resistance precedes other aspects of their metabolic syndrome. *J. Appl. Physiol.* 84:1311–15

160. Storlien LH, Hulbert AJ, Else PL. 1998. Polyunsaturated fatty acids, membrane function and metabolic diseases such as diabetes and obesity. *Curr. Opin. Clin Nutr. Metab. Care* 1:559–63

161. Ruben JA. 1996. Evolution of endothermy in mammals, birds and their ancestors. In *Phenotype and Evolutionary Adaptation,* ed. IA Johnston, AF Bennett pp. 347–76. Cambridge, MA: Cambridge Press

162. Perez-Campo R, Lopez-Torres M, Cadenas S, Rojas C, Barja G. 1998 The rate of free-radical production as a determinant of the rate of aging: evidence from the comparative approach. *J. Comp. Physiol.* 168:149–58

Annu. Rev. Physiol. 2000. 62:237–60

Functional Consequences of Altering Myocardial Adrenergic Receptor Signaling

W. J. Koch,[1] R. J. Lefkowitz,[2,3] and H. A. Rockman[2]

[1]Departments of Surgery, Pharmacology and Cancer Biology, [2]Medicine and [3]Biochemistry and [3]The Howard Hughes Medical Institute, Duke University Medical Center, Durham, North Carolina 27710; e-mail: koch0002@mc.duke.edu

Key Words   gene-targeted mice, adrenergic receptors, G protein signaling, desensitization, heart failure

■ **Abstract**   From the ability to successfully manipulate the mouse genome has come important transgenic and gene-targeted knockout models that impact many areas of biomedical research. Genetically engineered mouse models geared toward the study of cardiovascular regulation have recently been described and provide powerful tools to study normal and compromised cardiac physiology. The genetic manipulation of the adrenergic receptor (AR) signaling system in the heart, including its regulation by desensitizing kinases, has shed light on the role of this signaling pathway in the regulation of cardiac contractility. One major finding, supported by several mouse models, is that in vivo contractility can be enhanced via alteration of myocardial AR signaling. Thus genetic manipulation of this critical receptor system in the heart represents a novel therapeutic approach for improving function of the failing heart.

ADRENERGIC SIGNALING IN THE HEART

Adrenergic receptors (ARs), first described by Ahlquist in 1948 (1), belong to the superfamily of membrane proteins that activate heterotrimeric guanine nucleotide (G) binding proteins (2). α_1 and β-ARs exist in the myocardium and mediate several physiological aspects of heart function via stimulation by the sympathetic transmitters, epinephrine and norepinephrine. In the heart, agonist occupancy of β-ARs leads to the primary activation of the adenylyl cyclase (AC) stimulatory G protein, Gs, which leads to increases in intracellular cAMP and protein kinase A (PKA) activity (3). There are three identified β-AR subtypes, designated β_1, β_2, and β_3, that have distinct molecular functional and pharmacological characteristics (2). The β_1-AR is the most abundant subtype in the mammalian heart, approaching 75 to 80% of total β-ARs (3). β_2-ARs were thought to be the only other β-AR in the heart; however, the existence of β_3-ARs in human myocardium has recently been described (4). Both β_1- and β_2-ARs couple to AC in the heart, resulting in positive inotropy via cAMP and calcium entry (5). Interestingly, under certain conditions, β_2-ARs can also couple to the adenylyl cyclase inhibitory G protein, Gi (6, 7).

Activated α_1-ARs, which exist as three subtypes (α_{1A}, α_{1B}, and α_{1C}) (8), primarily couple to the G protein, Gq, which activates phospholipase C (PLC). This results in increases in the second messengers inositol trisphosphate and diacylglyceral (DAG), which lead to enhanced intracellular calcium and activation of protein kinase C (PKC) (9). α_{1A} and α_{1B}-ARs have been shown to exist in myocytes (10), and these as well as other Gq coupled receptors, such as those for angiotensin II and endothelin I, have been implicated in myocyte growth and hypertrophy (11, 12).

ARs undergo extensive regulation with the most rapid form being the targeted phosphorylation of activated receptors leading to G protein uncoupling, a process termed desensitization (13). This process is initiated by phosphorylation of the agonist-occupied receptor on intracellular residues. Phosphorylation of receptors can be accomplished by second messenger–dependent kinases such as PKA and PKC, as an example of a classical feedback mechanism, and also by a family of kinases known as the G protein-coupled receptor kinases (GRKs) (14). Homologous desensitization of ARs, as well as other G protein–coupled receptors, requires not only the actions of GRKs but also the binding of a second protein, β-arrestin, which binds to phosphorylated receptors and sterically intradicts further coupling to Gs (2, 13, 14). There are six members of the GRK family (14). The β-adrenergic receptor kinase (βARK1), also known as GRK2, is the primary GRK expressed in the heart, whereas GRK3 (also known as βARK2), GRK5, and GRK6 are also found in the myocardium (14, 15). GRKs are serine/threonine kinases, which share the characteristic of phosphorylating only agonist-occupied receptors, thereby triggering desensitization.

The GRKs also share the requirement of having to be targeted to the plasma membrane prior to activation (13, 14). For example, βARK1 (and GRK3) is primarily a cytosolic enzyme that must translocate to the membrane in order to phosphorylate its activated receptor substrate. The translocation of βARK1 (GRK2) is due to a specific physical interaction between βARK1 and the membrane-bound βγ subunits of G proteins ($G_{\beta\gamma}$) (16, 17). This physical interaction between $G_{\beta\gamma}$ and βARK1 has been mapped to an approximate 100 amino acid region located within the carboxyl-terminal domain of the enzyme (17). Interestingly, this region overlaps with a pleckstrin homology (PH) domain. PH domains are sequences with high affinity for acidic phospholipids and membrane binding (18, 19). Thus βARK1, as well as GRK3, are targeted to the membranes via $G_{\beta\gamma}$ and membrane phospholipids that stabilize this association. Importantly, peptides derived from the carboxyl-terminal domain of βARK1, including the last 194 amino acid residues known as the βARKct, are effective inhibitors of βARK1 activity via inhibition of $G_{\beta\gamma}$ binding (17, 20).

Alterations of Adrenergic Signaling in Cardiovascular Disease

Alterations in adrenergic signaling are important in a number of cardiac diseases. Undoubtedly, the alterations that take place in the β-AR system during the progression of heart failure (HF) are the most well characterized (3). As the heart begins to fail, compensatory mechanisms are initiated to maintain cardiac output and systemic blood pressure. One of these mechanisms involves the sympathetic nervous system, which increases its myocardial outflow of norepinephrine in an attempt to stimulate contractility (21). This increase in agonism can lead to β-AR desensitization. Reduction of cardiac β-AR density in the failing human heart was first observed by Bristow et al in 1982 (22). In addition, remaining receptors appear desensitized (22). β_1-ARs have been shown to be selectively reduced, although β_2-ARs are not altered in HF (23, 24). Interestingly, the levels of myocardial βARK1 have been shown to be significantly elevated in human HF, which represent a potential mechanism for the loss of β-AR responsiveness seen in this disease (24). Another potential contributing factor to decreased β-AR signaling in HF is increased levels of myocardial Gαi (25). The loss of cardiac β_1-ARs is critical because it results in a greater percentage of β_2-ARs, as well as α_1-ARs, which may therefore alter cardiac function.

Ischemic heart disease is also characterized by abnormal AR signaling. In chronic ischemia, alterations in myocardial β-AR signaling mirror those found in chronic HF (3, 26), including the upregulation of Gαi and βARK1 (27, 28). Interestingly, elevation of βARK1 may be among the earliest changes noted in heart disease and likely triggered by heightened sympathetic nervous system activity (29, 30). In addition to βARK1 being elevated in HF and ischemia, it is also found to be increased in pressure overload myocardial hypertrophy (31) and mild human hypertension (32).

The exact role of α_1-ARs in the heart is not well understood; however, α_1-AR signaling may be important in myocardial hypertrophy, which is a critical adaptive response following almost any myocardial injury (33, 34). Myocardial hypertrophy can lead to myocyte contractile dysfunction in the ischemic heart that ultimately progresses to HF (35). Recently, upregulation of the Gαq/PLC pathway was found in myocardial infarction border zones, suggesting that these signaling molecules play a critical role in surviving myocytes after myocardial infarction (36).

The ability to manipulate the expression of myocardial ARs or GRKs in vivo through the use of gene-targeted mice has recently proved feasible. Combining transgenic technology with sophisticated physiological measurements of cardiac hemodynamics is an extremely powerful strategy to study the regulation of myocardial contractility (37). The goal of this review is to highlight studies in genetically engineered mice with altered AR and GRK signaling that have provided unique experimental models for the study of receptor signaling in both normal and diseased myocardium. Importantly, some of these models have suggested novel therapeutic approaches for improving the function of the compromised heart, which may lead to new therapies for heart disease.

GENETICALLY ENGINEERED MOUSE MODELS OF ALTERED MYOCARDIAL β-AR SIGNALING

Myocardial-Targeted Overexpression of the β_2-AR

Transgenic technology, coupled with the availability of cardiac-specific promoters has made it possible to target ARs specifically to the myocardium. The use of the murine α-myosin heavy chain gene (αMyHC) promoter has revolutionized the field of myocardial transgenesis as this promoter is cardiac specific and supports robust transgene expression (38). Furthermore, the αMyHC promoter is not functional in ventricular myocytes until around birth, thus bypassing potential developmental problems by specific transgene overexpression (38). Using the human β_2-AR linked to the αMyHC promoter, our laboratory was able to overexpress β_2-ARs in all chambers of the mouse heart (39). The resultant mice (named TG4s) had unexpectedly robust β_2-AR overexpression, which was in the range of 20 to 30 pmoles per mg membrane protein (39). This extraordinary level of overexpression was >200-fold over endogenous myocardial β-AR expression (~75 fmole per mg membrane protein). Considering that normally β_2-ARs make up 25 to 30% of the total β-AR population in the heart, this transgenic overexpression level approaches three orders of magnitude higher than wild-type hearts. In fact, the density of receptors in these transgenic hearts is as high or higher than values reached in cell culture. TG4 mice, when compared with their nontransgenic littermate controls (NLCs), have the phenotype of maximal β-AR myocardial signaling, both biochemically and physiologically (39). This includes enhanced cardiac function, which at baseline levels (non-stimulated) is equal to or greater than NLC function in vivo with maximum doses of the β-agonist isoproterenol. In fact, an interesting characteristic of TG4 mice is that there is no additional contractility response, as measured by LV dP/dt$_{max}$, in response to isoproterenol administration. In addition to enhanced systolic function, TG4 mice are characterized by enhanced myocardial relaxation that is accompanied by down regulation of the sarcoplasmic reticulum protein, phospholamban (40). In addition to the TG4 mice with 200-fold β_2-AR overexpression, a second study using the αMyHC-β_2-AR transgene has demonstrated that β_2-AR overexpression at much lower levels (30–50-fold) also results in enhanced biochemical and physiologic function in vivo (41).

The findings in the various β_2-AR overexpressing transgenic mice led to the hypothesis that the maximal activation of myocardial signaling and function in the absence of agonist was due to a marked increase in spontaneously isomerized receptors present in the active conformation (42). G protein-coupled receptors such as β_2-ARs are thought to exist as an equilibrium between R, the predominant inactive form of the receptor and R*, the activated form of the receptor that couples to G proteins (42). In the absence of agonist stimulation, there is a low percentage of the total receptor density R*. However, in the case of transgenic mice overexpressing the β_2-AR, it is easy to see that with 200-fold overexpression as in TG4 mice, even this minor fraction of receptors thought to naturally undergo agonist-independent conformational changes (from R to R*) becomes significant and results in activation of myocardial signaling and the corresponding physiology (42). Thus when wild-type receptors are overexpressed at a high enough level, they effectively function as though they are constitutively active. Mutated constitutively active (CAM) ARs have been described in detail and result from point mutations within the third intracellular domain of the receptor protein (43). Using the αMyHC promoter, we have also generated transgenic mice with myocardially targeted overexpression of a CAM-β_2-AR (44). Interestingly, unlike TG4s, the phenotype of the CAM-β_2-AR transgenic mice, under normal conditions, is similar to NLCs due to the fact that there is only a modest threefold overexpression of the CAM-β_2-AR (44). One property of CAM receptors is that they are inherently unstable proteins. However, treatment of CAM-β_2-AR mice with various β-AR ligands stabilizes the CAM-β_2-AR protein, and receptor over-expression in the heart increases 50-fold, which leads to an increase in in vivo cardiac function, approaching the phenotype of TG4s (44). Thus these mice serve as a novel model for ligand-induced stabilization of a constitutively active, but inherently unstable, protein.

The fact that β_2-ARs can couple to Gi in addition to Gs has recently been exploited to demonstrate that a contributing factor to the loss of agonist-responsiveness in the TG4 mice is β_2-AR coupling to Gi proteins in the hearts of these animals (45). In this study, treatment of myocytes from TG4 animals with the Gi-inhibitory pertussis toxin restored β-AR responsiveness, demonstrating that significant Gi coupling is taking place in these animals (45).

It is interesting to note that for the TG4 mice, which have significantly enhanced heart rates and contractility from birth, minimal pathology is present. We have found in TG4 animals, >1 year of age, slight fibrosis and collagen replacement in areas of TG4 hearts affecting no more than ~10% of the total myocardium (WJ Koch, RJ Lefkowitz & HA Rockman, unpublished observations). We also studied in vivo physiology in animals >1 year of age and found that these mice still have significantly enhanced cardiac contractility (Figure 1). Thus these mice demonstrate the paucity of cardiac pathology even after a very long duration of hyper-contractility due to the high expression of β_2-ARs in the heart. This underscores the potential for genetic engineering as a novel means for enhancing ventricular function and replacing lost receptors found in HF.

Myocardial-Targeted Overexpression of the β_1-AR

The β_1-AR, which is the most abundant β-AR subtype endogenously expressed in the myocardium, has also been the focus of transgenic overexpression studies.

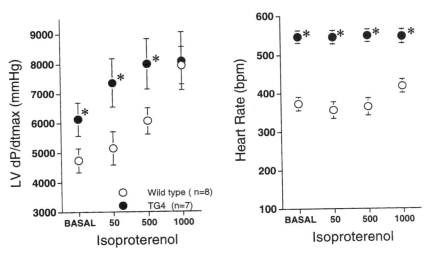

Figure 1 In vivo assessment of LV contractile function in older β_2-AR overexpressing (TG4) mice. Cardiac catheterization was performed in intact anesthetized mice using a 1.8 Fr. high-fidelity micromanometer. Two measured parameters (the maximal first derivative of LV pressure, LV dP/dtmax, and heart rate) are shown at baseline and after progressive doses of isoproterenol in wild-type (o) (n = 8), and TG4 (•) (n = 7) mice that were between 12 and 14 months of age. Data were analyzed with a repeated measures ANOVA and post hoc analysis by Newman-Keuls, *$p < 0.0005$ wild-type.

The first report of a β_1-AR transgenic mouse was a mouse model using the atrial-specific, human atrial natriuretic factor (ANF) promoter (46). These mice, which have modest overexpression (five to sixfold) limited to the atria, have a limited phenotype. However, recent studies have shown that these mice have decreased heart rate variability, and atrial strips from these transgenic mice do show enhanced basal contractility which, like the β_2-AR overexpressing mice, does not respond further to isoproterenol (47).

Recently, the β_1-AR was targeted to the ventricular myocardium by the use of the αMyHC promoter (48). These mice, with 5- to 15-fold overexpression, have a phenotype of dilated cardiomyopathy and HF with significant ventricular remodeling, including fibrosis, already present in young mice (48). This is consistent with the pathology caused by chronic catecholamine administration. Importantly, this is in contrast to the transgenic mice overexpressing β_2-ARs, such as the TG4, which at even much more robust receptor overexpression levels have enhanced contractility with no cardiomyopathy or HF present (see Figure 1).

Transgenic mice with myocardial-targeted Gαs overexpression also develop cardiac pathology (49), indicating a similarity to β_1-AR overexpression, but not to β_2-AR overexpression. In fact, these transgenic mouse models strongly support the hypothesis that β_1- and β_2-AR signaling in the heart is fundamentally different.

Thus, β_2-AR overexpression offers increased inotropy without the apparent deleterious effects on the heart seen with overexpression of β_1-ARs or Gαs. These models may provide insight into novel therapeutic strategies for enhancing β_2-AR signaling, but not β_1-AR signaling, in conditions of compromised heart function.

Cardiovascular Characterization of β-AR Knockout Mice

Cardiovascular consequences have also been demonstrated in gene-targeted mice with disruption of β-ARs and have recently been reviewed in detail (50). The β_1-AR knockout is generally embryonic lethal; a majority of mice homozygote for β_1-AR gene disruption die in utero (51). This embryonic mortality is reduced somewhat when the mice are outbred (51). Surviving β_1-AR knockout mice are viable, and resting heart rate and blood pressure appear normal (51, 52). It has been found that the chronotropic reserve in β_1-AR knockout mice is attenuated because exercise-induced increases in heart rates are significantly less than in corresponding wild-type mice (52). Interestingly, despite the presence of β_2-ARs in these mouse hearts, there was no contractility response to β-agonist administration, strongly suggesting that the β_1-AR is the predominant mediator of catecholamine-induced chronotropy and inotropy (52). These results suggest that in the mouse heart, β_2-ARs under endogenous conditions do not play a major role in cardiac contractile function. Further supporting this hypothesis are preliminary findings in a β_2-AR knockout mouse, which has limited changes in cardiac physiology (50). Importantly, these data add to the hypothesis that β_1-AR and β_2-AR signaling in the myocardium are fundamentally different.

GENETICALLY ENGINEERED MOUSE MODELS OF ALTERED MYOCARDIAL α_1-AR SIGNALING

Myocardial-Targeted Overexpression of Wild-Type and CAM α_1-ARs

Interesting transgenic mouse models have been developed that overexpress either the CAM or wild-type α_{1B}-AR (53, 54). Both lines of mice were generated using the αMyHC promoter. As stated above, α_1-ARs in the heart have been implicated in myocardial hypertrophy, and signaling through α_1-ARs or other receptors coupled to the Gq/PLC signaling pathway has been implicated in pressure and/or volume overload-induced hypertrophy (10–12). Direct proof that α_1-ARs can cause myocardial hypertrophy has been difficult to obtain in vivo because the administration of α-agonists evokes peripheral vascular effects that secondarily induce myocardial hypertrophy. Importantly, when the CAM α_{1B}-AR are targeted to the myocardium of transgenic mice, the adult hearts are significantly larger with ventricular myocyte size increased by 62% (53). Thus continual myocardial α_1-AR signaling induced by CAM α_{1B}-ARs can induce ventricular hypertrophy independent of any peripheral hemodynamic changes. These mice also have other properties associated with hypertrophy, including increased ventricular ANF expression and increased signaling through the Gq/PLC pathway associated with significantly elevated basal levels of myocardial DAG and inositol phosphate (53, 55).

In separate lines of transgenic mice with >40-fold wild-type α_{1B}-AR overexpression, basal myocardial α_1-AR signaling as measured by DAG levels is significantly increased to levels similar to those in CAM α_{1B}-AR mice (54). In contrast to the CAM α_{1B} mice, the hearts of the wild-type α_{1B}-AR overexpressors do not develop cardiac hypertrophy despite significant increases in ventricular ANF mRNA (54). An interesting phenotype in these animals, however, is that in vivo response to isoproterenol is significantly depressed, indicating molecular cross-talk between myocardial α_1- and β-AR systems (54, 56). Two mechanisms potentially contributing to this depressed β-AR activity in vivo following enhanced α_{1B}-AR signaling have been uncovered. The first is that the overexpressed α_{1B}-ARs couple to pertussis toxin-sensitive G proteins, which could negatively affect β-AR signaling (54). Second, since Gq/PLC signaling is enhanced in these mice, myocardial PKC activity is enhanced (56). Interestingly, PKC can phosphorylate and activate βARK1 (57). Indeed, we found increased βARK1 activity in the hearts of wild-type α_{1B}-AR overexpressors, leading to enhanced β-AR desensitization (54).

Myocardial Expression of a Peptide Inhibitor of Gq Signaling

Because it is evident that signaling through α_1-ARs and subsequent Gq activation can lead to myocardial hypertrophy in vivo, we recently documented that Gαq activation is the final common trigger of ventricular hypertrophy in response to pressure overload (58). To accomplish this, a specific peptide inhibitor (GqI) targeting the receptor-Gq interface was characterized extensively in in vitro studies. The peptide used was the last 54 amino acid residues of the murine α-subunit of Gq, which is the region of the Gαq protein that interacts with activated receptors (58). In vitro studies document that the GqI peptide specifically inhibits Gq signaling while not affecting Gs or Gi signaling (58). Subsequently, transgenic mice were created with αMyHC-targeted GqI expression. These animals have specifically attenuated myocardial Gq signaling as assessed by MAP kinase activation in response to angiotensin II, endothelin I, and phenylephrine (58).

Ventricular pressure overload was surgically induced in these mice by transverse aortic constriction (TAC), which in NLC mice results in a reproducible and significant left ventricular (LV) hypertrophy after 7 days (59). When TAC was applied to the GqI transgenic mice, they developed significantly less LV hypertrophy at any given pressure load compared with that of NLC mice, demonstrating that pressure overload induces ventricular hypertrophy through Gq (58) (Figure 2). Thus these mice provide a unique model for targeting the receptor-Gq inter-

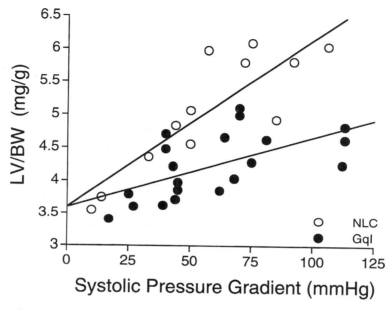

Figure 2 Hypertrophic response to pressure overload in GqI transgenic mice compared with non-transgenic littermate controls (NLCs). The index of left ventricular mass (LVW/BW) is plotted against the systolic pressure gradient produced by transverse aortic constriction (TAC) for each NLC mouse (n = 12) and transgenic mouse with myocardial-targeted expression of the GqI (n = 20) (open and filled circles, respectively). The slopes of the linear regression for NLC [y = 0.025x + 3.61, r = 0.85 (r is the correlation coefficient)] and GqI (y = 0.011x + 3.61, r = 60) animals were significantly different (P < 0.0005, ANOVA) (from reference 58).

face. This points toward a possible novel strategy for preventing pathophysiological signaling by simultaneously blocking multiple receptors coupled to a single class of G proteins. Class-specific G protein inhibition offers potentially significant advantages over single receptor antagonists, especially in conditions where multiple hormones or neurotransmitters may be involved such as in hypertension and myocardial hypertrophy. For example, if multiple agents that couple to Gq are involved in hypertrophy such as angiotensin II and endothelin I, inhibiting Gq signaling will be much more effective than using only an angiotensin II receptor antagonist since the Gq inhibitor would inhibit both signals.

Cardiovascular Characterization of α_{1B}-AR Knockout Animals

The α_{1B}-AR has also been studied in mice using a gene targeting approach to delete the gene for this important cardiovascular receptor (60). Total α_1-AR binding sites in the myocardium are reduced by 74% in homozygous ($-/-$) α_{1B}-AR knockout mice, demonstrating that this isoform in the mouse heart is the primary α_1-AR expressed (60). In α_{1B}-AR ($-/-$) mice, blood pressure response to phenylephrine is significantly decreased, and phenylephrine-induced contraction of aortic rings is significantly decreased, which suggests that the α_{1B}-AR is a mediator of blood pressure elevation in response to α_1-AR stimulation in vivo (60).

GENETICALLY ENGINEERED MOUSE MODELS OF ALTERED GRK EXPRESSION AND/OR ACTIVITY

Genetic Manipulation of Myocardial βARK1 Activity

In addition to altering myocardial AR signaling by targeting receptors, novel information regarding myocardial signaling and function has been obtained through the genetic manipulation of GRK expression and/or activity. The focus of a majority of work in this area is βARK1 (or GRK2) which, as stated above, is the primary GRK expressed in the myocardium. The activity of βARK1 has been manipulated in the hearts of transgenic mice either by overexpressing the enzyme itself or by expressing a peptide inhibitor of βARK1 (βARKct) (20). The βARKct is a peptide made up of the last 194 amino acids of βARK1, which contains the $G_{\beta\gamma}$ binding domain. Interestingly, these two lines of mice (βARK1 overexpression and βARKct expression) have reciprocally altered in vivo cardiac physiology as measured by LV function. Mice overexpressing βARK1 have attenuated response to isoproterenol stimulation, whereas animals expressing βARKct have enhanced LV dP/dt_{max} at baseline and an augmented response to isoproterenol administration. This reciprocal nature of the physiology has been demonstrated both in vivo and in cultured myocytes isolated from these transgenic hearts (20, 61). The physiological phenotypes of these two transgenic lines of mice indicate a critical role for βARK1 in normal cardiac regulation and function. In addition to attenuation of β-AR-induced inotropy, in vivo myocardial contractile responses to angiotensin II are also attenuated in βARK1 overexpressing transgenic mice (62).

The overall importance of βARK1 in cardiovascular regulation has been further emphasized by a gene disruption study in which βARK1 gene ablation leads to embryonic death with severe cardiac malformations (63). Homozygous ($-/-$) βARK1 knockout embryos were found in several litters, and the timing of the lethality in ($-/-$) embryos appears to be variable, occurring between gestational days 7.5 and 15 (63). Surprisingly, obvious cardiac abnormalities were found in all ($-/-$) embryos from gestational day 11 onward. Distinct abnormalities in the myocardium of the βARK1 ($-/-$) embryos resemble the "thin myocardium syndrome" observed with the targeted inactivation of several transcription factors (64). The findings in βARK1 knockout animals suggest a possible role for βARK1 in the normal migration, differentiation, or proliferation of myocardial cells from pre-cardiac mesoderm and in the normal development of the heart (63). Importantly, heterozygous ($+/-$) βARK1-deleted mice have no developmental abnormalities and age normally (65). Recently, we demonstrated that these mice have a cardiac phenotype of enhanced contractility similar to the βARKct transgenic animals (65). Furthermore, hybrid gene-targeted mice that are heterozygous for the βARK1 gene knockout with concurrent βARKct expression in the heart have even further enhancement of in vivo cardiac function (65). Thus, as depicted in Figure 3, these mice demonstrate that the level of contractile function in the heart in vivo is determined by the level of βARK1 expression and/or activity. These data have important implications in disease states, such as HF, where βARK1 activity is increased since even partial inhibition of βARK1 activity can lead to improved functional catecholamine responsiveness.

Myocardial-Targeted Overexpression of GRK3 and GRK5

Following the study of βARK1 overexpressing animals, a second GRK, GRK5, which is highly expressed in the myocardium, was targeted to the hearts of transgenic mice using the αMyHC promoter (62). GRK5-overexpressing transgenic animals were similar to the βARK1 mice in that they had severely attenuated β-AR signaling and loss of β-AR-mediated inotropic reserve (62). Importantly, the first evidence for in vivo substrate selectivity between different GRKs was found in these mice; in vivo cardiac responses to angiotensin II were not significantly altered in GRK5-overexpressing mice, which differs from the loss of angiotensin II–mediated contractile properties in the βARK1 mice (62). This finding is in contrast to in vitro studies that demonstrated, in a heterologous cell system, that both βARK1 and GRK5 when overexpressed, could phosphorylate and desensitize angiotensin II receptors (66).

In vivo differences in GRK substrate selectivity were also found in recently described animals with myocardial targeted GRK3 overexpression (15). These animals revealed the surprising and unexpected finding that β_1-ARs are not in vivo substrates for GRK3 (also known as βARK2). These findings were unexpected due to the previously held belief that βARK1 and GRK3 are isozymes that both desensitize β_1-ARs in vitro (67, 68). Interestingly, in these GRK3-overexpressing mice, cardiac signaling via the thrombin receptor was desensitized (15). The in vivo differences between βARK1 and GRK3 support the hypothesis that the activation of different G protein–coupled receptors leads to specific $G_{\beta\gamma}$ isoforms being released with differential affinities for these two $G_{\beta\gamma}$-dependent GRKs.

Data From Novel Hybrid Transgenic Mice

To further investigate in vivo GRK substrate selectivity, hybrid transgenic mice have been created that overexpress an individual GRK in the myocardium with concurrent cardiac overexpression of receptors. Thus the hearts of these mice

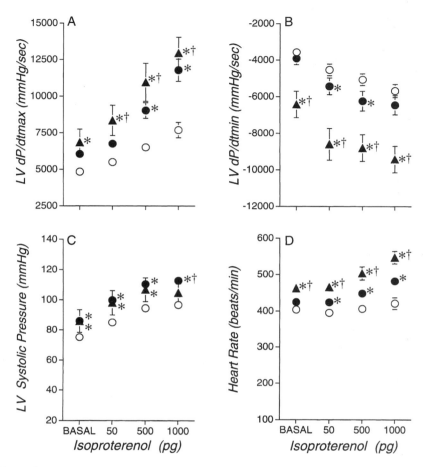

Figure 3   In vivo assessment of LV contractile function in response to β-agonist stimulation. Cardiac catheterization was performed in intact anesthetized mice using a 1.8 Fr. high-fidelity micromanometer. Parameters measured were LV systolic and end diastolic pressure, the maximal and minimal first derivative of LV pressure (LV dP/dt$_{max}$, min and heart rate). Four measured parameters are shown at baseline and after progressive doses of isoproterenol in wild-type (○) n = 26, and βARK1(+/−) (●) (n = 19), and βARK1(+/−)/βARKct (▲) (n = 9) mice. (A) LV dP/dt$_{max}$; (B) LV dP/dt$_{min}$; (C) LV systolic pressure; (D) heart rate. Data were analyzed with a repeated measures ANOVA and post hoc analysis by Newman-Keuls, *p<0.005 either βARK1(+/−) or βARK1(+/−)/βARKct versus wild type; †p<0.05 βARK1(+/−) versus βARK1(+/−)/βARKct. A significant between-group main effect in response to isoproterenol was found for (A) LV dP/dt$_{max}$ (p<0.0001); (B) LV dP/dt$_{min}$ (p<0.0001); (C) LV systolic pressure (p<0.005); and (D) heart rate (p<0.005). The pattern of change between groups was statistically different for (A) LV dP/dt$_{max}$ (p<0.0001) and (D) heart rate (p<0.0001) (from reference 65).

effectively serve as novel in vivo reaction vessels to study the specific interactions between GRKs and additional myocardial receptor systems. Recently, we carried out research in which the GRKs were overexpressed in the myocardium with concomitant overexpression of the CAM or wild-type α_{1B}-ARs (69). In addition, we studied GRK and TG4 hybrid mice (70). In the case of the GRK/α_{1B}-AR hybrid mice, interesting data were collected, demonstrating novel GRK selectivity (69). As described above, transgenic mice overexpressing the CAM α_{1B}-AR have the phenotype of myocardial hypertrophy. Thus in hybrid mice with concomitant cardiac expression of the CAM α_{1B}-AR and a specific GRK, the interaction between the kinase and the receptor can be assessed by studying any reduction in cardiac hypertrophy. Interestingly, CAM α_{1B}-AR-induced hypertrophy was attenuated by concurrent overexpression of GRK3 or GRK5, whereas no change in myocardial hypertrophy was detected by βARK1 overexpression (69). This lack of effect of βARK1 on α_{1B}-ARs in vivo was also demonstrated with a wild-type α_{1B}-AR/βARK1 hybrid transgenic mouse line, as well as by studying endogenous myocardial α_1-AR signaling (69). Thus although βARK1 is critical in regulating the effects of the sympathetic nervous system through myocardial β-ARs, it does not appear to play a role in signaling through α_1-ARs, which may become important in cardiovascular disease when β_1-ARs are down regulated. These findings are in contrast to α_{1B}-AR desensitization studies in vitro, where βARK1 was found to be capable of initiating desensitization in a cell culture overexpression system (71). Thus these data demonstrate the power of using genetically engineered animals to answer critical questions concerning the in vivo selectivity of GRKs. A summary of the data generated from these studies is shown in Table 1 where βARK1, GRK3, and GRK5 selectivity is shown for in vitro versus in vivo studies for a variety of important myocardial receptor systems.

TABLE 1   In vitro and in vivo selectivity of GRKs on the phosphorylation and/or desensitization of selected myocardial G protein–coupled receptors with corresponding references

	In Vitro			**In Vivo**		
Receptor	**βARK1**	**GRK3**	**GRK5**	**βARK1**	**GRK3**	**GRK5**
β_1-AR	Yes (68)	Yes (68)	Yes (68)	Yes (20)	No (15)	Yes (62)
β_2-AR	Yes (72)	Yes (67)	Yes (73)	Yes (70)	ns	Yes (70)
α_{1B}-AR	Yes (71)	Yes (71)	Yes/? (71)	No (69)	Yes (69)	Yes/?(69)
Angiotensin II	Yes (66)	Yes (66)	Yes (66)	Yes (62)	No (15)	No (62)
Adenosine	Yes (74, 75)	ns	ns	ns	ns	Yes (77)
Thrombin	No/? (76)	Yes (76)	ns	ns	Yes (15)	ns

ns = not studied; ? = results variable

ADRENERGIC RECEPTOR SIGNALING IN MURINE MODELS OF CARDIOVASCULAR DISEASE

Role of βARK1 in Myocardial Hypertrophy

Cardiac hypertrophy represents one of the most important adaptive responses to increased stress on the heart. Early stages of cardiac hypertrophy are compensatory in response to the increased mechanical load placed on the heart and act to normalize wall stress (78). However, it is now clear that sustained hypertrophy is maladaptive and can lead to decompensated HF (79). G protein–coupled receptors are critical in the initiation of myocardial hypertrophy and, as described above, signaling through Gq plays an obligatory role in the initiation of ventricular hypertrophy in vivo in response to pressure overload (58). β-AR signaling and functional abnormalities have been demonstrated in cardiac models of hypertrophy (80). In wild-type mice that undergo TAC to induce pressure overload hypertrophy, marked β-AR desensitization associated with a threefold increase in myocardial βARK1 activity is found (31). Enhanced βARK1 activity is not playing a role in the initiation of hypertrophy per se, as pressure overload by TAC in transgenic mice expressing the βARKct resulted in the same magnitude of ventricular hypertrophy (31). However, the β-AR desensitization seen after TAC in wild-type mice was completely reversed in βARKct animals, demonstrating that this cardiac dysfunction seen secondarily to cardiac hypertrophy was the result of augmented βARK1 levels.

Recently, we studied the βARKct inhibition of βARK1 in hypertrophy using a novel transgenic mouse model. The βARKct was targeted to the hearts of mice using a promoter that is functional during development unlike the αMyHC promoter. This promoter for the cardiac ankyrin repeat protein (CARP) actually turns off during adulthood (81). CARP-βARKct mice are viable and appear to be normal, and we have documented loss of the βARKct transgene expression after 2 to 3 weeks of life (82). Interestingly, CARP apparently belongs to the battery of fetal genes, such as the ANF gene, that can be activated in the adult heart by stress. Thus although adult CARP-βARKct transgenic mice have no enhanced contractility, when pressure overload is introduced by TAC, an induction of βARKct expression in ventricular myocardium is seen, which like that in the αMyHC-βARKct animals, results in enhanced β-AR responsiveness and reversal of βAR desensitization with pressure overload (82). Thus these mice represent a novel model of induced βARKct expression that is capable of normalizing βAR responsiveness following the development of ventricular hypertrophy induced by pressure overload.

Further experiments were recently carried out to investigate the role of βARK1 in the hypertrophic response. Interestingly, βARK1 is not elevated in a p21^{ras} overexpression mouse model of hypertrophy, demonstrating that increased βARK1 expression and activity is not a general characteristic of all forms of hypertrophy (31). Since hypertrophy is an early adaptive change to cardiac injury such as pressure overload or ischemia, one possible hypothesis for the initiation of biochemical changes in this condition is enhanced activity of the sympathetic nervous system. Therefore, we recently explored the effects of βARK1 expression after chronic infusion of either the β-AR agonist isoproterenol or the α_1-AR agonist phenylephrine (30). Both drugs were able to induce increases in cardiac mass to a comparable extent; however, only isoproterenol induced a twofold increase in myocardial βARK1 levels (30). These data were also confirmed in isolated cardiac myocytes, which showed that isoproterenol but not phenylephrine could increase the expression of βARK1 (30). Thus if the sympathetic nervous system is involved in the increased βARK1 expression in pressure overload animals or in other models of hypertrophy, it is mediated through β-ARs and not α_1-ARs. Furthermore, the increased βARK1 expression associated with isoproterenol treatment appears to be responsible for the β-AR uncoupling seen after chronic agonism, reinforcing the hypothesis that βARK1 is critically involved in the pathogenesis of β-AR dysfunction in HF. Since isoproterenol acting through β-ARs can induce the expression of βARK1, it is of importance to note that chronic β-blockade, including the chronic administration of carvedilol, a novel β-AR antagonist used successfully in the treatment of human HF, is able to decrease the expression and activity of βARK1 in the hearts of mice chronically treated with these agents (29). Thus the decreased βARK1 and resultant enhancement of cardiac β-AR signaling might represent a possible mechanism for the positive beneficial effect seen by β-blockade in HF.

Myocardial Expression of the βARKct and Resultant βARK Inhibition Rescues a Mouse Model of Cardiomyopathy and Heart Failure

Because βARK1 appears to play an important role in the progression of cardiac dysfunction, we recently carried out experiments in novel genetically engineered mice to elucidate a specific role for βARK1 in the pathogenesis of HF. A murine model of cardiomyopathy and HF has been described recently as a result of the gene disruption of the muscle lim protein (MLP), which is a conserved positive regulator of myogenic differentiation (83, 84). Mice that are homozygous ($-/-$) for the MLP gene knockout develop a cardiomyopathy, having several characteristics of the human disease including hypertrophy, dilatation, and loss of β-adrenergic inotropic reserve. Importantly, they also have biochemical abnormalities consistent with human HF, including β-AR uncoupling and enhanced βARK1 expression (83, 85). To determine whether altering β-AR function could also attenuate the cardiomyopathy seen in MLP ($-/-$) mice, animals were mated to transgenic mice that overexpress either the βARKct or β_2-ARs (TG4) (85). In vivo cardiac function was assessed by non-invasive echocardiography and invasive cardiac catheterization after the birth of these hybrid gene-targeted mice. Both MLP ($-/-$) and MLP ($-/-$)/β_2-AR mice had enlarged LV chambers with significantly reduced fractional shortening, demonstrating evidence of systolic dysfunction. Thus β_2-AR overexpression does not alter the phenotype of these MLP ($-/-$) HF animals (85). In contrast, LV chamber size and cardiac function were normal in the MLP ($-/-$) /βARKct mice (85). A representative M-mode echocardiogram shown in Figure 4 demonstrates the obvious cardiac dilatation and reduced function in the MLP ($-/-$) animals and the normalized systolic and diastolic function seen in the MLP ($-/-$) /βARKct mice. In addition to echo-

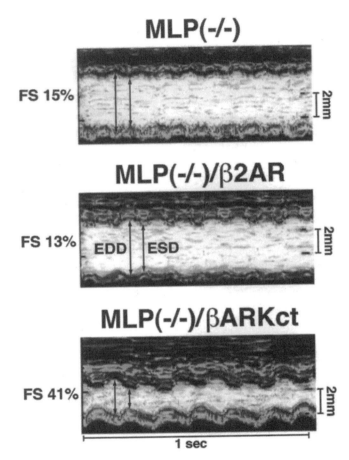

Figure 4 Analysis of cardiac function by echocardiography. Transthoracic M-mode echocardiographic tracings in a *MLP*($-/-$) (*upper panel*), a *MLP*($-/-$)/β_2AR (*middle panel*), and a *MLP*($-/-$)/βARKct mouse (*lower panel*). Left ventricular dimensions are indicated by the double-ended arrows. EDD, end diastolic dimension; ESD, end systolic dimension. Both the *MLP*($-/-$) and *MLP*($-/-$)/β_2AR mice have chamber dilatation with reduced wall motion, indicating depressed cardiac function, whereas chamber size and cardiac function are normal in the *MLP*($-/-$)/βARKct mouse (from reference 85).

cardiographic findings, basal LV contractility in the MLP $(-/-)$ / βARKct mice was significantly increased and responsiveness to β-agonism was normalized, demonstrating that βARKct expression in this mouse model of cardiomyopathy restores normal β-AR function.

These results demonstrate an important difference in these two transgenic models, both of which have increased contractility. βARKct expression preserves normal β-AR function presumably by inhibiting desensitization through endogenous $β_1$-ARs and rescues this mouse model of cardiomyopathy. In contrast, marked $β_2$-AR overexpression results in sustained β-AR stimulation that does not prevent the deterioration of cardiac function seen in this model. Taken together these data suggest that restoring normal control of $β_1$-AR signaling by inhibiting desensitization is an important mechanism for preventing the progressive deterioration of cardiac function in this model of HF. The findings further strengthen the hypothesis that βARK1 inhibition represents a potential novel therapeutic strategy for the treatment of the compromised heart.

Because the βARKct works through the inhibition of the $G_{βγ}$-βARK1 interaction, it is possible that inhibition of other $G_{βγ}$-dependent cell processes in myocytes is responsible for the extraordinary rescue of the mouse model of HF. One possibility is that $G_{βγ}$-dependent activation of MAP kinase could play a role in HF and that the βARKct would probably inhibit it (86). However, there is no direct evidence that MAP kinase plays a role in this model of cardiomyopathy, and the data in the MLP $(-/-)$/βARKct mice do demonstrate that β-AR desensitization is reversed due to βARKct expression (85). Furthermore, in a recently completed study using hybrid transgenic mice with concurrent myocardial βARK1 overexpression and βARKct expression, we have definitively demonstrated that the mode of βARKct action in the heart is the inhibition of enhanced βARK1 activity (87). In this study, blunted β-AR function in vivo caused by βARK1 expression in otherwise normal mouse hearts can be completely reversed when the βARKct is co-expressed, demonstrating that in vivo the βARKct is capable of inhibiting enhanced βARK1 activity such as that seen in HF (87). Thus although other $G_{βγ}$-dependent mechanisms may play a role, it seems clear that a primary action of the βARKct is to inhibit βARK1 activity, and this almost certainly participates in the rescue of the MLP $(-/-)$ HF phenotype.

$β_2$-AR Overexpression in a Model of Decompensated Hypertrophy

Contrasting rescue results between transgenic $β_2$-AR overexpression and βARKct expression have also been seen in a second murine model of cardiac dysfunction. Cross-breeding experiments between transgenic mice overexpressing $β_2$-AR and βARKct with mice that have transgenic overexpression of Gαq were recently reported (88). Gαq overexpression, driven by the αMyHC promoter, triggers events in the heart leading to a phenotype of eccentric hypertrophy and depressed ventricular function that resembles the phenotype of decompensated hypertrophy

(89). These animals have depressed β-AR function and thus the role of this β-AR dysfunction in the development of this failure phenotype was studied using the βARKct and $β_2$-AR transgenic mice. Interestingly, expression of the βARKct had no effect on this phenotype (88), which might be due to the fact that βARK1 upregulation is not seen in Gαq transgenic mice. Interestingly, cross-breeding with the TG4 mice, which have >200 fold overexpression of myocardial β-AR density, worsened the phenotype of the Gαq mice (88). However, a novel $β_2$-AR transgenic mouse line overexpressing the $β_2$-AR by 30-fold over endogenous levels was able to rescue the hypertrophy and basal ventricular function of the Gαq mice (88). Furthermore, the ventricular expression of ANF and skeletal α-actin, both molecular markers of hypertrophy, were also decreased in the mice with concomitant Gαq and low level $β_2$-AR overexpression. Thus these data suggest that while excessive uncontrolled enhancement of β-AR signaling is deleterious in the setting of a compromised heart, selective enhancement by overexpressing the $β_2$-AR subtype to limited levels restores not only cardiac contractility but also reverses cardiac hypertrophy. Moreover, it was recently reported that a human $β_2$-AR gene polymorphism, which results in a $β_2$-AR that has dysfunctional Gs coupling, negatively affects the outcome and prognosis of patients in congestive HF (90). Together these studies suggest that genetic addition of wild-type $β_2$-ARs to the myocardium, at least in this population of HF sufferers, might represent a novel therapeutic strategy.

CONCLUSIONS AND FUTURE DIRECTIONS

The use of gene-targeted mice to study the role of adrenergic signaling in cardiac contractility has yielded several novel models that have provided a broader understanding of the role of these G protein–coupled receptor signaling systems in the regulation of cardiac function both under normal conditions and in disease states. This includes models of enhanced function such as $β_2$-AR overexpression, and βARK1 inhibition through the expression of the peptide inhibitor βARKct. Early experiments have shown that both transgenic mouse models can rescue models of compromised heart function, and future experiments should elucidate whether $β_2$-AR overexpression or βARK1 inhibition will provide novel therapeutic strategies for the treatment of HF. In addition to the MLP ($-/-$) and Gαq overexpressing models of cardiomyopathy, several recent models recapitulate most or some of the physiological and biochemical characteristics of human HF. These models include transgenic mice overexpressing a mutant myosin heavy chain gene (91), transgenic mice overexpressing a CAM retinoic acid receptor controlled by the βMyHC promoter (92), a calsequestrin cardiac overexpressing transgenic mouse (93), and a transgenic mouse with myocardial overexpression of a dominant/negative CREB transcription factor (94). Through a strategy of cross-breeding these HF lines with the $β_2$-AR and βARKct transgenic mice described above, important information regarding the role of βARK1-mediated desensitization and β-AR overexpression in the failing heart should be revealed in the near future. Current experimental evidence strongly suggests a key role of cardiac GRK activity, and in particular βARK1 expression, in the pathogenesis of HF. Thus inhibition of βARK1 activity or lowering of its expression represents a novel target for the treatment for this devastating disease. The reduction of βARK1 expression can now be achieved with classical drugs such as β-blockers (29), and in animal models, reduction of its activity can be accomplished by the in vivo expression of peptide inhibitors such as the βARKct. Efforts are ongoing in our laboratory to deliver the βARKct transgene to the heart in vivo using adenoviruses to further test the hypothesis that inhibition of βARK1 activity in the setting of HF can result in enhanced myocardial performance. Along these lines, we have shown that infection of isolated cardiomyocytes with adenoviruses carrying the β₂-AR or βARKct transgene can increase the signaling and function activity of cardiomyocytes in culture including myocytes isolated from rabbits with congestive HF (95, 96). In addition to a gene therapy approach, the discovery of small molecules to inhibit βARK1 activity could lead to novel drugs that might prove more selective in improving performance of the failing heart.

In conclusion, gene manipulation in mice, coupled with powerful in vivo physiological technology, has shed considerable light on the role of adrenergic signaling, and its regulation by GRKs in modulating in vivo cardiac function. Concepts developed from these models have led to the elucidation of potentially novel therapeutic strategies for enhancing the function of the compromised heart. Only time will tell if these can be successfully extended to clinical practice.

Visit the Annual Reviews home page at www.AnnualReviews.org.

LITERATURE CITED

1. Ahlquist RP. 1948. A study of the adrenergic receptors. *Am. J. Physiol.* 153:586–86

2. Caron MG, Lefkowitz RJ. 1993. Catecholamine receptors: structure, function, and regulation. *Recent Prog. Horm. Res.* 48:277–19

3. Brodde OE. 1993. Beta-adrenoceptors in cardiac disease. *Pharmacol. Ther.* 60: 405–43

4. Gauthier C, Tavernier G, Charpentier F, Langin D, Le Marec H. 1996. Functional β₃-adrenoceptor in the human heart. *J. Clin. Invest.* 98:556–62

5. Bristow MR, Hershberger RE, Port JD, Rasmussen R. 1989. β₁ and β₂ adrenergic receptor mediated adenylyl cyclase stimulation in nonfailing and failing human ventricular myocardium. *Mol. Pharmacol.* 35:295–303

6. Daaka Y, Luttrell LM, Lefkowitz RJ. 1997. Switching of the coupling of the β₂-adrenergic receptor to different G proteins by protein kinase A. *Nature* 390:88–91

7. Xiao R-P, Avidonin P, Zhou Y-Y, Cheng H, Akhter SA, et al. 1999. Coupling of β₂-adrenoceptor to Gi proteins and its physiological relevance in murine cardiac myocytes. *Circ. Res.* 84:43–52

8. Hieble JP, Bylund DB, Clarke DE, Eikenburg DC, Langer SZ, et al. 1995. International union of pharmacology. X. Recommendation for nomenclautre of

α_1-adrenoceptors: consensus update. *Pharmacol. Rev.* 47:267–70

9. Exton JH. 1985. Mechanisms involved in alpha-adrenergic phenomena. *Am. J. Physiol.* 248:E663–68

10. Knowlton KU, Michel MC, Itani M, Shubeita HE, Ishihara K, et al. 1993. The α_{1A}-adrenergic receptor subtype mediates biochemical, molecular, and morphologic features of cultured myocardial cell hypertrophy. *J. Biol. Chem.* 268: 15374–80

11. Dostal DE, Baker KM. 1998. Angiotensin and endothelin: messengers that couple ventricular stretch to the Na^+/H^+ exchanger and cardiac hypertrophy. *Circ. Res.* 83:870–73

12. Simpson P, McGrath A. 1983. Norepinephrine-stimulated hypertrophy of cultured rat myocardial cells is an α_1 adrenergic response. *J. Clin. Invest.* 72:732–38

13. Lefkowitz RJ. 1998. G Protein-coupled receptors III. New roles for receptor kinases and β-arrestins in receptor signaling and desensitization. *J. Biol. Chem.* 273:18677–80

14. Inglese J, Freedman NJ, Koch WJ, Lefkowitz RJ. 1993. Structure and mechanism of the G protein-coupled receptor kinases. *J. Biol. Chem.* 268:23735–38

15. Iaccarino G, Rockman HA, Shotwell KF, Tomhave ED, Koch WJ. 1998. Myocardial-targeted overexpression of G protein-coupled receptor kinase-3 in transgenic mice: evidence for in vivo selectivity of GRKs. *Am. J. Physiol.* 275:H1298–306

16. Pitcher JA, Inglese J, Higgins JB, Arriza JL, Casey PJ, et al. 1992. Role of $\beta\gamma$-subunits of G proteins in targeting the β-adrenergic receptor kinase to membrane-bound receptors. *Science* 257: 1264–67

17. Koch WJ, Inglese J, Stone WC, Lefkowitz RJ. 1993. The binding site for the $\beta\gamma$ subunits of heterotrimeric G proteins

on the β-adrenergic receptor kinase. *J. Biol. Chem.* 268:8256–60

18. Inglese J, Koch WJ, Touhara K, Lefkowitz RJ. 1995. $G\beta\gamma$ interactions with PH domains and Ras-MAP kinase signaling pathways. *Trends Biochem. Sci.* 20:151–56

19. Touhara K, Koch WJ, Hawes BE, Lefkowitz RJ. 1993. Mutational analysis of the pleckstrin homology domain of the β-adrenergic receptor kinase. Differential effects on $G\beta\gamma$ and phosphatidylinositol 4,5–bisphosphate binding. *J. Biol. Chem.* 270:17000–5

20. Koch WJ, Rockman HA, Samama P, Hamilton RA, Bond RA, et al. 1995. Cardiac function in mice overexpressing the β-adrenergic receptor kinase or a βARK inhibitor. *Science* 268:1350–53

21. Leimbach WN, Wallin G, Victor RG, Aylward PE, Sundlof G, et al. 1986. Direct evidence from intraneural recordings for increased central sympathetic outflow in patients with failure. *Circulation* 73:913–19

22. Bristow MR, Ginsburg R, Minobe W, Cubicciotti R, Sageman WS, et al. 1982. Decreased catecholamine sensitivity and β-adrenergic receptor density in failing human hearts. *N. Engl. J. Med.* 307:205–11

23. Bristow MR, Minobe W, Raynolds MV, Port JD, Rasmussen R, et al. 1993. Reduced β_1 receptor messenger RNA abundance in the failing human heart. *J. Clin. Invest.* 92:2737–45

24. Ungerer M, Bohm M, Elce JS, Erdmann E, Lohse ML. 1993. Altered expression of β-adrenergic receptor kinase and β_1-adrenergic receptors in the failing heart. *Circulation* 87:454–63

25. Feldman AM, Cates AE, Veazey WE, Hershberger RE, Bristow MR, et al. 1988. Increase of the 40,000-mol wt pertussis toxin substrate (G protein) in the failing human heart. *J. Clin. Invest.* 82:189–97

26. Dhalla NS, Dixom IM, Rupp H, Barwin-

sky J. 1991. Experimental congestive heart failure due to myocardial infarction: sarcolemmal receptors and cation transporters. *Basic Res. Cardiol.* 86:13–23

27. Ungerer M, Kessebohm K, Kronsbein K, Lohse MJ, Richardt G. 1996. Activation of β-adrenergic receptor kinase during myocardial ischemia. *Circ. Res.* 79:455–46

28. Maurice JP, Shah A, Kypson AP, Hata J, White DC, et al. 1999. Molecular β-adrenergic signaling abnormalities in failing rabbit hearts after infarction. *Am. J. Physiol.* In press

29. Iaccarino G, Tomhave ED, Lefkowitz RJ, Koch WJ. 1998. Reciprocal in vivo regulation of myocardial G protein-coupled receptor kinase expression by β-adrenergic receptor stimulation and blockade. *Circulation* 98:1783–89

30. Iaccarino G, Dolber PC, Lefkowitz RJ, Koch WJ. 1999. β-adrenergic receptor kinase-1 levels in catecholamine-induced myocardial hypertrophy: regulation by β but not α₁ adrenergic stimulation. *Hypertension* 33:396–401

31. Choi D-J, Koch WJ, Hunter JJ, Rockman HA. 1997. Mechanism for β-adrenergic receptor desensitization in cardiac hypertrophy is increased β-adrenergic receptor kinase. *J. Biol. Chem.* 272:17223–29

32. Gros R, Benovic JL, Tan M, Feldman RD. 1997. G-protein-coupled receptor kinase activity is increased in hypertension. *J. Clin. Invest.* 99:2087–93

33. Anversa P, Loud AV, Levicky V, Guideri G. 1985. Left ventricular failure induced by myocardial infarction. I. Myocyte hypertrophy. *Am. J. Physiol.* 248:H876–82

34. Gidh-Jain M, Huang B, Jain P, Gick G, El-Sherif N. 1998. Alterations in cardiac gene expression during ventricular remodeling following experimental myocardial infarction. *J. Mol. Cell. Cardiol.* 30:627–37

35. Harding SE, MacLeod KT, Davies CH,

Wynne DG, Poole-Wilson PA. 1995. Abnormalities of the myocytes in ischaemic cardiomyopathy. *Eur. Heart J.* 16:74–81

36. Ju H, Zhao S, Tappia PS, Panagia V, Dixon IMC. 1998. Expression of Gqα and PLC-β in scar and border tissue in heart failure due to myocardial infarction. *Circulation* 97:892–99

37. James JF, Hewett TE, Robbins J. 1998. Cardiac physiology in transgenic mice. *Circ. Res.* 82:407–15

38. Subramaniam A, Jones WK, Gulick J, Wert S, Neumann J, et al. 1991. Tissue-specific regulation of the α-myosin heavy chain promoter in transgenic mice. *J. Biol. Chem.* 266:24613–20

39. Milano CA, Allen LF, Rockman HA, Dolber PC, McMinn TR, et al. 1994. Enhanced myocardial function in transgenic mice overexpressing the β₂-adrenergic receptor. *Science* 264:582–86

40. Rockman HA, Hamilton RA, Jones LR, Milano CA, Mao L, et al. 1996. Enhanced myocardial relaxation in vivo in transgenic mice overexpressing the β₂-adrenergic receptor is associated with reduced phospholamban protein. *J. Clin. Invest.* 97:1618–23

41. Turki J, Lorenz JN, Green SA, Donnelly ET, Jacinto M, et al. 1996. Myocardial signaling defects and impaired cardiac function of a human β-adrenergic receptor polymorphism expressed in transgenic mice. *Proc. Natl. Acad. Sci. USA* 93:10483–88

42. Bond RA, Leff P, Johnson TD, Milano CA, Rockman HA, et al. 1995. Physiological effects of inverse agonists in transgenic mice with myocardial overexpression of the β₂-adrenoceptor. *Nature* 374:272–76

43. Lefkowitz RJ, Cotecchia S, Samama P, Costa T. 1993. Constitutive activity of receptors coupled to guanine nucleotide regulatory proteins. *Trends Pharmacol. Sci.* 14:303–7

44. Samama P, Bond RA, Rockman HA,

Milano CA, Lefkowitz RJ. 1997. Ligand-induced overexpression of a consitutively active β_2-adrenergic receptor: pharmacological creation of a phenotype in transgenic mice. *Proc. Natl. Acad. Sci. USA* 94:137–41

45. Xiao RP, Avdonin P, Zhou YY, Cheng H, Akhter SA, et al. 1999. Coupling of β_2-adrenoceptor to Gi proteins and its physiological relevance in murine cardiac myocytes. *Circ. Res.* 84:43–52

46. Bertin B, Mansier P, Makeh I, Briand P, Rostene W, et al. 1993. Specific atrial overexpression of G protein coupled human β_1-adrenoceptors in transgenic mice. *Cardiovasc. Res.* 27:1606–12

47. Mansier P, Medigue C, Charlotte N, Vermeiren C, Coraboeuf E, et al. 1996. Decreased heart rat variability in transgenic mice overexpressing atrial β_1-adrenoceptors. *Am. J. Physiol.* 271: H1465–72

48. Engelhardt S, Hein L, Wiesmann F, Lohse MJ. 1999. Progressive hypertrophy and heart failure in β_1-adrenergic receptor transgenic mice. *Proc. Natl. Acad. Sci. USA* 96:7059–64

49. Iwase M, Bishop SP, Uechi M, Vatner DE, Shannon RP, et al. 1996. Adverse effects of chronic endogenous sympathetic drive induced by cardiac GSα overexpression. *Circ. Res.* 78:517–24

50. Rohrer DK. 1998. Physiological consequences of β-adrenergic receptor disruption. *J. Mol. Med.* 76:764–72

51. Rohrer DK, Desai KH, Jasper JR, Stevens ME, Regula DP, et al. 1996. Targeted disruption of the mouse β_1-adrenergic receptor gene: developmental and cardiovascular effects. *Proc. Natl. Acad. Sci. USA* 93:7375–80

52. Rohrer DK, Schauble EH, Desai KH, Kobilka BK, Bernstein D. 1998. Alterations in dynamic heart rate control in the β_1-adrenergic receptor knockout mouse. *Am. J. Physiol.* 274:H1184–93

53. Milano CA, Dolber PC, Rockman HA, Bond RA, Venable ME, et al. 1994. Myocardial expression of a constitutively active α_{1B}-adrenergic receptor in transgenic mice induces cardiac hypertrophy. *Proc. Natl. Acad. Sci. USA* 91:10109–13

54. Akhter SA, Milano CA, Shotwell KF, Cho MC, Rockman HA, et al. 1997. Transgenic mice with cardiac overexpression of α_{1B}-adrenergic receptors. In vivo α_1-adrenergic receptor-mediated regulation of β-adrenergic signaling. *J. Biol. Chem.* 272:21253–59

55. Harrison SN, Autelitano DJ, Wang BH, Milano C, Du XJ, et al. 1998. Reduced reperfusion-induced Ins(1,4,5)P3 generation and arrhythmias in hearts expressing constitutively active α_{1B}-adrenergic receptors. *Circ. Res.* 83:1232–40

56. Lemire I, Allen BG, Rindt H, Hebert TE, 1998. Cardiac-specific overexpression of α_{1B}-AR regulates β-AR activity via molecular crosstalk. *J. Mol. Cell. Cardiol.* 30:1827–39

57. Chuang TT, Levine H III, Deblasi A. 1995. Phosphorylation and activation of β-adrenergic receptor kinase by protein kinase C. *J. Biol. Chem.* 270:18660–65

58. Akhter SA, Luttrell LM, Rockman HA, Iaccarino G, Lefkowitz RJ, et al. 1998. Targeting the receptor-Gq interface to inhibit in vivo pressure overload myocardial hypertrophy. *Science* 280:574–77

59. Rockman HA, Ross RS, Harris AN, Knowlton KU, Steinhelper ME, et al. 1991. Segregation of atrial-specific and inducible expression of an atrial natriuretic factor transgene in an in vivo murine model of cardiac hypertrophy. *Proc. Natl. Acad. Sci. USA* 88:8277–81

60. Cavalli A, Lattion AL, Hummler E, Nenniger M, Pedrazzini T, et al. 1997. Decreased blood pressure response in mice deficient of the α_{1B}-adrenergic receptor. *Proc. Natl. Acad. Sci. USA* 94:11589–94

61. Korzick DH, Xiao RP, Ziman BD, Koch WJ, Lefkowitz RJ, et al. 1997. Transgenic manipulation of β-adrenergic receptor kinase modifies cardiac myocyte contraction to norepinephrine. *Am. J. Physiol.* 272:H590–96

62. Rockman HA, Choi D-J, Rahman NU, Akhter SA, Lefkowitz RJ, et al. 1996. Receptor specific in vivo desensitization by the G protein-coupled receptor kinase-5 in transgenic mice. *Proc. Natl. Acad. Sci. USA* 93:9954–59

63. Jaber M, Koch WJ, Rockman HA, Smith B, Bond RA, et al. 1996. Essential role of β-adrenergic receptor kinase-1 in cardiac development and function. *Proc. Natl. Acad. Sci. USA* 93:12974–79

64. Rossant J. 1996. Mouse mutants and cardiac development: new molecular insights into cardiogenesis. *Circ. Res.* 78:349–53

65. Rockman HA, Choi D-J, Akhter SA, Jaber M, Giros B, et al. 1998. Control of myocardial contractile function by the level of β-adrenergic receptor kinase-1 in gene-targeted mice. *J. Biol. Chem.* 273:18180–84

66. Oppermann M, Freedman NJ, Alexander RW, Lefkowitz RJ. 1996. Phosphorylation of the type 1A angiotensin II receptor by G protein-coupled receptor kinases and protein kinase C. *J. Biol. Chem.* 271:13266–72

67. Benovic JL, Onorato JJ, Arriza JL, Stone WC, Lohse M, et al. 1991. Cloning, expression, and chromosomal localization of β-adrenergic receptor kinase-2. A new member of the receptor kinase family. *J. Biol. Chem.* 266:14939–46

68. Freedman NJ, Liggett SB, Drachman DE, Pei G, Caron MG, et al. 1995. Phosphorylation and desensitization of the human β$_1$-adrenergic receptor: involvement of G protein-coupled receptor kinase and cAMP-dependent protein kinase. *J. Biol. Chem.* 270:17953–61

69. Eckhart AD, Duncan SJ, Akhter SA, Koch WJ. 1998. Specific myocardial interactions in vivo between G protein-coupled receptor kinases and α$_{1B}$-adrenergic receptors. *Circulation* 98:I-329

70. Akhter SA, Milano CA, Lefkowitz RJ, Koch WJ. 1996. Specific interactions between adrenergic receptors and receptor kinases in the hearts of hybrid transgenic mice. *Circulation* 94:I-408

71. Diviani D, Lattion AL, Larbi N, Kunapuli P, Pronin A, et al. 1996. Effect of different G protein-coupled receptor kinase on phophorylation and desensitization of the α$_{1B}$-adrenergic receptor. *J. Biol. Chem.* 271:5049–58

72. Benovic JL, DeBlasi A, Stone WC, Caron MG, Lefkowitz RJ. 1989. β-adrenergic receptor kinase: Primary structure delineates a multigene family. *Science* 246:235–40

73. Premont RT, Koch WJ, Inglese J, Lefkowitz RJ. 1994. Identification, purification and characterization of GRK5, a member of the family of G protein-coupled receptor kinases. *J. Biol. Chem.* 269:683–84

74. Nie Z, Mei Y, Ramkumar V. 1997. Short term desensitization of the α$_1$-adenosine receptors in DT$_1$MF-2 cells. *Mol. Pharmacol.* 52:456–64

75. Mundell SJ, Benovic JL, Kelly E. 1997. A dominant negative mutant of the G protein-coupled receptor kinase 2 selectively attenuates adenosine A$_2$ receptor desensitization. *Mol. Pharmacol.* 51:991–98

76. Ishii K, Chen J, Ishii M, Koch WJ, Freedman NJ, et al. 1994. Specific regulation of thrombin receptor signaling by a G protein-coupled receptor kinase. *J. Biol. Chem.* 269:1125–30

77. Tsimikas S, Koch WJ, Lefkowitz RJ, Rockman HA. 1996. Desensitization of adenosine A1 receptors with cardiac overexpression of the G protein-coupled receptor kinase 6 in transgenic mice. *Circulation* 94:I-408

78. Grossman W, Jones D, McLaurin LP. 1975. Wall stress and patterns of hypertrophy in the human left ventricle. *J. Clin. Invest.* 56:56–64

79. Lorell BH. 1997. Transition from hypertrophy to failure. *Circulation* 96:3824–27

80. Bohm M, Moll M, Schmid B, Paul M, Ganten D, et al. 1994. β-adrenergic

neuroeffector mechanisms in cardiac hypertrophy of renin transgenic rats. *Hypertension* 24:653–62

81. Zou Y, Evans S, Chen J, Kuo HC, Harvey RP, et al. 1997. CARP, a cardiac ankyrin repeat protein, is downstream in the Nkx2–5 homeobox gene pathway. *Development* 124:793–804

82. Manning BS, Koch WJ. 1998. Altering β-adrenergic receptor (AR) kinase activity and βAR signaling in the developing mouse heart. *Circulation* 98:I-329

83. Arber S, Hunter JJ, Ross J Jr, Hongo M, Sansig G, et al. 1997. MLP-deficient mice exhibit a disruption of cardiac cytoarchitectural organization, dilated cardiomyopathy, and heart failure. *Cell* 88:393–403

84. Arber S, Halder G, Caroni P. 1994. Muscle LIM protein, a novel essential regulator of myogenesis, promotes myogenic differentiation. *Cell* 79:221–31

85. Rockman HA, Chien KR, Choi D-J, Iaccarino G, Hunter JJ, et al. 1998. Expression of a β-adrenergic receptor kinase 1 inhibitor prevents the development of heart failure in gene-targeted mice. *Proc. Natl. Acad. Sci. USA* 95:7000–5

86. Koch WJ, Hawes BE, Allen LF, Lefkowitz RJ. 1994. Direct evidence that G_i-coupled receptor stimulation of mitogen-activated protein kinase is mediated by Gβγ activation of p21^{ras}. *Proc. Natl. Acad. Sci. USA* 91:12706–10

87. Akhter SA, Eckhart AD, Rockman HA, Shotwell KF, Lefkowitz RJ, et al. 1999. In vivo inhibition of elevated myocardial β-adrenergic receptor kinase activity in hybrid transgenic mice restores normal β-adrenergic signaling and function. *Circulation.* 100:648–53

88. Dorn GW, Tepe NM, Lorenz JN, Davis MG, Koch WJ, et al. 1999. Low- and high-transgenic expression of β2-adrenergic receptors differentially affects cardiac hypertrophy and function in Gαq overexpressing mice. *Proc. Natl. Acad. Sci. USA.* 96:6400–5

89. D'Angelo DD, Sakata Y, Lorenz JN, Biovin GP, Walsh RA, et al. 1997. Transgenic Gαq overexpression induces cardiac contractile failure in mice. *Proc. Natl. Acad. Sci. USA* 94:8121–26

90. Liggett SB, Wagoner LE, Craft LL, Hornung RW, Hoit BD, et al. 1998. The ile164 β2-adrenergic receptor polymorphism adversely affects the outcome of congestive heart failure. *J. Clin. Invest.* 102:1534–39

91. Vikstrom KL, Factor SM, Leinwand LA. 1996. Mice expressing mutant myosin heavy chains are a model for familial hypertrophic cardiomyopathy. *Mol. Med.* 2:556–67

92. Colbert MC, Hall DG, Kimball TR, Witt SA, Lorenz JN, et al. 1997. Cardiac compartment-specific overexpression of a modified retinoic acid receptor produces dilated cardiomyopathy and congestive heart failure in transgenic mice. *J. Clin. Invest.* 100:1958–68

93. Cho MC, Rapacciuolo A, Koch WJ, Kobayashi Y, Jones L, Rockman HA. 1999. Defective β-adrenergic receptor signaling precedes the development of dilated cardiomyopathy in transgenic mice with calsequestrin overexpression. *J. Biol. Chem.* 274:22251–56

94. Fentzke RC, Korcarz CE, Lang RM, Lin H, Leiden JM. 1998. Dilated cardiomyopathy in transgenic mice expressing a dominant-negative CREB transcription factor in the heart. *J. Clin. Invest.* 101:2415–26

95. Drazner MH, Peppel KC, Dyer S, Grant AO, Koch WJ, et al. 1997. Potentiation of β-adrenergic signaling by adenoviral-mediated gene transfer in adult rabbit ventricular myocytes. *J. Clin. Invest.* 99:288–96

96. Akhter SA, Skaer CA, Kypson AP, McDonald PH, Peppel KC, et al. 1997. Restoration of β-adrenergic signaling in failing cardiac ventricular myocytes via adenoviral-mediated gene transfer. *Proc. Natl. Acad. Sci. USA* 94:12100–5

Annu. Rev. Physiol. 2000. 62:261–87

REMODELING THE CARDIAC SARCOMERE USING TRANSGENESIS

Jeffrey Robbins

*Department of Pediatrics, Division of Molecular Cardiovascular Biology,
Children's Hospital Research Foundation, Cincinnati, Ohio 45229–3039;
e-mail: jeff.robbins@chmcc.org*

Key Words   mouse genetics, heart, muscle, hypertrophy, cardiac disease

■ **Abstract**   An underpinning of basic physiology and clinical medicine is that specific protein complements underlie cell and organ function. In the heart, contractile protein changes correlating with functional alterations occur during both normal development and the development of numerous pathologies. What has been lacking for the majority of these observations is an extension of correlation to causative proof. More specifically, different congenital heart diseases are characterized by shifts in the motor proteins, and the genetic etiologies of a number of different dilated and hypertrophic cardiomyopathies have been established as residing at loci encoding the contractile proteins. To establish cause, or to understand development of the pathophysiology over an animal's life span, it is necessary to direct the heart to synthesize, in the absence of other pleiotropic changes, the candidate protein. Subsequently one can determine whether or how the protein's presence causes the effects either directly or indirectly. By affecting the heart's protein complement in a defined manner, the potential to establish the function of different proteins and protein isoforms exists. Transgenesis provides a means of stably modifying the mammalian genome. By directing expression of engineered proteins to the heart, cardiac contractile protein profiles can be effectively remodeled and the resultant animal used to study the consequences of a single, genetic manipulation at the molecular, biochemical, cytological, and physiological levels.

INTRODUCTION

Structure-function relationships between, among, and within the contractile proteins have been intensely studied for the last 50 years. With the advent of modern biochemical separation techniques, it became apparent that at the protein level multiple isoforms occurred that varied in a muscle-type-specific and developmental-stage-specific manner. Molecular genetic techniques led to the isolation of unique genes and the genetic diversity of the contractile protein isoforms became clear (1–4). Subsequently, questions of isoform functionality began to be more precisely addressed in isolated systems.

0066–4278/00/0315–0261$12.00

The ability to stably modify the mammalian genetic apparatus through transgenesis and gene targeting has opened up new avenues for exploring the physiological consequences of contractile protein isoform substitutions or even, potentially, site-directed mutagenic studies. Previously, one was largely restricted to studying functional consequences of the different isoforms or modified protein domains in isolated, biochemically defined in vitro systems. However, now it is possible to make changes or substitutions in these proteins and study the consequences within the whole organ and whole animal context. A protein or protein's domain can be analyzed over time and under different physiological conditions.

An initial concern in applying the transgenic approach for remodeling the cardiac sarcomere was extensive data from lower organisms showing that gene dosage effects could lead to significant deficits in sarcomere assembly, integrity and ultimately function (5–7). Another potentially fatal flaw in applying transgenic over-expression to the general system was that transcription factors might be present in such rate-limiting amounts as to cause "squelching" of endogenous gene expression if promoters derived from genes encoding the endogenous contractile apparatus were used. Extensive data are now available so that, at least for contractile protein remodeling using promoters derived from the contractile protein gene sets, these concerns are invalid (8–11). Because of these data, cardiac-specific expression of a transgene has rapidly become a widely used paradigm for establishing mechanistic links between the appearance of a protein, or mutated form of a protein, and any resultant changes in overall organ function and/or morbidity/mortality over the animal's life span.

For the heart, there are unambiguous data showing that both the kinetics of the cross-bridge cycle as well as force production can be regulated independently of changes in the primary sequences of the contractile proteins (12). However, the identification of mutations in the myosin heavy chains (13), light chains (14), actins (15), tropomyosin and troponins (16, 17), and myosin binding protein C (18), as the genetic basis for at least some dilated and hypertrophic cardiomyopathies, emphasizes the importance of understanding structure-function relationships of the cardiac contractile proteins at the whole animal and whole organ levels. The demonstration that mutations in the major contractile proteins, as well as isoform shifts, can accompany development of cardiovascular disease (19–21) provides a compelling rationale for exploring these processes in a comprehensive fashion. Gene targeting and transgenesis provide the means to create animal models that can then be used to understand functional consequences of altered cardiac contractile protein isoform or mutated cardiac protein expression. This review focuses on transgenic approaches as they have been applied to exploring questions of isoform functionality and the long-term consequences of altered contractile protein expression, as well as on creation of animal models directed at understanding the pathogenic processes responsible for dilated and hypertrophic cardiomyopathy.

TRANSGENESIS AND CONTRACTILE PROTEINS: BASIC CONSIDERATIONS

Context

It is important to emphasize the limitations of transgenesis. Normally, one must generate multiple lines so that potential artifacts can be ruled out and the effects of high expression levels studied. Transgenesis involves the random insertion of exogenous DNA sequences into the genome. This contrasts with gene targeting in which homologous recombination is used to insert DNA at a precise site (22). With transgenesis, DNA can be inserted in varying copy numbers, and the site at which insertion takes place can have dramatic effects on ultimate transcriptional levels. Most transgenes require integration into a region of "open chromatin" in order to be expressed, and *cis*-acting sequences surrounding the integration site can have a dominant effect on tissue-specific and temporal expression patterns (23–25). However, the flanking regions of some genes can direct position independent expression. This was first demonstrated for the β globin gene, and the DNA elements responsible for the phenomenon were termed locus control regions (26). These sequences can stabilize an open chromatin conformation so that transgene expression levels occur independently of chromosomal context.

The physical act of inserting a large piece of DNA into the genetic apparatus is not always innocuous, and there are numerous examples of insertional mutagenic events resulting from transgenesis (27–30). Fortunately, the majority of these events result in recessive phenotypes and, as long as the transgene is carried in a heterozygous state with one normal allele present, no phenotype occurs. However, the possibility of an insertional mutagenic event often precludes breeding the transgene to homozygosity.

Abundance and Promoter Strength

The contractile proteins make up the majority of the cardiomyocytes' protein mass and are expressed at very high levels with steady state RNA transcripts numbering in the tens of thousands. To efficiently replace a significant proportion of the endogenous protein pool with a transgenically encoded protein a very active transcriptional apparatus or promoter must be incorporated as part of the transgenic construct. Early transgenic experiments used sequences such as the cytoplasmic actin or cytomegalovirus promoters that drove expression in a number of tissue types, including the heart (31, 32). Systemic expression of a transgene can seriously complicate the resultant phenotype because of the confounding effects of transgene expression in other organs or tissues. The development of promoters whose expression was restricted to the cardiac compartment enhanced the utility of transgenesis for remodeling the cardiac contractile apparatus. The ideal promoter should drive high levels of expression in a cardiac-specific manner at appropriate times during development. It should also display a minimum of position-dependent effects with expression levels being partially or completely insulated from the chromosomal context. Thus expression should be copy number dependent, but position independent, so that multiple lines of mice will show varying levels of expression. This allows construction of a dosage response curve, in which severity of phenotype can be correlated with the degree of transgenic replacement (Figure 1, see color insert). This can, in some cases, offer a significant advantage over the more precise (and time-consuming) gene targeting approach in which the targeted allele is present only in one or two copies. Often, the heterozygote is asymptomatic while the homozygote is nonviable (33–36).

Identification of cardiac-specific transcriptional regulatory elements was initiated using in vitro approaches and was centered on muscle cell line transfections. These experiments were only partially successful in identifying required elements because a true cardiogenic cell line did not exist and because of the inherent limitations of an in vitro environment in which the transfected regulatory elements are not integrated into the chromosome. Isolation of lines that more faithfully recapitulate cardiomyocyte differentiation and maintenance (37, 38) may, in the future, circumvent these difficulties. Often, active promoters characterized exclusively in vitro had little or no detectable expression in transgenic hearts (11, 39–41). Recently, a number of cardiac-specific promoters have been characterized, not only in vitro but also in vivo, either by injection directly into the heart (40, 42) or by testing the sequences in transgenic mice (8, 39, 43, 44). Not surprisingly, the most successful and widely used elements are derived from contractile genes themselves, with a particular focus on the myosin heavy and light chains (reviewed in 45). Of these, the α-myosin heavy chain (MyHC) promoter has been used most widely, because of its high levels of homogenous expression in both the adult atria and ventricles, its high degree of cardiac specificity, and the presence of sequences necessary for copy number-dependent and position-independent expression (9, 11, 44, 46). Importantly, transgenic expression with the full-length α-MyHC promoter appears to be homogenous across the cardiomyocyte population (9, 47, 48).

As noted above, possible gene dosage effects must be considered when attempting to modify contractile proteins, as perturbing the overall stoichiometries of the contractile protein pools could have dramatic and detrimental effects on sarcomeric structure and function. Surprisingly, in initial transgenic experiments in which the ventricular isoform of the myosin light chain (MLC) was overexpressed using the α-MyHC promoter, no overall increase in the protein pool could be detected despite 10-fold increases in steady-state levels of the transgenically encoded transcript (10, 49). Regulation of the stoichiometry did not occur at transcription, as no down-regulation of endogenous transcripts could be detected. Further experimentation also ruled out the possibility of modifications in translational initiation or efficiency (50) and, although it has not been proven formally, it appears most likely that the cardiomyocyte is able to regulate contractile protein stoichiometries at the post-translational level, possibly by controlling protein turnover.

This phenomenon considerably enhances the value of the transgenic approach for studying structure-function relationships of the contractile proteins because it essentially allows one to replace the endogenous protein simply by over-expressing the transgenically encoded sequences at sufficient levels (Figure 2, see color insert). That is, the cardiomyocyte can essentially be considered a closed vessel with two inlets (endogenous and transgenic gene expression) and one outlet (the rate of target protein turnover). If the transgenic message is present in significant excess over the endogenous transcript, and the two transcripts are translated at equal efficiencies, after a period of time, the endogenous product will be diluted out (assuming both proteins are incorporated into the sarcomere at roughly equal efficiencies). It is important to formally test the lack of gene dosage effects by over-expressing the wild type (endogenous) protein in a parallel set of lines, along with the mutated construct. The mutation can then be compared, not only to a nontransgenic cohort, but also to a cohort that expresses the normal protein. This ensures that no phenotype results simply from the levels of transgenic expression of the contractile protein being studied.

Dominant-Negative Contractile Protein Gene Mutations

Except in the cases where transgenic expression is so high as to effectively reduce steady-state protein levels to zero, detection of a phenotype depends upon the dominance of the transgenically encoded protein. For contractile proteins this often appears to be the case as exemplified by extensive data on a group of diseases known as the familial hypertrophic cardiomyopathies (FHC). These autosomal-dominant cardiomyopathies are inherited, rather than acquired as a secondary consequence to altered cardiac load (51), and cause hypertrophic cardiomyopathy as measured by an increase in mass. FHC is characterized by unexplained cardiac hypertrophy without increased cardiac load or in the absence of other systemic abnormalities. Clinically, the autosomal-dominant diseases show variable penetrance, with hypertrophy occurring in either ventricle, and there is almost always involvement of the intraventricular septum. Histologically, there is well-characterized disarray at both the myocyte and myofiber levels. Bizarre nuclear morphology and karyomegaly are also often present, although these characteristics can be age dependent (52). The histopathology also often includes extensive fibrosis that can be either focal or interstitial in nature (53). As a group of diseases, the FHCs are not common, with independent studies yielding estimates that 1:500 individuals are affected (54, 55). However, FHC is a major cause of sudden death in otherwise healthy appearing young adults. Even within a family in which the disease is due to a single genetic defect, the severity, onset, and penetrance of the pathology is highly variable. This is presumably due to the existence of modifier loci, although this has not yet been formally demonstrated. Penetrance is usually age related, with onset usually occurring in adolescence (53, 56, 57).

Beginning with the seminal paper of Geisterfer-Lowrance et al (13), a genetic basis for the primary etiology of the disease began to be established. FHC mapped to chromosome 14q11 and a point mutation in exon 13 of the beta cardiac MyHC gene (*β-MyHC*) was present in all affected individuals from particular kindreds. The gene encodes the major motor protein responsible for contraction in the adult ventricle. The mutation converted a highly conserved arginine residue (Arg403) to a glutamine (Arg403Gln). Since that initial observation, over 60 different point mutations leading to various amino acid substitutions have now been mapped to *β-MyHC:* Mutations in this gene account for ~30% of FHC in the general population. The large number of different mutations and their various locations in the MyHC molecule partially explains the disease's widely varying severity: Different mutations have different effects on MyHC's ability to carry out its function. For example, the Arg403Gln mutation is highly penetrant and has severe effects on morbidity and mortality of the affected patient population. The residue is located near the nucleotide-binding pocket, and is at a site in the myosin head that participates in actin-myosin interactions. Thus the mutation lies at and near critical sites for motor function (58, 59).

Early on, it was recognized that FHC mapped to multiple loci. Soon after the first reports linking the disease to *β-MyHC*, gene linkage/positional cloning approaches defined other disease loci and identified mutations in other sarcomeric protein genes: chromosome 1q31 (cardiac troponin T), 15q2 (α-tropomyosin), 3p (ventricular isoform of the regulatory myosin light chain), 11p13-q13 (cardiac myosin binding protein-C), and 12q2 (ventricular isoform of the cardiac essential myosin light chain) (14, 17, 18, 57, 60, 61). Almost certainly, additional loci will be identified, as demonstrated by the recent reports that mutations in the inhibitory subunit of cardiac troponin (16) and cardiac actin (15) are also linked to inheritable cardiovascular disease.

These mutated alleles are present in the human population in the heterozygous state, indicating that they are dominant negatives. Thus modeling these diseases by transgenesis becomes feasible. These multiple examples support the statement that contractile protein mutations/isoform replacements will generally behave as dominant negatives—a necessity if transgenic approaches are to be pursued. In fact, there are now ample data supporting these points, both from the naturally occurring mutations that cause disease and from transgenic experiments already performed. The proteins studied to date are shown in Table 1, and the insights gained into isoform functionality, functional domains, and site-directed mutations important both for the normal function of the contractile proteins and implicated in disease processes are outlined below.

THICK FILAMENT

Myosin

Considering its central importance to cardiac function, it is not surprising that myosin has been a focus of both transgenic and gene targeting approaches. It is the single most abundant muscle protein, constituting greater than 50% of myo-

TABLE 1 Transgenic manipulation of contractile proteins

Transgene	Phenotype
Rat α-MyHCArg403Gln + δ468-527 linked to rat α-MyHC promoter (72)	Low level of transgenic protein (10% of total myosin) still produced a bi-ventricular hypertrophy with 1 male showing dilated cardiomyopathy. Left ventricles showed myocyte disarray and fibrosis.
Mouse myosin light chain 2v linked to mouse α-MyHC promoter (10)	Complete shift in the atrial isoform to the transgenically encoded protein. Isolated atrial myocytes show a decrease in unloaded shortening velocity. No overt pathology or hypertrophy presents in the hearts over the lifetime of the animals.
Mouse myosin light chain 2f linked to mouse α-MyHC promoter (9)	Complete MLC2a to MLC2f shift, partial MLC2v to MLC2f shift. No overt pathology or hypertrophy. Significant decreases in left ventricular function were measured in the isolated working heart preparation.
Mouse essential myosin light chain 1a linked to mouse α-MyHC promoter (91)	Complete ELC1v to ELC1a shift. No overt pathology or hypertrophy. Significant increases in motor velocity and in V_{max} of unloaded velocity of shortening using skinned fibers isolated from left ventricle. Significant increase in left ventricular function.
Human essential myosin light chain 1v, both wild-type and FHC mutation (Met149Val) (95)	No phenotype apparent when normal ELC1v was expressed. Mutant protein expression was not quantitated, but mice showed significant papillary muscle hypertrophy, mimicking the human disease.
Mouse myosin binding protein C, both wild-type and a mutation causing FHC linked to mouse α-MyHC promoter (102)	No phenotype apparent when normal protein was expressed and replaced endogenous species. Mutant protein expression resulted in histopathologic changes in sarcomere ultrastructure.
Mouse γ-enteric actin linked to mouse α-MyHC promoter (36)	When expressed in α-cardiac actin null animal (a knockout was performed by gene targeting), expression rescued the null (lethal) phenotype. However, hearts showed deficits in left ventricular function.
Mouse β-tropomyosin linked to mouse α-MyHC promoter (115)	34-fold in β-Tm protein to 55% of total Tm in cells resulting in partial $\alpha\alpha$ to $\alpha\beta$ shift. Working heart preparation shows significant decreases in left ventricular relaxation times. Myofilament Ca^{2+} activation is affected and maximum developed tension was reduced.
Mouse tropomodulin linked to mouse α-MyHC promoter (133)	Dilated cardiomyopathy
Mouse skeletal troponin C linked to rat α-MyHC promoter (124)	Partial replacement of cardiac TnC with skeletal TnC in some cardiomyocytes. Decrease in acidosis sensitivity of tension-pCa relationship.
Mouse wild-type and truncated troponin T (mutation linked to FHC) linked to rat α-MyHC promoter (129)	Mice expressing wild-type protein were normal. Mice expressing the FHC mutation showed increased morbidity and mortality and only mice with < 5–10% incorporation of the transgenic protein were viable. Both systole and diastole were impaired, and decreases in both cardiomyocyte number and mass were measured.
Mouse missense troponin T (Arg92Gln) (FHC mutation) linked to mouse cardiac TnT promoter (147)	Significant cardiomyocyte disarray and interstitial fibrosis.

fibrillar mass and 15–30% of total muscle protein. Myosin is a hexameric protein made up of two heavy chains ($M_r \sim 229{,}000$) and four light chains ($M_r \sim 18{,}000$–27,000). The heavy chains consist of two separate domains; a globular head region and a rod region that assumes an α-helical coiled coil. The ATPase activity underlying muscle contraction is localized at the amino-terminal end, which corresponds to the globular head and neck of the molecule. High-resolution X-ray crystal structures of the head region (62, 63) have provided significant insights into the functionally important domains of the molecule (58, 64). The binding sites for actin and ATP are located in the globular head, whereas the light chains lie just distil to the head, in the so-called neck or hinge region. The two types of MLCs—essential and regulatory—likely have structural and regulatory roles in cardiac muscle contraction. The regulatory light chain is phosphorylatable through the protein kinase A pathway, but the role of phosphorylation in cardiac myosin activity is unknown.

In the vertebrate heart there are three MyHC isoforms whose relative amounts depend upon the developmental stage, the particular region of the heart, and the animal. Two heavy chain genes are expressed, α and β, which give rise to the two unique homodimers, V_1 and V_3 respectively. An intermediate heterodimeric form, V_2, is made up of α and β gene products. Each of these forms displays different electrophoretic mobilities in polyacrylamide under non-denaturing conditions, and each has a different intrinsic ATPase activity; V_1 is the most active (by about three to fourfold) and V_3 the least. The isoform population correlates with the different intrinsic muscle shortening velocities observed between species and within a species as the heart responds to chronic stress or conditioning (65, 66). Thus the adult mouse ventricle, which has a heart rate of 500–800 beats per min (67), contains essentially only V_1, whereas V_3 predominates in the human ventricle.

Extensive circumstantial evidence and biochemical data support the hypothesis that the speed of contraction is dependent upon the MyHC isoform present (66, 68), and studies have confirmed that the sliding velocity of the myosin-actin complex correlates with the particular MyHC isoform (69). Alpert and associates noted early on that the ATPase activity of the MyHC is lower in the failing rodent heart and postulated that molecular changes in MyHC play a major role in functional adaptation of the hypertrophied heart to chronic overload (65). During this process, α-MyHC, which has a relatively high ATPase activity, is down regulated and synthesis of the β-MyHC-encoded V_3 increases. The resultant lower ATPase activity presumably mediates a negative inotropic effect resulting in reduced myocardial contractility by decreasing the cross-bridge cycling rate. However, systolic ejection is increased because of increased tension. By carefully measuring the energetics, Alpert's group showed that there is an overall increase in the efficient use of chemical energy to generate mechanical force. While it is generally accepted that the isoform shifts result in different functional endpoints, it was thought, until recently, that the human ventricle did not undergo such a transition: The myosin is and remains in the adult, V_3. However, an isoform shift does occur in the human ventricle, with a mixture of MyHC isoforms present and α-MyHC accounting for as much as 34% of the total transcript (20). In the left ventricle significant down-regulation (by 67–84%) of β-MyHC accompanied development of congestive heart failure (19, 20).

In light of these data, it was exciting when mutations in human *β-MyHC* were identified as being responsible for between 30–40% of FHC cases (70). Both gene targeting and transgenic approaches were quickly directed at making the murine models. Dozens of different mutations in β-MyHC are linked to FHC, but one of the most severe is Arg403Gln. As is the case for the majority of MyHC FHC mutations, this residue is contained within the globular head region, and crystallographic data indicate that it is close to the actin-myosin interface (58). The effects of the mutation were analyzed in vitro and showed that the protein had normal ATPase activity in the absence of actin, but the V_{max} of the actin-activated ATPase was reduced by approximately fourfold (71). Although different isoforms are present in human and mouse hearts (β-MyHC and α-MyHC respectively), the amino acid sequences flanking this residue are 100% conserved between the proteins, providing a strong rationale for targeting the residue in the murine system. A rat α-MyHC cDNA containing the mutated residue, as well as an internal deletion of amino acids 468–527, was over-expressed in transgenic animals using the rat α-MyHC promoter (72). Despite significant transcript levels, only 2 to 12% of the total MyHC appeared to be transgenically encoded. However, consistent with the concept that these mutations behave as dominant negatives, even a small amount of transgenic protein produced a detectable phenotype that recapitulated aspects of the human disease (73, 74). The left ventricle showed significant pathology, with foci of myocyte disarray, degenerating myofibrils, and fibrosis. Gender differences developed over time with the females developing progressive left ventricular hypertrophy relative to the males, although in a single line some males developed a left ventricular dilated cardiomyopathy (72, 73).

Although gene targeting is frequently used for loss-of-function studies by producing a knockout or null allele, methodology exists that allows precise, site-directed mutations to be produced. These "in-out" (75) or "tag-and-exchange" (76) experiments involve two gene targeting events carried out in series, and this approach was used to create a murine model of the Arg403Gln mutation (34). Mice homozygous for the FHC mutation (human homozygotes have never been described) were born with an overtly normal heart but invariably died within a week. Detailed studies on the neonatal mice using high-frequency echocardiography showed normal cardiac dimensions and function (77). However, over a 2-day period, the hearts rapidly developed a fulminant dilated cardiomyopathy, characterized by wall thinning and loss of systolic function. The histopathology revealed foci of myofibrillar disarray, characteristic of hypertrophic cardiomyopathy. As expected from the human pedigrees and transgenic data outlined above, the mutant allele was dominant with heterozygotes developing asymmetric left ventricular hypertrophy and enlarged left atria. Myocyte disarray and progressive fibrosis were also evident. Significant gender effects were apparent, with the males being affected more severely, although both sexes showed increasing cardiac dysfunction and histopathology as they aged. The males also showed abnormal electrophysiological parameters, as measured using surface electrocardiograms (78, 79), with prolonged sinus node recovery and ventricular repolarization. Excitation-contraction coupling was altered as determined by measurement of Ca^{2+} cycling and contractile activation in trabeculae derived from the heterozygotes (80). The data showed that increased Ca^{2+} could be mobilized (peak intracellular Ca^{2+}), but contractility was not maintained at high stimulation rates. Male mice were also twice as likely to display ventricular tachycardia during programmed ventricular stimulation. The isolated working heart preparation revealed abnormal left ventricular function (34), and contractile abnormalities in both diastole and systole were confirmed by measuring in situ pressure-volume relationships (81). Both chamber filling and pressure relaxation were delayed, while the systolic pressure rise was accelerated. In contrast to these in situ studies, using an isolated isovolumic heart preparation, abnormalities were noted only in diastole with the hearts demonstrating, work load-dependent diastolic dysfunction (82).

Neither the knock-in nor transgenic models exactly mimic all aspects of the human MyHC Arg403Gln FHC phenotype. However, the experiments unambiguously show that the mutated MyHC acts as a poison peptide, affecting sarcomeric function at the level of cross-bridge cycling (71, 82–84) and provides definitive proof for the genetic basis of FHC.

The Myosin Light Chains

Both the regulatory and essential MLCs have been the subjects of focused transgenic studies. Atrial- and ventricular-specific genes and isoforms exist, and extensive biochemical data show that these proteins confer unique kinetic behavior to the contractile apparatus (21, 85–87). As noted above, FHC can also be caused by mutations in either the essential or regulatory MLCs (14), and isoform shifts in these proteins can accompany dilated cardiomyopathy (88), hypertrophy (89), and congenital heart disease (21, 86).

In order to approach questions of isoform function, a series of MLC replacements were carried out in transgenic mice using the α-MyHC promoter to drive expression. Initial experiments involved expression of the ventricular isoform of the regulatory light chain, MLC2v, in atria and ventricles (10, 49). Although the transgenic transcript could be detected at high levels relative to endogenous gene expression, there was no effect on the steady-state mRNA levels encoding related contractile proteins, including the endogenous MLC2v transcripts. Despite increasing MLC2v mRNA in the ventricle by four- to tenfold, no commensurate increase in the protein could be detected, in either the total protein or myofilament pools. Thus the usual correlation between mRNA and protein levels does not hold in the face of significant transgenic over-expression (10). Although no increase in MLC2v protein could be detected in the ventricles, complete replacement of the atrial isoform with MLC2v occurred in transgenic atria. There was no sign of overt pathology, hypertrophy, or dilation over the lifetime of the animals. No functional changes could be detected in the isolated working heart preparation. However, at the level of the cardiomyocyte, subtle alterations occurred. Atrial myocytes were enzymatically disaggregated and field-stimulated at multiple frequencies. Subsequently their mechanical properties and Ca^{2+} kinetics were studied using video edge detection and FURA 2-AM, respectively (90). Enhancement of the mechanical properties of the atrial cardiomyocytes could be detected with the speeds of shortening and relengthening at maximum Ca^{2+} stimulation, both being increased significantly. These data indicate that light chain isoform content can directly influence cross-bridge cycling times.

A similar transgenic strategy was used to explore light chain isoform functionality by replacing both cardiac regulatory light chains with the skeletal (fast) isoform (MLC2f). Multiple lines carrying varying copies of the transgene were made: As the number of copies increased, steady-state levels of transgenic mRNA also increased (9). Although transgenic over-expression resulted in equal levels of MLC2f RNA in all four cardiac compartments, significant differences in the degree of protein replacement between the atria and ventricles were observed. In the atria, replacement was essentially complete at low or moderate copy number ($>3 \leq 10$ copies). In the ventricles, despite high copy numbers ($>20 \leq 34$ copies), and a tenfold excess of MLC2f mRNA relative to MLC2v, replacement was $<40\%$. By breeding the different lines with one another such that additive mRNA accumulations resulted, 70% replacement was measured. A working hypothesis is that MLC2v has a high affinity, relative to MLC2f, for its endogenous contractile machinery, and preferentially competes against transgenic MLC2f during sarcomere assembly. Presumably, unbound protein is rapidly degraded, and stoichiometric amounts of total MLC are maintained (Figure 2). Thus by increasing the steady-state levels of MLC2f relative to MLC2v, one can drive replacement more completely. Functionally, replacement of the endogenous isoforms with ectopic MLC2f led to modest deficits in both cardiac contractility and relaxation (12–14%), as measured in the isolated working heart preparation. No pathology was detected nor was there any activation of the hypertrophic response (9).

As noted above, isoform transitions can accompany development of cardiac disease. Morano and colleagues noted that some patients suffering from congenital heart diseases such as tetralogy of Fallot, double outlet right ventricle, and infundibular pulmonary stenosis underwent a partial essential light chain (ELC)1 ventricle→ELC1 atrial isoform shift in the ventricle. This shift correlated with increases in cross-bridge cycling kinetics as measured in skinned fibers derived from the diseased muscle (21, 86). The α-MyHC promoter was used to transgenically over-express ELC1a in the mouse heart in order to replace ELC1v with ELC1a in the ventricle. A series of transgenic lines, showing varying levels of replacement were generated, and the kinetic and contractile properties of the motors analyzed (91). Using the in vitro motility assay as a measure of unloaded motor velocity (92, 93), transgenically modified fibers showed significant increases (25–40%) in the velocity of actin translocation (91). A similar increase was observed in the unloaded velocity of shortening (V_{max}), as measured using the slack test on skinned fibers derived from the papillary muscle. Contractility and relaxation ($\pm$ dP/dt) also increased, as measured using both the Langendorff and isolated working heart preparations. Thus increases in both unloaded and loaded motor velocity translated into improved cardiac function. The experiments showed that correlations noted in a clinical population could be tested rigorously by transgenic remodeling of the cardiac contractile apparatus.

This approach was extended to the study of a light chain mutation that causes FHC. Epstein and colleagues previously showed that a Met149Val mutation in the ventricular isoform of ELC1 caused a striking hypertrophy that was largely restricted to the papillary muscle, resulting in a mid-ventricular obstruction (14). They suggested that the mutation disrupted the stretch-activation response of the papillary muscle. Although this phenomenon is well characterized in insect flight muscles and contributes significantly to oscillatory power generation in the rapidly (150 beats/s) contracting sarcomeres (94), it is not clear that the human heart uses this mechanism in a physiologically significant manner. Both the wild-type and mutant genes were expressed in transgenic mice. Although no phenotype could be detected as a result of transgenic expression for the normal allele, multiple lines of mice that expressed the mutant ELC1v recapitulated the human phenotype (95), exhibiting significant papillary muscle hypertrophy in aged adult animals. When the transgenic papillary muscles were examined by subjecting the fibers to rapid and repeated oscillations in length, distortions in the stretch-activation response of the Met149Val fibers, relative to nontransgenic or transgenic fibers expressing wild-type ELC1v, were noted. At frequencies corresponding to physiologic human heart rates, oscillatory power was significantly reduced. The authors speculate it is this reduction that triggers the hypertrophic response.

Myosin Binding Protein C

Of the proteins identified as causing FHC, this thick filament protein is the least well understood; it probably has both structural and signaling roles in the heart. Myosin binding protein C (MyBP-C) is relatively large ($M_r \sim 130{,}000$) and represents $\sim$2–4% of total myofibrillar protein (96). Slow skeletal, fast skeletal, and cardiac-specific isoforms exist. The protein probably plays some role in thick filament assembly because it has both MyHC- and titin-binding domains located at the carboxyl terminus (97). It is restricted to the A band of the sarcomere and forms a series of 7 to 9 transverse bands spaced at 43 nm intervals. The protein belongs to the immunoglobulin superfamily, and the three isoforms show a highly conserved structure consisting of IgI and fibronectin (Fn) domains (98). It can bind to myosin directly in vitro (99) and can organize thick filaments into uniform structures when both MyHC and MyBP-C are co-transfected into non-muscle COS cells (98). As is the case of MyHC, a large number of mutations (>30) in cardiac MyBP-C have been linked to FHC and account for $\sim$15% of FHC cases.

However, unlike MyHC, most MyBP-C mutations result in reading frame shifts and premature termination as a result of nonsense codons (18, 60, 100, 101).

The lack of understanding the basic function of an abundant cardiac protein, coupled with its importance in human disease, makes MyBP-C an attractive target for a transgenic approach to understanding its structure-function relationships. Both wild-type and mutated MyBP-C proteins have now been expressed at high levels in the hearts of transgenic mice (102). As is the case for the other thick filament contractile proteins, the cardiomyocyte rigorously controls overall protein pool levels in the face of significant transgenic over-expression. No increase in the overall protein level of MyBP-C occurs either for the wild-type or MyBP-C protein containing the FHC mutation. Consistent with these data, no phenotype at the molecular, cellular, histologic, biochemical, or whole organ levels was observed in the hearts that over-expressed the wild-type protein.

In the transgenic animals the mutated protein mimicked a defined FHC mutation in which both the myosin- and titin-binding sites were deleted; approximately one third of the molecule's carboxyl terminus was missing. The truncated protein was stable and incorporated into the sarcomere. However, incorporation was not restricted to the A band and the protein only weakly bound to the other myofibril proteins, as measured by biochemical extraction techniques. Mice in whom approximately 60% of the total MyBP-C consisted of the transgenically encoded protein were selected for detailed study. No effects on morbidity or mortality were observed and no overt hypertrophy or dilation could be detected. However, histopathologic changes in both the ventricles and atria were apparent, with frequent areas of abnormal staining visible when cells were treated with hematoxylin and eosin. Ultrastructural analyses showed that individual cardiomyocytes, or parts of cardiomyocytes, had undergone sarcomere dissolution, with only small fragments of sarcoplasmic reticulum and a few mitochondria present. Other cardiomyocytes appeared to be completely normal. Incomplete penetrance of the phenotype, as well as the lack of hypertrophy, is consistent with the human phenotype (60, 103). Isolated working heart preparations carried out on young adult animals showed no differences. However, kinetic studies on skinned fiber preparations revealed both increased Ca^{2+} sensitivity and decreased maximum power output (102).

Taken together these experiments on thick filament remodeling illustrate some common principals. First, they show that a mutation in a protein that is an intrinsic part of the contractile apparatus can cause disease. Second, the models provide a means of gaining insight into the compensatory and pathologic processes, which occur longitudinally. Third, the models offer possible reagents for investigating the variable penetrance of the disease, which remains completely obscure. Why are some individuals affected and others not? The unaffected individuals express the mutant protein, but whether force production is affected and somehow compensated for is unknown. Variable penetrance is also observed in the mouse models in which inbred strains are used and the genetics are well defined. Therefore, theoretically, relevant modifier loci can be identified. Fourth, the degree of replacement is a function of both the steady-state levels of transcript and the affinity of the transgenic protein, relative to the endogenous species that is being replaced for the contractile apparatus. Fifth, complete replacement is not necessary or even, in some cases, desirable (Figure 1) for producing a measurable phenotype. As noted above, FHC is a dominant disease trait, and in hearts where only partial contractile protein isoform shifts are present, significant changes in contractile function occur (74).

THIN FILAMENT PROTEINS

In cardiac muscle, activation of cross-bridge cycling is mediated by Ca^{2+} flux and is controlled at the thin filament level. In addition to containing the actin cables with which the myosin head interacts during transduction of chemical energy into mechanical force, the cardiac thin filament also consists of the tropomyosin (Tm)-troponin (TnI, TnT, TnC) complex. In a series of elegant and complex cooperative interactions, these proteins mediate Ca^{2+} activation by controlling the critical transition between a weakly bound, or blocked state and the strongly bound (force-generating) state of the myofilament (104–106). The effective rate of this process, as well as the number of productive cross-bridges formed during each cardiac cycle, is regulated by post-translational covalent modification of a subset of these proteins, as well as by non-covalent means. Shifts in the isoform population also have major functional ramifications (2). There are mutations in actin, Tm, TnI, and TnT that cause either dilated (actin) or hypertrophic cardiomyopathy (15, 16, 61).

Actin

The different contractile protein isoforms expressed in the heart in response to external and internal stimuli underlie its changing physiologic profiles during development and in response to pathogenic processes. Yet sequences of the different isoforms are often closely conserved. Alpha-cardiac and α-skeletal actin, the two isoforms transcribed in the mammalian heart, are closely related, differing at only four amino acids out of 375 residues (107, 108). Two of these changes are localized at the amino terminus (α-cardiac actin; Asp-Asp-Glu-Glu versus Asp-*Glu*-*Asp*-Glu for α-skeletal actin), which is a critical region for thin-thick filament interaction (3, 4, 109). Unique isoform functionality is implied by data obtained from a naturally occurring mutation. Alpha-skeletal actin is the predominant isoform in the developing heart but is down regulated in most species during cardiac maturation. Concomitant up-regulation of α-cardiac actin gene transcription effects a switch in the predominant thin filament protein (in humans significant amounts of α-skeletal actin continue to be expressed in the adult heart). Thus α-cardiac actin predominates in the normal adult mouse heart. However, the BALB/c strain contains a naturally occurring genetic lesion at the actin promoter,

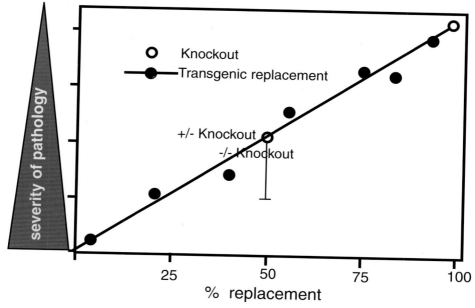

Figure 1 Possible dose-response relationships in transgenic and gene-targeted animals. In transgenesis, expression is copy number dependent if a suitable promoter is used and, assuming the transcript is targeted to the correct cellular location, the degree of replacement is a simple function of the transgenic transcript level and the protein's affinity for the contractile apparatus. Thus a series of lines can be derived that show varying replacement levels, and these different degrees of replacement can often be correlated with the severity of the phenotype and/or rapidity of onset. The phenotypic consequences of a gene targeting experiment directed toward components of the contractile apparatus are often very difficult to detect in the heterozygous state (+/- knockout), whereas the homozygous (-/- knockout) often presents as an embryonic lethal.

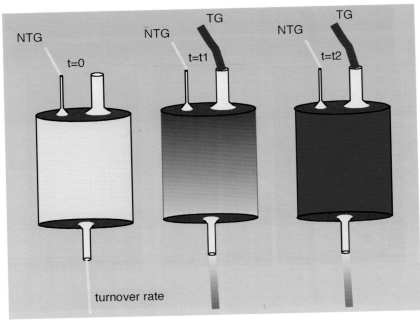

Figure 2 Hypothetical scheme for transgenic replacement of contractile proteins. The total mass of the contractile protein being targeted remains constant and is depicted as a filled cylinder. At t = 0, the transgene is off and the steady-state level is determined by the rates of endogenous synthesis (top inlet, yellow) and apparent turnover (bottom inlet). At t = t1, transgene synthesis is activated and the steady-state level of transgenic transcript is 5- to 10-fold greater than that of the endogenous mRNA (whose effective synthetic rate is unaffected). To maintain constant mass, turnover rate of the protein pool effectively increases, leading to a dilution of the endogenous protein. At t = t2, endogenous protein levels are essentially reduced to zero. Empirically, assuming the transgenic protein has approximately equal affinity for the ectopic contractile apparatus as the endogenous species, t1 ~ 4 weeks and t2 ~ 7--10 weeks if the transgenic transcript levels are 3- to 7-fold greater than that of the endogenous target.

leading to increased amounts of the α-skeletal isoform relative to α-cardiac actin (110, 111). Using the isolated working heart preparation, hearts of this strain were hyper-contractile compared with other mouse strains whose actin complement consists mostly of α-cardiac actin (112).

A combination of gene targeting and transgenic approaches was used to study cardiac actin isoform function. The cardiac α-actin gene was disrupted using homologous recombination in embryonic stem cells in order to study the consequences of its loss of function (36). During normal fetal cardiac development, both α-cardiac and α-skeletal actin are co-expressed along with transient expression of the vascular smooth muscle isoform. Although a majority of the homozygous null animals died during development, 40–45% lived for 1–14 days post-birth. The survival of these animals resulted from increased expression of both the α-skeletal and vascular smooth muscle isoforms, which were up regulated in the homozygous nulls. Combining a transgenic approach with the gene targeted animals, Lessard et al showed that the homozygote nulls could be rescued to adulthood by transgenic cardiac expression of enteric smooth muscle γ-actin (36). However, the hearts of these animals were considerably enlarged and hypodynamic, as measured in the isolated working heart preparation. Additionally, transgenically expressed enteric smooth muscle γ-actin reduced cardiac contractility in both the wild-type and heterozygous null backgrounds. These data convincingly demonstrate that despite the almost exact conservation sequence between the different actin isoforms specificity is important for normal cardiac function over the animal's lifetime (36).

Tropomyosin

Tropomyosin (Tm) is a rigid rod-shaped protein that binds along the length of the actin filament. Each molecule covers approximately seven actin monomers and partially overlaps in a head-to-tail arrangement with the adjoining Tm monomer. Tm stabilizes and stiffens the filament and, in the absence of Ca^{2+}, blocks the myosin-binding site of actin (reviewed in 106, 113). Situated on the Tm-actin complex are the three troponin (Tn) subunits: I, C, and T (named for their inhibitory, calcium, and tropomyosin binding activities, respectively). The carboxyl terminus of TnT binds at Tm's carboxyl end and is responsible for positioning the complex along the thin filament. TnI binds to actin and in this conformation inhibits the actin-activated myosin ATPase. Inhibition is reversible and Ca^{2+} sensitive in the presence of the intact troponin complex. Troponin C binds up to four molecules of Ca^{2+}, although during systole Ca^{2+} is bound to only one site. Calcium binding is thought to effect a molecular switch in binding affinities, strengthening the TnC-TnT and TnC-TnI interactions while weakening the TnT-Tm and TnI (Tm-actin) binding. The actin-myosin cross-bridge is then released from steric hindrance, and tension develops as a result of achieving the strongly bound state (114). However, the exact molecular events underlying the molecular transduction of this signal are not well understood (105, 106).

Tm isoform functionality was explored in the heart using transgenesis. The α- and β-striated Tms have 87% identity at the amino acid level, and normally form $\alpha\beta$ heterodimers (compared to the $\alpha\alpha$ or $\beta\beta$ species). The ratios vary in different striated fiber types. In the mouse heart, α/β ratios increase from 5:1 to 50:1 during maturation and the $\alpha\alpha$ homodimer becomes the predominant species. Cardiac-specific transgenic over-expression of β-Tm led to a 150-fold increase in mRNA levels, relative to the endogenous transcript. This, in turn, led to a 34-fold increase in β-Tm protein, with the cardiomyocytes now consisting of 45% α and 55% β and a resultant shift in Tm content from $\alpha\alpha{\rightarrow}\alpha\beta$. In contrast to all other experiments carried out to date with contractile protein isoform replacement, the massive increases in β-Tm transcript and/or protein lead to a decrease in the α-Tm transcripts (and protein), indicating the existence of cross-talk at the RNA and protein levels (115).

Protein analyses of several striated muscle types show that the relative proportions of the $\alpha\alpha$-homodimer and $\alpha\beta$-heterodimer are associated with the speed of contraction (116, 117) and, in the heart, pressure-overload hypertrophy leads to an increase in β-tropomyosin expression (118). In transgenic animals, over-expression of the protein did not cause any overt cardiac pathology or changes in the expression of other contractile protein genes. Cardiomyocyte structure and ultrastructure were also unaffected. However, diastolic function was slightly decreased as measured in the isolated working heart. When force measurements on isolated cardiac muscle fiber bundles were carried out, subtle changes in switch behavior were noted. The fibers showed an increase in the ability of strong cross-bridge binding to activate the thin filament. Additionally, sensitivity of myofilament activation was increased, and the usual rightward shift of the Ca^{2+}-force relationship, a function of cAMP-dependent phosphorylation of TnI, was significantly blunted (119). Thin filament sensitivity to activation by Ca^{2+} can be mediated, at least in part, by the relative ratios of the Tm isoforms, and changes in the relative proportion of the isoforms could play a role in myofilament desensitization via phosphorylation of TnI by the PKC and PKA pathways. Additional studies using detergent-extracted fibers and isolated myocytes derived from the transgenic hearts showed that tropomyosin substitution had a detrimental effect on both the maximal velocity of shortening and relengthening (120). Maximum tension developed by the skinned fibers was also reduced. However, these data must be treated with caution as no real control was possible: Over-expression at very high levels was carried out in the face of normal levels of tropomyosin expression, and the protein pools were not rigorously controlled. Although in the later, myofilament studies, mice over-expressing α-tropomyosin were used in control experiments, the level of over-expression that was achieved is not clear (120). Thus gene dosage effects may have had a partial or even major role in determining some of the observed phenotypes. Consistent with this caveat is that at even higher levels of expression, severe cardiac pathologies develop in both the ventricles and atria (121). Repeating these experiments, or variants thereof in the tropomyosin null or heterozygote null backgrounds now available (122, 123) has the potential of resolving this important issue.

The Troponins

The TnI/TnC/TnT troponin complex is the basis for control of cardiac contraction via Ca^{2+} and fiber-type specific isoforms exist (2). The α-MyHC promoter was used to express high levels of skeletal troponin C (sTnC) in the heart (124). Expression of the skeletal isoform resulted in a shift in the mid-point of the tension-pCa relationship and resulted in decreased sensitivity of the tension-pCa relationship to reduced pH. This result is consistent with the hypothesis that cardiac TnC helps determine the pH sensitivity and is partially responsible for the contractile functional depression that occurs after an acute myocardial ischemic episode and the resultant acidosis.

At least nine mutations in the cardiac troponin T (cTnT) have been linked to FHC. These consist of both missense mutations and two nonsense mutations, which cause truncations in the mature protein. The TnT mutations in the human are particularly severe and although hypertrophy is mild or undetectable, sudden death is relatively frequent (125). Most of the other experiments exploring isoform functionality of the different troponins have been carried out in vitro (126–128) and are beyond the scope of this review. However, recently two FHC mutations have been modeled in transgenic mice. One of the human mutations consists of a splice site donor mutation (G→A, intron 15) that results in a frameshift. The resulting RNA encodes a protein that is missing 28 amino acids at the carboxyl terminus but has 7 amino acids not present in the normal peptide (17). The analogous construct was made using the mouse cTnT. Multiple lines expressing this construct, as well as wild type cTnT (as a control), were generated. Mice expressing the wild-type protein appeared completely normal and, despite high levels of transgenic expression and substitution of the transgenically encoded protein for the endogenous species, sarcomere stoichiometry was rigorously maintained. However, expression of the truncated TnT severely compromised viability. Nine lines were generated but one founder died, and only three other lines expressed the transgene—all at very low levels, implying that high levels of expression were embryonic lethal (129). In fact, the viable lines showed only 5% incorporation of the mutant protein into the TnT pool. Subsequent breeding of the heterozygotes to one another to increase mutant protein levels showed that the homozygous animals were not viable, dying only hours after birth. The heterozygotes displayed a phenotype that reflects aspects of the human disease; histopathology revealed characteristic myocyte disorganization and degeneration. Cardiac function was significantly compromised as measured in the isolated working heart, with both contractility and relaxation impaired. In addition, overall ventricular mass was significantly decreased, resulting from a significant myocyte loss before birth (18–27%), and a 17% decrease in the mass of the remaining cardiomyocytes.

Similar results were obtained in a separate group of experiments in which one of the missense mutations, Arg92Gln was expressed (130). Again, very low levels of the mutant protein were obtained in multiple lines (0–10% of the total cTnT pool), confirming the dominant-negative behavior of the TnT mutations. Cardiac myocyte disarray was also present, and in this model significant interstitial fibrosis occurred. Both M-mode and Doppler analyses revealed significant diastolic dysfunction but no hypertrophy. However, it may be that as a large cohort of these animals is aged, additional pathology will present.

Tropomodulin

Transgenesis can also be used to gain insight into protein function in gain-of-function experiments. Tropomodulin is an actin-capping protein that appeared, in both biochemical and in vitro transfection experiments, to be involved in the control of actin filament length in striated muscle (131, 132). To explore the function of this protein in the heart, the α-MyHC promoter was used to drive cardiac expression (133). Over-expression of tropomodulin resulted in extensive myofibril dysgenesis and abnormal sarcomeric assembly. Sarcomere disarray resulted in a compromise of function at the whole organ level, and a majority of the animals developed dilated cardiomyopathy, confirming the importance of the protein in maintaining actin filament length and the central role it plays in generating and maintaining normal myofilament structure.

FUTURE DIRECTIONS

Currently, transgenesis as applied to remodeling the contractile apparatus has been limited; its general applicability in exploring structure-function in vivo will increase dramatically in the near term. Significant advances in better controlling transgene expression more precisely to directed regions of the heart (and temporally as well) will occur. The MLC2v promoter shows promise in directing ventricular-specific expression (8, 134), and as cardiac-region specific patterns of expression are defined, other promoters will undoubtedly be developed that will allow directed transgene expression to restricted locations such as the conduction system (135).

The use of conditional transgenics, in which transgene expression is turned on/off at will over the animal's life time, would be a tremendous advantage in exploring the physiologic basis of the cardiac phenotype. Even with the best cardiac-specific promoters, transgenesis paints with a broad stroke. For example, the most widely used promoter, derived from *α-MyHC,* is expressed in the early heart tube, as well as in the developing atria (136), and this early developmental expression has the potential of confounding any phenotype seen post-term. Unfortunately, the current systems such as the tetracycline (on/off), ecdysone, or RU486-based approaches are not robust enough to be used effectively for turning contractile gene expression on/off. The few successes that have been reported in transgenic animal myocardia are restricted to strong biological amplifiers/signals (137–141). The technology needs to be refined to be directly applicable for controlling abundant proteins such as those that make up the contractile apparatus. Improved conditional systems are a high priority, and the reagents are undergoing constant development (142).

The limitations, both in terms of the models themselves and our ability to analyze them must constantly be considered. Murine cardiac physiology is very different from that of larger mammals; the resting heart rate of a mouse is some ten times faster than that of humans. Conclusions drawn on the basis of changes observed in the mouse may not be valid for mammals with considerably slower heart rates. Physiologic measurements in the mouse, although dramatically improved in the last five years (reviewed in 143, 144), are still primitive compared with what has been accomplished in larger animals (145), and much development work in murine physiology remains.

An exciting development will be the application of functional genomics to the varied transgenic models. High-resolution maps of the mouse genome are being constructed and eventual completion of the mouse genome project (e.g. www.mpimg-berlin-dahlem.mpg.de/~rodent/sampleDB.html, www-genome.wi .mit.edu) will be completed within the next five years. This, coupled with our ability to analyze the genetic output (the transcriptome) of a tissue or cell type at any particular time (146), offers the physiologist the potential to understand the total system as a function of the transcriptional program at a level of resolution unimagined even a few years ago. These massive databases, when transferred into useful information, will undoubtedly lead to new targets for study and insights into the physiologic consequences of altered cardiac contractile protein function.

Visit the Annual Reviews home page at www.AnnualReviews.org.

LITERATURE CITED

1. Swynghedauw B. 1986. Developmental and functional adaptation of contractile proteins in cardiac and skeletal muscles. *Physiol. Rev.* 66:710–71
2. Schiaffino S, Reggiani C. 1996. Molecular diversity of myofibrillar proteins: gene regulation and functional significance. *Physiol. Rev.* 76:371–423
3. Biben C, Hadchouel J, Tajbakhsh S, Buckingham M. 1996. Developmental and tissue-specific regulation of the murine cardiac actin gene in vivo depends on distinct skeletal and cardiac muscle-specific enhancer elements in addition to the proximal promoter. *Dev. Biol.* 173:200–12
4. Buckingham M, Alonso S, Bugaisky G, Barton P, Cohen A, et al. 1985. The actin and myosin multigene families. *Adv. Exp. Med. Biol.* 182:333–44
5. Cripps RM, Becker KD, Mardahl M, Kronert WA, Hodges D, Bernstein SI. 1994. Transformation of *Drosophila melanogaster* with the wild-type myosin heavy-chain gene: rescue of mutant phenotypes and analysis of defects caused by overexpression. *J. Cell Biol.* 126:689–99
6. Bernstein SI, O'Donnell PT, Cripps RM.

1993. Molecular genetic analysis of muscle development, structure, and function in Drosophila. *Int. Rev. Cytology.* 143: 63–152

7. Beall CJ, Sepanski MA, Fryberg EA. 1989. Genetic dissection of Drosophila myofibril formation: Effects of actin and myosin heavy chain null alleles. *Genes Dev.* 3:131–40

8. Hunter JJ, Zhu H, Lee KJ, Kubalak S, Chien KR. 1993. Targeting gene expression to specific cardiovascular cell types in transgenic mice. *Hypertension.* 22: 608–17

9. Gulick J, Hewett TE, Klevitsky R, Buck S, Moss RL, Robbins J. 1997. Transgenic remodeling of the regulatory myosin light chains in the mammalian heart. *Circ. Res.* 80:655–64

10. Palermo J, Gulick J, Colbert M, Fewell J, Robbins J. 1996. Transgenic remodeling of the contractile apparatus in the mammalian heart. *Circ. Res.* 78:504–9

11. Subramaniam A, Jones WK, Gulick J, Wert S, Neumann J, Robbins J. 1991. Tissue specific regulation of the α-myosin heavy chain gene promoter in transgenic mice. *J. Biol. Chem.* 266:24216–25

12. Winegrad S. 1997. Endothelial cell regulation of contractility of the heart. *Annu. Rev. Physiol.* 59:505–25

13. Geisterfer-Lowrance AA, Kass S, Tanigawa G, Vosberg HP, McKenna W, et al. 1990. A molecular basis for familial hypertrophic cardiomyopathy: a beta cardiac myosin heavy chain gene missense mutation. *Cell.* 62:999–1006

14. Poetter K, Jiang H, Hassanzadeh S, Master SR, Chang A, et al. 1996. Mutations in either the essential or regulatory light chains of myosin are associated with a rare myopathy in human heart and skeletal muscle. *Nat. Genet.* 13:63–69

15. Olson TM, Michels VV, Thibodeau SN, Tai YS, Keating MT. 1998. Actin mutations in dilated cardiomyopathy, a heritable form of heart failure. *Science.* 280:750–52

16. Kimura A, Harada H, Park J, Nishi H, Satoh M, et al. 1997. Mutations in the cardiac troponin I gene associated with hypertrophic cardiomyopathy. *Nat. Genet.* 16:379–82

17. Thierfelder L, Watkins H, MacRae C, Lamas R, McKenna W, et al. 1994. Alpha-tropomyosin and cardiac troponin T mutations cause familial hypertrophic cardiomyopathy: a disease of the sarcomere. *Cell.* 77:701–12

18. Bonne G, Carrier L, Bercovici J, Cruaud C, Richard P, et al. 1995. Cardiac myosin binding protein-C gene splice acceptor site mutation is associated with familial hypertrophic cardiomyopathy. *Nat. Genet.* 11:438–40

19. Nakao K, Minobe W, Roden R, Bristow MR, Leinwand LA. 1997. Myosin heavy chain gene expression in human heart failure. *J. Clin. Invest.* 100:2362–70

20. Lowes BD, Minobe W, Abraham WT, Rizeq MN, Bohlmeyer TJ, et al. 1997. Changes in gene expression in the intact human heart—downregulation of alpha-myosin heavy chain in hypertrophied, failing ventricular myocardium. *J. Clin. Invest.* 100:2315–24

21. Morano M, Zacharzowski U, Maier M, Lange PE, Alexi MV, et al. 1996. Regulation of human heart contractility by essential myosin light chain isoforms. *J. Clin. Invest.* 98:467–73

22. Melton DW. 1994. Gene targeting in the mouse. *BioEssays.* 16:633–38

23. Allen ND, Cran DG, Barton SC, Hettle S, Reik W, Surani MA. 1988. Transgenes as probes for active chromosomal domains in mouse development. *Nature.* 333:852–55

24. Bonifer C, Hecht A, Saueressig H, Winter DM, Sippel AE. 1991. Dynamic chromatin: the regulatory domain organization of eukaryotic gene loci. *J. Cell. Biochem.* 47:99–108

25. Palmiter RD, Brinster RL. 1985. Transgenic mice. *Cell* 41:343–45
26. Grosveld F, van Assendelft GB, Greaves DR, Kollias G. 1987. Position-independent, high-level expression of the human β-globin gene in transgenic mice. *Cell* 51:975–85
27. Costantini F, Radice G, Lee JL, Chada KK, Perry W, Son HJ. 1989. Insertional mutations in transgenic mice. *Prog. Nucleic Acid Res. Mol. Biol.* 36:159–69
28. Friedman RA, Ryan AF. 1992. Transgenic mice. Current applications to the study of the auditory and vestibular systems. *Otolaryngol. Clin. North Am.* 25:1017–26
29. Krulewski TF, Neumann PE, Gordon JW. 1989. Insertional mutation in a transgenic mouse allelic with Purkinje cell degeneration. *Proc. Natl. Acad. Sci. USA* 86:3709–12
30. Singh G, Supp DM, Schreiner C, McNeish J, Merker HJ, et al. 1991. Legless insertional mutation: morphological, molecular, and genetic characterization. *Genes Dev.* 5:2245–55
31. Babinet C, Morello D, Renard JP. 1989. Transgenic mice. *Genome* 31:938–49
32. Field LJ. 1993. Transgenic mice in cardiovascular research. *Annu. Rev. Physiol.* 55:97–114
33. Huang X, Pi Y, Lee KJ, Henkel AS, Gregg RG, et al. 1999. Cardiac troponin I gene knockout: a mouse model of myocardial troponin I deficiency. *Circ. Res.* 84:1–8
34. Geisterfer-Lowrance AA, Christe M, Conner DA, Ingwall JS, Schoen FJ, et al. 1996. A mouse model of familial hypertrophic cardiomyopathy. *Science* 272: 731–34
35. Jones WK, Grupp IL, Doetschman T, Grupp G, Osinska H, et al. 1996. Ablation of the murine alpha myosin heavy chain gene leads to dosage effects and functional deficits in the heart. *J. Clin. Invest.* 98:1906–17
36. Kumar A, Crawford K, Close L, Madison M, Lorenz J, et al. 1997. Rescue of cardiac alpha-actin-deficient mice by enteric smooth muscle gamma-actin. *Proc. Natl. Acad. Sci. USA* 94:4406–11
37. Makino S, Fukuda K, Miyoshi S, Konishi F, Kodama H, et al. 1999. Cardiomyocytes can be generated from marrow stromal cells in vitro. *J. Clin. Invest.* 103:697–705
38. Claycomb WC, Lanson NA Jr, Stallworth BS, Egeland DB, Delcarpio JB, et al. 1998. HL-1 cells: a cardiac muscle cell line that contracts and retains phenotypic characteristics of the adult cardiomyocyte. *Proc. Natl. Acad. Sci. USA* 95:2979–84
39. Rindt H, Gulick J, Knotts S, Neumann J, Robbins J. 1993. In vivo analysis of the murine beta-myosin heavy chain gene promoter. *J. Biol. Chem.* 268:5332–38
40. Buttrick PM, Kaplan ML, Kitsis RN, Leinwand LA. 1993. Distinct behavior of cardiac myosin heavy chain gene constructs in vivo. Discordance with in vitro results. *Circ. Res.* 72:1211–17
41. Kitsis RN, Leinwand LA. 1992. Discordance between gene regulation in vitro and in vivo. *Gene Exp.* 2:313–18
42. Buttrick PM, Kass A, Kitsis RN, Kaplan ML, Leinwand LA. 1992. Behavior of genes directly injected into the rat heart in vivo. *Circ. Res.* 70:193–98
43. Hunter JJ, Tanaka N, Rockman HA, Ross JJ, Chien KR. 1995. Ventricular expression of a MLC-2v-*ras* fusion gene induces cardiac hypertrophy and selective diastolic dysfunction in transgenic mice. *J. Biol. Chem.* 270:23173–78
44. Knotts S, Rindt H, Neumann J, Robbins J. 1994. In vivo regulation of the mouse beta myosin heavy chain gene. *J. Biol. Chem.* 269:31275–82
45. Izumo S, Shioi T. 1998. Cardiac transgenic and gene-targeted mice as models of cardiac hypertrophy and failure: a problem of (new) riches. *J. Card. Fail.* 4:263–70
46. Knotts S, Rindt H, Robbins J. 1995. Posi-

tion independent expression and developmental regulation is directed by the beta myosin heavy chain gene's 5' upstream region in transgenic mice. *Nucleic Acids Res.* 23:3301–9

47. Soonpaa MH, Field LJ. 1998. Survey of studies examining mammalian cardiomyocyte DNA synthesis. *Circ. Res.* 83: 15–26

48. Agah R, Frenkel PA, French BA, Michael LH, Overbeek PA, Schneider MD. 1997. Gene recombination in post-mitotic cells: Targeted expression of Cre recombinase provokes cardiac-restricted, site-specific rearrangement in adult ventricular muscle in vivo. *J. Clin. Invest.* 169–79

49. Palermo J, Gulick J, Ng W, Grupp IL, Grupp G, Robbins J. 1995. Remodeling the mammalian heart using transgenesis. *Cell. Mol. Biol. Res.* 41:501–9

50. James J, Osinska H, Kimball T, Klevitsky R, Robbins J. 1999. Transgenic overexpression of a motor protein at high levels results in severe cardiac pathology. *Transgenic Res.* 8:9–22

51. Grossman W, Jones D, McLaurin LP. 1975. Wall stress and patterns of hypertrophy in the human left ventricle. *J. Clin. Invest.* 56:56–64

52. Maron BJ, Spirito P, Wesley Y, Arce J. 1986. Development and progression of left ventricular hypertrophy in children with hypertrophic cardiomyopathy. *N. Engl. J. Med.* 315:610–14

53. Schwartz K, Mercadier JJ. 1996. Molecular and cellular biology of heart failure. *Curr. Opin. Cardiol.* 11:227–36

54. Marian AJ, Mares AJ, Kelly DP, Yu QT, Abchee AB, et al 1995. Sudden cardiac death in hypertrophic cardiomyopathy. Variability in phenotypic expression of beta-myosin heavy chain mutations. *Eur. Heart J.* 16:368–76

55. Codd MB, Sugrue DD, Gersh BJ, Melton LD. 1989. Epidemiology of idiopathic dilated and hypertrophic cardiomyopathy. A population-based study in Olmsted County, Minnesota, 1975–1984. *Circulation* 80:564–72

56. Roberts R, Marian AJ, Bachinski L. 1996. Molecular genetics of hypertrophic cardiomyopathy. *J. Cardiac Fail.* 2(4 Suppl):S87–95

57. Watkins H, Seidman JG, Seidman CE. 1995. Familial hypertrophic cardiomyopathy: a genetic model of cardiac hypertrophy. *Hum. Mol. Gen.* 1721:1721–27

58. Rayment I, Smith C, Yount RG. 1996. The active site of myosin. *Annu. Rev. Physiol.* 58:671–702

59. Rayment I, Holden HM, Sellers JR, Fananapazir L, Epstein ND. 1995. Structural interpretation of the mutations in the beta-cardiac myosin that have been implicated in familial hypertrophic cardiomyopathy. *Proc. Natl. Acad. Sci. USA* 92:3864–68

60. Carrier L, Bonne G, Bahrend E, Yu B, Richard P, et al. 1997. Organization and sequence of human cardiac myosin binding protein C gene (MYBPC3) and identification of mutations predicted to produce truncated proteins in familial hypertrophic cardiomyopathy. *Circ. Res.* 80:427–34

61. Watkins H, McKenna WJ, Thierfelder L, Suk HJ, Anan R, et al. 1995. Mutations in the genes for cardiac troponin T and alpha-tropomyosin in hypertrophic cardiomyopathy. *N. Engl. J. Med.* 332: 1058–64

62. Xie X, Harrison DH, Sichlicting I, Sweet RM, Kalabokis VN, et al. 1994. Structure of the regulatory domain of scallop myosin at 2.8 Å resolution. *Nature* 368:306–12

63. Rayment I, Rypniewski WR, Schmidt BK, Smith R, Tomchick DR, et al. 1993. Three-dimensional structure of myosin subfragment-1: a molecular motor. *Science* 261:50–58

64. Rayment I. 1996. The structural basis of the myosin ATPase activity. *J. Biol. Chem.* 271:15850–53

65. Alpert NA, Mulieri LA. 1986. Functional

consequences of altered cardiac myosin isoenzymes. *Med. Sci. Sports Exerc.* 18:309–13

66. Barany M. 1967. ATPase activity of myosin is correlated with the speed of muscle shortening. *Science* 231:597–600

67. Fewell JG, Osinska H, Klevitsky R, Ng W, Sfyris G, et al. 1997. A treadmill exercise regimen for identifying cardiovascular phenotypes in transgenic mice. *Am. J. Physiol.* 273:H1595–605

68. Pagani ED, Julian FJ. 1984. Rabbit papillary muscle myosin isozymes and velocity of muscle shortening. *Circ. Res.* 54:586–94

69. Yamashita H, Sugiura S, Serizawa T, Sugimoto T, Iizuka M, et al. 1992. Sliding velocity of isolated rabbit cardiac myosin correlates with isozyme distribution. *Am. J. Physiol.* 263:H464–72

70. Seidman CE, Seidman JG. 1998. Molecular genetics of inherited cardiomyopathies. In *Molecular Basis of Cardiovascular Disease: A Companion to Brunwald's Heart Disease,* ed. KR Chien, JL Breslow. JM Leiden, pp. 251–63. New York: Saunders

71. Sweeney HL, Straceski AJ, Leinwand LA, Tikunov BA, Faust L. 1994. Heterologous expression of a cardiomyopathic myosin that is defective in its actin interaction. *J. Biol. Chem.* 269:1603–5

72. Vikstrom KL, Factor SM, Leinwand LA. 1995. A murine model for hypertrophic cardiomyopathy. *Z. Kardiol.* 84(Suppl.) 4:49–54

73. Vikstrom KL, Factor SM, Leinwand LA. 1996. Mice expressing mutant myosin heavy chains are a model for familial hypertrophic cardiomyopathy. *Mol. Med.* 2:556–67

74. Vikstrom KL, Leinwand LA. 1996. Contractile protein mutations and heart disease. *Curr. Opin. Cell Biol.* 8:97–105

75. Valancius V, Smithies O. 1991. Testing an "in-out" targeting procedure for making subtle genomic modifications in

mouse embryonic stem cells. *Mol. Cell. Biol.* 11:1402–8

76. Askew GR, Doetschman T, Lingrel JB. 1993. Site-directed point mutations in embryonic stem cells: a gene-targeting tag-and-exchange strategy. *Mol. Cell. Biol.* 13:4115–24

77. Fatkin D, Christe ME, Aristizabal O, McConnell BK, Srinivasan S, et al. 1999. Neonatal cardiomyopathy in mice homozygous for the Arg403Gln mutation in the alpha cardiac myosin heavy chain gene. *J. Clin. Invest.* 103:147–53

78. Berul CI, Christe ME, Aronovitz MJ, Seidman CE, Seidman JG, Mendelsohn ME. 1997. Electrophysiological abnormalities and arrhythmias in alpha MHC mutant familial hypertrophic cardiomyopathy mice. *J. Clin. Invest.* 99:570–76

79. Berul CI, Christe ME, Aronovitz MJ, Maguire CT, Seidman CE, et al. 1998. Familial hypertrophic cardiomyopathy mice display gender differences in electrophysiological abnormalities. *J. Interv. Cardiol. Electrophysiol.* 2:7–14

80. Gao WD, Perez NG, Seidman CE, Seidman JG, Marban E. 1999. Altered cardiac excitation-contraction coupling in mutant mice with familial hypertrophic cardiomyopathy. *J. Clin. Invest.* 103: 661–66

81. Georgakopoulos D, Christe ME, Giewat M, Seidman CM, Seidman JG, Kass DA. 1999. The pathogenesis of familial hypertrophic cardiomyopathy: early and evolving effects from an alpha-cardiac myosin heavy chain missense mutation. *Nat. Med.* 5:327–30

82. Spindler M, Saupe KW, Christe ME, Sweeney HL, Seidman CE, et al. 1998. Diastolic dysfunction and altered energetics in the alphaMHC403/+ mouse model of familial hypertrophic cardiomyopathy. *J. Clin. Invest.* 101:1775–83

83. Lankford EB, Epstein ND, Fananapazir L, Sweeney HL. 1995. Abnormal contractile properties of muscle fibers expressing beta-myosin heavy chain

gene mutations in patients with hypertrophic cardiomyopathy. *J. Clin. Invest.* 95:1409–14

84. Blanchard E, Seidman C, Seidman JG, LeWinter M, Maughan D. 1999. Altered crossbridge kinetics in the alpha-MHC403/+ mouse model of familial hypertrophic cardiomyopathy. *Circ. Res.* 84:475–83

85. Lowey S, Risby D. 1971. Light chains from fast and slow muscle myosins. *Nature* 234:81–85

86. Morano I, Hädicke K, Hasse H, Böhm M, Erdmann E, Schaub MC. 1997. Changes in essential myosin light chain isoform expression provide a molecular basis for isometric force regulation in the failing human heart. *J. Mol. Cell. Cardiol.* 29:1177–87

87. Morano I, Hädicke K, Grom S, Koch A, Schwinger RH, et al. 1994. Titin, myosin light chains and C-protein in the developing and failing human heart. *J. Mol. Cell. Cardiol.* 26:361–68

88. Margossian SS, White HD, Caulfield JB, Norton P, Taylor S, Slayter HS. 1992. Light chain 2 profile and activity of human ventricular myosin during dilated cardiomyopathy. Identification of a causal agent for impaired myocardial function. *Circulation* 85:1720–33

89. Schaub MC, Tuchschmid CR, Srihari T, Hirzel HO. 1984. Myosin isoenzymes in human hypertrophic hearts. Shift in atrial myosin heavy chains and in ventricular myosin light chains. *Eur. Heart J.* 5(Suppl F):85–93

90. Pawloski-Dahm CM, Song G, Kirkpatrick DL, Palermo J, Gulick J, et al. 1998. Effects of total replacement of atrial myosin light chain-2 with the ventricular isoform in atrial myocytes of transgenic mice. *Circulation* 97:1508–13

91. Fewell JG, Hewett TE, Sanbe A, Klevitsky R, Hayes E, et al. 1998. Functional significance of cardiac myosin essential light chain isoform switching in transgenic mice. *J. Clin. Invest.* 101:2630–39

92. Warshaw DM, Desrosiers JM, Work SS, Trybus KM. 1990. Smooth muscle myosin cross-bridge interactions modulate actin filament sliding velocity in vitro. *J. Cell. Biol.* 111:453–63

93. Nguyen TT, Hayes E, Mulieri LA, Leavitt BJ, ter Keurs HE, et al. 1996. Maximal actomyosin ATPase activity and in vitro myosin motility are unaltered in human mitral regurgitation heart failure. *Circ. Res.* 79:222–26

94. Tohtong R, Yamashita H, Graham M, Haeberle J, Simcox A, Maughan D. 1995. Impairment of muscle function caused by mutations of phosphorylation sites in myosin regulatory light chain. *Nature* 374:650–53

95. Vemuri R, Lankford EB, Poetter K, Hassanzadeh S, Takeda K, et al. 1999. The stretch-activation response may be critical to the proper functioning of the mammalian heart. *Proc. Natl. Acad. Sci. USA* 96:1048–53

96. Offer G, Moos C, Starr R. 1973. A new protein of the thick filaments of vertebrate skeletal myofibrils. Extractions, purification and characterization. *J. Mol. Biol.* 74:653–76

97. Freiburg A, Gautel M. 1996. A molecular map of the interactions between titin and myosin-binding protein C. Implications for sarcomeric assembly in familial hypertrophic cardiomyopathy. *Eur. J. Biochem.* 235:317–23

98. Seiler SH, Fischman DA, Leinwand LA. 1996. Modulation of myosin filament organization by c-protein family members. *Mol. Biol. Cell.* 7:113–27

99. Gilbert R, Kelly MG, Mikawa T, Fischman DA. 1996. The carboxyl terminus of myosin binding protein C (MyBP-C, C-protein) specifies incorporation into the A-band of striated muscle. *J. Cell Sci.* 109:101–11

100. Yu B, French JA, Carrier L, Jeremy RW, McTaggart DR, et al. 1998. Molecular pathology of familial hypertrophic cardiomyopathy caused by mutations in the

cardiac myosin binding protein C gene. *J. Med. Genet.* 35:205–10

101. Watkins H, Conner D, Thierfelder L, Jarcho JA, MacRae C, et al. 1995. Mutations in the cardiac myosin binding protein-C gene on chromosome 11 cause familial hypertrophic cardiomyopathy. *Nat. Genet.* 11:434–37

102. Yang Q, Sanbe A, Osinska H, Hewett TE, Klevitsky R, Robbins J. 1998. A mouse model of myosin binding protein C human familial hypertrophic cardiomyopathy. *J. Clin. Invest.* 102:1292–300

103. Charron P, Dubourg O, Desnos M, Isnard R, Hagege A, et al. 1998. Genotype-phenotype correlations in familial hypertrophic cardiomyopathy. A comparison between mutations in the cardiac protein-C and the beta-myosin heavy chain genes. *Eur. Heart J.* 19:139–45

104. Holmes KC. 1996. Muscle proteins—their actions and interactions. *Curr. Opin. Struct. Biol.* 6:781–89

105. Solaro RJ, Vaneyk J. 1996. Altered interactions among thin filament proteins modulate cardiac function. *J. Mol. Cell. Cardiol.* 28:217–30

106. Solaro RJ, Rarick HM. 1998. Troponin and tropomyosin: proteins that switch on and tune in the activity of cardiac myofilaments. *Circ. Res.* 83:471–80

107. Vandekerckhove J, Weber K. 1979. The complete amino acid sequence of actins from bovine aorta, bovine heart, bovine fast skeletal muscle, and rabbit slow skeletal muscle. A protein-chemical analysis of muscle actin differentiation. *Differentiation* 14:123–33

108. Vandekerckhove J, Weber K. 1984. Chordate muscle actins differ distinctly from invertebrate muscle actins. The evolution of the different vertebrate muscle actins. *J. Mol. Biol.* 179:391–413

109. Buckingham ME. 1985. Actin and myosin multigene families: their expression during the formation of skeletal muscle. *Essays Biochem.* 20:77–109

110. Garner I, Sassoon D, Vandekerckhove J,

Alonso S, Buckingham ME. 1989. A developmental study of the abnormal expression of alpha-cardiac and alpha-skeletal actins in the striated muscle of a mutant mouse. *Dev. Biol.* 134:236–45

111. Garner I, Minty AJ, Alonso S, Barton PJ, Buckingham ME. 1986. A 5′ duplication of the alpha-cardiac actin gene in BALB/c mice is associated with abnormal levels of alpha-cardiac and alpha-skeletal actin mRNAs in adult cardiac tissue. *EMBO J.* 5:2559–67

112. Hewett TE, Grupp IL, Grupp G, Robbins J. 1994. Alpha-skeletal actin is associated with increased contractility in the mouse heart. *Circ. Res.* 74:740–46

113. Tobacman LS. 1996. Thin filament-mediated regulation of cardiac contraction. *Annu. Rev. Physiol.* 58:447–81

114. Solaro RJ. 1995. Troponin C-troponin I interactions and molecular signalling in cardiac myofilaments. *Adv. Exper. Med. Biol.* 382:109–15

115. Muthuchamy M, Grupp IL, Grupp G, O'Toole BA, Kier AB, et al. 1995. Molecular and physiological effects of overexpressing striated muscle beta-tropomyosin in the adult murine heart. *J. Biol. Chem.* 270:30593–603

116. Schachat F, Brigg M, Williamson E, McGinnis H, Diamond M, Brandt P. 1990. Expression of fast thin filament proteins: defining fiber architectypes in a molecular continuum. In *The Dynamic State of Muscle Fibers,* ed D Pette, pp. 279–91. Berlin: de Gruyter

117. Muthuchamy M, Rethinasamy P, Wieczorek DF. 1997. Tropomyosin structure and function. *Trends Cardiovasc. Med.* 7:124–28

118. Izumo S, Nadal-Ginard B, Mahdavi V. 1988. Protooncogene induction and reprogramming of cardiac gene expression produced by pressure overload. *Proc. Natl. Acad. Sci. USA* 85:339–43

119. Palmiter KA, Kitada Y, Muthuchamy M, Wieczorek DF, Solaro RJ. 1996. Exchange of beta- for alpha-tropomyosin

in hearts of transgenic mice induces changes in thin filament response to Ca^{2+}, strong cross-bridge binding, and protein phosphorylation. *J. Biol. Chem.* 271:11611–14

120. Wolska BM, Keller RS, Evans CC, Palmiter KA, Phillips RM, et al. 1999. Correlation between myofilament response to Ca^{2+} and altered dynamics of contraction and relaxation in transgenic cardiac cells that express beta-tropomyosin. *Circ. Res.* 84:745–51

121. Muthuchamy M, Boivin GP, Grupp IL, Wieczorek DF. 1998. Beta-tropomyosin overexpression induces severe cardiac abnormalities. *J. Mol. Cell. Cardiol.* 30:1545–57

122. Blanchard EM, Iizuka K, Christe M, Conner DA, Geisterfer-Lowrance A, Schoen FJ, et al. 1997. Targeted ablation of the murine alpha-tropomyosin gene. *Circ. Res.* 81:1005–10

123. Rethinasamy P, Muthuchamy M, Hewett T, Boivin G, Wolska BM, et al. 1998. Molecular and physiological effects of alpha-tropomyosin ablation in the mouse. *Circ. Res.* 82:116–23

124. Metzger JM, Parmacek MS, Barr E, Pasyk K, Lin WI, et al. 1993. Skeletal troponin C reduces contractile sensitivity to acidosis in cardiac myocytes from transgenic mice. *Proc. Natl. Acad. Sci. USA* 90:9036–40

125. Seidman CE, Seidman JG. 1998. Molecular genetic studies of familial hypertrophic cardiomyopathy. *Basic. Res. Cardiol.* 93:13–26

126. Westfall MV, Samuelson LC, Metzger JM. 1996. Troponin I isoform expression is developmentally regulated in differentiating embryonic stem cell-derived cardiac myocytes. *Dev. Dyn.* 206:24–38

127. Sweeney HL, Feng HS, Yang Z, Watkins H. 1998. Functional analyses of troponin T mutations that cause hypertrophic cardiomyopathy: insights into disease pathogenesis and troponin function. *Proc. Natl. Acad. Sci. USA* 95:14406–10

128. Lin D, Bobkova A, Homsher E, Tobacman LS. 1996. Altered cardiac troponin T in vitro function in the presence of a mutation implicated in familiar hypertrophic cardiomyopathy. *J. Clin. Invest.* 97:2842–48

129. Tardiff JC, Factor SM, Tompkins BD, Hewett TE, Palmer BM, et al. 1998. A truncated cardiac troponin T molecule in transgenic mice suggests multiple cellular mechanisms for familial hypertrophic cardiomyopathy. *J. Clin. Invest.* 101:2800–11

130. Oberst L, Zhao G, Park JT, Brugada R, Michael LH, et al. 1998. Dominant-negative effect of a mutant cardiac troponin T on cardiac structure and function in transgenic mice. *J. Clin. Invest.* 102:1498–505

131. Gregorio CC, Fowler VM. 1995. Mechanisms of thin filament assembly in embryonic chick cardiac myocytes: tropomodulin requires tropomyosin for assembly. *J. Cell Biol.* 129:683–95

132. Gregorio CC, Weber A, Bondad M, Pennise CR, Fowler VM. 1995. Requirement of pointed-end capping by tropomodulin to maintain actin filament length in embryonic chick cardiac myocytes. *Nature* 377:83–86

133. Sussman MA, Welch S, Cambon N, Klevitsky R, Hewett TE, et al. 1998. Myofibril degeneration caused by tropomodulin overexpression leads to dilated cardiomyopathy in juvenile mice. *J. Clin. Invest.* 101:51–61

134. Becker KD, Gottshall KR, Chien KR. 1996. Strategies for studying cardiovascular phenotypes in genetically manipulated mice. *Hypertension* 27:495–501

135. Kupershmidt S, Yang T, Anderson ME, Wessels A, Niswender KD, et al. 1999. Replacement by homologous recombination of the minK gene with lacZ reveals restriction of minK expression to the mouse cardiac conduction system. *Circ. Res.* 84:146–52

136. Ng WA, Grupp IL, Subramaniam A, Robbins J. 1991. Cardiac myosin heavy chain mRNA expression and myocardial function in the mouse heart. *Circ. Res.* 68:1742–50

137. Bowman JC, Steinberg SF, Jiang TR, Geenen DL, Fishman GI, Buttrick PM. 1997. Expression of protein kinase C beta in the heart causes hypertrophy in adult mice and sudden death in neonates. *J. Clin. Invest.* 100:2189–95

138. Fishman GI, Kaplan ML, Buttrick PM. 1994. Tetracycline-regulated cardiac gene expression in vivo. *J. Clin. Invest.* 93:1864–68

139. Passman RS, Fishman GI. 1994. Regulated expression of foreign genes in vivo after germline transfer. *J. Clin. Invest.* 94:2421–25

140. Yu ZH, Redfern CS, Fishman GI. 1996. Conditional transgene expression in the heart. *Circ. Res.* 79:691–97

141. Fishman GI. 1998. Timing is everything in life—conditional transgene expression in the cardiovascular system. *Circ. Res.* 82:837–44

142. Baron U, Schnappinger D, Helbl V, Gossen M, Hillen W, Bujard H. 1999. Generation of conditional mutants in higher eukaryotes by switching between the expression of two genes. *Proc. Natl. Acad. Sci. USA* 96:1013–18

143. Chien KR. 1996. Genes and physiology—molecular physiology in genetically engineered animals. *J. Clin. Invest.* 97:901–9

144. James JF, Hewett TE, Robbins J. 1998. Cardiac physiology in transgenic mice. *Circ. Res.* 82:407–15

145. Kass DA, Hare JM, Georgakopoulos D. 1998. Murine cardiac function: a cautionary tail. *Circ. Res.* 82:519–22

146. Iyer VR, Eisen MB, Ross DT, Schuler G, Moore T, et al. 1999. The transcriptional program in the response of human fibroblasts to serum. *Science* 283:83–87

147. Marian AJ, Zhao GL, Seta Y, Roberts R, Yu QT. 1997. Expression of a mutant (Arg(92)Gln) human cardiac troponin T, known to cause hypertrophic cardiomyopathy, impairs adult cardiac myocyte contractility. *Circ. Res.* 81:76–85

Annu. Rev. Physiol. 2000. 62:289–319

GENETIC DISSECTION OF CARDIAC GROWTH CONTROL PATHWAYS

W. Robb MacLellan[1] and Michael D. Schneider[2]

[1]The Cardiovascular Research Laboratories, Department of Medicine, UCLA School of Medicine, Los Angeles, California, 90076; [2]Molecular Cardiology Unit, Departments of Medicine, Cell Biology, and Molecular Physiology & Biophysics, Baylor College of Medicine, Houston, Texas, 77030–3498; e-mail: michaels@bcm.tmc.edu

Key Words　cardiac muscle, cell cycle, growth factors, hypertrophy, signal transduction

■ **Abstract**　Cardiac muscle cells exhibit two related but distinct modes of growth that are highly regulated during development and disease. Cardiac myocytes rapidly proliferate during fetal life but exit the cell cycle irreversibly soon after birth, following which the predominant form of growth shifts from hyperplastic to hypertrophic. Much research has focused on identifying the candidate mitogens, hypertrophic agonists, and signaling pathways that mediate these processes in isolated cells. What drives the proliferative growth of embryonic myocardium in vivo and the mechanisms by which adult cardiac myocytes hypertrophy in vivo are less clear. Efforts to answer these questions have benefited from rapid progress made in techniques to manipulate the murine genome. Complementary technologies for gain- and loss-of-function now permit a mutational analysis of these growth control pathways in vivo in the intact heart. These studies have confirmed the importance of suspected pathways, have implicated unexpected pathways as well, and have led to new paradigms for the control of cardiac growth.

OVERVIEW

Cardiac myocytes display two developmentally programmed forms of growth, which have been investigated systematically chiefly for ventricular muscle. In utero, ventricular mass is augmented by cardiac myocyte proliferation, hyperplasia, which decreases progressively in late-gestation embryos and ceases soon after birth. In post-natal life, ventricular myocytes permanently exit the cell cycle (an operational definition discussed further below), negating or constraining further increases in cell number. Therefore, in normal post-natal growth and in adult cardiac myocytes subjected to an increased hemodynamic burden, adaptive increases in cardiac mass are achieved preponderantly through the increase in cell size known as hypertrophy. The questions that surround the regulation of these divergent but also similar processes are numerous. What mitogens, receptors, and signaling proteins are essential for cardiac myocytes proliferation during embryo-genesis? Do different growth factors mediate proliferation in different compart-ments of the heart? What developmentally regulated mechanisms preclude later proliferative growth? Is hypertrophy a *forme fruste* of hyperplasia?

This review focuses on the progress that has been made in the field of cardiac growth control and on its implications for understanding both cardiac develop-ment and disease. We attempt to summarize the current status of research in the field, with a particular emphasis on transgenic models, and critically discuss lim-itations of the existing knowledge. More than other mammals, mice are amenable to genetic manipulation, allowing the creation of invaluable in vivo models. Not only can genes be overexpressed in a tissue-restricted fashion by microinjection of a transgene into fertilized oocytes, but also gene deletions can be created through homologous recombination in embryonic stem cells. Thus, in mice, these reciprocal genetic approaches can both be exploited to dissect cardiac growth control pathways. Investigators have begun a systematic analysis of relevant can-didate genes, creating gain- and loss-of-function mutations in putative regulators. In addition, knowledge of cardiac growth control has benefited from genetically unbiased studies, where genes essential for cardiac growth have been disclosed by random mutagenesis, including retroviral and transgene insertions.

HYPERPLASIA AND HYPERTROPHY

Cardiac Myocyte Proliferation

Analysis of cardiac myocyte growth during murine development indicates that cardiac myocyte DNA synthesis occurs primarily in utero; a second peak early after birth corresponds to cardiac myocytes' binucleation (1). In mid-gestation, day 12 post coitum (pc), a labeling index of 33% was observed, which progres-sively decreased to 2% at birth. During fetal growth, karyokinesis and cytokinesis are coupled, resulting in increases in mononucleated cardiac myocytes. At day 4–6 post-natally, the labeling index increased transiently to 10%, then rapidly returned to baseline levels. During this latter phase, karyokinesis occurs in the absence of cytokinesis, resulting in binucleation of ventricular myocytes, without an overall increase in cell number. The mechanism responsible for this uncoupling of nuclear division from cell division in neonatal cardiac myocytes and its func-tional significance are unknown; however, a similar process called endoredupli-cation has been documented in both Drosophila and in other mammalian cells (2). For the normal adult mouse ventricle, estimates of DNA labeling have ranged from 0.04% to < 0.005% (1, 3–6). Results in mice receive emphasis here because they are more directly relevant than those found in other mammals for interpreting the phenotypes resulting from genetic alterations (see below).

The inviolability of adult cardiac myocytes' irreversible exit from the cell cycle has recently been challenged, suggesting instead that in several species, some limited capacity may be retained for cell cycle reentry (7). While this topic remains controversial (8, 9), counter examples such as the newt, which is permissive for adult ventricular myocyte regeneration, long have been known (10). Resolving the disputed capability of adult mammalian ventricular myocytes to resume proliferation in response to mitogenic or hemodynamic stimuli—distinguishing between scant (7) and none (8)—falls beyond the scope of this review. More importantly, however, it is essential to separate the ability to synthesize DNA (increased ploidy or even nucleation) from the further claim of cell division. Whether reported discrepancies represent true species differences among mammals in the potential for cardiac myocyte DNA synthesis, or simply reflect technical differences such as the choice and duration of growth stimuli or method of measurement, remain to be determined. Despite these discrepancies, even optimistic estimates confine DNA synthesis to a minute fraction of adult ventricular myocytes. This suggests that genetic manipulations permitting DNA synthesis, even if small in absolute terms, could have profound effects on the relative rate of S phase entry. What additional gene or genes might be required for mitosis is itself another matter.

Cardiac Hypertrophy

Hypertrophic growth of cardiac myocytes can be initiated by nominally mitogenic stimuli, canonical cardiac agonists, or passive mechanical stress, each leading to the induction of immediate-early transcription factors such as Fos, Myc, and Jun (11), followed by characteristic changes in cardiac-specific gene expression (12, 13). These changes have often been referred to as reactivation of a fetal gene program, given the re-expression of several genes not normally expressed in the adult ventricle but seen in the embryonic and neonatal heart. Common examples are the re-expression of atrial natriuretic factor and genes for fetal isoforms of contractile proteins, such as skeletal α-actin, atrial myosin light chain-1, and β-myosin heavy chain. This can be accompanied by down-regulation of genes normally expressed at higher levels in the adult than in the embryonic ventricle, such as α-myosin heavy chain and the sarcoplasmic reticulum calcium pump, SERCA2a.

Recently, it was recognized that hypertrophic growth and the fetal program are also accompanied by myocyte loss through apoptosis and by replacement fibrosis (14). Intrinsic changes in cardiac myocytes' mechanical performance, myocyte loss to apoptosis, and myocyte encasement by fibrosis have been postulated to mediate the eventual decline in myocardial function that occurs with the transition from hypertrophy to failure. Thus, investigators have been intrigued by extracellular signals and their cytoplasmic mediators, which together might explain these diverse aspects of hypertrophy (12, 13). Multiple candidate pathways have been identified including adrenergic signals, peptide growth factors, and cytokines. Many secreted factors are induced with hypertrophy, including TGFβ (15), insulin-like growth factor-1 (16), angiotensinogen (17), the precursor of angiotensin II, endothelin-1 (18), and cardiotropin-1(19), and can act on cardiac myocytes directly, evoking transcriptional responses at least partially similar to those induced by load itself (20–24). More recently, research has focused on how these ligands are coupled to transcription factors that mediate the re-induction of the fetal program and the nature of the link between growth signals and apoptosis. Thus, as summarized in Figure 1, hierarchical mechanisms that have been proposed for the modulation of multiple cardiac genes in hypertrophy include transcription factor phosphorylation and dephosphorylation, immediate-early gene induction, up-regulation of cardiac-restricted transcription factors, and autocrine/paracrine circuits.

CARDIAC GROWTH CONTROL PATHWAYS

Growth Factors, Cytokines, and Receptors

Numerous putative growth regulatory molecules have been implicated in mediating cardiac myocyte proliferation and/or hypertrophy in vitro; fewer have had this role tested in vivo. The determination that a particular ligand is necessary

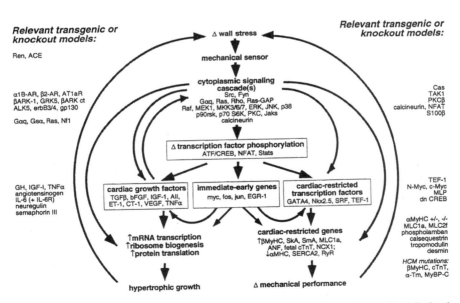

Figure 1   A genetic dissection of pathways for load-induced cardiac hypertrophy. Mechanical stress, working through integrins or alternative mechanical sensors, activates diverse cytoplasmic signaling pathways, leading to hypertrophic growth (which normalizes wall stress) and the associated fetal gene program (which includes adverse, as well as beneficial, responses). Specific proteins that have been implicated in this circuit via genetic models in vivo are highlighted at the left and right of the figure (reprinted with permission of M Abdellatif & M Schneider; 24a).

and sufficient to modulate myocardial growth can be problematic because interpretation of a cardiac phenotype is difficult in the presence of widespread abnormalities. Analogously, one obstacle to interpreting the results of certain transgenic models is the mutually dependent interaction of the heart with the fetal circulation and extracardiac tissues. The heart, by virtue of its central role in the cardiovascular system, is sensitive not only to defects primarily affecting the myocardium but also to any extrinsic change that affects its work load, such as mutations altering vasculogenesis or body mass. Additionally, a particular agonist can be critical for one form of growth but dispensable for the other.

To conclusively document a role for any putative factor in cardiac growth, the consequences of both overproduction and deletion of the factor or its cognate receptor should be known. For some proteins, such as insulin-like growth factor-1 (IGF-I) and gp130, these complementary data exist. Others await definitive proof. This review highlights not only the invaluable information transgenic studies have provided in identifying critical cardiac growth factors, but also the pitfalls associated with interpreting phenotypes in these mice and limitations that persist in the existing knowledge.

Insulin-Like Growth Factor-I   IGF-I-deficient mice display a generalized retardation of growth with no specific cardiac phenotype and die soon after birth of respiratory failure (25, 26). Therefore, interpretation of a primary role for IGF-I in cardiac growth versus secondary effects in this model is impossible. To circumvent the immediate lethality that results from an absolute lack of IGF-I, mice were engineered that express IGF-I at ~30% of normal levels (27). They survive to adulthood and are intermediate in size between the wild-type and IGF-I-deficient animals. These mice display no alteration in LV mass when corrected for body weight, and have a normal adaptive hypertrophic response to increased hemodynamic load produced by supraaortic banding (27). In complementary gain-of-function studies, transgenic mice with IGF-I targeted to the heart, under the control of the α-myosin heavy chain (α-MHC) promoter (28), or mice lacking the IGF-II receptor, which functions to bind and inactivate IGF-I (29), both display cardiomegaly resulting from cardiac myocyte hyperplasia. This observation concurs with in vitro evidence suggesting that IGF-I modulates myocyte proliferation rather than hypertrophy (30). Therefore, while IGF-I is capable of inducing cardiac myocyte proliferation, it is not clear that normal cardiac development or adaptive growth requires this signal.

gp130-Mediated Factors   Recently, cytokines were recognized to play a critical role in the development and homeostasis of many organ systems. One family in particular, including IL-6, IL-11, leukemia inhibitory factor, cardiotropin-1, ciliary neurotrophic factor, and oncostatin M, which share the common signal transducer gp130 in their receptors, has been implicated in both normal and pathological cardiac growth (31, 32). Mice deficient for gp130 die in utero between E12.5 and birth with ventricular hypoplasia, suggesting this signaling pathway is critical for proliferative cardiac growth (33).

This early lethality highlights the paradox that genetic models, which succeed in proving a protein's essential function, cannot be used to examine the protein's role in any later biological context, as is required for animal models of adult disease. To achieve a conditional deletion, the recognition site for a DNA recombinase (e.g. loxP sites, for the phage recombinase, Cre) can be inserted into the introns flanking a critical gene segment, by standard homologous recombination in ES cells (34, 35). Although the tagged (floxed) gene is expressed normally, and the resulting animal is phenotypically normal in the absence of recombinase, mating such animals to lines that carry a transgene for Cre, or viral delivery of Cre, allows the tagged gene to be deleted exclusively in cells that express the recombinase, and thus allows a conditional phenotype to be determined. Refinements of this approach, using lineage-specific promoters, drug-inducible promoters, or drug-dependent recombinase fusion proteins can be used for temporal or cell-type control over recombination. Importantly, ongoing DNA synthesis is not required for this form of recombination to function effectively, and even postmitotic cardiac myocytes are amenable to Cre-mediated recombination (36).

Thus, in the case of gp130, mice that had this gene conditionally deleted after birth developed cardiac defects—in addition to neurological, hematopoietic, immunological, hepatic, and pulmonary abnormalities—suggesting a broad role for gp130-dependent cytokines (37). These mice displayed myocardial thinning, presumably a result of a reduction in myocyte size. Mice lacking individual members of this cytokine family or their receptors—IL-6 (38), LIF (39, 40), CNTF (41), IL-11Rα (42)—exhibited widespread and varied phenotypes; however, none demonstrated specific cardiac defects. More recently, gp130 was deleted exclusively in ventricular cardiac myocytes using this Cre/lox technology (43). Surprisingly, these mice developed normally and displayed no overt cardiac phenotype. However, when these mice were subjected to a hemodynamic stress, they developed marked abnormalities including the rapid development of a dilated cardiomyopathy associated with myocyte apoptosis. These data demand a reinterpretation of the postulated critical role of gp130-mediated signaling in normal cardiac development and demonstrate the hazard inherent in interpreting a primary role for a factor in cardiac growth, as inferred from the conventional gp130 knockout. These studies refute the concept that gp130-mediated signaling is necessary for normal cardiac development, but instead indicate that this pathway is crucial for myocyte survival in the development of compensatory hypertrophy. The physiologically relevant ligand for gp130 in the heart is unknown; however, one potential candidate is cardiotrophin-1, a cytokine cloned on the basis of its ability to induce cardiac hypertrophy (44), which signals through the gp130 pathway (45) and has been shown to reduce cardiac myocyte apoptosis (46).

Another potentially relevant candidate ligand for gp130 in the heart is IL-6, which is produced by cultures of fetal cardiac myocytes (47) and is up-regulated in adult myocardium in response to many pathological stimuli (48). To further explore the role of IL-6 in cardiac growth, transgenic mice were created that overexpress IL-6 or the IL-6 receptor in the heart (49). Surprisingly, while neither transgene exhibited increased cardiac growth, dramatic myocardial hypertrophy occurred when the two lines were crossed. Although this suggests that activation of gp130-dependent pathways is sufficient to stimulate cardiac growth, the physiological relevance of IL-6-dependent signals is questionable since neither ligand nor receptor alone is sufficient to stimulate this process.

The Transforming Growth Factor Beta (TGFβ) Superfamily TGFβ family members have been implicated in cardiogenesis and cardiac hypertrophy by virtue of their temporally related expression patterns (15, 50) and their ability to reproduce certain aspects of these processes in culture (20, 21, 51). The absence of TGFβ1 can disrupt yolk sac vasculogenesis, with death in mid-gestation, but survivors develop normally, with inflammation in multiple organs after birth (52–54). One confounding aspect of this null phenotype is maternal rescue by transplacental passage of TGFβ1 from the heterozygous mother (55). By immunosuppression to prevent the lethal inflammation in TGFβ1-null mice (55), or by mating the mutation into the *scid* background, it has been possible to generate embryos truly lacking this growth factor (56); cardiac defects were seen in the former case, but not in the latter, suggesting the likelihood that factitious effects were responsible, rather than an essential function of the peptide. A second concern is redundancy. The absence of TGFβ2 causes cardiac malformations akin to Tetralogy of Fallot (ventricular septal defects and defects of outflow tract septation) (57); however, cardiac myogenesis per se is not impaired, and the absence of TGFβ3 results in cleft palate, without cardiac abnormalities (58). However, direct proof is lacking for a role of TGFβ in cardiac growth regulation, in part because combinatorial deletions affecting two or all three members of this family have not been reported. In a conventional deletion of the TGFβ type II receptor, the principal reported defects were in yolk sac hematopoiesis and vasculogenesis, with death at 10.5 days of gestation.

In contrast, mice that overexpress an activated TGFβ type I receptor, ALK5[L193A,P194A,T204D], in embryonic ventricles caused an arrest to looping morphogenesis, resulting in a linear, dilated, hypoplastic heart tube (59). The ventricular hypoplasia was associated with precocious induction of p21, a cyclin-dependent kinase inhibitor capable of causing cell cycle arrest in a wide variety of tissues. This suggests that an ALK5-sensitive pathway mediates looping and that perhaps looping itself is related to differential myocyte growth rates. Although these data suggest that a TGFβ receptor can affect cardiac myocyte proliferation, other members of this family might signal through ALK5, and it is not clear what role TGFβ normally, if ever, plays.

Fibroblast Growth Factors Another difficulty arises when interpretation of role for a factor is impossible due to embryonic lethality even prior to heart tube formation. This is the case for FGF-1, which can induce cell cycle re-entry by cultured neonatal myocytes (21). Because multiple members of the FGF family are expressed in the heart, e.g. FGF-18 (60), deleting single FGFs could prove more problematic than deleting FGF receptors, where a much smaller number of isoforms is known to exist. In avian embryos, a dominant-inhibitory FGFR1 decreased the clonal expansion of infected myocytes relative to a control virus, suggesting that endogenous FGF is a necessary mitogen for proliferating ventricular muscle cells (61). However, a direct assessment of this receptor's role in mammalian cardiac development is impossible by conventional homologous recombination because FGFR1-deficient embryos can generate mesoderm but display severe early growth defects (62, 63). Further investigations into the role of FGF-1 in cardiac growth await the creation of tissue-specific deletions, as discussed above for the gp130 receptor.

Angiotensin   The overexpression of many growth-promoting factors in myocardium in transgenic animals has resulted in increased ventricular mass; however, their relevance to the control of normal cardiac growth can be doubtful on the basis of gain-of-function alone. Overexpression of the angiotensin II type I receptor (AT_1) by the α-MHC promoter results in massive atrial enlargement secondary to hyperplasia and early mortality, presumably as a result of disturbances in heart rate and atrioventricular conduction (64). Because angiotensin II induces a hypertrophic response in cultured neonatal ventricular myocytes (23), it was surprising that morphology of the ventricles and ventricular myocytes in transgenic animals was normal despite elevated levels of AT_1 receptor. This is not likely due to a deficiency of signaling intermediaries since forced expression of a constitutively active α_{1B}-adrenergic receptor, which shares similar signaling pathways, results in ventricular hypertrophy in adult transgenic mice (65). However, despite the attractiveness of ascribing a role in cardiac myocyte proliferation to these molecules, it must be remembered that genetic manipulations resulting in enhanced cardiac growth do not necessarily imply a requirement for embryonic growth nor a role in normal myocardial hyperplasia. This is illustrated by the normal cardiac phenotype in angiotensinogen-deficient mice (66), as well as AT_{1A}/AT_{1B} (67) or AT_2 (68) receptor knockouts, and by the preservation of early and delayed responses to load in mice lacking the AT_{1A} receptor (69–72). Although the permutations mentioned above remain to be tested in the context of mechanical stress, these findings suggest that the renin-angiotensin system is sufficient to augment cardiac growth, but is not required under normal or pathological conditions. In contrast, an essential role was shown for β-adrenergic receptor kinase 1 (beta ARK1), a member of the G protein–coupled receptor kinase (GRK) family that mediates agonist-dependent phosphorylation and desensitization of G protein–coupled receptors (73). Mice lacking the kinase die prior to E15.5, with a hypoplastic myocardium similar to that discussed below for the transcription factors N-myc, TEF-1, RXRα, and WT-1.

Neuregulin   Other factors that regulate embryonic cardiac myocyte proliferation are largely speculative. However, occasionally transgenic mice with abnormalities of cardiac growth identify a novel set of regulators for this process, illustrated by the loss of trabeculae associated with neural crest defects seen in mice lacking the epidermal growth factor (EGF) homologue, neuregulin (74) or its receptors Erb2 (75) and Erb4 (76). Both ErbB2 and ErbB4 receptors are expressed on neonatal and adult ventricular myocytes. Soluble neuregulin provokes an approximate twofold increase in embryonic cardiac myocyte proliferation and promotes survival by inhibiting apoptosis in serum-deprived myocyte primary cultures. Neuregulin is also capable of inducing hypertrophic growth in both neonatal and adult ventricular myocytes, which is accompanied by enhanced expression of prepro-atrial natriuretic factor and skeletal α-actin (77). The essential role of neuregulin was also established using retroviral gene transfer of a hammerhead ribozyme to ablate the factor's expression, resulting in failure of trabeculation and embryonic lethality that resembled the neuregulin deficiency in mice (78).

Vascular Endothelial Growth Factor (VEGF)   Deletion of even one allele for VEGF is sufficient to disrupt normal vasculogenesis in the embryo; however, a less expected feature of the heterozygous mice is marked cardiac hypoplasia (79), something not seen with mutations of either VEGF receptor Flt-1 (80) or Flk-1 (81). Because cardiac myocytes do not express these receptors for VEGF, this result is consistent with the possibility of a third, alternative receptor, but more likely is indicative of a paracrine mechanism, mediated by the defect in formation of endocardial cells, a subset of the endothelium. This latter mechanism is also favored by the occurrence of similar cardiac growth retardation in mice lacking other essential endothelial growth factor receptors Tie-1 or Tie-2 (82), or lacking the Tie-2 ligand, angiopoietin-1 (83).

Signal Transducers

The intracellular signaling cascades that regulate cardiac growth have been less well studied despite the fact the multiple pathways have been linked to the hypertrophic phenotype in cell culture. The best studied are the G protein–coupled receptors and their signaling pathways. Myocardial overexpression of their downstream effectors Gαq (84, 85) or PKC (86, 87) resulted in pathological hypertrophy associated with contractile dysfunction and sometimes overt failure. While these studies confirm the importance of G protein–coupled receptors in cardiac growth, these relationships are dealt with in greater detail in the accompanying review by Koch, Lefkowitz & Rockman (87a).

Calmodulin, Calcineurin, and Other Calcium-Dependent Pathways   Intracellular Ca^{2+} homeostasis has been postulated to play a central role in the signaling pathway of many ligands. A role for calcium-dependent signaling molecules, particularly the activation of calmodulin, has been well established in the growth and proliferation of non-myocyte cells (88). Consistent with the notion of Ca^{2+} regulating cardiac growth is the observation that numerous factors that induce cardiac hypertrophy, including mechanical stretch (89), phenylephrine (90), angiotensin II (91, 92), and endothelin (92), also increase intracellular Ca^{2+} levels. (93). Overexpression of calmodulin in the developing ventricle, using the ANF promoter, resulted in cardiac myocyte hyperplasia at early developmental stages and hypertrophy at later time points (94). This was not simply a result of a global elevation in intracellular Ca^{2+} since overexpression of a calmodulin mutant equally capable of buffering calcium but unable to activate calmodulin-dependent target enzymes had no effect on cardiac growth. The basis is unknown for this temporal pattern of hyperplasia then hypertrophy, both resulting from forced expression of calmodulin. However, the possibilities include greater activity of the ANF promoter driving the transgene in embryonic rather than in post-natal ventricles, developmentally regulated differences in calmodulin target proteins, or time-dependent up-regulation of cell cycle inhibitors (see below). Interestingly, another calcium-binding protein, S100β, is induced in the myocardium following infarction (95) and reportedly inhibits hypertrophy (growth, as well as fetal gene induction) induced by norepinephrine in transgenic mice (96). Thus, induction of a signaling protein in hypertrophy could reflect counter-regulatory adaptation, rather than mediation.

One connection between calmodulin and activation of growth pathways in the myocardium was recently elucidated. GATA-4 has been identified as the critical element mediating the induction in vivo of the β-myosin heavy chain (97) and AT_{1A} receptor (98) in pressure-overloaded hearts. In a search for cardiac factors capable of interacting with GATA-4, a novel cardiac growth pathway was identified. NFAT3 was isolated from an embryonic library as a GATA-4-interacting factor functioning as a coactivator when bound to GATA-4 at promoters with GATA-4 binding sites (99). Elevations in intracellular calcium to dephosphorylation of NFAT by the calmodulin-dependent phosphatase, calcineurin, resulted in NFAT translocation to the nucleus and gene activation. When constitutively activated, calcineurin and NFAT each provoke cardiac hypertrophy in transgenic mice (99). Cyclosporine A or FK506, well-established inhibitors of this pathway, are effective in blocking several (but not all) genetic models of myocardial hypertrophy (85, 100–104).

Deletion of FKBP12, a modulator of the ryanodine receptor (sarcoplasmic reticulum calcium release channel) (105), results in a striking, selective defect in the compact layer of ventricular myocardium, resembling the human disorder, noncompaction of the left ventricle, and is accompanied by increased trabecular growth (106). Conceivably, this defect in cardiac morphogenesis may be the consequence of the prolonged channel openings and altered calcium homeostasis. Alternatively, FKBP12 also binds the inositol-1,4,5-triphosphate receptor (105) and other cellular proteins including the kinase domain of type I receptors for the TGFβ family (107). However, because receptor mutagenesis has shown that interaction with FKBP12 is dispensable for TGFβ receptor function (108), and because

TGFβ signaling was not affected by the absence of FKBP12 (106, 109), potential defects in TGFβ signaling are unlikely to explain the pathogenesis of noncompaction caused by this mutation.

Ras and Ras-Associated Proteins   The p21ras proto-oncogene is a central component of many mitogenic signaling pathways and has been implicated in hypertrophic responses in cultured cardiac muscle cells (110). Myosin light chain-2v driven oncogenic H-Ras resulted in increased ventricular mass through cardiac myocyte hypertrophy with no discernable hyperplasia and a selective prolongation of cardiac relaxation (111). This result is somewhat surprising, not merely because Ras is a critical component of many mitogenic signaling cascades, but more specifically because Ras can down-regulate the Cdk inhibitor, p27 (112), whose high expression in the adult heart may contribute to the normal post-mitotic phenotype (113). An echocardiographically selected substrain of the Ras transgenic mice exhibited a more severe phenotype (114). Although it is still unclear if this reflects selection for a more susceptible genetic background, rather than selection for higher expression, this study is worth noting for the principle that phenotypes arising from a genetic intervention are not fixed and immutable, but rather depend on additional factors, beyond the presence of the transgene alone.

Embryonic lethality ascribed to hypoplastic myocardium was seen in mice lacking the neurofibromatosis gene (Nf1) (115), which encodes a Ras GTPase-activating protein. Inducing the intrinsic GTPase activity of Ras results in GTP hydrolysis, thus restoring active (GTP-bound) Ras to the inactive (GDP-bound) state. Such studies—hypoplasia, following the deletion of a nominal growth inhibitor—highlight the complexities in interpreting the phenotype of ventricular hypoplasia. First, appropriate caution should be exercised before concluding a direct, critical role for these proteins in cardiac myocyte proliferation. With disruption of the Nf1 gene, defects are observed not only in the myocardium but also in sympathetic ganglia and other neural crest-derived tissues (115). The hypoplastic phenotype could conceivably result from decreased myocyte proliferation, but equally could arise from a failure of cardiac myocyte recruitment, increased cell death, precocious terminal differentiation, or deficient recruitment of key complementary lineages. Second, it may be simplistic to presume a growth-inhibitory biochemical function of Nf1: the prototype for Ras GTPase-activating proteins serves a dual role, acting in part as a Ras effector, which mediates agonist-dependent phosphorylation of RNA polymerase II (116, 117).

Mitogen-Activated Protein (MAP) Kinases   Another pathway that mediates diverse extracellular stimuli involves the MAP kinase superfamily of serine/threonine kinases. One downstream member of the family, p38, was found to be activated in mice after transverse aortic banding (118), and in cell culture, the immediate upstream activators for p38, MAP kinase kinase-3 and -6, can induce characteristic changes of cardiac hypertrophy, i.e. an increase in cell size, enhanced sarcomeric organization, and elevated ANF expression (119, 120). Two questions arise from these observations: How does p38 becomes activated following a mechanical load? Is an increase in the function of a p38 activator sufficient for one or more components of the hypertrophic phenotype in vivo? TGFβ-activated kinase, TAK1, is a novel MAP kinase kinase kinase that has been implicated as a mediator of TGFβ signaling, at least in mink lung cells (121). TAK1 activity is up-regulated during pressure-overload cardiac hypertrophy in mice (D Zhang & M Schneider, unpublished observations); thus, TAK1 is an attractive candidate, perhaps among others, for regulating downstream MAP kinases, including p38, in this setting. Mice that express a constitutively active form of TAK1 in the myocardium display myocyte hypertrophy, re-induction of fetal cardiac genes, contractile dysfunction, interstitial fibrosis, and apoptosis, resulting in markedly accelerated premature death (D Zhang & M Schneider, unpublished observations).

Transcription Factors

Myc Insights into the factors that couple extracellular stimuli with transcriptional regulation in heart have benefited from the accumulation of null mutations created to investigate factors in nonmuscle systems. C-myc is the prototypical member of a family of sequence-specific DNA-binding proteins that are postulated to act as third messengers for ligand-dependent signals (122) and are implicated in the regulation of growth in a variety of tissues (123). The myc family proteins, which include c-myc, N-myc, and L-myc, are transcription factors with a basic helix-loop-helix-leucine zipper (bHLHZ) structure that activates transcription as part of a heteromeric complex with a protein termed Max. Max also forms heterodimers with the bHLHZ proteins Mad1, Mxi-1, Mad3, Mad4, and Mnt. These alternate heterodimers actively repress transcription and therefore antagonize the actions of c-myc. Deregulated expression of c-myc is associated with many cancers, and over-expression of this protein in quiescent fibroblasts induces cell cycle reentry (124). Myc promotes proliferative growth through multiple mechanisms including upregulating many genes, for example Cdc25A, cyclin E, cyclin A, and ornithine decarboxylase (ODC), involved in cell cycle progression. In addition it is an upstream regulator of cyclin-dependent kinases and functionally antagonizes the action of at least one Cdk inhibitor, p27 (125). Therefore, a network is formed that both positively and negatively regulates gene expression, proliferation, apoptosis, and differentiation. Although not expressed in the heart under normal physiological conditions, cardiac c-myc expression is induced in many pathological conditions including hemodynamic stress such as pressure overload (126, 127) or multiple pharmacological stimuli (23, 128). Given the critical role c-myc plays in normal cellular proliferation, it is not surprising that both c-myc and N-myc appear necessary for normal cardiac growth. Transgenic mice with forced expression of c-myc in the myocardium develop an increase in cardiac mass secondary to myocyte hyperplasia, but differentiated normally, as assessed by relative levels of cardiac and skeletal α-actin (129). However, the c-myc transgene is not sufficient for sustained proliferation after birth and appears instead to transiently delay the exit of the cardiac myocytes from the cell cycle. An additional intriguing feature of the c-myc gain-of-function is that, although hyperplasia is induced during cardiac embryogenesis, the ultimate exit of the myocytes from the cell cycle actually is accelerated in the transgenic line (130). There are two possible explanations, either of which might reconcile these seemingly dichotomous effects: The timing of growth arrest is established by counting the number of cell divisions (131) or Myc might accelerate a cell-intrinsic timer (132). Although c-myc-deficient mice die prematurely in utero at E10.5, with multiple abnormalies including an enlarged heart and pericardial effusion (133), this clearly is not the hypoplastic phenotype one would extrapolate from the gain-of-function study: A plausible explanation for the discrepancy is that endogenous c-myc, in fact, is poorly expressed in the embryonic heart, where its expression is virtually confined to endothelial cells, in capillaries, and to the endocardium (134).

By contrast, targeted mutations of an alternate myc family member, N-myc, resulted in embryonic lethality around E11, with hypoplasia in diverse organs plus defects in the endocardial cushion and the atrial and ventricular septa (135). To obviate the early lethality of this complete N-myc deficiency, compound het-erozygotes were engineered (one inactivated plus one hypomorphic N-myc gene) that express N-myc at ~15% of normal levels and survive to E14 (134). Notably, a selective defect results in the outer compact layer of ventricular myocardium, sparing atrial myocardium and the inner trabecular layer, which maps well to the spatial distribution of N-myc in the compact layer alone. Conceptually, this phe-notype could result from a direct role of N-myc in cardiac myocyte cell cycle progression or from precocious differentiation of the subepicardial myocytes lead-ing to permanent cell cycle exit. A mechanistic explanation for the overt cardiac phenotypes in these N-myc-deficient mice thus remains elusive years after the initial publication of the knockouts and should be taken as a cautionary note, illustrating potential difficulties in discovering the precise pathogenetic basis behind a genetically evoked phenotype.

Retinoid Acid Receptor Family Retinoic acid (RA), the principal metabolite of vitamin A, is the activating ligand for a superfamily of non-steroid nuclear hor-mone receptors that function as ligand-dependent transcription factors, have diverse effects on cell differentiation and proliferation, and can be vital for normal development (136). Embryonic vitamin A deficiency leads to a variety of con-genital abnormalities, including malformations in the aortic arch and heart, and is associated with precocious differentiation of the subepicardial myocytes (com-pact layer) (137). There are two families of distantly related nuclear RA receptors: RARs (α, β, and γ), which are activated by both all-*trans* RAs, and 9-*cis* RA and RXRs (α, β, and γ), which are activated solely by 9-*cis* RA. Although mice deficient for RARα or RARγ are viable with a normal cardiac phenotype (138, 139), mice with a null mutation of the RXRα gene die in utero between day E13.5 and E16.5 with grossly abnormal hearts (140, 141), the major cardiac defect being hypoplasia in the compact ventricular layer, consistent with the selective effect of vitamin A deficiency discussed above (137). Although the trabecular layer is diminished, it is much less affected. These defects result in ventricular septal defects in most homozygous mice. Despite these extensive abnormalities, the hearts of homozygous embryos contract and express normal levels of several cardiac-specific genes (α-MHC, cardiac α-actin, and atrial myosin light chain); persistent expression of myosin light chain 2a, an atrial isoform, with failure to form a thick-walled ventricle, suggests a persistent atrial-like phenotype (142). Electron microscopy examination of wild-type and mutant embryos revealed early differentiation of the peripheral myocytes in the compact layer, suggesting that RXRα null mutant cannot maintain the cardiac myocytes in an undifferentiated state. However, this apparent difference in propensity for differentiation did not translate into differences in the mitotic index or rates of DNA synthesis by cardiac myocytes.

These detailed investigations of RXRα are also noteworthy for several insights. First, combinatorial deletions reveal cardiovascular functions of some retinoic acid receptors that are not evident in the single mutations (143). Second, the myocardial defect must be indirect (not cell-autonomous) because no cardiac phenotype results from a conditional, Cre-mediated deletion selective for ventricular myocytes (144) and because cardiac myocytes lacking RXRα normally contribute to the compact layer of the ventricle when interspersed with wild-type ones in chimeric mice (145). In this latter case, the mutant phenotype is seen only in highly chimeric embryos.

To assess the effects of excessive retinoid signaling on cardiac development, transgenic mice were created that overexpress a constitutively active RAR in either fetal or adult ventricles. While expression of a constitutively active RARα in the adult ventricle had no apparent effect, expression in embryonic myocardium, using the β-MHC promoter, resulted in a dilated cardiomyopathy, with impaired systolic function and changes in cardiac gene expression that are characteristic of hypertrophy (146). The primary target or targets for RARα in this setting are not known.

TEF-1 First identified as an SV40 enhancer-binding protein, TEF-1 is the prototype for a family of transcription factors that have been implicated in basal, cardiac-restricted transcription (147, 148) and in gene induction during cardiac hypertrophy (149–151). Disruption of the TEF-1 gene by a retroviral insertion led to embryonic lethality, with hypoplastic myocardium and reduced trabeculation, although a number of cardiac-specific transcripts, including known targets for TEF-1, were seemingly expressed at normal levels (152).

HIF-1a In contrast to these numerous hypoplastic phenotypes resulting from deficient cardiac growth, hyperplasia of the presumptive myocardium, resulting in ventricular obstruction, occurs in mice lacking HIF-1a, the hypoxia-inducible transcription factor (153). The concurrent reduction in vascularization is attributable to the defective expression of VEGF, an angiogenic factor that is known to be induced by tissue hypoxia via HIF-1a, but the surprising increase in cardiac cell number departs from the hypoplastic myocardium described earlier for VEGF$^{+/-}$ mice. Hence, the increase in cardiac cell number is unlikely to be due to impaired VEGF production or vasculogenesis, and may indicate a more direct role for HIF-1a in cardiac morphogenesis. Although at least two growth inhibitors, p53 and p21, are dependent on the presence of this transcription factor (154), overt cardiac hyperplasia is not seen in the corresponding knockout mice (155).

Cell Cycle Regulators

Cyclins Proper cell cycle coordination (Figure 2) integrates external growth signals with the sequential upregulation and activation of a series of cyclins and their associated catalytic partners, cyclin-dependent kinases (Cdk). Passage

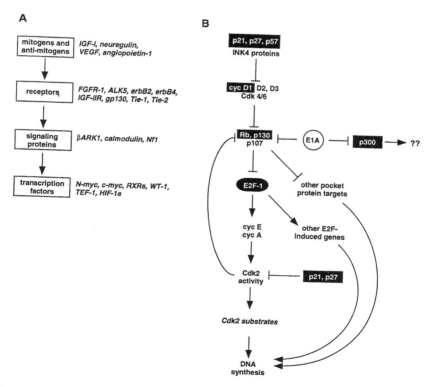

Figure 2 A genetic dissection of the post-mitotic cardiac phenotype. Signal transduction by diverse mitogens (*A*) ultimately converges on cyclin-dependent protein kinases, their activators, their substrates, and their inhibitors (*B*). Highlighted proteins have been implicated as positive or negative regulators of the cardiac cell cycle via genetic models in vivo.

through G_1 into S phase in mammals is sequentially regulated by the G1 cyclins (D1–3, E and A) (156, 157). D cyclins activate Cdk4 and Cdk6; E and A cyclins activate Cdk2. All three Cdks are known to phosphorylate tumor suppressor pocket proteins (Rb, p107, and p130), disinhibiting E2F transcription factors that are bound by the pocket domain and enabling the transcription of E2F-dependent genes required for S phase entry. Whereas these G1 cyclins have classically been associated with proliferative growth, it has recently been suggested that G1 Cdk activity is critical for hypertrophic growth as well (158).

Cyclin D1 and D3 are detected in embryonic myocardium and are down-regulated during the neonatal period, which correlates with cardiac myocyte cell cycle exit (1, 159). Transgenic mice that over-express cyclin D1 under the control of the α-MHC promoter display a 40% increase in heart weight, ascribed to a twofold increase in cardiac myocyte number at 14 days (159). Ongoing DNA synthesis was detected even in adult ventricular myocytes. However, while the labeling index of .05% was a large relative increase above rates observed in control animals (<0.0003%), the absolute magnitude nonetheless was small, consistent with the need for additional cell cycle activators, or the presence of cell cycle inhibitors or, most likely, both. Markers of cardiac differentiation were expressed normally in the α-MHC-cyc D1 transgenic mice, suggesting that if forced expression of cyc D1 affects the differentiation of cardiac myocytes, as is true for skeletal myocytes (160, 161), then this is at most a temporary delay. Enhanced DNA synthesis in adult cardiac myocytes was associated with multinucleation and the appearance of large, aberrant nuclei; cell division was not observed.

Pocket Proteins The only validated substrates for cyc D–activated Cdks are pocket proteins, whose phosphorylation is seen as an essential target of mitogenic signaling for S phase entry. Beyond this, a developmentally regulated transition from p107 to Rb expression is postulated to mediate the irreversibility of cell cycle exit in the post-mitotic skeletal muscle myotubes based on differences in the cell cycle of myocytes containing one pocket protein rather than the other (162, 163). Given that the same progression from p107 to Rb occurs in cardiac muscle (9), it is logical to assume, as a working hypothesis, that these factors are important for cardiac myocytes cell cycle exit as well.

To begin to dissect the importance of pocket protein members in mediating cardiac cell cycle control, investigators have exploited the ability of certain proteins produced by DNA tumor viruses to bind and inactivate this class of proteins. Adenovirus E1A, SV40 large T antigen, and human papilloma virus E7 all share a conserved LXCXE motif for binding the pocket domain and can coerce cell cycle re-entry even in post-mitotic cells, displacing cellular E2F transcription factors from the pocket and releasing E2F-dependent genes from the inhibition imposed by pocket proteins' intrinsic repressor domain (164, 165). In differentiated cells, these Rb-inactivating proteins also result in the down-regulation of tissue-specific genes (166–168). Two potential mechanism(s) for de-differentiation provoked by pocket protein binding include disruption of pocket protein interactions with tissue-specific transcription factors or cell cycle-dependent inactivation of the tissue-specific factors.

The first of these tumor suppressor-binding proteins to be studied in cardiac muscle was SV40 large T antigen. Expression of T antigen in cultured neonatal rat cardiac myocytes resulted in proliferation, with reportedly normal expression of cardiac-specific proteins (169). Later studies, using retroviral delivery of temperature-sensitive T antigen, indicated that sarcomeric myosin heavy chains and certain other indicators of cardiac differentiation were expressed only conditionally and could not be detected at 33°C, the permissive temperature for function of the mutant T antigen (170). Possibly, these conflicting claims can be reconciled with the very long half-life of sarcomeric proteins. In analogous studies of forced cell cycle re-entry discussed below, sarcomeric α-actin protein content was found to be maintained at times when the corresponding promoters and α-actin protein synthesis were suppressed (171).

To elucidate the function of pocket proteins in vivo, transgenic mice were created that express T antigen under a variety of muscle-specific promoters. T antigen driven by the atrial naturietic factor promoter results in atrial myocyte hyperplasia, atrial tumors, and arrhythmias (172). In addition to atrial myocyte hyperplasia, ventricular myocyte hyperplasia results when T antigen is expressed in the heart using the α-MHC (173); expression controlled by the β-MHC promoter, which is also active in slow-twitch skeletal muscle, results in cardiac and skeletal muscle myopathy (174). One useful offshoot of the T antigen transgenic mice has been the isolation and analysis of cardiac myocytes derived from transplantable atrial tumor lines (175) for grafting studies (176) and biochemical characterization (177, 178). Similar studies have been performed in cardiac muscle using E1A which, like SV40 large T antigen, can disrupt pocket protein function. It is agreed that E1A both reactivates DNA synthesis and down-regulates cardiac-restricted promoters, but the relative importance of pocket proteins versus other targets is disputed (179–181) (discussed further below).

Rb is the predominant pocket protein expressed in adult myocardium, p107 is preferentially expressed in the embryonic ventricle, and p130 is expressed at both stages (9). This temporal pattern, similar to findings in skeletal muscle, is consistent with the supposition that developmentally regulated changes in pocket protein composition likely contribute to the post-mitotic phenotype. However, Rb-deficient mice die in mid-gestation, with marked abnormalities in neural and hematopoietic tissue (182–184) and, consequently, cannot be used to test the function of Rb in any adult context. For this reason, Rb is an especially attractive candidate for a conditional deletion (described above). A cardiac-restricted deletion of Rb has been implemented successfully, using the Cre/lox system (185), that resulted in cardiac enlargement and sustained DNA synthesis similar to that seen from forced expression of cyclin D1 (159). Both studies thus are equally consistent with the existence of inhibitors distal to Rb, or with only an incomplete relief of pocket protein function.

Deletion of p130 resulted, surprisingly, in strain-specific embryonic lethality, well-tolerated in a C57BL/6J background, but causing growth arrest and death by E11–13 in a Balb/cJ-enriched background (186). Increased proliferation and apoptosis were seen in the brain and neural tube, as might be predicted from Rb (182–184). The cardiac phenotype, and likely cause of death, was a thin-walled, dilated myocardium, with defective looping and chamber formation; at E10.5, PCNA staining was decreased and apoptosis was absent. While apoptosis at earlier times cannot be excluded as a basis for the hypocellular myocardium, these findings are consistent with a requirement for p130 for normal myocyte proliferation, analogous to bifunctional effects of other cell cycle regulators (187, 188), or with loss of a trophic signal from some other cell type. This study also serves as a noteworthy example that second-site modifier genes can markedly alter cardiac phenotypes even in the setting of defined mutations.

P300 One key finding of investigations using E1A to manipulate the cardiac cell cycle was evidence that cellular targets apart from pocket proteins also could mediate G_1 exit and/or de-differentiation, including the transcriptional coactivator p300 (179, 180) and perhaps others (181). p300 is a structural and functional homologue of CBP, which binds the cyclic AMP response element-binding protein (CREB) (189–191). Analysis of its developmental expression patterns shows ubiquitous expression, including the heart at all time points examined (192). p300-deficient mice die in utero, the embryos appearing runted at the earliest time points studied and displaying cardiac, neurological, and yolk sac abnormalities (192). Death of the embryos was presumed secondary to a hypoplastic ventricle with poor trabeculation and reduced rates of DNA synthesis, associated with large pericardial effusions and suggestive of cardiac compromise. This corroborates previous evidence for the importance of p300 in cardiac differentiation (179, 180) and establishes that p300 is essential for normal cardiac development.

Cdk Inhibitors In recent years the identification of factors that negatively regulate cell cycle progression has begun to resolve the mechanisms underscoring the growth arrest observed with such diverse processes as DNA damage, terminal differentiation, and replicative senescence. Cdk inhibitors comprise two functionally distinct groups. The Ink4 family includes four members, $p15^{Ink4b}$, $p16^{Ink4a}$, $p18^{Ink4c}$, and $p19^{Ink4d}$, which have selective inhibitory activity against Cdk4 and Cdk6 (193). These proteins competitively bind G1 Cdks, preventing their interaction with cyclin D and effectively inhibiting their catalytic activity. p16-null mice have abnormal hematopoiesis, are predisposed to sarcomas and B-cell lymphomas, and have a reportedly normal cardiac phenotype (194). p18-deficient mice develop gigantism and widespread organomegaly, involving the pituitary gland, spleen, and thymus especially. These organs were disproportionately enlarged and hyperplastic, whereas cardiac enlargement was no greater than expected for the increase in body size (195).

By contrast, the Cip/Kip family—$p21^{WAF1/Cip1}$, $p27^{Kip1}$, and $p57^{Kip2}$—diverge in their C-terminal ends but possess a conserved N-terminal domain that binds both to cyclins and to Cdks (193). p21 is induced in the differentiation of a variety of post-mitotic cell types including cardiac muscle cells (196). Mice that lack p21 are phenotypically normal with no discernable developmental defects and display no increased incidence of tumor growth. However, fibroblasts from p21-deficient mice demonstrate defective G1 checkpoint control in response to radiation-induced DNA damage (197). The lack of a dramatic phenotype is presumably secondary to redundancies in the action of Cdk inhibitors and the ability of other family members to substitute functionally. Although p27 likewise is widely expressed, p27 mRNA was abundant in human heart (198), and p27 accumulates, at least at the protein level, during loss of growth in the cardiac myocytes (199). In contrast to the minimal phenotype of p21-deficient mice, p27 null mice showed generalized hyperplasia (200); like p18-deficient mice, an increase in heart weight occurs proportional to increased body size. The third Cip/Kip family member, p57, more restricted in its distribution, was detected in myocardium by E10.5, and subsequently increased in expression, peaking at E17.5 (201). p57-deficient mice typically died in the perinatal period, with multiple developmental defects (201). Although no obvious cardiac abnormality was observed, p57 mutant mice displayed increased apoptosis in heart muscle.

Given the overlapping patterns of expression and similar biochemical properties of the Cip/Kip Cdk inhibitors in vitro, discerning the importance of these factors in cardiac development and their postulated contributions to the post-mitotic phenotype will likely require combinatorial inactivation, such as was applied to cooperation between p21 and p57 in skeletal muscle development (202, 203). In addition, more refined analytical methods, such as flow cytometry to sample DNA content in thousands of cells, can detect subtle disregulation of growth where no overt phenotype is observed. With this approach, we have seen not only the increase in G_1 exit previously reported for cardiac myocytes lacking p27 (113), but also a similar, if smaller, effect in p21-null mice and mice hemizygous for p27 (S Zhang & M Schneider, unpublished observations).

However, the crux of the matter is not cell cycle distribution under basal conditions, where little or no impetus to S phase entry might exist, but rather the impact of deleting these inhibitors under provokable conditions, where disruption of cell cycle constraints might more plausibly be expected to have impact. For example, mice lacking the tumor suppressor p53 were threefold more susceptible to reactivation of DNA synthesis in the adult myocardium in vivo, following apical injection of adenovirus encoding E2F-1 (204). Because the prevalence for apoptosis induced by E2F-1 was unaffected by absence of p53, this increase points instead to a p53-dependent inhibition of G_1 exit itself. Such studies highlight the combinatorial power of viral gene delivery to genetically altered recipients.

CONCLUSIONS

This review has attempted to summarize recent advances—substantive, dramatic, or both—that have been made in our understanding of cardiac growth control. The ability to dissect cardiac growth control pathways through in vivo genetic manipulations has confirmed some predictions, challenged others, and, especially, accelerated the pace for novel insights including serendipitous ones. This, in turn, has changed paradigms and refocused research. Much of our own work could be said to address a revisionist model of the post-mitotic phenotype, in which the lock on the cell cycle is constructed not merely by Rb, but also by programmed up-regulation of p21 and p27, which both shield Rb from inactivation (hyper-phosphorylation) and suppress the function of E2F-dependent Cdks. The recent addition of conditional and tissue-restricted deletions to the arsenal of the modern biologist, and high-throughput methods for expression profiling, will only expand the utility of genetically altered mice for in vivo models of human disease and as a platform for drug discovery.

Visit the Annual Reviews home page at www.AnnualReviews.org.

LITERATURE CITED

1. Soonpaa MH, Kim KK, Pajak L, Franklin M, Field LJ. 1996. Cardiomyocyte DNA synthesis and binucleation during murine development. *Am. J. Physiol.* 271:H2183–89

2. Grafi G. 1998. Cell cycle regulation of DNA replication: the endoreduplication perspective. *Exp. Cell. Res.* 244:372–78

3. Soonpaa MH, Field LJ. 1994. Assessment of cardiomyocyte DNA synthesis during hypertrophy in adult mice. *Am. J. Physiol.* 266:H1439–45

4. Soonpaa MH, Field LJ. 1997. Assessment of cardiomyocyte DNA synthesis in the normal and injured adult mouse heart. *Am. J. Physiol.* 272:H220–26

5. Nakagawa M, Hamaoka K, Hattori T, Sawada T. 1988. Postnatal DNA synthesis in hearts of mice: autoradiographic and cytofluorometric investigations. *Cardiovas. Res.* 22:575–83

6. Rumyantsev PP. 1977. Interrelations of the proliferation and differentiation processes during cardiac myogenesis and regeneration. *Int. Rev. Cytol.* 51:187–273

7. Anversa P, Kajstura J. 1998. Ventricular myocytes are not terminally differentiated in the adult mammalian heart. *Circ. Res.* 83:1–14

8. Soonpaa MH, Field LJ. 1998. Survey of studies examining mammalian cardiomyocyte DNA synthesis. *Circ. Res.* 83:15–26

9. MacLellan WR, Schneider MD. 1998. The cardiac cell cycle. In *Cardiac Development,* ed. R Harvey, N Rosenthal, pp. 405–27. San Diego: Academic

10. Soonpaa MH, Oberpriller JO, Oberpriller JC. 1994. Factors altering DNA synthesis in the cardiac myocyte of the adult newt, *Notophthalmus viridescens. Cell Tissue Res.* 275:377–82

11. Parker TG, Schneider MD. 1991. Growth factors, proto-oncogenes, and plasticity of the cardiac phenotype. *Annu. Rev. Physiol.* 53:179–200

12. Komuro I, Yazaki Y. 1993. Control of cardiac gene expression by mechanical stress. *Annu. Rev. Physiol.* 55:55–75

13. Sadoshima J, Izumo S. 1997. The cellular and molecular response of cardiac myocytes to mechanical stress. *Annu. Rev. Physiol.* 59:551–71

14. MacLellan WR, Schneider MD. 1997. Death by design—programmed cell death in cardiovascular biology and disease. *Circ. Res.* 81:137–44

15. Takahashi N, Calderone A, Izzo NJ, Maki TM, Marsh JD, et al. 1994. Hypertrophic stimuli induce transforming

growth factor-beta(1) expression in rat ventricular myocytes. *J. Clin. Invest.* 94:1470–76

16. Donohue TJ, Dworkin LD, Lango MN, Fliegner K, Lango RP, et al. 1994. Induction of myocardial insulin-like growth factor-I gene expression in left ventricular hypertrophy. *Circulation* 89:799–809

17. Baker KM, Chernin MI, Wixson SK, Aceto JF. 1990. Renin-angiotensin system involvement in pressure-overload cardiac hypertrophy in rats. *Am. J. Physiol.* 259:H324–32

18. Yorikane R, Sakai S, Miyauchi T, Sakurai T, Sugishita Y, et al. 1993. Increased production of endothelin-1 in the hypertrophied rat heart due to pressure overload. *FEBS Lett.* 332:31–34

19. Ishikawa M, Saito Y, Miyamoto Y, Kuwahara K, Ogawa E, et al. 1996. cDNA cloning of rat cardiotrophin-1 (CT-1): augmented expression of CT-1 gene in ventricle of genetically hypertensive rats. *Biochem. Biophys. Res. Commun.* 219:377–81

20. Parker TG, Chow K-L, Schwartz RJ, Schneider MD. 1990. Differential regulation of skeletal α-actin transcription in cardiac muscle by two fibroblast growth factors. *Proc. Natl. Acad. Sci. USA* 87:7066–70

21. Parker TG, Packer SE, Schneider MD. 1990. Peptide growth factors can provoke "fetal" contractile protein gene expression in rat cardiac myocytes. *J. Clin. Invest.* 85:507–14

22. Shubeita HE, McDonough PM, Harris AN, Knowlton KU, Glembotski CC, et al. 1990. Endothelin induction of inositol phospholipid hydrolysis, sarcomere assembly, and cardiac gene expression in ventricular myocytes: a paracrine mechanism for myocardial cell hypertrophy. *J. Biol. Chem.* 265:20555–62

23. Sadoshima J, Izumo S. 1993. Molecular characterization of angiotensin II-induced hypertrophy of cardiac myocytes and hyperplasia of cardiac

fibroblasts: critical role of the AT1 receptor subtype. *Circ. Res.* 73:413–23

24. Wollert KC, Taga T, Saito M, Narazaki M, Kishimoto T, et al. 1996. Cardiotrophin-1 activates a distinct form of cardiac muscle cell hypertrophy–assembly of sarcomeric units in series via gp130 leukemia inhibitory factor receptor-dependent pathways. *J. Biol. Chem.* 271:9535–45

24a. Abdellatif M, Schneider MD. 1999. Transcriptional circuits mediating cardiac hypertrophy and heart failure. In *Pathogenetic Basis of Myocardial Diseases,* ed. R Virmani, JT Willerson. New York: Springer-Verlag. In press

25. Baker J, Liu JP, Robertson EJ, Efstratiadis A. 1993. Role of insulin-like growth factors in embryonic and postnatal growth. *Cell* 75:73–82

26. Liu JP, Baker J, Perkins AS, Robertson EJ, Efstratiadis A. 1993. Mice carrying null mutations of the genes encoding insulin-like growth factor-I (Igf-1) and type-1 IGF receptor (Igf1r). *Cell* 75:59–72

27. Lembo G, Rockman HA, Hunter JJ, Steinmetz H, Koch WJ, et al. 1996. Elevated blood pressure and enhanced myocardial contractility in mice with severe IGF-1 deficiency. *J. Clin. Invest.* 98:2648–55

28. Reiss K, Cheng W, Ferber A, Kajstura J, Li P, et al. 1996. Overexpression of insulin-like growth factor-1 in the heart is coupled with myocyte proliferation in transgenic mice. *Proc. Natl. Acad. Sci. USA* 93:8630–35

29. Lau MMH, Stewart CEH, Liu Z, Bhatt H, Rotwein P, et al. 1994. Loss of the imprinted IGF2/cation-independent mannose-6–phosphate receptor results in fetal overgrowth and perinatal lethality. *Genes Dev.* 8:2953–63

30. Kajstura J, Cheng W, Reiss K, Anversa P. 1994. The IGF-1-IGF-1 receptor system modulates myocyte proliferation but

not myocyte cellular hypertrophy in vitro. *Exp. Cell Res.* 215:273–83

31. Hirano T, Nakajima K, Hibi M. 1997. Signaling mechanisms through gp130: a model of the cytokine system. *Cytokine Growth Factor Rev.* 8:241–52

32. Taga T, Kishimoto T. 1997. Gp130 and the interleukin-6 family of cytokines. *Annu. Rev. Immunol.* 15:797–819

33. Yoshida K, Taga T, Saito M, Suematsu S, Kumanogoh A, et al. 1996. Targeted disruption of gp130, a common signal transducer for the interleukin 6 family of cytokines, leads to myocardial and hematological disorders. *Proc. Natl. Acad. Sci. USA* 93:407–11

34. Sauer B. 1998. Inducible gene targeting in mice using the Cre/lox system. *Methods* 14:381–92

35. Rossant J, McMahon A. 1999. "Cre"-ating mouse mutants—a meeting review on conditional mouse genetics. *Genes Dev.* 13:142–45

36. Agah R, Frenkel PA, French BA, Michael LH, Overbeek PA, et al. 1997. Gene recombination in postmitotic cells: Targeted expression of Cre recombinase provokes cardiac-restricted, site-specific rearrangement in adult ventricular muscle in vivo. *J. Clin. Invest.* 100:169–79

37. Betz UAK, Bloch W, vandenBroek M, Yoshida K, Taga T, et al. 1998. Postnatally induced inactivation of gp130 in mice results in neurological, cardiac, hematopoietic, immunological, hepatic, and pulmonary defects. *J. Exp. Med.* 188:1955–65

38. Kopf M, Baumann H, Freer G, Freudenberg M, Lamers M, et al. 1994. Impaired immune and acute-phase responses in interleukin-6-deficient mice. *Nature* 368:339–42

39. Stewart CL, Kaspar P, Brunet LJ, Bhatt H, Gadi I, et al. 1992. Blastocyst implantation depends on maternal expression of leukaemia inhibitory factor. *Nature* 359:76–79

40. Escary JL, Perreau J, Dumenil D, Ezine S, Brulet P. 1993. Leukaemia inhibitory factor is necessary for maintenance of haematopoietic stem cells and thymocyte stimulation. *Nature* 363:361–64

41. Masu Y, Wolf E, Holtmann B, Sendtner M, Brem G, et al. 1993. Disruption of the CNTF gene results in motor neuron degeneration. *Nature* 365:27–32

42. Robb L, Li R, Hartley L, Nandurkar HH, Koentgen F, et al. 1998. Infertility in female mice lacking the receptor for interleukin 11 is due to a defective uterine response to implantation. *Nat. Med.* 4:303–8

43. Hirota H, Chen J, Betz UA, Rajewsky K, Gu Y, et al. 1999. Loss of a gp130 cardiac muscle cell survival pathway is a critical event in the onset of heart failure during biomechanical stress. *Cell* 97:189–98

44. Pennica D, King KL, Shaw KJ, Luis E, Rullamas J, et al. 1995. Expression cloning of cardiotrophin 1, a cytokine that induces cardiac myocyte hypertrophy. *Proc. Natl. Acad. Sci. USA* 92:1142–46

45. Pennica D, Shaw KJ, Swanson TA, Moore MW, Shelton DL, et al. 1995. Cardiotrophin-1–biological activities and binding to the leukemia inhibitory factor receptor gp130 signaling complex. *J. Biol. Chem.* 270:10915–22

46. Sheng ZL, Knowlton K, Chen J, Hoshijima M, Brown JH, et al. 1997. Cardiotrophin 1 (CT-1) inhibition of cardiac myocyte apoptosis via a mitogen-activated protein kinase-dependent pathway. Divergence from downstream CT-1 signals for myocardial cell hypertrophy. *J. Biol. Chem.* 272:5783–91

47. Metcalf D, Willson TA, Hilton DJ, Di RL, Mifsud S. 1995. Production of hematopoietic regulatory factors in cultures of adult and fetal mouse organs: measurement by specific bioassays. *Leukemia* 9:1556–64

48. Kukielka GL, Smith CW, Manning AM, Youker KA, Michael LH, et al. 1995. Induction of interleukin-6 synthesis in the myocardium. Potential role in postre-

perfusion inflammatory injury. *Circulation* 92:1866–75

49. Hirota H, Yoshida K, Kishimoto T, Taga T. 1995. Continuous activation of gp130, a signal-transducing receptor component for interleukin 6-related cytokines, causes myocardial hypertrophy in mice. *Proc. Natl. Acad. Sci. USA* 92:4862–66

50. Akhurst RJ, Lehnert SA, Faissner A, Duffie E. 1990. TGF beta in murine morphogenetic processes: the early embryo and cardiogenesis. *Development* 108:645–56

51. Brand T, MacLellan WR, Schneider MD. 1993. A dominant-negative receptor for type-beta transforming growth factors created by deletion of the kinase domain. *J. Biol. Chem.* 268:11500–3

52. Shull MM, Ormsby I, Kier AB, Pawlowski S, Diebold RJ, et al. 1992. Targeted disruption of the mouse transforming growth factor-beta 1 gene results in multifocal inflammatory disease. *Nature* 359:693–99

53. Dickson MC, Martin JS, Cousins FM, Kulkarni AB, Karlsson S, et al. 1995. Defective haematopoiesis and vasculogenesis in transforming growth factor-beta 1 knock out mice. *Development* 121:1845–54

54. Kulkarni AB, Huh CG, Becker D, Geiser A, Lyght M, et al. 1993. Transforming growth factor beta 1 null mutation in mice causes excessive inflammatory response and early death. *Proc. Natl. Acad. Sci. USA* 90:770–74

55. Letterio JJ, Geiser AG, Kulkarni AB, Roche NS, Sporn MB, et al. 1994. Maternal rescue of transforming growth factor-beta 1 null mice. *Science* 264:1936–38

56. Diebold RJ, Eis MJ, Yin M, Ormsby I, Boivin GP, et al. 1995. Early-onset multifocal inflammation in the transforming growth factor beta 1–null mouse is lymphocyte mediated. *Proc. Natl. Acad. Sci. USA* 92:12215–19

57. Sanford LP, Ormsby I, Gittenberger-de Groot AC, Sariola H, Friedman R, et al.

1997. TGF beta 2 knockout mice have multiple developmental defects that are nonoverlapping with other TGF beta knockout phenotypes. *Development* 124:2659–70

58. Proetzel G, Pawlowski SA, Wiles MV, Yin MY, Boivin GP, et al. 1995. Transforming growth factor-beta 3 is required for secondary palate fusion. *Nat. Genet.* 11:409–14

59. Charng MJ, Frenkel PA, Lin Q, Yumada M, Schwartz RJ, et al. 1998. A constitutive mutation of ALK5 disrupts cardiac looping and morphogenesis in mice. *Dev. Biol.* 199:72–79

60. Hu MC, Qiu WR, Wang YP, Hill D, Ring BD, et al. 1998. FGF-18, a novel member of the fibroblast growth factor family, stimulates hepatic and intestinal proliferation. *Mol. Cell. Biol.* 18:6063–74

61. Mima T, Ueno H, Fischman DA, Williams LT, Mikawa T. 1995. Fibroblast growth factor receptor is required for in vivo cardiac myocyte proliferation at early embryonic stages of heart development. *Proc. Natl. Acad. Sci. USA* 92:467–71

62. Yamaguchi TP, Harpal K, Henkmeyer M, Rossant J. 1994. *fgfr-1* is required for embryonic growth and mesodermal patterning during mouse gastrulation. *Genes Dev.* 8:3032–44

63. Deng C-X, Wynshaw-Boris A, Shen MM, Daugherty C, Ornitz DM, et al. 1994. Murine FGFR-1 is required for early postimplantation growth and axial organization. *Genes Dev.* 8:3045–57

63a. Schultz JE, Witt SA, Nieman ML, Reiser PJ, Engle SJ, et al. 1999. Fibroblast growth factor-2 mediates pressure-induced hypertrophic response. *J. Clin. Invest.* 104:709–19

64. Hein L, Stevens ME, Barsh GS, Pratt RE, Kobilka BK, et al. 1997. Overexpression of angiotensin AT(1) receptor transgene in the mouse myocardium produces a lethal phenotype associated with myo-

cyte hyperplasia and heart block. *Proc. Natl. Acad. Sci. USA* 94:6391–96

65. Milano CA, Dolber PC, Rockman HA, Bond RA, Venable ME, et al. 1994. Myocardial expression of a constitutively active α1B- adrenergic receptor in transgenic mice induces cardiac hypertrophy. *Proc. Natl. Acad. Sci. USA* 91:10109–13

66. Tanimoto K, Sugiyama F, Goto Y, Ishida J, Takimoto E, et al. 1994. Angiotensinogen-deficient mice with hypotension. *J. Biol. Chem.* 269:31334–37

67. Oliverio MI, Kim HS, Ito M, Le T, Audoly L, et al. 1998. Reduced growth, abnormal kidney structure, and type 2 (AT2) angiotensin receptor-mediated blood pressure regulation in mice lacking both AT1A and AT1B receptors for angiotensin II. *Proc. Natl. Acad. Sci. USA* 95:15496–501

68. Ichiki T, Labosky PA, Shiota C, Okuyama S, Imagawa Y, et al. 1995. Effects on blood pressure and exploratory behavior of mice lacking angiotensin II type-2 receptor. *Nature* 377:748–50

69. Kudoh S, Komuro I, Hiroi Y, Zou YZ, Harada K, et al. 1998. Mechanical stretch induces hypertrophic responses in cardiac myocytes of angiotensin II type 1a receptor knockout mice. *J. Biol. Chem.* 273:24037–43

70. Harada K, Komuro I, Shiojima I, Hayashi D, Kudoh S, et al. 1998. Pressure overload induces cardiac hypertrophy in angiotensin II type 1A receptor knockout mice. *Circulation* 97:1952–59

71. Harada K, Komuro I, Zou YZ, Kudoh S, Kijima K, et al. 1998. Acute pressure overload could induce hypertrophic responses in the heart of angiotensin II type 1a knockout mice. *Circ. Res.* 82:779–85

72. Hamawaki M, Coffman TM, Lashus A, Koide M, Zile MR, et al. 1998. Pressure-overload hypertrophy is unabated in mice devoid of AT(1A) receptors. *Am. J. Physiol.* 43:H868–73

73. Jaber M, Koch WJ, Rockman H, Smith B, Bond RA, et al. 1996. Essential role of beta-adrenergic receptor kinase 1 in cardiac development and function. *Proc. Natl. Acad. Sci. USA* 93:12974–79

74. Meyer D, Birchmeier C. 1995. Multiple essential functions of neuregulin in development. *Nature* 378:386–90

75. Lee KF, Simon H, Chen H, Bates B, Hung MC, et al. 1995. Requirement for neuregulin receptor ErbB2 in neural and cardiac development. *Nature* 378:394–98

76. Gassmann M, Casagranda F, Orioli D, Simon H, Lai C, et al. 1995. Aberrant neural and cardiac development in mice lacking the ErbB4 neuregulin receptor. *Nature* 378:390–94

77. Zhao YY, Sawyer DR, Baliga RR, Opel DJ, Han XQ, et al. 1998. Neuregulins promote survival and growth of cardiac myocytes. Persistence of ErbB2 and ErbB4 expression in neonatal and adult ventricular myocytes. *J. Biol. Chem.* 273:10261–69

78. Zhao JJ, Lemke G. 1998. Selective disruption of neuregulin-1 function in vertebrate embryos using ribozyme-tRNA transgenes. *Development* 125:1899–907

79. Ferrara N, Carver-Moore K, Chen H, Dowd M, Lu L, et al. 1996. Heterozygous embryonic lethality induced by targeted inactivation of the VEGF gene. *Nature* 380:439–42

80. Fong GH, Rossant J, Gertsenstein M, Breitman ML. 1995. Role of the flt-1 receptor tyrosine kinase in regulating the assembly of vascular endothelium. *Nature* 376:66–70

81. Shalaby F, Rossant J, Yamaguchi TP, Gertsenstein M, Wu XF, et al. 1995. Failure of blood-island formation and vasculogenesis in flk-1-deficient mice. *Nature* 376:62–66

82. Sato TN, Tozawa Y, Deutsch U, Wolburgbuchholz K, Fujiwara Y, et al. 1995. Distinct roles of the receptor tyrosine

kinases tie-1 and tie-2 in blood vessel formation. *Nature* 376:70–74

83. Suri C, Jones PF, Patan S, Bartunkova S, Maisonpierre PC, et al. 1996. Requisite role of angiopoietin-1, a ligand for the TIE2 receptor, during embryonic angiogenesis. *Cell* 87:1171–80

84. Adams JW, Sakata Y, Davis MG, Sah VP, Wang YB, et al. 1998. Enhanced G alpha q signaling: A common pathway mediates cardiac hypertrophy and apoptotic heart failure. *Proc. Natl. Acad. Sci. USA* 95:10140–45

85. Mende U, Kagen A, Cohen A, Aramburu J, Schoen FJ, et al. 1998. Transient cardiac expression of constitutively active G alpha q leads to hypertrophy and dilated cardiomyopathy by calcineurin-dependent and independent pathways. *Proc. Natl. Acad. Sci. USA* 95:13893–98

86. Bowman JC, Steinberg SF, Jiang T, Geenen DL, Fishman GI, et al. 1997. Expression of protein kinase C beta in the heart causes hypertrophy in adult mice and sudden death in neonates. *J. Clin. Invest.* 100:2189–95

87. Wakasaki H, Koya D, Schoen FJ, Jirousek MR, Ways DK, et al. 1997. Targeted overexpression of protein kinase C beta 2 isoform in myocardium causes cardiomyopathy. *Proc. Natl. Acad. Sci. USA* 94:9320–25

87. Koch WJ, Lefkowitz RJ, Rockman HA. 2000. Functional consequences of altering myocardial adrenergic receptor signaling. *Annu. Rev. Physiol.* 62:In press

88. Takuwa N, Zhou W, Takuwa Y. 1995. Calcium, calmodulin and cell cycle progression. *Cell Signal.* 7:93–104

89. Le Guennec JY, White E, Gannier F, Argibay JA, Garnier D. 1991. Stretch-induced increase of resting intracellular calcium concentration in single guinea-pig ventricular myocytes. *Exp. Physiol.* 76:975–78

90. Sei CA, Irons CE, Sprenkle AB, Mcdonough PM, Brown JH, et al. 1991. The alpha-adrenergic stimulation of atrial natriuretic factor expression in cardiac myocytes requires calcium influx, protein kinase-C, and calmodulin-regulated pathways. *J. Biol. Chem.* 266:15910–16

91. Sadoshima J, Qiu ZH, Morgan JP, Izumo S. 1995. Angiotensin II and other hypertrophic stimuli mediated by G protein-coupled receptors activate tyrosine kinase, mitogen-activated protein kinase, and 90–kD S6 kinase in cardiac myocytes: the critical role of Ca^{2+}-dependent signaling. *Circ. Res.* 76:1–15

92. Touyz RM, Fareh J, Thibault G, Tolloczko B, Lariviere R, et al. 1996. Modulation of Ca^{2+} transients in neonatal and adult rat cardiomyocytes by angiotensin II and endothelin-1. *Am. J. Physiol.* 270:H857–68

93. Kelly RA, Eid H, Kramer BK, O'Neill M, Liang BT, et al. 1990. Endothelin enhances the contractile responsiveness of adult rat ventricular myocytes to calcium by a pertussis toxin-sensitive pathway. *J. Clin. Invest.* 86:1164–71

94. Gruver CL, Demayo F, Goldstein MA, Means AR. 1993. Targeted developmental overexpression of calmodulin induces proliferative and hypertrophic growth of cardiomyocytes in transgenic mice. *Endocrinology* 133:376–88

95. Tsoporis JN, Marks A, Kahn HJ, Butany JW, Liu PP, et al. 1997. S100 beta inhibits alpha(1)-adrenergic induction of the hypertrophic phenotype in cardiac myocytes. *J. Biol. Chem.* 272:31915–21

96. Tsoporis JN, Marks A, Kahn HJ, Butany JW, Liu PP, et al. 1998. Inhibition of norepinephrine-induced cardiac hypertrophy in s100beta transgenic mice. *J. Clin. Invest.* 102:1609–16

97. Hasegawa K, Lee SJ, Jobe SM, Markham BE, Kitsis RN. 1997. *cis*-acting sequences that mediate induction of beta-myosin heavy chain gene expression during left ventricular hypertrophy due to aortic constriction. *Circulation* 96:3943–53

98. Herzig TC, Jobe SM, Aoki H, Molkentin

JD, Cowley AW, et al. 1997. Angiotensin II type(1a) receptor gene expression in the heart: AP-1 and GATA-4 participate in the response to pressure overload. *Proc. Natl. Acad. Sci. USA* 94:7543–48

99. Molkentin JD, Lu JR, Antos CL, Markham B, Richardson J, et al. 1998. A calcineurin-dependent transcriptional pathway for cardiac hypertrophy. *Cell* 93:215–28

100. Meguro T, Hong C, Asai K, Takagi G, McKinsey TA, et al. 1999. Cyclosporine attenuates pressure-overload hypertrophy in mice while enhancing susceptibility to decompensation and heart failure. *Circ. Res.* 84:735–40

101. Ding B, Price RL, Borg TK, Weinberg EO, Halloran PF, et al. 1999. Pressure overload induces severe hypertrophy in mice treated with cyclosporine, an inhibitor of calcineurin. *Circ. Res.* 84:729–34

102. Walsh RA. 1999. Calcineurin inhibition as therapy for cardiac hypertrophy and heart failure: requiescat in pace? *Circ. Res.* 84:741–43

103. Luo Z, Shyu KG, Gualberto A, Walsh K. 1998. Calcineurin inhibitors and cardiac hypertrophy. *Nat. Med.* 4:1092–93

104. Sussman MA, Lim HW, Gude N, Taigen T, Olson EN, et al. 1998. Prevention of cardiac hypertrophy in mice by calcineurin inhibition. *Science* 281:1690–93

105. Marks AR. 1996. Cellular functions of immunophilins. *Physiol. Rev.* 76:631–49

106. Shou WN, Aghdasi B, Armstrong DL, Guo QX, Bao SD, et al. 1998. Cardiac defects and altered ryanodine receptor function in mice lacking FKBP12. *Nature* 391:489–92

107. Wang TW, Donahoe PK, Zervos AS. 1994. Specific interaction of type I receptors of the TGF-beta family with the immunophilin FKBP-12. *Science* 265: 674–76

108. Charng M-J, Kinnunen P, Hawker J, Brand T, Schneider MD. 1996. FKBP-12 recognition is dispensable for signal generation by type I TGFb receptors. *J. Biol. Chem.* 271:22941–44

109. Bassing CH, Shou WN, Muir S, Heitman J, Matzuk MM, et al. 1998. FKBP12 is not required for the modulation of transforming growth factor beta receptor I signaling activity in embryonic fibroblasts and thymocytes. *Cell Growth Differ.* 9: 223–28

110. Thorburn A, Thorburn J, Chen SY, Powers S, Shubeita HE, et al. 1993. H-Ras-dependent pathways can activate morphological and genetic markers of cardiac muscle hypertrophy. *J. Biol. Chem.* 268:2244–49

111. Hunter JJ, Tanaka N, Rockman HA, Ross J, Chien KR. 1995. Ventricular expression of a MLC-2v-ras fusion gene induces cardiac hypertrophy and selective diastolic dysfunction in transgenic mice. *J. Biol. Chem.* 270:23173–78

112. Takuwa N, Takuwa Y. 1997. Ras activity late in G(1) phase required for p27(kip1) downregulation, passage through the restriction point, and entry into S phase in growth factor-stimulated NIH 3T3 fibroblasts. *Mol. Cell. Biol.* 17:5348–58

113. Poolman RA, Li J-M, Brooks G. 1997. Altered expression of cell cycle regulatory proteins in p27 knockout mice. *Circulation* 96:I-6 (Abstr.).

114. Gotshall KR, Hunter JJ, Tanaka N, Dalton N, Becker KD, et al. 1997. Ras-dependent pathways induce obstructive hypertrophy in echo-selected transgenic mice. *Proc. Natl. Acad. Sci. USA* 94:4710–15

115. Jacks T, Shih TS, Schmitt EM, Bronson RT, Bernards A, et al. 1994. Tumour predisposition in mice heterozygous for a targeted mutation in Nf1. *Nat. Genet.* 7:353–61

116. Abdellatif M, Schneider MD. 1997. An effector-like function of Ras GTPase-activating protein predominates in cardiac muscle cells. *J. Biol. Chem.* 272:525–33

117. Abdellatif M, Packer SE, Michael LH,

Zhang D, Charng MJ, et al. 1998. A Ras-dependent pathway regulates RNA polymerase II phosphorylation in cardiac myocytes: implications for cardiac hypertrophy. *Mol. Cell. Biol.* 18:6729–36

118. Wang YB, Huang SA, Sah VP, Ross J, Brown JH, et al. 1998. Cardiac muscle cell hypertrophy and apoptosis induced by distinct members of the p38 mitogen-activated protein kinase family. *J. Biol. Chem.* 273:2161–68

119. Wang YB, Su B, Sah VP, Brown JH, Han JH, et al. 1998. Cardiac hypertrophy induced by mitogen-activated protein kinase kinase 7, a specific activator for c-jun NH2–terminal kinase in ventricular muscle cells. *J. Biol. Chem.* 273:5423–26

120. Nemoto S, Sheng ZL, Lin AN. 1998. Opposing effects of Jun kinase and p38 mitogen-activated protein kinases on cardiomyocyte hypertrophy. *Mol. Cell. Biol.* 18:3518–26

121. Yamaguchi K, Shirakabe T, Shibuya H, Irie K, Oishi I, et al. 1995. Identification of a member of the MAPKKK family as a potential mediator of TGF-beta signal transduction. *Science* 270:2008–11

122. Amati B, Alevizopoulos K, Vlach J. 1998. Myc and the cell cycle. *Front. Biosci.* 15:D250–68

123. Evan GI, Littlewood TD. 1993. The role of c-myc in cell growth. *Curr. Opin. Genet. Dev.* 3:44–49

124. Steiner P, Philipp A, Lukas J, Godden-kent D, Pagano M, et al. 1995. Identification of a myc-dependent step during the formation of active g(1) cyclin-cdk complexes. *EMBO J.* 14:4814–26

125. Vlach J, Hennecke S, Alevizopoulos K, Conti D, Amati B. 1996. Growth arrest by the cyclin-dependent kinase inhibitor p27(Kip1) is abrogated by c-Myc. *EMBO J.* 15:6595–604

126. Izumo S, Nadal-Ginard B, Mahdavi V. 1988. Proto-oncogene induction and reprogramming of cardiac gene expres-sion produced by pressure overload. *Proc. Natl. Acad. Sci. USA* 85:339–43

127. Mulvagh SL, Michael LH, Perryman MB, Roberts R, Schneider MD. 1987. A hemodynamic load in vivo induces cardiac expression of the cellular oncogene, c-myc. *Biochem. Biophys. Res. Commun.* 147:627–36

128. Starksen NF, Simpson PC, Bishopric N, Coughlin SR, Lee WMF, et al. 1986. Cardiac myocyte hypertrophy is associated with c-myc protooncogene expression. *Proc. Natl. Acad. Sci. USA* 83:8348–50

129. Jackson T, Allard MF, Sreenan CM, Doss LK, Bishop SP, et al. 1990. The c-myc proto-oncogene regulates cardiac development in transgenic mice. *Mol. Cell. Biol.* 10:3709–16

130. Machida N, Brissie N, Sreenan C, Bishop SP. 1997. Inhibition of cardiac myocyte division in c-myc transgenic mice. *J. Mol. Cell. Cardiol.* 29:1895–902

131. Reddel RR. 1998. Genes involved in the control of cellular proliferative potential. *Ann. NY Acad. Sci.* 854:8–19

132. Conlon I, Raff M. 1999. Size control in animal development. *Cell* 96:235–44

133. Davis AC, Wims M, Spotts GD, Hann SR, Bradley A. 1993. A null c-myc mutation causes lethality before 10.5 days of gestation in homozygotes and reduced fertility in heterozygous female mice. *Genes Dev.* 7:671–82

134. Moens CB, Stanton BR, Parada LF, Rossant J. 1993. Defects in heart and lung development in compound heterozygotes for two different targeted mutations at the N-myc locus. *Development* 119:485–99

135. Moens CB, Auerbach AB, Conlon RA, Joyner AL, Rossant J. 1992. A targeted mutation reveals a role for N-myc in branching morphogenesis in the embryonic mouse lung. *Genes Dev.* 6:691–704

136. Kastner P, Mark M, Chambon P. 1995. Nonsteroid nuclear receptors: What are genetic studies telling us about their role in real life? *Cell* 83:859–69

137. Kastner P, Messaddeq N, Mark M,

Wendling O, Grondona JM, et al. 1997. Vitamin A deficiency and mutations of RXR alpha, RXR beta and RAR alpha lead to early differentiation of embryonic ventricular cardiomyocytes. *Development* 124:4749–58

138. Li E, Sucov HM, Lee KF, Evans RM, Jaenisch R. 1993. Normal development and growth of mice carrying a targeted disruption of the alpha1 retinoic acid receptor gene. *Proc. Natl. Acad. Sci. USA* 90:1590–94

139. Lohnes D, Kastner P, Dierich A, Mark M, LeMeur M, et al. 1993. Function of retinoic acid receptor gamma in the mouse. *Cell* 73:643–58

140. Sucov HM, Dyson E, Gumeringer CL, Price J, Chien KR, et al. 1994. RXR alpha mutant mice establish a genetic basis for vitamin A signaling in heart morphogenesis. *Genes Dev.* 8:1007–18

141. Kastner P, Grondona JM, Mark M, Gansmuller A, LeMeur M, et al. 1994. Genetic analysis of RXR alpha developmental function: convergence of RXR and RAR signaling pathways in heart and eye morphogenesis. *Cell* 78:987–1003

142. Dyson E, Sucov HM, Kubalak SW, Schmidschonbein GW, Delano FA, et al. 1995. Atrial-like phenotype is associated with embryonic ventricular failure in retinoid x receptor alpha -/- mice. *Proc. Natl. Acad. Sci. USA* 92:7386–90

143. Lee RY, Luo JM, Evans RM, Giguere V, Sucov HM. 1997. Compartment-selective sensitivity of cardiovascular morphogenesis to combinations of retinoic acid receptor gene mutations. *Circ. Res.* 80:757–64

144. Chen J, Kubalak SW, Chien KR. 1998. Ventricular muscle-restricted targeting of the RXR alpha gene reveals a non-cell-autonomous requirement in cardiac chamber morphogenesis. *Development* 125:1943–49

145. Tran CM, Sucov HM. 1998. The RXR alpha gene functions in a non-cell-autonomous manner during mouse car-diac morphogenesis. *Development* 125:1951–56

146. Colbert MC, Hall DG, Kimball TR, Witt SA, Lorenz JN, et al. 1997. Cardiac com-partment-specific overexpression of a modified retinoic acid receptor produces dilated cardiomyopathy and congestive heart failure in transgenic mice. *J. Clin. Invest.* 100:1958–68

147. Farrance IKG, Mar JH, Ordahl CP. 1992. M-CAT binding factor is related to the SV40 enhancer binding factor, TEF-1. *J. Biol. Chem.* 267:17234–40

148. Farrance IKG, Ordahl CP. 1996. The role of transcription enhancer factor-1 (TEF-1) related proteins in the formation of M-CAT binding complexes in muscle and non-muscle tissues. *J. Biol. Chem.* 271: 8266–74

149. MacLellan WR, Lee TC, Schwartz RJ, Schneider MD. 1994. Transforming growth factor-beta response elements of the skeletal alpha-actin gene: combina-torial action of serum response factor, YY1, and the SV40 enhancer-binding protein, TEF-1. *J. Biol. Chem.* 269: 16754–60

150. Karns LR, Kariya K, Simpson PC. 1995. M-CAT, CArG, and Sp1 elements are required for alpha(1)-adrenergic induc-tion of the skeletal alpha-actin promoter during cardiac myocyte hypertrophy-transcriptional enhancer factor-1 and protein kinase C as conserved transduc-ers of the fetal program in cardiac growth. *J. Biol. Chem.* 270:410–17

151. Stewart AFR, Suzow J, Kubota T, Uey-ama T, Chen HH. 1998. Transcription factor RTEF-1 mediates alpha(1)-adren-ergic reactivation of the fetal gene pro-gram in cardiac myocytes. *Circ. Res.* 83:43–49

152. Chen Z, Friedrich GA, Soriano P. 1994. Transcriptional enhancer factor 1 disrup-tion by a retroviral gene trap leads to heart defects and embryonic lethality in mice. *Genes Dev.* 8:2293–301

153. Iyer NV, Kotch LE, Agani F, Leung SW,

Laughner E, et al. 1998. Cellular and developmental control of O2 homeostasis by hypoxia-inducible factor 1 alpha. *Genes Dev.* 12:149–62

154. Carmeliet P, Dor Y, Herbert JM, Fukumura D, Brusselmans K, et al. 1998. Role of HIF-1alpha in hypoxia-mediated apoptosis, cell proliferation and tumour angiogenesis. *Nature* 394:485–90

155. Donehower LA, Harvey M, Slagle BL, McArthur MJ, Montgomery CA, et al. 1992. Mice deficient for p53 are developmentally normal but susceptible to spontaneous tumours. *Nature* 356:215–21

156. Weinberg RA. 1995. The retinoblastoma protein and cell cycle control. *Cell* 81:323–30

157. Hunter T. 1997. Oncoprotein networks. *Cell* 88:333–46

158. Tamamori M, Ito H, Hiroe M, Terada Y, Marumo F, et al. 1998. Essential roles for G(1) cyclin-dependent kinase activity in development of cardiomyocyte hypertrophy. *Am. J. Physiol.* 44:H2036–40

159. Soonpaa MH, Koh GY, Pajak L, Jing SL, Wang H, et al. 1997. Cyclin D1 overexpression promotes cardiomyocyte DNA synthesis and multinucleation in transgenic mice. *J. Clin. Invest.* 99:2644–54

160. Skapek SX, Rhee J, Spicer DB, Lassar AB. 1995. Inhibition of myogenic differentiation in proliferating myoblasts by cyclin D1-dependent kinase. *Science* 267:1022–24

161. Guo K, Walsh K. 1997. Inhibition of myogenesis by multiple cyclin-Cdk complexes. Coordinate regulation of myogenesis and cell cycle activity at the level of E2F. *J. Biol. Chem.* 272:791–97

162. Schneider JW, Gu W, Zhu L, Mahdavi V, Nadal-Ginard B. 1994. Reversal of terminal differentiation mediated by p107 in Rb(−/−) muscle cells. *Science* 264:1467–71

163. Novitch BG, Mulligan GJ, Jacks T, Lassar AB. 1996. Skeletal muscle cells lacking the retinoblastoma protein display defects in muscle gene expression and accumulate in S and G(2) phases of the cell cycle. *J. Cell Biol.* 135:441–56

164. Sellers WR, Rodgers JW, Kaelin WG. 1995. A potent transrepression domain in the retinoblastoma protein induces a cell cycle arrest when bound to E2F sites. *Proc. Natl. Acad. Sci. USA* 92:11544–48

165. Chow KNB, Starostik P, Dean DC. 1996. The Rb family contains a conserved cyclin-dependent kinase-regulated transcriptional repressor motif. *Mol. Cell. Biol.* 16:7173–81

166. Gu W, Schneider JW, Condorelli G, Kaushal S, Mahdavi V, et al. 1993. Interaction of myogenic factors and the retinoblastoma protein mediates muscle cell commitment and differentiation. *Cell* 72:309–24

167. Tiainen M, Spitkovsky D, Jansen-Durr P, Sacchi A, Crescenzi M. 1996. Expression of E1A in terminally differentiated muscle cells reactivates the cell cycle and suppresses tissue-specific genes by separable mechanisms. *Mol. Cell. Biol.* 16:5302–12

168. Jones DL, Alani RM, Munger K. 1997. The human papillomavirus E7 oncoprotein can uncouple cellular differentiation and proliferation in human keratinocytes by abrogating p21(Cip1)-mediated inhibition of cdk2. *Gene Dev.* 11:2101–11

169. Sen D, Dunnmon P, Henderson S, Gerard RD, Chien KR. 1988. Terminally differentiated neonatal rat myocardial cells proliferate and maintain specific differentiated functions following expression of SV40 large T antigen. *J. Biol. Chem.* 263:19132–36

170. Jahn L, Sadoshima J, Greene A, Parker C, Morgan KG, et al. 1996. Conditional differentiation of heart- and smooth muscle-derived cells transformed by a temperature-sensitive mutant of SV40 t antigen. *J. Cell Sci.* 109:397–407

171. Kirshenbaum LA, Abdellatif M, Chakraborty S, Schneider MD. 1996. Human E2F-1 reactivates cell cycle progression

in ventricular myocytes and represses cardiac gene transcription. *Dev. Biol.* 179:402–11

172. Field LJ. 1988. Atrial natriuretic factor-SV40 T antigen transgenes produce tumors and cardiac arrhythmias in mice. *Science* 239:1029–33

173. Katz EB, Steinhelper ME, Delcarpio JB, Daud AI, Claycomb WC, et al. 1992. Cardiomyocyte proliferation in mice expressing alpha-cardiac myosin heavy chain-SV40 T-antigen transgenes. *Am. J. Physiol.* 262:H1867–76

174. DeLeon JR, Federoff HJ, Dickson DW, Vikstrom KL, Fishman GI. 1994. Cardiac and skeletal myopathy in beta myosin heavy-chain simian virus 40 tsA58 transgenic mice. *Proc. Natl. Acad. Sci. USA* 91:519–23

175. Steinhelper ME, Lanson NAJ, Dresdner KP, Delcarpio JB, Wit AL, et al. 1990. Proliferation in vivo and in culture of differentiated adult atrial cardiomyocytes from transgenic mice. *Am. J. Physiol.* 259:H1826–34

176. Koh GY, Soonpaa MH, Klug MG, Field LJ. 1993. Long-term survival of AT-1 cardiomyocyte grafts in syngeneic myocardium. *Am. J. Physiol.* 264:H1727–33

177. Daud AI, Lanson NA, Claycomb WC, Field LJ. 1993. Identification of SV40 large T-antigen-associated proteins in cardiomyocytes from transgenic mice. *Am. J. Physiol.* 264:H1693–700

178. Claycomb WC, Lanson NA, Stallworth BS, Egeland DB, Delcarpio JB, et al. 1998. HL-1 cells: a cardiac muscle cell line that contracts and retains phenotypic characteristics of the adult cardiomyocyte. *Proc. Natl. Acad. Sci. USA* 95: 2979–84

179. Kirshenbaum LA, Schneider MD. 1995. Adenovirus E1A represses cardiac gene transcription and reactivates DNA synthesis in ventricular myocytes, via alternative pocket protein- and p300-binding domains. *J. Biol. Chem.* 270:7791–94

180. Liu Y, Kitsis RN. 1996. Induction of DNA synthesis and apoptosis in cardiac myocytes by E1A oncoprotein. *J. Cell Biol.* 133:325–34

181. Bishopric NH, Zeng GQ, Sato B, Webster KA. 1997. Adenovirus E1A inhibits cardiac myocyte-specific gene expression through its amino terminus. *J. Biol. Chem.* 272:20584–94

182. Jacks T, Fazeli A, Schmitt EM, Bronson RT, Goodell MA, et al. 1992. Effects of an Rb mutation in the mouse. *Nature* 359:295–300

183. Lee EYHP, Chang CY, Hu NP, Wang YCJ, Lai CC, et al. 1992. Mice deficient for Rb are nonviable and show defects in neurogenesis and haematopoiesis. *Nature* 359:288–94

184. Clarke AR, Maandag ER, van Roon M, van der Lugt NM, van der Valk M, et al. 1992. Requirement for a functional Rb-1 gene in murine development. *Nature* 359:328–30

185. MacLellan WR, Frenkel PA, Vooijs M, Berns A, Schneider MD. 1998. Cardiac-restricted gene targeting of the retinoblastoma gene using the Cre/LoxP system. *Circulation* 98:I-608

186. LeCouter JE, Kablar B, Whyte PFM, Ying CY, Rudnicki MA. 1998. Strain-dependent embryonic lethality in mice lacking the retinoblastoma-related p130 gene. *Development* 125:4669–79

187. Weinberg RA. 1996. E2F and cell proliferation: a world turned upside down. *Cell* 85:457–59

188. LaBaer J, Garrett MD, Stevenson LF, Slingerland JM, Sandhu C, et al. 1997. New functional activities for the p21 family of CDK inhibitors. *Genes Dev.* 11:847–62

189. Arany Z, Sellers WR, Livingston DM, Eckner R. 1994. E1A-associated p300 and CREB-associated CBP belong to a conserved family of coactivators. *Cell* 77:799–800

190. Arany Z, Newsome D, Oldread E, Livingston DM, Eckner R. 1995. A family of transcriptional adaptor proteins tar-

geted by the E1A oncoprotein. *Nature* 374:81–84

191. Lundblad JR, Kwok RP, Laurance ME, Harter ML, Goodman RH. 1995. Adenoviral E1A-associated protein p300 as a functional homologue of the transcriptional co-activator CBP. *Nature* 374:85–88

192. Yao TP, Oh SP, Fuchs M, Zhou ND, Ch'ng LE, et al. 1998. Gene dosage-dependent embryonic development and proliferation defects in mice lacking the transcriptional integrator p300. *Cell* 93:361–72

193. Sherr CJ, Roberts JM. 1995. Inhibitors of mammalian G(1) cyclin-dependent kinases. *Genes Dev.* 9:1149–63

194. Serrano M, Lee HW, Chin L, Cordon-cardo C, Beach D, et al. 1996. Role of the INK4a locus in tumor suppression and cell mortality. *Cell* 85:27–37

195. Franklin DS, Godfrey VL, Lee HY, Kovalev GI, Schoonhoven R, et al. 1998. CDK inhibitors p18(INK4c) and p27(Kip1) mediate two separate pathways to collaboratively suppress pituitary tumorigenesis. *Genes Dev.* 12:2899–911

196. Parker SB, Eichele G, Zhang PM, Rawls A, Sands AT, et al. 1995. p53-independent expression of p21(Cip)1 in muscle and other terminally differentiating cells. *Science* 267:1024–27

197. Deng CX, Zhang PM, Harper JW, Elledge SJ, Leder P. 1995. Mice lacking p21(C/P1/WAF1) undergo normal development, but are defective in G1 checkpoint control. *Cell* 82:675–84

198. Polyak K, Lee MH, Erdjument-Bromage H, Koff A, Roberts JM, et al. 1994. Cloning of p27Kip1, a cyclin-dependent kinase inhibitor and a potential mediator of extracellular antimitogenic signals. *Cell* 78:59–66

199. Flink IL, Oana S, Maitra N, Bahl JJ, Morkin E. 1998. Changes in E2F complexes containing retinoblastoma protein family members and increased cyclin-dependent kinase inhibitor activities during terminal differentiation of cardiomyocytes. *J. Mol. Cell. Cardiol.* 30:563–78

200. Kiyokawa H, Kineman RD, Manovato-dorova KO, Soares VC, Hoffman ES, et al. 1996. Enhanced growth of mice lacking the cyclin-dependent kinase inhibitor function of p27(Kip1). *Cell* 85:721–32

201. Yan YM, Lee MH, Massagué J, Barbacid M. 1997. Ablation of the CDK inhibitor p57(Kip2) results in increased apoptosis and delayed differentiation during mouse development. *Genes Dev.* 11:973–83

202. Zhang P, Wong C, DePinho RA, Harper JW, Elledge SJ. 1998. Cooperation between the Cdk inhibitors p27(KIP1) and p57(KIP2) in the control of tissue growth and development. *Genes Dev.* 12:3162–67

203. Zhang PM, Wong C, Liu D, Finegold M, Harper JW, et al. 1999. p21(CIP1) and p57(KIP2) control muscle differentiation at the myogenin step. *Genes Dev.* 13:213–24

204. Agah R, Kirshenbaum LA, Truong LD, Chakraborty S, Abdellatif M, et al. 1997. Adenoviral delivery of E2F-1 directs cell cycle re-entry and p53-independent apoptosis in post-mitotic adult myocardium in vivo. *J. Clin. Invest.* 100:2722–28

Annu. Rev. Physiol. 2000. 62:321–51

Genetically Engineered Models with Alterations in Cardiac Membrane Calcium-Handling Proteins

Helen Kiriazis and Evangelia G. Kranias
Department of Pharmacology and Cell Biophysics, University of Cincinnati College of Medicine, Cincinnati, Ohio 45267–0575; e-mail: kraniaeg@email.uc.edu

Key Words Ca^{2+}-ATPase, phospholamban, calsequestrin, ryanodine receptor, Na^{+}/Ca^{2+} exchanger

■ **Abstract**   Regulation of intracellular Ca^{2+} provides a means by which the strength and duration of cardiac muscle contraction is altered on a beat-to-beat basis. Ca^{2+} homeostasis is maintained by proteins of the outer cell membrane or sarcolemma and the sarcoplasmic reticulum, which is the major intracellular Ca^{2+} storage organelle. Recently, genetic engineering techniques designed to induce specific mutations, manipulate expression levels, or change a particular isoform of various membrane Ca^{2+}-handling proteins have provided novel approaches in elucidating the physiological role of these gene products in the mammalian heart. This review summarizes findings in murine genetic models with alterations in the expression levels of the sarcolemmal Ca^{2+}-ATPase and Na^{+}/Ca^{2+} exchanger, which move Ca^{2+} across the cell membrane, and the sarcoplasmic reticulum proteins, which are involved in Ca^{2+} sequestration (Ca^{2+}-ATPase and its regulator, phospholamban), Ca^{2+} storage (calsequestrin), and Ca^{2+} release (ryanodine receptor, FK506-binding protein and junctin) during excitation-contraction coupling. Advances in genetic technology, coupled with the development of miniaturized technology to assess cardiac function at multiple levels in the mouse, have added a wealth of new information to our understanding of the functional role of each of these membrane Ca^{2+}-handling proteins in cardiac physiology and pathophysiology. Furthermore, these genetic models have provided valuable insights into the compensatory cross-talk mechanisms between the major membrane Ca^{2+}-handling proteins in the mammalian heart.

INTRODUCTION

This chapter focuses on genetically engineered models with alterations in Ca^{2+}-handling proteins of the sarcoplasmic reticulum and the sarcolemma, which are associated with alterations in cardiac function. In cardiac excitation-contraction, a small amount of Ca^{2+} enters the cell through the L-type Ca^{2+} channels and causes the release of Ca^{2+} from the sarcoplasmic reticulum store, via the Ca^{2+}

0066–4278/00/0315–0321$12.00

release channels or ryanodine receptors, for the initiation of contraction. Subsequently, relaxation is mediated by the rapid removal of cytosolic Ca^{2+}, which is predominantly re-sequestered into the sarcoplasmic reticulum by a Ca^{2+}-ATPase and extruded through the sarcolemma via the Na^+/Ca^{2+} exchanger and a Ca^{2+}-ATPase (Figure 1). The physiological role of several of these cardiac Ca^{2+} cycling proteins and their cross-talk with other regulatory mechanisms in the heart has recently been elucidated through the generation of genetically engineered animal models described below.

SARCOPLASMIC RETICULUM Ca^{2+}-ATPases

The rate of Ca^{2+} sequestration by the sarcoplasmic reticulum ATP-dependent Ca^{2+}-pump is a major determinant of the muscle relaxation rate. There are three highly homologous genes encoding the sarco(endo)plasmic reticulum Ca^{2+}-ATPase: *SERCA1, SERCA2,* and *SERCA3* (1). SERCA1a and SERCA1b are isoforms expressed in adult and neonatal fast-twitch skeletal muscle, respectively (2). SERCA2a is the cardiac and slow-twitch skeletal isoform (3), and SERCA2b is

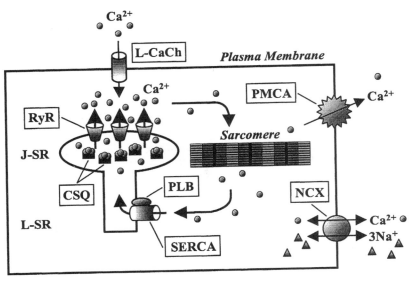

Figure 1 Ca^{2+} cycling and Ca^{2+} handling proteins of the cardiomyocyte. L-CaCh, L-type Ca^{2+} channel; RyR, ryanodine receptor; CSQ, calsequestrin; SERCA, sarcoplasmic reticulum Ca^{2+}-ATPase; PLB, phospholamban; PMCA, plasma membrane Ca^{2+}-ATPase; NCX, Na^+/Ca^{2+} exchanger; J-SR, junctional sarcoplasmic reticulum; L-SR, longitudinal sarcoplasmic reticulum.

expressed in smooth muscle and non-muscle tissues (4). SERCA3 is expressed in non-muscle tissues and mainly in epithelial and endothelial cells (5).

The cardiac isoform, SERCA2a, is abundantly expressed in the ventricular and atrial compartments of the mammalian heart. The role of the SERCA2 pump in the regulation of Ca^{2+} homeostasis and contractility in the heart has been recently defined by generating genetically engineered mice in which either SERCA2 is overexpressed in the cardiac compartment or ablated (knocked-out) using homologous recombination in embryonic stem cells.

Transgenic Mice with SERCA2 Overexpression in the Heart

Using a human cytomegalovirus immediate early enhancer linked to the chicken β-actin promoter, transgenic mice overexpressing a rat SERCA2 transgene were generated (6). SERCA2a mRNA was increased 2.6-fold, while protein levels were increased by only 1.2-fold. There were no alterations in the protein levels of the ryanodine receptor, calsequestrin, phospholamban, or Na$^+$/Ca^{2+} exchanger in the transgenic hearts (6).

Overexpression of SERCA2 was associated with increased rates of myocyte relengthening and shortening, as well as an increase in the percent cell shortening. The rate of intracellular Ca^{2+}-decline was accelerated in myocytes loaded with either Indo-1 (6) or Fluo-3 (7). The amplitude of the [Ca^{2+}]$_i$ transient was not significantly increased, although the sarcoplasmic reticulum Ca^{2+} content was increased by 29% in transgenic myocytes. There were no alterations in the function of the L-type Ca^{2+} channel, whereas the Na$^+$/Ca^{2+} exchanger was down-regulated by ~10% (7). The alterations at the cellular level also reflect similar alterations at the tissue level and in vivo (6). The time to half-relaxation and to half-maximum post-rest potentiation were both significantly shorter in isolated papillary muscles, suggesting that sarcoplasmic reticulum loading during a rest interval occurred faster in transgenic hearts. Furthermore, in vivo cardiac function evaluated by cardiac catheterization indicated that the basal rates of contraction and relaxation were significantly higher in transgenic hearts compared with wild-type. Isoproterenol stimulation augmented these contractile parameters in both groups. Under maximal isoproterenol stimulation, there were no differences between the transgenic and wild-type hearts. However, since the rate of relaxation (-dP/dt) can be affected by loading conditions, the preload independent measure of isovolumic relaxation, Tau, was also evaluated. Tau was significantly shorter in transgenics compared with wild-types and was unchanged by isoproterenol, indicating that the basal relaxation velocity in transgenic hearts was at its maximal value (6).

In another study, the rat SERCA2a cDNA driven by the α-myosin heavy chain promoter was overexpressed in mouse hearts (8). Two independent transgenic lines expressing 4-fold and 8-fold SERCA2 mRNA levels over those of control wild-type mice were obtained. However, despite the high mRNA levels, the protein levels were increased by only 1.3-fold and 1.5-fold in the transgenic hearts.

These observations were similar to those by He et al (6) and suggested that the mechanisms regulating SERCA2a protein levels are complex. Consistent with the increases in protein, the maximum velocity of the sarcoplasmic reticulum Ca^{2+}-transport rate was increased by 37% in the line overexpressing SERCA2a by 1.3-fold (Figure 2). However, the EC_{50} of the SERCA2a for Ca^{2+} was not altered, indicating that an increase in the relative stoichiometry of SERCA2a/phospholamban from 1/1 in wild-type hearts to 1.3/1 in transgenic hearts does not alter this intrinsic property of the Ca^{2+}-pump. These findings are in contrast to those of phospholamban genetically engineered hearts, where changes in the SERCA2a/phospholamban ratio correlated with alterations in the EC_{50} of SERCA2a for Ca^{2+} (see below). One explanation for this apparent discrepancy is that a change of only 30% in the ratio of SERCA2a/phospholamban, observed in SERCA2a overexpressing hearts, is too small to reflect an alteration in SERCA2a's EC_{50} for Ca^{2+}. Alternatively, the sarcoplasmic reticulum Ca^{2+} transport assay may not be sensitive enough to detect small changes in EC_{50} values. The increases in SERCA2a levels in the transgenic hearts reflected increases in contractile parameters assessed in work-performing preparations. Furthermore, the hearts expressing 1.5-fold SERCA2a exhibited higher stimulation of contractility than those expressing 1.3-fold SERCA2a. The stimulatory effects of SERCA2a overexpression were also associated with increases in the Ca^{2+} transient amplitude and contractile force in Fura-2 loaded isometrically contracting trabeculae (8).

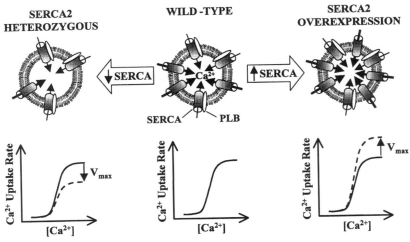

Figure 2 (*top*) Schematic representation of sarcoplasmic reticulum Ca^{2+}-ATPase (SERCA) and phospholamban (PLB) in native sarcoplasmic reticulum vesicles from SERCA2 heterozygous, wild-type and SERCA2 overexpression hearts. (*bottom*) Graphs illustrating Ca^{2+} uptake rate against Ca^{2+} concentration in sarcoplasmic reticulum vesicles from the three groups. Reduction in SERCA levels is associated with a decrease in the maximum velocity of the Ca^{2+} uptake rate (V_{max}), whereas an increase in SERCA levels augments the V_{max} value.

Thus overexpression of SERCA2a appears to result in relatively small increases in protein expression in the sarcoplasmic reticulum membrane but significant elevation of cardiac contractile parameters, as observed in two independent studies. It is difficult to compare the degree of stimulatory effects by the different levels of SERCA2a overexpression in these studies because different methods were used for the analysis of the obtained phenotype. However, it is interesting to note that He et al (6) reported maximal in vivo stimulation of Tau by 1.2-fold overexpression of SERCA2a, whereas Baker et al (8) observed a SERCA2a dosage effect, which was higher in 1.5-fold than 1.3-fold SERCA2a overexpressing work-performing hearts.

SERCA2 Heterozygous Mice

To gain a better understanding of the SERCA2 role in vivo, the promoter and 5' end of this gene were targeted in embryonic stem cells, using homologous recombination (9). Homozygous SERCA2 null mutants were not observed, indicating that SERCA2 deficiency resulted in lethality. Heterozygous mutant hearts expressed 55% of the mRNA and 65% of the protein levels of SERCA2 compared with wild-types (100%). The reduction in SERCA2 protein was associated with a similar reduction in the maximal velocity of sarcoplasmic reticulum Ca²⁺-uptake (Figure 2). However, EC_{50} values of the Ca²⁺-uptake were unchanged, indicating that the apparent decrease in the relative SERCA2/phospholamban from 1/1 in wild-type hearts to ~0.65/1 in SERCA2 heterozygous hearts did not result in changes of this intrinsic property of SERCA2. Thus altered SERCA2 levels do not result in changes in the EC_{50} of the Ca²⁺ transport system. These data are similar to those in SERCA2 overexpression hearts, as discussed above, but different than results obtained in phospholamban genetically altered mice, in which alterations in SERCA2/phospholamban closely correlated with alterations in the EC_{50} values of SERCA2 for Ca²⁺ (see below).

The reduction in SERCA2 levels and in sarcoplasmic reticulum Ca²⁺ transport reflects decreases in systolic ventricular pressure, rates of contraction and relaxation, and mean arterial blood pressure, assessed using transducers in the left ventricle and the right femoral artery. Dobutamine stimulated cardiac contractile parameters but the maximally elevated parameters in SERCA2 heterozygous hearts were significantly lower than those in wild-type hearts, consistent with reduced levels of SERCA2. Thus two functional copies of the *SERCA2* gene are required to maintain proper SERCA2 levels and Ca²⁺ homeostasis in the heart.

Transgenic Mice with Ectopic Expression of the Fast-Twitch Skeletal Muscle Sarcoplasmic Reticulum Ca²⁺-ATPase in the Heart

To determine whether the fast-twitch skeletal muscle sarcoplasmic reticulum Ca²⁺-ATPase isoform can functionally substitute for the cardiac SERCA2a isoform in the heart, a transgenic mouse overexpressing the rat SERCA1a specifically in the heart (driven by the α-myosin heavy chain promoter) was generated (10). Overexpression of SERCA1 resulted in a 2.5-fold increase in total SERCA protein, which was associated with decreases of 50% in the endogenous SERCA2a levels. It is interesting to note that high levels of SERCA1 protein overexpression may be achieved using the same promoter as for overexpression of SERCA2a, but in the case of SERCA2a, the highest protein expression levels were only 1.5-fold higher compared with wild-types (8). The reasons for these different levels of overexpression of the two SERCA isoforms are not known.

The increased SERCA protein was associated with similar increases in the steady-state SERCA phosphoenzyme intermediate, whereas the maximal velocity of the sarcoplasmic reticulum Ca^{2+} transport was increased by only 1.7-fold. There were no alterations in the expression levels of phospholamban, calsequestrin, actin, and tropomyosin in the transgenic hearts. The increases in sarcoplasmic reticulum Ca^{2+} transport rates reflected increases in the rates of shortening and relengthening as well as the rate of decay of the Ca^{2+} signal in ventricular myocytes. These changes were accompanied by similar alterations at the organ level, using work-performing heart preparations. It is interesting to note that the enhanced contractile parameters in hearts overexpressing SERCA1a by 2.5-fold were comparable to those observed in hearts overexpressing SERCA2a by 1.5-fold, indicating that the increased SERCA1a levels in the sarcoplasmic reticulum of transgenic hearts may not all be participating in Ca^{2+} sequestration, and that Ca^{2+} cycling in these hearts may be limited by other protein(s). Finally, the generation of the transgenic model overexpressing SERCA1a in the heart indicates that SERCA1a can substitute for SERCA2a in vivo, and this may provide another means for therapeutic approaches via gene therapy in the failing heart.

PHOSPHOLAMBAN

Phospholamban is a 52–amino acid phosphoprotein found in sarcoplasmic reticulum membranes of cardiac, slow-twitch skeletal and smooth muscles. The levels of phospholamban expression in slow-twitch skeletal and smooth muscles are much lower compared with that found in cardiac muscle, and its regulatory effects have been studied mainly in cardiac muscle. In vitro studies, using purified cardiac sarcoplasmic reticulum membranes, have shown that phospholamban can be phosphorylated at three distinct sites by various protein kinases: serine[10] by protein kinase C, serine[16] by cAMP-dependent protein kinase, and threonine[17] by Ca^{2+}-calmodulin-dependent protein kinase (11). Each phosphorylation site is associated with stimulation of the apparent affinity of the Ca^{2+}-ATPase for Ca^{2+} (11–20). Phospholamban is also phosphorylated in vivo during β-adrenergic stimulation of the heart (21, 22). Phosphorylation occurs on both serine[16] and threonine[17] of phospholamban, which are the cAMP-dependent protein kinase and Ca^{2+}-calmodulin-dependent protein kinase substrate sites, respectively. Phosphorylation of phospholamban in vivo has been postulated to be responsible, at least partially, for the lusitropic and inotropic effects of β-agonists in vivo.

Although considerable information on the mechanism by which phospholamban regulates the sarcoplasmic reticulum Ca^{2+}-ATPase activity was generated from in vitro and in vivo studies, the physiological role of this protein in modulating basal myocardial contractility was only recently revealed through the generation and characterization of genetically engineered mouse models with altered expression of phospholamban protein levels.

Phospholamban-Deficient Mice

In this mouse model, the coding region in the murine phospholamban gene was ablated, using homologous recombination in embryonic stem cells, and mice heterozygous and homozygous for the phospholamban-ablated gene were generated (23, 24). The phospholamban-heterozygous mice expressed 40% of the phospholamban protein levels present in wild-types, whereas the phospholamban-homozygous mice expressed no phospholamban mRNA or protein. Reduction or ablation of phospholamban was not associated with any phenotypic alterations at the gross morphology or ultrastructural levels (25). However, there were increases in the affinity of the sarcoplasmic reticulum Ca^{2+}-ATPase for Ca^{2+} (Figure 3). Furthermore, an apparent linear correlation between the levels of phospholamban and the Ca^{2+}-affinity of the sarcoplasmic reticulum Ca^{2+}-ATPase was observed, indicating that phospholamban is a major regulator of this intrinsic property of the enzyme (23, 24). The alterations at the sarcoplasmic reticulum level reflect similar alterations at the cellular level. Reduction or ablation of phospholamban results in enhanced myocyte mechanics (extent of cell shortening, rate of contraction, and rate of relengthening) and Ca^{2+} kinetics in Fura-2 or Indo-1 loaded myocytes (26, 27). Assessment of the spontaneous Ca^{2+} sparks (elementary release events) in isolated myocytes indicates that these sparks are three times more frequent and are larger in phospholamban-knockout than in wild-type cells (28). These alterations in the dynamics of cardiac myocyte mechanics are associated with parallel alterations in cardiac contractile parameters, assessed in work-performing heart preparations under identical venous returns, afterloads, and heart rates. The rates of contraction (+dP/dt) and relaxation (-dP/dt) are significantly higher in phospholamban-heterozygous hearts compared with wild-types and even higher in phospholamban-deficient hearts compared with phospholamban-heterozygotes. The increases in contractile parameters at the myocyte and organ levels upon reduction or ablation of phospholamban reflect similar increases at the intact animal level (29). A Millar micro-tip transducer was inserted into the right carotid artery and advanced into the left ventricle for direct measurement of ventricular pressure and contractile parameters in phospholamban-knockout, phospholamban-heterozygous, and wild-type mice. There were no differences in heart rate or left ventricular end-diastolic pressure. However, the cardiac basal parameters for contraction and relaxation were higher in phospholamban-

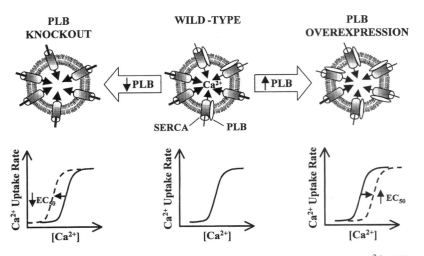

Figure 3 (*top*) Schematic representation of sarcoplasmic reticulum Ca^{2+}-ATPase (SERCA) and phospholamban (PLB) in native sarcoplasmic reticulum vesicles from PLB-knockout, wild-type and PLB overexpression hearts. (*bottom*) Graphs illustrating Ca^{2+} uptake rate against Ca^{2+} concentration in sarcoplasmic reticulum vesicles from the three groups. Ablation of PLB is associated with a leftward shift in the EC_{50} value, indicating an increase in the affinity of SERCA for Ca^{2+}, whereas overexpression of PLB induces a rightward shift in the EC_{50} corresponding to a decrease in the affinity of SERCA for Ca^{2+}.

heterozygous and even more so in phospholamban-knockout mice compared with wild-types. Similarly, ablation of phospholamban was associated with significant increases in the velocity of circumferential fiber shortening (corrected for heart rate), peak aortic velocity, mean aortic acceleration, and peak early diastolic transmitral velocity in the intact mouse using M-mode and Doppler echocardiography (30).

The basal cardiac rates of contraction and relaxation in isolated myocytes, perfused hearts, or in intact mice were linearly correlated with the levels of phospholamban in these hearts, indicating that phospholamban is a major regulator of myocardial contractility (24, 29). The elevated contractile parameters of the phospholamban-knockout and phospholamban-heterozygous hearts could be stimulated by isoproterenol, but to a much lower extent than those of wild-type hearts. Under maximal isoproterenol stimulation, the values in all three groups were similar (31, 24).

To determine whether phospholamban ablation and the resultant hyperdynamic cardiac function were associated with any alterations in the protein levels of the major Ca^{2+}-handling proteins, the levels of these proteins were assessed (25). The cardiac sarcoplasmic reticulum Ca^{2+}-ATPase, calsequestrin, Na^+/Ca^{2+} exchanger, myosin, actin, troponin I, and troponin T levels were not altered, but the ryanodine receptor protein levels were significantly decreased (25%) upon ablation of phospholamban. This might reflect an attempt to regulate Ca^{2+} release from the sarcoplasmic reticulum, which had a significantly higher diastolic Ca^{2+} content in phospholamban-knockout compared with wild-type sarcoplasmic reticulum. This increase in sarcoplasmic reticulum Ca^{2+} content, which was available for subsequent release, resulted in faster inactivation of the Ca^{2+} channel current, as assessed in ventricular myocytes (32). Examination of ATP levels revealed no alterations, although oxygen consumption, determined in work-performing preparations, increased (1.6-fold) to meet the increased ATP utilization in the hyperdynamic phospholamban-knockout hearts. The increases in oxygen consumption were associated with increases (2.2-fold) in the active fraction of the mitochondrial pyruvate dehydrogenase, suggesting increased tricarboxylic acid cycle turnover and ATP synthesis. ^{31}P nuclear magnetic resonance studies demonstrated decreases in phosphocreatine levels and increases in ADP and AMP levels in phospholamban-knockout compared with wild-type hearts. However, there are no differences in creatine kinase activity or creatine kinase reaction velocity (25). Thus it appears that metabolic adaptations established a new energetic steady state such that the increased ATP demands in the hyperdynamic phospholamban-knockout hearts could be met.

To determine whether the attenuated response of the phospholamban-knockout hearts to β-agonists was associated with any alterations in the β-signaling pathway, the β-adrenergic receptor density, adenylyl cyclase activity, tissue cAMP levels, and the basal phosphoprotein patterns in the heart were examined (31). No alterations were found. Isoproterenol perfusion resulted in similar increases in tissue cAMP levels and the degree of phosphorylation of troponin I, C-protein, and the 15-kDa sarcolemmal protein in both the wild-type and phospholamban-knockout hearts. Furthermore, the phospholamban-knockout mice exercised as well as wild-type animals, as measured by duration of exercise and peak oxygen consumption (33). The oxygen pulse (peak oxygen consumption/heart rate) curve was also normal in the knockout mice, suggesting that stroke volume and oxygen extraction could be increased during graded treadmill exercise. Thus phospholamban ablation did not appear to compromise cardiac performance during maximal cardiovascular stress provided by graded treadmill exercise. A longitudinal study of phospholamban-knockout mice and their isogenic wild-types indicated that the hyperdynamic cardiac function of the phospholamban-knockout hearts persisted throughout the aging process, without any alterations in heart-to-body mass ratio, cardiac cell length, or sarcomere length. Furthermore, phospholamban ablation did not compromise the animal's life span (34).

Phospholamban is also present in smooth muscle, although expression in this tissue is much lower than in the heart. The availability of the phospholamban-knockout model allowed elucidation of the functional role of this protein in vascular smooth muscle contractility (35). Ablation of phospholamban was associated with a faster time course of force development with phenylephrine stimulation, and decreased sensitivity to both phenylephrine and potassium chloride in aortic smooth muscle. These effects were abolished by sarcoplasmic reticulum inhibition. Thus phospholamban appears to be an important regulator of contractility in vascular smooth muscle, as well.

Transgenic Mice with Reinsertion of the Missing Phospholamban Gene in the Phospholamban-Deficient Heart

To determine whether re-introduction of the missing gene could reverse the hyperdynamic function of phospholamban-deficient hearts, phospholamban expression in the cardiac compartment of the null background was directed using the α-myosin heavy chain promoter (36). The mouse phospholamban cDNA fragment containing the coding region and the endogenous polyadenylation signal sequence was ligated to the α-myosin heavy chain promoter, and a SV40 polyadenylation signal was ligated at the 3' end of the phospholamban cDNA. The degree of reversal was proportional to the level of phospholamban expression. The successful use of transgenesis in the genetically altered murine background offered a unique system for studying phospholamban structural and functional relations in vivo. Studies have been conducted in which specific phospholamban mutants were used to address the functional significance of dual site phospholamban phosphorylation during β-adrenergic stimulation and the functional unit of phospholamban in vivo.

During β-adrenergic stimulation of cardiac muscle, both serine[16] and threonine[17], which are the substrates of cAMP-dependent and Ca^{2+}-calmodulin-dependent protein kinases in vitro, respectively, are phosphorylated in beating hearts. Although the phosphorylation of these two sites appears to be totally independent in vitro, phosphorylation of threonine[17] in vivo occurs mainly by agents that elevate cAMP levels. To better elucidate the functional significance of the two phosphorylation sites, a site-specific mutation converting serine[16] to alanine[16] in the phospholamban coding region was introduced, and cardiac-specific expression of mutant phospholamban in the null background was directed. Transgenic lines expressing similar levels (0.7-fold) of phospholamban-mutant or phospholamban-wild-type in the knockout background were studied in parallel. Both forms of phospholamban were capable of inhibiting the basal contractile parameters of the knockout hearts to the same extent, indicating that the phospholamban-mutant was capable of modulating basal contractility in a manner similar to wild-type phospholamban. However, isoproterenol stimulation was associated with much lower enhancement of the contractile parameters in phospholamban-mutant compared with phospholamban-wild-type hearts. The maximal increases in the rates of contraction ($+dP/dt$) and relaxation ($-dP/dt$) in mutant hearts were comparable to those of phospholamban-knockout hearts under β-adrenergic stimulation. These findings suggest that mutation of serine[16] in phospholamban compromises the contribution of this phosphoprotein to the stimulatory responses of the cardiac contractile parameters to isoproterenol. Actually, inclusion of ³²P-orthophosphate in the perfusion buffer indicated no ³²P-labeling of the phospholamban-mutant but equal phosphorylation of troponin I and C-protein in the phospholamban-mutant and wild-type hearts. To exclude the possibility that the lack of phospholamban threonine[17] phosphorylation in vivo was due to conversion of the adjacent serine[16] to alanine[16] residue, cardiac homogenates were incubated in vitro under optimal conditions for Ca²⁺-calmodulin-dependent phosphorylation. The degree of mutant phospholamban phosphorylation on threonine[17] was similar to that of wild-type phospholamban, demonstrating that the mutant form was capable of being phosphorylated on threonine[17]. Thus in vivo phosphorylation of threonine[17] requires prior phosphorylation of serine[16] in phospholamban, and prevention of phosphoserine formation results in attenuation of the β-agonist stimulatory responses in the mammalian heart.

To elucidate the active form of phospholamban in vivo, since both phospholamban monomers as well as phospholamban pentamers are active in inhibiting the affinity of the sarcoplasmic reticulum Ca²⁺-ATPase for Ca²⁺ (37, 38), a mutation (cysteine[41] to phenylalanine[41]) in the coding region, which results in phospholamban monomers, was introduced. Cardiac-specific expression of phospholamban-mutant (monomers) or phospholamban-wild-type (pentamers) molecules in the null background were directed using the α-myosin heavy chain promoter (39). Transgenic lines expressing similar levels of mutant-phospholamban or wild-type phospholamban were obtained, and their cardiac phenotypes were analyzed in parallel. Sarcoplasmic reticulum Ca²⁺-transport assays indicate similar decreases in SERCA2 Ca²⁺ affinity by mutant or wild-type phospholamban. However, the time constants of relaxation and Ca²⁺ transient decline in isolated cardiomyocytes were diminished to a greater extent by wild-type than mutant phospholamban, even without significant differences in the amplitudes of myocyte contraction or Ca²⁺ transients between the two groups. Langendorff perfusions also indicated that mutant phospholamban was not capable of depressing the enhanced relaxation parameters of the phospholamban-knockout hearts to the same extent as wild-type phospholamban. Moreover, in vivo assessment of mouse hemodynamics revealed a greater depression of cardiac function in wild-type than in mutant phospholamban hearts. Thus the mutant or monomeric form of phospholamban was not as effective in slowing Ca²⁺ decline or relaxation in cardiomyocytes, hearts, or in intact animals as was wild-type or pentameric phospholamban, indicating that pentameric assembly of phospholamban may be necessary for optimal regulation of myocardial contractility in vivo.

Transgenic Mice Overexpressing Phospholamban in the Heart

The functional stoichiometry of phospholamban to sarcoplasmic reticulum Ca²⁺-ATPase is not currently known. To attempt to define this stoichiometry in vivo, cardiac-specific overexpression of phospholamban, using the cardiac-specific α-myosin heavy chain promoter, was carried out. Transgenic mice expressed twofold higher levels of phospholamban in the heart compared with their wild-type littermates. No phenotypic alterations, no changes in heart-to-body mass ratio, heart-to-lung mass ratio, and cardiomyocyte size could be detected. Isolated unloaded cardiac myocytes from transgenic mice exhibited diminished shortening fraction and decreased rates of shortening and relengthening compared with wild-type cardiomyocytes. The decreases in contractile parameters of transgenic cardiomyocytes reflect decreases in the amplitude of the Ca^{2+} signal and prolongation in the time for decay of the Ca^{2+} signal, which is associated with a decrease in the apparent affinity of the sarcoplasmic reticulum Ca^{2+}-ATPase for Ca^{2+} (Figure 3), compared with wild-type cardiomyocytes. In vivo analysis of left ventricular systolic function using M-mode and pulsed-wave Doppler echocardiography revealed decreases in fractional shortening and mean velocity of circumferential fiber shortening (corrected for heart rate) in the transgenic mice. The differences in contractile parameters and Ca^{2+} kinetics in transgenic cardiomyocytes and the depressed left ventricular systolic function in transgenic mice were abolished upon isoproterenol stimulation, which resulted in phosphorylation of phospholamban and relief of its inhibitory effects on the sarcoplasmic reticulum Ca^{2+}-ATPase. Thus these studies indicate that a fraction of the sarcoplasmic reticulum Ca^{2+}-ATPases are not functionally regulated by phospholamban in vivo.

Phospholamban overexpression is not only associated with inhibition of contractile parameters in ventricular muscle but also in atrial muscle. The levels of phospholamban are threefold higher in the atrial muscles of the overexpressing mice compared with their isogenic wild-types. Atrial phospholamban overexpression is associated with depressed rates of contraction and relaxation. Isoproterenol stimulation results in significant increases in time-to-peak tension and half-relaxation time. Similar results were obtained when phospholamban-overexpression was targeted only to the atria. When levels of phospholamban were increased eight- to ninefold in the left atrium (40), Ca^{2+} uptake by sarcoplasmic reticulum was depressed, the time course of contraction was prolonged, and basal developed tension was decreased. The depressant effects of phospholamban were also reversed by isoproterenol in this study (40).

Phospholamban overexpression in atrial myocytes was not associated with any alterations in cell capacitance, voltage dependence of the Ca^{2+} channel current, and average current density. However, the fast component of inactivation of the Ca^{2+} channel current was significantly reduced in phospholamban overexpression myocytes (41), indicating a fine-tuning cross-talk between sarcoplasmic reticulum Ca^{2+} load and the kinetics of inactivation of the sarcolemmal Ca^{2+} channel, consistent with the data obtained with the phospholamban-knockout myocytes.

CALSEQUESTRIN

Calsequestrin is a high-capacity, low-to-moderate affinity Ca^{2+}-binding protein in the sarcoplasmic reticulum lumen (42) where it is essentially anchored to the junctional sarcoplasmic reticulum membrane (43). Calsequestrin, junctin, triadin, and the ryanodine receptor are hypothesized to form a functional complex at the cardiac junctional sarcoplasmic reticulum, which coordinates Ca^{2+} release per beat (44). In mammals there are two known isoforms of calsequestrin, cardiac and fast-skeletal muscle types, each encoded by different genes (45). The cardiac isoform is highly conserved between species (45). The recently deduced amino acid sequence of mouse cardiac calsequestrin is composed of 396 amino acid residues and has a protein homology of 90% compared to canine or rabbit cardiac calsequestrin (46). Expression of cardiac calsequestrin appears to be under tight control. It is the only isoform expressed in the developing, adult, and aging heart (45). In addition, unlike other Ca^{2+}-handling proteins, cardiac calsequestrin expression levels remain essentially unchanged in end-stage heart failure. Transgenesis was used to override this seemingly tight control on the expression level of calsequestrin and enabled the assessment of the overexpression effects of this protein in the heart.

Transgenic Mice with Cardiac-Specific Overexpression of Calsequestrin

Valuable insights on the physiological role of calsequestrin have been gained from the generation of two transgenic mouse models with the specific overexpression of cardiac calsequestrin in the heart (46, 47). In one model, the transgene construct, which was used for mouse embryo microinjections, consisted of the α-myosin heavy chain promoter, the entire canine cardiac calsequestrin protein coding region (including the signal peptide sequence), and the transcriptional terminator SV40 polyadenylation signal sequence (47). Immunoblot analysis of ventricular homogenates from the resultant transgenic mice revealed a 10-fold higher calsequestrin expression level compared with wild-type mice (47). In another model, the transgenic construct consisted of the α-myosin heavy chain promoter, the entire mouse cardiac calsequestrin protein coding region (including the signal peptide sequence), and the human growth hormone polyadenylation signal sequence (46). Three transgenic lines were identified and immunoblot analysis of cardiac homogenates from these lines revealed mouse cardiac calsequestrin protein levels increased by 20-, 43-, and 56-fold, respectively, compared with homogenates of wild-type hearts (46).

An interesting feature of mouse hearts with overexpression of cardiac calsequestrin was the development of cardiac hypertrophy (46, 47), although the degree of hypertrophy did not correlate with the overall amount of cardiac calsequestrin. Transgenic lines showing 20-, 43-, and 56-fold overexpression of mouse cardiac calsequestrin were characterized by a 30, 66, and 43% increase in the heart-to-body mass ratio, respectively (46), whereas 10-fold overexpression of canine cardiac calsequestrin resulted in ~100% increase in the heart-to-body mass ratio (47). Hypertrophy was also confirmed at the myocyte level (46, 47). Echocardiographic assessment of transgenic hearts revealed that the hypertrophy was concentric in nature, i.e. an increase in left ventricular wall thickness relative to cavity size (48). However, hearts with overexpression of canine cardiac calsequestrin progressed from concentric hypertrophy at 7 weeks of age to dilated cardiomyopathy at 13 weeks of age (49). The hypertrophic response of hearts was associated with induction of a fetal gene program, namely, increases in atrial natriuretic factor, α-skeletal actin, and β-myosin heavy chain transcripts (46).

Electron microscopic analysis on 4-week hearts overexpressing canine cardiac calsequestrin revealed the presence of many vesicles, presumably filled with calsequestrin (47). Junctions between the sarcoplasmic reticulum and the surface membrane or transverse tubules were reduced. Furthermore, junctions were smaller with fewer feet, and the calsequestrin content was not clumped; rather, it was more dispersed in comparison to wild-type myocardium (47). Myofibril and mitochondrial organization was disrupted, which, at least partly, accounted for the notable absence of clear striations in ventricular myocytes (as observed in light microscopy) isolated from these transgenic animals (47). Immunofluorescence microscopy was employed to examine the subcellular localization of calsequestrin in the transgenic adult ventricles overexpressing mouse cardiac calsequestrin. Calsequestrin-specific transverse-striated staining patterns (with a periodicity of $\sim$2 μm) were similar between ventricular tissue sectioned from transgenic and wild-type hearts, except that the former had much increased staining, consistent with the presence of more calsequestrin (46). There were only a few areas in sections from these transgenic hearts with a somewhat irregular staining pattern, suggesting some disruption of the terminal cisternae at the level of the Z-disc (46).

In addition to data from immunoblotting and histological analyses, indicating that calsequestrin was indeed overexpressed in transgenic hearts, functional confirmation of the presence of an increased amount of calsequestrin and Ca^{2+} storage in the sarcoplasmic reticulum was obtained with the application of caffeine. Caffeine, which opens the ryanodine receptors of the sarcoplasmic reticulum, caused a significantly greater sarcoplasmic reticulum Ca^{2+} release in transgenic myocytes in comparison to wild-type myocytes (46, 47). Surprisingly, despite the enhanced Ca^{2+} storage capacity of the sarcoplasmic reticulum, the amplitude of Ca^{2+} transients elicited upon depolarization was markedly reduced in transgenic myocytes (46, 47) (Figure 4). Even the frequency of Ca^{2+} sparks was reduced (47). Hence, there is an apparent impairment of Ca^{2+} release from the sarcoplasmic reticulum in transgenic hearts. The resultant lower amplitudes of Ca^{2+} release per beat in the vicinity of the sarcolemmal L-type Ca^{2+} channels of transgenic myocytes would be expected to induce a prolongation in the inactivation of the L-type Ca^{2+} current, as was the case (46, 47).

The transgenic animals expressing the canine-derived isoform are characterized by a marked downregulation of the junctional sarcoplasmic reticulum proteins: ryanodine receptor, triadin, and junctin (47). Although these proteins, along with calsequestrin, have been implicated as playing a role during normal Ca^{2+} release (44), it was hypothesized that a reduction in their protein expression levels was not the sole factor leading to the observed attenuation in Ca^{2+} release (47). Rather, a defect in L-type Ca^{2+} channel/ryanodine receptor signaling was pro-

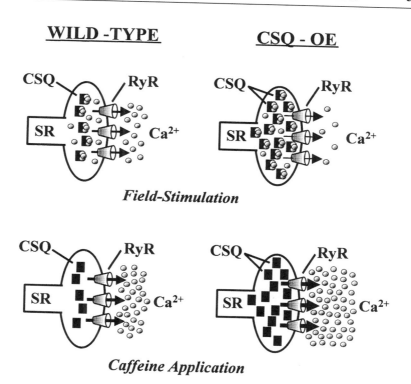

Figure 4   Schematic illustration of Ca^{2+} release from the sarcoplasmic reticulum in wild-type and calsequestrin overexpression (CSQ-OE) hearts. Field-stimulation resulted in less Ca^{2+} release in CSQ-OE versus wild-types. In contrast, upon the application of caffeine there was a markedly augmented sarcoplasmic reticulum Ca^{2+} release in transgenic hearts.

posed (47). Recent data on these mice suggest that low concentrations of caffeine (0.5 mM) alleviate defects in Ca^{2+}-induced Ca^{2+} release, probably by enhancing the Ca^{2+} sensitivity of the ryanodine receptors (50). It is interesting to note that although overexpression of murine cardiac calsequestrin does not affect the protein levels of ryanodine receptor, triadin, and junctin, Ca^{2+} release from the sarcoplasmic reticulum is also depressed (46). Furthermore, protein levels of FKBP12 (a FK506-binding protein, see below), which stabilize ryanodine receptors, were significantly reduced, possibly representing a compensatory mechanism to promote more Ca^{2+} release from the sarcoplasmic reticulum (46). A decrease in L-type Ca^{2+} current density, implying a reduced Ca^{2+} influx across the sarcolemma could have, at least partly, led to the attenuated sarcoplasmic reticulum Ca^{2+} release (46). Because there are more calsequestrin molecules in the sarcoplasmic reticulum per se, it is likely that they may have contributed to the impairment of normal Ca^{2+} release (see below).

Interestingly, proteins affecting the uptake of Ca^{2+} into the sarcoplasmic reticulum (Ca^{2+}-ATPase, phospholamban), were augmented or relatively unchanged. Sarcoplasmic reticulum Ca^{2+}-ATPase protein levels and phospholamban levels were markedly upregulated in hearts overexpressing mouse cardiac calsequestrin, although, due to parallel changes in these proteins, the ratio between the Ca^{2+}-ATPase and its inhibitor was unchanged (46). Hearts overexpressing canine cardiac calsequestrin had a modest (less than 30%) increase in sarcoplasmic reticulum Ca^{2+}-ATPase levels and no change in phospholamban levels (47). In vitro studies using cardiac homogenates revealed an enhanced Ca^{2+} uptake in the transgenic group, which was attributed to the modest increase in the Ca^{2+}-pumps or the expanded volume of the sarcoplasmic reticulum (47). An increase in the maximal velocity of the sarcoplasmic reticulum Ca^{2+}-pump, due to augmented levels of this protein, may be an adaptive mechanism to promote an increase in the amplitude of the Ca^{2+} transient (46).

Consistent with the reduction in Ca^{2+}-induced Ca^{2+} release from the sarcoplasmic reticulum, contractile parameters were depressed. This was evident in mice overexpressing murine cardiac calsequestrin at the cellular and organ levels and in vivo (46). Higher levels of calsequestrin expression were not associated with any further depression of contractile parameters (46). Animals overexpressing canine cardiac calsequestrin also showed depressed cardiac function (49, 51). Both the murine and canine cardiac calsequestrin overexpressing hearts have altered force-frequency relations with respect to wild-type hearts and exhibit pulsus alternans at high frequencies of stimulation, implying abnormal intracellular Ca^{2+} handling (51, 52). Recent data indicate that ablating phospholamban and thus promoting more Ca^{2+} cycling into the sarcoplasmic reticulum of hearts with 20-fold overexpression of mouse cardiac calsequestrin, restores the contractile parameters to normal levels (53).

Thus transgenesis reveals that it is possible to overexpress calsequestrin by many-fold in the lumen of the sarcoplasmic reticulum despite the seemingly tight regulation of calsequestrin expression in cardiac tissue during development, aging, and pathological conditions. The lumen is able to accommodate extra calsequestrin molecules and, consequently, additional Ca^{2+} ions. Evaluation of transgenic animals with calsequestrin overexpression indicates that calsequestrin regulates the amount of Ca^{2+} stored in the sarcoplasmic reticulum and the amount of Ca^{2+} released during excitation-contraction coupling (46, 47). Under normal conditions, Ca^{2+} release from sarcoplasmic reticulum of transgenic hearts is much depressed, leading to poor function. The cardiac hypertrophic response evident in this model may be an attempt to correct the contractile dysfunction. However, this also complicates the evaluation of the effects of calsequestrin overexpression per se. For instance, the appearance of pulsus alternans, evident in hearts with overexpression of calsequestrin, is also observed in pressure overload hypertrophy. Despite these limitations, the calsequestrin overexpression models provide the opportunity to further dissect the functional characteristics of this protein. The fact that the sarcoplasmic reticulum Ca^{2+} store is filled with Ca^{2+}, yet reduced levels are released per beat, warrants further investigation. It was suggested that the increased sarcoplasmic reticulum luminal Ca^{2+} concentration directly inhibits the ryanodine receptors (47). However, it may be that the free luminal Ca^{2+} concentration is now lower in transgenic hearts because of the extra sarcoplasmic reticulum Ca^{2+} buffered by more molecules of calsequestrin, thus reducing the amount of Ca^{2+} available for release (46) (Figure 4). In fact, ablating phospholamban restores function (53) by presumably promoting more Ca^{2+} uptake into the sarcoplasmic reticulum and elevating the free luminal Ca^{2+} concentration. If Ca^{2+} needs to first dissociate from calsequestrin before being released, then association and dissociation constants are also important. Perhaps the presence of more calsequestrin molecules around the Ca^{2+} release sites hinders Ca^{2+} release by their continuous association and dissociation with Ca^{2+}, or by simply crowding the exit. As ryanodine receptors are open for only a finite time during excitation-contraction coupling, such a phenomenon in itself may be implicated in reducing the total amount of Ca^{2+} released and altering the kinetics of Ca^{2+} release from the sarcoplasmic reticulum.

THE Ca²⁺ RELEASE COMPLEX

Ca^{2+} is released from the sarcoplasmic reticulum via the ryanodine receptors. There are three subtypes of ryanodine receptors in mammalian tissues (RyR1, RyR2, and RyR3); RyR2 is the predominant cardiac isoform (54). Ryanodine receptors are located in the sarcoplasmic reticulum membrane (terminal cisternae) juxtaposed to the sarcolemma (surface or transverse tubules). Ryanodine receptor channels are tetramers, i.e. consisting of four ~560 kDa ryanodine receptor subunits (54). The foot structures, which are seen ultrastructurally and span the gap between the sarcolemma and sarcoplasmic reticulum, correspond to the cytoplasmic domains of the ryanodine receptor channels (55). Ryanodine receptors are associated with a number of proteins, namely FKBP, junctin, triadin, and calsequestrin (Figure 5).

FKBPs are known for their immunosuppressive properties; however, a number have been found to make complexes with other proteins. FKBP12, a 12-kDa FKBP, associates with the skeletal muscle ryanodine receptor (56). Four FKBP12 molecules are associated with each ryanodine receptor channel, i.e. one FKBP12 per ryanodine receptor subunit (56). The analogous situation is present in cardiac muscle except that another isoform, FKBP12.6, selectively binds the cardiac ryanodine receptor (57). However, FKBP12 is also detectable in the cytoplasm of cardiac muscle. FKBP modulates the gating properties of ryanodine receptors in skeletal muscle, but there are conflicting data concerning its role in cardiac muscle (cf 57–59). Planar lipid bilayer experiments indicate that FKBP12 stabilizes skeletal ryanodine receptor channel opening, reducing the opening probability, but the channels that do open are more likely to reach full conductance levels (60).

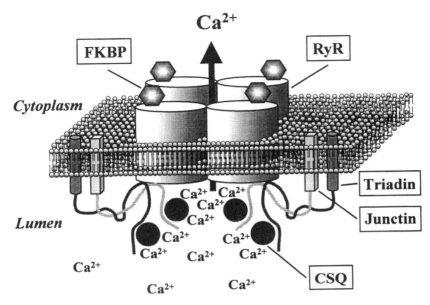

Figure 5 Schematic representation depicting the relation between ryanodine receptor (RyR), FK506-binding protein (FKBP), calsequestrin (CSQ), junctin, and triadin. Junctin and triadin have been proposed to interact with RyR, CSQ, and with each other (44).

Two other proteins associated with the ryanodine receptor, junctin, and triadin have been partially characterized, and a junctin overexpression transgenic model has been generated (see below). Although they are products of different genes, these proteins have remarkable similarities and are possibly involved in physically anchoring calsequestrin to the Ca^{2+} release site of the sarcoplasmic reticulum (44) (see Figure 5). Junctin is a 26-kDa protein (42, 44), whereas there are three cardiac muscle isoforms of triadin (with apparent M_r of 35,000, 40,000, and 92,000) (61). A model depicting the putative organization of the ryanodine receptor, calsequestrin, junctin, and triadin, working in concert to coordinate Ca^{2+} release from the sarcoplasmic reticulum, has been recently proposed (44).

Ryanodine Receptor-Deficient Mice

RyR2 was recently targeted by Takeshima et al (62). The authors introduced a *loxP* sequence into the 5'-untranslated region of exon 1 of the mouse *RyR2* gene, and another *loxP* sequence was inserted into intron 1; the resultant homologously recombined gene (*crr*^ml) was used to generate mutant mice. Mutant mice homozygous for *crr*^ml exhibit no phenotype (indicating that the *crr*^ml mutation is a silent mutation in *RyR2*).

In addition, embryonic stem cells containing crr^{m1} were further treated (with an adenoviral vector containing Cre recombinase) to obtain a recombinant mutant gene (crr^{m2}), which lacked the sequences flanked by the *loxP* sites. This resulted in the removal of 48 base pairs of the first protein-coding sequence and the partial sequence of intron 1 from the *RyR2* gene. Embryonic stem cells containing crr^{m2} were used to generate mutant mice, but there were no live mice homozygous for crr^{m2} produced. These mice would be expected to completely lack a functional cardiac ryanodine receptor. Upon further investigation, it was discerned that homozygous mutants (crr^{m2}/crr^{m2}) were present in the early embryonic stage but died in utero around embryonic day 10. These mutants had no histological abnormalities at embryonic day 8.5, although ultrastructural examination of cardiac myocytes revealed that the rough endoplasmic reticulum was somewhat swollen. Clear differences were evident between the mutant and control embryos at embryonic day 9.5. Specifically, a delayed developmental progress was noted for the mutants, and histological examination of the ventricular wall of mutant hearts revealed an abnormal arrangement of myocytes in the myocardium and a disorganized epicardium. In addition, cardiac myocytes of embryonic day 9.5 mutant animals failed to show Ca^{2+} transients upon application of caffeine, whereas caffeine-induced Ca^{2+} transients were observed in control embryonic myocytes. Although hearts from both groups displayed spontaneous rhythmic contractions at embryonic day 9.5, which was consistent with the presence of spontaneous Ca^{2+} oscillations in cardiac myocytes, this feature was not attributed to the sarcoplasmic reticulum, as ryanodine treatment of wild-type myocytes had little effect on the spontaneous Ca^{2+} transients. Hence, in the embryonic heart, it seems that the ryanodine receptor does not contribute to Ca^{2+} signaling during excitation-contraction coupling. A notable characteristic in the mutant embryos was that the cardiac sarcoplasmic reticulum became vacuolated and engorged with Ca^{2+} prior to death. The authors propose that in the embryonic stage, the ryanodine receptors have an important function in providing a route for Ca^{2+} leak from the developing cardiac sarcoplasmic reticulum, allowing the maintenance of normal luminal Ca^{2+} concentrations. It is interesting to note that heterozygous mice ($+/crr^{m2}$) for the targeted allele were asymptomatic and had normal morphological and physiological characteristics.

As described above, transgenic mice completely lacking the cardiac ryanodine receptor die in utero, prior to the cardiac ryanodine receptor undertaking its principal role during excitation-contraction coupling (62). However, transgenic mice generated using the recombinant mutant gene, crr^{m1}, may be a valuable model to study sarcoplasmic reticulum Ca^{2+} release during excitation-contraction coupling in the adult, where the sarcoplasmic reticulum takes on a more dominant role in supplying Ca^{2+} to the myofibrils. In these animals, the *RyR2* gene expression levels can be regulated by the introduction of Cre recombinase.

Furthermore, myotubes that lack the skeletal ryanodine receptor (dyspedic-myotubes, obtained from mice homozygous for a disrupted *RyR1* gene), provide a useful system to investigate muscle-specific differences in excitation-contraction coupling. For instance, expression of cardiac ryanodine receptors in cultured dyspedic myotubes (by nuclear injection of rabbit RyR2 cDNA), demonstrated that the introduced cardiac ryanodine receptor can support Ca^{2+}-induced Ca^{2+} release, but not skeletal-type excitation-contraction coupling, which is not dependent on the entry of extracellular Ca^{2+} (63). However, the injection of RyR1 cDNA, restored skeletal-type excitation-contraction coupling (64).

FKBP12-Deficient Mice

In order to evaluate the in vivo role of FKBP12, Shou et al (65) targeted the deletion of *FKBP12* exons 3 and 4, which encode important functional domains, to generate FKBP12-deficient mice. FKBP12 mRNA and protein were absent in these homozygous mutant animals. The majority of mutant mice died between embryonic day 14.5 and birth, due to severe dilated cardiomyopathy and ventricular septal defects. Histological abnormalities of FKBP12-deficient hearts at embryonic day 14.5 resembled a human congenital heart disorder. The mutant embryos had other notable abnormalities, probably secondary to the cardiac dysfunction, e.g. edema, hemorrhage, and necrosis of the liver. However, seven FKBP12-deficient mice did survive for several weeks post-partum, but died (apparently) due to a cardiac-related wasting syndrome, and one FKBP12-deficient animal survived past adulthood. In vivo left ventricular function and chamber dimensions were obtained from the single surviving FKBP12-deficient mouse at 14 months of age using echocardiography. This animal had a ventricular septal defect, and the left ventricular chamber was considerably dilated. Furthermore, left ventricular function was depressed relative to a control heart, as indicated by decreases in fractional shortening and ejection fraction. There was an interesting correlation between the cardiac phenotype of the FKBP12-deficient mice and the cardiac phenotype of pediatric organ transplant patients, who had received high doses of FK506 as an immunosuppressant therapy.

As mentioned above, FKBP12 is known to bind to the skeletal ryanodine receptor and impart a modulating role on the channel. However, in cardiac myocardium it is believed that FKBP12.6 is important, not FKBP12. The FKBP12-deficient mouse model has provided some interesting insights in this regard. Despite the absence of this protein, skeletal muscle morphology appears normal in FKBP12-deficient mice. Nonetheless, gating characteristics of skeletal muscle ryanodine receptors (reconstituted into planar lipid bilayers) display the expected phenotype in the absence of FKBP12 (as determined from in vitro studies), i.e. an increased probability of opening and the appearance of subconductance states. Surprisingly, a similar effect on the gating properties of the ryanodine receptors was observed in cardiac muscle, indicating that FKBP12 may have a physiological role in this tissue (at least in the embryonic developmental stage). In addition, preliminary findings using cultured ventricular myocytes from embryonic day 18.5 mice, indicate an increased frequency and duration of Ca^{2+} sparks in FKBP12-deficient hearts (66). Low levels of FKBP12.6 mRNA (which were not upregulated in FKBP12-deficient mice) were found in cardiac and skeletal muscles at embryonic day 18.5 (65). It seems that FKBP12 is indeed involved in coordinating the subunits of the ryanodine receptor tetramer, as previously suggested (54, 60). The absence of detrimental consequences in skeletal muscle, although cardiac muscle was severely affected, is probably due to differences in excitation-contraction coupling between the tissues (65).

Transgenic Mice with Cardiac-Specific Overexpression of Junctin

Ramesh et al (67) recently generated a transgenic model with the overexpression of canine junctin in mouse cardiac tissue in order to study the contribution of this protein to the architecture at the Ca^{2+} release site of the sarcoplasmic reticulum. Ventricles from 5-week-old mice had 5- to 10-fold overexpression of junctin. Preliminary data indicate that the overexpression of junctin facilitates the association between the sarcoplasmic reticulum and transverse tubules. The junctional sarcoplasmic reticulum cisternae had a more tightly zippered appearance in the transgenic model, and this zippered appearance is also evident in non-junctional regions. In addition, junctional sarcoplasmic reticulum cisternae cover a relatively greater surface of the transverse tubule profile in overexpressing myocardium.

THE PLASMA MEMBRANE Ca^{2+}-PUMP

The plasma membrane Ca^{2+}-ATPase is a ubiquitous enzyme proposed to mediate the transport of Ca^{2+} from the cytosol to the extracellular space during muscle relaxation and participate in the regulation of Ca^{2+} homeostasis. There are multiple plasma membrane Ca^{2+}-ATPase isoforms encoded by four genes, and each gene transcript is alternatively spliced, yielding multiple gene products (68). Plasma membrane Ca^{2+}-ATPase isoforms 1, 2, and 4 are expressed in cardiac muscle (69). The functional role of the plasma membrane Ca^{2+}-ATPase in cardiac muscle was recently addressed through transgenesis.

Transgenic Rats with Cardiac-Specific Overexpression of the Plasma Membrane Ca^{2+}-ATPase

Transgenic rats overexpressing the human plasma membrane Ca^{2+}-ATPase (PMCA4) cDNA in the heart using the ventricular-specific myosin light chain-2 promoter were generated (70). Transgenic rats overexpressed plasma membrane Ca^{2+}-ATPase by 2.5-fold in neonatal myocytes and 1.6-fold in adult myocytes. Consistent with this level of overexpression, the Ca^{2+}-ATPase activity was increased to 12.6 µmol ADP/mg/h compared with 7.1 µmol ADP/mg/h in wild-types, assessed in purified plasma membrane preparations. Examination of cardiac function, using in vivo hemodynamic measurements, indicates that overexpression of plasma membrane Ca^{2+}-ATPase has no effect on either baseline contractile parameters or peak performance obtained by volume loading. Furthermore, electrophysiological studies in Fura-2 loaded myocytes suggest no changes in voltage-dependence and in activation or inactivation properties of the L-type Ca^{2+}-current. However, when the sarcoplasmic reticulum function is blocked by thapsigarpin and ryanodine, the time constant of the $[Ca^{2+}]_i$ decline is significantly smaller in transgenic than in wild-type myocytes.

Thus overexpression of the plasma membrane Ca^{2+}-ATPase does not appear to have any effect on cardiac function except when the sarcoplasmic reticulum function is abolished. Even then the observed changes are so small that they may not be of any physiological significance. It is interesting to note that the degree of plasma membrane Ca^{2+}-ATPase overexpression (1.6-fold) is higher than that of SERCA2 (1.2–1.5-fold) (6, 8), yet there are no significant physiological alterations, unlike overexpression of SERCA2. These findings on the functional effects of plasma membrane Ca^{2+}-ATPase overexpression appear consistent with studies in wild-type isolated myocytes, which show that 1–2% of the $[Ca^{2+}]_i$ decline during cardiac muscle relaxation is mediated by both plasma membrane Ca^{2+}-ATPase and the mitochondrial Ca^{2+}-uniporter, whereas the Na^+/Ca^{2+} exchanger accounts for 25% and SERCA2 for 75% of this decline (71).

It has been suggested that the plasma membrane Ca^{2+}-ATPase is involved in growth and differentiation (72). To study this further, primary low-density cultures of neonatal cardiomyocytes from transgenic and wild-type rats were used as a model system for hypertrophy. Transgenic myocytes exhibit a significantly higher rate of protein synthesis under various stimuli, such as fetal calf serum, phenylephrine, and isoproterenol. These effects of plasma membrane Ca^{2+}-ATPase may involve regulation of the α-adrenergic and β-adrenergic growth signals through its localization in caveolae, as evidenced by biochemical and immunocytochemical studies. Several important signaling molecules such as Gsa, nitric synthase, and IP_3-sensitive Ca^{2+} channels are localized to caveolae, and the plasma membrane Ca^{2+}-ATPase may either directly interact with these molecules or modulate subcellular Ca^{2+} pools. Thus while the plasma membrane Ca^{2+}-ATPase's role in the regulation of excitation-contraction coupling in heart is problematic, it may modulate myocardial growth through adjusting caveolar signal transduction.

THE CARDIAC Na^+/Ca^{2+} EXCHANGER

The major physiological role of the cardiac Na^+/Ca^{2+} exchanger is to extrude Ca^{2+} from the cell, by operating in the efflux or forward mode, i.e. efflux of one Ca^{2+} ion coupled to the influx of three Na^+ ions. However, the exchanger can operate in either direction (73). In its influx or reverse mode it couples Ca^{2+} ion entry to Na^+ ion efflux, explaining the observed inotropic effects of cardiac glycosides. It has also been suggested that Ca^{2+} entry via the exchanger can directly trigger sarcoplasmic reticulum Ca^{2+} release (74).

In the steady state, the same amount of Ca^{2+} entering the cell from the extracellular space must be actively removed across the sarcolemma (against its concentration gradient), ensuring that there is no net gain or loss of cell Ca^{2+} per beat, thereby maintaining cellular Ca^{2+} homeostasis (75, 76). The Na^+/Ca^{2+} exchanger in its influx mode competes with the powerful Ca^{2+}-ATPase of the sarcoplasmic reticulum for cytosolic Ca^{2+} and is responsible for ~10% (in mouse, rat) to 30% (in rabbit, ferret, guinea pig) of the decline in the intracellular Ca^{2+} concentration during cardiac relaxation (27, 71, 75, 76). Hence, in comparison to rabbit, the Ca^{2+}-ATPase of the sarcoplasmic reticulum plays a more dominant role in the removal of Ca^{2+} from the cytosol during a twitch in mouse and rat, implying that in these species the Na^+/Ca^{2+} exchanger is a relatively weaker competitor. Moreover, in mouse and rat, the exchanger seems to be involved in Ca^{2+} entry during rest (leading to a net gain of Ca^{2+}), thus contributing to rest-potentiation, in contrast to other species; e.g. rabbit and ferret show rest-decay (75, 77). Interestingly, the resting intracellular Na^+ concentration is relatively higher in mouse and rat, in comparison to rabbit (75, 78). As the driving force of the exchanger is very much dependent on the chemical gradient across the sarcolemma and the membrane potential, species differences in Na^+ ion concentrations and action potentials underlie species differences in the mode of operation of the Na^+/Ca^{2+} exchanger during rest and during contraction (75).

Since the original cloning of the cardiac sarcolemmal canine Na^+/Ca^{2+} exchanger (79), this isoform has been cloned from several species, including human and mouse, which have similar levels of sequence identity to canine (80). The cardiac Na^+/Ca^{2+} exchanger consists of 970 amino acids, including an NH_2-terminal cleaved signal sequence, 11 hydrophobic (putative transmembrane) domains, and a hydrophilic (intracellular) loop, which represents more than one half of the protein (79). Antisense oligonucleotide studies, designed to knock-down the cardiac exchanger in cultured cardiac myocytes, have provided insight into the function of this protein in Ca^{2+} homeostasis (81, 82). Further insights have been gained from overexpression of the Na^+/Ca^{2+} exchanger in mouse hearts, in which the exchanger normally has only a minor functional role.

Transgenic Mice with Cardiac-Specific Overexpression of the Na⁺/Ca²⁺ Exchanger

To determine the physiological role of the cardiac sarcolemmal Na^+/Ca^{2+} exchanger, transgenic mice overexpressing this protein in the heart were generated (83). The transgene construct, which was used for microinjection into nuclei of fertilized mouse eggs, consists of an α-myosin heavy chain promoter, open reading frame of the canine cardiac Na^+/Ca^{2+} exchanger, and SV40 polyadenylation signal sequence (transcriptional terminator). Eight transgenic lines were obtained. The amount of protein overexpression was not determined quantitatively, due to possible differences in the affinity of the antibody, which was raised against the canine cardiac Na^+/Ca^{2+} exchanger, for the endogenous (mouse) cardiac exchanger and the introduced (canine) exchanger. However, Western and Northern blot analyses, and indirect immunofluorescence microscopy, demonstrate that the Na^+/Ca^{2+} exchanger is overexpressed in the hearts of transgenic animals (83). Importantly, the overexpressed exchanger was functionally active. Many studies have been subsequently undertaken with this transgenic model to ascertain the functional properties of the exchanger.

Prior to discussing the effects of the overexpression on Na^+/Ca^{2+} exchange, it is important to assess whether the introduction of the transgene has led to changes in the myocardium, other than the intentional overexpression of the exchanger. It seems that there were essentially no compensatory changes in this model. Body and heart masses were normal (83). The latter was further supported by the finding that the myocyte cell capacitance, an indicator of cell size, was unchanged (83). Furthermore, heart rate and blood pressure were not significantly changed (83). Protein expression levels of sarcoplasmic reticulum Ca^{2+}-ATPase, phospholamban, and calsequestrin were unaltered (77, 84). The sarcoplasmic reticulum Ca^{2+} content was unchanged in comparison to non-transgenic control hearts (78, 83), although one study reported an increase (77). The latter finding was attributed to altered kinetics of the sarcoplasmic reticulum Ca^{2+}-ATPase (see below). The Ca^{2+} channel current density was not changed (78, 83), implying that the sarcolemmal L-type Ca^{2+} channels were unaffected. Moreover, the intracellular resting Na^+ concentration was unaffected by the transgene (77, 78), and diastolic Ca^{2+} levels did not change significantly (77, 78, 83).

Basal force of contraction of isolated atrial preparations was similar between transgenic and wild-type groups (84). However, application of BDF 9148, a Na^+ channel agonist, resulted in a concentration-dependent increase in the force of contraction in preparations from transgenic animals, which was attributed to the presence of elevated levels of a functional Na^+/Ca^{2+} exchanger (84). Interestingly, isolated perfused hearts from male transgenic mice had an increased basal contractile function in comparison to male wild-type hearts, whereas differences between female transgenic and wild-type hearts did not achieve statistical significance (85). Isolated ventricular myocyte studies revealed that the amplitude of cell shortening was similar between the transgenic and wild-type mice (77), and the amplitude of the Ca^{2+} transient was unchanged (77, 78, 83). However, the kinetics of the intracellular Ca^{2+} transients were altered, although the changes were not concordant between studies. Specifically, one study, in which cells were paced at 0.25 Hz, reported prolongation in time-to-peak systolic intracellular Ca^{2+} in transgenic myocytes (78). However, another study, in which 0.5 Hz was employed, found a significant faster time-to-peak Ca^{2+} transient compared with non-transgenic cells, and this was also reflected in the relatively shorter time-to-peak twitch (77). Twitch relaxation was significantly faster in transgenic myocytes (77), as was the decline of the Ca^{2+} transient (77, 78), signifying an increased Ca^{2+} efflux during relaxation as a direct consequence of overexpression (78).

The decline of caffeine-induced Ca^{2+} transients was found to be markedly enhanced (two- to threefold) in the transgenic model, whereas the amplitude was unchanged (78, 83). Similar measurements taken while inhibiting the Na$^+$/Ca^{2+} exchanger revealed little difference between the transgenic and wild-type myocytes, supporting the involvement of the Na$^+$/Ca^{2+} exchanger in the former observation (78). However, Terracciano et al (77) found a greater Ca^{2+} release in transgenic myocytes upon caffeine application, suggesting an augmented sarcoplasmic reticulum Ca^{2+} content. It has been demonstrated that an increased peak intracellular Ca^{2+} concentration stimulates the kinetics of sarcoplasmic reticulum Ca^{2+} uptake (86). Hence, it was suggested that the apparent enhanced rates of cytoplasmic Ca^{2+} removal in transgenic myocytes [e.g. subsequent to caffeine application or upon re-warming after rapid-cooling (even when the exchanger was rendered inactive)], may not be purely the result of overexpression of the exchanger but partly due to increased rates of Ca^{2+} uptake by the sarcoplasmic reticulum (77). The increased sarcoplasmic reticulum Ca^{2+} content in the transgenic myocytes may be the result of enhanced Ca^{2+} influx via the exchanger leading to loading of the sarcoplasmic reticulum (77). However, as noted above, in normal twitches the amplitude of the Ca^{2+} transient is not different between transgenic and wild-type animals and, therefore, during the twitch, the observed enhanced rate of cytoplasmic Ca^{2+} removal may be due to the overexpressed exchanger rather than enhanced Ca^{2+} uptake by the sarcoplasmic reticulum. Also, as the amplitude of the Ca^{2+} transient is similar in both the transgenic and wild-type groups, this implies that the enhanced Ca^{2+} efflux via the exchanger, noted in the transgenic animals, must be balanced by enhanced Ca^{2+} influx. The latter is presumably achieved by Na$^+$/Ca^{2+} exchange as the L-type Ca^{2+} current density was unchanged between the groups (78).

The possibility of Ca^{2+} entering the cell via the exchanger directly eliciting Ca^{2+} release from the sarcoplasmic reticulum has also been investigated using this transgenic model. An earlier study failed to show the occurrence of this phenomenon in mice overexpressing the exchanger (83), possibly because of an insufficient concentration of Na$^+$ in the voltage-clamp pipette solution (78). However, Yao et al (78) suggest that their findings, obtained while blocking the L-type Ca^{2+} channel, are consistent with Ca^{2+} influx via the exchanger triggering sarcoplasmic reticulum Ca^{2+} release in transgenic myocytes. One should keep in mind, however, that the location of the overexpressed exchangers may be more advantageous for directly influencing the release of Ca^{2+} from the sarcoplasmic reticulum, whereas in the normal heart, this phenomenon may not be feasible. In addition, the presence of functional L-type Ca^{2+} channels may alter the putative contribution of the exchanger to sarcoplasmic reticulum Ca^{2+} release (78).

Ca^{2+} influx via the Na$^+$/Ca^{2+} exchanger has been implicated in the detrimental effects on cardiac tissue incurred upon ischemia/reperfusion. The Na$^+$/Ca^{2+} exchanger overexpression model allows further investigations on the role of the exchanger in ischemia/reperfusion-induced myocyte Ca^{2+} overload (85). Isolated hearts were subjected to 20 min of ischemia followed by 40 min of reperfusion. Post-ischemic cardiac function was markedly depressed in male transgenic hearts, in comparison to male wild-type hearts, suggesting that the exchanger does work in the Ca^{2+} influx mode during the ischemia/reperfusion protocol employed; i.e. the presence of more exchanger in male transgenic hearts led to increased injury. Male transgenic hearts displayed pulsus alternans during reperfusion, consistent with intracellular Ca^{2+} overload, and had lower recoveries of energy metabolites. Unexpectedly, female hearts with overexpression of the Na^+/Ca^{2+} exchanger showed a functional recovery from ischemia/reperfusion that was similar to that of wild-type female hearts. This protective nature in female transgenic mice was partially attributed to female-specific hormones, e.g. estrogen. In fact, transgenic hearts obtained from ovariectomized females did show lower post-ischemic functional recovery. This gender difference in susceptibility to ischemia/reperfusion injury seems to pertain to Na^+/Ca^{2+} exchanger overexpression animals, as hearts obtained from normal wild-type females had a similar response to the ischemia/reperfusion protocol as did male wild-type hearts.

CONCLUDING REMARKS

Tight regulation of intracellular Ca^{2+} is imperative for maintenance of Ca^{2+} homeostasis and normal cardiac function. In fact, myocardial dysfunction has been associated with abnormal Ca^{2+} handling. Genetically engineered models targeting membrane Ca^{2+} handling proteins in the heart have proven to be valuable for aiding our understanding of the physiological and pathological role of these proteins. With further advances in transgenic technology, it may be possible to control the level of expression of a specific gene product and limit cardiac compensatory changes, such as hypertrophy in order to identify changes solely due to the altered gene product of interest. In addition, the ability to manipulate the particular time-point at which a gene is switched on or off in a tissue-specific manner and the introduction of specific mutations in the gene of interest will greatly advance our understanding of regulation of cardiac Ca^{2+} homeostasis. These may also lead to the development of molecular approaches for therapeutic treatments of cardiac Ca^{2+} dysfunction in human heart disease.

ACKNOWLEDGMENTS

We greatly appreciate Dr. Yoji Sato for valuable discussions regarding this manuscript and assistance with figures. This work was supported by National Institutes of Health grants HL26057, P40-RR12358 and HL52318.

Visit the Annual Reviews home page at www.AnnualReviews.org.

LITERATURE CITED

1. Arai M, Matsui H, Periasamy M. 1994. Sarcoplasmic reticulum gene expression in cardiac hypertrophy and heart failure. *Circ. Res.* 74:555–64

2. Brandl CJ, Green NM, Korczak B, MacLennan DH. 1986. Two Ca^{2+} ATPase genes: homologies and mechanistic implications of deduced amino acid sequences. *Cell* 44:597–607

3. Zarain-Herzberg A, MacLennan DH, Periasamy M. 1990. Characterization of rabbit cardiac sarco(endo)plasmic reticulum Ca^{2+}-ATPase gene. *J. Biol. Chem.* 265:4670–77

4. Lytton J, Zarain-Herzberg A, Periasamy M, MacLennan DH. 1989. Molecular cloning of the mammalian smooth muscle sarco(endo)plasmic reticulum Ca^{2+}-ATPase. *J. Biol. Chem.* 264:7059–65

5. Anger M, Samuel JL, Marotte F, Wuytack F, Rappaport L, Lompré A-M. 1994. In situ mRNA distribution of sarco(endo)plasmic reticulum Ca^{2+}-ATPase isoforms during ontogeny in the rat. *J. Mol. Cell. Cardiol.* 26:539–50

6. He H, Giordano FJ, Hilal-Dandan R, Choi DJ, Rockman HA, et al. 1997. Overexpression of the rat sarcoplasmic reticulum Ca^{2+} ATPase gene in the heart of transgenic mice accelerates calcium transients and cardiac relaxation. *J. Clin. Invest.* 100:380–89

7. Yao A, Su Z, Dillmann WH, Barry WH. 1998. Sarcoplasmic reticulum function in murine ventricular myocytes overexpressing SR CaATPase. *J. Mol. Cell. Cardiol.* 30:2711–18

8. Baker DL, Hashimoto K, Grupp IL, Ji Y, Reed T, et al. 1998. Targeted overexpression of the sarcoplasmic reticulum Ca^{2+}-ATPase increases cardiac contractility in transgenic mouse hearts. *Circ. Res.* 83:1205–14

9. Periasamy M, Reed TD, Liu LH, Ji Y, Loukianov E, et al. 1999. Impaired cardiac performance in heterozygous mice with a null mutation in the sarco(endo)plasmic reticulum Ca^{2+}-ATPase isoform 2 (SERCA2) gene. *J. Biol. Chem.* 274:2556–62

10. Loukianov E, Ji Y, Grupp IL, Kirkpatrick DL, Baker DL, Loukianova T, et al. 1998. Enhanced myocardial contractility and increased Ca^{2+} transport function in transgenic hearts expressing the fast-twitch skeletal muscle sarcoplasmic reticulum Ca^{2+}-ATPase. *Circ. Res.* 83: 889–97

11. Kirchberger MA, Tada M, Katz AM. 1974. Adenosine 3′:5′-monophosphate-dependent protein kinase-catalyzed phosphorylation reaction and its relationship to calcium transport in cardiac sarcoplasmic reticulum. *J. Biol. Chem.* 249:6166–73

12. Katz AM, Tada M, Kirchberger MA. 1975. Control of calcium transport in the myocardium by the cyclic AMP-protein kinase system. *Adv. Cyclic Nucleotide Res.* 5:453–72

13. Le Peuch CJ, Haiech J, Demaille JG. 1979. Concerted regulation of cardiac sarcoplasmic reticulum calcium transport by cyclic adenosine monophosphate-dependent and calcium-calmodulin-dependent phosphorylations. *Biochemistry* 18:5150–57

14. Kranias EG, Mandel F, Wang T, Schwartz A. 1980. Mechanism of the stimulation of calcium ion dependent adenosine triphosphatase of cardiac sarcoplasmic reticulum by adenosine 3′,5′-monophosphate dependent protein kinase. *Biochemistry* 19:5434–39

15. Kirchberger MA, Antonetz T. 1982. Calmodulin-mediated regulation of calcium transport and (Ca^{2+} + Mg^{2+})-activated ATPase activity in isolated cardiac sarcoplasmic reticulum. *J. Biol. Chem.* 257:5685–91

16. Davis BA, Schwartz A, Samaha FJ, Kranias EG. 1983. Regulation of cardiac sarcoplasmic reticulum calcium transport by calcium-calmodulin-dependent phosphorylation. *J. Biol. Chem.* 258:13587–91

17. Movsesian MA, Nishikawa M, Adelstein RS. 1984. Phosphorylation of phospholamban by calcium-activated, phospholipid-dependent protein kinase. Stimulation of cardiac sarcoplasmic reticulum calcium uptake. *J. Biol. Chem.* 259:8029–32

18. Hicks MJ, Shigekawa M, Katz AM. 1979. Mechanism by which cyclic adenosine 3′:5′-monophosphate-dependent protein kinase stimulates calcium transport in cardiac sarcoplasmic reticulum. *Circ. Res.* 44:384–91

19. Kimura Y, Inui M, Kadoma M, Kijima Y, Sasaki T, Tada M. 1991. Effects of monoclonal antibody against phospholamban on calcium pump ATPase of cardiac sarcoplasmic reticulum. *J. Mol. Cell. Cardiol.* 23:1223–30

20. Kranias EG. 1985. Regulation of Ca^{2+} transport by cyclic 3′,5′-AMP-dependent and calcium-calmodulin-dependent phosphorylation of cardiac sarcoplasmic reticulum. *Biochim. Biophys. Acta* 844:193–99

21. Kranias EG, Solaro RJ. 1982. Phosphorylation of troponin I and phospholamban during catecholamine stimulation of rabbit heart. *Nature* 298:182–84

22. Lindemann JP, Jones LR, Hathaway DR, Henry BG, Watanabe AM. 1983. β-Adrenergic stimulation of phospholamban phosphorylation and Ca^{2+}-ATPase activity in guinea pig ventricles. *J. Biol. Chem.* 258:464–71

23. Luo W, Grupp IL, Harrer J, Ponniah S, Grupp G, et al. 1994. Targeted ablation of the phospholamban gene is associated with markedly enhanced myocardial contractility and loss of β-agonist stimulation. *Circ. Res.* 75:401–9

24. Luo W, Wolska BM, Grupp IL, Harrer JM, Haghighi K, et al. 1996. Phospholamban gene dosage effects in the mammalian heart. *Circ. Res.* 78:839–47

25. Chu G, Luo W, Slack JP, Tilgmann C, Sweet WE, et al. 1996. Compensatory mechanisms associated with the hyperdynamic function of phospholamban-deficient mouse hearts. *Circ. Res.* 79:1064–76

26. Wolska BM, Stojanovic MO, Luo W, Kranias EG, Solaro RJ. 1996. Effect of ablation of phospholamban on dynamics of cardiac myocyte contraction and intracellular Ca^{2+}. *Am. J. Physiol.* 271:C391–97

27. Li L, Chu G, Kranias EG, Bers DM. 1998. Cardiac myocyte calcium transport in phospholamban knockout mouse: relaxation and endogenous CaMKII effects. *Am. J. Physiol.* 274:H1335–47

28. Santana LF, Kranias EG, Lederer WJ. 1997. Calcium sparks and excitation-contraction coupling in phospholamban-deficient mouse ventricular myocytes. *J. Physiol.* 503:21–29

29. Lorenz JN, Kranias EG. 1997. Regulatory effects of phospholamban on cardiac function in intact mice. *Am. J. Physiol.* 273:H2826–31

30. Hoit BD, Khoury SF, Kranias EG, Ball N, Walsh RA. 1995. In vivo echocardiographic detection of enhanced left ventricular function in gene-targeted mice with phospholamban deficiency. *Circ. Res.* 77:632–37

31. Kiss E, Brittsan AG, Edes I, Grupp IL, Grupp G, Kranias EG. 1998. Thyroid hormone-induced alterations in phospholamban-deficient mouse hearts. *Circ. Res.* 83:608–13

32. Masaki H, Sato Y, Luo W, Kranias EG, Yatani A. 1997. Phospholamban deficiency alters inactivation kinetics of L-type Ca^{2+} channels in mouse ventricular myocytes. *Am. J. Physiol.* 272:H606–12

33. Desai KH, Schauble E, Luo W, Kranias E, Bernstein D. 1999. Phospholamban

deficiency does not compromise exercise capacity. *Am. J. Physiol.* 276:H1172–77

34. Slack JP, Grupp IL, Tilgmann C, Luo W, Tamura T, et al. 1997. Effects of age on the hyperdynamic cardiac function of phospholamban knockout mice. *Circulation* 96:I-179 (Abstr.)

35. Lalli J, Harrer JM, Luo W, Kranias EG, Paul RJ. 1997. Targeted ablation of the phospholamban gene is associated with a marked decrease in sensitivity in aortic smooth muscle. *Circ. Res.* 80:506–13

36. Luo W, Chu G, Sato Y, Zhou Z, Kadambi VJ, Kranias EG. 1998. Transgenic approaches to define the functional role of dual site phospholamban phosphorylation. *J. Biol. Chem.* 273:4734–39

37. Simmerman HK, Kobayashi YM, Autry JM, Jones LR. 1996. A leucine zipper stabilizes the pentameric membrane domain of phospholamban and forms a coiled-coil pore structure. *J. Biol. Chem.* 271:5941–46

38. Kimura Y, Asahi M, Kurzydlowski K, Tada M, MacLennan DH. 1998. Phospholamban domain Ib mutations influence functional interactions with the Ca²⁺-ATPase isoform of cardiac sarcoplasmic reticulum. *J. Biol. Chem.* 273: 14238–41

39. Chu G, Li L, Sato Y, Harrer JM, Kadambi VJ, et al. 1998. Pentameric assembly of phospholamban facilitates inhibition of cardiac function in vivo. *J. Biol. Chem.* 273:33674–80

40. Neumann J, Boknik P, DePaoli-Roach AA, Field LJ, Rockman HA, et al. 1998. Targeted overexpression of phospholamban to mouse atrium depresses Ca²⁺ transport and contractility. *J. Mol. Cell. Cardiol.* 30:1991–2002

41. Masaki H, Sako H, Kadambi VJ, Sato Y, Kranias EG, Yatani A. 1998. Overexpression of phospholamban alters inactivation kinetics of L-type Ca²⁺ channel currents in mouse atrial myocytes. *J. Mol. Cell. Cardiol.* 30:317–25

42. Mitchell RD, Simmerman HK, Jones LR.

1988. Ca²⁺ binding effects on protein conformation and protein interactions of canine cardiac calsequestrin. *J. Biol. Chem.* 263:1376–81

43. Franzini-Armstrong C, Kenney LJ, Varriano-Marston E. 1987. The structure of calsequestrin in triads of vertebrate skeletal muscle: a deep-etch study. *J. Cell. Biol.* 105:49–56

44. Zhang L, Kelley J, Schmeisser G, Kobayashi YM, Jones LR. 1997. Complex formation between junctin, triadin, calsequestrin, and the ryanodine receptor. Proteins of the cardiac junctional sarcoplasmic reticulum membrane. *J. Biol. Chem.* 272:23389–97

45. Yano K, Zarain-Herzberg A. 1994. Sarcoplasmic reticulum calsequestrins: structural and functional properties. *Mol. Cell. Biochem.* 135:61–70

46. Sato Y, Ferguson DG, Sako H, Dorn GW II, Kadambi VJ, et al. 1998. Cardiac-specific overexpression of mouse cardiac calsequestrin is associated with depressed cardiovascular function and hypertrophy in transgenic mice. *J. Biol. Chem.* 273:28470–77

47. Jones LR, Suzuki YJ, Wang W, Kobayashi YM, Ramesh V, et al. 1998. Regulation of Ca²⁺ signaling in transgenic mouse cardiac myocytes overexpressing calsequestrin. *J. Clin. Invest.* 101:1385–93

48. Sato Y, Kadambi VJ, Ball N, Hoit BD, Walsh RA, Kranias EG. 1998. Calsequestrin overexpression produces left ventricular hypertrophy and increased fractional shortening. *J. Mol. Cell. Cardiol.* 30:A166 (Abstr.)

49. Cho M-C, Rapacciuolo A, Koch WJ, Kobayashi Y, Jones L, Rockman HA. 1998. Progressive dilated cardiomyopathy in transgenic mice with calsequestrin overexpression. *Circulation* 98:I-837 (Abstr.)

50. Wang W, Morad M. 1999. Caffeine restores Ca²⁺ signaling and spark formation in transgenic myocytes over-

expressing calsequestrin. *Biophys. J.* 76:A464 (Abstr.)

51. Knollmann BC, Duc J, Groth A, Weissman NJ, Cleemann L, Morad M. 1998. Cardiac phenotype of transgenic mice overexpressing calsequestrin. *Circulation* 98:I-490 (Abstr.)

52. Kadambi VJ, Sato Y, Ball N, Kranias EG, Walsh RA, Hoit BD. 1998. Transgenic overexpression of calsequestrin produces pulsus alternans in vivo. *J. Mol. Cell. Cardiol.* 30:A47 (Abstr.)

53. Sato Y, Yamamoto S, Yatani A, Kranias EG. 1998. Rescue of the depressed contractile parameters in calsequestrin overexpressing hearts by phospholamban ablation. *Circulation* 98:I-53 (Abstr.)

54. Marks AR. 1997. Intracellular calcium-release channels: regulators of cell life and death. *Am. J. Physiol.* 272:H597–605

55. Flucher BE, Franzini-Armstrong C. 1996. Formation of junctions involved in excitation-contraction coupling in skeletal and cardiac muscle. *Proc. Natl. Acad. Sci. USA* 93:8101–6

56. Jayaraman T, Brillantes A-M, Timerman AP, Fleischer S, Erdjument-Bromage H, et al. 1992. FK506 binding protein associated with the calcium release channel (ryanodine receptor). *J. Biol. Chem.* 267:9474–77

57. Timerman AP, Onoue H, Xin H-B, Barg S, Copello J, et al. 1996. Selective binding of FKBP12.6 by the cardiac ryanodine receptor. *J. Biol. Chem.* 271:20385–91

58. McCall E, Li L, Satoh H, Shannon TR, Blatter LA, Bers DM. 1996. Effects of FK-506 on contraction and Ca^{2+} transients in rat cardiac myocytes. *Circ. Res.* 79:1110–21

59. Xiao R-P, Valdivia HH, Bogdanov K, Valdivia C, Lakatta EG, Cheng H. 1997. The immunophilin FK506–binding protein modulates Ca^{2+} release channel closure in rat heart. *J. Physiol.* 500:343–54

60. Brillantes A-MB, Ondriaš K, Scott A, Kobrinsky E, Ondriašová E, et al. 1994. Stabilization of calcium release channel (ryanodine receptor) function by FK506–binding protein. *Cell* 77:513–23

61. Guo W, Jorgensen AO, Jones LR, Campbell KP. 1996. Biochemical characterization and molecular cloning of cardiac triadin. *J. Biol. Chem.* 271:458–65

62. Takeshima H, Komazaki S, Hirose K, Nishi M, Noda T, Iino M. 1998. Embryonic lethality and abnormal cardiac myocytes in mice lacking ryanodine receptor type 2. *EMBO J.* 17:3309–16

63. Nakai J, Ogura T, Protasi F, Franzini-Armstrong C, Allen PD, Beam KG. 1997. Functional nonequality of the cardiac and skeletal ryanodine receptors. *Proc. Natl. Acad. Sci. USA* 94:1019–22

64. Nakai J, Dirksen RT, Nguyen HT, Pessah IN, Beam KG, Allen PD. 1996. Enhanced dihydropyridine receptor channel activity in the presence of ryanodine receptor. *Nature* 380:72–75

65. Shou W, Aghdasi B, Armstrong DL, Guo Q, Bao S, et al. 1998. Cardiac defects and altered ryanodine receptor function in mice lacking FKBP12. *Nature* 391:489–92

66. Song L-S, Shou W, Boheler KR, Xiao R-P, Stern MD, et al. 1999. Ca^{2+} sparks and coupled gating of ryanodine receptors in prenatal FKBP12 knockout mouse cardiac myocytes. *Biophys. J.* 76:A385 (Abstr.)

67. Ramesh V, Zhong L, Franzini-Armstrong C, Jones L. 1999. Structural alterations in cardiac calcium release units resulting from overexpression of junctin. *Biophys. J.* 76:A470 (Abstr.)

68. Carafoli E. 1992. The Ca^{2+} pump of the plasma membrane. *J. Biol. Chem.* 267:2115–18

69. Stauffer TP, Guerini D, Carafoli E. 1995. Tissue distribution of the four gene products of the plasma membrane Ca^{2+} pump. A study using specific antibodies. *J. Biol. Chem.* 270:12184–90

70. Hammes A, Oberdorf-Maass S, Rother T, Nething K, Gollnick F, et al. 1998. Over-

expression of the sarcolemmal calcium pump in the myocardium of transgenic rats. *Circ. Res.* 83:877–88

71. Bassani JW, Bassani RA, Bers DM. 1994. Relaxation in rabbit and rat cardiac cells: species-dependent differences in cellular mechanisms. *J. Physiol.* 476: 279–93

72. Hammes A, Oberdorf-Maass S, Jenatschke S, Pelzer T, Maass A, et al. 1996. Expression of the plasma membrane Ca²⁺-ATPase in myogenic cells. *J. Biol. Chem.* 271:30816–22

73. Glitsch HG, Reuter H, Scholz H. 1970. The effect of the internal sodium concentration on calcium fluxes in isolated guinea-pig auricles. *J. Physiol.* 209:25–43

74. Eisner DA, Trafford AW, Díaz ME, Overend CL, O'Neill SC. 1998. The control of Ca release from the cardiac sarcoplasmic reticulum: regulation versus autoregulation. *Cardiovasc. Res.* 38: 589–604

75. Bers DM. 1991. *Excitation-Contraction Coupling and Cardiac Contractile Force.* Dordrecht: Kluwer

76. Bers DM, Bassani JW, Bassani RA. 1996. Na-Ca exchange and Ca fluxes during contraction and relaxation in mammalian ventricular muscle. *Ann. NY Acad. Sci.* 779:430–42

77. Terracciano CMN, De Souza AI, Philipson KD, MacLeod KT. 1998. Na⁺-Ca²⁺ exchange and sarcoplasmic reticular Ca²⁺ regulation in ventricular myocytes from transgenic mice overexpressing the Na⁺-Ca²⁺ exchanger. *J. Physiol.* 512: 651–67

78. Yao A, Su Z, Nonaka A, Zubair I, Lu L, et al. 1998. Effects of overexpression of the Na⁺-Ca²⁺ exchanger on $[Ca^{2+}]_i$ transients in murine ventricular myocytes. *Circ. Res.* 82:657–65

79. Nicoll DA, Longoni S, Philipson KD. 1990. Molecular cloning and functional expression of the cardiac sarcolemmal Na⁺-Ca²⁺ exchanger. *Science* 250:562–65

80. Schulze DH, Kofuji P, Valdivia C, He S, Luo S, et al. 1996. Alternative splicing of the Na⁺-Ca²⁺ exchanger gene, NCX1. *Ann. NY Acad. Sci.* 779:46–57

81. Lipp P, Schwaller B, Niggli E. 1995. Specific inhibition of Na-Ca exchange function by antisense oligodeoxynucleotides. *FEBS Lett.* 364:198–202

82. Slodzinski MK, Blaustein MP. 1998. Na⁺/Ca²⁺ exchange in neonatal rat heart cells: antisense inhibition and protein half-life. *Am. J. Physiol.* 275:C459–67

83. Adachi-Akahane S, Lu L, Li Z, Frank JS, Philipson KD, Morad M. 1997. Calcium signaling in transgenic mice overexpressing cardiac Na⁺-Ca²⁺ exchanger. *J. Gen. Physiol.* 109:717–29

84. Bäumer AT, Flesch M, Kilter H, Philipson KD, Böhm M. 1998. Overexpression of the Na⁺-Ca²⁺ exchanger leads to enhanced inotropic responsiveness to Na⁺-channel agonist without sarcoplasmic reticulum protein changes in transgenic mice. *Biochem. Biophys. Res. Commun.* 249:786–90

85. Cross HR, Lu L, Steenbergen C, Philipson KD, Murphy E. 1998. Overexpression of the cardiac Na⁺/Ca²⁺ exchanger increases susceptibility to ischemia/reperfusion injury in male, but not female, transgenic mice. *Circ. Res.* 83: 1215–23

86. Bers DM, Berlin JR. 1995. Kinetics of $[Ca]_i$ decline in cardiac myocytes depend on peak $[Ca]_i$. *Am. J. Physiol.* 268:C271–77

Annu. Rev. Physiol. 2000. 62:353–75

DIAPAUSE

M. B. Renfree and G. Shaw

Department of Zoology, The University of Melbourne, Parkville, Victoria 3052, Australia; e-mail: m.renfree@zoology.unimelb.edu.au

Key Words pre-implantation development, marsupial mammal, delayed implantation, prolactin, blastocyst.

■ **Abstract** Embryonic diapause, or delayed implantation as it is sometimes known, is said to occur when the conceptus enters a state of suspended animation at the blastocyst stage of development. Blastocysts may either cease cell division so that their size and cell numbers remain constant, or undergo a period of very slow growth with minimal cell division and expansion. Diapause has independently evolved on many occasions. There are almost 100 mammals in seven different mammalian orders that undergo diapause. In some groups, such as rodents, kangaroos, and mustelids, it is widespread, whereas others such as the Artiodactyla have only a single representative (the roe deer). In each family the characteristics of diapause differ, and the specific controls vary widely from lactational to seasonal, from estrogen to progesterone, or from photoperiod to nutritional. Prolactin is a key hormone controlling the endocrine milieu of diapause in many species, but paradoxically it may act either to stimulate or inhibit growth and activity of the corpus luteum. Whatever the species-specific mechanisms, the ecological result of diapause is one of synchronization: It effectively lengthens the active gestation period, which allows mating to occur and young to be born at times of the year optimal for that species.

INTRODUCTION

A variety of mechanisms to enhance reproductive fitness have evolved in diverse species including insects, fishes, birds, and mammals (17). Most of the processes result in a delay of parturition to ensure optimal nutritional and seasonal environments for survival of the infant, and the fact that the processes involved are so diverse implies that the pressure to protect reproduction is one of the fundamental forces in evolution. Among the mechanisms that have evolved for this purpose are sperm storage, delayed development, and embryonic diapause (delayed implantation). Delayed development and delayed fertilization (sperm storage) have been reviewed elsewhere, and the focus of this discussion is on embryonic diapause in the mammal, a widespread phenomenon that occurs in at least seven orders: Marsupialia, Insectivora, Chiroptera, Edentata, Carnivora, Rodentia, and Artiodactyla (52). Embryonic diapause delays the development of the embryo, which is arrested at the blastocyst stage, and understanding of the

0066–4278/00/0315–0353$12.00

mechanism(s) by which diapause occurs will provide insights into the normal events in this critical and poorly understood biological process. Embryonic diapause has been found in about 70 eutherian species and 30 marsupial species (Table 1).

There are other forms of arrested development in mammals. Bats are an especially interesting group in which reproductive delays are achieved through several

TABLE 1 Occurrence of embryonic diapause in mammals

Frequency	Taxon	Number of species
Most genera	MARSUPIALS	
	Order Diprotodonta	
	Macropodidae	22
	Tarsipedidae	1
	EUTHERIANS	
	Order Carnivora	
	Family Mustelidae	15
	Ursidae	6
	Otariidae	7
	Phocidae	13
Several genera	MARSUPIALS	
	Acrobatidae	2
	Burramyidae	3
	EUTHERIANS	
	Order Rodentia	12
	Cricetidae	5
	Muridae	1
	Chinchillidae	
Few genera	EUTHERIANS	
	Order Insectivora	
	Soricidae	3
	Talpidae	1
	Order Chiroptera	
	Pteropidae	1
	Vespertilionidae	2
	Order Edentata	
	Dasypodidae	2
	Order Artiodactyla	
	Cervidae	1

Data compiled from References 3, 52, 74, 76.

mechanisms such as sperm storage (delayed fertilization), delayed implantation (diapause), and delayed development. These strategies are rare at tropical latitudes but are the norm at higher latitudes (6). Despite the very wide range of reproductive strategies used by bats, very few bat species have diapause. One, the bent winged bat *Miniopterus schreibersii,* has both delayed implantation and delayed development (18, 109). Delayed development is said to occur when gestation is lengthened by slowing post-blastocyst embryonic development, usually in response to an environmental cue such as temperature. This form of delay may also occur in hamsters (57). Australian sea lions have an 18-month reproductive cycle of which 3.5 to 5 months is due to embryonic diapause (36), so it is possible that the additional time may be due to delayed development. Delayed development or delayed implantation may also occur in Pere David's deer *Elaphurus davidianus,* because its gestation is not influenced by season and is significantly longer than for other deer species, except the roe deer, which has diapause (12). Delayed fertilization is also a mechanism for extending the period of time between mating and birth, again usually due to seasonal constraints or changes in climate that occur with changes in latitude. Delayed development and delayed fertilization have been well reviewed elsewhere (6, 52, 70) and thus are not discussed further here.

Although the mouse is probably the species studied in most detail (112), the reproductive physiology that makes it a convenient laboratory species makes it a poor representative of the remarkable range of mechanisms and responses of the blastocysts, corpora lutea, and uteri that occur in the 80 or so other nonrodent species with embryonic diapause. This review therefore concentrates on more recent work on the control of embryonic diapause in wild mammals, with particular attention to the tammar wallaby *Macropus eugenii* and to the Western spotted skunk *Spilogale putorius latifrons.*

CHARACTERISTICS OF DIAPAUSE IN MAMMALS

In all mammals, development of the embryo depends on complex interactions with the uterus, but despite the fundamental and practical significance of this process, we still know relatively little of the signals passing between the uterus and mother in early pregnancy. For physiologists and developmental biologists, embryonic diapause provides a powerful, but as yet poorly exploited, tool to understand the uterine control of early embryonic development in mammals. There are three phases of embryonic diapause: the entry into diapause and arrest of cell division; the maintenance of diapause; and reactivation after diapause. All attention to date has been on the latter two phases, but almost nothing is known of the molecular or metabolic mechanisms by which embryonic development is halted. Much more is known about the control of reactivation (Table 2).

In mammals whose embryos undergo a period of embryonic diapause, blastocysts remain either totally quiescent or expand at a very low slow rate (Figure 1).

TABLE 2 Embryonic diapause in mammals

| State of blastocyst | Implantation delay | | State of corpus luteum |
	Facultative	Obligate (seasonal)	
No growth, unilaminar blastocyst with zona pellucida	Kangaroos and wallabies	Tammar and Bennett's wallabies	Quiescent
No growth, unilaminar blastocyst without zona pellucida	Laboratory mouse Laboratory rat	—	Active
Some growth, unilaminar blastocyst with zona pellucida	—	Mustelids Bears Seals Honey Possum Feathertail Glider Pygmy Possum	Quiescent
Some growth, unilaminar blastocyst without zona pellucida	—	Roe deer Armadillo?	Active
Implanted but undifferentiated	—	Bats	?

References: 3, 9, 52, 53, 74, 76.

Diapause may be maintained by inhibitory factors in the uterus, and the presence or absence of a needed (stimulatory) factor may control reactivation. In mice, reactivation from diapause is associated with increased metabolic activity and trophoblast outgrowth (112). Trophoblast outgrowth does not occur in the absence of certain amino acids, serum factors or glucose, or in the presence of reduced levels of certain ions, suggesting that the uterus could control the embryo by regulating these components of uterine secretions. However, the low levels of these components in uterine fluids from diapausing females argue against this. Furthermore, while outgrowth is prevented, embryo metabolism is not reduced, suggesting that outgrowth and metabolism may be independently controlled by uterine factors.

ENTRY INTO DIAPAUSE

Most studies on diapause and its control have focused on reactivation. The entry into diapause requires signals such as the presence or absence of a sucking stimulus, the onset of short or long days, or the availability of nutrition (33). The majority of seasonally breeding mammals have a timed pattern of prolactin secretion, with peak concentrations in spring or summer and a nadir in autumn or winter (19). Photoperiod influences prolactin secretion via its effects on the secre-

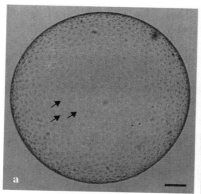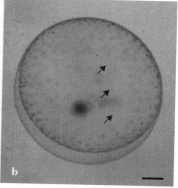

Figure 1 Blastocysts of a marsupial, the feathertailed glider *Acrobates pygmaeus* (*a*) and a eutherian, the Western spotted skunk *Spilogale putorius latifrons* (*b*). In both species the blastocyst slowly expands during diapause. This feathertailed glider blastocyst is at the end of the second phase of diapause. It is about 1.8 mm in diameter and has about 2000 cells whose nuclei give the embryo a speckled appearance. It is entirely unilaminar and has no inner cell mass but is also surrounded by a shell membrane distinct from the zona pellucida. There can be variation in size between the two to three blastocysts in each uterus, but most have reached this size by day 30 of pouch life and undergo little further expansion until the end of lactation (111). Skunk blastocysts remain in diapause for 200 days, growing only slowly to reach 1.2 mm in diameter in April, before starting more rapid growth and endoderm formation in early reactivation, after which they implant. This 1.5 mm skunk blastocyst is in the early stage of reactivation but is indistinguishable in gross appearance from a diapausing blastocyst. The inner cell mass is visible as the dark structure within the blastocyst. The membrane surrounding this blastocyst started out as the zona pellucida, but because it does not thin out as the embryo expands, it must acquire new material in the uterus. (Skunk photo provided by RA Mead). Scale bar 0.2 mm.

tion of melatonin. Both hormones influence either the onset or maintenance of diapause (42, 52, 74). Seasonal diapause occurs in 47 eutherian species (81) and at least 2 marsupial species (52, 73). Sandell (81) hypothesizes that delay in seasonally breeding eutherian species has evolved to maximize female choice or mate competition, so that by mating earlier and delaying birth female fitness will increase. However this hypothesis does not address or explain the types of seasonal delay that occur in certain marsupial species. For these species, it seems most likely that the primary ecological advantage is to ensure that either mating can occur or that young are born at the optimal time of the year for each individual species.

In most marsupial species, the young are born toward the end of the luteal phase so that the mothers' return to estrus and ovulation is suppressed by the sucking of the neonate. By contrast, in the macropodids (kangaroos and wallabies), the single young is born at the end of the pro-estrous phase, and ovulation and fertilization occur postpartum (75). The resulting conceptus develops to a 100-cell blastocyst and then enters dormancy. In most macropodid marsupials, the entry into diapause occurs in the first 6 to 8 days after birth, but apart from the 48 h immediately after birth, hormonal profiles and endometrial responses have been described in only a very small number of animals in which entry into diapause occurred after d7 post-coitus (pc) in lactating females (77, 105, 108). Estrogen is high immediately postpartum (39, 86), but the influence of steroids on oviducal or uterine secretions between ovulation and formation of the early blastocyst, which then enters diapause, has not been tested. Likewise, the uterine secretions at this early stage of development have not been analysed for growth factors, nor has it been determined whether specific cytokines or growth factors are induced or inhibited by steroids.

The best studied macropodid marsupial is the tammar wallaby *Macropus eugenii*. Development of their embryos at the blastocyst stage is completely halted

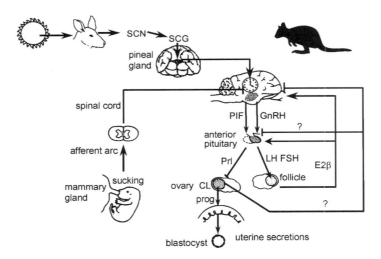

Figure 2 Schematic summary of the lactational and seasonal control of diapause in the tammar, *Macropus eugenii*. Between January and May, diapause is controlled by the lactational inhibition of corpus luteum (CL) growth in response to a sucking-induced prolactin (Prl) release from the pituitary. From then until the summer solstice, photoperiod takes over this role. Photoperiodic information relayed through the suprachiasmatic nucleus (SCN) modulates pineal melatonin secretion through its innervation via the superior cervical ganglion (SCG). Gonadotrophin secretion is not seasonally regulated, so follicles can grow at all times of year but, except in animals in their first year of age, the presence of a quiescent CL inhibits gonadotrophin secretion, follicle growth, and estrus for most of the year. GnRH, gonadotrophin releasing hormone; LH, luteinizing hormone; E2β, estradiol-17β; FSH, follicle-stimulating hormone; Prog, progesterone; PIF, prolactin-inhibiting factor. Lines with arrowheads indicate stimulation; lines with bars indicate inhibition (redrawn from 75).

in the tammar under the influence of the sucking stimulus, which releases prolactin from the pituitary thereby inhibiting the development of the corpus luteum (CL). Reactivation requires a fall in prolactin, which releases the CL from inhibition. Gonadotropins are not needed for reactivation of the CL. Luteal progesterone stimulates the uterus to reactivate the embryo. The CL, although held in quiescence by prolactin, itself prevents a new ovulation in the opposite ovary (Figure 2). In diapause there is no cell division, and no growth in either the embryo or the CL. Diapause can be maintained for at least 11 months in the absence of ovarian hormones with no loss of viability, but, remarkably, reactivation requires only a single hormone—progesterone. The fact that both progesterone and estradiol can trigger reactivation but only progesterone can maintain development suggests that several regulatory factors are needed to establish normal reactivation. After May, seasonal (photoperiod) cues mediated by melatonin maintain diapause, so although the pouch young are weaned in about September/October, the embryos remain in diapause until the longest day, which in the southern hemisphere occurs on December 22, after which the decreasing daylength allows reactivation. Thus in a normal cycle, females give birth after an active gestation of only 26.5 days at the end of January during the height of summer (77) and mate a few hours later. Ovulation occurs within 48 h pc. It takes about 7 days for the new blastocyst to form (see Figure 3), and the resulting embryo remains in diapause for 11 months. Tammars are therefore pregnant 364 days of the year, and the only day they are not is the day they give birth!

Perhaps the most remarkable aspect of entry into diapause occurs in the tammar at puberty. Unlike other species, gonadotrophin secretion in the tammar is not inhibited in the non-breeding season, and males are fertile the year round. Female tammars enter puberty at the time of permanent pouch exit when they are about 10-months old, most come into estrus and mate, but seasonal (photoperiodic) factors prevent the CL from fully developing and they enter diapause without ever experiencing a sucking inhibition (59, 115). These pubertal females retain their diapausing blastocysts until after the longest day when reactivation occurs.The unique feature here is that the female tammar wallaby does not become a seasonally breeding mammal until after puberty when it has acquired a CL (115).

It was long suspected that diapause occurred in some small possums, and this supposition has now been confirmed in the honey possum *Tarsipes rostratus* (72, 73, 116); the pygmy possums *Cercartetus concinnus, C. nanus,* and *C. lepidus* (110); and the feathertail possums *Acrobates pygmaeus* and *Distoechurus pennatus* (110, 111). *Burramys parvus,* the mountain pygmy possum, is the only member of this group in which diapause is known to be absent (73). In all these possums, diapause occurs during the unilaminar blastocyst stage, and unlike macropodid marsupials, there is continued slow growth of the blastocyst. Growth occurs in two phases, a relatively fast phase followed by a plateau when blastocysts do not expand much further. The CL also expands slowly throughout diapause (110, 111). The endocrine control is unknown, but the peaks in the time

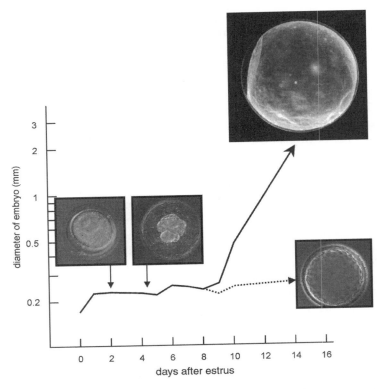

Figure 3 Growth and development of the newly fertilized egg of the tammar post-estrus in the absence of a sucking pouch young (solid line) and in the presence of the suckling inhibition of post blastocyst growth (dotted line). Ovulation occurs about 40–48 h after estrus (78). The insets show the different embryonic stages. At 2 days after estrus the recently fertilized egg recovered from the oviduct shows a distinct pronucleus. The egg is surrounded by a mucoid coat and shell membrane secreted in the oviduct, and within these membranes some sperm are visible. By 4 days, the embryo is cleaving, which leads to formation of an early blastocyst by about d6–7 pc (not shown) (105). If there is sucking or seasonal inhibition (dotted line), the blastocysts remains unilaminar in a state of quiescence. Without inhibition (solid line), development is indistinguishable until about day 8 when growth starts, and by day 15 there is a 4 mm bilaminar blastocyst. Growth curve redrawn from 108.

of births coincide with peaks in the numbers of flowering plants that provide an important food source via their pollen and nectar. However, again unlike in the kangaroos and wallabies, reactivation does not appear to be controlled by lactation, as removal of the sucking stimulus at any stage has no influence in the timing of births in the honey possum (MB Renfree, unpublished observations). Much more work is needed on this group of marsupials.

Diapause and the Cell Cycle

Entry of mouse embryos into quiescence appears to be triggered during the eighth-cell cycle and is independent of the cell number but may require a specific nucleo-cytoplasmic ratio (28). There have been no recent studies of the stage of the cell cycle of the diapausing blastocyst in any of the 96 species of mammal that undergo diapause. Sherman & Barlow (88) and Surani (101) measured the DNA content of rat blastocysts in diapause and concluded that they were arrested in G1. However, it is not possible to distinguish between G0 and G1 on DNA content alone. Given the lack of measurable metabolic activity, it is likely that the diapausing blastocyst cells of tammars are arrested in the G0 phase of the cell cycle and that reactivation requires a suite of specific growth factors. It will be interesting to define the stage of the cell cycle that blastocysts enter diapause, using the molecular probes for cyclins now available.

MAINTENANCE AND TERMINATION OF DIAPAUSE

Maintenance of Diapause

Diapause is maintained for periods ranging from brief (4–10 days as in rats and mice) to lengthy (10 months in badgers and 11 months in wallabies). In seals, the delay is variable between species, ranging from 1 to 5 months, and occurs in at least 13 phocid species and 7 otariid species (3, 9, 10). The most unusual pattern of reproduction in a diapausing seal is that of the Australian sea lion, which has a non-annual, aseasonal reproductive cycle of 18 months of which 3 to 5 months is diapause (36). In another carnivore, the spotted skunk, diapause lasts for about 200 days and is believed to be maintained by an insufficiency of uterine conditions (50). The early blastocysts are less than 0.4 mm diameter, but slowly expand to 1.1 mm during diapause. Although the trophoblast cells increase in number, there is no increase in the number of cells in the inner cell mass (53). In mink, after ovulation, the CL involutes, and progesterone secretion remains basal (25, 26). However cells from mink diapausing blastocysts divide in vitro, suggesting that reactivation is the terminal differentiation event (25). The control of diapause in mustelids such as the mink differs from marsupials.

In the tammar, the diapausing embryo is only 0.25 mm in diameter and shows no signs of growth or cell division. Remarkably, despite this inactivity, all the embryos survive and viable diapausing embryos can be maintained in the uterus for 2 years after ovariectomy (CH Tyndale-Biscoe, personal communication). Diapausing blastocysts have not yet been successfully reactivated in vitro despite numerous attempts, suggesting that diapause is not maintained simply by presence of an inhibitory uterine factor (MB Renfree & CH Tyndale-Biscoe, unpublished observations).

Ovarian Steroids in Diapause and Reactivation

Ovarian steroids play an important role in controlling uterine secretions and embryonic growth. Changes in ovarian steroids accompany reactivation after diapause in many species (Figure 4). In the mouse, estrogen is essential for blastocyst implantation in a progesterone-primed uterus, but the precise effects of estrogen on reactivation are still unclear (63). Estrogens alter transcription of a number of genes such as the EGF receptor gene (61). Recent work suggests that ovarian estrogen interacts with nuclear estrogen receptors to make the uterus receptive, whereas its metabolite, 4-hydroxy-estradiol-17β, synthesized in the uterus from estradiol, acts as a paracrine hormone to mediate blastocyst activation for implantation, which is successful only if these two hormones act synchronously (64).

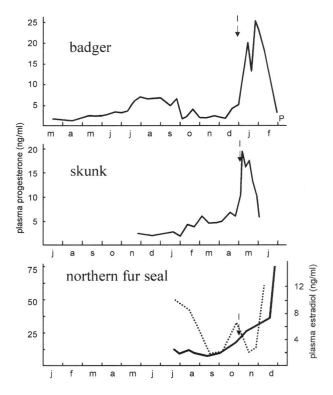

Figure 4   Steroid profiles during seasonal reactivation in three canivore species, the European *badger Meles meles,* the Western spotted skunk *S. putorius latifrons,* and the Northern fur seal *Callorhius ursinus.* In all three species progesterone rises steeply around the time of reactivation. In badgers and skunks, estrogen does not appear to affect diapause (15, 50), whereas a surge in estrogen occurs immediately before blastocyst activation in the seal (21). However, exogenous steroids do not induce reactivation.

Similarly, in the Western spotted skunk, EGF receptor is low during diapause but significantly increases after reactivation, suggesting it may be a prerequisite for implantation (62).

In seals, the control of reactivation is far from clear. Progesterone remains low during diapause and increases just before or at reactivation of the blastocyst (10, 20, 35, 36). There is a prominent surge of estrogen just before reactivation in both phocid and otariid seals (Figure 4) (21, 36, 67), although single intramuscular injections of either progesterone or estradiol or both fail to induce reactivation. In the only ungulate species known to have embryonic diapause, the roe deer *Capreolus capreolus,* there is an obligatory delay of about 5 to 6 months (1, 2, 89). The roe deer blastocyst enters diapause when the conceptus is relatively small (34, 82). Diapause can be terminated experimentally by transferring the blastocysts to an activated uterus (13). Plasma estradiol, progesterone, and prolactin increase after implantation, but the increase in endometrial secretion follows increases in protein synthesis in the conceptus, implicating a fetal cue for reactivation (47).

In mink, plasma progesterone concentrations increase coincident with the resumption of blastocyst growth (100). In the spotted skunk, plasma LH, prolactin, and progesterone are relatively low during diapause but gradually rise during the long pre-implantation period. However, although there is a reduction in the concentrations of both estrogen and progesterone receptors during the peri-implantation period, receptors can be detected during delayed implantation, suggesting that diapause is not due to a low number of ER and PR and that reactivation is not associated with an increase in uterine steroid receptors (54). Estrogen concentration is highly variable but declines during blastocyst activation, so it is possible that a transient rise occurs. In contrast to action in rats and mice, exogenous estrogen does not induce implantation. Ovariectomy decreases uterine weight in mink, skunk, and weasel (49, 50, 53). Exogenous progesterone maintains blastocyst viability but fails to induce reactivation or implantation. Similarly, various combinations of steroids in several other mustelid species have failed to induce implantation (51). Thus the precise combination of hormones required to induce blastocyst implantation in even a single species of carnivore remains unknown (51).

In the wallaby, diapause can be terminated by removing the pouch young (RPY) or by injecting progesterone, although the timing differs between these two methods of experimental reactivation and the time taken from estrus (see Figure 5) (79). Ovariectomy or lutectomy between 2 and 4 days after removal of the sucking pouch young does not prevent the initiation of blastocyst growth, but these blastocysts later collapse (14, 104, 119). However, removal of the CL after day 8 allows development to term. Estradiol 17β can also induce onset of mitoses and blastocyst expansion, but development fails by day 8 (29). Thus the CL must be present for at least the first few days to mediate the effects of the loss of the sucking stimulus.

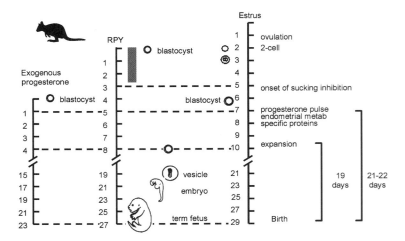

Figure 5 Intervals from exogenous progesterone injection, removal of pouch young (RPY), and estrus to the withdrawal or onset of sucking inhibition, the early rise in progesterone (progesterone pulse), the increase in endometrial wet weight, and the first measurable expansion of the blastocyst and birth. Although not shown, the progesterone pulse also coincides with an estradiol-17β pulse after RPY. Note that while the timing from injection, RPY, or estrus to the early progesterone pulse or to expansion is variable, the duration of pregnancy from the pulse is more or less constant and takes 21 to 22 days (108), and from expansion to birth 19 days. Based on data in References 29, 37, 42a, 69, 69a, 79, 86, 105.

Prolactin: The Hormone of Diapause

Prolactin appears to be a key hormone in both lactational and seasonal control of diapause, but it has different actions in different groups. In seals, reactivation does not appear to be linked to weaning (8, 9). Prolactin is luteotrophic and may function in embryonic reactivation, although it declines throughout diapause in Antarctic fur seals *Arctocephalus gazella* (10). In mink and spotted skunk, prolactin secretion is necessary for blastocyst and luteal development (26, 56, 65). In the skunk, however, melatonin does not inhibit prolactin secretion, but it does reduce the inhibitory effects of dopamine on prolactin secretion (80). Bromocriptine suppresses endogenous prolactin and prevents increase in prolactin receptor mRNA, suggesting that prolactin up-regulates its receptor and maintains the LH receptor in the mink CL (25). Administration of prolactin to mink or skunk hastens implantation, but does not directly induce it (53).

In macropodid marsupials, in contrast, prolactin acts to suppress growth and steroid secretion of the CL. Prolactin receptors are present on the CL (84, 99), and diapausing blastocysts may be readily reactivated by a single injection of the dopamine agonist bromocriptine, which inhibits prolactin secretion (31, 41, 48, 106). Prolactin is released in response to the sucking stimulus, and diapause is abolished if the sucked mammary gland is denervated, even when lactation continues (71). The sucking stimulus must be withdrawn for at least 72 h to allow the CL to escape inhibition (37). If the young are replaced after 72 h, reactivation is not inhibited, even though lactation continues. Experimental manipulation of photoperiod results in the loss of a characteristic dawn pulse of prolactin (48a), and there must be a loss of at least three consecutive dawn pulses for the blastocyst and CL to be irrevocably committed to reactivation (42). Similarly, after melatonin injections, the dawn prolactin pulse is abolished by the third day (107). Hypophysectomy induces reactivation due to the removal of the inhibitory effects of prolactin (41a), so the hypothalamic-pituitary axis must be sensitive to the lack of sucking inhibition on three successive days.

In the bent-winged bat, LH may be required for luteal maintenance (5), but prolactin can induce reactivation of the quiescent CL and promote initiation of implantation, whereas exogenous progesterone has no effect (4).

Uterine Secretions During Diapause and Reactivation

Numerous changes occur in the uterine environment of the skunk during blastocyst reactivation, characterized by an increase in uterine proteins, including at least one uterine-specific protein of 24 kDa (49, 55). The CLs of ferrets may secrete a basic protein that acts with progesterone to induce implantation (53). Cyclooxygenase-2 (COX-2), regulated by the implanting blastocyst, is required for implantation in the mouse, whereas expression of the uterine COX-1 gene is influenced by ovarian steroids (16). During delay in the skunk, COX-1 and COX-2 are not expressed, but are first detected in the uterus and trophoblast before blastocyst attachment, and their levels correlate with an influx of serum proteins when embryonic development resumes (23).

In tammars the uterine environment plays a key role in regulating development, since during the first two-thirds of gestation an acellular mucoid coat and keratinous shell prevent cell-cell contact between the endometrium and embryonic cells. The uterine fluid is a product of the endometrial lining of the uterus. In tammars, several uterine-specific prealbumins are present in fluid recovered from uteri during reactivation (69), and both progesterone and estradiol can stimulate rapid and dramatic changes in uterine protein secretion (85, 87). The uterine changes that maintain pregnancy are controlled by an early transient rise in progesterone (see Figure 6), but since ovariectomy after day 7 does not affect the continuation of pregnancy, the need for progesterone is brief. Diapausing blastocysts transferred to the uteri of recipients at day 8 RPY reactivate and develop normally, whereas reactivated day 8 blastocysts die if transferred to the uteri of recipients in diapause (104). Thus the uterine conditions promoting reactivation last until at least day 8 after RPY.

Metabolic Reactivation After Diapause

The specific controls that depress metabolism of the dormant embryo and then reactivate it to implant at a later time are unknown, although several studies have provided clues to the mechanisms and the changes that occur, (e.g. 45, 102, 112,

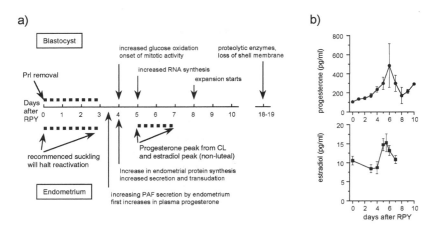

Figure 6 Summary of the key hormonal and metabolic steps during reactivation of the tammar (*a*) embryo and endometrial responses and (*b*) progesterone and oestradiol profiles. Rising progesterone stimulates uterine changes that result in embryonic reactivation. The role of the peak of estradiol on day 5 is unclear. Progesterone alone will induce reactivation and support pregnancy. Exogenous estradiol starts growth of blastocysts, which later collapse and die (redrawn from 85, 86).

113). Mouse blastocysts are under inhibition by the uterine environment, whereas there is no evidence of direct inhibition during diapause in the tammar (75, 85, 112). The earliest signs of blastocyst reactivation in the skunk coincide with a decrease in the amount of glycogen and lipid, and there is an increase in RNA and protein synthesis in the trophectoderm and inner cell mass (53).

In the mouse, mitoses and cell numbers increase within 12 h of a reactivating signal, when pyruvate may be the primary energy source. However, after 16 h, glucose appears to be the predominant energy source for the mouse blastocyst (92). These changes take much longer in the tammar. The tammar uterus becomes more secretory by day 4 of gestation after RPY, and embryo metabolism increases by day 5 RPY (93, 95) (Figure 6). There is no significant increase in carbohydrate uptake or production during the first 5 days after reactivation, after which there is a proportional decrease in lactate production suggestive of a metabolic switch at or around day 5 (91, 93). Glutamine and palmitate oxidation also increase after day 4, suggestive of a highly oxidative metabolism, as occurs in ruminant species (94, 95). Amino acids and fatty acids are therefore likely to supplement the energy supplied by carbohydrates during the early stages of reactivation. As noted above, removal of the suckled pouch young during the breeding season terminates diapause within 72 h (37) leading to a distinct increase in metabolic activity of the embryo (91, 93, 95). By day 4 oxidative metabolism of glucose has substantially increased, providing a fourfold increase in ATP production. By day 5, RNA synthesis increases. These changes are dependent on progesterone-induced changes in uterine secretions. By day 3 there is greater progesterone secretion by the CL, and by day 4–5 uterine protein synthesis has increased. The female hormones also appear to induce the production of a sequence of factors that regulate different stages of reactivation and expansion (Figure 6). For example, platelet-activating factor (PAF) appears to be induced by the rising progesterone secretion and may stimulate blastocyst development (46). The specific nature of these uterine regulatory factors is still not known, although in our studies using gel-electrophoresis, uterine-specific proteins were found from day 4 (69, 85). We have also used mouse blastocysts as a bioassay for wallaby uterine secretions (94, 103). Reactivated wallaby uterine exudates increase mouse blastocyst glucose metabolism and lactate production, but quiescent exudates are not capable of inducing diapause in mouse embryos (94), indicating that stimulatory factors are produced in the tammar uterus at reactivation, while not excluding the possibility of inhibitor production during diapause.

Influence of Cytokines and Growth Factors

In rodents reactivation of delayed implanting embryos may be mediated by both uterine secretions and cellular interactions between the embryo and endometrial epithelium (22, 114). Unlike that in rodents, the reactivating tammar blastocyst is completely enclosed in a keratinous shell membrane so it must be changes in the uterine secretions that regulate reactivation. Several unique polypeptides are found in the uterine secretions at the termination of diapause that may include growth factors important for the stimulation of embryonic growth (69), in much the same way that Weitlauf and colleagues (58, 114) have described for the mouse. Of the known growth factors, LIF (leukemia-inhibiting factor), IGF (insulin-like growth factors), EGF (epidermal growth factor), PDGF (platelet-derived growth factor), FGF (fibroblast growth factor), and TGF-β (transforming growth factor β) are present in the uterus and embryo and are active during embryogenesis (40, 44, 83, 97). By addition of purified growth factors to cultured embryos and by gene knockout studies, both LIF and EGF have been shown to be essential for normal development of mouse embryos in the peri-implantation period (96–98).

It is clear from work on eutherian mammals that many growth factors in the uterine secretions may regulate embryonic metabolism and development through paracrine and autocrine interactions (11, 83). The clear separation of embryonic reactivation and implantation in the tammar provides an interesting contrast to the most-studied species, the mouse.

LIF is essential for growth but not differentiation of the blastocyst (96). In mice, LIF is produced in the endometrial glands specifically on day 4 of pregnancy and is essential for implantation (96, 98). Embryos in LIF−/− knockout mothers develop to blastocysts but do not implant by day 7. At this stage they look like embryos in diapause with no cell proliferation (96). When the blastocysts from LIF−/− knockout mothers are transferred to wild-type foster mothers, the result is viable offspring (97). Analysis of expression in pseudopregnant and delayed implanting mice indicates that LIF expression is maternally controlled by estrogen; thus its expression coincides with blastocyst formation and always precedes implantation (7). In pigs, uterine LIF production is upregulated when the embryo starts producing significant amounts of estrogen (118). Estradiol, not progesterone, induces LIF synthesis by bovine oviduct cells (68). In rabbits, by contrast, progesterone regulates LIF expression (117), and progesterone inhibits LIF secretion in cultures of human endometrium (38). In mink, uterine LIF levels are low during diapause but increase transiently on the first two days of reactivation (90). Similarly, LIF mRNA is not abundant during diapause in the skunk but increases when blastocysts resume development, remaining high until implantation (43). Although prolactin, progesterone, and estradiol do not increase uterine concentrations of LIF in the skunk above that found in ovariectomized controls, the timing of its expression is consistent with a role for LIF in preparation of the uterus for implantation.

LIF could affect the embryo directly or act in an autocrine fashion on the uterus to alter secretory activity (40, 96) that may be essential for continued development. Contrasting the timing of expression of LIF between mice, mustelids, and wallabies may help define the physiological control of metabolic activation, mitosis, blastocyst expansion, and implantation.

The IGFs are also important regulators of embryo growth. IGF-1 and -2 modulate glucose uptake by mouse blastocysts by regulating the GLUT-1 glucose transporter (60). In tammars, the substantial increases in glucose uptake and utilization that accompany reactivation from diapause suggest that the switch in the metabolic pathway apparently regulated by intracellular glucose concentration (93) may in fact be modulated by IGF.

If growth factors in uterine secretions control pre-implantation embryonic development in a similar way, it would explain the need for synchrony between embryo and uterus after diapause. One of the earliest interactions so far defined is the induction of heparin-binding EGF-like growth factor at the site of apposition of the mouse blastocyst to the uterine epithelium after termination of delay by estrogen (24). EGF-related growth factors and up-regulation of EGF receptors may be a prerequisite for blastocyst activation and implantation in the spotted skunk (62). As discussed above, changes in the cyclooxygenases also appear to be important (23), and successful implantation occurs only when the activated blastocyst coincides with a receptive uterus (64). Two members of the EGF family, betacellulin and epiregulin, are expressed only in the mouse uterine luminal epithelium and underlying stroma adjacent to the implanting blastocyst (22). These growth factors are absent during diapause but are rapidly induced by estrogen, which activates the blastocyst. Another growth factor that participates in the implantation process but is produced only when the blastocyst is activated is neu differentiation factor (NDF) (66), again demonstrating the requirement for synchrony between the implanting blastocyst and the reactivating uterus. Clearly a complex network of cell-signaling events is required for successful reactivation of the blastocyst after embryonic diapause.

CONCLUSIONS

Diapause is a fascinating phenomenon by which some mammals can effectively extend the gestation period. The selective advantage of this phenomenon is clearly profound judging by the diversity of mammals in which diapause has evolved. Understanding its control has contributed much to our understanding of reproductive endocrinology and the control of early embryonic growth in mammals. Although most work continues to be based on the mouse, rodent reproduction has diverged remarkably from most mammals, and studies summarized here on several species may be more representative. These studies highlight the importance of prolactin as a key endocrine regulator linking environmental stimuli such as photoperiod or lactation with ovarian control. Although estradiol and progesterone clearly play a central role in regulating the interactions between uterus and embryo, other hormones must also be involved since neither hormone terminates diapause in all species. Understanding the endocrine control of diapause in all species may reveal pathways of control that have been overlooked in the common laboratory animals and humans. Although there is great diversity in endocrine controls, it is likely that the signals that control the blastocyst are more conserved. Diapause and reactivation probably involve several independently controlled steps. A range of growth factors secreted by the uterus may regulate diapause, and studies of the mechanisms by which these growth factor work are now starting to unravel the molecular biological controls of diapause.

ACKNOWLEDGMENTS

We are especially grateful to Dr. Rodney Mead for providing the beautiful photograph of the Western spotted skunk blastocyst. We thank our numerous graduate students, colleagues, and collaborators for their contributions to the research on marsupials. Our research has been supported by the Australian Research Council and the Australian National Health and Medical Research Council.

Visit the Annual Reviews home page at www.AnnualReviews.org.

LITERATURE CITED

1. Aitken RJ. 1974. Delayed implantation in roe deer (*Capreolus capreolus*). *J. Reprod. Fertil.* 39:225–33

2. Aitken RJ. 1981. Aspects of delayed implantation in the roe deer (*Capreolus capreolus*). *J. Reprod. Fertil. Suppl.* 29:83–95

3. Atkinson S. 1997. Reproductive biology of seals. *Rev. Reprod.* 2:175–94

4. Bernard RT, Bojarski C. 1994. Effects of prolactin and hCG treatment on luteal activity and the conceptus during delayed implantation in Schreibers' long-fingered bat (*Miniopterus schreibersii*). *J. Reprod. Fertil.* 100:359–65

5. Bernard RT, Bojarski C, Millar RP. 1991. Plasma progesterone and luteinizing hormone concentrations and the role of the

corpus luteum and LH gonadotrophs in the control of delayed implantation in Schreibers' long-fingered bat (*Miniopterus schreibersii*). *J. Reprod. Fertil.* 93: 31–42

6. Bernard RT, Cumming GS. 1997. African bats: evolution of reproductive patterns and delays. *Q. Rev. Biol.* 72:253–74

7. Bhatt H, Brunet L, Stewart CL. 1991. Uterine expression of leukemia inhibitory factor coincides with the onset of blastocyst implantation. *Proc. Natl. Acad. Sci. USA* 88:11408–12

8. Boyd IL. 1984. The relationship between body condition and the timing of implantation in pregnant grey seals (*Halichoerus grypus*). *J. Zool.* 203:113–23

9. Boyd IL. 1991. Changes in plasma progesterone and prolactin concentrations during the annual cycle and the role of prolactin in the maintenance of lactation and luteal development in the Antarctic fur seal (*Arctocephalus gazella*) *J. Reprod. Fertil.* 91:637–47

10. Boyd IL. 1991. Environmental physiological factors controlling the reproductive cycles of pinnipeds. *Can. J. Zool.* 69:1135–48

11. Brigstock DR, Heap RB, Brown KD. 1989. Polypeptide growth factors in uterine tissues and secretions. *J. Reprod. Fertil.* 85:747–58

12. Brinklow BR, Loudon AS. 1993. Gestation periods in the Pere David's Deer (*Elaphurus davidianus*): evidence for embryonic diapause or delayed development. *Reprod. Fertil. Dev.* 5:567–75

13. Broich A, Hildebrandt T, Lange A, Gilles M, Hermes R, et al. 1998. Experimental investigation of embryonic diapause in European roe deer (*Capreolus capreolus*). *J. Reprod. Fertil.* 22:33–34

14. Bryant SL, Rose RW. 1986. Growth and role of the corpus luteum throughout delayed gestation in the potoroo, *Potorous tridactylus*. *J. Reprod. Fertil.* 76: 409–14

15. Canivenc R, Bonnin M. 1981. Environmental control of delayed implantation in the European badger (*Meles meles*). *J. Reprod. Fertil. Suppl.* 29:25–33

16. Chakraborty I, Das SK, Wang J, Dey SK. 1996. Developmental expression of the cyclo-oxygenase-1 and cyclo-oxygenase-2 genes in the peri-implantation mouse uterus and their differential regulation by the blastocyst and ovarian steriods. *J. Mol. Endocrinol.* 16:107–22

17. Clutter ME, ed. 1978. *Dormancy and Developmental Arrest. Experimental Analysis in Plants and Animals.* New York: Academic

18. Crichton EG, Seamark RF, Krutzsch PH. 1989. The status of the corpus luteum during pregnancy in *Miniopterus schreibersii* (Chiroptera: Vespertilionidae) with emphasis on its role in developmental delay. *Cell Tissue Res.* 258:183–201

19. Curlewis JD. 1992. Seasonal prolactin secretion and its role in seasonal reproduction: a review. *Reprod. Fertil. Dev.* 4:1–23

20. Daniel JC. 1975. Concentrations of circulating progesterone during early pregnancy in the Northern fur seal, *Callorhinus ursinus*. *J. Fish. Res. Bd. Can.* 32:65–66

21. Daniel JC. 1981. Delayed implantation in the northern fur seal (*Callorhinus ursinus*) and other pinnipeds. *J. Reprod. Fertil. Suppl.* 29:35–50

22. Das SK, Das N, Wang J, Lim H, Schryver B, Plowman GD, Dey SK. 1997. Expression of betacellulin and epiregulin genes in the mouse uterus temporally by the blastocyst solely at the site of its apposition is coincident with the "window" of implantation. *Dev. Biol.* 190:178–90

23. Das SK, Wang J, Key SK, Mead RA. 1999. Spatiotemporal expression of cyclooxygenase 1 and cyclooxygenase 2 during delayed implantation and the peri-implantation period in the western spotted skunk. *Biol. Reprod.* 60:893–99

24. Das SK, Wang XN, Paria BC, Damm D, Abraham JA, et al. 1994. Heparin-binding EGF-like growth factor gene is induced in the mouse uterus temporally by the blastocyst solely at the site of its apposition: a possible ligand for interaction with blastocyst EGF-receptor in implantation. *Development* 120:1071–83

25. Douglas DA, Houde A, Song JH, Farookhi R, Concannon PW, Murphy BD. 1998. Luteotropic hormone receptors in the ovary of the mink (*Mustela vison*) during delayed implantation and early-postimplantation gestation. *Biol. Reprod.* 59:571–78

26. Douglas DA, Song JH, Houde A, Cook GM, Murphy BD. 1997. Luteal and placental characteristics of carnivore gestation: expression of genes for luteotrophic receptors and steroidogenic enzymes. *J. Reprod. Fertil. Suppl.* 51:153–66

27. Douglas DA, Song JH, Moreau GM, Murphy BD. 1998. Differentiation of the corpus luteum of the mink (*Mustela vison*): mitogenic and steroidogenic potential of luteal cells from embryonic diapause and postimplantation gestation. *Biol. Reprod.* 58:1163–69

28. Evsikov SV, Vagyna IN, Solomko AP. 1996. Mechanisms of cell number regulation in the peri-implantation mouse blastocyst. *J. Exp. Zool.* 276:201–8

29. Fletcher TP, Jetton AE, Renfree MB. 1988. Influence of progesterone and oestradiol 17β on blastocysts of the tammar wallaby during seasonal diapause. *J. Reprod. Fertil.* 83:193–200

30. Deleted in proof

31. Fletcher TP, Shaw G, Renfree MB. 1990. Effects of bromocriptine at parturition in the tammar wallaby, *Macropus eugenii. Reprod. Fertil. Dev.* 2:79–88

32. Flint AP. 1981. A unifying hypothesis for the control of blastocyst growth based on observations of the pig. *J. Reprod. Fertil. Suppl.* 29:215–27

33. Flint APF, Renfree MB, Weir BJ, eds. 1981. *Embryonic Diapause in Mammals.*

Cambridge, UK: J. Reprod. Fertil. Suppl. 29. 260 pp

34. Flint AP, Krzywinski A, Sempere AJ, Mauger R, Lacroix A. 1994. Luteal oxytocin and monoestry in the roe deer *Capreolus capreolus. J. Reprod. Fertil.* 101:651–56

35. Gales NJ, Costa DP. 1997. The Australian sea lion: a review of an unusual life history. *In Marine Mammal Research in the Southern Hemisphere*, ed. M Hindell, C Kemper. pp. 78–87. Sydney: Beaty & Sons

36. Gales NJ, Williamson, P. Higgins LV, Blackberry MA, James I. 1997. Evidence for a postimplantation period in the Australian sea lion (*Neophoca cinerea*). *J. Reprod. Fertil.* 111:159–63

37. Gordon K, Renfree MB, Short RV, Clarke IJ. 1988. Hypothalamo-pituitary portal blood concentrations of β-endorphin during suckling in the ewe. A possible role for endogenous opiates in the lactational inhibition of reproduction. *J. Reprod. Fertil.* 79:397–408

38. Hambatsoumian E, Torpin JL, Moreau JF, Freydman R, Chaouat G. 1998. In vivo administration of progesterone inhibits the secretion of endometrial leukaemia inhibitory factor in vitro. *Mol. Hum. Reprod.* 4:1039–44

39. Harder JD, Hinds LA, Horn CA, Tyndale-Biscoe CH. 1984. Oestradiol in follicular fluid and in utero-ovarian venous and peripheral plasma during parturition and postpartum oestrus in the tammar, *Macropus eugenii. J. Reprod. Fertil.* 72:551–58

40. Harvey MB, Leco KJ, Arcellana-Panlilio MY, Zhang X, Edwards DR, Schultz GA. 1995. Roles of growth factors during peri-implantation development. *Hum. Reprod.* 10:712–18

41. Hearn CM, Shaw G, Short RV, Renfree MB. 1998. Effects of cabergoline on reproduction in three families of Australian marsupials. *J. Reprod. Fertil.* 113:151–75

41a. Hearn JP. 1974. The pituitary gland and implantation in the tammar wallaby *Macropus eugenii. J. Reprod. Fertil.* 39: 235–41

42. Hinds LA. 1994. Prolactin, a hormone for all seasons: endocrine regulation of seasonal breeding in the Macropodidae. *Oxford Rev. Reprod. Biol.* 16:247–99

42a. Hinds LA, Tyndale-Biscoe CH 1982. Plasma progesterone levels in the pregnant and non-pregnant tammar, *Macropus eugenii. J. Endocrinol.* 93:99–107

43. Hirzel DJ, Wang J, Das SK, Dey SK, Mead RA. 1999. Changes in uterine expression of leukemia inhibitory factor during pregnancy in the Western spotted skunk. *Biol. Reprod.* 60:484–92

44. Kane MT, Morgan PM, Coonan C. 1997. Peptide growth factors and preimplantation development. *Hum. Reprod. Update* 3:137–57

45. Kaye PL. 1997. Preimplantation growth factor physiology. *Rev. Reprod.* 2:121–27

46. Kojima T, Hinds LA, Muller WJ, O'Neill C, Tyndale-Biscoe CH. 1993. Production and secretion of progesterone in vitro and presence of platelet activating factor (PAF) in early pregnancy of the marsupial, *Macropus eugenii. Reprod. Fertil. Dev.* 5:15–25

47. Lambert RTK, Ashworth CJ, Beattie L, Gebbie FE, Hutchinson JSM, et al. 1998. Temporal changes in reproductive hormones during embryonic diapause and reactivation of the blastocyst in the European roe deer (*Capreolus capreolus*). *J. Reprod. Fertil. Abst. Ser.* 22:88

48. Loudon ASI, Brinklow BR, Gulland FD, Boyle J. Flint APF. 1990. Roles of prolactin and the uterus in the control of luteal regression in the Bennett's wallaby (*Macropus rufogriseus rufogriseus*). *Reprod. Fertil. Dev.* 2:71–78

48a. McConnell SJ, Tyndale-Biscoe CH, Hinds LA. 1986. Change in duration of elevated concentrations of melatonin is the major factor in photoperiod response

of the tammar, *Macropus eugenii. J. Reprod. Fertil.* 77:623–32

49. Mead RA. 1975. Effects of hypophysectomy on blastocyst survival, progesterone secretion and nidation in the spotted skunk. *Biol. Reprod.* 12:526–33

50. Mead RA. 1981. Delayed implantation in mustelids with special emphasis on the spotted skunk. *J. Reprod. Fertil. Suppl.* 29:11–24

51. Mead RA. 1986. Role of the corpus luteum in controlling implantation in mustelid carnivores. *Ann. NY Acad. Sci.* 476:25–35

52. Mead RA. 1993. Embryonic diapause in vertebrates. *J. Exp. Zool.* 266:629–41

53. Mead RA. 1995. Hormonal control of implantation in some carnivores. *In Molecular and Cellular Aspects of Periimplantation Processes,* ed. SK Dey, pp. 48–66. Serono Symp. USA. Norwell, MA: Springer

54. Mead RA, Eroschenko VP. 1995. Changes in uterine estrogen and progesterone receptors during delayed implantation and early implantation in the spotted skunk. *Biol. Reprod.* 53:827–33

55. Mead RA, Rourke AW, Swannack A. 1979. Changes in uterine protein synthesis during delayed implantation in the western spotted skunk and its regulation by hormones. *Biol. Reprod.* 21:39–46

56. Murphy BD, Rajkumar K, Gonzalez Reyna A, Silversides DW. 1993. Control of luteal function in the mink (*Mustela vison*). *J. Reprod. Fertil. Suppl.* 47:181–88

57. Newkirk KD, Mcmillan HJ, Wynne-Edwards KE. 1997. Length of delay to birth of a second litter in dwarf hamsters (Phodopus): evidence for post-implantation embryonic diapause. *J. Exp. Zool.* 278:106–14

58. Nieder GL, Weitlauf HM. 1985. Effects of metabolic substrates and ionic environment on in vitro activation of delayed implanting mouse blastocysts. *J. Reprod. Fertil.* 73:151–57

59. Nurse SC, Renfree MB. 1994. Pubertal development of the pouch and tests in a marsupial. *J. Reprod. Fertil.* 101:279–85

60. Pantaleon M, Kaye PL. 1996. IGFI and insulin regulate glucose transport in mouse blastocysts via IGFI receptor. *Mol. Reprod. Dev.* 44:71–76

61. Paria BC, Das SK, Andrews GK, Dey SK. 1993. Expression of the epidermal growth factor receptor gene is regulated in mouse blastocysts during delayed implantation. *Proc. Natl. Acad. Sci. USA* 90:55–59

62. Paria BC, Das SK, Mead RA, Dey SK. 1994. Expression of epidermal growth factor receptor in the preimplantation uterus and blastocyst of the western spotted skunk. *Biol. Reprod.* 51:205–13

63. Paria BC, Huet-Hudson YM, Dey SK. 1993. Blastocyst's state of activity determines the "window" of implantation in the receptive mouse uterus. *Proc. Natl. Acad. Sci. USA* 90:10159–62

64. Paria BC, Lim H, Wang XN, Leihr J, Das SK, Dey SK. 1998. Coordination of differential effects of primary estrogen and catecholestrogen on two distinct targets mediates embryo implantation in the mouse. *Endocrinology* 139:5235–46

65. Polejaeva IA, Reed WA, Bunch TD, Ellis LC, White KL. 1997. Prolactin-induced termination of obligate diapause of mink (*Mustela vison*) blastocysts in vitro and subsequent establishment of embryonic stem-like cells. *J. Reprod. Fertil.* 109:229–36

66. Reese J, Brown N, Das SK, Dey SK. 1998. Expression of neu differentiation factor during the periimplantation period in the mouse uterus. *Biol. Reprod.* 58:719–27

67. Reijnders PG. 1990. Progesterone and oestradiol-17 beta concentration profiles throughout the reproductive cycle in harbour seals (*Phoca vitulina*). *J. Reprod. Fertil.* 90:403–9

68. Reinhart KC, Dubey, RK, Mummery CL, vanRooijen M, Keller PJ, Marrinelar S. 1998. Synthesis and regulation of leukaemia inhibitory factor in cultured bovine oviduct cells by hormones. *Mol. Hum. Reprod.* 4:301–8

69. Renfree MB. 1973. Proteins in the uterine secretions of the marsupial *Macropus eugenii*. *Dev. Biol.* 32:41–49

69a. Renfree MB. 1973. The composition of fetal fluids of the marsupial *Macropus eugenii*. *Dev. Biol.* 33:62–79

70. Renfree MB. 1978. Embryonic diapause in mammals–developmental strategy. In *Mechanisms of Dormancy and Developmental Arrest.* ed. ME Clutter, pp. 1–46. New York: Academic

71. Renfree MB. 1979. Initiation of development of diapausing embryo by mammary denervation during lactation in a marsupial. *Nature* 278:549–51

72. Renfree MB. 1980. Embryonic diapause in the honey possum *Tarsipes spencerae*. *Search* 11:81

73. Renfree MB. 1981. Embryonic diapause in marsupials. *J. Reprod. Fertil. Suppl.* 29:67–68

74. Renfree MB. 1993. Diapause, pregnancy, and parturition in Australian marsupials. *J. Exp. Zool.* 266:450–62

75. Renfree MB. 1994. Endocrinology of pregnancy, parturition, and lactation in marsupials. In *Marshall's Physiology of Reproduction, Vol. 3. Pregnancy and Lactation,* ed. GE Laming, pp. 677–766. London: Chapman & Hall

76. Renfree MB, Calaby JH. 1981. Background to delayed implantation and embryonic diapause. *J. Reprod. Fertil. Suppl.* 29:1–9

77. Renfree MB, Fletcher, TP, Blanden DR, Lewis PR, Shaw G, et al. 1989. Physiology and behavioural events around the time of birth in macropodid marsupials. In *Kangaroos, Wallabies and Rat Kangaroos.* ed. G Grigg, P Jarman, ID Hume, pp. 323–37. Sydney: Beatty & Sons

78. Renfree MB, Lewis A. 1996. Cleavage in vivo and in vitro in the marsupial *Macropus eugenii. Reprod. Fertil. Dev.* 8:725–42

79. Renfree MB, Tyndale-Biscoe CH. 1973. Intra-uterine development after diapause in the marsupial. *Macropus eugenii. Dev. Biol.* 32:28–40

80. Rozell MD, Mead RA. 1993. Effect of melatonin on pituitary secretion of prolactin in vitro during delayed implantation and the periimplantation period in the spotted skunk. *J. Exp. Zool.* 267:524–32

81. Sandell M. 1990. The evolution of seasonal delayed implantation. *Q. Rev. Biol.* 65:23–42

82. Schams D, Barth D, Karg H. 1980. LH, FSH and progesterone concentration peripheral plasma of the female roe deer (*Capreolus capreolus*) during the rutting season. *J. Reprod. Fertil.* 60:109–14

83. Schultz GA, Heyner S. 1993. Growth factors in preimplantation mammalian embryos. *Oxford Rev. Reprod. Biol.* 15: 43–81

84. Sernia C, Tyndale-Biscoe CH. 1979. Prolactin receptors in the mammary gland, corpus luteum and other tissues of the tammar wallaby, *Macropus eugenii. J. Endocrinol.* 83:79–89

85. Shaw G. 1996. The uterine environment in early pregnancy in the tammar wallaby. *Reprod. Fertil. Dev.* 8:811–18

86. Shaw G, Renfree MB. 198. Concentrations of oestradiol-17β in plasma and corpora lutea through pregnancy in the tammar, *Macropus eugenii. J. Reprod. Fertil.* 72:29–37

87. Shaw G, Renfree MB. 1986. Uterine and embryonic metabolism after embryonic diapause in the tammar wallaby (*Macropus eugenii*). *J. Reprod. Fertil.* 76: 339–47

88. Sherman MI, Barlow, PW. 1972. Deoxyribonucleic acid content in delayed mouse blastocysts *J. Reprod. Fertil.* 29:123–26

89. Short RV, Hay MF. 1966. Delayed implantation in the roe deer, *Capreolus capreolus. Symp. Zool. Soc. London* 15:173–94

90. Song JH, Houde A, Murphy BD. 1998. Cloning of leukemia inhibitory factor (LIF) and its expression in the uterus during embryonic diapause and implantation in the mink (*Mustela vison*). *Mol. Reprod. Dev.* 51:13–21

91. Spindler RE, Renfree MB, Gardner DK. 1995. Metabolic assessment of wallaby blastocysts during embryonic diapause and subsequent reactivation. *Reprod. Fertil. Dev.* 7: 1157–62

92. Spindler RE, Renfree MB, Gardner DK. 1996. Carbohydrate uptake by quiescent and reactivated mouse blastyocysts. *J. Exp. Zool.* 276:132–37

93. Spindler RE, Renfree MB, Shaw G, Gardner DK. 1998. Reactivating tammar wallaby blastocysts oxidise glucose. *Biol. Reprod.* 58:1425–31

94. Spindler RE, Renfree MB, Shaw G, Gardner DK. 1999. Mouse embryos used as a bioassay to determine control of marsupial embryonic diapause. *J. Exp. Zool.* 1:283:590–99

95. Spindler RE, Renfree MB, Shaw G, Gardner DK. 1999. Reactivating tammar wallaby blastocysts oxidise fatty acids and amino acids. *J. Reprod.Fertil.* 115:79–86

96. Stewart CL. 1994. Leukaemia inhibitory factor and the regulation of pre-implantation development of the mammalian embryo. *Mol. Reprod. Dev.* 39:233–38

97. Stewart CL, Cullinan EB. 1997. Preimplantation development of the mammalian embryo and its regulation by growth factors. *Dev. Genet.* 21:91–101

98. Stewart CL, Kaspar P, Brunet LJ, Bhatt H. Gadi I, et al. 1992. Blastocyst implantation depends on maternal expression of leukaemia inhibitory factor. *Nature* 359:76–79

99. Stewart F. Tyndale-Biscoe CH. 1982. Prolactin and luteinizing hormone recep-

tors in marsupial corpora lutea: relationship to control of luteal function. *J. Endocrinol.* 92:63–72

100. Stoufflet I, Mondain-Monval M, Simon P, Martinet L. 1989. Patterns of plasma progesterone, androgen and oestrogen concentrations and in vitro ovarian steroidogenesis during embryonic diapause and implantation in the mink (*Mustela vison*). *J. Reprod. Fertil.* 87:209–21

101. Surani MAH. 1975. Zona pellucida denudation, blastocyst proliferation and attachment in the rat. *J. Embryol. Exp. Morphol.* 33:343–53

102. Surani MAH, Fishel SB. 1981. Embryonic and uterine factors in delayed implantation in rodents. *J. Reprod. Fertil. Suppl.* 29:159–72

103. Thornber EJ, Renfree MB, Wallace GI. 1981. Biochemical studies of intrauterine components of the tammar wallaby *Macropus eugenii* during pregnancy. *J. Embryol. Exp. Morphol.* 62:325–38

104. Tyndale-Biscoe CH. 1970. Resumption of development by quiescent blastocysts transferred to primed, ovariectomized recipients in the marsupial, *Macropus eugenii. J. Reprod. Fertil.* 23:25–32

105. Tyndale-Biscoe CH. 1979. In *Maternal Recognition of Pregnancy Ciba Found. Symp. 64.* pp. 173–90 Amsterdam: Excerpta Medica

106. Tyndale-Biscoe CH, Hinds LA. 1984. Seasonal patterns of circulating progesterone and prolactin and response to bromocriptine in the female tammar *Macropus eugenii. Gen. Comp. Endocrinol.* 53:58–68

107. Tyndale-Biscoe CH, Hinds LA, McConnell SJ. 1986. Seasonal breeding in a marsupial: opportunities of a new species for an old problem. *Rec. Prog. Horm.* 1986. 42:471–512

108. Tyndale-Biscoe H, Renfree MB. 1987. *Reproductive Physiology of Marsupials.* Cambridge, UK: Cambridge Univ. Press. 476 pp.

109. Wallace GI. 1978. A histological study of the early stages of pregnancy in the bent winged bat (*Miniopterus schreibersii*) in the north-eastern New South Wales, Australia (32°27′S). *J. Zool.* 185:519–37

110. Ward SJ. 1990. Reproduction in the western pygmy-possum, *Cercartetus concinnus* (Marsupialia: Burramyidae), with notes on reproduction of some other small possum species. *Aust. J. Zool.* 38:423–38

111. Ward S, Renfree MB. 1988. Reproduction in males of the feathertail gliders, *Acrobates pygmeaus* (Marsupialia). *J. Zool.* 216:241–52

112. Weitlauf HM. 1994. Biology of implantation. In *The Physiology of Reproduction,* ed. E Knobil, JD O'Neill, pp. 391–440. New York: Raven. 2nd ed.

113. Weitlauf HM, Kiessling AA. 1981. Activation of 'delayed implanting' mouse embryos in vitro *J. Reprod. Fertil. Suppl.* 29:191–202

114. Weitlauf HM, Suda-Hartman M. 1988. Changes in secreted uterine proteins associated with embryo implantation in the mouse. *J. Reprod. Fertil.* 84:539–49

115. Williams SC, Fletcher TP, Renfree MB. 1998. Puberty in the female tammar wallaby. *Biol. Reprod.* 58:1117–22

116. Wooller RD, Renfree MB, Russell ER, Dunning A, Green SW, Duncan P. 1981. Seasonal changes in population of the nectar-feeding marsupial *Tarsipes spencerae* (Marsupialia: Tarsipedidae). *J. Zool.* 195:267–79

117. Yang ZM, Chen DB, Le SP, Harper MJ. 1996. Differential hormonal regulation of leukemia inhibitory factor (LIF) in rabbit and mouse uterus. *Mol. Reprod. Dev.* 43:470–76

118. Yelich JV, Pomp D, Geisert RD. 1997. Ontogeny of elongation and gene expression in the early developing porcine conceptus. *Biol. Reprod.* 57:1256–65

119. Young IR, Renfree MB. 1979. The effects of corpus luteum removal during gestation on parturition in the tammar wallaby, *Macropus eugenii. J. Reprod. Fertil.* 56:249–54

Annu. Rev. Physiol. 2000. 62:377–411

MULTIPLE ENDOCRINE NEOPLASIAS

A. O. Hoff, G. J. Cote, and R. F. Gagel

Section of Endocrine Neoplasia and Hormonal Disorders, Department of Internal Medicine Specialties, University of Texas M.D. Anderson Cancer Center, Houston, Texas 77030; e-mail: rgagel@mdanderson.org

Key Words MEN1, MEN2, RET proto-oncogene, menin, von Hippel-Lindau disease, neurofibromatosis, Carney complex

■ **Abstract** The multiple endocrine neoplasia syndromes form a distinct group of genetic tumor syndromes. They include multiple endocrine neoplasia types 1 and 2, von Hippel Lindau syndrome, neurofibromatosis, and Carney complex. Research over the past decade has identified a molecular basis for each of these syndromes. This knowledge has revolutionized not only the clinical management but also has illuminated the field of human cancer research by the identification of new and important genes critical for regulation of cell growth, differentiation, and death. This review focuses on the structure, physiologic function, and molecular abnormalities of the genes involved in these syndromes.

INTRODUCTION

The multiple endocrine neoplasia syndromes are autosomal dominant syndromes characterized by overproduction of a variety of hormonal substances. The fascination with these syndromes, out of proportion to their frequency in the population, derives from the multiple and sometimes Byzantine syndromes that occur in affected kindreds. These include hypercalcemia, hypercorticism, carcinoid syndrome, peptic ulceration caused by excessive gastrin, watery diarrhea caused by vasoactive intestinal peptides, hyperprolactinemia, acromegaly, hyperinsulinism, and several others. These syndromes include multiple endocrine neoplasia (MEN) types 1 and 2 (MEN1 and MEN2), von Hippel Lindau (VHL) syndrome, neurofibromatosis (NF) type 1 (NF1), and Carney complex (Table 1). Although these syndromes were recognized early in the twentieth century, their natural history and molecular causes have been elucidated only during the past 25 years. Recent findings include the identification of three new genes involved in cell growth and the assemblage of the components of a novel tyrosine kinase receptor system. In this review we define these syndromes and focus on the remarkable progress of the last eight years.

TABLE 1   Genetic syndromes with endocrine neoplastic components

Syndrome	Neoplastic features
Multiple endocrine neoplasia type 1	Pituitary Parathyroid glands Pancreatic islets Adrenal cortex Cutaneous angiofibromas Lipomas
Multiple endocrine neoplasia type 2A	C-cell of the thyroid (MTC) Adrenal medulla (pheochromocytoma) Parathyroid glands
Multiple endocrine neoplasia type 2B	C-cell of the thyroid (MTC) Adrenal medulla (pheochromocytoma) Intestinal ganglioneuromatosis Marfanoid features
von Hippel Lindau syndrome	Adrenal medulla (pheochromocytoma) Pancreatic islets Hemangioblastomas of the central nervous system Retinal angiomas Renal cell carcinomas Visceral cysts
Neurofibromatosis type 1	Neurofibromas Inconstant development of endocrine tumors Adrenal medulla (pheochromocytoma) C-cell (MTC) Parathyroid neoplasia Somatostatin-producing carcinoid tumors
Carney complex	Pituitary Thyroid Testicular Adrenal cortex Myxomas of heart, breast, and skin Cutaneous spotty pigmentation

MULTIPLE ENDOCRINE NEOPLASIA TYPE 1

The association of tumors of the parathyroid glands, pancreatic islet cells, adrenal cortex, and anterior pituitary gland characterizes MEN1 (1, 2). Primary hyperparathyroidism, present in 90 to 97% of MEN1 carriers, is usually the first manifestation of MEN1 and consists of multiglandular, asymmetric parathyroid hyperplasia or adenomas. Multiple surgical procedures throughout life may be required because of regrowth of parathyroid tissue. The second most common manifestation of MEN1 is neoplastic transformation of the pancreatic islet cells, found in 40 to 75% of gene carriers. Of these carriers, 30 to 50% eventually develop hepatic metastases, the most common cause of death in MEN1. A number of clinical syndromes caused by excessive hormone production have been identified, with overproduction of gastrin, insulin, and glucagon the most common. The issues guiding treatment of the pancreatic tumors are complex. It is necessary to balance the long-term side effects of diabetes caused by total pancreatectomy with the 30 to 35% probability that a tumor will metastasize if not removed. The most common approach to management is to delay a surgical procedure until a patient has developed clinical symptoms caused by hormone excess or an easily identifiable tumor. In some families there is a high frequency of malignant islet cell tumors, and in these a more aggressive surgical approach may be appropriate. Pituitary adenomas are the third manifestation of MEN1 and occur in ~30% of gene carriers (3). The most common are prolactin- and growth hormone-secreting tumors. Other associated abnormalities include adrenal cortical adenomas (4), carcinoid tumors, lipomas, angiofibromas (5), collagenomas (5), and thyroid adenomas.

Identification of the MEN1 Gene

In 1988, Larsson et al mapped the *MEN1* gene to chromosome 11q13 by linkage analysis and showed loss of heterozygosity (LOH) at this locus in MEN 1 tumors, indicating that *MEN1* was likely a tumor suppressor gene (6). Positional cloning was used to identify the *MEN1* gene; meiotic recombination and tumor loss-of-heterozygosity analysis narrowed the region containing the *MEN1* gene to <300 kb (7–10). Systematic examination of each of the genes in this region led to the identification of the *MEN1* gene (11, 12). It contains 10 exons, one of which is untranslated, and encodes a 610-amino-acid protein, called menin (11) (Figure 1).

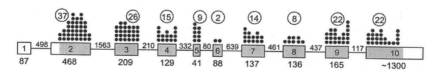

Figure 1 The *MEN1* gene and the distribution of mutations. Schematic illustration of the *MEN1* gene depicting coding regions (shaded areas) and exon and intron sizes (bp). The circled numbers are the total numbers of unique mutations reported to occur in each exon with the solid circles providing relative locations. Mutation data are derived from the Human Gene Mutation Database, from which more detailed information can be obtained (12a; http://www.uwcm.ac.uk/uwcm/mg/hgmd0.html). Drawing is not to scale.

Germline Mutations of the MEN1 Gene in MEN1 Families

A total of ~150 germline mutations of the *MEN1* gene have been identified (11, 13–19). The mutations are distributed across the 9 coding exons of the gene (Figure 1). Most result in premature protein truncation caused by frameshift mutations (deletions or insertions) and nonsense mutations, findings consistent with a loss of function of the tumor suppressor gene mechanism for transformation. Some of the missense mutations may involve important functional areas of the gene and lead to a dysfunctional protein, although this has not been proven with certainty. The distribution of mutations across the coding region of the *MEN1* gene makes mutational analysis in MEN1 families unpredictable and tedious. There are no true "hot spots," but some mutations occur more frequently; those involving codons 83, 84, 209–211, and 514–516 account for 25% of germline mutations in *MEN1* (20). These areas contain unstable DNA sequences [dinucleotide repeats or poly(C)^7 tracts] rendering them more susceptible to insertions or deletions (20). There are still a number of MEN1 kindreds without an identifiable *MEN1* mutation, a figure that approaches 50% in some series (13, 15, 18). Possible explanations for this wide range could be the use of different detection techniques [dideoxy fingerprinting (ddF), single strand conformation polymorphism (SSCP), and DNA sequencing] or the presence of mutations in noncoding regions of the *MEN1* gene.

Germline Mutations in Sporadic MEN1

Germline mutations of the *MEN1* gene have been reported in sporadic cases of MEN1, defined as an individual with two of three MEN1 manifestations who is the first such case in a family. In one report, 8 of 11 cases had a *MEN1* mutation (13), and the mutations in these patients were similar to those in MEN1 kindreds. In the three cases in which no mutation was identified, all had single gland parathyroid neoplasia with either pituitary or pancreatic tumors, raising the possibility that these cases do not represent MEN1. In a third report, none of eight patients with two or three tumors seen in MEN1 and a negative family history and 4 of 6 with a family history had *MEN1* mutations (21). Several de novo *MEN1* mutations have been described in sporadic MEN1 (13, 18).

Because primary hyperparathyroidism is the most common manifestation of MEN1 and linkage analysis performed in some kindreds with familial isolated hyperparathyroidism showed possible linkage to chromosome 11q13, the *MEN1* gene was considered a possible candidate gene. However, most kindreds with familial isolated hyperparathyroidism studied so far do not have a *MEN1* gene mutation (13, 18). The one exception is a Japanese family with a codon 184 mutation (22).

MEN1 Mutations in Sporadic Endocrine Tumors

Somatic mutations of tumor suppressor genes have been identified in many sporadic endocrine tumors, reinforcing their causative role in tumor formation. LOH in sporadic parathyroid, pituitary, and pancreatic islet tumors provides evidence for a deficiency of menin in their causation (8, 9, 23–29). Somatic mutations of the *MEN1* gene are found in 12 to 21% of parathyroid tumors (30–32), 33% of gastrinomas (33), 36% of carcinoid tumors of the lung (34), 17% of lipomas, 0.03% of pituitary adenomas (35–37), and 17% of insulinomas (33). It is interesting that the incidence of LOH of 11q in endocrine tumors is higher than the incidence of *MEN1* gene mutations, indicating the potential existence of another tumor suppressor gene in the region. For example, in one report, 7 adrenocortical tumors (5 of 5 adrenocortical carcinomas and 2 of 21 nonsecreting benign adenomas) were found to have chromosome 11q13 LOH, but none had an identifiable *MEN1* mutation (38).

Mechanism of Tumor Suppression by Menin

Menin is a 610-amino-acid protein that has no homology to any known protein. Menin has two nuclear localization signals and is located primarily in the nucleus (39). Its localization in the nucleus has led to the hypothesis that menin might be important in regulation of cell growth, leading to growth arrest either directly or by regulation of other genes. Using a yeast two-hybrid screen, Agarwal et al were able to demonstrate that menin interacts with the AP1 (activated protein 1) transcription factor *junD* (40). The AP-1 family includes a rapidly growing group of homo- or heterodimeric transcription factors composed of *jun* (v-*jun*, c-*jun*, *junB*, and *junD*), *fos* (v-*fos*, c-*fos*, *fosB*, *fra1*, and *fra2*), and activating transcription factor subunits that bind to a common DNA site, the AP-1–binding site (41). They regulate transcription by binding to a consensus TRE(12-*O*-tetradecanoyl-phorbol-13-acetate)–responsive element. The AP-1 transcription factor family is involved in regulation of cell proliferation and death (41) via activation of different sets of target genes. *junD*, in contrast to other members of this transcription family, is expressed in quiescent cells, is minimally activated by growth factors, and has an inhibitory effect on cell growth (41, 42). It has been shown that the N-terminal domain of menin is critical for *junD* binding. Menin interacts with *junD* but with no other members of the AP-1 family (e.g. c-*jun* and *junB*) (40). Missense mutations of the region between menin codons 139 and 142 inhibited menin-*junD* interaction, whereas missense mutations flanking this region do not (Figure 2). Overexpression of menin in several cell lines led to repression of JunD-mediated transcriptional activation (40). To determine whether all menin missense mutations interfere with the interaction of menin and *junD*, five naturally occurring mutations were examined. Mutant menin with L22R and H139Y bound *junD* but did not repress *junD*-mediated transcription; H139D and A242V did not bind *junD* efficiently and did not repress *junD* activity (40). W436R bound and showed some ability to repress *junD*. These results suggest that no single mechanism accounts for the effect of menin in regulating *junD* and cell growth (Figure 2). The fact that menin, a tumor suppressor, causes repression of *junD* activity, a known cell growth inhibitor, was surprising. Further studies will be necessary to better delineate whether the menin-*junD* interaction regulates cell growth.

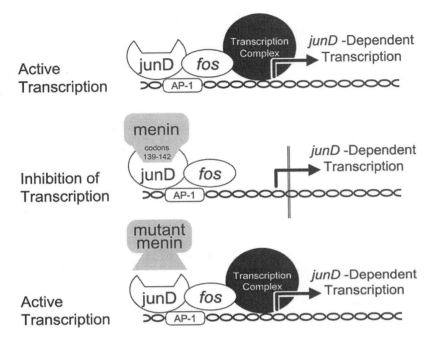

Figure 2 A model for the action of menin. The transcription factors *junD* and *fos* are known to interact with activated protein 1 (AP-1) enhancer elements to stabilize the formation of an active transcription complex. The interaction of *junD* with menin, which is mediated through codons 139–142, prevents *junD*-dependent transcription by an as yet undefined mechanism. MEN1-causing mutations prevent menin association with *junD*, allowing transcription to occur.

Lack of Genotype-Phenotype Correlation in MEN1

No genotype-phenotype correlation exists in MEN1. Kindreds with predominant clinical presentations such as prolactinoma (43) or carcinoid tumors (44, 45) have a broad spectrum of inactivating mutations. One example is found in three reported families with the prolactinoma variant of MEN1. Two families have different germline mutations of the *MEN1* gene (R460X and Y312X), and, in the third, the mutation has not yet been localized (13, 43, 46). In addition a single MEN1 DNA change may cause diverse manifestations in different families. For example, a study of five unrelated families with the same 4-bp deletion (CAGT) in codons 210 and 211 revealed a wide range of tumors without clear genotype correlation (47). All the affected family members had hyperparathyroidism, four out of five families had gastrinomas, and one family had insulinomas. Prolactinomas were present in four out of five families, and the family without prolactinoma developed carcinoids.

MULTIPLE ENDOCRINE NEOPLASIA TYPE 2

Multiple endocrine neoplasia type 2 (MEN2) is a genetic syndrome characterized by the neoplasia of the neuroendocrine cells within the thyroid gland, adrenal medulla, and parathyroid gland. MEN type 2A (MEN2A) consists of medullary thyroid cancer (MTC) (95%), pheochromocytoma (50%), and hyperparathyroidism (20%) (2, 48). Variants of MEN2A include familial MTC (FMTC), in which MTC is the only manifestation (49); MEN2A associated with cutaneous lichen amyloidosis (50–52) (a pruritic skin lesion located over the upper back with scratching and excoriation); and MEN2A associated with Hirschsprung disease (failure of normal colonic neural development) (53) (Table 1).

MEN type 2B (MEN2B) is characterized by MTC, pheochromocytoma, a marfanoid habitus, and neuromas of the lips, tongue, and gastrointestinal tract (54–56). Hyperparathyroidism is rare in MEN2B, and the MTC develops earlier and generally pursues a more aggressive course than that found in MEN2A (Table 1). All variants of MEN2 include medullary thyroid carcinoma, and 15 to 25% of those affected die from it.

The constellation of neuroendocrine neoplasia and neurologic and skeletal abnormalities suggested that the causative gene(s) was likely to be involved in normal differentiation of neural crest derivatives and in neurologic and bone development. It was therefore no surprise that the causative gene for MEN2, the *RET* proto-oncogene, plays an important role in central and peripheral nerve development and function.

The RET Proto-Oncogene

The *RET* proto-oncogene encodes a cell surface tyrosine kinase receptor that has a large extracellular domain, a single transmembrane region, and two cytoplasmic tyrosine kinase domains (57–59). The extracellular domain includes a cadherin-ligand–binding site, which may be important for cell-cell signaling (60), and a cysteine-rich extracellular region that is important for receptor dimerization. The *RET* proto-oncogene contains 21 exons spanning >60 kb of genomic DNA (61, 62). The first exon of this gene is separated from the remaining coding exons by a large intron of 24 kb. At least 10 different isoforms of *RET* have been identified and result from alternative 5′ and 3′ splicing sites; the significance of these different isoforms is unclear.

The transforming effect of *RET* was discovered in 1985 when a rearranged form of this gene (*RE*arranged during *T*ransfection) was shown to transform NIH 3T3 cells, a model used to identify genes with oncogenic potential (63). A naturally occurring form of a *RET* rearrangement was discovered in 1990 in papillary thyroid carcinoma (PTC) and named the *PTC* oncogene (64–66). Subsequent studies identified *RET* rearrangements in approximately 30 to 35% of PTC in the United States and Europe. The *PTC* rearrangement is rarely found in Japan (67–69). At least three different rearrangements of *RET* have been identified in PTC

(*PTC1, PTC2,* and *PTC3*) (Figure 3). In each, the tyrosine kinase domain of the *RET* proto-oncogene is fused downstream of another constitutively expressed gene (*H4,* RIα, or *ELE-1*). The constitutive expression of *H4,* R1α, and *ELE-1* in the thyroid follicular cell results in continuous expression of the *RET* proto-oncogene (70).

Physiologic Functions of *RET*

The *RET* proto-oncogene has an important function in the migration and development of tissues arising from the neural crest. It is expressed in tissues of neural-crest derivation, including C cells of the thyroid gland, adrenal medulla, parasympathetic and sympathetic ganglia, enteric ganglia, and urogenital tract (71, 72). It is also expressed in parathyroid cells derived from the branchial arches. Targeted disruption of the *RET* proto-oncogene in mice causes kidney agenesis and a failure of enteric neuronal development, a phenotype that is similar to Hirchsprung disease (73, 74). In fact, inactivating mutations of the *RET* proto-oncogene cause Hirschsprung disease (congenital megacolon).

Glial cell line-derived neurotrophic factor (GDNF) is a ligand for the *RET* receptor (75–78). GDNF is a potent survival factor for central and peripheral neurons and is essential for renal and enteric neuronal development. The observation that *GDNF-* or *RET*-deficient mice failed to develop kidneys and the normal enteric neuronal system led to the recognition that GDNF is a ligand for the *RET* receptor (73, 79–81). GDNF is a member of the transforming growth factor beta superfamily, but it differs from other members in that it signals through a receptor tyrosine kinase (RET) instead of a serine/threonine kinase receptor.

In a parallel search for a GDNF receptor, a 468-amino-acid protein that bound GDNF was isolated from an embryonic rat midbrain cDNA library. This protein was designated GDNF receptor-α (GDNFR-α) and is now called GFRα − 1 (75,

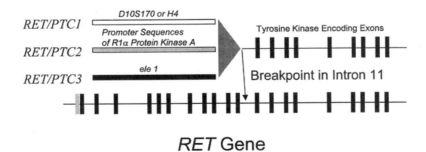

Figure 3   Papillary thyroid carcinoma rearrangements of the *RET* proto-oncogene. Rearrangements of the *RET* gene results in unregulated over-expression of the tyrosine kinase domain. These rearrangements occur in ~30% of all papillary thyroid carcinomas and are called *RET/PTC1, RET/PTC2,* and *RET/PTC3*. The breakpoint for the rearrangements is located within intron 11 just downstream of exons encoding the transmembrane domain.

82). GFRα-1 is a glycosyl-phosphatidylinositol cell surface protein that lacks cytoplasmic and transmembrane domains. It is expressed in GDNF-responsive cells and binds GDNF with high affinity. Binding of GDNF to GFRα-1 activates the *RET* receptor and forms a multisubunit receptor system in which GFRα-1 is a ligand-binding component and RET is the signaling component (Figure 4) (75). Targeted disruption of *GFRα-1* causes a phenotype nearly identical to that seen in the GDNF and RET knockout models (83).

Other GDNF-binding genes have been identified (84–88). *GFRα-2* was identified by its sequence homology to *GFRα-1;* it binds GDNF and can also mediate GDNF signaling through RET (Figure 4). Two additional members of the GFRα family, *GFRα-3* and *GFRα-4,* have been cloned (Figure 4). Neurturin, persephin, and artemin are three additional GDNF-like neurotrophic factors (Table 2) (89– 92). Neurturin (NTN) has 40% homology with GDNF and was isolated from Chinese hamster ovary cells based on its ability to promote survival of sympathetic neurons. Like GDNF, it supports survival of a variety of neurons including peripheral, sensory, motor, and midbrain dopaminergic neurons. It is, in addition, expressed in tissues outside the nervous system (thyroid, heart, lung, kidney, and gastrointestinal tract), suggesting a physiologic role in these tissues. NTN also signals through the RET/GFRα-1 or RET/GFRα-2 receptor complex (Figure 4). There is evidence that GDNF binds preferentially to a GFRα-1/RET receptor,

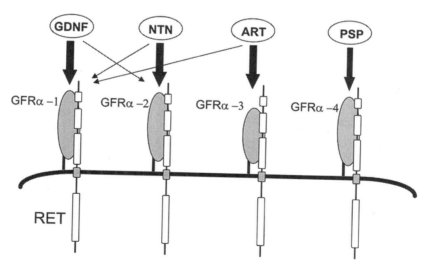

Figure 4 The ligand-receptor interactions with the RET transmembrane tyrosine kinase. Large arrows indicate favored ligand/GFRα/RET interactions, and smaller arrows show alternative interactions. The GFRα-1/RET receptor complex is capable of interaction with GDNF, NTN, and ART, whereas the GFRα-4/RET complex is thought to interact only with PSP. Abbreviations: GDNF, glial-derived neurotrophic factor; NTN, neurturin; ART, artemin; PSP, persephin. Adapted from Baloh et al (92).

TABLE 2 Expression of ligands and the GFRα/RET receptor complexes[a]

Gene	Chromosomal location	Expression	Receptor	Ligand
Glial cell-derived neurotrophic factor (GDNF)	5p13.1-p13.3	Brain, thyroid, lung, kidney, GI tract	GFRα-1, RET	
Neurturin (NTN)	19p13.3	Brain, PNS, thyroid, heart, lung, GI tract, kidney, liver	GFRα-2, RET	
Artemin (ART)			GFRα-3, RET	
Persephin (PSP)	19p13.3	Brain, heart, kidney, liver	GFRα-4, RET	
GFRα-1	10q26	Brain, PNS, thyroid, heart, lung, GI tract, kidney, liver		GDNF ≫ Neurturin
GFRα-2	8p21-22	Brain, PNS, thyroid, heart, lung, GI tract, kidney, liver		Neurturin > GDNF
GFRα-3	5q31.1-q31.3	PNS, thyroid, heart, lung, GI tract, kidney, liver		Artemin
GFRα-4				Persephin
RET proto-oncogene	10q11.2	Brain, PNS, thyroid, heart, lung, GI tract, kidney, liver		

[a]Abbreviations: GDNF, glial cell-derived neurotrophic factor; GI, gastrointestinal tract; NTN, neurturin; GFRα-1, previously referred to as GDNFR-α; GFRα-2, previously referred to as TmR-2, NTNR-a, RETL2, GDNF-β. Updated from reference 207.

whereas NTN interacts with a greater affinity with the GFRα-2/RET complex (Table 2) (93). Persephin, the third member of this family, has ~40% homology with GDNF and NTN and also promotes survival of motor and dopaminergic neurons. Persephin, like GDNF, promotes ureteric bud branching, an important developmental step in kidney morphogenesis. In contrast to GDNF and NTN, it does not support survival of peripheral neurons. Persephin binds efficiently only to GFRα-4 (Figure 4), signals through RET/GFRα-4, and does not interact with either GFRα-1/RET or GFRα-2/RET (91). Neither GDNF nor NTN signal through RET/GFRα-4 (94). Artemin, the most recently cloned member of the GDNF ligand family, supports both peripheral and central neurons and signals preferentially through the GFRα3-RET receptor complex (Figure 4) (92).

GDNF- and RET-deficient animals have kidney agenesis caused by a failure of interaction between the ureteric bud and metanephric mesenchyme. During the process of embryogenesis, the kidney or metanephros develops in response to an interaction between the ureteric bud (where GFRα-1/RET is expressed) and the metanephric mesenchyme (where GDNF is expressed). The role that this receptor system has in embryonic development is shown most clearly by GDNF/GFRα-1/RET interactions in the developing kidney. GDNF acts as a chemoattractant for ureteric bud and nephric duct cells expressing RET, enticing migration of these cells towards the metanephric mesenchyme (95). Similarly, RET-expressing neural crest cells in gastrointestinal tract development, destined to become enteric neurons, are directed into the developing gut endoderm by temporal and spatial expression of GDNF.

The *RET* Proto-Oncogene in MEN2A and MEN2B

Genetic mapping studies in MEN2A and MEN2B families localized the responsible gene to chromosome 10q11.2 (96–99) in 1987. Further narrowing of the disease gene region identified an area of 480 kb that includes the *RET* proto-oncogene. Mulligan et al analyzed RET cDNAs obtained from seven tumors from six patients with MEN2A to identify missense mutations of a cysteine-rich extracellular domain (100). Each of the identified mutations caused a cysteine substitution for another amino acid. Using SSCP and DNA sequencing, Donnis-Keller et al subsequently confirmed these observations in patients with MEN2A and FMTC (101). In 1994, further investigation from three groups reported a Met-918/Thr *RET* proto-oncogene tyrosine kinase domain mutation in patients with MEN2B (102–104). In the 6 years since these seminal observations, genetic analysis of families around the world has provided a clearer view of mutations in MEN2. Most affect the cysteine-rich domain; in a minority, missense mutations of the cytoplasmic tyrosine kinase domain are found (Figure 5).

Genotype-Phenotype Correlation in MEN2

The International RET Mutation Consortium analyzed 477 independent MEN2 families with MEN2A (43%), MEN2B (17%), and FMTC (7%) (105). Of MEN2 families examined, >95% have a *RET* proto-oncogene mutation. The most common is a codon Cys-634–Arg substitution. A codon-634 mutation with any amino acid substitution is most commonly associated with classic MEN2A with MTC, pheochromocytoma, and hyperparathyroidism. Kindreds with the MEN2A/cutaneous lichen amyloidosis syndrome also have codon-634 mutations (105). Mutations at codons 609, 611, 618, and 620 are most commonly associated with FMTC, but MEN2A is also found. There have been no reports of pheochromocytoma in association with a codon-609 mutation (105). Moers et al reported that a MEN2A family with a cys618ser mutation has a lower incidence of pheochromocytoma and hyperparathyroidism and a higher life expectancy than families with a codon-634 mutation (106). Mutations at codons 768 and 891 are specific

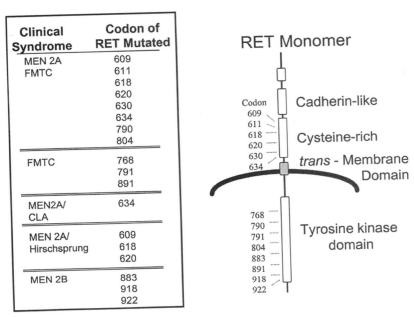

Clinical Syndrome	Codon of RET Mutated
MEN 2A	609
FMTC	611
	618
	620
	630
	634
	790
	804
FMTC	768
	791
	891
MEN2A/ CLA	634
MEN 2A/ Hirschsprung	609
	618
	620
MEN 2B	883
	918
	922

Figure 5 Mutations of the *RET* proto-oncogene that are associated with hereditary medullary thyroid carcinoma. Abbreviations: MEN2A, multiple endocrine neoplasia type 2A; FMTC, familial medullary thyroid carcinoma; MEN2A/CLA, MEN2A with cutaneous lichen amyloidosis; MEN2A/Hirshsprung, MEN2A associated with Hirshsprung disease; and MEN2B, multiple endocrine neoplasia type 2B. Updated from reference 207.

for FMTC (107, 108). The MEN2A/ Hirschsprung disease variant has been found in kindreds with codon-609, -618, and -620 mutations only (105, 109, 110). Kindreds with codon-804 mutations most commonly have FMTC, but a few kindreds with MEN2A have been described. Of all MEN2B families, >95% have a Met-918/Thr mutation (105); other rare intracellular mutations associated with MEN2B involve codons 883 and 922 (111, 112)

Use of Genetic Information in Patient Management

What sets MEN2 apart from other genetic cancer syndromes is the usefulness of molecular information in treatment decisions. Most importantly, the decision to perform a prophylactic thyroidectomy, with the goal of removing the thyroid gland before metastasis occurs, is influenced by the results of genetic analysis. A secondary but equally important use of genetic testing is the exclusion of the 50% of family members without a *RET* mutation from further screening. The usefulness of genetic testing for clinical decisions makes it essential that *RET* mutations be accurately identified. All current techniques use polymerase chain reaction amplification of genomic DNA followed by DNA sequencing. Broad screening methodology such as SSCP or hybridization approaches such as allele-specific hybridization have a sufficiently high rate of error that they are not suitable for clinical decision making. Direct DNA sequencing with or without confirmation by restriction analysis has been adapted by most laboratories as the "gold standard" for detecting mutations in this disorder. It is possible to use this labor-intensive approach because 90% of known mutations occur in two small exons and because the remainder are found in four additional exons. Others have used denaturing gradient gel electrophoresis (113). The need for accuracy in analysis makes it necessary to perform a second analysis, preferably using a different primer set, to confirm either the positive or negative result. A discussion of these issues is beyond the scope of this review but is provided elsewhere (2, 114–116).

Several commercial laboratories are now equipped to perform genetic testing. [A list of commercial laboratories performing genetic testing is available on the University of Texas MD Anderson Cancer Center Section of the Endocrine Neoplasia and Hormonal Disorders Web Site (http://endocrine.mdacc.tmc.edu)].

Genetic Abnormalities in Individual Clinical Syndromes

men2a   The most common mutations in MEN2A are located in exons 10 and 11 of the *RET* proto-oncogene, which encode the highly conserved cysteine-rich domain (Table 3, Figure 5). The mutations involve eight codons and represent missense mutations that substitute a cysteine for another amino acid (codons 609/611/618/620/630/634) or small nucleotide insertions (codons 635/637). Codon-634 mutations are the most common and are found in 85% of MEN2A patients (105). A single coding change (Cys-634-Arg) accounts for 52% of all codon-634 mutations and a second (Cys-634-Tyr) for an additional 26% (105).

One unique cysteine-rich domain mutation was identified in a kindred with a high incidence of parathyroid disease and no pheochromocytoma (117). This kindred has a duplication of 12 bp in the cysteine-rich domain that results in the insertion of four amino acids, including an additional cysteine residue, between codons 634 and 635. Intracellular tyrosine kinase domain mutations at codons 790 and 804 have been reported, but are rare, in MEN2A kindreds (118–120) (Table 3, Figure 5).

Familial MTC   Most of the *RET* mutations identified in FMTC also involve the extracellular, cysteine-rich domain. The International RET Mutation Consortium identified a Cys-618-Ser substitution in 33% of FMTC patients (105). The second most common mutation was a Cys-634-Tyr substitution in 30% of FMTC patients. None of the FMTC kindreds had a Cys-634-Arg mutation, the most common cause of MEN2A. Mutations of the intracellular tyrosine kinase domain codons 768, 790, 791, 804, and 891 have also been identified in FMTC (105, 107, 120) (Figure 5, Table 3).

TABLE 3 Mutations of the RET proto-oncogene associated with MEN2 and hereditary MTC

Affected codon	Amino acid change (normal→mutant)	Nucleotide change (normal→mutant)	Clinical syndrome	Percentage of all *MEN2* mutations
609	cys→arg	TGC→CGC	MEN2A/FMTC	0–1
	cys→gly	TGC→GGC		
	cys→tyr	TGC→TAC		
611	cys→ser	TGC→AGC	MEN2A/FMTC	2–3
	cys→arg	TGC→CGC		
	cys→tyr	TGC→TAC		
	cys→phe	TGC→TTC		
	cys→trp	TGC→TGG		
618	cys→ser	TGC→AGC	MEN2A/FMTC	3–5
	cys→arg	TGC→CGC		
	cys→gly	TGC→GGC		
	cys→tyr	TGC→TAC		
	cys→ser	TGC→TCC		
	cys→phe	TGC→TTC		
620	cys→ser	TGC→AGC	MEN2A/FMTC	6–8
	cys→arg	TGC→CGC		
	cys→gly	TGC→GGC		
	cys→tyr	TGC→TAC		
	cys→ser	TGC→TCC		
	cys→phe	TGC→TTC		
	cys→trp	TGC→TGG		
630	cys→tyr	TGC→TAC	MEN2A/FMTC	0–1
	cys→ser	TGC→TCC		
	cys→phe	TGC→TTC		

(continued)

Identification of Germline RET Mutations in Apparent Sporadic MTC Systematic screening of patients with MTC and no family history of thyroid carcinoma
has identified germline *RET* proto-oncogene mutations in 6–7% (121–125). A
few are examples of de novo mutations; the majority derive from families in
which there is poor documentation of medical conditions or separation of family
members through adoption, war, or emigration. The a priori probability that 6%
of patients with apparent sporadic MTC have germline *RET* mutations suggests
that routine screening should be performed. Identification of a single family member with a *RET* mutation frequently leads to the identification of other gene carriers in the family.

TABLE 3 (continued)

Affected codon	Amino acid change (normal→mutant)	Nucleotide change (normal→mutant)	Clinical syndrome	Percentage of all *MEN2* mutations
634	cys→ser	TGC→AGC	MEN 2A	80–90
	cys→arg	TGC→CGC		
	cys→gly	TGC→GGC		
	cys→tyr	TGC→TAC		
	cys→ser	TGC→TCC		
	cys→phe	TGC→TTC		
	cys→trp	TGC→TGG		
635	thr ser cys ala	ACGAGCTGTGCC	MEN2A	Rare
637	cys arg thr	TGCCGCACG	MEN2A	Rare
768	glu→asp	GAG→GAC	FMTC	Rare
790	leu→phe	TTG→TTC	MEN2A/FMTC	Rare
	leu→phe	TTG→TTT		
791	tyr→phe	TAT→TTT	FMTC	Rare
804	val→met	GTG→ATG	MEN2A/FMTC	0–1
	val→leu	GTG→TTG		
883	ala→phe	GCT→TTT	MEN2B	Rare
891	ser→ala	TCG→GCG	FMTC	Rare
918	met→thr	ATG→ACG	MEN2B	3–5
922	ser→tyr	TCC→TAC	MEN2B	Rare

MEN2A Cutaneous Lichen Amyloidosis   MEN2A associated with a pruritic cutaneous lesion over the upper back (cutaneous lichen amyloidosis) has been reported in >18 kindreds (51, 52, 105). The pathogenesis is unknown, but the deposition of amyloid may result from chronic irritation caused by the intense pruritus experienced by these patients. All reported families have codon-634 mutations (105).

MEN2B   Of individuals with MEN2B, 95% have a germline Met-918-Thr mutation (102, 103). Other less frequent mutations include a handful of Ala-883-Phe and Ser-922-Tyr mutations (111, 112) (Figure 5, Table 3). There is one reported case of MEN2B with two germline point mutations, Val-804-Met and Tyr-806-Cys, in the same allele (126).

Mutations in Sporadic MTC and Pheochromocytomas   Of sporadic MTCs studied, ~25–35% have a somatic *RET* Met-918-Thr mutation of the *RET* proto-oncogene identical to the germline mutation found in MEN2B (121, 124, 127). Tumors harboring this mutation are thought to have a more aggressive course

(128); however, this observation needs to be confirmed in a larger series of patients. Other infrequent somatic mutations involve codons 630, 634, 766, 768, 804, and 883 (107, 119, 129–133). Mutations of the *RET* proto-oncogene have been found in sporadic pheochromocytomas but in much lower frequency. Most involve codon 918 (134, 135).

Inactivating Mutations of the *RET* Proto-Oncogene

Hirschsprung Disease   Hirschsprung disease or congenital colonic aganglion-osis affects ~1 in 5000 newborns (136). Of these, ~10% are hereditary with autosomal dominant, autosomal recessive, or polygenic transmission. Affected individuals usually present in the neonatal period with intestinal obstruction or severe constipation, the result of disorganized or absent autonomic innervation of the gastrointestinal tract. It was the association of Hirschsprung disease with MEN2A, the identification of a child with Hirschsprung disease with a chromosome 10q deletion (137), and the Hirschsprung phenotype in mice with targeted disruption of GDNF, GFRα-1, or RET (79, 81, 138, 139) that led to the identification of *RET* and *GDNF* mutations in this disorder (140–151).

RET is expressed at the very earliest stages of enteric nervous system development, at the time of entry of neural crest cells into the foregut mesenchyme (71). One possible role of the GDNF/RET/GFRα-1 receptor system is to provide survival signals to neural crest progenitors to form the enteric nervous system, whereas extensive apoptosis of these cells occurs in RET-deficient animals. RET expression in neural crest cells and its interaction with GDNF expressed in gut endoderm serve to promote migration of the neural crest cells into the gut (152).

The molecular background of Hirschsprung disease is complex. At least five genes have been implicated in its pathogenesis: *GDNF, RET,* the *NTN* gene, endothelin-β , and the endothelin-β receptor (149). Mutations of these genes have been reported in families with Hirschsprung disease (140–148, 150, 151). In addition, combined mutations of *RET* and *GDNF, RET* and the *NTN* gene, or *RET* and endothelin receptor-β genes have been reported in some affected individuals (149).

Mutations of the *RET/GDNF* receptor complex have also been identified in the variant of Hirschsprung disease associated with congenital central hypoventilation (Ondine's curse). One is a novel mutation involving codon 1039 (exon 19) (153). Eight families with Hirschsprung and MEN 2A have mutations in codons 609, 618, and 620, with the latter being most common (105, 109, 110, 154, 155).

How Activating Mutations of the *RET* Proto-Oncogene Cause Oncogenesis

The transformation potential of the mutant *RET* proto-oncogene has been demonstrated by NIH 3T3 fibroblast transformation assay and by nude mice experiments in which cells were transfected with *RET* mutated at codon 634

(Cys-634-Arg or Cys-634-Tyr) or codon 918 (Met-918-Thr) (156–158). Extracellular cysteine-rich (codon-634) and tyrosine kinase (codon-918) domain mutations cause constitutive activation of the *RET* receptor. Codon-634 mutations also induce ligand-independent homodimerization of RET leading to tyrosine kinase activation (Figure 6). Constitutive dimerization, in the absence of ligand, is thought to occur because the unpaired cysteine residues form intermolecular disulfide bonds (159). The codon-918 mutation alters the substrate specificity of the kinase domain, thereby activating growth-stimulating pathways (Figure 6). It is unclear whether maximal activation of RET in MEN2B requires not only the mutation-induced activation of the receptor but also ligand-receptor interaction (Figure 6). This question has been raised because NIH 3T3 cells that express a mutant *RET* cDNA (Met-918-Thr) have a lower growth rate than cells expressing mutant *RET* with a codon-634 mutation. Although the most likely explanation for this observation was the use of a short RET isoform with altered tyrosine kinase activity, this phenomenon may be caused by a lack of GDNF/RET interaction in the subcutaneous tumor transplantation location (158, 159). There is precedent for this type of ligand-receptor interaction in oncogenesis. Studies with chimeric constructs (ligand-binding domain of the epidermal growth factor receptor fused to the catalytic domain of RET) show that the transforming efficiency

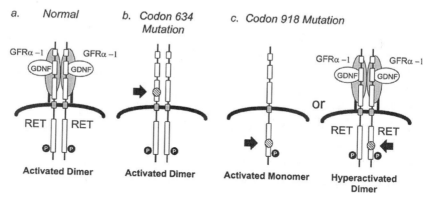

Figure 6 The RET/GFRα signaling system and the effect of *RET* mutations on activation and dimerization. (*a*) Interaction of glial-derived neurotrophic factor (GDNF) with the receptor complex formed by GFRα-1 and the transmembrane tyrosine kinase, RET. Association of GDNF with this complex stabilizes dimerization and autophosphorylation of RET and leads to activation of several kinase pathways (see Figure 7). (*b*) The impact of a codon-634 mutation on receptor activation. In vitro studies (described in the text) have shown that this mutation leads to ligand-independent dimerization and activation of RET. (*c*) The impact of a codon-918 mutation on receptor activation. Two pathways have been described. The first involves autophosphorylation of RET creating an activated monomer. In the second pathway, dimer formation can occur with mutant or normal (shown) RET to create a hyperactivated receptor dimer complex.

is higher in the presence of epidermal growth factor (160). Furthermore, Bongarzone et al showed that the activity of RET mutated at codon 918 is increased by stable dimerization of the receptor, an experiment performed by expressing a double mutant receptor (Cys-634-Arg) and (Met-918-Thr) in cells exposed to high concentrations of GDNF (161).

Another difference between codon-634 and -918 mutations is the different phosphorylation of tyrosine residues in the catalytic core region. Through differential mutation of tyrosine residues in the kinase domain, Tyr-905 (corresponding to Tyr-416 of the Src protein) mediates the transforming activity of a codon-634 mutation, whereas Tyr-864 and Tyr-952 are critical for the transforming activity of a codon-918 mutation (162). A remaining question is whether GFRα-1 has a role in the transformation process. No mutations of GFRα-1 have been reported in MEN2, in vitro transformation studies do not address the question of whether GFRα-1 is required for transformation.

There is a tight correlation between genotype and phenotype with *RET* mutations. Activating mutations are invariably associated with MEN2, and inactivating mutations are associated with Hirschsprung disease. There are a few crossovers, such as the activating mutations of codons 609, 618, and 620, that are associated with both MTC and Hirschsprung disease. It is unclear what effect the *RET* mutation causing Ondine's curse and Hirschsprung disease has on RET receptor function. Within the general category of activating mutations, there is a hierarchy of transformation potential that may be explained by the magnitude of *RET* activation and/or by differential activation of intracellular pathways. For example, Carlomagno et al showed that a Cys-620-Tyr mutation (associated with FMTC) has a lower transformation potential than a Cys-634-Tyr mutation (associated with MEN2A) (163). This observation has been confirmed by Ito et al, who showed that *RET* with a codon-634 mutation not only had a higher transforming capability than *RET* with codon-609, -611, -618, -620, or -630 mutations but also had several-fold-higher levels of RET protein expression (164).

RET Signal Transduction

Tyrosine kinase receptors transmit extracellular signals to the nucleus through a large network of interacting proteins, mediated through mitogen-activated protein kinases (MAPK). The MAPK superfamily of serine-threonine kinases has an important role in regulation of proliferation, differentiation, and apoptosis. There are three known subfamilies: the extracellular signal-regulated protein kinases (ERK1 and ERK2), the JNK or c-Jun amino-terminal kinases (also called stress-activated protein kinases), and the p38 kinases (165, 166). The intracellular domain of *RET* contains 14 tyrosine residues, which serve as docking sites for adaptor proteins (Shc, PLCγ, Grb2) that contain Src homology 2 (SH2) or phosphotyrosine-binding domains. When these adaptor proteins are bound to the phosphorylated receptor, a small protein, Sos, is recruited to the plasma membrane, leading to activation of Ras, Raf, and ERK1/2 (Figure 7). Ras is known to activate

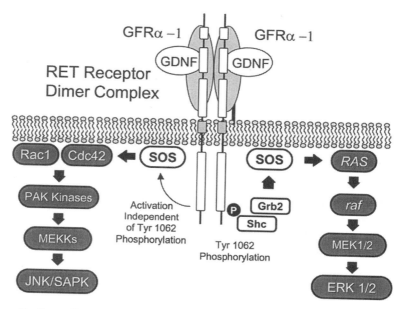

Figure 7   Intracellular signaling pathways activated by the GDNF-GFRα-1/RET signaling system. Two different signaling pathways, JNK/SAPK and ERK 1/2, are known to be activated (described in text). The ERK 1/2 pathway is initiated by autophosphorylation of tyrosine codon 1062. Adapted from reference 207.

both ERK1/2 and JNK. Mutation of specific tyrosine residues abrogates the transforming activity of RET, confirming the importance of these pathways (167–170).

RET activation by GDNF or by mutations that cause MEN2A and MEN2B leads to activation of a Ras-MAPK pathway (171). Although RET can activate the JNK pathway through a Ras-mediated effect, the main activators of JNK seem to be the small GTPases of the Rho/Rac family including Rac1 and Cdc42 (Figure 7) (172). Activated Rac1 and Cdc42 can initiate a kinase cascade that stimulates MEKK1/MKK4/JNK. The observation that dominant-negative constructs for Cdc-42 and Rac-1 impair RET-mediated JNK activation (172) show that this cascade is important. There is evidence that mutant RET (codons 634, 918, and the RET/PTC1 rearrangement) and the GDNF-activated wild-type receptor also activate the JNK pathway (172).

Additional evidence that activation of ERK and JNK pathways by RET is distinct and that JNK activation is not Ras-dependent was obtained by experiments with a mutant RET in which tyrosine residue 1062, part of a docking site for the Shc phosphotyrosine-binding domain, was mutated. Mutation of this residue abolished phosphorylation of Shc and blocked activation of the Ras/ERK pathway but did not affect JNK activation (Figure 7). Furthermore a dominant-negative Ras (RasN-17) did not impair JNK activation by RET (172), providing additional evidence for two distinct pathways. Although the evidence is incomplete, it is thought that activation of both JNK and ERK 1/2 pathways is required for transformation.

VON HIPPEL-LINDAU DISEASE

VHL disease is an autosomal dominant neoplastic disorder characterized by renal-cell carcinoma (RCC) in ~70% of the individuals by age 60 years, retinal and cerebellar hemangioblastomas, pheochromocytomas, islet cell tumors, endolymphatic tumors, and renal, pancreatic, and epididymal cysts (173). Type 1 (65–75% of total) is characterized by the absence and type 2 (25–35% of total) by the presence of pheochromocytoma. There is a further subdivision of type 2 VHL: type 2A is characterized by the presence of pheochromocytoma without RCC; type 2B includes both pheochromocytoma and RCC (Table 1). Islet cell tumors occur in 15 to 20% of patients with VHL, predominantly those with the type-2 variant. Kindreds presenting with autosomal dominant transmission of pheochromocytomas and/or islet cell tumors should be examined for central nervous system tumors and RCC.

The VHL gene is a tumor suppressor gene identified in 1993 by positional cloning of a genetic locus on chromosome 3p25 (174). It contains 3 exons and has a 213-amino-acid coding sequence. A total of >500 VHL kindreds have been analyzed, and most have germline mutations of the VHL gene (175). These mutations are distributed throughout the coding sequence; ~70% are deletion, frameshift, or nonsense mutations that lead to inactivation by producing a truncated or nonfunctional protein. These inactivating mutations are associated with a low incidence of pheochromocytoma (Figure 8). The remaining 30% are missense mutations associated with an increased probability of pheochromocytoma development (176). In one report, the cumulative pheochromocytoma prevalence by age 50 in patients with missense mutations was 59%, whereas those with protein-truncating mutations had a 9% prevalence of pheochromocytoma (Figure 8) (177). Mutations that alter an arginine residue at codon 167 are associated with a >80% probability of pheochromocytoma development by age 50 (177).

Somatic VHL gene mutations have also been identified in sporadic, nonfamilial tumors. Loss of the wild-type VHL allele and somatic mutation of the other allele are found in 50 to 75% of sporadic RCCs (178). Methylation of the VHL promoter is found in another 15% of sporadic RCCs, leading to underexpression of the VHL protein (179). VHL mutations are also found frequently in sporadic hemangioblastomas but are infrequent in sporadic pheochromocytomas (180). Despite frequent LOH of chromosome 3p in other sporadic cancers (breast, lung, testicular, and ovarian), VHL mutations are rare in these tumors (173).

Missense mutations of the VHL gene have provided a tool to identify proteins that interact with VHL, namely a multiprotein complex involved in several cel-

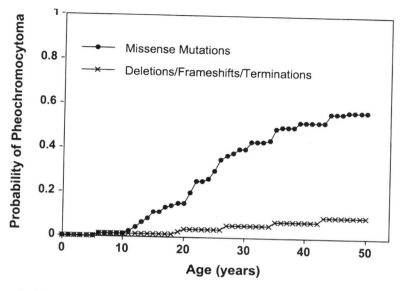

Figure 8 Missense mutations of the *VHL* gene are associated with a higher risk of pheochromocytoma. This graph compares the cumulative age-related risk for pheochromocytoma in patients with missense *VHL* gene mutations (closed circles) versus patients with deletions or nonsense or frameshift *VHL* mutations (*x*). The risk of pheochromocytoma is higher in patients with missense mutations, 59% at age 50 years compared with 9% at age 50 in patients with other *VHL* mutations. (Reprinted with permission from 177).

lular processes that include transcription elongation, regulation of hypoxia-induced genes, fibronectin matrix assembly, and possibly ubiquitin ligases.

Elongin A, B, and C form a multiunit transcription elongation complex termed elongin or SIII (Figure 9). The complex enhances the rate of transcription by preventing RNA polymerase from acting at certain pause sites. The VHL protein competes with elongin A for binding to the elongin B and C complex (Figure 9), thereby inhibiting the elongin function. The point of interaction is the carboxy-terminal portion of VHL (codons 157–189, frequently mutated) (Figure 9) (181, 182). Therefore, one function of the VHL protein is to down-regulate transcription activity of certain genes involved in cell growth. However, the greatest concentration of VHL/elongin is in the cytoplasm, where it may interact with other components of the elongin complex. These include Cullin 2 (Cul 2) and a RING-box protein (Rbx1) (183–186). Cul 2 is a member of the Cullin protein family, part of the E3 ubiquitin ligase complex that targets proteins for ubiquitin-mediated proteolysis. Rbx1 is a part of the SCF^{Cdc4} complex, also involved in ubiquitination. These findings indicate that another function of the VHL complex may be degradation of yet unidentified proteins involved in cell cycle regulation. Other functions of the VHL protein include repression of hypoxia-inducible genes and

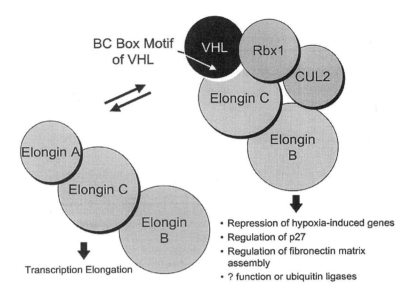

Figure 9 Proposed structure and functions of the VHL-elonginC-eloninB complex (VCB complex). The elonginBC complex interacts with a short BC-box motif in the VHL protein. This complex then interacts with Cul2 (through elonginC-Cul2 association) and Rbx1. A large part of the VHL mutations alter the BC box, disrupting the VCB complex. The figure also lists the proposed functions of the VCB complex.

regulation of fibronectin matrix assembly (187, 188). Exactly how the loss of these regulatory functions of VHL leads to neoplastic changes is unclear.

NEUROFIBROMATOSIS

There are two types of NF, NF 1 and NF 2. NF 1 or von Recklinghausen disease (189) accounts for >95% of the NF cases (190) and can involve any organ system. Manifestations include café au lait macules, neurofibromas, axillary or inguinal freckling, optic nerve glioma, Lisch nodules (iris hamartomas), and more (191).

A variety of neoplastic endocrine manifestations have been described in NF 1, including pheochromocytoma, hyperparathyroidism, MTC, and somatostatin-producing carcinoid tumors of the duodenal wall (2).

The *NF-1* gene is located on chromosome 17q11.2 and encodes a protein called neurofibromin (192, 193), which is homologous to the yeast and mammalian p21*ras* GTPase-activating proteins (194–196). The GTPase domain of neurofibromin binds to *ras* and increases the conversion of guanosine triphosphate (GTP) to guanosine diphosphate (GDP). Loss of neurofibromin function leads to uncontrolled p21*ras* activation and transformation through uncontrolled MAPK activation. The *NF-1* gene acts as tumor suppressor gene. Identified inactivating mutations include insertions, deletions, and missense point mutations (190, 197, 198). NF-1 is an autosomal dominant disorder, but 30 to 50% of all cases are thought to represent de novo mutations, most of which are of paternal origin (190).

CARNEY COMPLEX

Carney complex is a rare autosomal dominant disorder characterized by spotty pigmentation of the skin (lentiginosis) and multiple neoplasias, including myxomas at various sites (cardiac, breast, and skin) and endocrine tumors (199). Primary pigmented nodular adrenocortical disease, an ACTH-independent, primary adrenal form of hypercortisolism, occurs in 32% of patients with Carney complex (200). Other endocrine tumors include adrenocortical carcinomas, follicular thyroid carcinomas, growth hormone-producing pituitary tumors, and testicular tumors (201–203). There is evidence of genetic heterogeneity in Carney complex; analysis of 11 kindreds linked the disease to chromosome 2p16, whereas other kindreds appear to map to chromosome 17q2 (203–205). A series of overlapping clones, likely to contain the 2p16 gene, has been constructed (206).

SUMMARY

Ten years ago there was little information regarding the molecular causes of any of the multiple endocrine neoplasia syndromes. The identification of causative genes for MEN1, MEN2, VHL, and NF1, and the mapping of the gene for Carney complex have not only led to improvement in the clinical managment of these syndromes, but also to the identification of several novel signaling systems. For example, the insight gained from the GDNF/GFRα-1/RET signaling system is of great importance in the development of therapeutic strategies for degenerative neuronal disorders. Investigators working on MEN1 and VHL are slowly unraveling the components of these important signal transduction pathways. With the discovery of menin/junD interactions and the relationship between the VHL gene product and elongin B and C, a new regulatory complex for transcription that affects several cellular functions has been identified.

Despite these impressive advances, much work remains. Little is known about the subsequent mutational events that result in progression of the transformation process. It is also not known why mutation or deletion of the MEN1, VHL, or NF1 genes, ubiquitously expressed, causes unique combinations of endocrine tumors rather than generalized neoplastic transformation. It is also unclear why germline mutations of the *RET* proto-oncogene, a gene expressed widely in neural cell types, do not cause brain or spinal cord tumors. The splendid progress of the last 10 years suggests that answers to many of these questions will be forthcoming during the next decade and that they will contribute greatly to our understanding of neuroendocrine cell differentiation, growth, and death.

Visit the Annual Reviews home page at www.AnnualReviews.org.

LITERATURE CITED

1. Skogseid B, Rastad J, Oberg K. 1994. Multiple endocrine neoplasia type 1. Clinical features and screening. *Endocrinol. Metab. Clin. North Am.* 23:1–18

2. Gagel RF. 1997. Multiple endocrine neoplasia. In *Williams Textbook of Endocrinology,* ed. JD Wilson, DW Foster, PR Larsen, H Kronenberg, pp. 1627–49. Philadelphia: Saunders

3. Burgess JR, Shepherd JJ, Parameswaran V, Hoffman L, Greenaway TM. 1996. Spectrum of pituitary disease in multiple endocrine neoplasia type 1 (MEN 1): clinical, biochemical, and radiological features of pituitary disease in a large MEN1 kindred. *J. Clin. Endocrinol. Metab.* 81:2642–46

4. Burgess JR, Harle RA, Tucker P, Parameswaran V, Davies P, et al. 1996. Adrenal lesions in a large kindred with multiple endocrine neoplasia type I. *Arch. Surg.* 131:699–702

5. Darling TN, Skarulis MC, Steinberg SM, Marx SJ, Spiegel AM, Turner M. 1997. Multiple facial angiofibromas and collagenomas in patients with multiple endocrine neoplasia type 1. *Arch. Dermatol.* 133:853–57

6. Larsson C, Skogseid B, Oberg K, Nakamura Y, Nordenskjold M. 1988. Multiple endocrine neoplasia type 1 gene maps to chromosome 11 and is lost in insulinoma. *Nature* 332:85–87

7. Bystrom C, Larsson C, Blomberg C, Sandelin K, Falkmer U, et al. 1990. Localization of the MEN1 gene to a small region within chromosome 11q13 by deletion mapping in tumors. *Proc. Natl. Acad. Sci. USA* 87:1968–72

8. Dong Q, Debelenko LV, Chandrasekhar-appa SC, Emmert-Buck MR, Zhuang Z, et al. 1997. Loss of heterozygosity at 11q13: analysis of pituitary tumors, lung carcinoids, lipomas, and other uncommon tumors in subjects with familial multiple endocrine neoplasia type 1. *J. Clin. Endocrinol. Metab.* 82:1416–20

9. Lubensky IA, Debelenko LV, Zhuang Z, Emmert-Buck MR, Dong Q, et al. 1996. Allelic deletions on chromosome 11q13 in multiple tumors from individual MEN1 patients. *Cancer Res.* 56:5272–78

10. The European Consortium on MEN1. 1997. Linkage disequilibrium studies in multiple endocrine neoplasia type 1 (MEN1). *Hum. Genet.* 100:657–65

11. Chandrasekharappa SC, Guru SC, Manickam P, Olufemi S-E, Collins FS, et al. 1997. Positional cloning of the gene for multiple endocrine neoplasia type 1. *Science* 276:404–7

12. Lemmens I, Van de Ven WJ, Kas K, Zhang CX, Giraud S, et al. 1997. Identification of the multiple endocrine neoplasia type 1 (MEN1) gene. The European Consortium on MEN1. *Hum. Mol. Genet.* 6:1177–83

12a. Krawczak M, Cooper DN. 1997. The human gene mutation database. *Trends Genet.* 13:121–22)

13. Agarwal SK, Kester MB, Debelenko LV, Heppner C, Emmert-Buck MR, et al. 1997. Germline mutations of the MEN1 gene in familial multiple endocrine neoplasia type 1 and related states. *Hum. Mol. Genet.* 6:1169–75

14. Lemmens I, Van de Ven WJ, Kas K, Zhang CX, Giraud S, et al. 1997. Identification of the multiple endocrine neoplasia type 1 (MEN1) gene. The

European Consortium on MEN1. *Hum. Mol. Genet.* 6:1177–83

15. Cote GJ, Lee JE, Evans DB, Huang E, Schultz PN, et al. 1998. Five novel mutations in the familial multiple endocrine neoplasia type 1 (MEN 1) gene. *Hum. Mutat.* 12:219 (Abstr.)

16. Giraud S, Zhang CX, Serova-Sinilnikova O, Wautot V, Salandre J, et al. 1998. Germ-line mutation analysis in patients with multiple endocrine neoplasia type 1 and related disorders. *Am. J. Hum. Genet.* 63:455–67

17. Poncin J, Abs R, Velkeniers B, Bonduelle M, Abramowicz M, et al. 1999. Mutation analysis of the MEN1 gene in Belgian patients with multiple endocrine neoplasia type 1 and related diseases. *Hum. Mutat.* 13:54–60

18. Teh BT, Kytola S, Farnebo F, Bergman L, Wong FK, et al. 1998. Mutation analysis of the MEN1 gene in multiple endocrine neoplasia type 1, familial acromegaly and familial isolated hyperparathyroidism. *J. Clin. Endocrinol. Metab.* 83:2621–26

19. Sakurai A, Shirahama S, Fujimori M, Katai M, Itakura Y, et al. 1998. Novel MEN1 gene mutations in familial multiple endocrine neoplasia type 1. *J. Hum. Genet.* 43:199–201

20. Thakker RV. 1998. Multiple endocrine neoplasia—syndromes of the twentieth century. *J. Clin. Endocrinol. Metab.* 83:2617–20

21. Dackiw A, Cote G, Fleming J, Schultz P, Stanford P, et al. 2000. Screening for MEN1 mutations in patients with atypical endocrine neoplasia. *Surgery.* In press

22. Fujimori M, Shirahama S, Sakurai A, Hashizume K, Hama Y, et al. 1998. Novel V184E MEN1 germline mutation in a Japanese kindred with familial hyperparathyroidism. *Am. J. Med. Genet.* 80:221–22

23. Bale AE, Norton JA, Wong EL, Fryburg JS, Maton PN, et al. 1991. Allelic loss on chromosome 11 in hereditary and sporadic tumors related to familial multiple endocrine neoplasia type 1. *Cancer Res.* 51:1154–57

24. Debelenko LV, Zhuang Z, Emmert-Buck MR, Chandrasekharappa SC, Manickam P, et al. 1997. Allelic deletions on chromosome 11q13 in multiple endocrine neoplasia type 1-associated and sporadic gastrinomas and pancreatic endocrine tumors. *Cancer Res.* 57:2238–43

25. Falchetti A, Morelli A, Amorosi A, Tonelli F, Fabiani S, et al. 1997. Allelic loss in parathyroid tumors from individuals homozygous for multiple endocrine neoplasia type 1. *J. Clin. Endocrinol. Metab.* 82:2278–82

26. Lammie GA, Peters G. 1991. Chromosome 11q13 abnormalities in human cancer. *Cancer Cells* 3:413–20

27. Patel P, O'Rahilly S, Buckle V, Nakamura Y, Turner RC, Wainscoat JS. 1990. Chromosome 11 allele loss in sporadic insulinoma. *J. Clin. Pathol.* 43:377–78

28. Radford DM, Ashley SW, Wells SAJ, Gerhard DS. 1990. Loss of heterozygosity of markers on chromosome 11 in tumors from patients with multiple endocrine neoplasia syndrome type 1. *Cancer Res.* 50:6529–33

29. Weil RJ, Vortmeyer AO, Huang S, Boni R, Lubensky IA, et al. 1998. 11q13 allelic loss in pituitary tumors in patients with multiple endocrine neoplasia syndrome type 1. *Clin. Cancer Res.* 4:1673–78

30. Heppner C, Kester MB, Agarwal SK, Debelenko LV, Emmert-Buck MR, et al. 1997. Somatic mutation of the MEN1 gene in parathyroid tumours. *Nat. Genet.* 16:375–78

31. Farnebo F, Teh BT, Kytola S, Svensson A, Phelan C, et al. 1998. Alterations of the MEN1 gene in sporadic parathyroid tumors. *J. Clin. Endocrinol. Metab.* 83:2627–30

32. Carling T, Correa P, Hessman O, Hedberg J, Skogseid B, et al. 1998. Parathyroid MEN1 gene mutations in relation to

clinical characteristics of nonfamilial primary hyperparathyroidism. *J. Clin. Endocrinol. Metab.* 83:2960–63

33. Zhuang Z, Vortmeyer AO, Pack S, Huang S, Pham TA, et al. 1997. Somatic mutations of the MEN1 tumor suppressor gene in sporadic gastrinomas and insulinomas. *Cancer Res.* 57:4682–86

34. Debelenko LV, Brambilla E, Agarwal SK, Swalwell JI, Kester MB, et al. 1997. Identification of MEN1 gene mutations in sporadic carcinoid tumors of the lung. *Hum. Mol. Genet.* 6:2285–90

35. Tanaka C, Yoshimoto K, Yamada S, Nishioka H, Ii S, et al. 1998. Absence of germ-line mutations of the multiple endocrine neoplasia type 1 (MEN1) gene in familial pituitary adenoma in contrast to MEN1 in Japanese. *J. Clin. Endocrinol. Metab.* 83:960–65

36. Zhuang Z, Ezzat SZ, Vortmeyer AO, Weil R, Oldfield EH, et al. 1997. Mutations of the MEN1 tumor suppressor gene in pituitary tumors. *Cancer Res.* 57:5446–51

37. Prezant TR, Levine J, Melmed S. 1998. Molecular characterization of the MEN1 tumor suppressor gene in sporadic pituitary tumors. *J. Clin. Endocrinol. Metab.* 83:1388–91

38. Heppner C, Reincke M, Agarwal SK, Mora P, Allolio B, et al. 1999. MEN1 gene analysis in sporadic adrenocortical neoplasms. *J. Clin. Endocrinol. Metab.* 84:216–19

39. Guru SC, Goldsmith PK, Burns AL, Marx SJ, Spiegel AM, et al. 1998. Menin, the product of the MEN1 gene, is a nuclear protein. *Proc. Natl. Acad. Sci. USA* 95:1630–34

40. Agarwal SK, Guru SC, Heppner C, Erdos MR, Collins RM, et al. 1999. Menin interacts with the AP1 transcription factor JunD and represses JunD-activated transcription. *Cell* 96:143–52

41. Karin M, Liu Z, Zandi E. 1997. AP-1 function and regulation. *Curr. Opin. Cell Biol.* 9:240–46

42. Hirai SI, Ryseck RP, Mechta F, Bravo R, Yaniv M. 1989. Characterization of junD: a new member of the jun proto-oncogene family. *EMBO J.* 8:1433–39

43. Petty EM, Green JS, Marx SJ, Taggart RT, Farid N, Bale AE. 1994. Mapping the gene for hereditary hyperparathyroidism and prolactinoma (MEN1Burin) to chromosome 11q: evidence for a founder effect in patients from Newfoundland. *Am. J. Hum. Genet.* 54:1060–66

44. Teh BT, McArdle J, Chan SP, Menon J, Hartley L, et al. 1997. Clinicopathologic studies of thymic carcinoids in multiple endocrine neoplasia type 1. *Medicine* 76:21–29

45. Teh BT, Zedenius J, Kytola S, Skogseid B, Trotter J, et al. 1998. Thymic carcinoids in multiple endocrine neoplasia type 1. *Ann. Surg.* 228:99–105

46. Olufemi SE, Green JS, Manickam P, Guru SC, Agarwal SK, et al. 1998. Common ancestral mutation in the MEN1 gene is likely responsible for the prolactinoma variant of MEN1 (MEN1Burin) in four kindreds from Newfoundland. *Hum. Mutat.* 11:264–69

47. Bassett JH, Forbes SA, Pannett AA, Lloyd SE, Christie PT, et al. 1998. Characterization of mutations in patients with multiple endocrine neoplasia type 1. *Am. J. Hum. Genet.* 62:232–44

48. Sipple JH. 1961. The association of pheochromocytoma with carcinoma of the thyroid gland. *Am. J. Med.* 31:163–66

49. Farndon JR, Leight GS, Dilley WG, Baylin SB, Smallridge RC, et al. 1986. Familial medullary thyroid carcinoma without associated endocrinopathies: a distinct clinical entity. *Br. J. Surg.* 73:278–81

50. Nunziata V, Giannattasio R, di Giovanni G, D'Armiento MR, Mancini M. 1989. Hereditary localized pruritus in affected members of a kindred with multiple endocrine neoplasia type 2A (Sipple's syndrome). *Clin. Endocrinol.* 30:57–63

51. Bugalho MJ, Limbert E, Sobrinho LG, Clode AL, Soares J, et al. 1992. A kindred with multiple endocrine neoplasia type 2A associated with pruritic skin lesions. *Cancer* 70:2664–67

52. Gagel RF, Levy ML, Donovan DT, Alford BR, Wheeler T, Tschen JA. 1989. Multiple endocrine neoplasia type 2a associated with cutaneous lichen amyloidosis. *Ann. Intern. Med.* 111:802–6

53. Verdy M, Weber AM, Roy CC, Morin CL, Cadotte M, Brochu P. 1982. Hirschsprung's disease in a family with multiple endocrine neoplasia type 2. *J. Pediatr. Gastroenterol. Nutr.* 1:603–7

54. Carney JA, Go VL, Sizemore GW, Hayles AB. 1976. Alimentary-tract ganglioneuromatosis. A major component of the syndrome of multiple endocrine neoplasia type 2b. *N. Engl. J. Med.* 295:1287–91

55. Carney JA, Sizemore GW, Hayles AB. 1978. Multiple endocrine neoplasia type 2b. *Pathobiol. Annu.* 8:105–53

56. Rashid M, Khairi MR, Dexter RN, Burzynski NJ, Johnston CC Jr. 1975. Mucosal neuroma, pheochromocytoma and medullary thyroid carcinoma: multiple endocrine neoplasia type 3. *Med. (Baltim.)* 54:89–112

57. Takahashi M, Cooper GM. 1987. *ret* transforming gene encodes a fusion protein homologous to tyrosine kinases. *Mol. Cell. Biol.* 7:1378–85

58. Takahashi M, Buma Y, Iwamoto T, Inaguma Y, Ikeda H, Hiai H. 1988. Cloning and expression of the ret proto-oncogene encoding a tyrosine kinase with two potential transmembrane domains. *Oncogene* 3:571–78

59. Takahashi M. 1988. Structure and expression of the ret transforming gene. *IARC* 92:189–97

60. Takeichi M. 1991. Cadherin cell adhesion receptors as a morphogenetic regulator. *Science* 251:1451–55

61. Pasini B, Hofstra RM, Yin L, Bocciardi R, Santamaria G, et al. 1995. The physi-

cal map of the human RET proto-oncogene. *Oncogene* 11:1737–43

62. Myers SM, Eng C, Ponder BA, Mulligan LM. 1995. Characterization of RET proto-oncogene 3′ splicing variants and polyadenylation sites: a novel C-terminus for RET. *Oncogene* 11:2039–45

63. Takahashi M, Ritz J, Cooper GM. 1985. Activation of a novel human transforming gene, ret, by DNA rearrangement. *Cell* 42:581–88

64. Bongarzone I, Pierotti MA, Monzini N, Mondellini P, Manenti G, et al. 1989. High frequency of activation of tyrosine kinase oncogenes in human papillary thyroid carcinoma. *Oncogene* 4:1457–62

65. Grieco M, Santoro M, Berlingieri MT, Melillo RM, Donghi R, et al. 1990. PTC is a novel rearranged form of the ret proto-oncogene and is frequently detected in vivo in human thyroid papillary carcinomas. *Cell* 60:557–63

66. Ishizaka Y, Ushijima T, Sugimura T, Nagao M. 1990. cDNA cloning and characterization of ret activated in a human papillary thyroid carcinoma cell line. *Biochem. Biophys. Res. Commun.* 168: 402–8

67. Bongarzone I, Butti MG, Coronelli S, Borrello MG, Santoro M, et al. 1994. Frequent activation of RET protooncogene by fusion with a new activating gene in papillary thyroid carcinomas. *Cancer Res.* 54:2979–85

68. Wajjwalku W, Nakamura S, Hasegawa Y, Miyazaki K, Satoh Y, et al. 1992. Low frequency of rearrangements of the ret and trk proto-oncogenes in Japanese thyroid papillary carcinomas. *Jpn. J. Cancer Res.* 83:671–75

69. Santoro M, Dathan NA, Berlingieri MT, Bongarzone I, Paulin C, et al. 1994. Molecular characterization of RET/PTC3; a novel rearranged version of the RET proto-oncogene in a human thyroid papillary carcinoma. *Oncogene* 9:509–16

70. Edery P, Eng C, Munnich A, Lyonnet S.

1997. RET in human development and oncogenesis. *Bioessays* 19:389–95

71. Pachnis V, Mankoo B, Costantini F. 1993. Expression of the c-ret proto-oncogene during mouse embryogenesis. *Development* 119:1005–17

72. Attie-Bitach T, Abitbol M, Gerard M, Delezoide AL, Auge J, et al. 1998. Expression of the RET proto-oncogene in human embryos. *Am. J. Med. Genet.* 80:481–86

73. Schuchardt A, D'Agati V, Larsson-Blomberg L, Costantini F, Pachnis V. 1994. Defects in the kidney and enteric nervous system of mice lacking the tyrosine kinase receptor Ret. *Nature* 367:380–83

74. Schuchardt A, D'Agati V, Larsson-Blombert L, Costantini F, Pachnis V. 1995. RET-deficient mice: an animal model for Hirschsprung's disease and renal agenesis. *J. Intern. Med.* 238:327–32

75. Treanor JJS, Goodman L, de Sauvage F, Stone DM, Poulsen KT, et al. 1996. Characterization of a multicomponent receptor for GDNF. *Nature* 382:80–83

76. Durbec P, Marcos-Gutierrez CV, Kilkenny C, Suvanto P, Smith D, et al. 1996. GDNF signalling through the ret receptor tyrosine kinase. *Nature* 381:789–93

77. Trupp M, Arenas E, Falnzilber M, Nilsson AS, Sieber BA, et al. 1996. Functional receptor for GDNF encoded by the c-ret proto-oncogene. *Nature* 381:785–88

78. Jing S, Wen D, Yu Y, Holst PL, Luo Y, et al. 1996. GDNF-induced activation of the Ret protein tyrosine kinase is mediated by GDNFR-a, a novel receptor for GDNF. *Cell* 85:1113–24

79. Pichel JG, Shen L, Sheng HZ, Granholm AC, Drago J, et al. 1996. Defects in enteric innervation and kidney development in mice lacking GDNF. *Nature* 382:73–76

80. Sanchez MP, Silos-Santiago I, Frisen J, He B, Lira SA, Barbacid M. 1996. Renal agenesis and the absence of enteric neurons in mice lacking GDNF. *Nature* 382:70–73

81. Moore MW, Klein RD, Farinas I, Sauer H, Armanini M, et al. 1996. Renal and neuronal abnormalities in mice lacking GDNF. *Nature* 382:76–79

82. Jing S, Wen D, Yu Y, Holst PL, Luo Y, et al. 1996. GDNF-induced activation of the ret protein tyrosine kinase is mediated by GDNFR-alpha, a novel receptor for GDNF. *Cell* 85:1113–24

83. Cacalano G, Farinas I, Wang LC, Hagler K, Forgie A, et al. 1998. GFRalpha1 is an essential receptor component for GDNF in the developing nervous system and kidney. *Neuron* 21:53–62

84. Jing S, Yu Y, Fang M, Hu Z, Holst PL, et al. 1997. GFRalpha-2 and GFRalpha-3 are two new receptors for ligands of the GDNF family. *J. Biol. Chem.* 272:33111–17

85. Baloh RH, Tansey MG, Golden JP, Creedon DJ, Heuckeroth RO, et al. 1997. TrnR2, a novel receptor that mediates neurturin and GDNF signaling through Ret. *Neuron* 18:793–802

86. Sanicola M, Hession C, Worley D, Carmillo P, Ehrenfels C, et al. 1997. Glial cell line-derived neurotrophic factor-dependent RET activation can be mediated by two different cell-surface accessory proteins. *Proc. Natl. Acad. Sci. USA* 94:6238–43

87. Klein RD, Sherman D, Ho WH, Stone D, Bennett GL, et al. 1997. A GPI-linked protein that interacts with Ret to form a candidate neurturin receptor. *Nature* 387:717–21

88. Suvanto P, Wartiovaara K, Lindahl M, Arumae U, Moshnyakov M, et al. 1997. Cloning, mRNA distribution and chromosomal localisation of the gene for glial cell line-derived neurotrophic factor receptor beta, a homologue to GDNFR-alpha. *Hum. Mol. Genet.* 6:1267–73

89. Heuckeroth RO, Kotzbauer P, Copeland NG, Gilbert DJ, Jenkins NA, et al. 1997.

Neurturin, a novel neurotrophic factor, is localized to mouse chromosome 17 and human chromosome 19p13.3. *Genomics* 44:137–40

90. Kotzbauer PT, Lampe PA, Heuckeroth RO, Golden JP, Creedon DJ, et al. 1996. Neurturin, a relative of glial-cell-line-derived neurotrophic factor. *Nature* 384:467–70

91. Milbrandt J, de Sauvage FJ, Fahrner TJ, Baloh RH, Leitner ML, et al. 1998. Persephin, a novel neurotrophic factor related to GDNF and neurturin. *Neuron* 20:245–53

92. Baloh RH, Tansey MG, Lampe PA, Fahrner TJ, Enomoto H, et al. 1998. Artemin, a novel member of the GDNF ligand family, supports peripheral and central neurons and signals through the GFRalpha3-RET receptor complex. *Neuron* 21:1291–302

93. Horger BA, Nishimura MC, Armanini MP, Wang LC, Poulsen KT, et al. 1998. Neurturin exerts potent actions on survival and function of midbrain dopaminergic neurons. *J. Neurosci.* 18:4929–37

94. Enokido Y, de Sauvage F, Hongo JA, Ninkina N, Rosenthal A, et al. 1998. GFR alpha-4 and the tyrosine kinase Ret form a functional receptor complex for persephin. *Curr. Biol.* 8:1019–22

95. Tang MJ, Worley D, Sanicola M, Dressler GR. 1998. The RET-glial cell-derived neurotrophic factor (GDNF) pathway stimulates migration and chemoattraction of epithelial cells. *J. Cell Biol.* 142:1337–45

96. Mathew CG, Chin KS, Easton DF, Thorpe K, Carter C, et al. 1987. A linked genetic marker for multiple endocrine neoplasia type 2A on chromosome 10. *Nature* 328:527–28

97. Simpson NE, Kidd KK, Goodfellow PJ, McDermid H, Myers S, et al. 1987. Assignment of multiple endocrine neoplasia type 2A to chromosome 10 by linkage. *Nature* 328:528–30

98. Ishizaka Y, Itoh F, Tahira T, Ikeda I, Sug-imura T, et al. 1989. Human ret proto-oncogene mapped to chromosome 10q11.2. *Oncogene* 4:1519–21

99. Donghi R, Sozzi G, Pierotti MA, Biunno I, Miozzo M, et al. 1989. The oncogene associated with human papillary thyroid carcinoma (PTC) is assigned to chromosome 10 q11-q12 in the same region as multiple endocrine neoplasia type 2A (MEN2A). *Oncogene* 4:521–23

100. Mulligan LM, Kwok JB, Healey CS, Elsdon MJ, Eng C, et al. 1993. Germ-line mutations of the RET proto-oncogene in multiple endocrine neoplasia type 2A. *Nature* 363:458–60

101. Donis-Keller H, Dou S, Chi D, Carlson KM, Toshima K, et al. 1993. Mutations in the RET proto-oncogene are associated with MEN 2A and FMTC. *Hum. Mol. Genet.* 2:851–56

102. Hofstra RM, Landsvater RM, Ceccherini I, Stulp RP, Stelwagen T, et al. 1994. A mutation in the RET proto-oncogene associated with multiple endocrine neoplasia type 2B and sporadic medullary thyroid carcinoma. *Nature* 367:375–76

103. Eng C, Smith DP, Mulligan LM, Nagai MA, Healey CS, et al. 1994. Point mutation within the tyrosine kinase domain of the RET proto-oncogene in multiple endocrine neoplasia type 2B and related sporadic tumours. *Hum. Mol. Genet.* 3:237–41

104. Carlson KM, Dou S, Chi D, Scavarda N, Toshima K, et al. 1994. Single missense mutation in the tyrosine kinase catalytic domain of the RET protooncogene is associated with multiple endocrine neoplasia type 2B. *Proc. Natl. Acad. Sci. USA* 91:1579–83

105. Eng C, Clayton D, Schuffenecker I, Lenoir G, Cote G, et al. 1996. The relationship between specific RET proto-oncogene mutations and disease phenotype in multiple endocrine neoplasia type 2. International RET mutation consortium analysis. *JAMA* 276:1575–79

106. Moers AM, Landsvater RM, Schaap C,

Jansen-Schillhorn van Veen JM, de Valk IA, et al. 1996. Familial medullary thyroid carcinoma: not a distinct entity? Genotype-phenotype correlation in a large family. *Am. J. Med.* 101:635–41

107. Eng C, Smith DP, Mulligan LM, Healey CS, Zvelebil MJ, et al. 1995. A novel point mutation in the tyrosine kinase domain of the RET proto-oncogene in sporadic medullary thyroid carcinoma and in a family with FMTC. *Oncogene* 10:509–13

108. Hofstra RM, Fattoruso O, Quadro L, Wu Y, Libroia A, et al. 1997. A novel point mutation in the intracellular domain of the ret protooncogene in a family with medullary thyroid carcinoma. *J. Clin. Endocrinol. Metab.* 82:4176–78

109. Decker RA, Peacock ML. 1998. Occurrence of MEN 2a in familial Hirschsprung's disease: a new indication for genetic testing of the RET proto-oncogene. *J. Pediatr. Surg.* 33:207–14

110. Caron P, Attie T, David D, Amiel J, Brousset F, et al. 1996. C618R mutation in Exon 10 of the RET proto-oncogene in a kindred with multiple endocrine neoplasia type 2A and Hirschsprung's disease. *J. Clin. Endocrinol. Metab.* 81:27131–33

111. Kitamura Y, Goodfellow PJ, Shimizu K, Nagahama M, Ito K, et al. 1997. Novel germline RET proto-oncogene mutations associated with medullary thyroid carcinoma (MTC): mutation analysis in Japanese patients with MTC. *Oncogene* 14:3103–6

112. Gimm O, Marsh DJ, Andrew SD, Frilling A, Dahia PL, et al. 1997. Germline dinucleotide mutation in codon 883 of the RET proto-oncogene in multiple endocrine neoplasia type 2B without codon 918 mutation. *J. Clin. Endocrinol. Metab.* 82:3902–4

113. Peacock ML, Borst MJ, Sweet JD, Decker RA. 1996. Detection of RET mutations in multiple endocrine neoplasia type 2a and familial medullary thyroid carcinoma by denaturing gradient gel electrophoresis. *Hum. Mutat.* 7:100–4

114. Gagel RF, Cote GJ, Martins Bugalho MJG, Boyd AE, Cummings T, et al. 1995. Clinical use of molecular information in the management of multiple endocrine neoplasia type 2A. *J. Int. Med.* 238:333–41

115. Wohllk N, Cote GJ, Evans DB, Goepfert H, Ordonez NG, Gagel RF. 1996. Application of genetic screening information to the management of medullary thyroid carcinoma and multiple endocrine neoplasia type 2. *Endocrinol. Metab. Clin. North Am.* 25:1–25

116. Gagel RF. 1997. Unresolved issues in the genesis and management of multiple endocrine neoplasia type 2. *Horm. Metab. Res.* 29:135–37

117. Hoppner W, Ritter MM. 1997. A duplication of 12 bp in the critical cysteine rich domain of the RET proto-oncogene results in a distinct phenotype of multiple endocrine neoplasia type 2A. *Hum. Mol. Genet.* 6:587–90

118. Berndt I, Reuter M, Saller B, Frankraue K, Groth P, et al. 1998. A new hot spot for mutations in the ret protooncogene causing familial medullary thyroid carcinoma and multiple endocrine neoplasia type 2A. *J. Clin. Endocrinol. Metab.* 83:770–74

119. Scurini C, Quadro L, Fattoruso O, Verga U, Libroia A, et al. 1998. Germline and somatic mutations of the RET proto-oncogene in apparently sporadic medullary thyroid carcinomas. *Mol. Cell. Endocrinol.* 137:51–57

120. Bolino A, Schuffenecker I, Luo Y, Seri M, Silengo M, et al. 1995. RET mutations in exons 13 and 14 of FMTC patients. *Oncogene* 10:2415–19

121. Wohllk N, Cote GJ, Bugalho MM, Ordonez N, Evans DB, et al. 1996. Relevance of RET proto-oncogene mutations in sporadic medullary thyroid carcinoma. *J. Clin. Endocrinol. Metab.* 81:3740–45

122. Eng C, Mulligan LM, Smith DP, Healey CS, Frilling A, et al. 1995. Mutation of the RET protooncogene in sporadic medullary thyroid carcinoma. *Genes Chromosomes Cancer* 12:209–12

123. Decker RA, Peacock ML, Borst MJ, Sweet JD, Thompson NW. 1995. Progress in genetic screening of multiple endocrine neoplasia type 2A: Is calcitonin testing obsolete? *Surgery* 118:257–64

124. Komminoth P, Kunz EK, Matias-Guiu X, Hiort O, Christiansen G, et al. 1995. Analysis of RET proto-oncogene point mutations distinguishes heritable from nonheritable medullary thyroid carcinomas. *Cancer* 76:479–89

125. Zedenius J, Wallin G, Hamberger B, Nordenskjold M, Weber G, Larsson C. 1994. Somatic and MEN 2A de novo mutations identified in the RET proto-oncogene by screening of sporadic MTCs. *Hum. Mol. Genet.* 3:1259–62

126. Miyauchi A, Futami H, Hai N, Yokozawa T, Kuma K, et al. 1999. Two germline missense mutations at codons 804 and 806 of the RET proto-oncogene in the same allele in a patient with multiple endocrine neoplasia type 2B without codon 918 mutation. *Jpn. J. Cancer Res.* 90:1–5

127. Hofstra RM, Landsvater RM, Ceccherini I, Stulp RP, Stelwagen T, et al. 1994. A mutation in the RET proto-oncogene associated with multiple endocrine neoplasia type 2B and sporadic medullary thyroid carcinoma. *Nature* 367:375–76

128. Zedenius J, Larsson C, Bergholm U, Bovee J, Svensson A, et al. 1995. Mutations of codon 918 in the RET proto-oncogene correlate to poor prognosis in sporadic medullary thyroid carcinomas. *J. Clin. Endocrinol. Metab.* 80:3088–90

129. Uchino S, Noguchi S, Adachi M, Sato M, Yamashita H, et al. 1998. Novel point mutations and allele loss at the RET locus in sporadic medullary thyroid carcinomas. *Jpn. J. Cancer Res.* 89:411–18

130. Marsh DJ, Learoyd DL, Andrew SD, Krishnan L, Pojer R, et al. 1996. Somatic mutations in the RET proto-oncogene in sporadic medullary thyroid carcinoma. *Clin. Endocrinol.* 44:249–57

131. Bugalho MJ, Frade JP, Santos JR, Limbert E, Sobrinho L. 1997. Molecular analysis of the RET proto-oncogene in patients with sporadic medullary thyroid carcinoma: a novel point mutation in the extracellular cysteine-rich domain. *Eur. J. Endocrinol.* 136:423–26

132. Alemi M, Lucas SD, Sallstrom JF, Bergholm U, Akerstrom G, Wilander E. 1997. A complex nine base pair deletion in RET exon 11 common in sporadic medullary thyroid carcinoma. *Oncogene* 14:2041–45

133. Hofstra RM, Stelwagen T, Stulp RP, de Jong D, Hulsbeek M, et al. 1996. Extensive mutation scanning of RET in sporadic medullary thyroid carcinoma and of RET and VHL in sporadic pheochromocytoma reveals involvement of these genes in only a minority of cases. *J. Clin. Endocrinol. Metab.* 81:2881–84

134. Eng C, Mulligan LM. 1997. Mutations of the RET proto-oncogene in the multiple endocrine neoplasia type 2 syndromes, related sporadic tumours, and Hirschsprung disease. *Hum. Mutat.* 9:97–109

135. Lindor NM, Honchel R, Khosla S, Thibodeau SN. 1995. Mutations in the RET protooncogene in sporadic pheochromocytomas. *J. Clin. Endocrinol. Metab.* 80:627–29

136. Okamoto E, Ueda T. 1967. Embryogenesis of intramural ganglia of the gut and its relation to Hirschsprung's disease. *J. Pediatr. Surg.* 2:437–43

137. Martucciello EA. 1992. Chromosome 10 deletion in Hirschsprung's disease. *Pediatr. Surg. Int.* 7:308–10

138. Sanchez M, Silos-Santiago I, Frisen J, He B, Lira S, Barbacid M. 1996. Newborn mice lacking GDNF display renal agenesis and absence of enteric neurons, but

no deficits in midbrain dopaminergic neurons. *Nature* 382:70–73

139. Schuchardt A, D'Agati V, Larsson-Blomberg L, Costantini F, Pachnis V. 1994. Defects in the kidney and enteric nervous system of mice lacking the tyrosine kinase receptor Ret. *Nature* 367:380–83

140. Angrist M, Bolk S, Thiel B, Puffenberger EG, Hofstra RM, et al. 1995. Mutation analysis of the RET receptor tyrosine kinase in Hirschsprung's disease. *Hum. Mol. Genet.* 4:821–30

141. Angrist M, Bolk S, Halushka M, Lapchak PA, Chakravarti A. 1996. Germline mutations in glial cell-derived neurotrophic factor (GDNF) and RET in a Hirschsprung disease patient. *Nat. Genet.* 14:341–44

142. Attie T, Till M, Pelet A, Amiel J, Edery P, et al. 1995. Mutation of the endothelin-receptor B gene in Waardenburg-Hirschsprung disease. *Hum. Mol. Genet.* 4:2407–9

143. Attie T, Pelet A, Sarda P, Eng C, Edery P, et al. 1994. A 7 bp deletion of the RET proto-oncogene in familial Hirschsprung's disease. *Hum. Mol. Genet.* 3:1439–40

144. Attie T, Pelet A, Edery P, Eng C, Mulligan LM, et al. 1995. Diversity of RET proto-oncogene mutations in familial and sporadic Hirschsprung disease. *Hum. Mol. Genet.* 4:1381–86

145. Bidaud C, Salomon R, Van Camp G, Pelet A, Attie T, et al. 1997. Endothelin-3 gene mutations in isolated and syndromic Hirschsprung disease. *Eur. J. Hum. Genet.* 5:247–51

146. Edery P, Lyonnet S, Mulligan LM, Pelet A, Dow E, et al. 1994. Mutations of the RET proto-oncogene in Hirschsprung's disease. *Nature* 367:378–80

147. Edery P, Attie T, Amiel J, Pelet A, Eng C, et al. 1996. Mutation of the endothelin-3 gene in the Waardenburg-Hirschsprung disease (Shah-Waardenburg syndrome). *Nat. Genet.* 12:442–44

148. Lyonnet S, Edery P, Mulligan LM, Pelet A, Dow E, et al. 1994. Mutations of RET proto-oncogene in Hirschsprung disease. *C.R. Acad. Sci. III* 317:358–62

149. Doray B, Salomon R, Amiel J, Pelet A, Touraine R, et al. 1998. Mutation of the RET ligand, neurturin, supports multigenic inheritance in Hirschsprung disease. *Hum. Mol. Genet.* 7:1449–52

150. Hofstra RM, Osinga J, Tan-Sindhunata G, Wu Y, Kamsteeg EJ, et al. 1996. A homozygous mutation in the endothelin-3 gene associated with a combined Waardenburg type 2 and Hirschsprung phenotype (Shah-Waardenburg syndrome). *Nat. Genet.* 12:445–47

151. Svensson PJ, Anvret M, Molander ML, Nordenskjold A. 1998. Phenotypic variation in a family with mutations in two Hirschsprung-related genes (RET and endothelin receptor B). *Hum. Genet.* 103:145–48

152. Pachnis V, Durbec P, Taraviras S, Grigoriou M, Natarajan D. 1998. Neural injury, repair, and adaptation in the GI tract. III. Role Of the RET signal transduction pathway in development of the mammalian enteric nervous system. *Am. J. Physiol.* 275:G183–86

153. Amiel J, Salomon R, Attie T, Pelet A, Trang H, et al. 1998. Mutations of the RET-GDNF signaling pathway in Ondine's curse. *Am. J. Hum. Genet.* 62:715–17

154. Decker RA, Peacock ML, Watson P. 1998. Hirschsprung disease in MEN 2A: increased spectrum of RET exon 10 genotypes and strong genotype-phenotype correlation. *Hum. Mol. Genet.* 7:129–34

155. Reynolds LF, Eng C. 1995. RET mutations in multiple endocrine neoplasia type 2 and Hirschsprung disease. *Curr. Opin. Pediatr.* 7:702–9

156. Asai N, Iwashita T, Matsuyama M, Takahashi M. 1995. Mechanism of activation of the *ret* proto-oncogene by

multiple endocrine neoplasia 2A mutations. *Mol. Cell Biol.* 15:1613–19

157. Xing S, Smanik PA, Oglesbee MJ, Trosko JE, Mazzaferri EL, Jhiang SM. 1996. Characterization of ret oncogenic activation in MEN2 inherited cancer syndromes. *Endocrinology* 137:1512–19

158. Santoro M, Carlomagno F, Romano A, Bottaro DP, Dathan NA, et al. 1995. Activation of RET as a dominant transforming gene by germline mutations of MEN 2A and MEN 2B. *Science* 267:381–83

159. Marshall GM, Peaston AE, Hocker JE, Smith SA, Hansford LM, et al. 1997. Expression of multiple endocrine neoplasia 2B RET in neuroblastoma cells alters cell adhesion in vitro, enhances metastatic behavior in vivo, and activates Jun kinase. *Cancer Res.* 57:5399–405

160. Rizzo C, Califano D, Colucci-D'Amato GL, De Vita G, D'Alessio A, et al. 1996. Ligand stimulation of a Ret chimeric receptor carrying the activating mutation responsible for the multiple endocrine neoplasia type 2B. *J. Biol. Chem.* 271:29497–501

161. Bongarzone I, Vigano E, Alberti L, Borrello M, Pasini B, et al. 1998. Full activation of the MEN2B mutant ret by an additional MEN2A mutation or by ligand GDNF stimulation. *Oncogene* 16:2295–301

162. Iwashita T, Asai N, Murakami H, Matsuyama M, Takahashi M. 1996. Identification of tyrosine residues that are essential for transforming activity of the *ret* proto-oncogene with MEN 2A or MEN 2B mutation. *Oncogene* 12:481–87

163. Carlomagno F, Salvatore G, Cirafici AM, De Vita G, Melillo RM, et al. 1997. The different RET-activating capability of mutations of cysteine 620 or cysteine 634 correlates with the multiple endocrine neoplasia type 2 disease phenotype. *Cancer Res.* 57:391–95

164. Ito S, Iwashita T, Asai N, Murakami H, Iwata Y, et al. 1997. Biological properties of Ret with cysteine mutations correlate with multiple endocrine neoplasia type 2A, familial medullary thyroid carcinoma, and Hirschsprung's disease phenotype. *Cancer Res.* 57:2870–72

165. Seger R, Krebs EG. 1995. The MAPK signaling cascade. *FASEB J.* 9:726–35

166. Cobb MH, Goldsmith EJ. 1995. How MAP kinases are regulated. *J. Biol. Chem.* 270:14843–46

167. Lorenzo MJ, Gish GD, Houghton C, Stonehouse TJ, Pawson T, et al. 1997. RET alternate splicing influences the interaction of activated RET with the SH2 and PTB domains of Shc, and the SH2 domain of Grb2. *Oncogene* 14:763–71

168. Arighi E, Alberti L, Torriti F, Ghizzoni S, Rizzetti MG, et al. 1997. Identification of Shc docking site on Ret tyrosine kinase. *Oncogene* 14:773–82

169. Iwashita T, Asai N, Murakami H, Matsuyama M, Takahashi M. 1996. Identification of tyrosine residues that are essential for transforming activity of the ret proto-oncogene with MEN2A or MEN2B mutation. *Oncogene* 12:481–87

170. Asai N, Murakami H, Iwashita T, Takahashi M. 1996. A mutation at tyrosine 1062 in MEN2A-Ret and MEN2B-Ret impairs their transforming activity and association with shc adaptor proteins. *J. Biol. Chem.* 271:17644–49

171. Ohiwa M, Murakami H, Iwashita T, Asai N, Iwata Y, et al. 1997. Characterization of Ret-Shc-Grb2 complex induced by GDNF, MEN 2A, and MEN 2B mutations. *Biochem. Biophys. Res. Commun.* 237:747–51

172. Chiariello M, Visconti R, Carlomagno F, Melillo R, Bucci C, et al. 1998. Signalling of RET receptor tyrosine kinase through the C-Jun NH2-terminal protein kinases (JNKS)—evidence for a divergence of the erks and jnks pathways induced by RET. *Oncogene* 16:2435–45

173. Maher ER, Kaelin WG, Jr. 1997. von Hippel-Lindau disease. *Medicine* 76:381–91

174. Latif F, Kalman T, Gnarra J, Yao M, Duh F-M, et al. 1993. Identification of the von Hippel-Lindau disease tumor suppressor gene. *Science* 260:1317–20

175. Zbar B, Kishida T, Chen F, Schmidt L, Maher ER, et al. 1996. Germline mutations in the Von Hippel-Lindau disease (VHL) gene in families from North America, Europe, and Japan. *Hum. Mutat.* 8:348–57

176. Chen F, Kishida T, Yao M, Hustad T, Glavac D, et al. 1995. Germline mutations in the von Hippel-Lindau disease tumor suppressor gene: correlations with phenotype. *Hum. Mutat.* 5:66–75

177. Maher ER, Webster AR, Richards FM, Green JS, Crossey PA, et al. 1996. Phenotypic expression in von Hippel-Lindau disease: correlations with germline VHL gene mutations. *J. Med. Gen.* 33:328–32

178. Foster K, Prowse A, van den Berg A, Fleming S, Hulsbeek MM, et al. 1994. Somatic mutations of the von Hippel-Lindau disease tumour suppressor gene in non-familial clear cell renal carcinoma. *Hum. Mol. Genet.* 3:2169–73

179. Herman JG, Latif F, Weng Y, Lerman MI, Zbar B, et al. 1994. Silencing of the VHL tumor-suppressor gene by DNA methylation in renal carcinoma. *Proc. Natl. Acad. Sci. USA* 91:9700–4

180. Eng C, Crossey PA, Mulligan LM, Healey CS, Houghton C, et al. 1995. Mutations in the RET proto-oncogene and the von Hippel-Lindau disease tumour suppressor gene in sporadic and syndromic phaeochromocytomas. *J. Med. Genet.* 32:934–37

181. Duan DR, Pause A, Burgess WH, Aso T, Chen DY, et al. 1995. Inhibition of transcription elongation by the VHL tumor suppressor protein. *Science* 269:1402–6

182. Kibel A, Iliopoulos O, De Caprio JA, Kaelin WG Jr. 1995. Binding of the von Hippel-Lindau tumor suppressor protein to Elongin B and C. *Science* 269:1444–46

183. Lonergan KM, Iliopoulos O, Ohh M, Kamura T, Conaway RC, et al. 1998. Regulation of hypoxia-inducible mRNAs by the von Hippel-Lindau tumor suppressor protein requires binding to complexes containing elongins B/C and Cul2. *Mol. Cell. Biol.* 18:732–41

184. Pause A, Lee S, Worrell RA, Chen DY, Burgess WH, et al. 1997. The von Hippel-Lindau tumor-suppressor gene product forms a stable complex with human CUL-2, a member of the Cdc53 family of proteins. *Proc. Natl. Acad. Sci. USA* 94:2156–61

185. Kaelin WG, Iliopoulos O, Lonergan KM, Ohh M. 1998. Functions of the von Hippel-Lindau tumour suppressor protein. *J. Intern. Med.* 243:535–39

186. Kamura T, Koepp DM, Conrad MN, Skowyra D, Moreland RJ, et al. 1999. Rbx1, a component of the VHL tumor suppressor complex ans SCF ubiquitin ligase. *Science* 284:657–61

187. Pause A, Lee S, Lonergan KM, Klausner RD. 1998. The von Hippel-Lindau tumor suppressor gene is required for cell cycle exit upon serum withdrawal. *Proc. Natl. Acad. Sci. USA* 95:993–98

188. Ohh M, Yauch RL, Lonergan KM, Whaley JM, Stemmer-Rachamimov AO, et al. 1998. The von Hippel-Lindau tumor suppressor protein is required for proper assembly of an extracellular fibronectin matrix. *Mol. Cell* 1:959–68

189. Riccardi VM. 1981. Von Recklinghausen neurofibromatosis. *N. Engl. J. Med.* 305:1617–27

190. Karnes PS. 1998. Neurofibromatosis: a common neurocutaneous disorder. *Mayo Clin. Proc.* 73:1071–76

191. Neurofibromatosis. 1987. Natl. Inst. Health Consens. Dev. Conf. Consens. Statement 6:1–7

192. Xu GF, O'Connell P, Viskochil D, Cawthon R, Robertson M, et al. 1990. The neurofibromatosis type 1 gene encodes a protein related to GAP. *Cell* 62:599–608

193. Fountain JW, Wallace MR, Bruce MA, Seizinger BR, Menon AG, et al. 1989.

Physical mapping of a translocation breakpoint in neurofibromatosis. *Science* 244:1085–87

194. Ballester R, Marchuk D, Boguski M, Saulino A, Letcher R, et al. 1990. The NF1 locus encodes a protein functionally related to mammalian GAP and yeast IRA proteins. *Cell* 63:851–59

195. Martin GA, Viskochil D, Bollag G, McCabe PC, Crosier WJ, et al. 1990. The GAP-related domain of the neurofibromatosis type 1 gene product interacts with ras p21. *Cell* 63:843–49

196. Xu GF, Lin B, Tanaka K, Dunn D, Wood D, et al. 1990. The catalytic domain of the neurofibromatosis type 1 gene product stimulates ras GTPase and complements ira mutants of *S. cerevisiae*. *Cell* 63:835–41

197. Upadhyaya M, Cheryson A, Broadhead W, Fryer A, Shaw DJ, et al. 1990. A 90 kb DNA deletion associated with neurofibromatosis type 1. *J. Med. Genet.* 27:738–41

198. Wallace MR, Andersen LB, Saulino AM, Gregory PE, Glover TW, Collins FS. 1991. A de novo Alu insertion results in neurofibromatosis type 1. *Nature* 353:864–66

199. Carney JA, Gordon H, Carpenter PC, Shenoy BV, Go VLW. 1985. The complex of myxomas, spotty pigmentation, and endocrine overactivity. *Medicine* 64:270–83

200. Sarlis NJ, Chrousos GP, Doppman JL, Carney JA, Stratakis CA. 1997. Primary pigmented nodular adrenocortical disease: reevaluation of a patient with carney complex 27 years after unilateral adrenalectomy. *J. Clin. Endocrinol. Metab.* 82:1274–78

201. Stratakis CA, Courcoutsakis NA, Abati A, Filie A, Doppman JL, et al. 1997. Thyroid gland abnormalities in patients with the syndrome of spotty skin pigmentation, myxomas, endocrine overactivity, and schwannomas (Carney complex). *J. Clin. Endocrinol. Metab.* 82:2037–43

202. Rosenzweig JL, Lawrence DA, Vogel DL, Costa J, Gorden P. 1982. Adrenocorticotropin-independent hypercortisolemia and testicular tumors in a patient with a pituitary tumor and gigantism. *J. Clin. Endocrinol. Metab.* 55:421–27

203. Stratakis CA, Carney JA, Lin JP, Papanicolaou DA, Karl M, et al. 1996. Carney complex, a familial multiple neoplasia and lentiginosis syndrome. Analysis of 11 kindreds and linkage to the short arm of chromosome 2. *J. Clin. Invest.* 97:699–705

204. Casey M, Mah C, Merliss AD, Kirschner LS, Taymans SE, et al. 1998. Identification of a novel genetic locus for familial cardiac myxomas and Carney complex. *Circulation* 98:2560–66

205. Milunsky J, Huang XL, Baldwin CT, Farah MG, Milunsky A. 1998. Evidence for genetic heterogeneity of the Carney complex (familial atrial myxoma syndromes). *Cancer Genet. Cytogenet.* 106:173–76

206. Taymans S, Svetlana P, Kirschner L, Zhuang Z, Stratakis C. 1999. Amplification of chromosome 2p15-p16 in tumors from patients with carney complex. *Prog. Abstr., Endocrine Soc. Ann. Meet., 81st, (OR28–5)*, p. 101 (Abstr.)

207. Gagel RF, and Cote GJ. 1998. Pathogenesis of medullary thyroid carcinoma. In *Thyroid Cancer*, ed. F JA, pp. 85–103. Norwell, MA: Kluwer

Annu. Rev. Physiol. 2000. 62:413–37

LEPTIN

Rexford S. Ahima and Jeffrey S. Flier

*Department of Medicine, Division of Endocrinology, Beth Israel Deaconess
Medical Center, Harvard Medical School, Boston, Massachusetts 02215;
e-mail: jflier@caregroup.harvard.edu*

Key Words adipose tissue, feeding, metabolism, neuroendocrine

■ **Abstract** The discovery of the adipose-derived hormone leptin has generated
enormous interest in the interaction between peripheral signals and brain targets
involved in the regulation of feeding and energy balance. Plasma leptin levels correlate
with fat stores and respond to changes in energy balance. It was initially proposed
that leptin serves a primary role as an anti-obesity hormone, but this role is commonly
thwarted by leptin resistance. Leptin also serves as a mediator of the adaptation to
fasting, and this role may be the primary function for which the molecule evolved.
There is increasing evidence that leptin has systemic effects apart from those related
to energy homeostasis, including regulation of neuroendocrine and immune function
and a role in development.

INTRODUCTION

Evidence for the existence of a physiological system for homeostatic regulation
of body weight has accumulated over the past four decades. Kennedy (1) proposed
that the amount of energy stored in adipose mass represented the balance between
ingested calories and energy expenditure. Since adipose mass tends to be relatively stable over long periods in most mammals, he envisaged a homeostatic
mechanism that monitors changes in energy stores and elicits compensatory
changes in food intake and energy expenditure to maintain adipose mass at a set
point. This adipostatic model of body weight regulation is consistent with the
observation that a decrease in adiposity from fasting or surgical resection causes
hyperphagia, decreases energy expenditure, and eventually restores body weight
to the previous level (2–4). Conversely, weight gain from forced overfeeding
inhibits voluntary food intake (3, 4). Hervey (5) demonstrated that cross-circulation
(parabiosis) between rats rendered obese by lesions in the ventromedial hypothalamus (VMH) and control rats led to death from starvation in the latter. Based
on these results he suggested that increased levels of a circulating satiety factor
from the obese rats inhibited food intake in the non-lesioned lean rats. In contrast,
the obese rats were incapable of responding to elevated endogenous levels of the
presumed satiety factor because of the hypothalamic lesion. This latter view was

0066–4278/00/0315–0413$12.00

consistent with the known effects of VMH lesions on feeding and body weight regulation (6).

The concept of a circulating satiety factor was further strengthened by the discovery of recessive mutations, *obese* (*ob*) and *diabetes* (*db*), both of which led to hyperphagia, decreased energy expenditure, and early onset obesity in mice (7). Coleman (8, 9) and Hausberger (10) showed that parabiosis of wild-type mice and *ob/ob* mice suppressed weight gain in the latter, whereas parabiosis to *db/db* mice caused profound hypophagia in lean wild-type mice. Taken together, these results suggested that the *ob* locus was necessary for the production of a humoral satiety factor and that the *db* locus encoded a molecule required for response to this factor. Coleman's predictions more than two decades ago have been confirmed by the cloning of the *ob* and *db* genes (11). The product of the *ob* gene was named leptin (from the Greek root *leptos* meaning thin) because it caused marked reduction in food intake, body weight, and body fat when injected into leptin-deficient or normal mice (12). A rise in leptin levels was proposed to prevent obesity by decreasing appetite and increasing thermogenesis, through action in the brain (13, 14). However, as often happens when a new hormone or protein is discovered, the initial view of leptin as an anti-obesity hormone has been replaced by a more complex one. Here, we review major advances leading to our current understanding of the diverse roles of leptin in the regulation of metabolism, neuroendocrine, and immune function, and development.

THE *OB* GENE

The mouse *ob* gene was discovered through positional cloning and shown to encode a 4.5 kilobase mRNA transcript with a highly conserved 167-amino acid open reading frame that was unique in the GenBank database (11). Mouse and human *ob* genes have been localized to chromosomes 6 and 7q31.3, respectively (11, 15, 16). The *ob* gene encompases 650 kb and consists of 3 exons separated by 2 introns. The coding region for Ob protein is located in exons 2 and 3. Several regulatory elements have been identified within the *ob* gene promoter, including cyclic AMP and glucocorticoid response elements, and CCATT/enhancer and SP-1 binding sites (17–19). The sites responsible for adipose-specific expression and for regulated expression in responses to changes in adipose size or energy balance have not been identified. Analysis of the *ob* gene product revealed characteristics consistent with a secreted protein and a high degree of homology among species. For example, human leptin is 84% identical to mouse leptin and 83% identical to rat leptin. Leptin is synthesized mainly, but not exclusively (see below), by white adipose tissue and circulates as a 16-kDa protein. There is a strong positive correlation between leptin mRNA and protein levels in adipose tissue and circulating leptin levels (20–22). Structural analysis indicates that leptin is similar to cytokines (23, 24). Moreover, leptin contains an intrachain disulfide bond that appears to be necessary for its biological activity (25). So far, it is not known whether leptin is secreted by a constitutive or regulated mechanism; however, the former means is thought to be more likely because leptin does not appear to be stored in substantial amounts (26).

Mutations of the *ob* gene cause early onset obesity in mice (11–14). In C57Bl/6J *ob/ob* mice, a Cys-to-Thr substitution results in a stop codon at position 105 instead of arginine and in synthesis of a truncated protein that is incapable of being secreted (11, 27). mRNA expression of *ob* is increased in C57Bl/6J *ob/ob* mice, consistent with the view that the *ob* gene is under negative feedback regulation. In the *ob²J/ob²J* mouse mutant, a transposon inserted into the first intron of the *ob* gene prevents the synthesis of mature *ob* mRNA (11). Both *ob/ob* mouse mutants are leptin deficient, hyperphagic, hypothermic, and morbidly obese and have several metabolic and neuroendocrine abnormalities.

Human *ob* gene mutations are rare and were first reported in two children from a consanguineous Pakistani family in 1997 (28). In these patients, deletion of a single guanine nucleotide in codon 133 led to a frameshift mutation and synthesis of a truncated leptin protein that underwent proteosomal degradation (27). Strobel et al (29) identified three members of a Turkish family with a missense mutation (Cys-to-Thr) in codon 105. As with the *ob* mutation described above, the abnormal leptin protein encoded in these patients is incapable of being secreted (29). Human *ob* gene mutations cause hyperphagia, morbid obesity, and hypothalamic hypogonadism. Impairment of linear growth and decreased sympathetic tone (measured by cold pressor response) are less thoroughly documented (28, 29). However, unlike *ob/ob* mice (11–14) hyperinsulinemia, hyperglycemia, hypercorticism, and hypothermia have not as yet been reported in leptin-deficient humans (28, 29). The reasons for these species differences are not known, but they suggest substantial differences in the physiological actions of leptin between rodents and humans. As is discussed below, the relative importance of leptin as a signal for the adaptation to fasting may differ among these species.

REGULATION OF LEPTIN EXPRESSION

Leptin expression is influenced by the status of energy stores in fat, as evidenced by increased adipose *ob* mRNA and serum leptin levels in obese humans and other mammals (20–22, 30, 31) (Table 1). Moreover, adipocyte size is an important determinant of leptin synthesis, as larger adipocytes contain more leptin than smaller adipocytes in the same individual (30). Leptin levels in blood correlate with total body fat stores (20–22); however, it is not known whether increased triglyceride levels, lipid metabolites, or mechanical factors associated with increased adipocyte size influence leptin expression. Leptin levels increase within hours after a meal in rodents and after several days of overfeeding in humans (32–34). Leptin levels decrease within hours after initiation of fasting in both species (32, 35, 36). The changes in leptin expression in response to fasting and feeding are out of proportion to the corresponding changes in body weight or

TABLE 1   Regulation of leptin expression

Site	Increase	Decrease
Adipose tissue	Overfeeding Obesity (except ob mutation) Insulin Glucocorticoids Acute infection Cytokines (TNF-α, IL-1, LPS)	Fasting Testosterone Beta-adrenergic agonists Thiazolidinediones (in vitro) ? Thyroid hormone Cold exposure
Placenta	Insulin Glucocorticoids Hypoxia	Smoking Low birth weight
Skeletal muscle (rat)	Glucosamine Glucose Lipids	
Stomach fundus (rat)		Feeding Cholecystokinin

body fat (34, 36), suggesting that leptin serves as an indicator of energy stores, as well as a mediator of energy balance. On the other hand, because leptin levels do not rise in response to individual meals (37), leptin is not likely to serve as a meal-related satiety signal.

Regulation of leptin expression by nutrition is probably mediated in part by insulin. Leptin expression increases after peak insulin secretion during the feeding cycle (32, 38). Insulin stimulates leptin expression directly in isolated adipocytes (39) and increases leptin levels when injected into rodents (32). In contrast, leptin is decreased in low insulin states, such as streptozotocin-induced diabetes, and increases after insulin treatment (40). In humans leptin expression is correlated with insulin levels, increases several days after insulin infusion, and may be predictive of insulin resistance (41–43). Conversely, the fall in insulin levels may mediate the decline in leptin levels during fasting (36).

Leptin levels are regulated by other factors (Table 1). Glucocorticoids directly stimulate leptin synthesis in cultured adipocytes (44–46), and leptin expression increases in response to chronic elevation of cortisol in humans (47). In contrast to this positive relationship in free-living animals, plasma leptin and glucocorticoid levels are inversely related. Peak glucocorticoid levels coincide with the nadir of leptin at the beginning of the light cycle in humans (dark cycle in rodents), and the nadir of glucocorticoids is related to peak leptin levels at night (light cycle in rodents) (48–51). An inverse correlation between pulsatile leptin secretion and cortisol and adrenocorticotropin (ACTH) has been reported in humans (50). Leptin levels are higher in prepubertal rodents and boys and does not appear to be dependent on adipose mass or triglyceride level (49, 52, 53). The prepubertal increase in leptin expression precedes the rise in testosterone and estradiol and is postulated to be involved in the maturation of the gonadal axis (49, 53). Females have higher leptin levels than males when matched by age, weight, or body fat

(54, 55). This may be attributable to sex differences in body fat distribution and testosterone level (54, 56). Subcutaneous adipose tissue is more abundant and contains higher levels of leptin in females. Leptin synthesis is inhibited by testosterone but is not affected by ovarian sex steroids (56, 57).

Administration of thyroid hormone decreases leptin levels in rodents (58). Although levels of plasma leptin, thyroid-stimulating hormone (TSH), and adiposity correlate in euthyroid patients (59), there are conflicting reports on the effect of hypothyroidism and hyperthyroidism on leptin levels and on the interaction between leptin and the pituitary-thyroid axis in humans. Some studies have described an elevation of plasma leptin in hypothyroid patients and a decrease in hyperthyroid patients, but others have reported no significant alteration in leptin levels in these conditions or in response to replacement doses of thyroxine (59–62).

Leptin synthesis is stimulated by infection, endotoxin, and cytokines, e.g. tumor necrosis factor (TNF), leukemia inhibitory factor (LIF), and interleukin 1 (IL-1) (63–66). In addition to regulating feeding behavior and energy balance directly, the rise in leptin as a result of elevation of cytokine levels may also contribute to anorexia and weight loss in these inflammatory conditions (65, 67). Troglitazone decreases leptin synthesis in vitro (68), and cold exposure and catecholamines decrease leptin expression, most likely through activation of β-adrenergic receptors (69–72). The effects of thiazolidinediones and catecholamines on leptin levels are likely to be mediated by direct action on the *ob* gene, since binding sites for the respective nuclear transcription factors are present in the *ob* gene promoter (17, 18).

Initial studies indicated that leptin expression was synthesized only in adipose tissue. However, leptin is also synthesized in extra-adipose tissues including placenta, gastric fundic mucosa, skeletal muscle, and mammary epithelium (73–76) (Table 1). Placental leptin expression is stimulated by hypoxia, insulin, and glucocorticoids (77, 78). Leptin is synthesized by mammary epithelium, secreted in colustrum, and absorbed by the neonate (74). Feeding and administration of cholecystokinin or gastrin decrease leptin synthesis in the gastric fundus and increase plasma leptin (75). It is speculated that meal-related alterations in gastric and plasma leptin levels may be involved in the short-term regulation of appetite (75). Glucosamine infusion increases leptin expression in adipose tissue and induces de novo leptin synthesis in rat skeletal muscle (76). Glucose and lipid infusion have similar effects on leptin expression in these tissues, raising the possibility that leptin acts as a sensor of nutrient flux in adipose tissue and skeletal muscle (76).

THE *DB* GENE

Tartaglia et al (79) were the first to isolate the leptin receptor (Ob-R) from mouse choroid plexus using an expression cloning strategy. Because the sequence and expression of the initially cloned receptor are normal in *db/db* mice, they predicted that the *db* mutation affected a different receptor or an alternatively spliced iso-form. The latter explanation rapidly proved to be correct. Multiple splice variants of Ob-R mRNA encode at least six leptin receptor isoforms (80, 81) (Figure 1). The leptin receptor belongs to the family of class 1 cytokine receptors, which include receptors for interleukin 6 (IL-6), leukemia inhibitory factor (LIF), gran-ulocyte-colony stimulating factor (GCSF), and glycoprotein 130 (for review see 82). Leptin receptor isoforms share an identical extracellular ligand-binding domain at the amino terminus but differ at the carboxy terminus. Five isoforms, Ob-Ra, Ob-Rb, Ob-Rc, Ob-Rd, and Ob-Rf have transmembrane domains; how-ever, only Ob-Rb (the long receptor isoform) contains intracellular motifs required for activation of the JAK (janus kinase)-STAT (signal transducers and activators of transcription) signal transduction pathway (83–86) (Figure 1). Activation of ObRb, and to a lesser extent ObRa, promotes JAK-dependent signaling to path-ways other than STAT, such as MAP kinase (86), and the relative importance of these divergent signaling events in leptin action is unknown. Leptin binds with high affinity (nanomolar range) to an Ob-R homodimer, leading to activation of

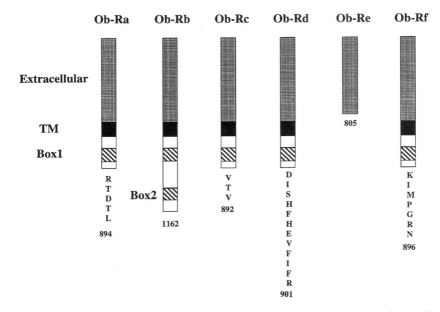

Figure 1 Domain structure of alternatively spliced leptin receptor (Ob-R) isoforms. Ob-R isoforms (ObRa-Ob-Rf) share a common extracellular leptin-binding domain, but differ at the carboxy terminus (intracellular domain). Only Ob-Rb, the long isoform, has all intracellular protein motifs necessary for signaling via the Jak-STAT signal transduction pathway. Terminal amino acid residues for various Ob-R isoforms are denoted by the alphabet code. Ob-Re lacks a transmembrane domain (TM) as well as intracellular motifs. Intracellular Box1 and Box2 domains are indicated by hatched boxes.

JAK2. It is not known whether Ob-Rb is capable of forming heterodimers with other receptor isoforms. Ob-Re lacks transmembrane and intracellular domains and circulates as a soluble receptor (80, 87).

Leptin receptor mutations cause early onset obesity in rodents (83, 88, 89). In C57Bl/Ks *db/db* mice, a premature stop codon inserted in the 3′-end of the Ob-Rb mRNA transcript leads to the synthesis of a truncated receptor that replaces the Ob-Rb isoform with the Ob-Ra isoform, which is incapable of mediating JAK-STAT signaling (84, 85). Ob-Ra and other splice variants are expressed normally in these *db/db* mice. Mice with db^{Pas}/db^{Pas} and db^{3J}/db^{3J} mutations lack transmembrane and intracytoplasmic domains and thus lack all receptor species (87, 90). *db* mutations cause leptin insensitivity, hyperphagia, metabolic derangement, morbid obesity, and neuroendocrine abnormalities, including hypercorticism and hypothalamic hypogonadism (12, 14, 91). A Gln-to-Pro substitution at amino acid position 269 in the extracellular domain decreases cell surface Ob-R expression in *fa/fa* rats and additionally reduces the signaling capacity of the receptor (83, 89). There are conflicting reports on the effect of intracerebroventricular (icv) leptin administration on feeding in *fa/fa* rats. Some studies have described a decrease in food intake in response to icv leptin injection; however, others have observed no such effect in these rats (93, 94). Obese Koletsky rats have a point mutation at amino acid position 763, which results in a stop codon in the extracellular domain and failure of expression of all isoforms of Ob-R (88, 95).

Ob-R mutations are extremely rare in humans. Clement et al (96) described the first cases of human Ob-R mutations in three sisters from a consanguineous Kabilian family. In these patients, a G→A substitution in the splice donor site of exon 16 resulted in a truncated leptin receptor lacking both transmembrane and intracellular domains. The mutant leptin receptor circulates at high concentrations and is capable of binding leptin (96). As with human *ob* gene mutations, human *db* mutation causes hyperphagia, early onset obesity, and hypothalamic hypogonadism. In addition, the secretion of thyrotropin and growth hormone is impaired in these patients. Unlike *db/db* mice, the human *db* mutation is not associated with hyperglycemia, hypercorticism, and hypothermia (91, 96).

LEPTIN TRANSPORT AND SITES OF ACTION

Leptin circulates as a 16-kDa protein and is partially bound to plasma proteins (97, 98). In one study, the proportion of bound leptin was reported to be higher in lean (~45%) compared with obese (~20%) individuals (98). The bound fraction of leptin can be as high as 80% in humans with a leptin receptor mutation due to binding of leptin to circulating leptin receptors (96). An additional pool of leptin is bound to tissue-binding sites and is likely to contribute to the maintenance of steady-state plasma leptin levels (99). Based on anatomic and functional data, it appears that leptin exerts its effects on energy balance mainly by acting in the brain. Intravenous leptin injection activates neurons in the arcuate, ventromedial, and dorsomedial hypothalamic nuclei and in brainstem neuronal circuits implicated in the regulation of feeding behavior and energy balance (100, 101). The long form leptin receptor (Ob-Rb) is present in these hypothalamic regions and colocalized with STAT3 and neuropeptide mediators of leptin action, such as neuropeptide Y (NPY) and proopiomelanocortin (POMC) (102–106). In contrast, short leptin receptor isoforms are expressed in chorioid plexus, vascular endothelium, and peripheral tissues, such as kidney, liver, lung, and gonads, where they may serve a transport and/or clearance role (104, 107). It is of interest that intracerebroventricular leptin injection inhibits food intake and decreases adiposity more potently that peripheral leptin administration (12–14).

Leptin enters the rat brain by a saturable transport mechanism (108), possibly by receptor-mediated transcytosis across the blood-brain barrier, as is the case for some other large proteins (109, 110). In support of this view, brain microvessels express high levels of the short form leptin receptor Ob-Ra and are also capable of binding and internalizing leptin (107, 111). Leptin target neurons in the arcuate, dorsomedial, ventromedial, and ventral premammillary nuclei lie within close proximity to the median eminence. Because capillaries in the median eminence lack tight junctions, as in other circumventricular organs, leptin may reach neurons in the adjacent ventrobasal hypothalamus through diffusion. Leptin may also be transported into the brain via cerebrospinal fluid (CSF) (112). It has also been suggested that Ob-Ra, which is highly expressed in the choroid plexus (the site of CSF production), could mediate blood-to-CSF leptin transport (107). However, leptin is present (albeit at a much lower fraction of the elevated circulating levels) in CSF of obese Koletsky rats, which totally lack leptin receptors, indicating that leptin receptors are not essential for leptin transport into CSF (95). More importantly, CSF leptin concentration is ~100-fold lower than plasma leptin and less than the K_d of the leptin receptor (79, 112). Therefore, it is unlikely that CSF leptin is a major source of leptin for targets in the brain.

Leptin is distributed widely in various tissues and is cleared mainly by the kidney (99, 113, 114). A role for the kidney in leptin clearance is consistent with elevation of leptin levels in patients with renal impairment and end-stage renal disease (115, 116). Leptin is filtered by the glomeruli and is thought to be degraded by renal epithelial cells (114). High levels of short form leptin receptors are present in the kidney, and leptin binds to the corticomedullary junction and renal papilla (117). These receptors may internalize and degrade leptin, as occurs in Chinese hamster ovary (CHO) cells expressing Ob-Ra (118). Leptin levels are higher in patients with liver cirrhosis (119, 120), suggesting that the liver may be involved in leptin synthesis or clearance. The liver is unlikely to be involved in leptin clearance because there is no net uptake of leptin by normal human liver (113). A study in rats has demonstrated that transdifferentiated stellate cells obtained from rat liver following injury are capable of synthesizing leptin (121). This finding in humans raises the possibility that the rise in leptin levels in cirrhosis is derived in part from hepatic synthesis.

LEPTIN ACTION IN THE BRAIN

The discovery of leptin has provided insight into the interaction between energy stores and hypothalamic centers that regulate feeding behavior and energy balance. Abnormalities of energy balance resulting from ventrobasal hypothamic lesions resemble those in *ob/ob* and *db/db* mice (reviewed in 122, 123). All these conditions are characterized by hyperphagia, decreased energy expenditure, and increased adiposity, and these features underscore the critical roles of leptin as an indicator of energy stores and the hypothalamus as a major effector organ for energy homeostasis. Leptin-sensitive neurons in the arcuate, ventromedial, and dorsomedial hypothalamic nuclei express neuropeptides/neurotransmitters implicated in the central regulation of energy balance. A detailed description of the neuroanatomy of leptin targets in the brain is beyond the scope of this article (122–124). Briefly, the long form leptin receptor (Ob-Rb) is coexpressed with neuropeptide Y (NPY), agouti-related peptide (AgRP), proopiomelanocortin (POMC), a precursor of α-melanocyte stimulating hormone (α-MSH), and cocaine- and amphetamine-regulated transcript (CART) in the arcuate hypothalamic nucleus (Figure 2). NPY and AgRP are expressed in the same neurons in the medial arcuate nucleus, whereas POMC and CART are coexpressed in the lateral arcuate nucleus. Intracerebral injection of NPY stimulates feeding (i.e. orexigenic). In contrast, α-MSH (a product of POMC) and CART inhibit feeding (i.e. anorexigenic). α-MSH is thought to regulate feeding through melanocortin 4 (MC4) receptors in the hypothalamus (125). AgRP antagonizes the actions of α-MSH at MC4 receptors and is therefore orexigenic (126).

Leptin-sensitive neurons in the arcuate hypothalamic neurons may influence feeding by regulating the expression of other orexigenic peptides, e.g. melanin-concentrating hormone (MCH) and possibly orexins/hypocretin in the lateral hypothalamic nucleus (Figure 2) (122, 123). Other neurotransmitters/neuropeptides suggested as potential mediators of leptin action in the brain include corticotropin-releasing hormone (CRH), cholecystokinin (CCK), glucagon-like peptide-1 (GLP-1), urocortin, bombesin, and serotonin (87, 127). The stimulatory effect of NPY and MCH on food intake is consistent with the elevation of the levels of these peptides in the hypothalamus in states of leptin deficiency, e.g. *ob/ob* mice and fasting, and the decrease in their expression in response to leptin administration (123, 124). In contrast, expression of the anorexigenic peptides POMC and CART is decreased in *ob/ob* mice and during fasting and increased in response to leptin administration (67, 123, 128).

Genetic ablation of putative neuropeptide mediators of leptin action in the brain does not always produce phenotypes predicted on the basis of pharmacological studies. For example, NPY deficiency or lack of Y1 and Y5 NPY receptors does not reduce feeding behavior or prevent weight gain, impair thermogenesis and neuroendocrine function, or impair responsiveness to leptin (129–131). Mice with mutation of the serotonin 5-HT2C receptor develop hyperphagia, late onset obesity, and hyperleptinemia but are still capable of responding normally to exog-

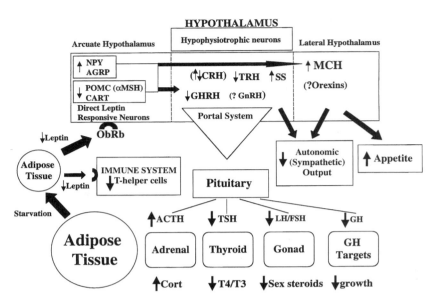

Figure 2 Role of leptin in the adaptation to starvation. The fall in leptin with starvation results in an increase in neuropeptide Y (NPY) and agouti-related peptide (AGRP) levels, and a decrease in proopiomelanocortin (POMC) and cocaine- and amphetamine-regulated transcript (CART) levels in the arcuate hypothalamic nucleus. NPY, POMC, AGRP, and CART neurons are directly responsive to leptin. NPY and AGRP stimulate feeding (orexigenic), whereas α-melanocyte stimulating hormone (a product of POMC) and CART inhibit feeding (anorexigenic). These neurons also project to the lateral hypothalamus and regulate the expression of melanin-concentrating hormone (MCH), a major stimulator of feeding. In addition, leptin targets in the arcuate hypothalamic nucleus respond to low leptin levels by regulating the neuroendocrine axis and decreasing sympathetic nervous output. The fall in leptin also leads to suppression of immune function. The metabolic and neuroendocrine adaptations to fasting mediated by leptin are likely to be of greater survival value in rodents since short-term starvation has more severe consequences in this species. CRH (corticotropin-releasing hormone), TRH (thyrotropin-releasing hormone), GHRH (growth hormone–releasing hormone), SS (somatostatin), GnRH (gonadotropin-releasing hormone), GH (growth hormone).

enous leptin (132). NPY appears to be partially responsible for hyperphagia, obesity, and neuroendocrine abnormalities in leptin-deficient *ob/ob* mice, as evidenced by partial amelioriation of these abnormalties in NPY-deficient *ob/ob* mice (133). In contrast to NPY deficiency, MCH deficiency causes hypophagia and failure of weight gain, in agreement with its suggested role as an orexigenic peptide (134). These findings suggest that the central effects of leptin and other feeding signals are likely mediated by neuronal networks expressing a complex array of hypothalamic neuropeptides/neurotransmitters.

In addition to regulating food intake, leptin-sensitive NPY/AgRP and POMC/CART neurons project to the paraventricular hypothalamic nucleus and probably mediate the effects of leptin on the neuroendocrine axis and autonomic function (122, 123). The fall in leptin levels suppresses thyroid function, in part by decreasing thyrotropin-releasing hormone (TRH) formation in the paraventricular hypothalamic nucleus (135). Ablation of the arcuate hypothalamic nucleus with monosodium glutamate prevents the fall in TRH mRNA expression with fasting, indicating that the effect of leptin on the thyrotropic axis is mediated, at least in part, through leptin-senstive NPY and POMC neurons (136). Leptin stimulates secretion of gonadotropin-releasing hormone (GnRH) in hypothalamic explants (137). However, this effect may not be mediated directly by leptin, since GnRH neurons do not express detectable levels of leptin receptors (138). Reports on regulation of CRH by leptin are variable. Leptin has been reported to increase basal CRH release from hypothalamic explants and to inhibit hypoglycemia-induced CRH release from hypothalamic explants (139, 140). Leptin is reported to stimulate CRH mRNA expression in the paraventricular hypothalamic nucleus in some studies (67), whereas others have not demonstrated a significant effect.

Although leptin activates STAT1, 3, and 5 in in vitro systems, intravenous leptin activates only STAT3 in the mouse hypothalamus (84, 85). STAT3 protein is expressed in NPY and POMC neurons in the arcuate hypothalamic nucleus, consistent with the concept that leptin regulates the transcription of these genes at least in part through the JAK-STAT signal transduction pathway (106). Leptin also regulates the expression of other STAT3 target genes in the hypothalamus, including c-*fos*, c-*jun*, *tis-11*, and SOCS-3 (a member of the suppressors of cytokine signaling family) (141). Leptin inhibits glucose-responsive neurons in the hypothalamus and insulin secretion by pancreatic β-cells, through effects on ATP-sensitive potassium channels (142, 143). In addition, leptin depolarizes paraventricular hypothalamic neurons (144), inhibits hypothalamic NPY release (145), and regulates vagal afferents in the stomach (146). The mechanisms underlying these rapid electrophysiological actions of leptin are not known but are not likely to involve STAT-mediated transcription.

Although studies in *ob/ob* mice and other rodents, often involving the administration of supraphysiological doses of leptin, have provided some insights into leptin action, it is not known how physiological alterations in leptin influence neuronal function. Ioffe et al (147) showed that there is a dose-effect of leptin such that neuroendocrine abnormalities, i.e. hypercorticism and central hypogonadism, are corrected by lower doses of leptin. In contrast, leptin concentrations above the normal fed level are required to inhibit feeding and prevent weight gain. Thermoregulation requires even higher leptin levels than are required for neuroendocrine regulation and maintenance of normal body weight. These results suggest that there are different thresholds for leptin for various functions and that responses to physiological alterations in leptin may be mediated by different subsets of neurons.

THE PHYSIOLOGICAL ROLE OF LEPTIN IN ENERGY HOMEOSTASIS

Leptin As Anti-Obesity Hormone

Administration of leptin to rodents decreases food intake and increases energy expenditure (12–14, 148). In contrast to starvation, weight loss after peripheral or central leptin administration is restricted to adipose tissue, with no loss of lean mass (148). Leptin activates lipid oxidation, at least in part, by inducing the expression of enzymes of lipid oxidation (149). In rats leptin also stimulates apoptosis of adipocytes (150). The ability of leptin to decrease body weight and body fat content led to the prevailing view that leptin is an anti-obesity hormone (reviewed in 87, 151, 152). However, this view must be reconciled with the failure of high endogenous leptin levels to prevent obesity in humans and other obese mammals (20–22). Hyperleptinemia is thought to be indicative of leptin resistance, which may play a role in the development of obesity (87, 151, 152). Mechanisms thought to underlie leptin resistance include dysregulation of leptin synthesis and/or secretion, abnormalities of brain leptin transport, and abnormalities of leptin receptors and/or post-receptor signaling.

Studies in obese rodents have provided some insights into the potential mechanisms of leptin resistance. However, there is as yet no direct explanation of the apparent lack of sensitivity of individuals to elevated leptin levels during the course of diet-induced obesity. CSF leptin transport may be limited in obesity, as evidenced by decreased plasma:CSF leptin ratio in obese individuals (112, 153). Because plasma:CSF ratios are markedly decreased in *fa/fa* and Koletsky rats with abnormalities of membrane leptin receptor expression, leptin resistance may arise from defects of receptor-mediated leptin transport into the brain (95). A polygenic mutation that leads to late onset obesity in New Zealand obese (NZO) mice may also offer some insight into the role of brain leptin transport in obesity. These mice are resistant to peripheral leptin administration, but do respond to intracerebroventricular leptin injection, consistent with defective brain leptin transport (148). Similarly, diet-induced obesity in rodents is characterized by insensitivity to peripheral leptin injection (154) but respond to intracerebroventricular leptin (154). In contrast, agouti (*Ay/a*) mice have impaired melanocortin (MC4) receptor signaling in the brain and are resistant to both peripheral and central leptin injection (148). Studies of leptin transport into brain in these models have not been reported.

A member of the suppressors of cytokine signaling family, SOCS-3, is a potential molecular mediator of leptin resistance (141). SOCS-3 mRNA levels are conserved by leptin-mediated STAT3 activation, and SOCS-3 protein potently inhibits leptin signaling. In support of its role as an inhibitor of leptin action in the brain, SOCS-3 expression is induced in the arcuate and dorsomedial hypothalamic nuclei of mice after leptin treatment (141). Leptin resistance may also be mediated by the SH2-containing tyrosine phosphatase, SHP-2, since leptin signaling is reported to be enhanced when the binding site on Ob-Rb for SHP-2 is mutated (155). Leptin resistance could also reside at steps downstream from the initial step of receptor interaction.

The role of leptin in body weight regulation may involve interactions with other metabolic signals, notably insulin and glucocorticoids (67). These hormones regulate the expression of similar neuropeptides in brain regions involved in feeding behavior and body weight regulation. Glucocorticoids have a permissive effect on obesity, as evidenced by the ability of adrenalectomy to ameliorate obesity (156–158). Conversely, hypercortisolism leads to abnormalities of adipose distribution (159). Further studies are needed to understand the interactions among these metabolic hormones.

Leptin As a Signal for Adaptation to Fasting

The widespread occurrence of leptin-resistant obesity may reflect the fact that inability to store energy efficiently at times of abundance is evolutionarily disadvantageous (151). According to this view, the dominant role of leptin in energy homeostasis is likely to be as a mediator of the adaptation to fasting (48, 151). Starvation triggers complex neural, metabolic, hormonal, and behavioral adaptations with the goal of maintaining the supply of energy substrates for use by the brain, protecting lean mass, and promoting survival. A major aspect of this adaptation is the capacity to switch from carbodydrate- to fat-based metabolism during fasting. This change is mediated predominantly by a fall in insulin and rise in counteregulatory hormones, i.e. glucagon, epinephrine, and glucocorticoids (67, 151, 160). Other adaptations to starvation include a decrease in thyroid and gonadal hormones, increased adrenal glucocorticoids, decreased body temperature, and increased appetite. The net effect of these adaptations is to stimulate gluconeogenesis to provide glucose for vital cellular function and supply fatty acids for use by skeletal muscle. Energy utilization is minimized during fasting, in part through suppression of thyroid thermogenesis and curtailment of procreation and growth. In addition, starvation is characterized by immune suppression, including decreased lymphocyte proliferation and helper T-cell cytokine production (161). The changes in thyroid hormones, glucocorticoids, and in body temperature are prominent in rodents but limited in humans (48, 162–164). Similarly, pertubations of the reproductive axis as a result of starvation develop more rapidly in rodents than humans (48, 165).

Starvation decreases leptin levels (21, 48). Because leptin-deficient *ob/ob* mice have similar metabolic, neuroendocrine, and immune abnormalities as those resulting from starvation (91), we reasoned that leptin deficiency is perceived as a state of continuous starvation in *ob/ob* mice and that the fall in leptin mediates the adaptation to fasting (48). To test this hypothesis, leptin was administered twice daily by intraperitoneal injection to mice during a 48-h fast. Prevention of the characteristic fall in leptin during fasting blunted the expected rise in corticosterone and ACTH and prevented the decrease in the levels of thyroid hormone, testosterone, and luteinizing hormone (48). Leptin administration during fasting also prevented a prolongation of estrus cycles (48). Studies in rats and non-human primates have also demonstrated that the fall in leptin with fasting is an important mediator of the somatotropic, thyroid, and reproductive alterations (135–138, 166, 167). Leptin stimulates inflammatory response, T-lymphocyte proliferation, and Th1 cytokine production during fasting in normal mice and in fed *ob/ob* mice, indicating that leptin is an important link between nutrition and the immune system (161).

Low leptin levels may contribute to the development of obesity. Leptin is inappropriately low (as a function of body fat) in some obese individuals (168); however, it is not known whether these individuals have defective leptin synthesis and/or release, and this finding has not yet been observed in all populations (169). Although the functional implications of this observation are yet to be determined, it is plausible that relatively low leptin is perceived as a starvation signal, leading to increased appetite and efficient energy utilization. In contrast, elevation of leptin levels may predispose to cachexia in patients with renal failure and infections by inhibiting appetite and increasing energy expenditure (65, 116). The plasma:CSF leptin ratio is normal in patients with anorexia nervosa during refeeding (prior to weight restoration) and may create a premature sense of satiety during refeeding (112, 170).

OTHER ACTIONS OF LEPTIN

Leptin has diverse effects on the neuroendocrine axis in addition to appetite and body weight regulation. Leptin appears to be necessary for maturation of the reproductive axis, as evidenced by its ability to restore puberty and fertility in *ob/ob* mice, accelerate puberty in wild-type mice, and facilitate reproductive behavior in rodents (171–174). Mutations of *ob* and *db* genes result in hypothalamic hypogonadism in humans (29), and low leptin and absence of a diurnal leptin rhythm occur with exercise-induced amenorrhea (51). Leptin stimulates gonadotropin release and inhibits insulin-like growth factor-mediated release of estradiol in ovarian follicular cells (137, 175). These results indicate that leptin signals the adequacy of energy stores for reproduction, by interacting with different target organs in the hypothalamic-pituitary-gonadal axis.

In rodents leptin is also capable of regulating the hypothalamic-pituitary-adrenal axis independent of its role in the adaptation to starvation. For example, leptin injection blunts ACTH and corticosterone secretion during restraint stress in rats and directly inhibits glucocorticoid synthesis and ACTH-stimulated glucocorticoid secretion in adrenal cortical cells (140, 176, 177). Taken together with its ability to regulate CRH synthesis and secretion (139, 140), these results show that leptin is capable of interacting with various components of the hypothalamic-pituitary-adrenal (HPA) axis. The absence of HPA activation in leptin-deficient humans suggests species differences that require additional study.

Leptin exerts acute effects on metabolism, independent of its role in long-term body weight regulation. For example, leptin decreases glucose and insulin levels acutely in *ob/ob* mice before detectable weight loss (49) and also stimulates gluconeogenesis and glucose metabolism in wild-type rodents (178–180). Leptin stimulates lipolysis, alters lipid partitioning in skeletal muscle, and is capable of increasing fatty acid synthesis in the liver (13, 180, 181). The extent to which these effects are mediated directly on peripheral targets or through the central nervous system is as yet unsettled. Local leptin expression in the stomach has been postulated to regulate satiety (75). The long form leptin receptor (Ob-Rb) is expressed in jejunal epithelium and responds to intravenous leptin administration by inducing STAT3, STAT5, and immediate early genes (182). Direct leptin signaling in the intestine may be involved in the regulation of nutrient absorption and intestinal motility. Leptin also increases sympathetic nerve activity in brown adipose tissue, adrenal gland, kidney, and hindlimb skeletal muscle (183). Thus in addition to increasing energy expenditure (at least in rodents) (13, 184), leptin may be involved in the regulation of cardiovascular and renal function via the central nervous system (183). Such a role may have important implications for the development of cardiovascular and renal complications in obesity and related diseases.

Leptin may play an important role in development, as evidenced by formation of leptin in placenta, widespread expression of leptin and its receptors in fetal tissues, and stimulation of hematopoiesis and angiogenesis by leptin (73, 185–187). Leptin is also likely to be involved in brain development. *ob/ob* and *db/db* mice have decreased brain weight, structural neuronal defects, impaired myelination, and deficiency of several neuronal and glial proteins (188–191). Chronic leptin administration increases brain weight, and restores whole brain protein content and the levels of some neuronal proteins, e.g. growth-associated protein (GAP-43), syntaxin 1, and SNAP-25 in *ob/ob* mice (190, 191).

CONCLUSION

The discovery of leptin marks an important milestone in our understanding of metabolic physiology and will stimulate further research into effector mechanisms in the brain and other organs involved in energy homeostasis. Our current understanding of the roles of leptin in metabolism and neuroendocrine regulation derives mainly from studies in rodents. Although there have been many reports of associations between leptin levels and various physiological and disease states in humans, there are no studies designed to evaluate the role of leptin directly in humans. Human recombinant leptin has been used in phase 1 trials for obesity. It is hoped that future studies will examine the effects of leptin administration on metabolism and on neuroendocrine and immune systems in humans. It is likely that the most important physiological role of leptin is as a signal for the switch between the starved and fed states. Although some leptin is thought to prevent obesity, most obesity occurs in the presence of increased leptin levels. Major tasks ahead include the determination of the molecular mechanisms for leptin resistance and the role, if any, of leptin in the pathophysiology of common obesity.

ACKNOWLEDGMENTS

This work was supported by National Institutes of Health grant DKR3728082 and Eli Lilly and Co. (JSF). RSA is supported by Pfizer Inc. Thanks to Stan Hileman and Jody Dushay for helpful suggestions.

Visit the Annual Reviews home page at www.AnnualReviews.org.

LITERATURE CITED

1. Kennedy GC. 1953. The role of depot fat in the hypothalamic control of food intake in the rat. *Proc. R. Soc. London Ser. B* 140:578–96

2. Faust IM, Johnson PR, Hirsch J. 1977. Adipose tissue regeneration following lipectomy. *Science* 197:391–93

3. Harris RBS, Kasser TR, Martin RJ. 1986. Dynamics of recovery of body composition after overfeeding, food restriction or starvation of mature female rats. *J. Nutr.* 116:2536–46

4. Harris RBS. 1990. Role of set point theory in regulation of body weight. *FASEB J.* 4:3310–18

5. Hervey GR. 1958. The effects of lesions in the hypothalamus in parabiotic rats. *J. Physiol.* 145:336–52

6. Hetherington AW, Ranson SW. 1940. Hypothalamic lesions and adiposity in the rat. *Anat. Rec.* 78:149–72

7. Ingalls AM, Dickie MM, Snell GD. 1950. Obesity, a new mutation in the house mouse. *J. Hered.* 41:317–18

8. Coleman DL, Hummel KP. 1969. Parabiosis of normal with genetically diabetic mice. *Am. J. Physiol.* 217:1298–304

9. Coleman DL. 1973. Effects of parabiosis of obese with diabetes and normal mice. *Diabetologia* 9:294–98

10. Hausberger FX. 1959. Parabiosis and transplantation experiments in hereditary obese mice. *Anat. Rec.* 130:313

11. Zhang Y, Proenca R, Maffei M, Barone M, Leopold L, et al. 1994. Positional cloning of the mouse obese gene and its human homologue. *Nature* 372:425–32

12. Halaas J, Gajiwala K, Maffei M, Cohen S, Chait B, et al. 1995. Weight-reducing effects of the plasma protein encoded by the obese gene. *Science* 269:543–46

13. Pelleymounter M, Cullen M, Baker M, Hecht R, Winters D, et al. 1995. Effects of the obese gene product on body weight regulation in ob/ob mice. *Science* 269:540–43

14. Campfield LA, Smith FJ, Guisez J, Devos R, Burn P. 1995. Recombinant mouse OB protein: evidence for a peripheral signal linking adiposity and central neural networks. *Science* 269:546–49

15. He Y, Chen J, Quon MJ, Reitman M. 1995. The mouse obese gene. *J. Biol. Chem.* 270:28887–91

16. Isse N, Ogawa Y, Tamura N, Masuzaki H, Mori K, et al. 1995. Structural organization and chromosomal assignment of the human obese gene. *J. Biol. Chem.* 270:27728–33

17. Gong DW, Bi S, Pratley RE, Weintraub BD. 1996. Genomic structure and promoter analysis of the human obese gene. *J. Biol. Chem.* 271:3971–74

18. Hwang CS, Mandrup S, MacDougald OA, Geiman DE, Lane MD. 1996. Transcriptional activation of the mouse obese (Ob) gene by CCAAT/enhancer binding protein α. *Proc. Natl. Acad. Sci. USA* 93:873–77

19. Miller SG, De Vos P, Guerre-Millo M, Wong K, Hermann T, et al. 1996. The adipocyte specific transcription factor C/EBPα modulates human ob gene expression. *Proc. Natl. Acad. Sci. USA* 93: 5507–11

20. Maffei MJ, Halaas J, Ravussin E, Pratley RE, Lee GM, et al. 1995. Leptin levels in human and rodent: measurement of plasma leptin and ob mRNA in obese and weight-reduced subjects. *Nat. Med.* 1:1155–61

21. Frederich RC, Hamann A, Anderson S, Lollman B. 1995. Leptin levels reflect body lipid content in mice: evidence for diet-induced resistance to leptin action. *Nat. Med.* 1:1311–14

22. Considine RV, Sinha MK, Heiman ML, Kriauciunas A, Stephens TW, et al. 1996. Serum immunoreactive leptin concentrations in normal weight and obese humans. *N. Engl. J. Med.* 334:292–95

23. Madej T, Boguski MS, Bryant SH. 1995. Threading analysis suggests that the obese gene product may be a helical cytokine. *FEBS Lett.* 373:13–18

24. Zhang F, Basinski MB, Beals JM, Briggs SL, Churgay LM, et al. 1997. Crystal structure of the obese protein leptin-E100. *Nature* 387:206–9

25. Grasso P, Leinung MC, Inher SP, Lee DW. 1997. In vitro effects of leptin-related synthetic peptides on body weight and food intake in female ob/ob mice: localization of leptin activity to domains between amino acid residues 106–140. *Endocrinology* 138:1413–18

26. Barr VA, Malide D, Zarnowski MJ, Taylor SI, Cushman SW. 1997. Insulin stimulates both leptin secretion and production by rat white adipose tissue. *Endocrinology* 138:4463–72

27. Rau H, Reaves BJ, O'Rahilly S, Whitehead JP. 1999. Truncated human leptin (?133) associated with extreme obesity undergoes proteosomal degradation after defective intracellular transport. *Endocrinology* 140:1718–23

28. Montague CT, Farooqui S, Whitehead JP, Soos MA, Rau H, et al. 1997. Congenital leptin deficiency is associated with severe early onset obesity in humans. *Nature* 387:903–8

29. Strobel A, Issad T, Camoin L, Ozata M, Strosberg AD. 1998. A leptin missense mutation associated with hypogonadism and morbid obesity. *Nat. Genet.* 18:213–15

30. Hamilton BS, Paglia D, Kwan AYM, Dietel M. 1995. Increased obese mRNA expression in omental fat cells from massively obese humans. *Nat. Med.* 1:953–56

31. Lonnqvist F, Arner P, Nordfors, Schalling W. 1995. Overexpression of the obese (ob) gene in adipose tissue of human obese subjects. *Nat. Med.* 1:950–53

32. Saladin R, Devos P, Guerre-Millo M, Leturge A, Girard J, et al. 1995. Transient increase in obese gene expression after food intake or insulin administration. *Nature* 377:527–29

33. Harris RBS, Ramsay TG, Smith SR, Bruch RC. 1996. Early and late stimulation of ob mRNA expression in meal-fed and overfed rats. *J. Clin. Invest.* 97:2020–26

34. Kolacznyski JW, Considine RV, Ohannesian J, Marco C, Caro JF. 1996. Responses of leptin to short-term fasting and refeeding in humans. *Diabetes* 45:1511–15

35. Frederich RC, Lollman B, Hamann A, Napolitano-Rosen A, Kahn B, et al. 1995. Expression of ob mRNA and its encoded protein in rodents. *J. Clin. Invest.* 96:1658–63

36. Boden G, Chen X, Mozzoli M, Ryan I. 1996. Effect of fasting on serum leptin in

normal human subjects. *J. Clin. Endo-crinol. Metab.* 81:3419–23

37. Korbonits M, Trainer PJ, Little JA, Edwards R, Kopelman PG, et al. 1997. Leptin levels do not change acutely with food administration in normal or obese subjects, but are negatively correlated with pituitary-adrenal activity. *Clin. Endocrinol.* 46:751–57

38. Sinha MK, Ohannesian JP, Heiman ML, Kriauciunas A, Stephens TW, et al. 1996. Nocturnal rise of leptin in lean, obese and non-insulin dependent diabetes mellitus subjects. *J. Clin. Invest.* 97:1344–47

39. Rentsch J, Chiesi M. 1996. Regulation of ob gene mRNA levels in cultured adi-pocytes. *FEBS Lett.* 379:55–59

40. MacDougald OA, Hwang CS, Fan H, Lane MD. 1995. Regulated expression of the obese gene product (leptin) in white adipose tissue and 3T3–L1 adipocytes. *Proc. Natl. Acad. Sci. USA* 92:9034–37

41. Kolaczynski JW, Nyce MR, Considine RV, Boden G, Nolan JJ, Henry R. 1996. Acute and chronic effects of insulin on leptin production in humans: studies in vivo and in vitro. *Diabetes* 45:699–701

42. Boden G, Chen X, Kolacynski JPM. 1997. Effects of prolonged hyperinsulin-emia on serum leptin in normal human subjects. *J. Clin. Invest.* 100:1107–13

43. Segal KR, Landt M, Klein S. 1996. Rela-tionship between insulin sensitivity and plasma leptin concentration in lean and obese men. *Diabetes* 45:988–91

44. Murakami T, Iida M, Shima K. 1995. Dexamethasone regulates obese expres-sion in isolated rat adipocytes. *Biochem. Biophys. Res. Commun.* 214:126–27

45. Slieker LJ, Sloop KW, Surface PL, Kriauciunas A, LaQuier F, et al. 1996. Regulation of ob mRNA and protein by glucocorticoids and cAMP. *J. Biol. Chem.* 271:5301–4

46. De Vos P, Saladin R, Auwerx J, Staels B. 1995. Induction of ob gene expression by corticosteroids is accompanied by body weight loss and reduced food intake. *J. Biol. Chem.* 270:15958–61

47. Cizza G, Lotsikas AJ, Licinio J, Gold PW, Chrousos GP. 1997. Plasma leptin levels do not change in patients with Cushing's disease shortly after correction of hypercortisolism. *J. Clin. Endocrinol. Metab.* 82:2747–50

48. Ahima RS, Prabakaran D, Mantzoros C, Qu D, Lowell BB, et al. 1996. Role of leptin in the neuroendocrine response to fasting. *Nature* 382:250–52

49. Ahima RS, Prabakaran D, Flier JS. 1998. Postnatal leptin surge and regulation of circadian rhythm of leptin by feeding: implications for energy homeostasis and neuroendocrine function. *J. Clin. Invest.* 101:1020–27

50. Licinio J, Mantzoros C, Negrao AB, Cizza G, Wong ML, et al. 1997. Human leptin levels are pulsatile and inversely related to pituitary-adrenal function. *Nat. Med.* 3:575–79

51. Laughlin GA, Yen SS. 1997. Hypolepti-nemia in women athletes: absence of a diurnal rhythm with amenorrhea. *J. Clin. Endocrinol. Metab.* 82:318–21

52. Devaskar SU, Ollesch C, Rajakumar RA, Rajakumar PA. 1997. Developmental changes in obese gene expression and circulating leptin peptide concentrations. *Biochem. Biophys. Res. Commun.* 238:44–47

53. Mantzoros C, Flier JS, Rogol AD. 1997. A longitudinal assessment of hormonal and physical alterations during normal puberty in boys. V. Rising leptin levels may signal the onset of puberty. *J. Clin. Endocrinol. Metab.* 82:1066–70

54. Rosenbaum M, Nicolson M, Hirsch J, Heymsfield SB, Gallagher D, et al. 1996. Effects of gender, body composition and menopause on plasma concentration of leptin. *J. Clin. Endocrinol. Metab* 81:3424–27

55. Saad ME, Damani S, Gingerich RL, Riad-Gabriel MG, Khan A, et al. 1997. Sexual dimorphism in plasma leptin con-

centration. *J. Clin. Endocrinol. Metab.*
82:579–84

56. Blum WF, Englaro P, Hanitsch S, Juul A, Hertel NT, et al. 1997. Plasma leptin levels in healthy children and adolescents: dependence on body mass index, fat mass, gender, pubertal stage, and testosterone. *J. Clin. Endocrinol. Metab.* 82: 2904–10

57. Castracane VD, Kraemer RR, Franken MA, Kraemer GR, Gimpel T. 1998. Serum leptin concentration in women: effect of age, obesity, and estrogen administration. *Fertil. Steril.* 70:472–77

58. Escobar-Morreale HF, Escobar del Rey F, Morreale de Escobar G. 1997. Thyroid hormones influence serum leptin concentrations in the rat. *Endocrinology* 138:4485–88

59. Pinkney JH, Goodrick SJ, Katz J, Johnson AB, Lightman SL, Coppack SW, et al. 1998. Leptin and the pituitary-thyroid axis: a comparative study in lean, obese, hypothyroid and hyperthyroid subjects. *Clin. Endocrinol.* 49:583–88

60. Mantzoros CS, Rosen HN, Greenspan SL, Flier JS, Moses AC. 1997. Short-term hyperthyroidism has no effect on leptin levels in man. *J. Clin. Endocrinol. Metab.* 82:497–99

61. Diekman MJ, Romijn JA, Endert E, Sauerwein H, Wiersinga WM. 1998. Thyroid hormones modulate serum leptin levels: observations in thyrotoxic and hypothyroid women. *Thyroid* 8:1081–86

62. Ozata M, Ozisik G, Bingol N, Corakci, Gundogan MA. 1998. The effects of thyroid status on plasma leptin levels in women. *J. Endocrinol. Invest.* 21:337–41

63. Bornstein SR, Licinio J, Tauchnitz R, Engelmann L, Negrao AB, Chrousos GP. 1998. Plasma leptin levels are increased in survivors of acute sepsis: associated loss of diurnal rhythm in cortisol and leptin secretion. *J. Clin. Endocrinol. Metab.* 83:280–83

64. Grunfeld C, Zhao C, Fuller J, Pollack A, Moser A, et al. 1996. Endotoxin and cytokines induce expression of leptin, the ob gene product, in hamsters. *J. Clin. Invest.* 97:2152–57

65. Sarraf P, Frederich RC, Turner EM, Ma G, Jaskowiak NT, et al. 1997. Multiple cytokines and acute inflammation raise mouse leptin levels: potential role in inflammatory anorexia. *J. Exp. Med.* 185:171–75

66. Janik JE, Curtis ED, Considine RV, Prager HC, Powers GC, et al. 1997. Interleukin 1 alpha increases serum leptin concentrations in humans. *J. Clin. Endocrinol. Metab.* 82:3084–86

67. Schwartz MW, Seeley R. 1997. Neuroendocrine responses to starvation and weight loss. *N. Engl. J. Med.* 336:1802–11

68. Kallen CB, Lazar MA. 1996. Antidiabetic thiazolidinediones inhibit leptin (ob) gene expression in 3T3-L1 adipocytes. *Proc. Natl. Acad. Sci. USA* 93:5793–96

69. Trayhurn P, Duncan JS, Rayner DV. 1996. Acute cold-induced suppression of Ob (obese) gene expression in white adipose tissue of mice: mediation by the sympathetic nervous system. *Biochem. J.* 311:729–33

70. Mantzoros CS, Qu D, Frederich RC, Susulic VS, Lowell BB, et al. 1996. Activation of beta(3) adrenergic receptors suppresses leptin expression and mediates leptin-independent inhibition of food intake in mice. *Diabetes* 45:909–14

71. Danahoo WT, Jensen DR, Yost TJ, Eckel RH. 1997. Isoproterenol and somatostatin decrease plasma leptin in humans: a novel mechanism regulating leptin secretion. *J. Clin. Endocrinol. Metab.* 82: 4139–43

72. Li H, Matheny M, Scarpace PJ. 1997. Beta 3-adrenergic-mediated suppression of leptin gene expression in rats. *Am. J. Physiol.* 272:E1031–36

73. Masuzaki H, Ogawa Y, Sagawa N, Hosoda K, Matsumoto T, et al. 1997. Nonadipose production of leptin: leptin

as a novel placenta-derived hormone in humans. *Nat. Med.* 3:1029–33

74. Casabiell X, Pineiro V, Tome MA, Peino R, Dieguez C, Casanueva FF. 1997. Presence of leptin in colostrum and/or breast milk from lactating mothers: a potential role in the regulation of neonatal food intake. *J. Clin. Endocrinol. Metab.* 82:4270–73

75. Bado A, Levasseur S, Attoub S, Kermogant S, Laigneau JP, et al. 1998. The stomach is a source of leptin. *Nature* 394:790–93

76. Wang J, Liu R, Hawkins M, Barzalai N, Rossetti L. 1998. A nutrient-sensing pathway regulates leptin gene expression in muscle and fat. *Nature* 393:684–88

77. Mise H, Sagawa N, Matsumoto T, Yura S, Nanno H, et al. 1998. Augumented placental production of leptin in pre-eclampsia: possible involvement of placental hypoxia. *J. Clin. Endocrinol. Metab.* 83:3225–29

78. Shekhawat PS, Garland JS, Shivpuri C, Mick GJ, Sasidharan A, et al. 1998. Neonatal cord blood leptin: its relationship to birth weight, body mass index, maternal diabetes, and steroids. *Pediatr. Res.* 43:338–43

79. Tartaglia L, Dembski M, Weng X, Deng N, Culpper J, et al. 1995. Identification and expression cloning of a leptin receptor. *Cell* 83:1263–71

80. Lee GH, Proenca R, Montez JM, Carroll K, Darvishzadeh JG, et al. 1996. Abnormal splicing of the leptin receptor in diabetic mice. *Nature* 379:632–35

81. Wang M-Y, Zhou YT, Newgard CB, Unger RH. 1998. A novel leptin receptor isoform in rat. *FEBS Lett.* 392:87–90

82. Tartaglia LA. 1997. The leptin receptor. *J. Biol. Chem.* 272:6093–96

83. Chua SC, Chung WK, Wu-Peng XS. 1996. Phenotypes of mouse *diabetes* and rat *fatty* due to mutations in the OB (leptin) receptor. *Science* 271:994–96

84. Vaisse C, Halaas JL, Horvarth CM, Darnell JE Jr, Stoffel M, Friedman JM. 1996.

Leptin activation of Stat3 in the hypothalamus of wild type and ob/ob mice but not db/db mice. *Nat. Genet.* 14:95–97

85. Ghilardi N, Ziegler S, Wiestner A, Stoffel R, Heim MH, Skoda RC. 1996. Defective STAT signaling by the leptin receptor in diabetic mice. *Proc. Natl. Acad. Sci. USA* 93:6231–35

86. Bjorbaek C, Uotani S, da Silva B, Flier JS. 1997. Divergent signaling capacities of the long and short isoforms of the leptin receptor. *J. Biol. Chem.* 272:32686–95

87. Friedman JM, Halaas JL. 1998. Leptin and the regulation of body weight in mammals. *Nature* 395:763–70

88. Takaya K, Ogawa Y, Hiraoka J, Hosoda K, Yamori Y, et al. 1996. Nonsense mutation of leptin receptor in the obese spontaneously hypertensive Koletsky rat. *Nat. Genet.* 14:130–31

89. White DW, Wang DW, Chua SC Jr, Morgenstern JP, Leibel RL. 1997. Constitutive and impaired signaling of leptin receptors containing the Gln-Pro extracellular domain mutation. *Proc. Natl. Acad. Sci. USA* 94:10657–62

90. Li C, Ioffe E, Fidahusein N, Connolly E, Friedman JM. 1998. Absence of soluble leptin receptor in plasma from db^{Pas}/db^{Pas} and other db/db mice. *J. Biol. Chem.* 273:10078–82

91. Bray GA, York DA. 1979. Hypothalamic and genetic obesity in experimental animals: an autonomic and endocrine hypothesis. *Physiol. Rev.* 59:719–90

92. da Silva BA, Bjorbaek C, Uotani S, Flier JS. 1998. Functional properties of leptin receptor isoforms containing the Gln-Pro extracellular domain mutation of the fatty rat. *Endocrinology* 139:3681–90

93. Cusin I, Rohner-Jeanrenaud F, Stricker-Krongard A, Jeanrenaud B. 1996. The weight reducing effect of an intracerebroventricular bolus injection of leptin in genetically obese fa/fa rats. Reduced sensitivity compared with lean animals. *Diabetes* 45:1446–50

94. Seeley RJ, van Dijk G, Campfield LA, Smith FJ, Burn P, et al. 1996. Intraventricular leptin reduces food intake and body weight of lean rats but not obese Zucker rats. *Horm. Metab. Res.* 28:664–68

95. Wu-Peng XS, Chua SCJ, Okada N, Liu SM, Nicolson M, Leibel RL. 1997. Phenotype of the obese Koletsky (f) rat due to Tyr763Stop mutation in the extracellular domain of the leptin receptor (Lepr): evidence for deficient plasma-to-CSF transport of leptin in both the Zucker and Kolestsky obese rat. *Diabetes* 46:513–18

96. Clement K, Vaisse C, Lahlous N, Cabroll S, Pelloux V, et al. 1998. A mutation in the human leptin receptor gene causes obesity and pituitary dysfunction. *Nature* 392:398–401

97. Houseknecht KL, Mantzoros CS, Kuliawat R, Hadro E, Flier JS, Kahn BB. 1996. Evidence for leptin binding to proteins in serum of rodents and humans: modulation with obesity. *Diabetes* 45: 1638–43

98. Sinha MK, Opentanova I, Ohannesian JP, Kolacynski JW, Hale L, et al. 1996. Evidence of free and bound leptin in human circulation. Studies in lean and obese subjects and during short-term fasting. *J. Clin. Invest.* 98:1277–82

99. Hill RA, Margetic S, Pegg GG, Gazzola C. 1998. Leptin: its pharmacokinetics and tissue distribution. *Int. J. Obes. Relat. Metab. Disord.* 22:765–70

100. Elmquist JK, Ahima RS, Maratos-Flier E, Flier JS, Saper CB. 1997. Leptin activates neurons in the ventrobasal hypothalamus and brainstem. *Endocrinology* 839–42

101. Elmquist JK, Ahima RS, Elias CS, Flier JS, Saper CB. 1998. Leptin activates distinct projections from the dorsomedial and ventromedial hypothalamic nuclei. *Proc. Natl. Acad. Sci. USA* 741–48

102. Schwartz M, Seeley RJ, Campfield LA, Burn P, Baskin DG. 1996. Identification of targets of leptin action in rat hypothalamus. *J. Clin. Invest.* 98:1101–6

103. Mercer JG, Hoggard N, Williams LM, Lawrence CB, Hannah LT, et al. 1996. Localization of leptin mRNA and the long form splice variant (Ob-Rb) in mouse hypothalamus and adjacent brain regions by in situ hybridization. *FEBS Lett.* 387:113–16

104. Elmquist JK, Bjorbaek C, Ahima RS, Flier JS. 1998b. Distributions of leptin receptor isoforms in the rat brain. *J. Comp. Neurol.* 395:535–47

105. Baskin DG, Breininger JF, Schwartz MW. 1999. Leptin receptor mRNA identifies a subpopulation of neuropeptide Y neurons activated by fasting in rat hypothalamus. *Diabetes* 48:828–33

106. Hakanssson ML, Meister B. 1998. Transcription factor STAT3 in leptin target neurons of the rat hypothalamus. *Neuroendocrinology* 68:420–27

107. Bjorbaek C, Elmquist JK, Michl P, Ahima RS, van Bueren A, et al. 1998. Expression of leptin receptor isoforms in brain microvessels. *Endocrinology* 139:3485–91

108. Banks WA, Kastin AJ, Huang W, Jaspan JP, Maness LM. 1996. Leptin enters the brain by a saturable system independent of insulin. *Peptides* 17:305–11

109. Pardridge WM. 1986. Receptor-mediated peptide transport through the blood-brain barrier. *Endocrinol. Rev.* 7:314–30

110. Schwartz MW, Figlewicz DP, Baskin DG, Woods SC, Porte JD Jr. 1992. Insulin in the brain: a hormonal regulator of energy balance. *Endocrinol. Rev.* 13: 387–14

111. Golden PL, Maccagnan TJ, Padridge WM. 1997. Human blood-brain barrier leptin receptor: binding and endocytosis in isolated human brain microvessels. *J. Clin. Invest.* 99:14–18

112. Schwartz MW, Peskind E, Raskind M, Boyko EJ, Porte D Jr, et al. 1996. Cerebrospinal fluid leptin concentrations:

relationship to plasma levels and to adiposity in humans. *Nat. Med.* 2:589–93

113. Jensen MD, Moller N, Nair KS, Eisenberg P, Landt M, Klein S. 1999. Regional leptin kinetics in humans. *Am. J. Clin. Nutr.* 69:18–21

114. Meyer C, Robson D, Rackovsky N, Nadkarni V, Gerich J, et al. 1997. Role of the kidney in human leptin metabolism. *Am. J. Physiol.* 273:E903–7

115. Sharma K, Considine RV, Michael B, Dunn SR, Weisberg LS, et al. 1997. Plasma leptin is partly cleared by the kidney and elevated in hemodialysis patients. *Kidney Int.* 51:1980–85

116. Merabet E, Dagogo-Jack S, Coyne DW, Klein S, Santiago JV, et al. 1997. Increased plasma leptin concentration in end-stage renal disease. *J. Clin. Endocrinol. Metab.* 82:847–50

117. Serradiel-Le Gal C, Raufaste D, Brossard G, Pouzat B, Marty E, et al. 1997. Characterization and localization of leptin receptors in the rat kidney. *FEBS Lett.* 404:185–91

118. Uotani S, Bjorbaek C, Tornoe J, Flier JS. 1999. Functional properties of leptin receptor isoforms. Internalization and degradation of leptin and ligand-induced receptor downregulation. *Diabetes* 48:279–86

119. Shimizu H, Kakizaki S, Tsuchiya T, Nagamine T, Takagi H, et al. 1998. An increase of circulating leptin in patients with liver cirrhosis. *Int. J. Obes. Relat. Metab. Disord.* 22:1234–38

120. McCullough AJ, Bugianesi E, Marchesini G, Kalhan SC. 1998. Gender-dependent alterations in serum leptin in alcoholic cirrhosis. *Gastroenterology* 115:947–53

121. Potter JJ, Womack L, Mezey E, Anania FA. 1998. Transdifferentiation of rat hepatic stellate cells results in leptin expression. *Biochem. Biophys. Res. Commun.* 244:178–82

122. Sawchenko PE. 1998. Toward a new neurobiology of energy balance, appetite and obesity: The anatomists weigh in. *J. Comp. Neurol.* 402:435–41

123. Elmquist JK, Elias CF, Saper CB. 1999. From lesions to leptin: hypothalamic control of food intake and body weight. *Neuron* 22:221–32

124. Flier JS, Maratos-Flier E. 1998. Obesity and the hypothalamus: novel peptides for new pathways. *Cell* 92:437–40

125. Seeley RJ, Yagaloff KA, Fisher SL, Burn P, Thiele TE, et al. 1997. Melanocortin receptors in leptin effects. *Nature* 390:49

126. Fan W, Boston BA, Kesterson RA, et al. 1997. Role of melanocortinergic neurons in feeding and the agouti obesity syndrome. *Nature* 385:165–68

127. Barrachina M, Martinez V, Wang L, Wei JY, Tache Y. 1997. Synergistic interaction between leptin and cholecystokinin to reduce short-term food intake in lean mice. *Proc. Natl. Acad. Sci. USA* 94:10455–60

128. Kristensen P, Judge ME, Thim L, Ribel U, Christjansen KN, et al. 1998. Hypothalamic CART is a new anorectic peptide regulated by leptin. *Nature* 393:72–76

129. Erickson JC, Clegg KE, Palmiter RD. 1996. Sensitivity to leptin and susceptibility to seizures of mice lacking neuropeptide Y. *Nature* 381:415–18

130. Pedrazzini T, Seydoux J, Kunster P, Aubert JF, Grouzmann E, et al. 1998. Cardiovascular response, feeding behavior and locomotor activity in mice lacking the NPY Y1 receptor. *Nat. Med.* 4:722–26

131. Marsh DJ, Hollopeter G, Kafer KE, Palmiter RD. 1998. Role of Y5 neuropeptide Y receptor in feeding and obesity. *Nat. Med.* 4:718–21

132. Nonogaki K, Starck AM, Dallman MF, Tecott LH. 1998. Leptin-independent hyperphagia and type 2 diabetes in mice with a mutated serotonin 5-HT2C receptor gene. *Nat. Med.* 4:1152–56

133. Erickson JC, Hollopeter G, Palmiter RD. 1996. Attenuation of the obesity syn-

drome of ob/ob mice by the loss of neuropeptide Y. *Science* 274:1704–7

134. Shimada M, Tritos N, Lowell BB, Flier JS, Maratos-Flier E, et al. 1999. Mice lacking melanin-concentrating hormone are hypophagic and lean. *Nature* 396:670–74

135. Legradi G, Emerson CH, Ahima RS, Flier JS, Lechan RM. 1997. Leptin prevents fasting-induced suppression of prothyrotropin-releasing hormone messenger ribonucleic acid in neurons of the hypothalamic paraventricular nucleus. *Endocrinology* 138:2569–76

136. Legradi G, Emerson CH, Ahima RS, Rand WM, Flier JS, Lechan RM. 1998. Arcuate nucleus ablation prevents fasting-induced suppression of ProTRH mRNA in the hypothalamic paraventricular nucleus. *Neuroendocrinology* 68: 89–97

137. Yu WH, Kimura M, Walczewska A, Karanth S, McCann SM. 1997. Role of leptin in hypothalamic-pituitary function. *Proc. Natl. Acad. Sci. USA* 94:1023–28

138. Finn PD, Cunningham MJ, Pau KY, Spies HG, Clifton DK, Steiner RA. 1998. The stimulatory effect of leptin on the neuroendocrine reproductive axis of the monkey. *Endocrinology* 139:4652–62

139. Costa A, Poma A, Martignoni E, Nappi G, Ur E, Grossman A. 1997. Stimulation of corticotropin-releasing hormone release by obese (ob) gene product, leptin, from hypothalamic explants. *NeuroReport* 8:1131–34

140. Heiman ML, Ahima RS, Craft LS, Schoner B, Stephens TW, Flier JS. 1997. Leptin inhibition of the hypothalamic-pituitary-adrenal axis in response to stress. *Endocrinology* 138:3859–63

141. Bjorbaek C, Elmquist JK, Franz JD, Shoelson SE, Flier JS. 1998. Identification of SOCS-3 as a potential mediator of central leptin resistance. *Mol. Cell* 1:619–25

142. Spanswick D, Smith MA, Groppi VE, Logan SD, Ashford ML, et al. 1997. Leptin inhibits hypothalamic neurons by activation of ATP-sensitive potassium channels. *Nature* 390:521–25

143. Kieffer TJ, Heller S, Leech CA, Holz GG, Habener JF. 1997 Leptin suppression of insulin secretion by the activation of ATP-sensitive K^+ channels in pancreatic β-cells. *Diabetes* 46:1087–93

144. Powis JE, Bains JS, Ferguson AV. 1998. Leptin depolarizes rat hypothalamic paraventricular nucleus neurons. *Am. J. Physiol* . 274:R1468–72

145. Glaum SR, Hara M, Binkodas VP, Lee CC, Polonsky KS, et al. 1996. Leptin, the obese gene product, rapidly modulates synaptic transmission in the hypothalamus. *Mol. Pharmacol.* 50: 230–35

146. Wang YH, Tache Y, Sheibel AB, Go VL, Wei JY, et al. 1997. Two types of leptin-responsive gastric vagal afferent terminals: an in vitro single-unit study in rats. *Am. J. Physiol.* 273:R833–37

147. Ioffe E, Moon B, Connolly E, Friedman JM. 1998. Abnormal regulation of the leptin gene in the pathogenesis of obesity. *Proc. Natl. Acad. Sci. USA* 95:11852–55

148. Halaas JL, Boozer C, Blair-West J, Fidahusein N, Denton DA, Friedman JM. 1998. Physiological response to long-term peripheral and central leptin infusion in lean and obese mice. *Proc. Natl. Acad. Sci. USA* 94:8878–83

149. Shimabukuro M, Koyama K, Chen G, Wang M-Y, Trieu F, et al. 1997. Direct antidiabetic effect of leptin through triglyceride depletion of tissues. *Proc. Natl. Acad. Sci. USA* 94:4637–41

150. Quian H, Azani MJ, Compton MM, Hartzell D, Hausman GH, Baile CA. 1997. Brain administration of leptin causes deletion of adipocytes by apoptosis. *Endocrinology* 139:791–94

151. Flier JS. 1998. Clinical review 94: What's in a name? In search of leptin's physiologic role. *J. Clin. Endocrinol. Metab.* 83:1407–13

152. Spiegelman BM, Flier JS. 1996. Adipo-

genesis and obesity: rounding out the big picture. *Cell* 87:377–89

153. Caro JF, Kolaczynski JW, Nyce MR, Ohannesian JP, Opentanova I, et al. 1997. Decreased cerebrospinal fluid/serum leptin ratio in obesity: a possible mechanism for leptin resistance. *Lancet* 348:159–61

154. Van Heek M, Compton DS, France CF, Tedesco RP, Fawzi AB, et al. 1997. Diet-induced obese mice develop peripheral, but not central, resistance to leptin. *J. Clin. Invest.* 99:385–90

155. Carpenter LR, Farruggela TJ, Symes A, Karow ML, Yancopoulos GD, et al. 1998. Enhancing leptin response by preventing SH2-containing phosphatase 2 interaction with ob receptor. *Proc. Natl. Acad. Sci. USA* 95:6061–66

156. Herberg L, Kley HK. 1975. Adrenal function and effect of a high fat diet on C57BL/6J and C57BL/6J ob/ob mice. *Horm. Metab. Res.* 7:410–15

157. Bruce BK, King BM, Phelps GR, Veitia MC. 1982. Effects of adrenalectomy and corticosterone adminstration on hypothalamic obesity in rats. *Am. J. Physiol.* 243:E152–57

158. Debons AF, Siclari E, Das KC, Fuhr B. 1982. Gold thioglucose-induced hypothalamic damage, hyperphagia, and obesity: dependence on the adrenal gland. *Endocrinology* 110:2024–29

159. Peeke PM, Chrousos GP. 1995. Hypercortisolism and obesity. *Ann. NY. Acad. Sci.* 771:665–76

160. Schwartz MW, Dallman MF, Woods SC. 1995. Hypothalamic response to starvation: implications for the study of wasting disorders. *Am. J. Physiol.* 269:R949–57

161. Lord GM, Matarese G, Howard JK, Baker RJ, Bloom SR, et al. 1998. Leptin modulates the T-cell immune response and reverses starvation-induced immunosuppression. *Nature* 294:897–91

162. Doring H, Schwarzer K, Nuesslein-Hildesheim B, Schmidt I. 1998. Leptin selectively increases energy expenditure of food-restricted lean mice. *Int. J. Obes. Relat. Metab. Disord.* 22:83–88

163. Cahill JG, Herrera MG, Morgan AP, Soeldner JS, Steinke J, et al. 1966. Hormone-fuel interrelationships during fasting. *J. Clin. Invest.* 45:1751–69

164. Sims EA, Horton ES. 1968. Endocrine and metabolic adaptation to obesity and starvation. *Am. J. Clin. Nutr.* 21:1455–70

165. Pirke K, Schweiger U, Strowitzki T, Tushl RJ, Laesck RG, et al. 1989. Dieting causes menstrual irregularities in normal weight young women through impairment of episodic luteinizing hormone secretion. *Fertil. Steril.* 51:263–68

166. Vuagnat BAM, Pierroz DD, Lalaoui M, Englaro P, Pralong FP, et al. 1998. Evidence for a leptin-neuropeptide Y axis for the regulation of growth hormone secretion in the rat. *Neuroendocrinology* 67:291–300

167. Nagatani S, Guthikonda P, Thompson RC, Tsukamura H, Maeda KI, Foster DL. 1998. Evidence for GnRH regulation by leptin: Leptin administration prevents reduced pulsatile LH secretion during fasting. *Neuroendocrinology* 67:370–76

168. Ravussin E, Pratley RE, Maffei M, Wang H, Friedman JM, et al. 1997. Relatively low plasma leptin concentrations precede weight gain in Pima Indians. *Nat. Med.* 3:238–40

169. Haffner SM, Mykkanen LA, Gonzalez CC, Stern MP. 1998. Leptin concentrations do not predict weight gain: the Mexico City Diabetes Study. *Int. J. Obes. Relat. Metab. Disord.* 22:695–99

170. Mantzoros C, Flier JS, Lesen MD, Brewerton TD, Jimerson DC. 1997. Cerebrospinal fluid leptin in anorexia nervosa: correlation with nutritional status and potential role in resistance to weight gain. *J. Clin. Endocrinol. Metab.* 82:1845–51

171. Chehab F, Lim M, Lu R. 1996. Correction of the sterility defect in homozygous obese female mice by treatment with the

human recombinant leptin. *Nat. Genet.* 12:318–20

172. Chehab FF, Mounzih K, Lu R, Lim ME. 1997. Early onset of reproductive function in normal female mice treated with leptin. *Science* 275:88–90

173. Ahima RS, Dushay J, Flier SN, Prabakaran D, Flier JS. 1997. Leptin accelerates the onset of puberty in normal female mice. *J. Clin. Invest.* 99:391–395

174. Wade GN, Lempicki RL, Panicker AK, Frisbee RM, Blaustein JD. 1997. Leptin facilitates and inhibits sexual behavior in female hamsters. *Am. J. Physiol.* 272:R1354–58

175. Zachow RJ, Magoffin DA. 1997. Direct intraovarian effects of leptin: impairment of the synergistic action on insulin-like growth factor I on follicle stimulating hormone dependent estradiol 17 beta production by rat ovarian granulosa cells. *Endocrinology* 138:847–50

176. Bornstein SR, Uhlmann K, Haidan A, Ehrhart-Bornstein M, Scherbaum. 1997. Evidence for a novel peripheral action of leptin as a metabolic signal to the adrenal gland: Leptin inhibits cortisol release directly. *Diabetes* 46:1235–38

177. Pralong FP, Roduit R, Waeber G, Castillo E, Mosimann F, et al. 1998. Leptin inhibits directly glucocorticoid secretion by normal human and rat adrenal gland. *Endocrinology* 139:4264–68

178. Rossetti L, Massillon D, Barzilai N, Vuguin P, Chen W, et al. 1997. Short term effects of leptin on hepatic gluconeogenesis and in vivo insulin action. *J. Biol. Chem.* 272:27758–63

179. Kamohara S, Burcelin R, Halaas JL, Friedman J, Charron M. 1997. Acute stimulation of glucose metabolism in mice by leptin treatment. *Nature* 389:374–77

180. Cohen SM, Werrman J, Tota M. 1998. ^{13}C NMR study of the effects of leptin treatment on kinetics of hepatic intermediary metabolism. *Proc. Natl. Acad. Sci. USA* 95:7385–90

181. Siegrist-Kaiser C, Pauli V, Juge-Aubry C, Boss O, Pernin A, et al. 1997. Direct effect of leptin on brown and white adipose tissue. *J. Clin. Invest.* 100:2858–64

182. Morton NM, Emilsson V, Liu YL, Cawthorne MA. 1998. Leptin action in intestinal cells. *J. Biol. Chem.* 273:26194–201

183. Haynes WG, Sivitz WJ, Morgan DA, Walsh SA, Mark AL. 1997. Sympathetic and cardiorenal actions of leptin. *Hypertension* 30:619–23

184. Scarpace PJ, Matheny M, Pollock BH, Turner N. 1997 Leptin increases uncoupling protein expression and energy expenditure. *Am. J. Physiol* 273:E226–30

185. Hoggard N, Hunter L, Duncan J, Williams LM, Trayhurn P, Mercer JC. 1997. Leptin and leptin receptor mRNA and protein expression in the murine fetus and placenta. *Proc. Natl. Acad. Sci. USA* 94:11073–78

186. Gainsford T, Willson TA, Metcalf D, Handman E, McFarlane C, et al. 1996. Leptin can induce proliferation, differentiation and functional activation of hemopoietic cells. *Proc. Natl. Acad Sci. USA* 93:14564–68

187. Sierra-Honigmann MR, Nath AK, Murakami C, Garcia-Cardena G, Papapetropoulos A, et al. 1998. Biologic action of leptin as an angiogenic factor. *Science* 281:1683–85

188. Bereiter DA, Jeanreneaud B. 1979. Altered neuroanatomical organization in the central nervous system of genetically obese (ob/ob) mice. *Brain. Res.* 165:249–60

189. Sena A, Sarlieve LL, Rebel G. 1985. Brain myelin of genetically obese mice. *J. Neurol. Sci.* 68:233–44

190. Steppan CM, Swick AG. 1999. A role for leptin in brain development. *Biochem. Biophys. Res. Commun.* 256:600–2

191. Ahima RS, Bjorbaek C, Osei SY, Flier JS. 1999. Regulation of neuronal and glial proteins by leptin: implications for brain development. *Endocrinology* 140:2755–62

Annu. Rev. Physiol. 2000. 62:439–66

THE MECHANISM OF ACTION OF THYROID HORMONES

Jinsong Zhang and Mitchell A. Lazar

Departments of Medicine, Biochemistry, and Genetics, and the Penn Diabetes Center, University of Pennsylvania School of Medicine, Philadelphia, Pennsylvania 19104; e-mail: lazar@mail.med.upenn.edu

Key Words thyroid hormone receptor, hormone action, transcription, repression, chromatin

■ **Abstract** Thyroid hormone is essential for normal development, differentiation, and metabolic balance. Thyroid hormone action is mediated by multiple thyroid hormone receptor isoforms derived from two distinct genes. The thyroid hormone receptors belong to a nuclear receptor superfamily that also includes receptors for other small lipophilic hormones. Thyroid hormone receptors function by binding to specific thyroid hormone-responsive sequences in promoters of target genes and by regulating transcription. Thyroid hormone receptors often form heterodimers with retinoid X receptors. Heterodimerization is regulated through distinct mechanisms that together determine the specificity and flexibility of the sequence recognition. Amino-terminal regions appear to modulate thyroid hormone receptor function in an isoform-dependent manner. Unliganded thyroid hormone receptor represses transcription through recruitment of a corepressor complex, which also includes Sin3A and histone deacetylase. Ligand binding alters the conformation of the thyroid hormone receptor in such a way as to release the corepressor complex and recruit a coactivator complex that includes multiple histone acetyltransferases, including a steroid receptor family coactivator, *p*300/*CREB*-binding protein–associated factor (PCAF), and *CREB* binding protein (CBP). The existence of histone-modifying activities in the transcriptional regulatory complexes indicates an important role of chromatin structure. Stoichiometric, structural, and sequence-specific rules for coregulator interaction are beginning to be understood, as are aspects of the tissue specificity of hormone action. Moreover, knockout studies suggest that the products of two thyroid hormone receptor genes mediate distinct functions in vivo. The increased understanding of the structure and function of thyroid hormone receptors and their interacting proteins has markedly clarified the molecular mechanisms of thyroid hormone action.

INTRODUCTION

Thyroid hormone (T3), produced by the thyroid gland, plays an important role in development, differentiation, and metabolism (1). The lack of T3 in early human development results in growth disturbances and severe mental retardation,

0066–4278/00/0315–0439$12.00

a disease called cretinism (2). Later in life, T3 plays an important role in metabolic balance (3). T3 action is mediated by nuclear T3 receptors (TRs) that can bind T3 with high affinity (1). TRs belong to the nuclear receptor superfamily that also includes the receptors for retinoids, vitamin D, fatty acids, and prostaglandins, as well as "orphan receptors" with no identified ligands (4–7). TR is encoded by two separate genes, designated TRα and TRβ, located in different chromosomes (17 and 3, respectively, in humans). Alternative splicing from each gene generates multiple TR isoforms, including TRα1, TRα2, and TRα3 from the TRα gene and TRβ1 and TRβ2 from the TRβ gene (reviewed in 1). Like other nuclear receptors, TRs have modular structures with six regions (A–F) and three functional domains (Figure 1).

The main function of a TR as a transcription factor is to regulate target gene expression directly through DNA response elements. The T3 response element (TRE) is composed of repeated DNA sequences with different configurations (8–11). Although TRs can bind to TREs as monomers or homodimers, the major form of TR bound to the TRE is the heterodimer with retinoid X receptor (RXR) (12–18). An important property of TRs is their ability to bind TREs constitutively independent of ligand occupancy (1, 4–6). Unliganded TR generally represses basal transcription. Ligand binding triggers a conformational change in the TR, resulting in activated transcription of its target gene. In the past few years, great progress in biochemical, functional, and structural studies has clarified the molecular mechanism of TR action. The purpose of this review is to summarize the current knowledge with emphasis on transcriptional regulation by multiple cofactor complexes.

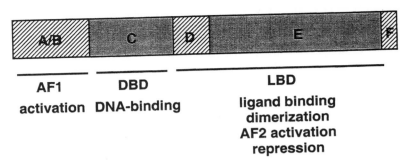

Figure 1   Modular structure of thyroid hormone receptor. Nuclear receptors, including TR, can be divided into six regions (A–F) with three functional domains: AF1, activation function 1 (A and B regions); DBD, DNA-binding domain (C region); LBD, ligand-binding domain (D, E, and F regions).

DNA-BINDING: SPECIFICITY AND FLEXIBILITY

The ability to bind specific sequences in target genes is crucial for TR function. The consensus sequence recognized by nuclear receptors often contains a hexamer AGGTCA known as the half site. Functional and efficient binding requires two of the half-site sequences with different configurations (19, 20). TR—as well as retinoic acid receptor (RAR), vitamin D receptor (VDR), and peroxisome proliferator-activated receptor (PPAR)—predominantly bind DNA response elements as heterodimers with RXRs (12–18). Heterodimer formation is thought to enhance DNA-binding affinity as well as provide target gene specificity, determined by the spacing between two half sites (5, 7). Accordingly, TR/RXR activates through the DR4 element (two half sites in one orientation spaced by four base pairs), whereas VDR/RXR and RAR/RXR activate through DR3 and DR5, respectively (the so-called 3–4–5 rule) (21). TR can also bind to other configurations of the two repeats, such as palindrome TRE and everted repeats (10, 22).

The DNA-binding domain is the most conserved region of the nuclear receptor superfamily. Structures of DNA-DNA-binding domain complexes have been determined for the glucocorticoid receptor (23), estrogen receptor (24), and Rev-Erb (25), as well as TR/RXR heterodimer (26). Two zinc-containing modules in the DNA-binding domain mediate the specific sequence recognition and confer spacing specificity. A DNA recognition helix (P box) in the carboxyl terminus of the first zinc finger mediates the half-site sequence recognition by directly contacting the major groove nucleotides. It is important that the P box can distinguish a single base change in the half site used by two subfamilies of the receptors (AGGACA for the glucocorticoid receptor versus AGGTCA for the estrogen and thyroid receptors) (21). In addition to the major groove contact, several members of the nuclear receptor family make additional minor groove contact through the carboxyl-terminal extension downstream of the second zinc-containing module, as shown in the crystal structures of TR/RXR bound to DR4 repeats (26). This carboxyl-terminal extension recognizes two additional nucleotides T, (A/G) at the 5′ of the hexamer and thus enhances the monomer binding affinity to the octamer (27). The structural basis for the spacing recognition results from the steric constraints imposed by a specific and weak interaction between the D box from the RXR DNA-binding domain (5′ position) and the T box from the DNA-binding domain of a receptor at 3′ position (7). This interaction also provides a weak dimerization interface (28–31). There is a strict binding polarity of TR/RXR heterodimer on DR4 such that RXR occupies the upstream half site and TR occupies the downstream half site (26, 32).

A stronger heterodimerization surface is located in the ligand-binding domain (33–36). Both dimerization surfaces contribute to the heterodimerization of RXR with TR, although DNA binding is required only for heterodimerization via the DNA-binding domain (37). In the crystal structure of the ligand-binding domain of unliganded RXR, the ligand-binding domain, a hydrophobic patch composed mainly of helix 9 and 10, is proposed to mediate the dimerization (38). This region includes the ninth heptad hydrophobic repeat that has been suggested by mutational analysis to correspond to the potential heterodimerization surface (32, 36, 39). Cooperative DNA-binding requires ligand-binding domain-mediated heterodimerization. By contrast, the DNA-binding domain heterodimerized surface restricts binding to specific half-site spacing (37). Thus, the two heterodimerized surfaces are not functionally redundant, but rather differentially determine the DNA-binding specificity as well as the flexibility. The flexibility of the hinge region allows permissive binding to these TREs with different half-site orientations, including inverted and everted repeats in addition to the directly repeated sites. These binding interactions are highly dependent on the presence of the ligand-binding domain dimerization surface (40, 41). This dependence suggests that flexible and cooperative TR/RXR binding to multiple TREs may require TR and RXR to form a solution heterodimer as the first step (37, 41).

TRα2 is an alternative splicing product of the TRα gene that lacks an intact ninth heptad and acquires a unique carboxyl-terminal region leading to an inability to bind T3 (1). Dominant negative activity of TRα2 requires DNA binding (42, 43). Loss of the ligand-binding domain dimerization surface abolishes the interaction with RXR in solution and impairs the ability of TRα2 to form heterodimers on some DR4 sites (41, 44). Unlike TRα1, which forms stable heterodimers equally well on four DR4 sites, TRα2 preferentially forms stable heterodimers on a subset of DR4 that contains two additional T(A/G) nucleotides before the downstream hexamer and is the optimal site for TR monomer binding. This difference is probably the consequence of additional contact with the A box of the DNA-binding domain (41).

Thus distinct mechanisms are used by TR isoforms to regulate the heterodimerization and DNA-binding activity. The unique carboxyl-terminal region of TRα2 can be phosphorylated in vivo and in vitro (45). Phosphorylation greatly reduces the monomeric binding affinity of TRα2 and impairs the heterodimer formation on permissive DNA-binding sites (45). The increased dominant-negative action of a nonphosphorylatable form of TRα2 suggests that phosphorylation may provide a means to regulate TR function (45).

UNIQUE FUNCTIONS OF AF1 DOMAIN: MODULATION OF THYROID HORMONE RECEPTOR ACTIVITY

The amino-terminal regions are least conserved among nuclear receptor sequences. This domain is highly divergent between TRα and TRβ isoforms, which suggests differential roles in transcriptional regulation. In addition, alternative splicing of the TRβ gene generates two isoforms, TRβ1 and TRβ2, with completely different amino-terminal domains (1). The amino-terminal domain is not required for T3-dependent transcriptional activation by rat TRβ1 (46), which suggests that the amino-terminal domain might modulate—rather than be essential for—TR function. The amino terminus of TRβ2 contains two distinct trans-activation regions that are important for the unique transcriptional properties of this isoform (47, 48).

The function of the amino-terminal domain appears to be mediated through interaction with basal transcriptional factors, especially with transcription factor IIB (49). Indeed, a sequence of 10 amino acids in chicken TRα1 amino-terminal domain, which contains a cluster of 5 basic amino acids, mediates interaction with transcription factor IIB, and the interaction correlates with its requirement for full transcriptional activation (49). At least two separate serine phosphorylation sites are present in the chicken amino-terminal domain (50, 51). Only one of the sites, [28]Ser-Ser-Glu-Cys-Leu-Val-Lys, is retained in the P75-gag-v-ErbA protein (52). v-ErbA is a mutant form of the chick TRα that has been corrupted by the avian erythroblastosis virus (53, 54). Activation of either protein kinase C or cAMP-dependent protein kinase greatly enhances the phosphorylation of this site in both p46c-ErbA and P75gag-v-ErbA in vivo (51). In addition, phosphorylation through this site appears to be necessary for the oncogenic properties of v-ErbA protein. Mutation of two serine residues to alanine or treatment with kinase inhibitors dramatically impairs oncogenic transformation. In contrast, conversion of two serines to threonines, which can still be phosphorylated by protein kinase A, retains v-ErbA oncogenic activity (52). Protein kinase A phosphorylation on this site dramatically reduced monomeric DNA-binding affinity (55). It is interesting that the cluster of five basic amino acids, [23]Lys-Arg-Lys-Arg-Lys[27], is located immediately before these two serine residues. These five basic residues appear to be involved in the modulation of multiple TR activities (56). Conversion of these residues to [23]Thr-Ile-Thr-Ile-Thr[27] abolishes transcription factor IIB interaction, significantly decreases T3-dependent transcriptional activation, and inhibits monomeric DNA binding (56). The similar effect of protein kinase A phosphory-lation might result from neutralizing the positive charges of the basic residues by introducing a negatively charged phosphate group. This effect also suggests a potential link between the amino-terminal region and the v-ErbA oncogenic activity.

In addition to modulating ligand-dependent activation function, the amino-terminal domain has also modulates ligand-independent interaction with core-pressors (57). Unlike TRα1 or TRβ1, TRβ2 fails to repress transcription in the absence of hormone. Consistent with this, it appears that the nuclear coreceptor (N-CoR) does not function for TRβ2 (57). Both TRβ1 and TRβ2 isoforms, how-ever, interact with corepressors equally well on DNA. This interaction suggests that the amino-terminal domain of TRβ2 can inactivate or mask the corepressor function through other unknown mechanisms (57).

MECHANISMS OF TRANSCRIPTIONAL REGULATION

As a transcriptional factor, a key function of the TR is to regulate the target gene expression in response to multiple signaling pathways. Tremendous effort and progress have recently been made in understanding the molecular mechanism of nuclear receptor action. Unlike steroid receptors, TR—as well as RAR, RXR, and PPAR—constitutively bind to DNA response elements in the absence and presence of the ligand. Unliganded TR represses the basal transcription. Ligand binding causes derepression and enhances transcriptional activation. Thus the biological significance of repression is to turn off target genes in the absence of hormone and to increase the magnitude of transcriptional activation by hormone ligand. A group of cofactor proteins (coactivators and corepressors) mediate repression and activation. Cofactors alone cannot bind DNA but instead they directly interact with DNA-bound nuclear receptors, as a result of which they are recruited to the proximity of the target gene promoter region and affect the rate of transcription.

A higher level of transcriptional regulation is provided by a change of chromatin structure. Open chromatin (euchromatin) is thought to facilitate the assembly of basal transcriptional machinery and increase the transcription rate. In contrast, a highly condensed chromatin (heterochromatin) blocks the entry of TATA-binding protein and leads to transcriptional repression. Chromatin structure can be greatly affected by acetylation of histones in the nucleosome octamer. Hyperacetylation of histones loosens the interaction between DNA and nucleosome by reducing the net positive charge. Conversely, histone deacetylation opposes the structural change of nucleosomes brought by histone acetylation. Both histone acetyltransferase and histone deacetylase activities are functionally associated with coactivators and corepressors, respectively, thus providing an enzymatic link to the activation and repression by nuclear receptors (Figure 2).

Activation Is Mediated by Multiple Coactivator Proteins

Transcriptional activation of liganded nuclear receptors, including TR, is mediated by coactivator proteins that associate with nuclear receptors in a ligand-dependent manner. Ectopic expression of coactivators leads to potentiation of the ligand-dependent transactivation function, and most of the coactivators contain activation domains. Early evidence for the existence of coactivators came from observations of ligand-dependent transcriptional interference, or squelching, such that cotransfection of one activated nuclear receptor reduces the transcriptional activity of another (58–61). Squelching occurs away from DNA and involves competition by the squelching receptor for binding to one or more limiting proteins required for transcriptional activity.

The first evidence for the existence of such limiting factors came from a biochemical approach with the ligand-binding domain of estrogen receptors (62). Two estrogen receptor–associated proteins (ERAP), ERAP-140 and ERAP-160, were found to associate with the glutathione S-transferase/estrogen receptor in the presence—but not in the absence—of estradiol or diethylstilbestrol. Mutational analysis indicated that this ligand-dependent interaction correlates with the ability to activate transcription. Moreover, the estrogen antagonist 4-hydroxytamoxifen (4-OHT) and the pure anti-estrogen ICI 164384 are unable to promote

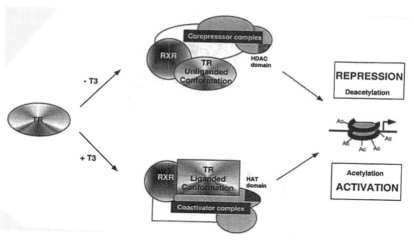

Figure 2   Model for activation and repression by thyroid hormone receptor. In the absence of T3, TR/RXR recruits a corepressor complex that has histone deacetylase (HDAC) activity. In the presence of T3, TR/T3/RXR releases the corepressor complex and recruits a coactivator complex that has histone acetyltransferase (HAT) activity. Enzymatic modification of nucleosomes by HDAC or HAT activity results in a closed or open chromatin structure that leads to transcriptional repression or activation.

the association of the estrogen receptor with ERAP. These data provide the evidence that ERAPs are estrogen coactivators. Similar biochemical approaches were used to characterize a glucocorticoid receptor coactivator (63). The 160-kDa forms of these proteins have included the first cloned coactivator, steroid receptor coactivator-1 (SRC-1).

SRC-1 was the first nuclear receptor coactivator to be cloned and characterized (64). SRC-1 associates with the progesterone receptor in the presence of agonist, but not in the presence of antagonist. In addition, SRC-1 enhances the ligand-dependent transcriptional activity of all the steroid receptors tested, including progesterone receptor, estrogen receptor, and glucocorticoid receptor. SRC-1 can reverse the ligand-dependent transcriptional interference of the progesterone receptor by cotransfected human estrogen receptor in the presence of the ligand estradiol, indicating that SRC-1 is a limiting cofactor recruited by both the liganded progesterone and estrogen receptors. SRC-1 also enhances the activity of liganded TR, RXR, and HNF-4 (65, 66). Furthermore, an amino-terminal–truncated SRC-1 containing the receptor-interacting domain exhibits strong dominant-negative activity on liganded progesterone and thyroid receptors. These results establish SRC-1 as a general common coactivator not only for receptors of this class. An important role of SRC-1 in T3 action is revealed by the fact that the mice without functional SRC-1 are T3 resistant (67).

Other members of the SRC family include TIF2/GRIP1 (68–74) and pCIP/ACTR/AIB1/TRAM1/RAC3 (75–81). In yeast cells, these coactivators dramatically enhance the transcriptional activity of nuclear receptors, including TR (82, 83). TIF2 is the human homolog of mouse GRIP1 protein. A novel fusion protein between MOZ and TIF2, which resulted from chromosomal translocation inv(8)(p11q13), associates with a distinct subtype of acute myeloid leukemia (84, 85). This subtype is usually associated with the t(8;16)(p11; p13), a translocation between *MOZ* and *CBP* genes (86). MOZ-TIF2 retains the histone acetyltransferase domain and also the CBP-binding domain of TIF2. The apparently identical phenotypes observed in both cases are likely caused by recruitment of CBP by the TIF2 part of the fusion protein. AIB1, which was also identified by its ability to bind and activate TR (79), is amplified in ∼10% of breast cancers and highly expressed in 60% of cases. Altered expression of AIB1 may contribute to steroid-dependent cancers (78, 79).

SRC-1 contains two intrinsic transferable activation domains, AD1 and AD2, which are needed to achieve maximum activity of steroid receptors (87). SRC-1 is capable of interacting not only with the carboxyl-terminal ligand-binding domain of the nuclear receptor, but also with the amino-terminal domain (87). Thus SRC-1 appears to be involved in both ligand-dependent AF2 and ligand-independent AF1 transactivation functions (87). In addition, in experiments with isolated AF1 (ABCD) and AF2 (EF) fragments, SRC-1 potentiates the functional interaction between AF1 and AF2 regions of the estrogen receptor in the presence of ligand E2, consistent with the role of SRC-1 on the full-length receptor (88, 89). Thus one of the roles of SRC-1 in estrogen receptor function, and potentially in that of other members of the nuclear receptor superfamily, is to act as an adaptor protein and promote the cross-talk between amino-terminal AF1 and carboxyl-terminal AF2 to achieve maximum synergistic activity. SRC-1 possesses intrinsic histone acetyltransferase activity through its carboxyl-terminal region and also interacts with another histone acetyltransferase, p300/CREB-binding protein–associated factor (90–93).

The interaction between TRβ and SRC-1 requires integrity of the carboxyl-terminal amphipathic helix (65, 94). This helix contains a consensus sequence φφXEφφ (φ represents a hydrophobic amino acid, X can be any amino acid, E is glutamic acid), also called the AF2 motif. Deletion of the six AF2 amino acids (amino acids 451–456) of TRβ abolishes the ligand-dependent association with SRC-1 in vitro and the coactivation function in vivo (65).

Physiologically, aberrant coactivator recruitment is a feature of an autosomal inherited disease, T3 resistance (RTH) (95–97). RTH is caused by mutations in the TRβ gene and is characterized by elevated serum-free T3 levels, increased levels of thyroid-stimulating hormone (TSH), and variable peripheral refractoriness to hormone action (96, 98). TRβ mutants from RTH patients exhibit impaired SRC-1 recruitment, with variable T3 binding affinity (94, 95). In some mutants, SRC-1 recruitment is disproportionately impaired compared with altered T3 affinity, which suggests that the inability of mutant TRs to interact with coactivators such as SRC-1 might be a determinant of dominant-negative activity (94, 97). Three clusters of RTH natural TRβ mutations (amino acids 310–353, 429–461, and 234–282) correspond to three boundaries of the ligand-binding cavity and to the receptor-coactivator surface composed of helices 3, 4, 5, and 12 (95, 99, 100). In addition to influencing coactivator recruitment, corepressors also appear to play an important role in RTH syndrome (see below).

Coactivators of the SRC family also associate with p300/CBP (69, 75, 76, 101). CBP was originally identified by its interaction and coactivation function for phosphorylated CREB (102, 103). p300 is a functional homolog of CBP (104, 105). p300/CBP is involved in nuclear receptor signaling (106–108) in that it directly interacts with nuclear receptors and potentiates their transcriptional activation function in vivo (106–108). p300/CBP also interacts with and mediates the activation of other transcriptional regulation factors, including AP-1 (109), p53 (110), STAT proteins (109, 111), NF-κB (112), C/EBP (113), and NF-E2 (114). Thus p300/CBP is a regulator of multiple signaling pathways (115).

Originally identified as a CBP-associated factor (93), PCAF has intrinsic histone deacetylase activity (93) and is a nuclear receptor coactivator (92). PCAF differs from other coactivators because it interacts with the DNA-binding domain of nuclear receptors and because the interaction is ligand independent (92). However, the ligand-independent association with corepressors inhibits the PCAF recruitment in the absence of the ligand and therefore may confer ligand dependency of PCAF association in vivo (92). PCAF also interacts with SRC family coactivators (76, 90, 116). Thus, PCAF, p300/CBP, and SRC family coactivators may form a multiprotein complex to mediate transactivation functions of diverse transcriptional factors. Microinjection studies suggest that different transcription factors have distinct requirements for coactivation complex formation (116). For example, TR activation function, but not STAT-1 function, is blocked by microinjection of PCAF antibody. Whereas PCAF is required for both nuclear receptor and CREB functions, the histone acetyltransferase activity of PCAF is indispensable for nuclear receptor function but is not essential for CREB function (116). In contrast, the histone acetyltransferase activity of CBP is required for CREB but not for nuclear receptor function (116).

In addition to the histone acetyltransferase-containing coactivators, a separate coactivator complex used by TR (117), VDR (118), and other classes of transcription factors (119) has also been identified. For TR this complex has been referred to as the TRAP (117). This complex does not appear to contain histone acetyltransferase activity and is transcriptionally active even in the absence of chromatin. It contains multiple polypeptides that are shared with a more general transcriptional regulatory complex referred to as the mediator complex SMCC (120, 121). The relative roles of the histone acetyltransferase and TRAP complexes are a subject of intense investigation. The roles of other TR coactivators, including TRIP230 (122) and p120 (123), are also unclear. A motif of LXXLL (Leu-XX-Leu-Leu; X is any amino acid) is present in most of the coactivators identified so far, including SRC-1, TIF2, and p300/CBP (124). This motif is necessary and sufficient to mediate the ligand-dependent interaction with nuclear receptors (124). It is interesting that the LXXLL motif is also involved in the interaction between CBP and SRC family coactivators (125). SRC family coactivators contain three LXXLL motifs (termed the NR box) in the central region of the proteins. These NR boxes are not functionally redundant. In contrast, other usages of NR boxes are receptor specific (125). TR interaction requires both the second and third NR boxes and correct spacing between them. It appears that the specificity of NR box usage is determined by the carboxyl-terminal sequences to the LXXLL motif (125). These carboxyl-terminal residues can make differential contacts with helices 1 and 3 (or 3′) of nuclear receptors (125). Thus the presence of multiple NR boxes in the coactivator protein provides the specificity and flexibility for the assembly of nuclear receptor-coactivator complexes that serve diverse biological functions.

Repression and the Corepressor—Histone Deacetylase Complex

TRs are located in the nucleus and bound to chromatin in the absence or presence of T3 (1, 4–6, 126). The most important difference between v-erbA and TRα is a 9-amino-acid deletion at the carboxyl terminus that removes the AF2 motif. This change greatly impairs the ligand-binding affinity of v-erbA but has little affect on its DNA binding. As the result, v-erbA acts as a strong dominant-negative inhibitor of c-erbA (127–129). Dominant negative activity requires v-erbA to bind DNA response element (130). Both v-erbA and c-erbA contain a transferable repression domain in the ligand-binding domain region (131). Mutation analysis reveals that two regions, located in the amino terminus (hinge region) and carboxyl terminus of v-erbA ligand-binding domain, are required for the repression function (131). Thus unliganded TR is capable of actively repressing the basal transcription (silencing), in contrast to the transcriptional activation mediated by the liganded TR.

Studies using in vitro transcription systems demonstrate that unliganded TR represses basal transcription in either HeLa nuclear extracts or defined reconstituted systems (132–134). Unliganded TR inhibits the formation of a functional preinitiation complex, probably through direct interaction with TBP and transcription factor IIB, which suggests a possible mechanism of active TR repression (132–134). However, functional assays strongly suggest the existence of a limiting corepressor protein involved in TR repression (135–137).

A major breakthrough has been the cloning of two corepressors, N-CoR/RIP13 (138, 139) and silencing mediator for retinoid and thyroid receptors (SMRT)/TRAC (140–142). N-CoR is a 270-kDa, ubiquitously expressed nuclear protein, identified by yeast two-hybrid screening with the ligand-binding domain of TR as the bait. SMRT was cloned by yeast two-hybrid screening as an RXR-interacting protein. N-CoR and SMRT share significant sequence homology, which suggests that they are members of a novel corepressor family. They show ligand-independent interaction with RAR and TR in vitro and exhibit modular structures, with carboxyl termini as the nuclear receptor-interacting regions and amino termini as the autonomous repression domains. They contain multiple transferable repression domains, which can repress transcription when fused to heterologous Gal4 DBD (138, 141, 143–145). N-CoR also serves as corepressor for other nuclear receptors, including orphan receptors Rev-Erb (146, 147) and COUP-TF (148, 149). Other classes of transcription regulatory complexes, such as POZ domain–containing repressors, also use N-CoR and/or SMRT (150, 151).

A region referred to as the CoR box in the hinge region (helix 1) of TR and RAR is required for the interaction with corepressors N-CoR and SMRT (138, 140, 152, 153). Consistent with this requirement, the hinge region mutation Pro-144–Arg in v-erbA abolishes repression and oncogenic transformation activity of v-erbA (154–156). N-CoR and SMRT each contain two independent receptor-interacting regions (ID1 and ID2) (146, 157–159). This similarity is likely related to the finding that two ligand-binding domains from two receptors are required for functional interaction with corepressors on DNA (160, 161), which suggests that stoichiometric and steric principles govern corepression function (160).

TR ninth heptad mutants and TRα2 cannot interact with RXR in solution and are defective in both repression and corepressor recruitment (33, 40, 135, 162). Although RXR is a poor repressor that only minimally interacts with corepressors on its own (40, 138, 142, 159, 163), recruitment of RXR via a heterologous dimerization interface complements repression-defective ninth-heptad TR mutants, which suggests an active role of RXR in repression by TR (40). RXR interaction with apo-TR requires an intact CoR box as well as the ninth heptad, but not AF2; conversely, AF2, but not the CoR box or ninth heptad of TR, is required for RXR interaction in the presence of T3 (40). Differential recognition of apo- and holo-TR by RXR is thus likely to play an important role in corepressor recruitment by TR/RXR heterodimer. TR homodimers also interact with N-CoR and SMRT (158, 160) and thus may also play a role in repression.

Small Unique Nuclear receptor Co-Repressor (SUN-CoR) is a 16-kDa nuclear protein identified by yeast two-hybrid screening with Rev-Erb as the bait (164); it shares no homology with N-CoR and SMRT. SUN-CoR contains a transferable repression domain and also interacts with and potentiates repression by TR. SUN-CoR also interacts with N-CoR in vitro and in vivo, which suggests that it may function as a component of the repression complex involved in repression by TR and orphan receptors. Another TR-interacting molecule, TRUP-1, inhibits activation by TR but not basal transcription on TRE-containing promoters (165).

Transcriptional repression by nuclear receptors varies among different cell types (166), which suggests a potential regulatory mechanism for cell-specific corepressor protein expression. However, the N-CoR and SMRT genes are ubiquitously expressed (138). By yeast two-hybrid screening, mSiah2, a mammalian homolog of the *Drosophila* "seven in absentia" (Sina) protein, was identified as an N-CoR–interacting protein (167). mSiah2- and Sina-mediated proteasomal regulation have been implicated in proteolysis of other proteins (166, 168, 169). mSiah2 specifically targets N-CoR for degradation, thereby inhibiting repression by Rev-Erb (which specifically relies on N-CoR as a corepressor) and blunting repression by TR. mSiah2 is expressed prominently in germ cells and cells of the nervous system, which explains at least some aspects of cell specificity of N-CoR protein expression and the magnitude of nuclear receptor repression.

What are the downstream targets of the corepressors? Recent studies support the existence of a multiprotein complex, including N-CoR/SMRT, Sin3, and histone deacetylase (170–177). In contrast to histone acetyltransferase activity, which results in an open chromatin environment and gene activation, histone deacetylase contributes to a more compact chromatin structure, excluding the recruitment of basal transcriptional machinery and thereby repressing the basal transcription. This corepressor-histone deacetylase complex thus provides an enzymatic link to the repression by unliganded nuclear receptors.

In addition to the histone deacetylase-dependent mechanism, nuclear receptors and corepressors may also use other histone deacetylase-independent mechanisms to repress transcription (178). Trichostatin A, a specific inhibitor of histone deacetylase, cannot relieve Sin3A-mediated repression (157). N-CoR and SMRT directly interact with transcription factor IIB, $TAF_{II}32$, and $TAF_{II}70$ (157, 179). These interactions may interfere with the formation of functional preinitiation complex and thus decrease the rate of initiation. In addition, experiments with coupled chromatin assembly and transcription suggest that apo-TR/RXR heterodimer and histone deacetylase use distinct mechanisms to repress transcription (180). However, histone deacetylase activity is also required for TR/RXR to repress, because trichostatin A can relieve its repression (180). The fact that apo-TR/RXR represses transcription under conditions of incomplete chromatin assembly suggests that deacetylase recruited by TR/RXR may have functions in repression other than facilitating the chromatin assembly (180).

Dysregulation of corepressor function often leads to human disease. Recruitment of corepressors appears to be a prerequisite for the ability of TRβ RTH mutants to exhibit strong dominant-negative inhibition (95, 181–184). Consistent with this assumption, all RTH mutants have normal DNA-binding activity (185).

Corepressor interaction is also essential for v-erbA oncogenic activity (140). Recruitment of corepressor-histone deacetylase complex is also linked to different types of myelogenous leukemia, including acute promyelocytic leukemia (153, 186–190) and acute myeloid leukemia (191–193). It is interesting that differential response to retinoic acid treatment for two types of acute promyelocytic leukemia correlates with the ability of retinoic acid to dissociate corepressors from the corresponding oncogenic fusion proteins. Additional contact to corepressor from the POZ-domain-containing PLZF moiety results in constitutive corepressor-histone deacetylase binding that fails to respond to retinoic acid treatment, whereas retinoic acid binding to PML-RAR releases corepressor complex and achieves complete remission.

Chromatin remodeling complexes provide additional levels of regulation of repression (194–200). The chromatin remodeling complex contains histone deacetylase and, in addition, ATPase activity. The coupling of histone deacetylase with remodeling activity may facilitate the assembly of a repressive chromatin structure. However, the role of the chromatin remodeling complex in transcriptional regulation needs more investigation.

STRUCTURAL BIOLOGY OF THE THYROID HORMONE RECEPTOR: ROLE OF THE LIGAND

Crystallographic structures of the ligand-binding domains from several unliganded and liganded nuclear receptors have been solved. These receptors include unliganded RXR (38), liganded TR (100), liganded RAR (201, 202), PPAR (203, 204), an agonist- or antagonist-bound estrogen receptor (205, 206), and a liganded progesterone receptor (207). The ligand-binding domains are composed mostly of α-helices. All the receptors exhibit a common fold with 12 helices arranged in three layers. Instructive information comes from the comparison of unliganded with liganded conformations. Overall, the liganded structure is more compact and stable than the unliganded structure, at least in part because the receptor folds around the ligand. The ligand becomes buried within the interior of the receptor and makes multiple contacts with several helices and β-strands to stabilize the conformation. This arrangement suggests that the ligand plays a structural role in triggering completion of the receptor fold. Likewise, the several hydrophobic cavities in unliganded RXR structures indicate that the fold cannot be completed without the ligand.

Most of the unliganded and liganded conformations can be superimposed except for a few important structural changes, which reveal the role of the ligand in receptor function. The most important change is the repositioning of helix 12, which contains the AF2 motif important in ligand-dependent transactivation. In unliganded RXR, helix 12 extends from the ligand-binding domain core, whereas in liganded TR, helix 12 folds back toward the ligand-binding domain, realigns with helix 3 and helix 4, and contacts the ligand, thereby closing the ligand cavity and generating a surface for coactivator recruitment (mousetrap model) (99, 100). With the release of helix 12, the Ω loop flips over underneath helix 6, carrying along the amino terminus of helix 3 (99, 100) and completing the fold around the ligand (Figure 3).

The repositioning of helix 12 plays an important role in nuclear receptor function. Consistent with the structural model, biochemical studies identified a hydrophobic cleft composed of helices 3–5 and 12 that is crucial for coactivator binding (99, 100). It is interesting that the core AF2 sequence φφXEφφ has an LXXLL motif (NR box), which is sufficient to bind to the coactivator-interacting surface. In antagonist-bound estrogen receptor, AF2 sterically prevents coactivator bind-

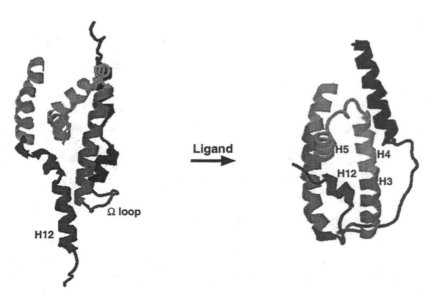

Figure 3 Ligand-induced conformational change of nuclear receptors. Structures that exhibit significant differences are *left,* unliganded RXR structure; *right,* liganded RAR structure. The structure of apo-TR has not been solved, and coordinates of ligand-bound TR are not currently available.

ing by mimicking the NR box to adopt the coactivator position (206). Liganded TR structures also provide important insights into the structural basis of RTH syndrome. RTH mutations essentially map to the boundaries of the ligand cavity, thus explaining the impaired T3 binding for almost all mutants (95, 208, 209).

LIFE WITHOUT THYROID RECEPTOR HORMONE: REDUNDANCY AND SPECIFICITY OF TRα AND TRβ

T3 action is mediated by two receptors, TRα and TRβ. Despite extensive studies to understand the mechanism of TR action, some in vivo functions remain undefined. Overall, the functional proteins encoded by TRα and TRβ genes have similar biochemical and functional properties. Both TRα1 and TRβ receptors bind T3 with high affinity. Unliganded receptors are potent repressors, and ligand binding converts them to transcriptional activators. The TRα and TRβ genes are coexpressed in some tissues (210–215). This arrangement raises the possibility that they are functionally redundant. Therefore, knockout mice that lack functional TRα and/or TRβ genes have been generated to study the differential roles of these genes for mediating T3 action.

TRα1 has been shown to be especially important for normal cardiac function. TRα1-specific knockout mice have lower heart rates under normal conditions and after T3 stimulation. They also show prolonged QRS- and QT_{end}-durations in electrocardiograms and have lower body temperatures but appear normal in overall behavior and reproduction (216). In contrast to relatively minor phenotypic abnormalities in TRα1 knockout mice, TRα$^{-/-}$ mice that are devoid of TRα1 and TRα2 become progressively hypothyroid and exhibit growth arrest, which leads to death within 5 weeks after birth (217). This phenotype could be caused by the additional absence of TRα2 but may also relate to the specific scheme used to delete the TRα gene, which might allow for expression of dominant negative proteins at the TRα locus (217).

TRβ is essential for auditory development. TRβ$^{-/-}$ mice exhibit a permanent deficit in hearing, for which other receptors do not compensate. Because TRβ does not control cochlear morphogenesis, TRα or other unidentified receptors may influence morphogenesis, and TRβ may mediate functional maturation of the ear (218). Inactivation of TRβ leads to hyperthyroxinemia (219), similar to what is observed in RTH, and is consistent with the negative regulation of the TSHβ gene by liganded TRβ. The elevated level of TSH in TRβ$^{-/-}$ mice suggests that TRα alone cannot complement deficient TRβ function. TRα$^{-/-}$ TRβ$^{-/-}$ mice have much higher levels of TSH, which suggests that TRα at least partially controls TSH expression (220). Thus partial redundancy may exist for a limited number of functions of TRα and TRβ gene products, but generally these products mediate specific functions in a time- and tissue-specific manner. The described double knockout has multiple abnormalities but at present does not appear to completely recapitulate the athyroid phenotype. This condition could be caused by an undiscovered third T3 receptor gene or by nongenomic effects of T3. Another fundamental difference between the absence of ligand and the absence of a receptor is that the absence of T3 locks the TR in a repressed state, whereas genes containing TREs would be in a relatively more active neutral state in the absence of TR. Future and additional studies of double knockouts will undoubtedly clarify the role of each TR gene product in thyroid physiology and will shed great light on the relative roles of repression and activation in TR function.

SUMMARY AND FUTURE DIRECTIONS

Our knowledge of mechanisms underlying T3 action has grown exponentially over the past decade with TR cloning, identification and cloning of the TR heterodimer partner RXR, and the identification of transcriptional coregulators. The challenge for the future is to better understand the underlying particularity of the mechanisms: specific functions of each TR isoform, specific functions of TR homo- and heterodimers, and specific functions for each TR coactivator and corepressor. This understanding will require an expanded view of TR target genes in each target tissue and cell type under different physiological conditions, which will be possible with the anticipated progress of the mapping of human and mouse genomes and new computational approaches to complex networks of gene regulation. The convergence of these technologies lends great promise to the hope of relating the molecular mechanism of T3 action to thyroid physiology.

Visit the Annual Reviews home page at www.AnnualReviews.org.

LITERATURE CITED

1. Lazar MA. 1993. Thyroid hormone receptors: multiple forms, multiple possibilities. *Endocr. Rev.* 14:184–93
2. Oppenheimer JH, Samuels HH. 1983. *The Molecular Basis of Thyroid Hormone Action.* New York: Academic
3. Utiger LEB, Utiger RD. 1991. *The Thyroid: a Fundamental and Clinical Text.* Philadelphia: Lippincott
4. Evans RM. 1988. The steroid and thyroid hormone receptor superfamily. *Science* 240:889–95
5. Mangelsdorf DJ, Thummel C, Beato M, Herrlich P, Schutz G, et al. 1995. The nuclear receptor superfamily: the second decade. *Cell* 83:835–39
6. Ribeiro RC, Kushner PJ, Baxter JD. 1995. The nuclear hormone receptor gene superfamily. *Annu. Rev. Med.* 46:443–53
7. Glass CK. 1994. Differential recognition of target genes by nuclear receptor monomers, dimers, and heterodimers. *Endocr. Rev.* 15:391–407
8. Umesono K, Murakami KK, Thompson CC, Evans RM. 1991. Direct repeats as selective response elements for the thyroid hormone, retinoic acid, and vitamin D3 receptors. *Cell* 65:1255–66
9. Naar AM, Boutin JM, Lipkin SM, Yu VC, Holloway JM, et al. 1991. The orientation and spacing of core DNA-binding motifs dictate selective transcriptional responses to three nuclear receptors. *Cell* 65:1267–79
10. Glass CK, Franco R, Weinberger C, Albert VR, Evans RM, et al. 1987. A c-Erb-A binding site in rat growth hormone gene mediates trans-activation by thyroid hormone. *Nature* 329:738–41
11. Brent GA, Larsen PR, Harney JW, Koenig RJ, Moore DD. 1989. Functional characterization of the rat growth hormone promoter elements required for induction by thyroid hormone with and without a co-transfected beta type thyroid hormone receptor. *J. Biol. Chem.* 264:178–82
12. Kliewer SA, Umesono K, Mangelsdorf DJ, Evans RM. 1992. Retinoid X receptor interacts with nuclear receptors in retinoic acid, thyroid hormone and vitamin D3 signalling. *Nature* 355:446–49
13. Zhang XK, Hoffmann B, Tran PB, Graupner G, Pfahl M. 1992. Retinoid X receptor is an auxiliary protein for thyroid hormone and retinoic acid receptors. *Nature* 355:441–46
14. Yu VC, Delsert C, Andersen B, Holloway JM, Devary OV, et al. 1991. RXR beta: a coregulator that enhances binding of retinoic acid, thyroid hormone, and vitamin D receptors to their cognate response elements. *Cell* 67:1251–66
15. Marks MS, Hallenbeck PL, Nagata T, Segars JH, Appella E, et al. 1992. H-2RIIBP (RXR beta) heterodimerization provides a mechanism for combinatorial diversity in the regulation of retinoic acid and thyroid hormone responsive genes. *EMBO J.* 11:1419–35
16. Leid M, Kastner P, Lyons R, Nakshatri H, Saunders M, et al. 1992. Purification, cloning, and RXR identity of the HeLa cell factor with which RAR or TR heterodimerizes to bind target sequences

efficiently. *Cell* 68:377–95 [published erratum in *Cell* 1992. 71(5):after 886]

17. Lazar MA, Berrodin TJ, Harding HP. 1991. Differential DNA binding by monomeric, homodimeric, and potentially heteromeric forms of the thyroid hormone receptor. *Mol. Cell. Biol.* 11:5005–15

18. Bugge TH, Pohl J, Lonnoy O, Stunnenberg HG. 1992. RXR alpha, a promiscuous partner of retinoic acid and thyroid hormone receptors. *EMBO J.* 11:1409–18

19. Forman BM, Samuels HH. 1990. Interactions among a subfamily of nuclear hormone receptors: the regulatory zipper model. *Mol. Endocrinol.* 4:1293–301

20. Umesono K, Giguere V, Glass CK, Rosenfeld MG, Evans RM. 1988. Retinoic acid and thyroid hormone induce gene expression through a common responsive element. *Nature* 336:262–65

21. Umesono K, Evans RM. 1989. Determinants of target gene specificity for steroid/thyroid hormone receptors. *Cell* 57:1139–46

22. Ribeiro RC, Apriletti JW, Yen PM, Chin WW, Baxter JD. 1994. Heterodimerization and deoxyribonucleic acid-binding properties of a retinoid X receptor-related factor. *Endocrinology* 135:2076–85

23. Luisi BF, Xu WX, Otwinowski Z, Freedman LP, Yamamoto KR, et al. 1991. Crystallographic analysis of the interaction of the glucocorticoid receptor with DNA. *Nature* 352:497–505

24. Schwabe JW, Chapman L, Finch JT, Rhodes D. 1993. The crystal structure of the estrogen receptor DNA-binding domain bound to DNA: how receptors discriminate between their response elements. *Cell* 75:567–78

25. Zhao Q, Khorasanizadeh S, Miyoshi Y, Lazar MA, Rastinejad, F. 1998. Structural elements of an orphan nuclear receptor-DNA complex. *Mol. Cell* 1:849–61

26. Rastinejad F, Perlmann T, Evans RM,

Sigler PB. 1995. Structural determinants of nuclear receptor assembly on DNA direct repeats. *Nature* 375:203–11

27. Katz RW, Koenig RJ. 1994. Specificity and mechanism of thyroid hormone induction from an octamer response element. *J. Biol. Chem.* 269:18915–20

28. Zechel C, Shen XQ, Chambon P, Gronemeyer H. 1994. Dimerization interfaces formed between the DNA binding domains determine the cooperative binding of RXR/RAR and RXR/TR heterodimers to DR5 and DR4 elements. *EMBO J.* 13:1414–24

29. Zechel C, Shen XQ, Chen JY, Chen ZP, Chambon P, et al. 1994. The dimerization interfaces formed between the DNA binding domains of RXR, RAR and TR determine the binding specificity and polarity of the full-length receptors to direct repeats. *EMBO J.* 13:1425–33

30. Perlmann T, Rangarajan PN, Umesono K, Evans RM. 1993. Determinants for selective RAR and TR recognition of direct repeat HREs. *Genes Dev.* 7:1411–22

31. Predki PF, Zamble D, Sarkar B, Giguere V. 1994. Ordered binding of retinoic acid and retinoid-X receptors to asymmetric response elements involves determinants adjacent to the DNA-binding domain. *Mol. Endocrinol.* 8:31–39

32. Kurokawa R, Yu VC, Naar A, Kyakumoto S, Han Z, et al. 1993. Differential orientations of the DNA-binding domain and carboxy-terminal dimerization interface regulate binding site selection by nuclear receptor heterodimers. *Genes Dev.* 7:1423–35

33. Au-Fliegner M, Helmer E, Casanova J, Raaka BM, Samuels HH. 1993. The conserved ninth C-terminal heptad in thyroid hormone and retinoic acid receptors mediates diverse responses by affecting heterodimer but not homodimer formation. *Mol. Cell Biol.* 13:5725–37

34. Forman BM, Yang CR, Au M, Casanova J, Ghysdael J, et al. 1989. A domain con-

taining leucine-zipper-like motifs mediate novel in vivo interactions between the thyroid hormone and retinoic acid receptors. *Mol. Endocrinol.* 3:1610–26

35. Glass CK, Lipkin SM, Devary OV, Rosenfeld MG. 1989. Positive and negative regulation of gene transcription by a retinoic acid-thyroid hormone receptor heterodimer. *Cell* 59:697–708

36. Zhang XK, Salbert G, Lee MO, Pfahl M. 1994. Mutations that alter ligand-induced switches and dimerization activities in the retinoid X receptor. *Mol. Cell Biol.* 14:4311–23

37. Perlmann T, Umesono K, Rangarajan PN, Forman BM, Evans RM. 1996. Two distinct dimerization interfaces differentially modulate target gene specificity of nuclear hormone receptors. *Mol. Endocrinol.* 10:958–66

38. Bourguet W, Ruff M, Chambon P, Gronemeyer H, Moras D. 1995. Crystal structure of the ligand-binding domain of the human nuclear receptor RXR-alpha. *Nature* 375:377–82

39. Leng X, Blanco J, Tsai SY, Ozato K, O'Malley BW, et al. 1995. Mouse retinoid X receptor contains a separable ligand-binding and transactivation domain in its E region. *Mol. Cell Biol.* 15:255–63

40. Zhang J, Zamir I, Lazar MA. 1997. Differential recognition of liganded and unliganded thyroid hormone receptor by retinoid X receptor regulates transcriptional repression. *Mol. Cell Biol.* 17:6887–97

41. Reginato MJ, Zhang J, Lazar MA. 1996. DNA-independent and DNA-dependent mechanisms regulate the differential heterodimerization of the isoforms of the thyroid hormone receptor with retinoid X receptor. *J. Biol. Chem.* 271:28199–205

42. Katz D, Berrodin TJ, Lazar MA. 1992. The unique C-termini of the thyroid hormone receptor variant, c-ErbA alpha 2, and thyroid hormone receptor alpha 1 mediate different DNA-binding and het-erodimerization properties. *Mol. Endocrinol.* 6:805–14

43. Katz D, Lazar MA. 1993. Dominant negative activity of an endogenous thyroid hormone receptor variant (alpha 2) is due to competition for binding sites on target genes. *J. Biol. Chem.* 268:20904–10

44. Yang YZ, Burgos-Trinidad M, Wu Y, Koenig RJ. 1996. Thyroid hormone receptor variant alpha2. Role of the ninth heptad in DNA binding, heterodimerization with retinoid X receptors, and dominant negative activity. *J. Biol. Chem.* 271:28235–42

45. Katz D, Reginato MJ, Lazar MA. 1995. Functional regulation of thyroid hormone receptor variant TR alpha 2 by phosphorylation. *Mol. Cell Biol.* 15: 2341–48

46. Thompson CC, Evans RM. 1989. Transactivation by thyroid hormone receptors: functional parallels with steroid hormone receptors. *Proc. Natl. Acad. Sci. USA* 86:3494–98

47. Sjoberg M, Vennstrom B. 1995. Ligand-dependent and -independent transactivation by thyroid hormone receptor beta 2 is determined by the structure of the hormone response element. *Mol. Cell Biol.* 15:4718–26

48. Langlois MF, Zanger K, Monden T, Safer JD, Hollenberg AN, et al. 1997. A unique role of the beta-2 thyroid hormone receptor isoform in negative regulation by thyroid hormone. Mapping of a novel amino-terminal domain important for ligand-independent activation. *J. Biol. Chem.* 272:24927–33

49. Hadzic E, Desai-Yajnik V, Helmer E, Guo S, Wu S, et al. 1995. A 10-amino-acid sequence in the N-terminal A/B domain of thyroid hormone receptor alpha is essential for transcriptional activation and interaction with the general transcription factor TFIIB. *Mol. Cell Biol.* 15:4507–17

50. Glineur C, Bailly M, Ghysdael J. 1989. The c-ErbA alpha-encoded thyroid hor-

mone receptor is phosphorylated in its amino terminal domain by casein kinase II. *Oncogene* 4:1247–54

51. Goldberg Y, Glineur C, Gesquiere JC, Ricouart A, Sap J, et al. 1988. Activation of protein kinase C or cAMP-dependent protein kinase increases phosphorylation of the c-ErbA-encoded thyroid hormone receptor and of the v-ErbA-encoded protein. *EMBO J.* 7:2425–33

52. Glineur C, Zenke M, Beug H, Ghysdael J. 1990. Phosphorylation of the v-ErbA protein is required for its function as an oncogene. *Genes Dev.* 4:1663–76

53. Weinberger C, Thompson CC, Ong ES, Lebo R, Gruol DJ, et al. 1986. The c-ErbA gene encodes a thyroid hormone receptor. *Nature* 324:641–46

54. Sap J, Munoz A, Damm K, Goldberg Y, Ghysdael J, et al. 1986. The c-ErbA protein is a high-affinity receptor for thyroid hormone. *Nature* 324:635–40

55. Tzagarakis-Foster C, Privalsky ML. 1998. Phosphorylation of thyroid hormone receptors by protein kinase A regulates DNA recognition by specific inhibition of receptor monomer binding. *J. Biol. Chem.* 273:10926–32

56. Hadzic E, Habeos I, Raaka BM, Samuels HH. 1998. A novel multifunctional motif in the amino-terminal A/B domain of T3Ralpha modulates DNA binding and receptor dimerization. *J. Biol. Chem.* 273:10270–78

57. Hollenberg AN, Monden T, Madura JP, Lee K, Wondisford FE. 1996. Function of nuclear co-repressor protein on thyroid hormone response elements is regulated by the receptor A/B domain. *J. Biol. Chem.* 271:28516–20

58. Zhang XJM, Bagchi MK. 1996. Ligand-dependent cross-talk between steroid and thyroid hormone receptors—evidence for common transcriptional coactivator(s). *J. Biol. Chem.* 271:14825–33

59. Barettino DRM, Stunnenberg HG. 1994. Characterization of the ligand-dependent

transactivation domain of thyroid hormone receptor. *EMBO J.* 13:3039–49

60. Conneely OM, Kettelberger DM, Tsai M-J, O'Malley BW. 1989. *Gene Regulation by Steroid Hormones.* New York: Springer-Verlag

61. Meyer ME, Gronemeyer H, Turcotte B, Bocquel MT, Tasset D, Chambon P. 1989. Steroid hormone receptors compete for factors that mediate their enhancer function. *Cell* 57:433–42

62. Halachmi S, Marden E, Martin G, Mackay H, Abbondanza C, Brown M. 1994. Estrogen receptor-associated proteins: possible mediators of hormone-induced transcription. *Science* 264:1455–58

63. Eggert M, Mows CC, Tripier D, Arnold R, Michel J, et al. 1995. A fraction enriched in a novel glucocorticoid receptor-interacting protein stimulates receptor-dependent transcription in vitro. *J. Biol. Chem.* 270:30755–59

64. Onate SA, TS, Tsai MJ, O'Malley BW. 1995. Sequence and characterization of a coactivator for the steroid hormone receptor superfamily. *Science* 270:1354–57

65. Jeyakumar M, Tanen MR, Bagchi MK. 1997. Analysis of the functional role of steroid receptor coactivator-1 in ligand-induced transactivation by thyroid hormone receptor. *Mol. Endocrinol.* 11:755–67

66. Wang JC, Stafford JM, Granner DK. 1998. SRC-1 and GRIP1 coactivate transcription with hepatocyte nuclear factor 4. *J. Biol. Chem.* 273:30847–50

67. Weiss RE, Xu J, Ning G, Pohlenz J, O'Malley BW, et al. 1999. Mice deficient in the steroid receptor co-activator 1 (SRC-1) are resistant to thyroid hormone. *EMBO J.* 18:1900–04

68. Voegel JJ, Heine MJ, Zechel C, Chambon P, Gronemeyer H. 1996. TIF2, a 160 kDa transcriptional mediator for the ligand-dependent activation function

AF-2 of nuclear receptors. *EMBO J.* 15:3667–75

69. Voegel JJ, Heine MJ, Tini M, Vivat V, Chambon P, et al. 1998. The coactivator TIF2 contains three nuclear receptor-binding motifs and mediates transactivation through CBP binding-dependent and -independent pathways. *EMBO J.* 17:507–19

70. Berrevoets CA, Doesburg P, Steketee K, Trapman J, Brinkmann AO. 1998. Functional interactions of the AF-2 activation domain core region of the human androgen receptor with the amino-terminal domain and with the transcriptional coactivator TIF2 (transcriptional intermediary factor2). *Mol. Endocrinol.* 12:1172–83

71. Leers J, Treuter E, Gustafsson JA. 1998. Mechanistic principles in NR box-dependent interaction between nuclear hormone receptors and the coactivator TIF2. *Mol. Cell Biol.* 18:6001–13

72. Hong H, Darimont BD, Ma H, Yang L, Yamamoto KR, et al. 1999. An additional region of coactivator GRIP1 required for interaction with the hormone-binding domains of a subset of nuclear receptors. *J. Biol. Chem.* 274:3496–502

73. Hong H, Kohli K, Garabedian MJ, Stallcup MR. 1997. GRIP1, a transcriptional coactivator for the AF-2 transactivation domain of steroid, thyroid, retinoid, and vitamin D receptors. *Mol. Cell Biol.* 17:2735–44

74. Hong H, Kohli K, Trivedi A, Johnson DL, Stallcup MR. 1996. GRIP1, a novel mouse protein that serves as a transcriptional coactivator in yeast for the hormone binding domains of steroid receptors. *Proc. Natl. Acad. Sci. USA* 93:4948–52

75. Torchia J, Rose DW, Inostroza J, Kamei Y, Westin S, et al. 1997. The transcriptional co-activator p/CIP binds CBP and mediates nuclear-receptor function. *Nature* 387:677–84

76. Chen H, Lin RJ, Schiltz RL, Chakravarti D, Nash A, et al. 1997. Nuclear receptor coactivator ACTR is a novel histone acetyltransferase and forms a multimeric activation complex with P/CAF and CBP/p300. *Cell* 90:569–80

77. Ghadimi BM, Schrock E, Walker RL, Wangsa D, Jauho A, et al. 1999. Specific chromosomal aberrations and amplification of the AIB1 nuclear receptor coactivator gene in pancreatic carcinomas. *Am. J. Pathol.* 154:525–36

78. Bautista S, Valles H, Walker RL, Anzick S, Zeillinger R, et al. 1998. In breast cancer, amplification of the steroid receptor coactivator gene AIB1 is correlated with estrogen and progesterone receptor positivity. *Clin. Cancer Res.* 4:2925–29

79. Anzick SL, Kononen J, Walker RL, Azorsa DO, Tanner MM, et al. 1997. AIB1, a steroid receptor coactivator amplified in breast and ovarian cancer. *Science* 277:965–68

80. Takeshita A, Cardone GR, Koibuchi N, Suen CS, Chin WW. 1997. TRAM-1, a novel 160-kDa thyroid hormone receptor activator molecule, exhibits distinct properties from steroid receptor coactivator-1. *J. Biol. Chem.* 272:27629–34

81. Li H, Gomes PJ, Chen JD. 1997. RAC3, a steroid/nuclear receptor-associated coactivator that is related to SRC-1 and TIF2. *Proc. Natl. Acad. Sci. USA* 94:8479–84

82. Olson DP, Sun B, Koenig RJ. 1998. Thyroid hormone response element architecture affects corepressor release from thyroid hormone receptor dimers. *J. Biol. Chem.* 273:3375–80

83. Walfish PG, Yoganathan T, Yang YF, Hong H, Butt TR, et al. 1997. Yeast hormone response element assays detect and characterize GRIP1 coactivator-dependent activation of transcription by thyroid and retinoid nuclear receptors. *Proc. Natl. Acad. Sci. USA* 94:3697–702

84. Carapeti M, Aguiar RC, Goldman JM, Cross NC. 1998. A novel fusion between MOZ and the nuclear receptor coactiva-

tor TIF2 in acute myeloid leukemia. *Blood* 91:3127–33

85. Liang J, Prouty L, Williams BJ, Dayton MA, Blanchard KL. 1998. Acute mixed lineage leukemia with an inv(8)(p11q13) resulting in fusion of the genes for MOZ and TIF2. *Blood* 92:2118–22

86. Borrow J, Stanton VP Jr, Andresen JM, Becher R, Behm FG, et al. 1996. The translocation t(8;16)(p11↑3) of acute myeloid leukaemia fuses a putative acetyltransferase to the CREB-binding protein. *Nat. Genet.* 14:33–41

87. Onate SA, Boonyaratanakornkit B, Spencer TE, Tsai SY, Tsai MJ, et al. 1998. The steroid receptor coactivator-1 contains multiple receptor interacting and activation domains that cooperatively enhance the activation function 1 (AF1) and AF2 domains of steroid receptors. *J. Biol. Chem.* 273:12101–8

88. McInerney EM, Tsai MJ, O'Malley BW, Katzenellenbogen BS. 1996. Analysis of estrogen receptor transcriptional enhancement by a nuclear hormone receptor coactivator. *Proc. Natl. Acad. Sci. USA* 93:10069–73

89. Kraus WL, McInerney EM, Katzenellenbogen BS. 1995. Ligand-dependent, transcriptionally productive association of the amino- and carboxyl-terminal regions of a steroid hormone nuclear receptor. *Proc. Natl. Acad. Sci. USA* 92:12314–18

90. Spencer TE, Burcin MM, Allis CD, Zhou J, Mizzen CA, et al. 1997. Steroid receptor coactivator-1 is a histone acetyltransferase. *Nature* 389:194–98

91. Ogryzko VV, Kotani T, Zhang X, Schlitz RL, Howard T, et al. 1998. Histone-like TAFs within the PCAF histone acetylase complex. *Cell* 94:35–44

92. Blanco JC, Minucci S, Lu J, Yang XJ, Walker KK, et al. 1998. The histone acetylase PCAF is a nuclear receptor coactivator. *Genes Dev.* 12:1638–51

93. Yang XJ, Ogryzko VV, Nishikawa J, Howard BH, Nakatani Y. 1996. A p300/

CBP-associated factor that competes with the adenoviral oncoprotein E1A. *Nature* 382:319–24

94. Collingwood TN, Rajanayagam O, Adams M, Wagner R, Cavailles V, et al. 1997. A natural transactivation mutation in the thyroid hormone beta receptor: impaired interaction with putative transcriptional mediators. *Proc. Natl. Acad. Sci. USA* 94:248–53

95. Collingwood TN, Wagner R, Matthews CH, Clifton-Bligh RJ, Gurnell M, et al. 1998. A role for helix 3 of the TRbeta ligand-binding domain in coactivator recruitment identified by characterization of a third cluster of mutations in resistance to thyroid hormone. *EMBO J.* 17:4760–70

96. Chatterjee VK. 1997. Resistance to thyroid hormone. *Horm. Res.* 48:43–46

97. Liu Y, Takeshita A, Misiti S, Chin WW, Yen PM. 1998. Lack of coactivator interaction can be a mechanism for dominant negative activity by mutant thyroid hormone receptors. *Endocrinology* 139:4197–4204

98. Brucker-Davis F, Skarulis MC, Grace MB, Benichou J, Hauser P, et al. 1995. Genetic and clinical features of 42 kindreds with resistance to thyroid hormone. The National Institutes of Health Prospective Study. *Ann. Intern. Med.* 123:572–83

99. Feng W, Ribeiro RC, Wagner RL, Nguyen H, Apriletti JW, et al. 1998. Hormone-dependent coactivator binding to a hydrophobic cleft on nuclear receptors. *Science* 280:1747–49

100. Wagner RL, Apriletti JW, McGrath ME, West BL, Baxter JD, et al. 1995. A structural role for hormone in the thyroid hormone receptor. *Nature* 378:690–97

101. Yao TP, Ku G, Zhou N, Scully R, Livingston DM. 1996. The nuclear hormone receptor coactivator SRC-1 is a specific target of p300. *Proc. Natl. Acad. Sci. USA* 93:10626–31

102. Kwok RP, Lundblad JR, Chrivia JC,

Richards JP, Bachinger HP, et al. 1994. Nuclear protein CBP is a coactivator for the transcription factor CREB. *Nature* 370:223–26

103. Chrivia JC, Kwok RP, Lamb N, Hagiwara M, Montminy MR, et al. 1993. Phosphorylated CREB binds specifically to the nuclear protein CBP. *Nature* 365:855–59

104. Arany Z, Sellers WR, Livingston DM, Eckner R. 1994. E1A-associated p300 and CREB-associated CBP belong to a conserved family of coactivators. *Cell* 77:799–800

105. Lundblad JR, Kwok RP, Laurance ME, Harter ML, Goodman RH. 1995. Adenoviral E1A-associated protein p300 as a functional homologue of the transcriptional co-activator CBP. *Nature* 374:85–88

106. Chakravarti D, LaMorte VJ, Nelson MC, Nakajima T, Schulman IG, et al. 1996. Role of CBP/P300 in nuclear receptor signalling. *Nature* 383:99–103

107. Kamei Y, Xu L, Heinzel T, Torchia J, Kurokawa R, et al. 1996. A CBP integrator complex mediates transcriptional activation and AP-1 inhibition by nuclear receptors. *Cell* 85:403–14

108. Hanstein B, Eckner R, DiRenzo J, Halachmi S, Liu H, et al. 1996. p300 is a component of an estrogen receptor coactivator complex. *Proc. Natl. Acad. Sci. USA* 93:11540–45

109. Horvai AE, Xu L, Korzus E, Brard G, Kalafus D, et al. 1997. Nuclear integration of JAK/STAT and Ras/AP-1 signaling by CBP and p300. *Proc. Natl. Acad. Sci. USA* 94:1074–79

110. Avantaggiati ML, Ogryzko V, Gardner K, Giordano A, Levine AS, et al. 1997. Recruitment of p300/CBP in p53-dependent signal pathways. *Cell* 89:1175–84

111. Bhattacharya S, Eckner R, Grossman S, Oldread E, Arany Z, et al. 1996. Cooperation of Stat2 and p300/CBP in signalling induced by interferon-alpha. *Nature* 383:344–47

112. Perkins ND, Felzien LK, Betts JC, Leung K, Beach DH, et al. 1997. Regulation of NF-kappaB by cyclin-dependent kinases associated with the p300 coactivator. *Science* 275:523–27

113. Mink S, Haenig B, Klempnauer KH. 1997. Interaction and functional collaboration of p300 and C/EBPbeta. *Mol. Cell Biol.* 17:6609–17

114. Cheng X, Reginato MJ, Andrews NC, Lazar MA. 1997. The transcriptional integrator CREB-binding protein mediates positive cross talk between nuclear hormone receptors and the hematopoietic bZip protein p45/NF-E2. *Mol. Cell Biol.* 17:1407–16

115. Janknecht R, Hunter T. 1996. Transcription: a growing coactivator network. *Nature* 383:22–23

116. Korzus E, Torchia J, Rose DW, Xu L, Kurokawa R, et al. 1998. Transcription factor-specific requirements for coactivators and their acetyltransferase functions. *Science* 279:703–7

117. Fondell JD, Ge H, Roeder RG. 1996. Ligand induction of a transcriptionally active thyroid hormone receptor coactivator complex. *Proc. Natl. Acad. Sci. USA* 93:8329–33

118. Rachez C, Suldan Z, Ward J, Chang CP, Burakov, D, et al. 1998. A novel protein complex that interacts with the vitamin D3 receptor in a ligand-dependent manner and enhances VDR transactivation in a cell-free system. *Genes Dev.* 12:1787–800

119. Ryu S, Zhou S, Ladurner AG, Tjian R. 1999. The transcriptional cofactor complex CRSP is required for activity of the enhancer-binding protein Sp1. *Nature* 397:446–50

120. Gu W, Malik S, Ito M, Yuan CX, Fondell JD, et al. 1999. A novel human SRB/MED-containing cofactor complex, SMCC, involved in transcription regulation. *Mol. Cell* 3:97–108

121. Sun X, Zhang Y, Cho H, Rickert P, Lees E, et al. 1998. NAT, a human complex

containing Srb polypeptides that functions as a negative regulator of activated transcription. *Mol. Cell* 2:213–22

122. Chang KH, Chen Y, Chen TT, Chou WH, Chen PL, et al. 1997. A thyroid hormone receptor coactivator negatively regulated by the retinoblastoma protein. *Proc. Natl. Acad. Sci. USA* 94:9040–45

123. Monden T, Wondisford FE, Hollenberg AN. 1997. Isolation and characterization of a novel ligand-dependent thyroid hormone receptor-coactivating protein. *J. Biol. Chem.* 272:29834–41

124. Heery DM, Kalkhoven E, Hoare S, Parker MG. 1997. A signature motif in transcriptional co-activators mediates binding to nuclear receptors. *Nature* 387:733–36

125. McInerney EM, Rose DW, Flynn SE, Westin S, Mullen TM, et al. 1998. Determinants of coactivator LXXLL motif specificity in nuclear receptor transcriptional activation. *Genes Dev.* 12:3357–68

126. Tsai MJ, O'Malley BW. 1994. Molecular mechanisms of action of steroid/thyroid receptor superfamily members. *Annu. Rev. Biochem.* 63:451–86

127. Evans RM. 1989. The v-ErbA oncogene is a thyroid hormone receptor antagonist. *Int. J. Cancer Suppl.* 4:26–28

128. Forrest D, Munoz A, Raynoschek C, Vennstrom B, Beug H. 1990. Requirement for the C-terminal domain of the v-ErbA oncogene protein for biological function and transcriptional repression. *Oncogene* 5:309–16

129. Zenke M, Munoz A, Sap J, Vennstrom B, Beug H. 1990. v-ErbA oncogene activation entails the loss of hormone-dependent regulator activity of c-ErbA. *Cell* 61:1035–49

130. Selmi S, Samuels HH. 1991. Thyroid hormone receptor/and v-ErbA: a single amino acid difference in the C-terminal region influences dominant negative activity and receptor dimer formation. *J. Biol. Chem.* 266:11589–93

131. Baniahmad A, Kohne AC, Renkawitz R.

1992. A transferable silencing domain is present in the thyroid hormone receptor, in the v-ErbA oncogene product and in the retinoic acid receptor. *EMBO J.* 11:1015–23

132. Fondell JD, Roy AL, Roeder RG. 1993. Unliganded thyroid hormone receptor inhibits formation of a functional preinitiation complex: implications for active repression. *Genes Dev.* 7:1400–10

133. Fondell JD, Brunel F, Hisatake K, Roeder RG. 1996. Unliganded thyroid hormone receptor alpha can target TATA-binding protein for transcriptional repression. *Mol. Cell Biol.* 16:281–87

134. Baniahmad A, Ha I, Reinberg D, Tsai S, Tsai MJ, et al. 1993. Interaction of human thyroid hormone receptor beta with transcription factor TFIIB may mediate target gene derepression and activation by thyroid hormone. *Proc. Natl. Acad. Sci. USA* 90:8832–36

135. Casanova J, Helmer E, Selmi-Ruby S, Qi JS, Au-Fliegner M, et al. 1994. Functional evidence for ligand-dependent dissociation of thyroid hormone and retinoic acid receptors from an inhibitory cellular factor. *Mol. Cell Biol.* 14:5756–65

136. Qi JS, Desai-Yajnik V, Greene ME, Raaka BM, Samuels HH. 1995. The ligand-binding domains of the thyroid hormone/retinoid receptor gene subfamily function in vivo to mediate heterodimerization, gene silencing, and transactivation. *Mol. Cell Biol.* 15:1817–25

137. Tong GX, Jeyakumar M, Tanen MR, Bagchi MK. 1996. Transcriptional silencing by unliganded thyroid hormone receptor beta requires a soluble corepressor that interacts with the ligand-binding domain of the receptor. *Mol. Cell Biol.* 16:1909–20

138. Horlein AJ, Naar AM, Heinzel T, Torchia J, Gloss B, et al. 1995. Ligand-independent repression by the thyroid hormone receptor mediated by a nuclear receptor co-repressor. *Nature* 377:397–404

139. Seol W, Choi HS, Moore DD. 1995. Isolation of proteins that interact specifically with the retinoid X receptor: two novel orphan receptors. *Mol. Endocrinol.* 9: 72–85

140. Chen JD, Evans RM. 1995. A transcriptional co-repressor that interacts with nuclear hormone receptors. *Nature* 377:454–57

141. Ordentlich P, Downes M, Xie W, Genin A, Spinner NB, et al. 1999. Unique forms of human and mouse nuclear receptor corepressor SMRT. *Proc. Natl. Acad. Sci. USA* 96:2639–44

142. Sande S, Privalsky ML. 1996. Identification of TRACs (T3 receptor-associating cofactors), a family of cofactors that associate with, and modulate the activity of, nuclear hormone receptors. *Mol. Endocrinol.* 10:813–25

143. Nagy L, Kao HY, Chakravarti D, Lin RJ, Hassig CA, et al. 1997. Nuclear receptor repression mediated by a complex containing SMRT, mSin3A, and histone deacetylase. *Cell* 89:373–80

144. Li H, Leo C, Schroen DJ, Chen JD. 1997. Characterization of receptor interaction and transcriptional repression by the corepressor SMRT. *Mol. Endocrinol.* 11:2025–37

145. Chen JD, Umesono K, Evans RM. 1996. SMRT isoforms mediate repression and anti-repression of nuclear receptor heterodimers. *Proc. Natl. Acad. Sci. USA* 93:7567–71

146. Zamir I, Harding HP, Atkins GB, Horlein A, Glass CK, et al. 1996. A nuclear hormone receptor corepressor mediates transcriptional silencing by receptors with distinct repression domains. *Mol. Cell Biol.* 16:5458–65

147. Burke LJ, Downes M, Laudet V, Muscat GE. 1998. Identification and characterization of a novel corepressor interaction region in RVR and Rev-ErbA alpha. *Mol. Endocrinol.* 12:248–62

148. Bailey PJ, Dowhan, DH, Franke K, Burke LJ, Downes M, et al. 1997. Transcriptional repression by COUP-TF II is dependent on the C-terminal domain and involves the N-CoR variant, RIP13delta1. *J. Steroid Biochem. Mol. Biol.* 63:165–74

149. Shibata H, Nawaz Z, Tsai SY, O'Malley BW, Tsai MJ. 1997. Gene silencing by chicken ovalbumin upstream promoter-transcription factor I (COUP-TFI) is mediated by transcriptional corepressors, nuclear receptor-corepressor (N-CoR) and silencing mediator for retinoic acid receptor and thyroid hormone receptor (SMRT). *Mol. Endocrinol.* 11:714–24

150. Huynh KD, Bardwell VJ. 1998. The BCL-6 POZ domain and other POZ domains interact with the co-repressors N-CoR and SMRT. *Oncogene* 17:2473–84

151. Hong SH, David G, Wong CW, Dejean A, Privalsky ML. 1997. SMRT corepressor interacts with PLZF and with the PML-retinoic acid receptor alpha (RAR-alpha) and PLZF-RARalpha oncoproteins associated with acute promyelocytic leukemia. *Proc. Natl. Acad. Sci. USA* 94:9028–33

152. Kurokawa R, Soderstrom M, Horlein A, Halachmi S, Brown M, et al. 1995. Polarity-specific activities of retinoic acid receptors determined by a co-repressor. *Nature* 377:451–54

153. Grignani F, De Matteis S, Nervi C, Tomassoni L, Gelmetti V, et al. 1998. Fusion proteins of the retinoic acid receptor-alpha recruit histone deacetylase in promyelocytic leukaemia. *Nature* 391:815–18

154. Barlow C, Meister B, Lardelli M, Lendahl U, Vennstrom B. 1994. Thyroid abnormalities and hepatocellular carcinoma in mice transgenic for v-ErbA. *EMBO J.* 13:4241–50

155. Damm K, Beug H, Graf T, Vennstrom B. 1987. A single point mutation in erbA restores the erythroid transforming potential of a mutant avian erythroblas-

tosis virus (AEV) defective in both erbA and erbB oncogenes. *EMBO J.* 6:375–82

156. Damm K, Evans RM. 1993. Identification of a domain required for oncogenic activity and transcriptional suppression by v-ErbA and thyroid-hormone receptor alpha. *Proc. Natl. Acad. Sci. USA* 90:10668–72

157. Wong CW, Privalsky ML. 1998. Transcriptional repression by the SMRT-mSin3 corepressor: multiple interactions, multiple mechanisms, and a potential role for TFIIB. *Mol. Cell Biol.* 18:5500–10

158. Cohen RN, Wondisford FE, Hollenberg AN. 1998. Two separate NCoR (nuclear receptor corepressor) interaction domains mediate corepressor action on thyroid hormone response elements. *Mol. Endocrinol.* 12:1567–81

159. Seol W, Mahon MJ, Lee YK, Moore D. 1996. Two receptor interacting domains in the nuclear hormone receptor corepressor RIP13/N-CoR. *Mol. Endocrinol.* 10:1646–55

160. Zamir I, Zhang J, Lazar MA. 1997. Stoichiometric and steric principles governing repression by nuclear hormone receptors. *Genes Dev.* 11:835–46

161. Jeannin E, Robyr D, Desvergne B. 1998. Transcriptional regulatory patterns of the myelin basic protein and malic enzyme genes by the thyroid hormone receptors alpha1 and beta1. *J. Biol. Chem.* 273:24239–48

162. Tagami T, Kopp P, Johnson W, Arseven OK, Jameson JL. 1998. The thyroid hormone receptor variant alpha2 is a weak antagonist because it is deficient in interactions with nuclear receptor corepressors. *Endocrinology* 139:2535–44

163. Martin B, Renkawitz R, Muller M. 1994. Two silencing sub-domains of v-ErbA synergize with each other, but not with RXR. *Nucleic Acids Res.* 22:4899–905

164. Zamir I, Dawson J, Lavinsky RM, Glass CK, Rosenfeld MG, et al. 1997. Cloning and characterization of a corepressor and

potential component of the nuclear hormone receptor repression complex. *Proc. Natl. Acad. Sci. USA* 94:14400–5

165. Burris TP, Nawaz Z, Tsai MJ, O'Malley BW. 1995. A nuclear hormone receptor-associated protein that inhibits transactivation by the thyroid hormone and retinoic acid receptors. *Proc. Natl. Acad. Sci. USA* 92:9525–29

166. Harding HP, Lazar MA. 1995. The monomer-binding orphan receptor Rev-Erb represses transcription as a dimer on a novel direct repeat [published erratum in *Mol. Cell. Biol.* 1995. 11:6479]. *Mol. Cell Biol.* 15:4791–802

167. Zhang J, Guenther MG, Carthew RW, Lazar MA. 1998. Proteasomal regulation of nuclear receptor corepressor-mediated repression. *Genes Dev.* 12:1775–80

168. Tang AH, Neufeld TP, Kwan E, Rubin GM. 1997. PHYL acts to down-regulate TTK88, a transcriptional repressor of neuronal cell fates, by a SINA-dependent mechanism. *Cell* 90:459–67

169. Li S, Li Y, Carthew RW, Lai ZC. 1997. Photoreceptor cell differentiation requires regulated proteolysis of the transcriptional repressor Tramtrack. *Cell* 90:469–78

170. Laherty CD, Yang WM, Sun JM, Davie JR, Seto E, et al. 1997. Histone deacetylases associated with the mSin3 corepressor mediate mad transcriptional repression. *Cell* 89:349–56

171. Zhang Y, Iratni R, Erdjument-Bromage H, Tempst P, Reinberg D. 1997. Histone deacetylases and SAP18, a novel polypeptide, are components of a human Sin3 complex. *Cell* 89:357–64

172. Kadosh D, Struhl K. 1998. Histone deacetylase activity of Rpd3 is important for transcriptional repression in vivo. *Genes Dev.* 12:797–805

173. Zhang Y, Sun ZW, Iratni R, Erdjument-Bromage H, Tempst P, et al. 1998. SAP30, a novel protein conserved between human and yeast, is a compo-

nent of a histone deacetylase complex. *Mol. Cell* 1:1021–31

174. Alland L, Muhle R, Hou H Jr., Potes J, Chin L, et al. 1997. Role for N-CoR and histone deacetylase in Sin3-mediated transcriptional repression. *Nature* 387:49–55

175. Hassig CA, Fleischer TC, Billin AN, Schreiber SL, Ayer DE. 1997. Histone deacetylase activity is required for full transcriptional repression by mSin3A. *Cell* 89:341–47

176. Heinzel T, Lavinsky RM, Mullen TM, Soderstrom M, Laherty CD, et al. 1997. A complex containing N-CoR, mSin3 and histone deacetylase mediates transcriptional repression. *Nature* 387:43–48

177. Laherty CD, Billin AN, Lavinsky RM, Yochum GS, Bush AC, et al. 1998. SAP30, a component of the mSin3 corepressor complex involved in N-CoR-mediated repression by specific transcription factors. *Mol. Cell* 2:33–42

178. Pazin MJ, Kadonaga JT. 1997. What's up and down with histone deacetylation and transcription? *Cell* 89:325–28

179. Muscat GE, Burke LJ, Downes M. 1998. The corepressor N-CoR and its variants RIP13a and RIP13Delta1 directly interact with the basal transcription factors TFIIB, TAFII32 and TAFII70. *Nucleic Acids Res.* 26:2899–907

180. Wong J, Patterton D, Imhof A, Guschin D, Shi Y, et al. 1998. Distinct requirements for chromatin assembly in transcriptional repression by thyroid hormone receptor and histone deacetylase. *EMBO J.* 17:520–34

181. Tagami T, Jameson JL. 1998. Nuclear corepressors enhance the dominant negative activity of mutant receptors that cause resistance to thyroid hormone. *Endocrinology* 139:640–50

182. Yoh SM, Chatterjee VK, Privalsky ML. 1997. Thyroid hormone resistance syndrome manifests as an aberrant interaction between mutant T3 receptors and transcriptional corepressors. *Mol. Endocrinol.* 11:470–80

183. Nagaya T, Fujieda M, Seo H. 1998. Requirement of corepressor binding of thyroid hormone receptor mutants for dominant negative inhibition. *Biochem. Biophys. Res. Commun.* 247:620–23

184. Nagaya T, Eberhardt NL, Jameson JL. 1993. Thyroid hormone resistance syndrome: correlation of dominant negative activity and location of mutations. *J. Clin. Endocrinol. Metab.* 77:982–90

185. Nagaya T, Madison LD, Jameson JL. 1992. Thyroid hormone receptor mutants that cause resistance to thyroid hormone. Evidence for receptor competition for DNA sequences in target genes. *J. Biol. Chem.* 267:13014–19

186. Guidez F, Ivins S, Zhu J, Soderstrom M, Waxman S, et al. 1998. Reduced retinoic acid-sensitivies of nuclear receptor corepressor binding to PML- and PLZF-RARalpha underlie molecular pathogenesis and treatment of acute promyelocytic leukemia. *Blood* 91:2634–42

187. He LZ, Guidez F, Triboli C, Peruzzi D, Ruthardt M, et al. 1998. Distinct interactions of PML-RARalpha and PLZF-RARalpha with co-repressors determine differential responses to RA in APL. *Nat. Genet.* 18:126–35

188. Collins SJ. 1998. Acute promyelocytic leukemia: relieving repression induces remission. *Blood* 91:2631–33

189. Lin RJ, Nagy L, Inoue S, ShaoW, Miller WH Jr., et al. 1998. Role of the histone deacetylase complex in acute promyelocytic leukaemia. *Nature* 391:811–14

190. Jeanteur P. 1998. Acute promyelocytic leukemia, histone deacetylase, and response to retinoids. *Bull. Cancer* 85:301–3

191. Gelmetti V, Zhang J, Fanelli M, Minucci S, Pelicci PG, et al. 1998. Aberrant recruitment of the nuclear receptor corepressor-histone deacetylase complex by the acute myeloid leukemia fusion partner ETO. *Mol. Cell Biol.* 18:7185–91

192. Lutterbach B, Westendorf JJ, Linggi B, Patten A, Moniwa M, et al. 1998. ETO, a target of t(8;21) in acute leukemia, interacts with the N-CoR and mSin3 corepressors. *Mol. Cell Biol.* 18:7176–84

193. Wang J, Hoshino T, Redner RL, Kajigaya S, Liu JM. 1998. ETO, fusion partner in t(8;21) acute myeloid leukemia, represses transcription by interaction with the human N-CoR/mSin3/HDAC1 complex. *Proc. Natl. Acad. Sci. USA* 95:10860–65

194. Xue Y, Wong J, Moreno GT, Young MK, Cote J, et al. 1998. NURD, a novel complex with both ATP-dependent chromatin-remodeling and histone deacetylase activities. *Mol. Cell* 2:851–61

195. Zhang Y, LeRoy G, Seelig HP, Lane WS, Reinberg D. 1998. The dermatomyositis-specific autoantigen Mi2 is a component of a complex containing histone deacetylase and nucleosome remodeling activities. *Cell* 95:279–89

196. Wade PA, Jones PL, Vermaak D, Wolffe AP. 1998. A multiple subunit Mi-2 histone deacetylase from *Xenopus laevis* cofractionates with an associated Snf2 superfamily ATPase. *Curr. Biol.* 8:843–46

197. Mizuguchi G, Tsukiyama T, Wisniewski J, Wu C. 1997. Role of nucleosome remodeling factor NURF in transcriptional activation of chromatin. *Mol. Cell* 1:141–50

198. Martinez-Balbas MA, Tsukiyama T, Gdula D, Wu C. 1998. Drosophila NURF-55, a WD repeat protein involved in histone metabolism. *Proc. Natl. Acad. Sci. USA* 95:132–37

199. Georgel PT, Tsukiyama T, Wu C. 1997. Role of histone tails in nucleosome remodeling by Drosophila NURF. *EMBO J.* 16:4717–26

200. Tsukiyama T, Daniel C, Tamkun J, Wu C. 1995. ISWI, a member of the SWI2/SNF2 ATPase family, encodes the 140 kDa subunit of the nucleosome remodeling factor. *Cell* 83:1021–26

201. Klaholz BP, Renaud JP, Mitschler A, Zusi C, Chambon P, et al. 1998. Conformational adaptation of agonists to the human nuclear receptor RAR gamma. *Nat. Struct. Biol.* 5:199–202

202. Renaud JP, Rochel N, Ruff M, Vivat V, Chambon P, et al. 1995. Crystal structure of the RAR-gamma ligand-binding domain bound to all-*trans* retinoic acid. *Nature* 378:681–89

203. Uppenberg J, Svensson C, Jaki M, Bertilsson G, Jendeberg L, et al. 1998. Crystal structure of the ligand binding domain of the human nuclear receptor PPAR gamma. *J. Biol. Chem.* 273:31108–12

204. Nolte RT, Wisely GB, Westin S, Cobb JE, Lambert MH, et al. 1998. Ligand binding and co-activator assembly of the peroxisome proliferator-activated receptor-gamma. *Nature* 395:137–43

205. Brzozowski AM, Pike AC, Dauter Z, Hubbard RE, Bonn T, et al. 1997. Molecular basis of agonism and antagonism in the oestrogen receptor. *Nature* 389:753–58

206. Shiau AK, Barstad D, Loria PM, Cheng L, Kushner PJ, et al. 1998. The structural basis of estrogen receptor/coactivator recognition and the antagonism of this interaction by tamoxifen. *Cell* 95:927–37

207. Williams SP, Sigler PB. 1998. Atomic structure of progesterone complexed with its receptor. *Nature* 393:392–96

208. Apriletti JW, Ribeiro RC, Wagner RL, Feng W, Webb P, et al. 1998. Molecular and structural biology of thyroid hormone receptors. *Clin. Exp. Pharmacol. Physiol.* 25(Suppl.):S2–11

209. Ribeiro RC, Apriletti JW, Wagner RL, Feng W, Kushner PJ, et al. 1998. X-ray crystallographic and functional studies of thyroid hormone receptor. *J. Steroid Biochem. Mol. Biol.* 65:133–41

210. Bradley DJ, Young WSD, Weinberger C. 1989. Differential expression of alpha and beta thyroid hormone receptor genes in rat brain and pituitary. *Proc. Natl. Acad. Sci. USA* 86:7250–54

211. Bradley DJ, Towle HC, Young WSD. 1992. Spatial and temporal expression of alpha- and beta-thyroid hormone receptor mRNAs, including the beta 2-subtype, in the developing mammalian nervous system. *J. Neurosci.* 12:2288–302

212. Forrest D, Sjoberg M, Vennstrom B. 1990. Contrasting developmental and tissue-specific expression of alpha and beta thyroid hormone receptor genes. *EMBO J.* 9:1519–28

213. Forrest D, Hallbook F, Persson H, Vennstrom B. 1991. Distinct functions for thyroid hormone receptors alpha and beta in brain development indicated by differential expression of receptor genes. *EMBO J.* 10:269–75

214. Strait KA, Schwartz HL, Perez-Castillo A, Oppenheimer JH. 1990. Relationship of c-ErbA mRNA content to tissue triiodothyronine nuclear binding capacity and function in developing and adult rats. *J. Biol. Chem.* 265:10514–21

215. Strait KA, Schwartz HL, Seybold VS, Ling NC, Oppenheimer JH. 1991. Immunofluorescence localization of thyroid hormone receptor protein beta 1 and variant alpha 2 in selected tissues: cerebellar Purkinje cells as a model for beta 1 receptor-mediated developmental effects

of thyroid hormone in brain. *Proc. Natl. Acad. Sci. USA* 88:3887–91

216. Wikstrom L, Johansson C, Salto C, Barlow C, Campos Barros A, et al. 1998. Abnormal heart rate and body temperature in mice lacking thyroid hormone receptor alpha 1. *EMBO J.* 17:455–61

217. Fraichard A, Chassande O, Plateroti M, Roux JP, Trouillas J, et al. 1997. The T3R alpha gene encoding a thyroid hormone receptor is essential for post-natal development and thyroid hormone production. *EMBO J.* 16:4412–20

218. Forrest D, Erway LC, Ng L, Altschuler R, Curran T. 1996. Thyroid hormone receptor beta is essential for development of auditory function. *Nat. Genet* 13:354–57

219. Forrest D, Hanebuth E, Smeyne RJ, Everds N, Stewart CL, et al. 1996. Recessive resistance to thyroid hormone in mice lacking thyroid hormone receptor beta: evidence for tissue-specific modulation of receptor function. *EMBO J.* 15:3006–15

220. Gauthier K, Chassande O, PlaterotiM, Roux JP, Legrand C, et al. 1999. Different functions for the thyroid hormone receptors TRalpha and TRbeta in the control of thyroid hormone production and post-natal development. *EMBO J.* 18:623–31

Annu. Rev. Physiol. 2000. 62:467–91

ROLE OF CFTR IN THE COLON

R. Greger

*Physiologisches Institut, Albert-Ludwigs-Universität, Hermann-Herder-Strasse 7D,
79104 Freiburg, Germany; e-mail: Greger@ruf.uni-freiburg.de*

Key Words Cl^- secretion, Cl^- channel, diarrhea, cystic fibrosis

■ **Abstract** In contrast to the airways, the defects in colonic function in cystic fibrosis (CF) patients are closely related to the defect in CFTR. The gastrointestinal phenotype of CF transgenic mice closely resembles the phenotype in CF patients, which clearly indicates the crucial role of CFTR in colonic Cl^- secretion and the absence of an effective compensation.

In the colon, stimulation of CFTR Cl^- channels involves cAMP- or cGMP-dependent phosphorylation. Exocytosis is not involved. Activation of CFTR leads to coactivation of basolateral K_VLQT_1-type K^+ channels and inhibition of luminal Na^+ channels (ENaC). In contrast to cultured cells, Ca^{2+} does not activate luminal Cl^- channels in intact enterocytes. It activates basolateral SK4-type K^+ channels and luminal K^+ channels, which provide additional driving force for Cl^- exit. The magnitude of Cl^- secretion, however, completely depends on the presence of at least a residual CFTR function in the luminal membrane.

These findings have been clearly demonstrated by Ussing chamber experiments in colon epithelium biopsies of CF and normal individuals: Colonic Cl^- secretion in CF patients is variable and reflects the genotype; a complete defect of CFTR is paralleled by the absence of Cl^- secretion and unmasks Ca^{2+}-regulated K^+ channels in the luminal membrane; overabsorption of Na^+ in CF reflects the absence of ENaC inhibition by CFTR; and the functional status of CF colon can be mimicked by the complete suppression of cAMP stimulation in enterocytes of healthy individuals.

INTRODUCTION

The colon is placed strategically at the end of the gastrointestinal tract. This dictates its various functions: reclamation of water, in humans of approximately 1 liter per day; further digestion with the aid of saprophytic bacteria; absorption of short chain fatty acids and other contents; fine tuning of electrolyte excretion; production of stool, approximately 200 g per day; and storage of stool for defecation. The mucosal barrier function must be intact because otherwise bacteria would invade the blood stream. The feces contain a large fraction of solid matter, therefore the colonic wall must also be secured so that stool can pass through the lumen without mechanically damaging the mucosa. To meet all these requirements the colonic wall contains a specific mucosa, the respective circular and

0066–4278/00/0315–0467$12.00

longitudinal smooth muscle network, as well as its intrinsic nervous and autocrine system. The mucosa is structurally simple compared with the small intestine as it contains crypts but no villi. The mucosal surface is covered by mucus, which is produced by the goblet cells and is modified by water and electrolyte transport. The cell types in the colon comprise germinative cells at the base of the crypt, chromaffin cells, goblet cells, and enterocytes. The life span of an enterocyte is short, for example 4 to 8 days in humans. All enterocytes are produced at the base of the crypt (Figure 1). They travel up along the crypt axis as they mature, reach the surface, and are shed off. This maturation is in accord with a corresponding change in functional properties.

In terms of epithelial transport function the colonic mucosa absorbs and secretes electrolytes. The following transport processes have been reported for colonic mucosa: (a) electroneutral absorption of Na^+ and Cl^- via the parallel arrangement of Na^+/H^+ and Cl^-/HCO_3^- exchangers (1); (b) rheogenic Na^+ absorption via epithelial Na^+ channels (ENaC) (2, 3); (c) absorption of K^+ via the H^+/K^+-ATPase located in the luminal membrane (4); (d) absorption of short fatty acids mostly by the uptake of the anion (1); (e) K^+ secretion via K^+ channels

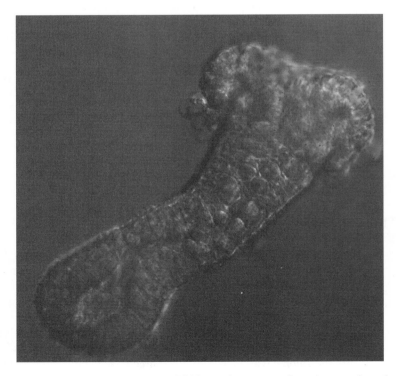

Figure 1   Isolated rat colonic crypt. DIC Nomarsky contrast. Length approximately 350 µm. Crypt base *lower left side,* surface cells *upper right side.*

in the luminal membrane (5); and (*f*) Cl⁻ secretion via luminal membrane Cl⁻ channels (3) (Figure 2). The transport of water is supposed to follow the osmotic gradient set by the direction of net ion transport but the detailed mechanisms have not been clarified.

This review focuses on the mechanisms of Cl⁻ secretion but also addresses the other processes inasmuch as they are e interdependent and regulated in a complex fashion. A short discussion is given comparing results obtained in cultured colonocytes and in intact colonic crypts.

CFTR AND CHLORIDE SECRETION

When stimulated by secretagogues, the colon secretes Na^+, Cl^- and water (1, 6). These secretagogues can be neurotransmitters such as acetylcholine (ACh), vasoactive intestinal peptide (VIP), locally liberated autacoids such as prostaglandins, guanylin, and bacterial toxins such as heat stable *Escherichia coli* toxin or choleratoxin (6–10). The rate of this secretion can be substantial, although it should be kept in mind that the major site of action of the strong secretagogues such as the bacterial toxins (the diarrhea-inducing effect) is in the small bowel and not in the colon.

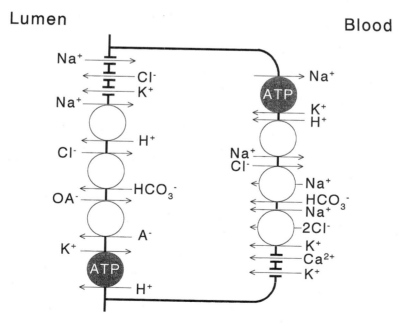

Figure 2 Transport processes in colonic enterocytes. Arrows, conductive pathways; circles, carrier systems; circles with ATP, ion pumps (-ATPases).

The crucial role of the cystic fibrosis transmembrane conductance regulator (CFTR) in Cl^- secretion is highlighted by the fact that on the one hand intestinal Cl^- secretion is defective in cystic fibrosis (CF), which leads to meconium ileus in approximately 10% of newborn CF children and obstructive gut disease (meconium ileus equivalent) at later ages (11, 12). On the other hand, it has been argued that less serious bacterially induced diarrhea in the heterozygous CF population has provided a genetic advantage, which has kept the incidence of CF mutations high (12). Whether this argument holds true has not been proven. It probably cannot be answered easily experimentally (13), but the data in CF knockout mice suggest that heterozygotes respond less to bacterial toxins than normal controls (11).

The properties of colonocytes change characteristically when they travel up from the base to the surface. The base and middle cells are the targets for cAMP-mediated Cl^- secretion, although even the surface cells make a minor contribution to this process (3, 14). Absorption of Na^+ via ENaC channels is mostly found in the surface and middle cells, but not in the base cells. The activation of Cl^- secretion by carbachol (or acetylcholine) is present all along the crypt axis (3).

The Concept of Chloride Secretion

The process whereby Cl^- is secreted in the colon is schematicized in Figure 3, which represents a mid-crypt cell. This secretory process generates a lumen-negative voltage, even with equal NaCl concentrations on both sides of the epithelium. Therefore, this process resembles active Cl^- secretion, and debate centers on whether a Cl^- pump is necessary to drive this process (15). Countering this hypothesis is the fact that there is no evidence for an ATP-driven Cl^- pump in this and other mammalian Cl^- transporting epithelia but rather a high density of the Na^+,K^+-ATPase. Alternatively, it was proposed that uphill Cl^- secretion is possible by coupling the cellular uptake of Cl^- on the basal cell pole to that of Na^+. This necessitates the preservation of a transmembrane gradient for Na^+ by the active Na^+ extrusion by the Na^+,K^+-ATPase. Cl^- could then leave the cell across the luminal membrane down its electrochemical gradient via Cl^- channels (16), which could also partially explain the lumen-negative voltage. This concept is supported by the finding that so-called loop diuretics such as bumetanide, furosemide, piretanide, and azosemide all inhibit Cl^- secretion in the colon when added to the blood side (17). The mechanism illustrated in Figure 3 is based on data showing basolateral Na^+- and K^+-coupled Cl^- uptake via the $Na^+2Cl^-K^+$ cotransporter, which originally was found in the thick ascending limb of the loop of Henle, the renal target of loop diuretics (18). The fact that Cl^- uptake is coupled to both cations is of high relevance. The K^+ ions taken up by the $Na^+2Cl^-K^+$ cotransporter recycle via K^+ channels present in the basolateral membrane. This K^+ recycling hyperpolarizes the cell and provides the driving force for Cl^- exit through Cl^- channels in the luminal membrane.

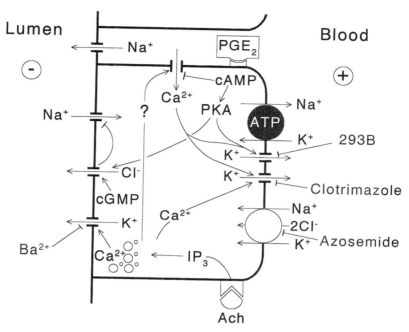

Figure 3 The mechanisms of Na$^+$ and Cl$^-$ absorption and secretion in colonic mid-crypt cells. Note that the cell is equipped with the machinery for NaCl absorption and NaCl secretion. NaCl secretion can be activated via agonists increasing cytosolic cAMP and via those increasing cytosolic Ca^{2+} ([Ca^{2+}]$_i$). Activated NaCl secretion inhibits NaCl absorption by a reciprocal inhibitory effect of CFTR Cl$^-$ channels on epithelial Na$^+$ channels (ENaC). cAMP produces a fall in [Ca^{2+}]$_i$ by reducing voltage-dependent Ca^{2+} influx. Hyperpolarization enhances and depolarization reduces Ca^{2+} influx. Ca^{2+} and cAMP act cooperatively on NaCl secretion: (*a*) cAMP not only enhances CFTR-type Cl$^-$ conductance, but also increases basolateral K$^+$ conductance via K$_V$LQT$_1$ K$^+$ channels. (*b*) Ca^{2+} not only activates SK4 type K$^+$ channels in the basolateral membrane, it also enhances the K$_V$LQT$_1$-mediated K$^+$ conductance. In addition, the two second messengers act differentially; cAMP reduces Ca^{2+} influx (see above) via depolarization, and Ca^{2+} activates a luminal K$^+$ conductance leading to K$^+$ secretion. In CF, CFTR type Cl$^-$ channels cannot be activated. Therefore, ENaC channels stay activated and Ca^{2+} mobilizing agonists enhance K$^+$ secretion (see also Figures 4 and 5). For symbols definition see legend to Figure 2.

Stated differently, rheogenic K$^+$ exit on the serosal side and rheogenic Cl$^-$ exit on the mucosal side are interdependent and produce the mucosa-negative voltage, which drives passive Na$^+$ secretion. In this sense the operation of the Na$^+$2Cl$^-$K$^+$ cotransporter rather than that of a Na$^+$Cl$^-$ cotransporter is very economical because it generates an overall metabolic ratio of 6 moles of Na$^+$

and Cl^- secreted for 1 mole ATP consumed rather than a ratio of 3 to 1, which is the ratio of the primary active pump, the Na^+,K^+-ATPase (19).

The Agonistic Pathways

The second messenger pathways to stimulate Cl^- secretion utilize at least cAMP, cGMP, and Ca^{2+}. Their putative targets are summarized in Figure 3. cAMP has its major effect on the CFTR Cl^- channels in the luminal membrane (20, 21). However, additional targets are very likely: cAMP-dependent protein phosphorylation has a stimulatory effect on basolateral K^+ channels, probably those of K_vLQT_1 type (22), and an inhibitory effect on Na^+/H^+ exchange in the luminal membrane (1). In addition, cAMP changes transcription on a more protracted time scale (23). The effects on ENaC are discussed below.

It has been suggested that CFTR is activated by cAMP by enhancing the number of copies in of the membrane (24–26), which could be effected by enhancing the rate of exocytosis or reducing the rate of endocytosis of CFTR-containing membrane vesicles (27). It has also been shown in immunolocalization experiments that CFTR moves from the cytosol to the plasma membrane when the cells are activated by enhancing cytosolic cAMP (25). Moreover, it has even been suggested that CFTR somehow controls membrane trafficking (28). Sheets of cultured A6 cells, stemming from frog kidney, and possessing a CFTR equivalent (29), have been shown to respond to cAMP by increases in membrane capacitance (30). CFTR expressing *Xenopus* oocytes activated by cAMP change their voltage clamp-induced current transients, as expected for a large increase in membrane capacitance (25). We have developed a new and sensitive method to monitor changes in membrane capacitance by patch-clamp techniques and find that Chinese hamster ovary cells, expressing CFTR and pretreated by forskolin, show the expected large increases in Cl^- conductance but only very small (if any) corresponding increases in membrane capacitance (31). Similar experiments have also recently been performed in isolated rat colonic crypts and in in vitro perfused rectal gland tubules of *Squalus acanthias*. In both preparations membrane capacitance increases by cAMP very slightly in contrast to the very marked increase in conductance. The small increase in membrane capacitance is most probably caused by the ensuing volume increase but not by exocytosis (32). These studies in tissues showing endogenous CFTR regulation suggest that activation by cAMP does not involve detectable exocytosis. In fact, CFTR activation can be shown in cell free (excised) membrane patches and involves the phosphorylation of the regulatory domain by protein kinase A (21, 33). It is unclear, however, which of the protein kinase A sites of this domain are necessary and used for phosphorylation (21).

cGMP increases Cl^- secretion in the intestine (7, 8). Its effect mimics that of cAMP. It has been proposed that cGMP, via cGMP regulated (G) protein kinase II (PKG II), activates CFTR (7, 34), with a similar mechanism proposed for the rectal gland (35). In addition, it is possible that cGMP also acts by inhibition of phosphodiesterase, which leads to an increase in cAMP.

The targets of elevated cytosolic Ca^{2+} ($[Ca^{2+}]_i$) are less clear. Ca^{2+} activates a small conductance K^+ channel in the basolateral membrane (36, 37), which we have identified as a SK4 K^+ channel (38). This channel has a single-channel conductance of approximately 15 pS. It is activated by $[Ca^{2+}]_i$ in the physiological range and is inhibited by imidazoles such as clotrimazole (39). In addition, Ca^{2+} apparently activates the K_vLQT_1 K^+ channel, which is also present in the basolateral membrane (22). An unidentified K^+ channel in the luminal membrane is also activated (5, 40). This mechanism can be shown by stimulating colon mucosa with acetylcholine in the absence of cAMP- producing agonists (41). Then a lumen-positive current (voltage) is produced, which can be prevented by the luminal application of Ba^{2+} (5). It is still not entirely clear whether increased $[Ca^{2+}]_i$ also activates Cl^- channels in the lumen membrane. In colonocytes acetylcholine, carbachol (CCH), ATP, and neurotensin all activate a Ca^{2+}-regulated Cl^- conductance (42–45). Similarly, in colonic mid-crypt and surface cells, the carcinogen dimethylhydrazine (DMH) leads to an altered CCH response. While CCH normally hyperpolarizes crypt cells (activation of K^+ channels), the voltage response is more complex after DMH pretreatment and always consists of a depolarization, caused by the activation of a Ca^{2+}-regulated Cl^- conductance (46). Hence, enterocytes that proliferate and depart from their differentiation program, as indicated by the absence of ENaC, possess Ca^{2+}-activated Cl^- channels. We recently reexamined this issue and measured whole-cell conductances of mid-colonic crypt cells in response to CCH and in the presence of K^+ channel blockers. We found that CCH had no detectable effect on whole-cell conductances under these conditions (R Greger, unpublished observation). Thus it seems reasonable to conclude that $[Ca^{2+}]_i$ does not detectably activate luminal Cl^- channels in intact colonic enterocytes. The situation is entirely different for cultured colonocytes and precancerous colon.

The Defect in Cystic Fibrosis

The defect in CF leads to a reduction or abolishment of Cl^- secretion. This causes meconium ileus in ~10% of the newborns with CF and the meconium ileus equivalent in the adult (11, 12, 47). Unlike the poor model character of CF knock-out mice for human lung disease in CF, the intestinal complications in these mice closely resemble those of CF patients. In fact, most of these mice die from intestinal complications (11). The details of mucus secretion in CF versus healthy controls are only partly understood. The amount of mucus appears to be enhanced in CF, and its composition may be altered. Mucus accumulates in glands of Lieberkühn. The goblet cells, at least in some CF knock-out mice, are hypertrophied and hyperplastic (11).

Colonic Cl^- secretion in CF is affected to a variable degree, which probably largely reflects the genotype (see below). It can be completely absent, which underscores the fact that there is no evidence for the presence of alternative Cl^- channels in the luminal membrane. It has been argued that, in this respect, the situation for respiratory epithelial cells may be more advantageous because there some data support the existence of Ca^{2+}-sensitive or otherwise activated Cl^- channels (48). In the CF colon, even agonists such as acetylcholine cannot support Cl^- secretion because this neurotransmitter, by enhancing cytosolic Ca^{2+} activity (49), apparently activates only Ca^{2+}-regulated K^+ channels (SK4) in the basolateral membrane (see above) and an unidentified Ca^{2+}-regulated K^+ channel in the luminal membrane (36, 38).

Activated CFTR normally downregulates ENaC type Na^+ channels present in the luminal membrane of intermediate and surface crypt cells (50). This cAMP-induced ENaC inactivation is absent in CF colon (11). Therefore, NaCl and H_2O absorption continues unimpeded, contributing to the concentration of mucus. The issue of ENaC CFTR interaction is discussed in detail below.

It has been suggested that activation of CFTR by cAMP leads to the coactivation of K_VLQT_1. This is based on observations in *Xenopus laevis* oocytes injected with CFTR cRNA (51). A comparable phenomenon is seen in colonic crypt cells. For example, after addition of forskolin, the luminal membrane Cl^- conductance is immediately increased, followed by a more delayed increase in the basolateral membrane K^+ conductance, which has been shown to be the target of the chromanol 293B and which is caused by K_VLQT_1 channels (52, 53). This type of CFTR-K^+-channel interaction must be indirect because the two channel proteins reside in different cell membranes. It cannot be excluded, on the basis of the data available for the colon, that the activation processes of the two conductances are coordinated in time but are not otherwise interrelated.

Testing Colon Function for the Diagnosis of Cystic Fibrosis

Mini-Ussing chambers have been constructed that allow examination of the gut from mice or even small biopsies from human rectum mucosa (41). This approach has now been used to examine material from otherwise healthy volunteers and CF patients. Three major findings have resulted: (*a*) the fact that Cl^- secretion cannot be appropriately stimulated in CF tissue, (*b*) the unexpected observation that carbachol induces a lumen-positive short circuit current in these patients, and (*c*) absence of inhibition of ENaC (41, 54, 79).

Figure 4 shows an example of an Ussing chamber experiment in rectum mucosa biopsies of a control subject and a CF patient. It is evident that cAMP stimulation led to the expected activation of Cl^- secretion in the biopsy of the normal individual but not in that of the CF patient. Furthermore, carbachol induced a transient and strong increase in the secretory current in the normal but not in the CF tissue; instead, the opposite effect, namely a lumen-positive voltage (and current) was seen. This lumen-positive current results from the activation of K^+ channels in the luminal membrane (5, 41). In the presence of indomethacin, the carbachol response is gradually attenuated in the intact tissue until after some

a
Non-CF rectal tissue

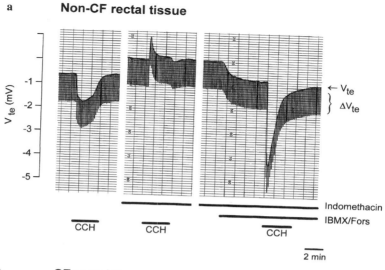

b
CF rectal tissue

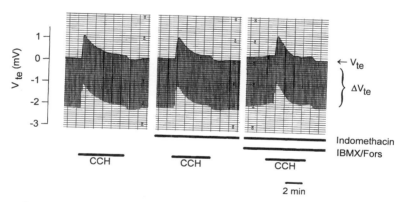

Figure 4 Ussing chamber analysis of human colonic mucosa. (A) Non-CF tissue. (B) CF tissue. Transepithelial voltage (V_{te}) is plotted as a function of time. The pulse amplitudes reflect the transepithelial resistance (R_{te}) and are caused by a pulsed current injection. CCH = carbachol 100 μmol/l, added to the serosal side. Indomethacin (10 μmol/l), forskolin (Fors, 1 μmol/l), and IBMX (isobutylmethylxanthine, 100 μmol/l) were also added to the serosal side. Experiments were carried out in the presence of amiloride (10 μmol/l) (A) Note that in non-CF tissue, CCH initially causes a lumen-negative V_{te} deflection that is augmented in the presence of IBMX/Fors. IBMX and Fors, by increasing cytosolic cAMP, also produce a lumen-negative change in V_{te}. This corresponds to Cl^- secretion. Therefore, CCH and IBMX/Fors enhance Cl^- secretion cooperatively. In the absence of IBMX/Fors and after 30 min exposure to indomethacin to reduce cytosolic cAMP, CCH causes a lumen-positive V_{te} deflection, unmasking CCH-induced K^+ secretion. (B) In CF tissue, CCH always (with and without indomethacin) causes a lumen-positive V_{te} deflection (K^+ secretion). Forskolin and IBMX do not change V_{te}, i.e. do not produce Cl^- secretion.

time the response looks like that in the CF tissue. This indicates that luminal K^+ channels are also activated by increases in cytosolic Ca^{2+} in the healthy epithelium but are masked by the concomitant and usually stronger cAMP-mediated activation of Cl^- channels. This observation highlights the fact that the response to carbachol in tissues of unknown origin cannot be taken per se as a criterion for diagnosing CF. The carbachol response must always be tested with controlled cAMP-activation status (fully activated or fully inactivated). Only a lumen-positive response persistent in the presence of cAMP can be taken as evidence for a CFTR defect (41).

Figure 5 depicts experiments in which the effect of amiloride was examined in the presence and absence of cAMP activation. The amiloride effect was atten-

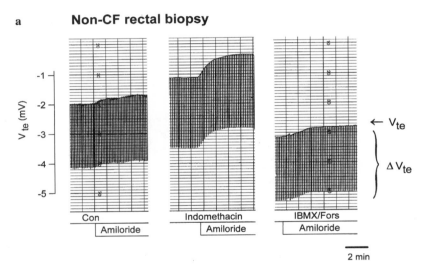

Figure 5 Ussing chamber analysis of human colonic mucosa. (*A*) Non-CF tissue. (*B*) CF tissue. Transepithelial voltage (V_{te}) is plotted as a function of time. The pulses reflect the transepithelial resistance (R_{te}) and are caused by a pulsed current injection. Amiloride, a selective blocker of ENaC (Amil, 10 μmol/l, mucosal side) is examined both, in the presence and absence of forskolin (Fors, 1 μmol/l) and IBMX (isobutylmethylxanthine, 100 μmol/l), added to the serosal side. (*A*) Note that in non-CF tissue, amiloride causes a lumen-positive V_{te} deflection (inhibition of NaCl absorption) that is strongly attenuated in the presence of IBMX/Fors. IBMX and Fors, by increasing cytosolic cAMP, also produce a lumen-negative change in V_{te}. This corresponds to Cl^- secretion. Thus IBMX/Fors (cAMP) enhances Cl^- secretion and, at the same time, inhibits Na^+ absorption. (*B*) In CF tissue, amiloride always (with and without forskolin/IBMX) causes a lumen-positive V_{te} deflection (inhibition of Na^+ absorption). Forskolin and IBMX do not change V_{te}, i.e. do not produce Cl^- secretion. Therefore, the defect in CF has two components: Cl^- secretion is diminished or absent, and Na^+ absorption is always maximal and not attenuated by cAMP-producing agonists.

b   **CF rectal biopsy**

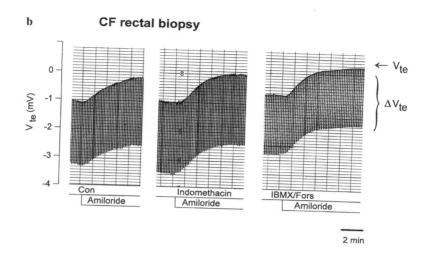

uated by cAMP in control tissue but was larger and not influenced by cAMP in CF tissue (55). This is caused by the interaction of CFTR with ENaC in normal tissue and the absence of such an interaction in CF tissue. The possible cellular mechanisms are discussed below.

It is clear that CF is characterized by a reduction or absence of cAMP-mediated CFTR activation. In addition the ENaC function is not inhibited. Inhibition of ENaC would help to avoid stickiness and compaction of gut contents and to ensure lubrication. Therefore, as in the airways, the pathophysiology of CF involves not only undersecretion but also overabsorption (11, 56).

The effect of Ca^{2+} mobilizing agonists such as carbachol is normally an activation of SK4 channels in the basolateral membrane (36, 38). This assists Cl^- secretion to the extent that the luminal membrane Cl^- conductance (CFTR) is activated by cAMP-dependent phosphorylation. Once the Cl^- conductance is inactivated, Ca^{2+}-regulated luminal K^+ channels are unmasked. Activation of these channels leads to K^+ secretion (5). This is the normal response in CF but can also occur in control tissue if cAMP production is inhibited (41).

Inhibitors of Chloride Secretion

Cl^- secretion can theoretically be inhibited at several levels (see Figure 3). The agonistic pathways can be interfered with at the level of neuronal control, at the level of the agonist receptors, and at the level of second messengers. Of relevance in this context are muscarinic antagonists and indomethacin. Both affect only one part of the activating pathways. The direct inhibition of the release of second messengers (Ca^{2+}, cAMP, cGMP) is probably not feasible. Therefore, effective inhibition must be targeted at the level of the membrane transport proteins.

Cl$^-$ channel inhibition has been widely examined (57–59). Unfortunately, the blockers, such as nitro-phenyl-propyl-amino-benzoate (NPPB), and even more potent compounds (57), designed (by ourselves) for the thick ascending limb of the loop of Henle, are poor inhibitors in the colon (60). All other inhibitors such as glibenclamide and DIDS (58, 61–63) cannot be regarded as specific inhibitors at the effective concentrations (100 µmol/l and higher). In our search for more potent blockers of cAMP-mediated Cl$^-$ secretion we arrived at chromanol structures (Figure 6). These compounds inhibit Cl$^-$ secretion reversibly, and some of the derivatives do so at nanomolar concentrations (52).

In our effort to characterize the target of these chromanols we identified novel K$^+$ channels in the basolateral membrane of the colon (22). These channels have now been identified on a molecular level as K$_V$LQT$_1$-type channels (53, 64). They have a very low single-channel conductance and can therefore be studied kinetically only by noise analysis (22, 65, 66). They are poorly blocked by Ba^{2+} and are activated by cAMP and probably also (indirectly?) by Ca^{2+} (67) (see above). There must be a very high density of these channels because they underlie a conductance >10 nS in a single colonocyte (68). Inhibition of these channels by 293B completely negates cAMP-stimulated Cl$^-$ secretion but has no effect on carbachol-mediated secretion. This is what one would expect on the basis of the scheme in Figure 3. The two K$^+$ channels can assist each other or they can compensate for the inactivation of the other. Such is the case when Cl$^-$ secretion is stimulated by cAMP, but when cytosolic Ca^{2+} activity is at its resting value (3). Then the Ca^{2+}-activated K$^+$ channel SK4 is inactivated because cytosolic Ca^{2+} falls further (69). The fall in [Ca^{2+}]$_i$ is caused by the ensuing cell depolarization, which reduces Ca^{2+} influx. If K$_V$LQT$_1$ channels were not activated in this instance, Cl$^-$ secretion would cease. The effect of chromanols such as 293B

——————————————————————————————————→

Figure 6 K$_V$LQT$_1$ channels in the basolateral membrane of colonic crypts. (*A*) Ussing chamber studies in rabbit colonic mucosa (taken from Reference 73). The equivalent short circuit current (I$_{sc}$, negative sign refers to Cl$^-$ secretion) is shown in the continuous presence of amiloride (10 µmol/l, mucosal side). Prostaglandin E$_2$ (PGE$_2$, 0.1 µmol/l) activates Cl$^-$ secretion. This current is blocked completely by the chromanol 293B (10 µmol/l, serosal side). In the presence of 293B carbachol (Cch, 10 µmol/l, serosal side) still generates Cl$^-$ secretion. As apparent from Figure 3, these data indicate that for Cl$^-$ secretion to proceed either one or both K$^+$ channels in the basolateral membrane (K$_V$LQT$_1$ or SK4) must be open. If K$_V$LQT$_1$, for instance, is blocked (by 293B), the SK4 can secure Cl$^-$ secretion. (*B*) Patch-clamp studies in an excised inside/out patch of the basolateral membrane of a crypt base cell. Pipette filled with NaCl Ringers, bath (cytosolic side, KCl Ringers). A noisy current, following the direction of the K$^+$ ion, is apparent in the upper trace. This current is blocked reversibly by the chromanol 293B (10 µmol/l, cytosolic side). The Lorentzian analysis of the noise reveals that it has well-defined kinetics (reflected by the corner frequency). 293B reduces the noise power density and leads to a small shift in the corner frequency. These data unmask a previously unknown K$^+$ channel of extremely small single-channel conductance that corresponds to K$_V$LQT$_1$.

may be useful in the treatment of secretory diarrhea because these compounds act from both sides of the epithelium with fairly similar IC_{50} values.

The SK4 K^+ channels are partly activated under resting conditions. They are tightly controlled by cytosolic Ca^{2+}, i.e. with a large Hill coefficient (Figure 7).

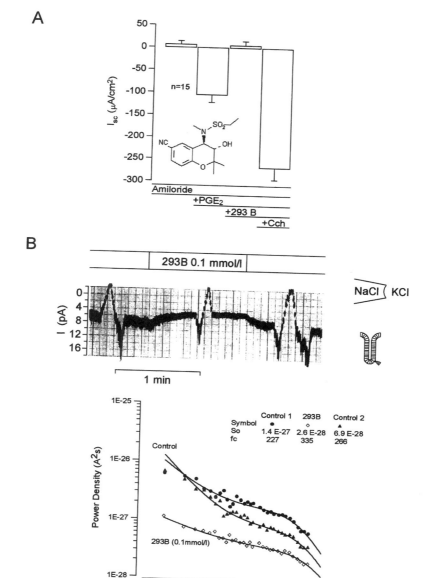

Slight increases in cytosolic Ca^{2+} lead to marked increases in SK4 activity (36). This channel has also been cloned from rat colon (38). It is a $\cong 15$ pS inwardly rectifying Ca^{2+}-regulated K^+ channel, which is blocked by Ba^{2+}. This channel can also be inhibited by imidazoles such as clotrimazole (Figure 7), NS004, or NS 1619 (5, 39, 70). NS004 has otherwise been described as an activator of CFTR (58, 71). SK4 is activated by the related drug 1-EBIO (72). Application of clotrimazole alone to the basolateral side of the colon has little effect even on the Cl^- secretion caused by carbachol, but it inhibits this component completely in the additional presence of 293B (38, 73, 74).

Cl^- secretion can also be blocked experimentally by loop diuretics binding to the colonic type of $Na^+ 2Cl^- K^+$ cotransporter (17, 68). Among the usual drugs used, azosemide proved superior to bumetanide, furosemide, piretanide, and torasemide. Therefore, the pharmacological fingerprint of the colonic form of this cotransporter is different from the renal type, where the sequence of IC_{50} values is bumetanide $=$ torasemide $>$ piretanide $>$ furosemide $=$ azosemide (75). These blockers are not useful from a practical standpoint because they would induce a maximal diuresis if used systemically at the concentrations necessary to inhibit intestinal secretion. Finally inhibition of the Na^+,K^+-ATPase pump is also practically irrelevant for obvious reasons.

CFTR AND SODIUM ION ABSORPTION

A unique aspect of epithelial physiology is the polarity of transport. The crypt cell represents one extreme case. A single cell must redirect vectorial NaCl and H_2O transport from absorption (under control of aldosterone) to secretion (under control of cAMP). When considering the scheme of Figure 3, the dilemma becomes clear. If ENaC and Cl^- (CFTR-type) channels were open at the same time the cell would take up NaCl (in the absorptive direction). However, if the $Na^+ 2Cl^- K^+$ cotransporter were operative, the cell would take up NaCl through

$\longrightarrow$

Figure 7 SK4 channels in the basolateral membrane of a colonic crypt. (*A*) Patch-clamp studies in an excised inside/out patch of the basolateral membrane of a crypt base cell. Pipette filled with NaCl Ringers, bath (cytosolic side, KCl Ringers). A current, following the direction of the K^+ ion and composed of several single K^+ channel currents, is apparent in the upper trace. This current is dependent on cytosolic Ca^{2+} activity. The mean channel activity (NPo) is half maximal at 20–30 nmol/l. (*B*) Patch-clamp studies in an excised inside/out patch of the basolateral membrane of a crypt base cell. Conditions as in (*A*). A current, following the direction of the K^+ ion and composed of several single K^+ channel currents, is apparent in the upper trace. This current is blocked concentration dependently by the imidazole clotrimazole (cytosolic side). The concentration response curve of the open probability of these channels reveals a half maximal inhibitory concentration of approximately 0.1 µmol/l. These single channel currents are caused by the Ca^{2+}-activated SK4 channels coexisting with $K_V LQT_1$ in the basolateral membrane.

both membranes, accumulate salt, swell, and eventually burst. Moreover, the cAMP pathway is primed to gear secretion, whereas it would support Na^+ driven absorption according to this scheme (Figure 3). The solution to this dilemma is both simple and elegant: Upregulation of CFTR by cAMP inhibits ENaC.

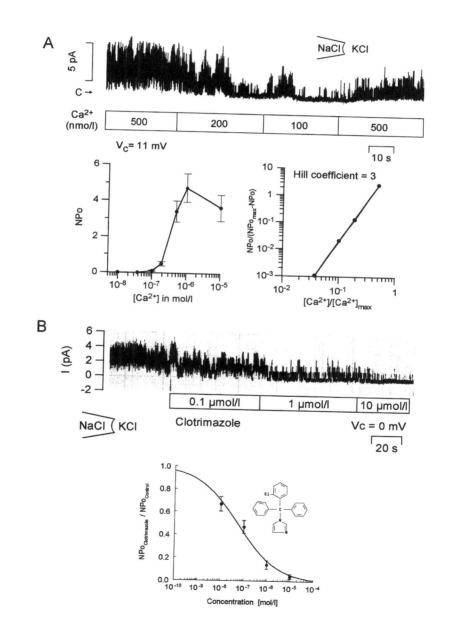

ENaC and CFTR Interaction

The inhibitory effect of CFTR on ENaC was first noted in MDCK cells and fibroblasts expressing CFTR, where it was shown that cAMP reduced the amiloride-inhibited Na^+ conductance (76). Shortly thereafter it was observed that ENaC was downregulated by activated CFTR but not by mutated CFTR (ΔF508 CFTR or G551D CFTR) in *Xenopus laevis* oocytes overexpressing these membrane transport proteins (77). These data, when extrapolated to intact tissue such as airway epithelia or colon, indicate that CF would not only cause a defect in NaCl (and H_2O) secretion but should pari passu also cause overabsorption. This effect was proposed for CF airway epithelia over a decade ago based on an increased amiloride effect in CF versus control individuals (78). Attenuation of the amiloride response by cAMP-activated CFTR has meanwhile been shown in the intact colonic mucosa of mouse, rat, and humans (79, 80), and it has also been demonstrated in CF tissue from both the respiratory tract and the colon that the ENaC conductance is larger (disinhibited) (Figure 6) when compared with control tissue (55, 79).

The mechanism of the interaction of CFTR with ENaC is not clear at present. Experiments using a two-hybrid assay suggest that it is the α subunit of ENaC that directly interacts with CFTR (81), but coimmunoprecipitation of both proteins has thus far not been successful. Recent studies with truncated CFTR indicate, on the one hand, that the first nucleotide-binding fold of CFTR is essential for the control of ENaC (82). Mutations of ENaC causing Liddle's syndrome, on the other hand, still are downregulated by CFTR (83). It has been proposed for the salivary gland duct that ENaC is controlled by cytosolic Cl^- activity via small GTP binding proteins (84). In fact, for the inhibition of Na^+, the Cl^- conducting function of CFTR seems to be mandatory. Mutations of CFTR with reduced Cl^- conduction properties also produce less inhibition of ENaC. Even with intact CFTR the inhibition of ENaC requires the presence and the conduction of chloride ions (85). In these experiments, substantial variations in cytosolic Cl^- or Na^+ activity were prevented. Therefore, the mechanism of this CFTR control over ENaC function awaits further clarification.

Although CFTR serves as a cAMP-controlled switch for the direction of Na^+ transport in secretory tissues, this function is absent in strictly absorptive epithelia such as the renal cortical-collecting duct or the sweat gland duct. In M1 cells, a cell line from mouse collecting duct, which has many properties of the intact collecting duct, cAMP downregulates ENaC via CFTR (86), but this apparently is not the case for the intact collecting duct where cAMP, produced in response to arginine vasopressin, increases ENaC conductance (87). In the sweat gland duct, ENaC and CFTR channels are present in the luminal membrane and secure NaCl absorption (88, 89). These observations suggest that a third, unknown component determines whether the reciprocal interaction of CFTR on ENaC is operational.

COLONOCYTES IN CULTURE AND COLONIC CRYPTS

The availability of colonic carcinoma cell lines and cell culture methods in general has had a large impact in the field. Studies of isolated colonic crypts is technically demanding. Patch clamp and cytosolic pH and Ca^{2+} measurements are difficult to perform in this preparation. Patch-clamp studies on the luminal membrane of colonic crypts are especially difficult because this membrane is covered by mucus. The situation is entirely different for colonocytes in culture because they are easy to study. Abundant Ussing chamber studies, patch-clamp studies, and studies on cytosolic second messengers have been performed in HT29, T84, and Caco-2 cells (34, 39, 63, 90–103).

In these cell lines Cl^- channels of different single-channel conductance have been found: small ones (4–12 pS) corresponding to CFTR, and other (?) small ones (around 4 pS) activated by Ca^{2+} and by cell swelling. In addition, an intermediate conductance (30–80 pS) Cl^- channel with outward rectification is abundant (104). While this latter type of channel (called ORCC or ICOR) was originally thought to be the epithelial Cl^- channel defective in CF (105–107), it has now been shown that ORCC (ICOR), under normal conditions, is rarely if at all active on the cell and is activated by excision (108, 109).

There is no evidence for the presence of small Cl^- channels other than CFTR in the luminal membrane of the intact crypt cells (11, 41). Whether such channels are present in the basolateral membrane is difficult to determine, even though several patch-clamp studies have been performed on this membrane (22, 36, 37, 110, 111). The principal conduction pathway is the SK4 K^+ channel and, after stimulation by cAMP, the K_VLQT_1 channels (22). When cytosolic Ca^{2+} increases above 1 μmol/l, an abundant non-selective cation channel of 25–35 pS is activated (36). The ICOR-type channel has also been found in excised patches from the basolateral membrane (36). Because of this background channel it is very difficult to detect small or very small conductance Cl^- channels.

The patterns of channel expression indicate that there are profound functional differences between colonic crypt cells and colonocytes. The ability to absorb Na^+ via ENaC channels has never been shown for colon carcinoma cell lines. In fact, this property is also lost when colon carcinoma is induced by dimethylhydrazine in rat colon (46). Another difference regards the secretion of mucus. There are subclones of HT_{29} cells that specifically secrete mucus (95, 98). In yet other clones the cAMP-regulated Cl^- conductance is gradually lost (R Greger, unpublished observation), whereas the Ca^{2+}-regulated Cl^- conductances usually remain robust. In addition, the cell layer arrangement, at least when grown on glass cover slips, is not uniform, and it is difficult to ascertain that all cells grow right-side up and with competent tight junctions. In retrospect, most colonocyte cultures can be regarded as a model for the secretory crypt base type cells. Even in this respect extrapolations appear problematic. The normal colonic crypt cells have such a short life span and undergo such rapid maturation and differentiation that it is no surprise that immortalized cell cultures from these cells get stuck at some early phase of maturation and may develop new phenotypes.

CONCLUSION

The different types of CF knockout and transgenic mice (11) have shown us how relevant CFTR is for normal intestinal function inasmuch as most of these animals die early on from gastrointestinal complications. For feces of normal consistency to be produced, functional CFTR is necessary. As in the respiratory tract, it is not quite clear how much of the pathology is related to the different functions of CFTR: its role as the pathway for Cl^- secretion, its role for mucus production, and its role to inhibit ENaC.

The CF defect in Cl^- conductance cannot be compensated for by any other Cl^- channel in the luminal membrane. Therefore, unlike the situation in the respiratory tract, cholinergic or purinergic stimulation is of no help in colonic Cl^- secretion in CF patients. Acetylcholine or ATP simply unmask Ca^{2+}-mediated K^+ secretion, which is overshadowed by the larger Cl^- secretion in normal colon. The CF defect in intestinal Cl^- secretion may well be the cause for the high frequency of CF mutations in heterozygotes. Heterozygotes may possess a genetic advantage in terms of less severe diarrhea in response to bacterial toxins (11, 12).

Fairly little is known about mucus pathology in CF. Alterations in glycoproteins in CF have been explained by endosomal pH changes (112, 113). Whether this is relevant in intestine is unclear. There is, however, little doubt that the amount of mucus produced is increased in CF intestine. How this relates to CFTR and its defects again is not clear, and it has recently been suggested that the electrolyte story in CF is linked causally to the mucus story (12): The disturbed electrolyte secretion might indeed generate oversecretion of mucus and the viscosity of this abundant mucus may be further increased by undersecretion and overabsorption.

The inhibitory role of CFTR on ENaC function has been unravelled only very recently. This basic principle allows for the redirection of NaCl and water transport within a single cell. Under the control of elevated aldosterone, NaCl absorption is activated and, conversely, under the influence of cAMP-producing secretagogues, CFTR permits NaCl secretion and the inhibition of NaCl absorption at the same time. The corresponding data for CF patients are just being summarized (55, 79). It is obvious that the complication caused by inappropriately active ENaC channels depends on the mineralocorticoid status. The importance of the defect in ENaC inhibition in CF patients correlates with the higher aldosterone activity.

Finally because the role of CFTR in colonic crypts under normal conditions and the defects in CF have recently been clarified to some extent, our understanding of these processes is greater than that of CFTR function and pathophysiology in the airways. Whereas the defects in colonic function in CF are closely related to the defect in CFTR, this relation is much more indirect in the airways where the residual function is determined largely by secondary effects of infection, inflammation, and fibrosis.

ACKNOWLEDGMENTS

The work in the author's laboratory has been continuously and generously supported by Deutsche Forschungsgemeinschaft.

Visit the Annual Reviews home page at www.AnnualReviews.org.

LITERATURE CITED

1. Binder HJ, Sandle GI. 1994. Electrolyte transport in the mammalian colon. In *Physiology of the Gastrointestinal Tract,* ed. LR Johnson, pp. 2133–71 New York: Raven

2. Barbry P, Hofman P. 1997. Molecular biology of Na^+ absorption. *Am. J. Physiol.* 273:G571–85

3. Greger R, Bleich M, Leipziger J, Ecke D, Mall M, Kunzelmann K. 1997. Regulation of ion transport in colonic crypts. *News Physiol. Sci.* 12:62–66

4. Cougnon M, Planelles G, Crowson MS, Shull GE, Rossier BC, Jaisser F. 1996. The rat distal colon P-ATPase α subunit encodes a ouabain-sensitive H^+, K^+-ATPase. *J. Biol. Chem.* 271:7277–80

5. Kerstan D, Gordjani N, Nitschke R, Greger R, Leipziger J. 1998. Luminal ATP induces K^+ secretion via $P2Y_2$ receptor in rat distal colonic mucosa. *Pflügers Arch.* 436:712–16

6. Field MJ, Semrad CE. 1993. Toxigenic diarrheas, cogenital diarrheas, and cystic fibrosis: disorders of intestinal ion transport. *Annu. Rev. Physiol.* 55:631–55

7. Markert T, Vaandrager AB, Gambaryan S, Pohler D, Hauser C, et al. 1999. Endogenous expression of type II cGMP-dependent protein kinase mRNA and protein in rat intestine. Implications for cystic fibrosis transmembrane conduc-

tance regulator. *J. Clin. Invest.* 96:822–30

8. Cuthbert AW, Hickman ME, Mac Vinish LJ, Evans MJ, Colledge WH, et al. 1994. Chloride secretion in response to guanylin in colonic epithelia from normal and transgenic cystic fibrosis mice. *Br. J. Pharmacol.* 112:31–36

9. Joo NS, London RM, Kim HD, Forte LR, Clarke LL. 1998. Regulation of intestinal Cl^- and HCO_3^- secretion by uroguanylin. *Am. J. Physiol.* 274:G663–64

10. Cohen MB, Witte DP, Hawkins JA, Currie MG. 1995. Immunohistochemical localization of guanylin in the rat small intestine and colon. *Biochem. Biophys. Res. Commun.* 209:803–8

11. Grubb BR, Boucher RC. 1999. Pathophysiology of gene-targeted mouse models for cystic fibrosis. *Physiol. Rev.* 79:S193–214

12. Quinton PM. 1999. Physiological basis of cystic fibrosis: a historical perspective. *Physiol. Rev.* 79:S3–22

13. Cuthbert AW, Halstead J, Ratcliff R, Colledge WH, Evans MJ. 1995. The genetic advantage hypothesis in cystic fibrosis heterocyzotes: a murine study. *J. Physiol.* 482.2:449–54

14. Köckerling A, Fromm M. 1993. Origin of cAMP-dependent Cl^- secretion from both crypts and surface epithelia of rat

intestine. *Am. J. Physiol.* 264:C1294–301

15. Gerencser GA, Purushotham KR, Meng HB. 1996. An electrogenic chloride pump in a zoological membrane. *J. Exp. Biol.* 275:256–61

16. Frizzell RA, Field MJ, Schultz SG. 1979. Sodium-coupled chloride transport by epithelial tissues. *Am. J. Physiol.* 236:F1–8

17. Heintze K, Stewart CP, Frizzell RA. 1983. Sodium-dependent chloride secretion across rabbit descending colon. *Am. J. Physiol.* 244:G357–65

18. Greger R. 1985. Ion transport mechanisms in thick ascending limb of Henle's loop of mammalian nephron. *Physiol. Rev.* 65:760–97

19. Greger R, Schlatter E, Gögelein H. 1986. Sodium chloride secretion in rectal gland of dogfish Squalus acanthias. *News Physiol. Sci.* 1:134–36

20. Strong TV, Boehm K, Collins FS. 1994. Localization of cystic fibrosis transmembrane conductance regulator mRNA in the human gastrointestinal tract by in situ hybridization. *J. Clin. Invest.* 93:347–54

21. Gadsby DC, Nairn AC. 1999. Control of CFTR channel gating by phosphorylation and nucleotide hydrolysis. *Physiol. Rev.* 79:S77–107

22. Warth R, Riedemann N, Bleich M, van Driessche W, Busch AE, Greger R. 1996. The cAMP-regulated and 293B-inhibited K^+ conductance of rat colonic crypt base cells. *Pflügers Arch.* 432:81–88

23. McDonald RA, Matthews RP, Idzerda RL, McKnight GS. 1995. Basal expression of the cystic fibrosis transmembrane conductance regulator gene is dependent on protein kinase A activity. *Proc. Natl. Acad. Sci. USA* 92:7560–64

24. Howard M, DuVall MD, Devor DC, Dong J-Y, Henze K, Frizzell RA. 1995. Epitope tagging permits cell surface detection of functional CFTR. *Am. J. Physiol.* 269:C1565–76

25. Takahashi H, Watkins SC, Howard M, Frizzell RA. 1996. CFTR-dependent membrane insertion is linked to stimulation of the CFTR chloride conductance. *Am. J. Physiol.* 271:C1887–94

26. Cunningham SA, Frizzell RA, Morris AP. 1995. Vesicular targeting and the control of ion secretion in epithelial cells: implications for cystic fibrosis. *J. Physiol.* 482P:27S-30

27. Greger R, Allert N, Fröbe U, Normann C. 1993. Increase in cytosolic Ca^{2+} regulates exocytosis and Cl^- conductance in HT_{29} cells. *Pflügers Arch.* 424:329–34

28. Bradbury NA, Jilling T, Berta G, Sorscher EJ, Bridges RJ, Kirk KL. 1992. Regulation of plasma membrane recycling by CFTR. *Science* 256:530–32

29. Sorensen JB, Larsen EH. 1998. Patch clamp on the luminal membrane of exocrine gland acini from frog skin (*Rana esculenta*) reveals the presence of cystic fibrosis transmembrane conductance regulator-like Cl^- channels activated by cyclic AMP. *J. Gen. Physiol.* 112:19–31

30. Zeiske W, Atia F, van Driessche W. 1998. Apical Cl^- channels in A6 cells. *J. Membr. Biol.* 166:169–78

31. Hug MJ, Thiele I, Greger R. 1997. The role of exocytosis in the activation of the chloride conductance in Chinese hamster ovary cells (CHO) stably expressing CFTR. *Pflügers Arch.* 434:779–84

32. Greger R, Thiele I, Warth R, Bleich M. 1998. Does stimulation of NaCl secretion in *in vitro* perfused rectal gland tubules of *Squalus acanthias* increase membrane capacitance? *Pflügers Arch.* 436:538–44

33. Tabcharani JA, Low W, Elie D, Hanrahan JW. 1990. Low-conductance chloride channel activated by cAMP in the epithelial cell line T_{84}. *FEBS Lett.* 270:157–64

34. Jarchau T, Häusler C, Markert T, Pöhler D, Vanderkerckhove J et al. 1994. Cloning, expression, and in situ localization of rat intestinal cGMP-dependent protein kinase II. *Proc. Natl. Acad. Sci. USA* 91:9426–30

35. Kottra G. 1995. Calcium is not involved in the cAMP-mediated stimulation of Cl^- conductance in the apical membrane of Necturus gallbladder epithelium. *Pflügers Arch.* 429:647–58

36. Bleich M, Riedemann N, Warth R, Kerstan D, Leipziger J, et al. 1996. Ca^{2+} regulated K^+ and non-selective cation channels in the basolateral membrane of rat colonic crypt base cells. *Pflügers Arch.* 432:1011–22

37. Sandle GI, McNicholas CM, Lomax RB. 1994. Potassium channels in colonic crypts. *Lancet* 343:23–25

38. Warth R, Hamm K, Bleich M, Kunzelmann K, von Hahn T, et al. 1999. Molecular and functional characterization of the small Ca^{2+} regulated K^+ channel (rSK4) of colonic crypts. *Pflügers Arch.* In press

39. Devor DC, Singh AK, Gerlach AC, Frizzell RA, Bridges RJ. 1997. Inhibition of intestinal Cl^- secretion by clotrimazole: direct effect on basolateral membrane K^+ channels. *Am. J. Physiol.* 273:C531–40

40. Butterfield I, Warhurst G, Jones MN, Sandle GI. 1997. Characterization of apical potassium channels induced in rat distal colon during potassium adaptation. *J. Physiol.* 501:537–47

41. Mall M, Bleich M, Schuerlein M, Kuehr J, Seydewitz HH, et al. 1998. Cholinergic ion secretion in human colon requires coactivation by cAMP. *Am. J. Physiol.* 275:G1274–81

42. Kunzelmann K, Tilmann M, Greger R. 1992. Ion transport in HT_{29} colonic carcinoma cells. *Adv. Comp. Envir. Physiol.* 16:237–51

43. Kunzelmann K, Kubitz R, Grolik M, Warth R, Greger R. 1992. Small conductance Cl^- channels in HT_{29} cells: activation by Ca^{2+}, hypotonic cell swelling and 8-Br-cGMP. *Pflügers Arch.* 421:238–46

44. Bajnath RB, Dekker K, Vaandrager AB, De Jonge HR, Groot JA. 1992. Biphasic

increase of apical Cl^- conductance by muscarinic stimulation of HT-29cl.19A human colon carcinoma cell line: evidence for activation of different Cl^- conductances by carbachol and forskolin. *J. Membr. Biol.* 127:81–94

45. Bajnath RB, De Jonge HR, Borgdorff AJ, Zuiderwijk M, Groot JA. 1997. Characterization of swelling-induced ion transport in HT-29Cl.19A cells. Role of inorganic and organic osmolytes during regulatory volume decrease. *Pflügers Arch.* 433:276–86

46. Bleich M, Ecke D, Schwartz B, Fraser G, Greger R. 1997. Effects of the carcinogen dimethylhydrazine (DMH) on the function of rat colonic crypts. *Pflügers Arch.* 433:254–59

47. Goodchild MC, Dodge JA. 1993. *Cystic Fibrosis.* pp. 1–212. London: Baillière Tindall

48. Pilewski JM, Frizzell RA. 1999. Role of CFTR in airway disease. *Physiol. Rev.* 79:S215–55

49. Leipziger J, Kerstan D, Nitschke R, Greger R. 1997. ATP increases $[Ca^{2+}]_i$ and ion secretion via a basolateral P2Y-receptor in rat distal colonic mucosa. *Pflügers Arch.* 434:77–83

50. Ecke D, Bleich M, Greger R. 1996. The amiloride inhibitabe Na^+ conductance of rat colonic crypt cells is suppressed by forskolin. *Pflügers Arch.* 431:984–86

51. Mall M, Kunzelmann K, Hipper A, Busch AE, Greger R. 1996. cAMP stimulation of CFTR-expressing *Xenopus* oocytes activates a chromanol-inhibitable K^+ conductance. *Pflügers Arch.* 432:516–22

52. Lohrmann E, Burhoff I, Nitschke RB, Lang HJ, Mania D, et al. 1995. A new class of inhibitors of cAMP-mediated Cl^- secretion in rabbit colon, acting by the reduction of cAMP-activated K^+ conductance. *Pflügers Arch.* 429:517–30

53. Bleich M, Briel M, Busch AE, Lang HJ, Gerlach U, et al. 1997. $K_V LQT_1$ channels

are inhibited by the K^+ channel blocker 293B. *Pflügers Arch.* 434:499–501

54. Mall M, Greger R, Seydewitz HH, Kuehr J, Brandis M, Kunzelmann K. 1999. Detection of defective cholinergic Cl^- secretion in rectal biopsies from cystic fibrosis patients. *Am. J. Physiol.* Submitted

55. Mall M, Bleich M, Greger R, Schreiber R, Kunzelmann K. 1998. The amiloride-inhibitable Na^+ conductance is reduced by the cystic fibrosis transmembrane conductance regulator in normal but not in cystic fibrosis airways. *J. Clin. Invest.* 102:15–21

56. Grubb BR, Boucher RC. 1999. Enhanced colonic Na^+ absorption in cystic fibrosis mice versus normal mice. *Am. J. Physiol.* 272:G393–400

57. Wangemann P, Wittner M, Di Stefano A, Englert HC, Lang HJ, et al. 1986. Cl^--channel blockers in the thick ascending limb of the loop of Henle. Structure activity relationship. *Pflügers Arch.* 407(Suppl. 2):S128–41

58. Schultz BD, Singh AK, Devor DC, Bridges RJ. 1999. Pharmacology of CFTR chloride channel activity. *Physiol. Rev.* 79:S109–44

59. Cabantchik ZI, Greger R. 1992. Chemical probes for anion transporters of mammalian cell membranes. *Am. J. Physiol.* 262:C803–27

60. Greger R, Nitschke RB, Lohrmann E, Burhoff I, Hropot M, et al. 1991. Effects of arylaminobenzoate-type chloride channel blockers on equivalent short circuit current in rabbit colon. *Pflügers Arch.* 419:190–96

61. Anderson MP, Welsh MJ. 1991. Calcium and cAMP activate different chloride channels in the apical membrane of normal and cystic fibrosis epithelia. *Proc. Natl. Acad. Sci. USA* 88:6003–7

62. Dawson DC, Smith SS, Mansoura MK. 1999. CFTR: Mechanism of anion conduction. *Physiol. Rev.* 79:S47–75

63. Kubitz R, Warth R, Allert N, Kunzel-mann K, Greger R. 1992. Small conductance chloride channels induced by cAMP, Ca^{2+}, and hypotonicity in HT_{29} cells: ion selectivity, additivity, and stilbene sensitivity. *Pflügers Arch.* 421:447–54

64. Busch AE, Busch GL, Ford E, Suessbrich H, Lang HJ, et al. 1997. The role of the I_{sK} protein in the specific pharmacological properties of the I_{Ks} channel complex. *Br. J. Pharmacol.* 122:187–89

65. Yang Y, Sigworth FJ. 1998. Single-channel properties of I_{Ks} potassium channels. *J. Gen. Physiol.* 112:665–78

66. Sesti F, Goldstein AN. 1998. Single-channel characteristics of wild-type I_{Ks} channels and channels formed with two MinK mutants that cause long QT syndrome. *J. Gen. Physiol.* 112:651–63

67. Kim SJ, Greger R. 1999. Voltage dependent, slowly activated K^+ current (I_{Ks}) and its augmentation by carbachol in rat pancreatic acini. *Pflügers Arch.* In press

68. Ecke D, Bleich M, Greger R. 1996. Crypt base cells show forskolin-induced Cl^- secretion but no cation inward conductance. *Pflügers Arch.* 431:427–34

69. Fischer K-G, Leipziger J, Rubini-Illes P, Nitschke R, Greger R. 1996. Attenuation of stimulated Ca^{2+} influx in colonic epithelial (HT_{29}) cells by cAMP. *Pflügers Arch.* 432:735–40

70. Rufo PA, Merlin D, Riegler M, Ferguson-Maltzman MH, Dickinson BL, et al. 1999. The antifungal antibiotic, clotrimazole, inhibits chloride secretion by human intestinal T84 cells via blockade of distinct basolateral K^+ conductances. Demonstration of efficacy in intact rabbit colon and in an in vivo model of cholera. *J. Clin. Invest.* 100 (12):3111–20

71. Gribkoff VK, Champigny G, Barbry P, Dworetzky SI, Meanwell NA, Lazdunski M. 1994. The substituted benzimidazolone NS004 is an opener of the cystic fibrosis chloride channel. *J. Biol. Chem.* 269:10983–86

72. Devor DC, Singh AK, Frizzell RA,

Bridges RJ. 1997. Modulation of Cl^- secretion by benzimidazolones. I. Direct activation of a Ca^{2+}-dependent K^+ channel. *Am. J. Physiol.* 271:L775–84

73. Ecke D, Bleich M, Lohrmann E, Hropot M, Englert HC, et al. 1995. A chromanol type of K^+ channel blocker inhibits forskolin—but not carbachol mediated Cl^- secretion in rat and rabbit colon. *Cell. Physiol. Biochem.* 5:204–10

74. Bleich M, Warth R, Schmidt-Hieber M, Schulz-Baldes A, Hasselblatt P, et al. 1999. Rescue of the mineralocorticoid receptor knock-out mouse. *Pflügers Arch.* 438(3):245–54

75. Greger R. 1995. Loop diuretics. In *Handbook of Experimental Pharmacology; Diuretics*, ed. R Greger, H Knauf, E Mutschler, pp. 221–74. Heidelberg/New York: Springer

76. Stutts MJ, Canessa CM, Olsen JC, Hamrick M, Cohn JA, et al. 1995. CFTR as a cAMP-dependent regulator of sodium channels. *Science* 269:847–50

77. Mall M, Hipper A, Greger R, Kunzelmann K. 1996. Wild type but not $\Delta F508$ CFTR inhibits Na^+ conductance when coexpressed in *Xenopus* oocytes. *FEBS Lett.* 381:47–52

78. Boucher RC, Stutts MJ, Knowles MR, Cantley L, Gatzy JT. 1986. Na^+ transport in cystic fibrosis respiratory epithelia. *J. Clin. Invest.* 78:1245–52

79. Mall M, Bleich M, Kühr J, Brandis M, Greger R, Kunzelmann K. 1999. CFTR-mediated inhibition of epithelial sodium conductance in human colon is defective in cystic fibrosis. *Am. J. Physiol.* In press

80. Ecke D, Bleich M, Greger R. 1996. The amiloride inhibitable Na^+ conductance of rat colonic crypt cells is suppressed by forskolin. *Pflügers Arch.* 431:984–86

81. Kunzelmann K, Kiser GL, Schreiber R, Riordan JR. 1997. Inhibition of epithelial Na^+ currents by intracellular domains of the cystic fibrosis transmembrane regulator. *FEBS Lett.* 400:341–44

82. Schreiber R, Hopf A, Mall M, Greger R, Kunzelmann K. 1999. The first-nucleotide binding domain of the cystic-fibrosis transmembrane conductance regulator is important for inhibition of the epithelial Na^+ channel. *Proc. Natl. Acad. Sci. USA* 96:5310–15

83. Hopf A, Schreiber R, Mall M, Greger R, Kunzelmann K. 1999. CFTR inhibits epithelial Na^+ channels carrying Liddle's syndrome mutations. *J. Biol. Chem.* 274(20):13894–99

84. Komwatana P, Dinudom A, Young JA, Cook DI. 1995. Control of the amiloride-sensitive Na^+ current in mouse salivary ducts by intracellular anions is mediated by a G protein. *J. Physiol.* 487:549–55

85. Briel M, Greger R, Kunzelmann K. 1998. Cl^- transport by cystic fibrosis transmembrane conductance regulator (CFTR) contributes to the inhibition of epithelial Na^+ channels (ENaCs) in *Xenopus* oocytes co-expressing CFTR and ENaC. *J. Physiol.* 508.3:825–36

86. Letz B, Korbmacher C. 1997. cAMP stimulates CFTR-like Cl^- channels and inhibits amiloride-sensitive Na^+ channels in mouse CCD cells. *Am. J. Physiol.* 272:C657–66

87. Schlatter E, Schafer JA. 1987. Electrophysiological studies in principal cells of rat cortical collecting tubules. ADH increases the apical membrane Na^+-conductance. *Pflügers Arch.* 409:81–92

88. Quinton PM. 1987. Physiology of sweat secretion. *Kidney Int.* 32:102–8

89. Schulz I. 1969. Micropuncture studies of the sweat formation in cystic fibrosis patients. *J. Clin. Invest.* 48:1470–77

90. Augeron C, Laboisse CL. 1984. Emergence of permanently differentiated cell clones in a human colonic cancer cell line in culture after treatment with sodium butyrate. *Cancer Res.* 44:3961–69

91. Bajnath RB, Van Hoeve MH, De Jonge HR, Groot JA. 1992. Regulation of apical Cl^- conductance and basolateral K^+ conductances by phorbol esters in HT-

29cl.19A cells. *Am. J. Physiol.* 263: C759–66

92. Benning N, Leipziger J, Greger R, Nitschke R. 1996. Effect of alkalinization of cytosolic pH by amines on intracellular Ca^{2+} activity in HT_{29} cells. *Pflügers Arch.* 432:126–33

93. Disser J, Hazama A, Frömter E. 1993. Chloride channel studies on HT29 cells with minimal levels of cAMP-mediated stimulation. *Pflügers Arch.* 422:R65 (Abstr.)

94. Greger R. 1994. Chloride channels of colonic carcinoma cells. In *Handbook of Membrane Channels,* ed. C Peracchia, pp. 229–44. San Diego: Academic

95. Jarry A, Merlin D, Hopfer U, Laboisse CL. 1994. Cyclic AMP-induced mucin exocytosis is independent of Cl^- movements in human colonic epithelial cells (HT29–Cl.16E). *Biochem. J.* 304:675–78

96. Kerst G, Fischer KG, Normann C, Kramer A, Leipziger J, Greger R. 1995. Ca^{2+} influx induced by store release and cytosolic Ca^{2+} chelation in HT_{29} colon carcinoma cells. *Pflügers Arch.* 430:653–65

97. Köttgen M, Leipziger J, Fischer KG, Nitschke R, Greger R. 1994. pH regulation in HT_{29} colon carcinoma cells. *Pflügers Arch.* 428:179–85

98. Kreusel KM, Fromm M, Schulzke JD, Hegel U. 1991. Cl^- secretion in epithelial monolayers of mucus-forming human colon cells (HT-29/B6). *Am. J. Physiol.* 261:C574–82

99. Warhurst G, Fogg KE, Higgs NB, Tonge A, Grundy J. 1994. Ca^{2+}-mobilising agonists potentiate forskolin- and VIP-stimulated cAMP production in human colonic cell line, HT29–cl.19A: role of $[Ca^{2+}]_i$ and protein kinase C. *Cell Calcium* 15:162–74

100. Mandel KG, Dharmsathaphorn K, McRoberts JA. 1986. Characterization of a cyclic AMP-activated Cl^- transport pathway in the apical membrane of a human colonic epithelial cell line. *J. Biol. Chem.* 261:704–12

101. Grasset E, Bernabeu J, Pinto M. 1985. Epithelial properties of human colonic carcinoma cell line Caco-2: effect of secretagogues. *Am. J. Physiol.* 248: C410–18

102. Sood R, Bear C, Auerbach W, Reyes E, Jensen T, et al. 1992. Regulation of CFTR expression and function during differentiation of intestinal epithelial cells. *EMBO J.* 11:2487–94

103. Tien XY, Brasitus TA, Kaetzel MA, Dedman JR, Nelson DJ. 1994. Activation of the cystic fibrosis transmembrane conductance regulator by cGMP in the human colonic cancer cell line, Caco-2. *J. Biol. Chem.* 269:51–54

104. Hayslett JP, Gögelein H, Kunzelmann K, Greger R. 1987. Characteristics of apical chloride channels in human colon cells (HT_{29}). *Pflügers Arch.* 410:487–94

105. Li M, McCann JD, Liedtke CM, Nairn AC, Greengard P, Welsh MJ. 1988. Cyclic AMP-dependent protein kinase opens chloride channels in normal but not cystic fibrosis airway epithelium. *Nature* 331:358–60

106. Frizzell RA, Rechkemmer G, Shoemaker RL. 1986. Altered regulation of airway epithelial cell chloride channels in cystic fibrosis. *Science* 233:558–60

107. Hwang TC, Lu L, Zeitlin L, Gruenert DC, Huganir R, Guggino WB. 1989. Cl^- channels in CF: lack of activation by protein kinase C and cAMP-dependent protein kinase. *Science* 244:1351–53

108. Kunzelmann K, Pavenstädt H, Greger R. 1989. Properties and regulation of chloride channels in cystic fibrosis and normal airway cells. *Pflügers Arch.* 415: 172–82

109. Kunzelmann K, Tilmann M, Hansen CP, Greger R. 1991. Inhibition of epithelial chloride channels by cytosol. *Pflügers Arch.* 418:479–90

110. Burckhardt BC, Gögelein H. 1992. Small

and maxi K $^+$ channels in the basolateral membrane of isolated crypts from rat distal colon: single channel and slow whole-cell recordings *Pflügers Arch.* 420:54–60

111. Diener M, Rummel W, Mestres P, Lindemann B. 1989. Single chloride channels in colon mucosa and isolated colonic enterocytes of the rat. *J. Membr. Biol.* 108:21–30

112. Barasch J, Kiss B, Prince A, Saiman L, Gruenert DC, Al-Awqati Q. 1999. Defective acidification of intracellular organelles in cystic fibrosis. *Nature* 352:70–73

113. Imundo L, Barasch J, Prince A, Al-Awqati Q. 1995. Cystic fibrosis epithelial cells have a receptor for pathogenic bacteria on their apical surface. *Proc. Natl. Acad. Sci. USA* 92:3019–23

Annu. Rev. Physiol. 2000. 62:493–513

Intracellular Ca²⁺ and Cl⁻ Channel Activation in Secretory Cells

J. F. Kidd and P. Thorn

Department of Pharmacology, University of Cambridge, Tennis Court Road, Cambridge, CB2 1QJ, United Kingdom; e-mail: pt207@cus.cam.ac.uk

Key Words acinar, InsP₃, CaMKII, DIDS

■ **Abstract** Molecular and functional evidence indicates that a variety of Ca^{2+}-dependent chloride ($Cl_{(Ca)}$) channels are involved in fluid secretion from secretory epithelial cells in different tissues and species. Most $Cl_{(Ca)}$ channels so far characterized have an I^- permeability greater than Cl^-, and most are sensitive to 4,4'-diisothiocyanatostilbene-2,2'-disulfonic acid (DIDS). Whole-cell $Cl_{(Ca)}$ currents show outward rectification. Single-channel current voltage relationships are linear with conductances ranging from 2 to 30 pS. Some $Cl_{(Ca)}$ channels are blocked by Ca^{2+}-calmodulin-dependent protein kinase (CAMKII) inhibitors. Others, such as the $Cl_{(Ca)}$ channels of parotid and submandibular acinar cells, appear to be directly regulated by Ca^{2+}. In native cells, the $Cl_{(Ca)}$ channels are located on the apical plasma membrane and activated by localized mechanisms of Ca^{2+} release. This positioning allows the $Cl_{(Ca)}$ channel to respond specifically to localized Ca^{2+} signals that do not invade other regions of the cell. The $Cl_{(Ca)}$ follows the rising phase of the Ca^{2+} signal, but in the falling phase hysteresis occurs where the $Cl_{(Ca)}$ current decays more rapidly than the underlying Ca^{2+}. The future elucidation of the identity and mechanisms of regulation of $Cl_{(Ca)}$ channels will be critical to our understanding of stimulus-secretion coupling.

INTRODUCTION

Fluid secretion is an essential mechanism for maintaining the function of the lungs, the gastrointestinal tract, and a diverse range of other organs. Several models of how fluid secretion is mediated by secretory epithelial cells in different tissues have been proposed (1–3); all are dependent on Cl^- movement across the apical plasma membrane. One important Cl^- channel, present in the apical plasma membrane of many secretory epithelial cells, is the cystic fibrosis transmembrane conductance regulator (CFTR). Mutations in this cAMP-dependent channel are responsible for the disruption of fluid secretion in the disease cystic fibrosis (CF). The channel has been cloned and identified in a wide range of tissues (4). Another group of ion channels that are apically located and may play an important role in fluid secretion are the Ca^{2+}-activated Cl^- ($Cl_{(Ca)}$) channels. This review aims to

0066–4278/00/0315–0493$12.00

summarize our current knowledge of the diversity of $Cl_{(Ca)}$ channels and the mechanisms underlying their Ca^{2+}-dependent activation.

Distribution and Characterization of $Cl_{(Ca)}$ Channels

Recently *bCLCA1*, a gene that encodes a bovine $Cl_{(Ca)}$ channel, was cloned (5), which led to the cloning of further homologous genes from mouse (*mCLCA 1*) (6) and human (*hCLCA1* and *hCLCA2*) cDNA libraries (7,7a). The mRNA of *mCLCA1* is expressed in many tissues including most secretory tissues. In contrast *bCLCA1* mRNA has been detected only in the trachea; *hCLCA1* mRNA has been detected in only the colonic mucosa and small intestine; and *hCLCA2* mRNA has been detected in only the lung, trachea, and mammary gland (7, 7a, 8). All four channel proteins show a high level of sequence identity at the amino acid level. They also form $Cl_{(Ca)}$ conductances with similar functional characteristics when expressed in cultured cells. These similarities suggest that they form a new family of Cl^- channels (8a). Further experiments in this field will increase our understanding of the diversity of $Cl_{(Ca)}$ channels. In the absence of this molecular information we focus herein on the functional characterization of $Cl_{(Ca)}$ conductances. On this basis, most $Cl_{(Ca)}$ currents described have greater permeability to I^- than Cl^-; most have outwardly rectifying whole-cell currents, and most are blocked by 4,4'-diisothiocyanatostilbene-2,2'-disulfonic acid (DIDS) (see Table 1). Suggesting a potential molecular diversity of $Cl_{(Ca)}$ channels are differences in measured single-channel conductances ranging from 2 to 30 pS and differences in calcium-calmodulin-dependent kinase II (CaMKII) sensitivity (see Table 2).

Tissue Distribution

There is functional evidence for the presence of $Cl_{(Ca)}$ channels in a wide variety of secretory epithelial cells. This evidence is discussed below.

Airway   Many studies in different species have shown that a rise in intracellular Ca^{2+} ($[Ca^{2+}]_i$) can stimulate transepithelial chloride secretion by airway epithelial cells (9–13). Using short-circuit current measurements, investigators showed that a $Cl_{(Ca)}$-dependent conductance is present in the apical membrane of human airway epithelia (9). In addition, whole-cell patch-clamp studies in cultured airway epithelial cells and cell lines have shown the presence of an outwardly rectifying $Cl_{(Ca)}$ current (9, 14, 15) that is activated by CaMKII (14), blocked by DIDS, and has a relative permeability sequence of $I^- > Cl^-$ (9).

Excised inside-out patches from airway epithelial cells of normal and CF patients show the presence of two different Cl^- channels activated by Ca^{2+} (16): a large outwardly rectifying channel with a conductance of around 50 pS and a smaller linear conductance channel of around 20 pS (15, 16). The 50 pS channel shows outward rectification in the single-channel conductance and has been termed the outwardly rectifying chloride channel (ORCC). It has been detected in many studies on airway epithelium (15, 17–20). However, despite some reports showing Ca^{2+}-dependence (15, 16), others have failed to show any effect of [Ca^{2+}]$_i$ (17, 21).

The smaller channel (20 pS), identified by Frizzell et al (15), is similar in conductance and Ca^{2+} sensitivity to a channel purified from bovine trachea which, when reconstituted in lipid bilayers, has a linear conductance of 25 to 30 pS (22, 23). In addition, this bovine tracheal channel was shown to be activated in a CaMKII-dependent manner, blocked by DIDS, and had a permeability sequence of I$^-$ > Cl$^-$ (23). A gene (*bCLCA1*) possibly encoding the channel was cloned from a bovine tracheal cDNA expression library using an antibody raised against the purified channel protein (5). Recently a homologous gene (*mCLCA1*) was cloned from mouse trachea (6). The single-channel properties of mCLCA1 remain to be determined although pharmacological (6) and expression studies (5, 8) suggest that it encodes a channel with properties different from those encoded by *bCLCA1*.

There is good evidence for Cl$_{(Ca)}$ channels in airway epithelial cells. These channels are distinct from the ORCC characterized in many airway epithelia, show CaMKII dependence, are blocked by DIDS, and have a permeability sequence of I$^-$ > Cl$^-$.

Intestine   There is conflicting information about the presence of Cl$_{(Ca)}$ channels in the apical membrane of intestinal epithelial cells. Much of this results from the use of cell lines, such as T84 and HT29, that clearly express a Cl$_{(Ca)}$ channel in their undifferentiated state (24) but apparently down-regulate this channel when forming differentiated monolayers (9, 25). The Cl$_{(Ca)}$ channel in undifferentiated HT29 or T84 cells has a conductance of 8–15 pS and shows sensitivity to CaMKII blockers (24, 26).

The earliest descriptions of mature monolayers of T84 cells indicated that no apical Cl$_{(Ca)}$ conductance was elicited by Ca^{2+}-mobilizing stimulation (27). This was confirmed directly in a patch-clamp study (9) showing whole-cell Cl$_{(Ca)}$ currents in undifferentiated cells but no apical Cl$_{(Ca)}$ conductance when the cells were grown on a permeable support and allowed to differentiate. In contrast, short-circuit currents, measured in an Ussing chamber (28) and ^{125}I flux studies on HT29 cells (25) suggest the presence of an apical Cl$_{(Ca)}$. These indirect measurements are difficult to interpret because an intracellular Ca^{2+} signal, in the presence of apical CFTR channels and basolateral K$_{(Ca)}$ channels, could give rise to transepithelial Ca^{2+}-dependent Cl$^-$ flux even in the absence of Cl$_{(Ca)}$ channels (27). However, more recent short-circuit current experiments report two different apical Cl$^-$ conductances, on the basis of DIDS sensitivity (29, 30). McEwan et al (29) showed DIDS block of a carbachol- (cholinergic agonist) induced apical Cl$^-$ conductance, suggestive of the presence of a Cl$_{(Ca)}$ channel. Another study performed on T84 monolayers shows evidence for apically and basolaterally located Cl$_{(Ca)}$ channels (29a). The most convincing evidence for an apically located Cl$_{(Ca)}$ channel comes from a study by Merlin et al (30). In this study the basolateral

TABLE 1 Pharmacology of $Cl_{(Ca)}$ channels

Cell type	DIDS[a]	NPPB[b]	NFA[c]	References
Sheep parotid acinar cells (whole-cell)	30 μM reduced current to 29.8% of control at +80 mV	300 μM reduced current by 94% of control at +80 mV	—	(57)
Rat parotid acinar cells (whole-cell)	500 μM reduced current by 49 ± 4% at +60 mV	—	—	(42)
Rat pancreatic acinar cells (inside-out excised patches)	100 μM gave no significant inhibition at −65 mV	100 μM gave no significant inhibition at −65 mV	—	(38)
Rat submandibular acinar cells (whole-cells)	1 mM reduced current to 27.9 ± 4.8% of control at +69 mV	100 μM reduced current to 55.1 ± 24.7 of control at +69 mV	—	(41)
Bovine tracheal cells (planar bilayer)	100 μM reduced P_o from 0.55 to 0.06 ± 0.02 at +40 mV	—	100 μM had no effect on channel P_o at +40 mV	(58)
Murine tracheal expressed in HEK293 (whole-cell)	300 μM reduced current to 15% at +100 mV	—	100 μM reduced current to 21% at +100 mV	(6)
T84 (whole-cell)	200 μM reduced current by 52 ± 12% of control at +50 mV	—	—	(26)
HPAF (whole-cell)	500 μM caused 13% inhibition of current at +60mV	—	100 μM caused 48% inhibition of current at +60mV	(47)
Canine pancreatic duct epithelial cells (whole-cell)	500 μM caused 75.6 ± 6.6% inhibition of current at +40 mV	500 μM caused almost complete loss of 1 efflux induced by A23187	—	(48)
Human biliary cell line (Mz8ChA-1) (cell-attached)	—	100 μM caused rapid channel closure	—	(51)
Rat bile duct epithelial cells (iodide efflux)	150 μM inhibited ionomycin stimulated efflux by 48 ± 9%	—	—	(53)

[a]DIDS [4,4′-diisothiocyanatostilbene-2,3′ disulfonic acid]; [b]NPPB [5-nitro-2-(3-phenylpropylamino)-benzoic acid]; [c]NFA [niflumic acid]

TABLE 2 How CaMKII inhibitors affect $Cl_{(Ca)}$ currents from different cell types

Cell type	Calmidazolium	KN-62	CaMK[a]	References
Human airway epithelial cell line (whole-cell)	—	—	20 μM reduced outward current by 71%	(14)
T84 (whole-cell)	25 μM inhibited ~ 90% of the current	10 μM reduced currents by ~80–90%	10 μM blocked currents	(61, 42)
HT 29 (excised inside-out patches)	—	—	50 μM inhibited channel activity	(24)
Cystic fibrosis–derived pancreatic epithelial cell line (CF-PAC1) (whole-cell)	—	—	20 μM abolished current	(49)
Human biliary cell line (Mz8ChA-1) (cell-attached patches)	100 μM decreased P_o or abolished channel activity	20 μM significantly inhibited ionomycin-stimulated iodide efflux	—	(51)

[a]CaMK is a CaMKII inhibitory peptide composed of residues of CaMKII responsible for calmodulin binding. The studies cited above used one of two peptides, 291-317 or 273-302.

membrane was permeabilized, therefore ruling out the possible involvement of basolateral $K_{(Ca)}$ channels in causing transepithelial Cl^- flux. They showed that Ca^{2+} mobilization with thapsigargin elicited an apical Cl^- current, with an I^- permeability greater than Cl^- that was abolished by DIDS (30).

No direct evidence for an apical $Cl_{(Ca)}$ current has been found in native colonic epithelium. Experiments have shown that Ca^{2+}-mediated transepithelial chloride secretion is absolutely dependent on the presence of CFTR. This has been demonstrated in the Cambridge CF mouse model (31) and also pharmacologically (32, 33). In addition, a study on jejunal and cecal preparations from CFTR-deficient (*Cftr* $-/-$) mice failed to show Ca^{2+}-mediated short circuit currents (35).

It is difficult to explain the conflicting data about the presence of a $Cl_{(Ca)}$ channel in cell lines but not in native cells. One possibility is that there is a progressive decrease in $Cl_{(Ca)}$ activity as the cells mature and differentiate. This decrease may be due to lowered expression or function of apical $Cl_{(Ca)}$ channels. This decrease in $Cl_{(Ca)}$ activity with time is supported by ^{125}I flux experiments that show a decrease in flux as cells mature (25) and also by the experiments of Anderson & Welsh (9, 25a) that show a decrease in $Cl_{(Ca)}$ current with time after differentiation. The mechanism of this down-regulation may be the result of the colocalization of CFTR and $Cl_{(Ca)}$ channels in the apical membrane of the mature cell, and might result from a direct interaction of the CFTR channel with the $Cl_{(Ca)}$ channel. In support of this scheme, heterologous expression of CFTR in *Xenopus* oocytes has been shown to decrease the amplitude of the endogenously expressed $Cl_{(Ca)}$ current only when CFTR is activated (34). In addition, in some tissues obtained from CF mice (various homozygous mutations in CFTR), which show a mild CF phenotype, the $Cl_{(Ca)}$ activity was up-regulated (35, 36).

$Cl_{(Ca)}$ is, at best, a minor component of the apical Cl^- conductance in native colonic epithelial cells. In cell lines, however, there is a great deal of evidence for $Cl_{(Ca)}$ channels.

Exocrine Glands   Fluid secretion in exocrine glands is controlled by both acinar and duct cells (1, 37). Exocrine acinar cells secrete fluid and enzymes in a Ca^{2+}-dependent manner. The $Cl_{(Ca)}$ channel forms the apical chloride efflux pathway, as suggested in early experiments (1), and now recently shown by cell-attached and excised inside-out patches from rat pancreatic acinar cells (38). Single-channel conductances of ~2 pS in rat lacrimal (39), submandibular (40), and pancreatic acinar cells (38) suggest that a similar channel is conserved in acinar cells from different glands. Another shared property of these conductances is the lack of effect of CaMKII inhibitors on $Cl_{(Ca)}$ currents (41, 42). In addition to $Cl_{(Ca)}$ channels, submandibular and pancreatic acinar cells have been shown to possess apical CFTR channels, although the functional significance of these channels is unclear (43, 43a). Exocrine duct cells in dog, rat, and human have now all been shown to possess $Cl_{(Ca)}$ currents that can be regulated by agonist-evoked Ca^{2+} signals (44, 47, 48). Studies in cell-attached patches from a CF pancreatic duct cell line (CFPAC-1) showed the presence of Cl$^-$ currents activated by the Ca^{2+} ionophore A23187 (45). Whole-cell studies performed in duct cells from a variety of tissues show that Ca^{2+} ionophores such as ionomycin evoke outwardly rectified Cl$^-$ currents (46, 48). These currents are similar in appearance to the whole-cell Cl$_{(Ca)}$ currents measured in acinar cells (55–58). However, unlike currents in acinar cells, these currents appear to be abolished by CaMKII inhibitors (49), suggesting that CaMKII regulates these channels in a similar way to that of the Cl$_{(Ca)}$ channels in airway cells.

Therefore, exocrine tissues appear to have two types of Cl$_{(Ca)}$ channel; one localized to the apical membrane of acinar cells that is not regulated by CaMKII and another present in the duct cells that is regulated by CaMKII.

Kidney Some Cl$^-$ channels in the apical membrane of cortical collecting duct cells have been shown to be Ca^{2+} dependent (50). These channels have been hypothesized to play a role either in cell volume regulation or in Cl$^-$ and HCO$_3^-$ secretion (50).

Gallbladder A Cl$_{(Ca)}$ channel has been described in a human cholangiocarcinoma cell line (51). This channel appears to be regulated by CaMKII (52) and has a linear conductance of 14 pS (51). A Cl$_{(Ca)}$ conductance has also been described in freshly isolated rat biliary epithelial cells. Whole-cell measurement of this current show that it is activated by application of ionomycin to the bath, is outwardly rectified, and is inhibited by DIDS (53).

Functional Characterization

Although Cl$_{(Ca)}$ currents have been detected in a wide variety of secretory cells, not all seem to have identical functional properties. This section discusses some of the most important functional characteristics of these currents and how they differ.

Conductance Single-channel conductances vary considerably. The smallest are found in acinar cells ~2pS (38–40). In other cells they range from 8 pS in T84 (26) cells to ~30 pS in the channel reconstituted from bovine trachea (22).

Most of the Cl$_{(Ca)}$ whole-cell currents show outward rectification, although the measured tail current amplitudes do not (9, 53, 55). In cultured human airway epithelial cells (from wild-type and CF patients), the rectification properties of the whole-cell currents of single cells contrasted with the linear current-voltage relationship attributable to the apical membrane of the cells grown as monolayers (9). Similar linearity was seen in excised and cell-attached patches from tracheal epithelial cells (15), in excised patches from rat biliary epithelial cells (51, 53), and in bilayer studies on the bovine tracheal channel (22). This suggests the outward rectification seen in whole-cell currents may be from channel recruitment rather than an innate property of the channels themselves. An example of the

$Cl_{(Ca)}$ whole-cell current, from mouse pancreatic acinar cells, with typical characteristics of outward rectification and time- and voltage-dependent activation, is shown in Figure 1.

$[Ca^{2+}]_i$ Dependence   Although many studies performed on $Cl_{(Ca)}$ conductances have shown that increasing $[Ca^{2+}]_i$ leads to an increase in activity, few have quantified this response. All these studies have been performed under steady-state conditions, which do not closely reflect physiological stimulation by Ca^{2+} spikes. Ideally Ca^{2+} dependence should be measured in response to rapid Ca^{2+} changes. However, this is technically difficult, and steady-state measures give at least an initial insight into the Ca^{2+} sensitivity of the channel.

One of the earliest studies was performed on the activation of $Cl_{(Ca)}$ in lacrimal acinar cells (56) using the whole-cell configuration of the patch-clamp technique to alter $[Ca^{2+}]_i$. The experiments showed that at $[Ca^{2+}]_i$ above 100 nM, the amplitude of outwardly rectifying $Cl_{(Ca)}$ currents increased. At very high concentrations (2 μM), the current ceased to show its distinctive outward rectification, i.e. the current-voltage relationship became more linear. This effect has also been observed in other acinar cells (55, 57).

In lacrimal acinar cells, the EC_{50} of Ca^{2+} dependence was ~1 μM, with the same value obtained at membrane potentials of $+20$ and -60 mV (56). In agreement with this figure, pancreatic acinar cells showed little $Cl_{(Ca)}$ current at 100 nM $[Ca^{2+}]_i$ but were fully activated at 1000 nM (58). A similar estimated EC_{50} for Ca^{2+} dependence of channel activation of 300 nM was found in rat parotid acinar cells at a membrane potential of -66 mV (55). However, at a depolarized membrane potential of $+74$ mV, the EC_{50} was lower, 61 nM (55).

The studies in lacrimal and parotid acinar cells agree that the steepness of the Ca^{2+} dependence of current activation is greater than one (55, 56). This suggests that the mechanism of activation is complex and may involve the binding of multiple Ca^{2+} ions to the channel (55).

Although a great deal is known about the steady-state Ca^{2+} dependence of $Cl_{(Ca)}$ in acinar cells, less is known about the channel from tracheal and intestinal epithelia. Excised patch studies on human tracheal epithelial cells show that the channel is inactive at 20 nM Ca^{2+}, activates immediately on excision into 180 nM, and is further activated at 760 nM (16). Bilayer studies on a $Cl_{(Ca)}$ purified from bovine trachea show that it is open even at 10 nM Ca^{2+}, with a significant increase in probability of opening (P_o) at concentrations greater than 3 μM (23). The differences in effects of Ca^{2+} on the reconstituted channel and on the channel in excised inside-out patches may indicate that the purified channel loses some accessory component that keeps it closed at low $[Ca^{2+}]_i$ or simply that there are two different channels.

Pharmacology   Blockers of the $Cl_{(Ca)}$, such as DIDS or 5-nitro-2-(3-phenylpropylamino)-benzoic acid (NPPB), are neither specific nor potent (Table 1). How-

a. Whole-cell currents

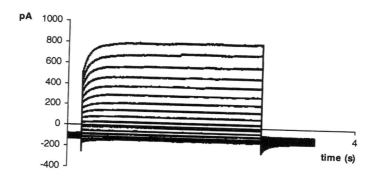

Voltage pulse protocol

b. Current voltage relationship

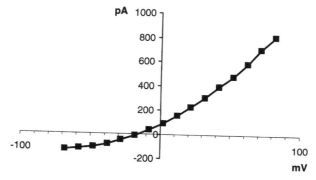

Figure 1 (*a*) A typical example of whole-cell Cl$_{(Ca)}$ currents recorded from a single freshly isolated mouse pancreatic acinar cell. Cell capacitance was measured at 19.7 pF. Currents were elicited using the voltage pulse protocol shown. (*b*) Current-voltage relationship showing the outwardly rectifying nature of the currents. Solutions contained (mM): [Cl]$_i$ = 53, [Cl$^-$]$_o$ = 144. Na$^+$ and K$^+$ in intracellular and extracellular solutions were replaced with *N*-methyl-D-glucamine (NMDG$^+$) in order to eliminate the contribution from Ca^{2+}-activated cation channels present in the cells. The measured free [Ca^{2+}] of the intracellular solution was 450 nM. The reversal potential of these currents is similar to the calculated Cl$^-$ equilibrium potential for these solutions. E$_{rev}$ = -20 mV; $\cong$ E$_c$l = -25 mV. (Cell isolation and current recordings were performed as described 86.)

ever, DIDS in particular has been used to distinguish the $Cl_{(Ca)}$ from other apical Cl^- conductances such as CFTR.

pH Regulation   A number of studies have shown that decreases in intracellular pH inhibit $Cl_{(Ca)}$ currents. This property of $Cl_{(Ca)}$ channels has been detected in many cell types: lacrimal acinar cells (59), parotid acinar cells (26), and T84 cells (26). The mechanism for channel activity inhibition is not known, neither is the physiological relevance. It has been postulated that inhibition of $Cl_{(Ca)}$ currents by reduced pH might be a negative feedback loop for HCO_3^- exit through these channels thereby preventing excessive cytosolic acidification (60).

Calmodulin and CaMKII Regulation   There is evidence to suggest that the activation of $Cl_{(Ca)}$ in tracheal and intestinal cells and colonic cell lines is dependent on phosphorylation by CaMKII (see Table 2). Excised patch studies of the $Cl_{(Ca)}$ channels from HT-29 and biliary cells showed rundown, consistent with cytosolic involvement in channel activation (51, 24). However, when calmodulin alone was added to the intracellular side of the patch, activity was not restored consistent with the involvement of a further regulatory substance (24). That this substance may be CaMKII has been shown by the inhibitory effect of kinase antagonists such as KN-62, calmidazolium, and CaMKII inhibitory peptides on the $Cl_{(Ca)}$ currents of T84, HT29, and tracheal cells (14, 24, 42, 61). Further evidence for a regulatory role for CaMKII comes from a study on the $Cl_{(Ca)}$ channel protein purified from bovine trachea (23), which showed that the sensitivity of the channel to Ca^{2+} is enhanced in the presence of CaMKII. In addition it was shown that the purified protein is phosphorylated by CaMKII (23). In contrast, experiments on the $Cl_{(Ca)}$ present in acinar cells failed to show evidence for CaMKII dependence. In excised patches from pancreatic and submandibular acinar cells, $Cl_{(Ca)}$ did not show rundown and could be directly activated by the application of Ca^{2+} to the bath (38, 40). Whole-cell studies in parotid and submandibular acinar cells showed that inhibitors of CaMKII fail to block $Cl_{(Ca)}$ currents (41, 42).

CaMKII may have other effects on the $Cl_{(Ca)}$ channel. Studies on the $Cl_{(Ca)}$ from bovine trachea (23) showed that in the presence of CaMKII, high concentrations of $[Ca^{2+}]_i$ (>2 μM) produce flicker block of the channel. This phenomenon has been described in $K_{(Ca)}$ channels (62, 63).

Dependence of $Cl_{(Ca)}$ on Endogenous Ca^{2+} Signals

In vivo the intracellular Ca^{2+} signal is generated by agonists that act both to release Ca^{2+} from intracellular Ca^{2+} stores and to promote Ca^{2+} influx across the plasma membrane. For many agonists the intracellular Ca^{2+} stores are the initial and primary source of Ca^{2+}, and therefore the relative position of the Ca^{2+} store to the $Cl_{(Ca)}$ channels becomes a crucial parameter in understanding stimulus-fluid secretion coupling. Many studies have been performed on the characterization of the Ca^{2+} signalling process in secretory epithelial cells, much of which has been recently reviewed (64–66), and is not covered here. Instead, we concentrate on experiments that have combined the measurement of the [Ca^{2+}]$_i$ signal with Cl$_{(Ca)}$ current and indicate the importance of the spatial and temporal aspects of the Ca^{2+} signal to the regulation of the Cl$_{(Ca)}$ channels.

In many cells the coexistence of the Cl$_{(Ca)}$ channel with K$_{(Ca)}$ channels is critical for fluid secretion (67). Both K$_{(Ca)}$ and Cl$_{(Ca)}$ currents can be recorded simultaneously with whole-cell patch-clamp techniques. With these methods the agonist-evoked Ca^{2+} signals have been shown to differentially affect the Cl$_{(Ca)}$ current and the K$_{(Ca)}$ current. In HT29 cells, stimulated with the Ca^{2+} mobilizing agonist neurotensin, the Cl$_{(Ca)}$ was activated first, followed by the K$_{(Ca)}$ (68). In addition, it was shown that the Cl$_{(Ca)}$ current is activated long before a rise in cytosolic Ca^{2+} is observed (measured as an average signal from the whole cell). These undifferentiated HT29 cells presumably show no polarized distribution of the plasma membrane channels, and as a result the authors conclude that Cl$_{(Ca)}$ has a higher sensitivity to [Ca^{2+}]$_i$ than K$_{(Ca)}$ (68). Furthermore they suggest that the Cl$_{(Ca)}$ channels are specifically activated by a Ca^{2+} rise localized to the sub-plasmalemmal region, which explains why the Cl$_{(Ca)}$ current is activated before a rise in global Ca^{2+} is observed. In a similar study, the activation of the K$_{(Ca)}$ of parotid acinar cells was also shown to precede a rise in global Ca^{2+} (69).

In differentiated secretory epithelial cells, both plasma membrane channels and Ca^{2+} stores would be expected to be precisely distributed because of the polarization of these cells. We now know that the acinar cell Ca^{2+} signal is complex both in time, where oscillations are observed, and in space, where discrete local Ca^{2+} signals are seen (64, 70). The first description of Ca^{2+} signal complexity in acinar cells came from recordings of Ca^{2+} oscillations, using fura-2 fluorescence in parotid acinar cells (71). Digital Ca^{2+} imaging revealed that these oscillations were initiated in the secretory pole and then spread as a wave across the cell (2, 71a). Although not recorded simultaneously, whole-cell currents indicate that the activation of a large Cl$^-$ current is temporally coincident with the secretory pole Ca^{2+} signal (2). This has now been shown in acinar cells of the airway (72) and in parotid acinar (73, 74) cells. In lacrimal acinar cells, imaging experiments were used to localize the Ca^{2+} signal associated with plasma membrane channel activation measured with whole-cell patch clamp (75). These experiments demonstrated activation of both Cl$_{(Ca)}$ and K$_{(Ca)}$ channels coincident with a Ca^{2+} signal localized to the apical portion of the cells. In a separate study of submandibular cells, a similar coactivation of the K$_{(Ca)}$ and the Cl$_{(Ca)}$ was seen in the cholinergic response (76).

Spatially Discrete Ca^{2+} Signals Specifically Activate the Cl$_{(Ca)}$ Channel

Further experiments showed that the Cl$^-$ current could be activated in an oscillatory manner by a Ca^{2+} signal that remained confined to the secretory pole of the cell. The oscillations were originally described in terms of spikes in the whole-cell Cl^- current elicited by the injection of low concentrations of $InsP_3$ (77). In these experiments, trains of short-lasting ($\sim$2s) $Cl_{(Ca)}$ current spikes, which were shown to be largely independent of extracellular Ca^{2+}, were established by the infusion of $InsP_3$ in to the cell (77). Further experiments measured global, average $[Ca^{2+}]$ but failed to detect any Ca^{2+} signal associated with acetylcholine-stimulated short-lasting Cl^- current spikes despite the observation of a Ca^{2+} signal induced by higher acetylcholine concentrations (78). By combining whole-cell patch-clamp recordings with digital Ca^{2+} imaging, a secretory pole Ca^{2+} spike was correlated with the Cl^- spikes (79). The local Ca^{2+} signal does not spread to the rest of the cell, and therefore it was concluded that the $Cl_{(Ca)}$ channels are closely associated ($<$1 μm) with the sites of Ca^{2+} release. The actual relationship between the Ca^{2+} signal and the activation of the Cl^- channel is not known, but we can draw some tentative conclusions.

Spatial Relationship of the Ca^{2+} Release Sites to the $Cl_{(Ca)}$ Channels

Does the plasma membrane Cl^- channel respond to local $[Ca^{2+}]_i$ close to the mouth of Ca^{2+} release channels, or is it responsive to the smaller changes in $[Ca^{2+}]$ seen in the bulk cytosol? The steady-state $[Ca^{2+}]$ required for half maximal activation of the acinar cell $Cl_{(Ca)}$ channel is around 300 nM at normal hyperpolarized potentials (55, 56). Therefore if we assume a similar value for the $Cl_{(Ca)}$ response to a dynamic Ca^{2+} signal (as opposed to steady-state), then the channel is sensitive to the range of agonist-evoked Ca^{2+} changes recorded in the bulk cytosol of the secretory pole (2, 80). Indeed the use of low-affinity Ca^{2+}-sensitive dyes has shown that although there is evidence that the agonist-evoked Ca^{2+} signal may have discrete pockets of large Ca^{2+} change ($\sim$10 μM), the $Cl_{(Ca)}$ current follows smaller ($<$1 μM) changes in bulk cytosolic Ca^{2+} (81). This evidence seems to favor a close ($<$1μm) but not intimate (nm) proximity between the Ca^{2+} release sites and the $Cl_{(Ca)}$ channels.

Structure of the Local Secretory Pole Ca^{2+} Signal

If the $Cl_{(Ca)}$ channels are responding to a bulk change in Ca^{2+}, what is the nature of the underlying Ca^{2+} release mechanism that gives rise to this change? We have previously discussed (70) the similarity between the local secretory pole Ca^{2+} spike and puffs of Ca^{2+} in *Xenopus* oocytes (82) that are believed to arise from clusters of $InsP_3$ receptors (83). The two Ca^{2+} release events have similar planar dimensions and similar peak Ca^{2+} amplitudes, although the kinetics of the acinar cell response is much slower (70). However, evidence suggests that the acinar cell signal may be more complex. It has been shown that Ca^{2+} wave velocity is not constant across all regions of the secretory pole (84), indicating that Ca^{2+} release sites are not homogeneously distributed in this region of the cell. Indeed, this may have physiological relevance as it has been shown that different Ca^{2+}-mobilizing agonists are capable of initiating a Ca^{2+} signal from different parts of the secretory pole (85). Direct evidence for inhomogeneities of Ca^{2+} release within the secretory pole has been obtained by studying trains of InsP$_3$-evoked spikes. Spike by spike comparison of the nature of the secretory pole Ca^{2+} signal showed that each spike is a composite response arising from Ca^{2+} release from a single small region of the secretory pole coupled with variable contributions of Ca^{2+} release from other adjoining sites within the secretory pole (66). It appears, therefore, that Ca^{2+} release in the secretory pole region may not be a unitary phenomenon, as it can be further subdivided into smaller Ca^{2+} release units. We suggest that the key process that coordinates Ca^{2+} release from these smaller units is the action of Ca^{2+} via Ca^{2+}-induced Ca^{2+} release at the InsP$_3$ receptor (66, 86). In this way release of Ca^{2+} from one site acts to entrain release of Ca^{2+} from the adjoining sites. Evidence to support this comes from experiments that show that the action of the Ca^{2+} buffer, ethylene glycol-bis-(β-aminoethyl ether)-*N,N,N′,N′*-tetraacetic acid (EGTA), in this system is to progressively localize the secretory pole Ca^{2+} signal and to break up the Ca^{2+} spike into spatially separate miniature Ca^{2+} release events (86). If this model of Ca^{2+} release in the secretory pole is correct, what is the consequence for the activation of the Cl$_{(Ca)}$ current? We could speculate that a system that relies on multiple Ca^{2+} release sites would be less susceptible to the stochastic variation that might arise from dependence on a single release site. The spikes in the secretory pole would thus be an average response of the action of multiple Ca^{2+} release events and therefore might be more robust and reproducible.

Hysteresis Between Cl$_{(Ca)}$ Current Decay and Ca^{2+} Signal Decay

Notwithstanding these complexities in the underlying Ca^{2+} signal, we still have fundamental questions as to the nature of the signal to which the Cl$_{(Ca)}$ channels respond. Does the Cl$_{(Ca)}$ respond differently to a change in Ca^{2+} as opposed to steady-state Ca^{2+}? In other systems, such as *Xenopus* oocytes, it has been shown that the Cl$_{(Ca)}$ current decays, even in the continued presence of elevated Ca^{2+} (89). This decay has been described as a tuning of the Cl$_{(Ca)}$ to respond to the rate of change in Ca^{2+}. In support of this notion, the Cl$_{(Ca)}$ current amplitude was closely correlated with the differential of the Ca^{2+} signal (89). Against this, isolated inside-out patches from *Xenopus* oocytes showed a Cl$_{(Ca)}$ channel that was not inactivated by changes in Ca^{2+} at the cytosolic surface (90). In smooth muscle, the Cl$_{(Ca)}$ current decay also precedes the decay of the Ca^{2+} signal. It has been shown that inhibitors of CAMKII can prevent inactivation (91).

The hysteresis between the Ca^{2+} signal and the Cl$_{(Ca)}$ current has been shown in acinar cells. Kasai & Augustine (2) showed that despite the maintenance of elevated [Ca^{2+}] at the secretory pole, the Cl$_{(Ca)}$ current declined. A typical example of the oscillatory response to InsP$_3$ in mouse pancreatic acinar cells is shown

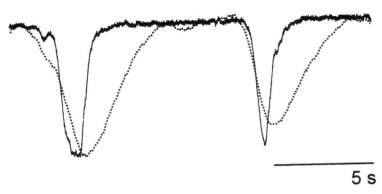

5 s

⌐⌐⌐⌐   normalized whole cell currents

······   normalized secretory pole
[Ca^{2+}]$_i$ response

Figure 2   Hysteresis between Cl$_{(Ca)}$ currents decay and [Ca^{2+}]$_i$ decay in single mouse pancreatic acinar cells. Ins(2,4,5)P$_3$ (8 μM) was injected through a whole-cell patch pipette to elicit trains of Ca^{2+} spikes in single mouse pancreatic acinar cells. The Cl$_{(Ca)}$ current was recorded (holding potential –30 mV) and the figure illustrates two of the captured spikes. Simultaneous digital fluorescence images (Calcium Green, ΔF/F ratio) (methods described Reference 86) of the secretory pole Ca^{2+} response are shown. The amplitudes of the first Cl$_{(Ca)}$ current spike and the Ca^{2+} spike were normalized. For each spike the Cl$_{(Ca)}$ peak precedes the Ca^{2+} peak, and the decay of the Cl$_{(Ca)}$ current is faster than that of the underlying Ca^{2+} signal. (These experiments were performed in collaboration with K Fogarty and D Tuft of the Biomedical Imaging Group, Department of Physiology, University of Massachusetts Medical School.)

in Figure 2 and illustrates the discrepancy between the Ca^{2+} signal decay and the Cl$_{(Ca)}$ current decay. For each spike the currents are almost fully recovered at a time when the Ca^{2+} measured in the secretory pole region is still substantially elevated. This discrepancy may be due to a local sub-plasmalemmal decrease in Ca^{2+} that is either too small or too local to be detected by imaging techniques (2). However, the potential role of phosphorylation in Cl$_{(Ca)}$ current decay has not been investigated in secretory epithelial cells. Recently it was shown that calmodulin is translocated to the apical pole region during agonist stimulation and therefore may well regulate the Cl$_{(Ca)}$ channel behavior (92).

Physiology of the Ca^{2+} Oscillations

The above data, showing Cl$_{(Ca)}$ current decay with an apparently continued elevation in Ca^{2+}, lead us to question the physiological significance of Ca^{2+} oscillations. The tuning of response elements to oscillatory Ca^{2+} signals is of widespread interest. For example, CaMKII (93) and gene expression (94) are preferentially responsive to oscillations in the Ca^{2+} signal. It is important to determine if the Cl$_{(Ca)}$ current response to the Ca^{2+} signal is optimized in a similar way to the oscillatory Ca^{2+} signal. We do not understand why secretory cells employ Ca^{2+} oscillations as opposed to a continuous Ca^{2+} rise. The oscillations may arise out of the need to reduce the energetic cost of producing a sustained Ca^{2+} signal (79, 95). Alternatively, Ca^{2+} oscillations may be essential in fine-tuning the activation of different channels involved in the secretory process, an idea suggested in the push-pull model of fluid secretion (2). This model proposes that an initial localized, Ca^{2+} rise in the secretory pole activates apically located Cl$_{(Ca)}$ channels (push phase), thus leading to the exit of Cl$^-$ from the apex of the cell. The apical Cl$_{(Ca)}$ channels then close through inactivation or a decrease in the local Ca^{2+} signal. The subsequent wave of Ca^{2+} across the cell leads to a rise in Ca^{2+} in the basal part of the cell that activates Ca^{2+}-dependent cation channels. This depolarizes the cell membrane, which results in the pull of Cl$^-$ into the cell through the basally located Cl$^-$ channels. This model therefore is absolutely dependent on Ca^{2+} oscillations activating apical and basally located Ca^{2+}-dependent channels alternately.

CONCLUSIONS

Functional and molecular evidence suggest that there are a number of Cl$_{(Ca)}$ channels with different functional properties. Studies on the recently cloned Cl$_{(Ca)}$ channels (CLCA) indicate that they represent a family of closely related channels with highly conserved molecular and functional properties. Comparison of the functional characteristics of these cloned CLCA channels with those of the native Cl$_{(Ca)}$ channels in exocrine acinar cells suggests that the acinar channels represent a separate family. In many secretory cells, there is evidence for the presence of multiple Cl$^-$ channel types. Therefore, in order to understand the physiological role of these Cl$_{(Ca)}$ channels in secretory cells further studies on the molecular structure, functional properties, and localization of the channel proteins will have to be carried out. In addition further experiments are needed to give us a more detailed understanding of the secretory process itself.

ACKNOWLEDGMENTS

Work in the authors' laboratory was funded by The Medical Research Council, The Biotechnological and Biological Science Research Council, and The Wellcome Trust.

Visit the Annual Reviews home page at www.AnnualReviews.org.

LITERATURE CITED

1. Petersen OH. 1992. Stimulus-secretion coupling: cytoplasmic calcium signals and the control of ion channels in exocrine acinar cells. *J. Physiol.* 448:1–51

2. Kasai H, Augustine GJ. 1990. Cytosolic Ca^{2+} gradients triggering unidirectional fluid secretion from exocrine pancreas. *Nature* 348:735–38

3. Scratcherd T, Hutson D, Case RM. 1981. Ionic transport mechanisms underlying fluid secretion by the pancreas. *Philos. Trans. R. Soc. London Ser. B* 296:167–78

4. Fuller CM, Benos DJ. 1992. CFTR! *Am. J. Physiol.* 263:C267–86

5. Cunningham SA, Awayda MS, Bubien JK, Ismailov II, Arrate MP, et al. 1995. Cloning of an epithelial chloride channel from bovine trachea. *J. Biol. Chem.* 270:31016–26

6. Gandhi R, Elble RC, Gruber AD, Schreur KD, Ji HL, et al. 1998. Molecular and functional characterization of a calcium-sensitive chloride channel from mouse lung. *J. Biol. Chem.* 273:32096–101

7. Gruber AD, Elble RC, Ji HL, Schreur KD, Fuller CM, Pauli BU. 1998. Genomic cloning, molecular characterization, and functional analysis of human CLCA1, the first human member of the family of Ca^{2+}-activated Cl^- channel proteins. *Genomics* 54:200–14

7a. Gruber AD, Schreuer KD, Hong-Long J, Fuller CM, Pauli BU. 1999. Molecular cloning and transmembrane structure of hCLCA2 from human lung, trachea and mammary gland. *Am. J. Physiol.* 276: C1261–70

8. Gruber AD, Gandhi R, Pauli BU. 1998. The murine calcium-sensitive chloride channel (mCaCC) is widely expressed in secretory epithelia and in other select tissues. *Histochem. Cell Biol.* 110:43–49

8a. Cuppoletti J, Malinowska DH. 1999. Ca^{2+}-activated Cl^- channels: focus on molecular cloning and transmembrane structure of hCLCA2 from human lung, trachea and mammary gland. *Am. J. Physiol.* 276:C1259–60

9. Anderson MP, Welsh MJ. 1991. Calcium and cAMP activate different chloride channels in the apical membrane of normal and cystic fibrosis epithelia. *Proc. Natl. Acad. Sci. USA* 88:6003–7

10. Winding B, Winding H, Bindslev N. 1992. Second messengers and ion channels in acetylcholine-induced chloride secretion in hen trachea. *Comp. Biochem. Physiol. C.* 103:195–205

11. Boucher RC, Cheng EH, Paradiso AM, Stutts MJ, Knowles MR, Earp HS. 1989. Chloride secretory response of cystic fibrosis human airway epithelia. Preservation of calcium but not protein kinase C- and A-dependent mechanisms. *J. Clin. Inv.* 84:1424–31

12. Willumsen NJ, Boucher RC. 1989. Activation of an apical Cl- conductance by Ca^{2+} ionophores in cystic fibrosis airway epithelia. *Am. J. Physiol.* 256:C226–33

13. Welsh MJ. 1987. Effect of phorbol ester and calcium ionophore on chloride secretion in canine tracheal epithelium. *Am. J. Physiol.* 253:C828–34

14. Wagner JA, Cozens AL, Schulman H, Gruenert DC, Stryer L, Gardner P. 1991. Activation of chloride channels in normal and cystic fibrosis airway epithelial cells by multifunctional calcium/calmodulin-dependent protein kinase. *Nature* 349:793–96

15. Frizzell RA, Rechkemmer G, Shoemaker RL. 1986. Altered regulation of airway epithelial cell chloride channels in cystic fibrosis. *Science* 233:558–60

16. Frizzell RA, Halm DR, Rechkemmer G, Shoemaker RL. 1986. Chloride channel regulation in secretory epithelia. *Fed. Proc.* 45:2727–31

17. Welsh MJ. 1986. An apical-membrane

chloride channel in human tracheal epithelium. *Science* 232:1648–50

18. Welsh MJ, Liedtke CM. 1986. Chloride and potassium channels in cystic fibrosis airway epithelia. *Nature* 322:467–70

19. Gabriel SE, Clarke LL, Boucher RC, Stutts MJ. 1993. CFTR and outward rectifying chloride channels are distinct proteins with a regulatory relationship. *Nature* 363:263–68

20. Egan M, Flotte T, Afione S, Solow R, Zeitlin PL, et al. 1992. Defective regulation of outwardly rectifying Cl$^-$ channels by protein kinase A corrected by insertion of CFTR. *Nature* 358:581–84

21. Kunzelmann K, Pavenstädt H, Greger R. 1989. Properties and regulation of chloride channels in cystic fibrosis and normal airway cells. *Pflügers Arch.* 415:172–82

22. Ran S, Fuller CM, Arrate MP, Latorre R, Benos DJ. 1992. Functional reconstitution of a chloride channel protein from bovine trachea. *J. Biol. Chem.* 267:20630–37

23. Fuller CM, Ismailov II, Keeton DA, Benos DJ. 1994. Phosphorylation and activation of a bovine tracheal anion channel by Ca^{2+}/calmodulin-dependent protein kinase II. *J. Biol. Chem.* 269:26642–50

24. Morris AP, Frizzell RA. 1993. Ca$^{(2+)}$-dependent Cl$^-$ channels in undifferentiated human colonic cells (HT-29). II. Regulation and rundown. *Am. J. Physiol.* 264:C977–85

25. Morris AP, Cunningham SA, Benos DJ, Frizzell RA. 1992. Cellular differentiation is required for cAMP but not Ca$^{(2+)}$-dependent Cl$^-$ secretion in colonic epithelial cells expressing high levels of cystic fibrosis transmembrane conductance regulator. *J. Biol. Chem.* 267:5575–83

25a. Anderson MP, Sheppard DN, Berger HA, Welsh MJ. 1992. Chloride channels in the apical membrane of normal and cystic fibrosis airway and intestinal epithelia. *Am. J. Physiol.* 263:L1–14

26. Arreola J, Melvin JE, Begenisich T. 1995. Inhibition of Ca^{2+}-dependent Cl-channels from secretory epithelial cells by low internal pH. *J. Membr. Biol.* 147:95–104

27. Dharmsathaphorn K, Pandol SJ. 1986. Mechanism of chloride secretion induced by carbachol in a colonic epithelial cell line. *J. Clin. Invest.* 77:348–54

28. Vajanaphanich M, Schultz C, Rudolf MT, Wasserman M, Enyedi P, et al. 1994. Long-term uncoupling of chloride secretion from intracellular calcium levels by Ins(3,4,5,6)P$_4$. *Nature* 371:711–14

29. McEwan GT, Hirst BH, Simmons NL. 1994. Carbachol stimulates Cl$^-$ secretion via activation of two distinct apical Cl$^-$ pathways in cultured human T84 intestinal epithelial monolayers. *Biochem. Biophys. Acta* 1220:241–47

29a. Vaandrager AB, Bajnath R, Groot JA, Bot AG, De Jonge HR. 1991. Ca^{2+} and cAMP activate different chloride efflux pathways in HT-29.cl19A colonic epithelial cell line. *Am J. Physiol.* 261:G958–65

30. Merlin D, Jiang L, Strohmeier GR, Nusrat A, Alper SL, et al. 1998. Distinct Ca^{2+}- and cAMP-dependent anion conductances in the apical membrane of polarized T84 cells. *Am. J. Physiol.* 275:C484–95

31. Cuthbert AW, MacVinish LJ, Hickman ME, Ratcliff R, Colledge WH, Evans MJ. 1994. Ion-transporting activity in the murine colonic epithelium of normal animals and animals with cystic fibrosis. *Pflügers Arch.* 428:508–15

32. Mall M, Bleich M, Schürlein M, Kühr J, Seydewitz HH, et al. 1998. Cholinergic ion secretion in human colon requires coactivation by cAMP. *Am. J. Physiol.* 275:G1274–81

33. Strabel D, Diener M. 1995. Evidence against direct activation of chloride

secretion by carbachol in the rat distal colon. *Eur. J. Pharm.* 274:181–91

34. Kunzelmann K, Mall M, Briel M, Hipper A, Nitschke R, et al. 1997. The cystic fibrosis transmembrane conductance regulator attenuates the endogenous Ca^{2+} activated Cl- conductance of Xenopus oocytes. *Pflügers Arch.* 435:178–81

35. Wilschanski MA, Rozmahel R, Beharry S, Kent G, Li C, et al. 1996. In vivo measurements of ion transport in long-living CF mice. *Biochem. Biophys. Res. Commun.* 219:753–59

36. Clarke LL, Grubb BR, Yankaskas JR, Cotton CU, McKenzie A, Boucher RC. 1994. Relationship of a non-cystic fibrosis transmembrane conductance regulator-mediated chloride conductance to organ-level disease in Cftr(-/-) mice. *Proc. Natl. Acad. Sci USA* 91:479–83

37. Case RM, Argent BE. 1990. Pancreatic secretion: in vivo, perfused gland, and isolated duct studies. *Meth. Enzymol.* 192:256–71

38. Zdebik A, Hug MJ, Greger R. 1997. Chloride channels in the luminal membrane of rat pancreatic acini. *Pflügers Arch.* 434:188–94

39. Marty A, Tan YP, Trautmann A. 1984. Three types of calcium-dependent channel in rat lacrimal glands. *J. Physiol.* 357:293–325

40. Martin DK. 1993. Small conductance chloride channels in acinar cells from the rat mandibular salivary gland are directly controlled by a G-protein. *Biochem. Biophys. Res. Commun.* 192:1266–73

41. Ishikawa T. 1996. A bicarbonate- and weak acid-permeable chloride conductance controlled by cytosolic Ca^{2+} and ATP in rat submandibular acinar cells. *J. Membr. Biol.* 153:147–59

42. Arreola J, Melvin JE, Begenisich T. 1998. Differences in regulation of Ca^{2+}-activated Cl- channels in colonic and parotid secretory cells. *Am. J. Physiol.* 274:C161–66

43. Zeng W, Lee MG, Yan M, Diaz J, Ben-

jamin I, et al. 1997. Immuno and functional characterization of CFTR in submandibular and pancreatic acinar and duct cells. *Am. J. Physiol.* 273:C442–55

43a. Zeng W, Min Goo L, Muallen S. 1997. Membrane-specific regulation of Cl^- channels by purinergic receptors in rat submandibular gland acinar and duct cells. *J. Biol. Chem.* 272:32956–65

44. Ashton N, Evans RL, Elliott AC, Green R, Argent BE. 1993. Regulation of fluid secretion and intracellular messengers in isolated rat pancreatic ducts by acetylcholine. *J. Physiol.* 471:549–62

45. Schoumacher RA, Ram J, Iannuzzi MC, Bradbury NA, Wallace RW, et al. 1990. A cystic fibrosis pancreatic adenocarcinoma cell line. *Proc. Natl. Acad. Sci. USA* 87:4012–16

46. Gray MA, Winpenny JP, Porteous DJ, Dorin JR, Argent BE. 1994. CFTR and calcium-activated chloride currents in pancreatic duct cells of a transgenic CF mouse. *Am. J. Physiol.* 266:C213–21

47. Winpenny JP, Harris A, Hollingsworth MA, Argent BE, Gray MA. 1998. Calcium-activated chloride conductance in a pancreatic adenocarcinoma cell line of ductal origin (HPAF) and in freshly isolated human pancreatic duct cells. *Pflügers Arch.* 435:796–803

48. Nguyen TD, Koh DS, Moody MW, Fox NR, Savard CE, et al. 1997. Characterization of two distinct chloride channels in cultured dog pancreatic duct epithelial cells. *Am. J. Physiol.* 272:G172–80

49. Chao AC, Kouyama K, Heist EK, Dong YJ, Gardner P. 1995. Calcium- and CaMKII-dependent chloride secretion induced by the microsomal $Ca^{(2+)}$-ATPase inhibitor 2,5–di-(tert-butyl)-1,4–hydroquinone in cystic fibrosis pancreatic epithelial cells. *J. Clin. Inv.* 96:1794–801

50. Light DB, Schwiebert EM, Fejes-Toth G, Naray-Fejes-Toth A, Karlson KH, et al. 1990. Chloride channels in the apical

membrane of cortical collecting duct cells. *Am. J. Physiol.* 258:F273–80

51. Schlenker T, Fitz JG. 1996. Ca^{2+}-activated Cl$^-$ channels in a human biliary cell line: regulation by Ca^{2+}/calmodulin-dependent protein kinase. *Am. J. Physiol.* 271:G304–10

52. McGill JM, Yen MS, Basavappa S, Mangel AW, Kwiatkowski AP. 1995. ATP-activated chloride permeability in biliary epithelial cells is regulated by calmodulin-dependent protein kinase II. *Biochem. Biophys. Res. Commun.* 208:457–62

53. Fitz JG, Basavappa S, McGill J, Melhus O, Cohn JA. 1993. Regulation of membrane chloride currents in rat bile duct epithelial cells. *J. Clin. Inv.* 91:319–28

54. Deleted in proof

55. Arreola J, Melvin JE, Begenisich T. 1996. Activation of calcium-dependent chloride channels in rat parotid acinar cells. *J. Gen. Physiol.* 108:35–47

56. Evans MG, Marty A. 1986. Calcium-dependent chloride currents in isolated cells from rat lacrimal glands. *J. Physiol.* 378:437–60

57. Ishikawa T, Cook DI. 1993. A Ca^{2+}-activated Cl- current in sheep parotid secretory cells. *J. Membr. Biol.* 135:261–71

58. Randriamampita C, Chanson M, Trautmann A. 1988. Calcium and secretagogues-induced conductances in rat exocrine pancreas. *Pflügers Arch.* 411:53–57

59. Park K, Brown PD. 1995. Intracellular pH modulates the activity of chloride channels in isolated lacrimal gland acinar cells. *Am. J. Physiol.* 268:C647–50

60. Begenisich T, Melvin JE. 1998. Regulation of chloride channels in secretory epithelia. *J. Membr. Biol.* 163:77–85

61. Worrell RT, Frizzell RA. 1991. CaMKII mediates stimulation of chloride conductance by calcium in T84 cells. *Am. J. Physiol.* 260:C877–82

62. McManus OB. 1991. Calcium-activated potassium channels: regulation by calcium. *J. Bioeng. Biomembr.* 23:537–60

63. Sakakibara M, Alkon DL, DeLorenzo R, Goldenring JR, Neary JT, Heldman E. 1986. Modulation of calcium-mediated inactivation of ionic currents by Ca^{2+}/calmodulin-dependent protein kinase II. *Biophys. J.* 50:319–27

64. Petersen OH, Petersen CC, Kasai H. 1994. Calcium and hormone action. *Annu. Rev. Physiol.* 56:297–319

65. Thomas AP, Bird GS, Hajnóczky G, Robb-Gaspers LD, Putney JW Jr. 1996. Spatial and temporal aspects of cellular calcium signaling. *FASEB J.* 10:1505–17

66. Thorn P, Moreton R, Berridge M. 1996. Multiple, coordinated Ca^{2+}-release events underlie the inositol trisphosphate-induced local Ca^{2+} spikes in mouse pancreatic acinar cells. *EMBO J.* 15:999–1003

67. Petersen OH. 1992. Ion channels. Ten years of patch-clamp studies. *Biochem. Pharmacol.* 43:1–3

68. Morris AP, Kirk KL, Frizzell RA. 1990. Simultaneous analysis of cell Ca^{2+} and Ca^{2+}-stimulated chloride conductance in colonic epithelial cells (HT-29). *Cell Regul.* 1:951–63

69. Foskett JK, Gunter-Smith PJ, Melvin JE, Turner RJ. 1989. Physiological localization of an agonist-sensitive pool of Ca^{2+} in parotid acinar cells. *Proc. Natl. Acad. Sci. USA* 86:167–71

70. Thorn P. 1996. Spatial domains of Ca^{2+} signaling in secretory epithelial cells. *Cell Calcium* 20:203–14

71. Gray PT. 1988. Oscillations of free cytosolic calcium evoked by cholinergic and catecholaminergic agonists in rat parotid acinar cells. *J. Physiol.* 406:35–53

71a. Yamamoto-Hino M, Atsushi A, Segawa A, Adachi E, et al. 1998. Apical vesicles bearing inositol 1,4,5-trisphosphate receptors in the Ca^{2+} initiation site of ductal epithelium of the submandibular gland. *J. Cell Biol.* 141:135–42

72. Sasaki T, Shimura S, Wakui M, Ohka-

wara Y, Takishima T, Mikoshiba K. 1994. Apically localized IP$_3$ receptors control chloride current in airway gland acinar cells. *Am.J. Physiol.* 267:L152–58

73. Hassoni AA, Gray PT. 1994. Flash photolysis studies of the localization of calcium release sites in rat parotid isolated acinar cells. *J. Physiol.* 478 Pt 3:461–67

74. Hassoni AA, Gray PT. 1994. The control of chloride conductance in rat parotid isolated acinar cells investigated by photo release of caged compounds. *Pflügers Arch.* 428:269–74

75. Tan YP, Marty A, Trautmann A. 1992. High density of Ca^{2+}-dependent K$^+$ and Cl$^-$ channels on the luminal membrane of lacrimal acinar cells. *Proc. Natl. Acad. Sci. USA* 89:11229–33

76. Smith PM, Gallacher DV. 1992. Acetylcholine- and caffeine-evoked repetitive transient Ca($^{2+}$)-activated K$^+$ and Cl$^-$ currents in mouse submandibular cells. *J. Physiol.* 449:109–20

77. Wakui M, Potter BV, Petersen OH. 1989. Pulsatile intracellular calcium release does not depend on fluctuations in inositol trisphosphate concentration. *Nature* 339:317–20

78. Osipchuk YV, Wakui M, Yule DI, Gallacher DV, Petersen OH. 1990. Cytoplasmic Ca^{2+} oscillations evoked by receptor stimulation, G-protein activation, internal application of inositol trisphosphate or Ca^{2+}: simultaneous microfluorimetry and Ca^{2+} dependent Cl- current recording in single pancreatic acinar cells. *EMBO J.* 9:697–704

79. Thorn P, Lawrie AM, Smith PM, Gallacher DV, Petersen OH. 1993. Local and global cytosolic Ca^{2+} oscillations in exocrine cells evoked by agonists and inositol trisphosphate. *Cell* 74:661–68

80. Toescu EC, Lawrie AM, Petersen OH, Gallacher DV. 1992. Spatial and temporal distribution of agonist-evoked cytoplasmic Ca^{2+} signals in exocrine acinar cells analysed by digital image microscopy. *EMBO J.* 11:1623–29

81. Ito K, Miyashita Y, Kasai H. 1997. Micromolar and submicromolar Ca^{2+} spikes regulating distinct cellular functions in pancreatic acinar cells. *EMBO J.* 16:242–51

82. Yao Y, Choi J, Parker I. 1995. Quantal puffs of intracellular Ca^{2+} evoked by inositol trisphosphate in Xenopus oocytes. *J. Physiol.* 482 (Pt 3):533–53

83. Mak DO, Foskett JK. 1997. Single-channel kinetics, inactivation, and spatial distribution of inositol trisphosphate (IP$_3$) receptors in Xenopus oocyte nucleus. *J. Gen. Physiol.* 109:571–87

84. Kasai H, Li YX, Miyashita Y. 1993. Subcellular distribution of Ca^{2+} release channels underlying Ca^{2+} waves and oscillations in exocrine pancreas. *Cell* 74:669–77

85. Xu X, Zeng W, Diaz J. Muallem S. 1996. Spatial compartmentalization of Ca^{2+} signaling complexes in pancreatic acini. *J. Biol. Chem.* 271:24684–90

86. Kidd JF, Fogarty, KE, Tuft R, Thorn P. 1999. The role of Ca^{2+} feedback in shaping InsP$_3$–evoked Ca^{2+} signals in mouse pancreatic acinar cells. *J. Physiol.* 520:187–201

87. Deleted in proof

88. Deleted in proof

89. Parker I, Yao Y. 1994. Relation between intracellular Ca^{2+} signals and Ca^{2+}-activated Cl$^-$ current in Xenopus oocytes. *Cell Calcium* 15:276–88

90. Gomez-Hernandez JM, Stühmer W, Parekh AB. 1997. Calcium dependence and distribution of calcium-activated chloride channels in Xenopus oocytes. *J. Physiol.* 502 (Pt 3):569–74

91. Wang YX, Kotlikoff MI. 1997. Inactivation of calcium-activated chloride channels in smooth muscle by calcium/calmodulin-dependent protein kinase. *Proc. Natl. Acad. Sci. USA* 94:14918–23

92. Craske M, Takeo T, Gerasimenko O, Vallant C, Torok K, et al. 1999. Hormone-induced secretory and nuclear

translocation of calmodulin: oscillations of calmodulin with the nucleus as an integrator. *Proc. Natl. Acad. Sci. USA* 96:4426–31

93. De Koninck P, Schulman H. 1998. Sensitivity of CaM kinase II to the frequency of Ca^{2+} oscillations. *Science* 279:227–30

94. Li W, Llopis J, Whitney M, Zlokarnik G, Tsien RY. 1998. Cell-permeant caged InsP$_3$ ester shows that Ca^{2+} spike frequency can optimize gene expression. *Nature* 392:936–41

95. Taylor CW. 1995. Why do hormones stimulate Ca^{2+} mobilization? *Biochem. Soc. Trans.* 23:637–42

Annu. Rev. Physiol. 2000. 62:515–34

THE Na-K-Cl COTRANSPORTER OF SECRETORY EPITHELIA

Mark Haas[1] and Bliss Forbush III[2]

[1]Department of Pathology, Johns Hopkins University School of Medicine, Baltimore, Maryland 21205; e-mail: mhaas@jhmi.edu; [2]Department of Cellular and Molecular Physiology, Yale University School of Medicine, New Haven, Connecticut 06510

Key Words   ion transport, K-Cl cotransport, bumetanide, furosemide, chloride

■ **Abstract**   The Na-K-Cl cotransporters are a class of ion transport proteins that transport Na, K, and Cl ions into and out of cells in an electrically neutral manner, in most cases with a stoichiometry of 1Na:1K:2Cl. To date, two Na-K-Cl cotransporter isoforms have been identified: NKCC1, which is present in a wide variety of secretory epithelia and non-epithelial cells; and NKCC2, which is present exclusively in the kidney, in the epithelial cells of the thick ascending limb of Henle's loop and of the macula densa. Both NKCC isoforms represent part of a diverse family of cation-chloride cotransport proteins that share a common predicted membrane topology; this family also includes Na-Cl cotransporters and multiple K-Cl cotransporter isoforms. In secretory epithelia, the regulation of NKCC1, which is typically present on the basolateral membrane, is tightly coordinated with that of other transporters, including apical Cl channels, to maintain cell volume and integrity during active salt and fluid secretion. Changes in intracellular [Cl] ([Cl]$_i$) appear to be involved in this regulation of NKCC1, which is directly phosphorylated by an unknown protein kinase in response to various secretagogues as well as reductions in [Cl]$_i$ and cell volume. This review focuses on structure-function relationships within NKCC1 and on recent developments pertaining to NKCC1 regulation at cellular and molecular levels.

INTRODUCTION

Na-K-Cl cotransporters mediate the electrically neutral transport of Na, K, and Cl ions across cell membranes, with a stoichiometry of 1Na:1K:2Cl in the overwhelming majority of cases (27, 28, 30, 70). Although the direction of net cotransport may be into or out of the cells depending on the sum of the chemical potential gradients of the transported ions (36), under physiological conditions in most cells net transport occurs from extracellular fluid to cytoplasm. Na-K-Cl cotransport in all cells and tissues is inhibited by the 5-sulfamoylbenzoic acid loop diuretics, which include (in order of increasing potency) furosemide, bumetanide,

0066–4278/00/0315–0515$12.00

515

and benzmetanide, although the inhibitory potency of these drugs for Na-K-Cl cotransport varies significantly between tissues and species (27, 69, 71).

Na-K-Cl cotransporters are present in many different tissues from a wide variety of animal species, where they serve a number of vital physiological functions (see References 27, 28, 30, 63, 70 for reviews). In most cell types studied to date, Na-K-Cl cotransport is activated by cell shrinkage and as such plays a potential role in the regulation of cell volume. As a major pathway for salt influx, the cotransporter also works in concert with other solute transport pathways to maintain cell volume, and it is well documented that secretory epithelial cells will lose salt and water when exposed to bumetanide or other loop diuretics (32, 55, 87). In some cells, Na-K-Cl cotransport activity may be involved in modulating cell growth and development (10, 72). The physiological role of Na-K-Cl cotransport is, however, most clearly defined in salt-transporting epithelia. In the absorptive epithelium of the thick ascending limb of Henle's loop of mammalian kidney, apical Na-K-Cl cotransporters act in concert with apical K channels, basolateral Cl channels, and the basolateral Na/K pump to mediate net NaCl absorption (24). In a wide variety of secretory epithelia, including those of the intestines (12, 25), airways (7), and salivary glands (65), a similar coordinated transport process occurs, only with reversed polarity: Cl enters the cells with Na and K via the basolateral cotransporter and is transported into the lumen via apical Cl channels; K taken up via the cotransporter and Na/K pump is recycled back across the basolateral membrane via K channels, and the lumen-negative transepithelial electrical potential generated by these transport processes drives passive Na transport from the serosa into the lumen (7, 12, 25, 65). Predictably, mice lacking NKCC1 exhibit decreased chloride secretion in the intestines and trachea (14a). NKCC1-deficient mice and Shaker-with-syndactylism mice (a radiation-induced strain with mutations in the gene encoding NKCC1 leading to marked reduction in its expression) are also profoundly deaf and exhibit behavior indicative of inner ear defects (10a, 12a, 14a), which is consistent with the prominent expression of NKCC1 protein on the basolateral membrane of strial marginal and vestibular dark cells and in neurons of the inner ear (8a, 10a). This review focuses on various aspects of Na-K-Cl cotransporters in secretory epithelia, including tissue distribution, structure-function correlations, regulation, and how this regulation is coordinated with that of Cl and K channels to produce a stimulated rate of transepithelial ion transport in response to secretagogues. We first briefly review the structural relationship of Na-K-Cl cotransporters in secretory epithelia to Na-K-Cl cotransporters in other tissues, and structurally related cation-chloride cotransporters.

Na-K-Cl COTRANSPORTER ISOFORMS AND THE CATION-CHLORIDE COTRANSPORTER SUPERFAMILY

Table 1 summarizes the properties of and homology between the seven known members of the cation-chloride cotransporter superfamily, which includes two Na-K-Cl (NKCC) cotransporter isoforms, one known Na-Cl cotransporter (NCC) isoform, and four K-Cl cotransporter (KCC) isoforms. As deduced from their cDNA sequences, each member of this superfamily shares a common secondary structure characterized by 12 predicted transmembrane domains, and hydrophilic, intracellular amino- and carboxy-terminal domains (Figure 1, see color insert). The greatest degree of homology between superfamily members is in the predicted transmembrane domains, as well as in putative intracellular loops connecting these domains, particularly the large loop connecting transmembrane domains 2 and 3 (Figure 1, see color insert). Significant homology is also seen in regions of the carboxy-terminal domain and to a lesser extent within the amino-terminal domain (11, 19, 20, 22, 36a, 63, 63a, 73–76, 88, 90).

It is possible that in the future, additional members of the cation-cotransporter superfamily will be added to those in Table 1, as has been the case with Na-H exchangers (2, 3). Considerable homology is known to exist between NKCC and KCC isoforms and DNA sequences present in cyanobacteria and *Caenorhabditis elegans* (74–76, 88). A number of additional cation-chloride cotransporters have been described with physiological properties different from known NKCC, NCC, and KCC isoforms, yet conceivably some or all of these may prove to be structurally related to the proteins listed in Table 1. These include electrogenic K-Cl cotransporters (49), bumetanide-sensitive, K-independent Na-Cl cotransporters (14, 82), and the Na-K-Cl cotransporter of squid giant axon, which has a reported stoichiometry of 2Na:1K:3Cl (80).

Of the two NKCC isoforms, NKCC1 is quite widespread in its tissue distribution, being present in many secretory epithelia as well as non-epithelial cells such as neurons, endothelial cells, and renal mesangial cells (44, 76, 77, 90). In the vast majority of secretory epithelia, including that of the shark rectal gland (Figure 2, panels *a-c*), the cotransporter is expressed on the basolateral membrane, but not apically, in a distribution similar to that of Na/K-ATPase (56, 57). By contrast, NKCC2, which is present only in the kidney, is expressed (as three different splice variants) on the apical membrane of the epithelial cells of the cortical and medullary thick ascending limb of Henle's loop and of the macula densa (44, 45, 66, 74, 89), and in subapical cytoplasmic vesicles within these cells (66). The one known exception to this basolateral NKCC1–apical NKCC2 paradigm is in choroid plexus epithelium, where NKCC1 is located on the apical membrane (Figure 2, panels *d-f*), again together with Na/K-ATPase (58, 77).

STRUCTURE-FUNCTION RELATIONSHIPS WITHIN NKCC1

Isenring, Forbush, and coworkers (38–40) constructed chimeras of human colonic and shark rectal gland NKCC1 cDNAs and expressed the corresponding proteins in HEK-293 cells in order to examine the roles of specific domains within NKCC1 in the binding of Na, K, Cl, and the loop diuretic bumetanide. Central to this approach are the well-established differences between human and shark NKCC1

TABLE 1   The cation-chloride cotransporter superfamily

NKCC1
Other name:	BSC2
Stoichiometry:	1Na:1K:2Cl
Distribution:	Secretory epithelia (basolateral membrane); choroid plexus (apical membrane); non-epithelial tissues
Inhibitors:	Bumetanide > furosemide, insensitive to thiazides
mRNA size:	7.0–7.5 kb
Protein mass:	~130 kDa (deglycosylated)
Homology:	~60% amino acid identity with NKCC2; ~45% amino acid identity with NCC; ~25% amino acid identity with KCC1 and KCC2

NKCC2
Other name:	BSC1
Stoichiometry:	1Na:1K:2Cl
Distribution:	Kidney (alternatively spliced variants in cortex and/or medulla)
Inhibitors:	Bumetanide > furosemide; insensitive to thiazides
mRNA size:	4.6–5.2 kb
Protein mass:	120–130 kDa (deglycosylated)
Homology:	~60% amino acid identity with NKCC1; 45–48% amino acid identity with NCC; ~25% amino acid identity with KCC1 and KCC2

NCC
Other name:	TSC
Stoichiometry:	1Na:1Cl, K-independent
Distribution:	Teleost urinary bladder, distal tubule of mammalian kidney (apical membrane)
Inhibitors:	Metolazone and other thiazide diuretics; insensitive to bumetanide
mRNA size:	3.0–4.4 kb
Protein mass:	~110 kDa (deglycosylated)
Homology:	~45% amino acid identity with NKCC1; 45–48% amino acid identity with NKCC2; ~25% amino acid identity with KCC1 and KCC2

KCC1
Stoichiometry:	1K:1Cl, Na-independent
Distribution:	Many organs and cell types including kidney, brain, heart, lung, liver, muscle, stomach, colon, placenta, erythrocytes
Inhibitors:	Furosemide > bumetanide; DIDS, DIOA; insensitive to thiazides
mRNA size:	3.8 kb
Protein mass:	~120 kDa (deglycosylated)
Homology:	65–71% amino acid identity with other KCC isoforms; ~25% amino acid identity with NKCC1, NKCC2 and NCC

KCC2
Stoichiometry:	Most likely 1K:1Cl, Na-independent
Distribution:	Neuronal-specific
Inhibitors:	Furosemide > bumetanide; DIDS and DIOA (low affinity)
mRNA size:	5.6 kb
Protein mass:	~125 kDa (deglycosylated)
Homology:	65–71% amino acid identity with other KCC isoforms; ~25% amino acid identity with NKCC1, NKCC2 and NCC

(continued)

TABLE 1 *Continued.*

KCC3	
Stoichiometry:	Most likely 1K:1Cl, Na-independent
Distribution:	Muscle, heart, kidney, brain
Inhibitors:	Furosemide > bumetanide
mRNA size:	6–7 kb (probable alternative splicing)
Protein mass:	~120 kDa (deglycosylated)
Homology:	65–71% amino acid identity with other KCC isoforms; 27–33% amino acid identity with NKCC1, NKCC2 and NCC
KCC4	
Stoichiometry:	Not yet tested
Distribution:	Many organs including kidney, liver, lung, muscle, brain, stomach, thyroid, pancreas, placenta
Inhibitors:	Furosemide, possibly others
mRNA size:	5.3 kb
Protein mass:	~115 kDa (unglycosylated)
Homology:	65–71% amino acid identity with other KCC isoforms; 27–33% amino acid identity with NKCC1, NKCC2 and NCC

with respect to ion and bumetanide affinities (76, 88). Although the predicted amino acid sequences of these cotransporters are 74% identical, the $K_{1/2}$ values for Na, K, and Cl and the K_i value for bumetanide are four- to sixfold higher in shark NKCC1 compared with its human homologue (76, 88). With the first set of chimeras, in which amino- and carboxy-terminal domains were exchanged between human and shark proteins, it was found that the affinities for Na, K, Cl, and bumetanide were determined entirely by the large, hydrophobic, central portion of NKCC1 containing the 12 putative membrane-spanning helices. Substitutions in amino- and carboxy-terminal domains did not affect these ion or inhibitor affinities, although mutants lacking either of these domains were not functional when expressed in HEK-293 cells, apparently due to minimal delivery of the mutant proteins to the cell surface (38).

Isenring et al (40) next produced two inverse shark-human NKCC1 chimeras with a junction point located at the start of the third putative transmembrane domain (TM). Each of these chimeric proteins exhibited Na and Rb (congener of K) affinities intermediate between those of shark and human NKCC1. Cl affinities of the chimeras showed small (but significant) differences from wild-type proteins, with the portion of the molecule distal to the junction point being the major determinant of Cl affinity. By contrast, bumetanide affinities of the chimeras were determined mainly by the part of the molecule proximal to the junction point, indicating that Cl and bumetanide binding sites on NKCC1 are at least partially distinct from one another (40). A point mutation of one pair of residues in TM2 of shark NKCC1 produced a Na affinity similar to that of the chimera having human sequence up to TM3 (but no change in Rb affinity), whereas mutation of

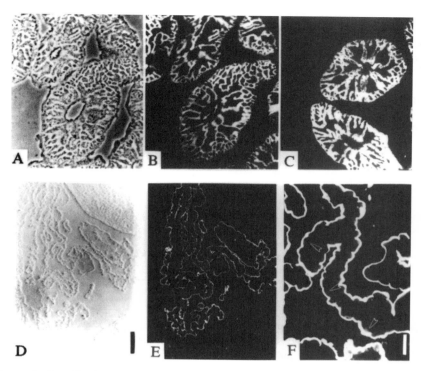

Figure 2   Localization of NKCC1 protein in epithelia of the shark rectal gland (*A–C*) and rat choroid plexus (*D–F*) by immunofluorescence using specific anti-NKCC1 antibodies. Panels *A–C* show photomicrographs of cryosections of shark rectal gland under phase contrast microscopy (*A*), stained with a monoclonal antibody (J4)(57) against shark NKCC1 (*B*), and stained with a monoclonal antibody against the α-subunit of Na,K-ATPase (*C*). Both antibodies stain the basolateral membrane, but not the apical membrane (arrows, panel *B*). Original magnification of each micrograph is X300. Panels *D–F* show photomicrographs of cryosections of rat choroid plexus under phase contrast microscopy (*D*), and stained with a rabbit polyclonal antibody against a portion of the carboxy-terminal region of mouse NKCC1 (44, 77) at low power (*E*) and higher power (*F*). Staining is localized to the apical membrane, with no staining of basolateral membranes (arrows, panel *F*). The bar in panel *D* 50 μm; in panel *F* 13 μm. Panels *A–C* are reproduced from Lytle et al (57) with copyright permission from the Am. Soc. Biochem. Mol. Biol. Inc.; panels *D–F* are reproduced from Plotkin et al (77) with copyright permission from the Am. Physiol. Soc.

a second pair of residues within TM2 produced a Rb affinity similar to that of the chimera but no change in Na affinity (40).

Finally, Isenring et al (39) employed additional chimeras and point mutations to further identify regions within NKCC1 that are involved in cation, Cl, and bumetanide binding. These studies showed that mutations in putative transmembrane domains beyond TM7 had no effect on ion affinities, but that bumetanide affinity is affected by mutations in TM11, 12, or both. A shark-human chimera with a junction point within TM7 had Na, K, and Cl affinities intermediate between those of shark and human NKCC1, whereas a chimera with human sequence through TM7 and shark sequence thereafter had ion affinities indistinguishable from those of human NKCC1, suggesting that TM7, like TM2, is involved in cation binding to NKCC1, and that TM7 is involved in Cl binding as well. This was further confirmed using a mutation in which all residues within TM7 of shark NKCC1 were replaced by their human counterparts (39). As TM1, 3, and 6 are fully conserved between human and shark NKCC1, this left only TM4 and 5 as additional potential modulators of ion and/or bumetanide binding. Chimeras with junction points after TM5 showed no significant difference in Na affinity to those with junction points at the start of TM3, but differences in Rb and Cl affinities were observed (39). Further studies with point mutations localized the affinity-modifying residues to TM4 rather than TM5. Thus in summary the binding and transport of Na by NKCC1 appears to involve primarily TM2 and 7; that of Rb involves mainly TM2, 4, and 7; that of Cl mainly TM4 and 7, with a lesser contribution of TM2. Bumetanide binding also involves residues in the same TM2–7 region, but in addition also residues in TM11 and/or 12. Regions of NKCC1 involved in determining ion and bumetanide affinities are indicated on the structural model of this protein shown in Figure 1.

REGULATION OF NKCC1

As noted above, NKCC1 in the basolateral membrane of secretory epithelia acts in concert with other transporters, namely apical Cl channels and basolateral K channels and Na/K pumps, to produce transepithelial Cl secretion. Thus any regulation of NKCC1 in these cells must be coordinated with that of these other transporters, otherwise the cells will develop potentially fatal imbalances in ion and water contents. In most secretory epithelia that exhibit hormone-stimulated transepithelial secretion, such as those of the airways and intestines, Cl channels in the apical membrane appear to represent the primary site of hormone action, although in some cases (particularly with some secretagogues using intracellular $[Ca^{2+}]$ rather than cyclic AMP [cAMP] as a second messenger) basolateral K channels may also be directly stimulated. Findings in the shark rectal gland (53–55) first suggested that stimulation of NKCC1 by the cAMP-dependent secretagogue vasoactive intestinal peptide (VIP) and other substances (e.g. forskolin) that raised intracellular cAMP levels did not involve a primary stimulation of NKCC1, but rather an effect secondary to apical Cl efflux via activated channels. For example, if $[K]_o$ is raised from 4 to 80 mM, a maneuver that depolarizes the cell and thus renders Cl efflux energetically unfavorable, cotransport activity becomes refractory to forskolin activation (55). This finding also correlates with the lack of a consensus phosphorylation site for cAMP-dependent protein kinase

(PKA) in the sequence of shark NKCC1 (88). Similar findings were also noted in mammalian airway epithelial cells, where raising basolateral $[K]_o$ completely inhibited basolateral cotransport activation by apical uridine triphosphate (UTP), a secretagogue that activates a non-CFTR apical Cl channel via a cAMP-independent mechanism, and markedly reduced cotransporter activation by cAMP-dependent secretagogues such as isoproterenol, although these cells also appear to exhibit some direct cotransport activation via cAMP (28, 34).

Although the activation of basolateral Na-K-Cl cotransport in response to secretagogues is indirect, it clearly involves biochemical modification (i. e. phosphorylation) of NKCC1 as opposed to a thermodynamic effect related to changes in ion gradients. The first evidence supporting this conclusion came from studies showing that [^{3}H]bumetanide binding, a marker of cotransporter activation (28, 30), was increased in airway epithelial cells in response to secretagogues including isoproterenol and apical UTP (31, 34). Lytle & Forbush (54) and Torchia et al (84) first demonstrated direct phosphorylation of NKCC1 in the shark rectal gland and avian salt gland, respectively; the former in response to forskolin and hypertonicity, and the latter in response to VIP and the calcium-dependent secretogogue carbachol. Later studies in airway epithelial cells (33) (depicted in Figure 3) and in rat parotid acini (83) confirmed NKCC1 phosphorylation in response to cAMP-dependent (e. g. isoproterenol) and cAMP-independent (e. g. apical UTP) secretagogues. To date, phosphorylation of NKCC1 has been demonstrated on serine and threonine but not on tyrosine residues (51, 54), although Na-K-Cl cotransport in some non-epithelial cells has been shown to be inhibited by high doses of the tyrosine kinase inhibitor genistein through a yet unknown mechanism (16). In the shark rectal gland, three specific sites of NKCC1 phosphorylation have now been definitively identified, each in the amino-terminal domain (Thr-184, Thr-189, and Thr-202; see Figure 1) (5, 54, 88). Each of these threonines is conserved in human NKCC1 (76) and in NKCC2 as well (19, 74), although actual phosphorylation of the latter protein remains to be determined. In a recent preliminary report (5), it was found that mutation of Thr-189 to Ala resulted in a protein that was expressed on the cell surface in levels comparable to wild-type shark NKCC1 and could be phosphorylated at other sites, but could not be activated.

The amino-terminal domain of NKCC1 (but not NKCC2) also contains the sequence arg-val-asn-phe that forms a consensus binding site for type 1 protein phosphatase (4; see Figure 1, color insert). When NKCC1 cDNAs containing mutations in this sequence were stably expressed in HEK-293 cells, cells expressing mutant and wild-type NKCC1s exhibited similar maximal levels of Na-K-Cl cotransport activity in response to a marked decrease in intracellular [Cl] ($[Cl]_i$) (see below). However, at higher levels of $[Cl]_i$, the mutants exhibited greater levels of cotransport activity than wild-type NKCC1, suggesting that preventing phosphatase binding results in greater constitutive activity of the cotransporter (4).

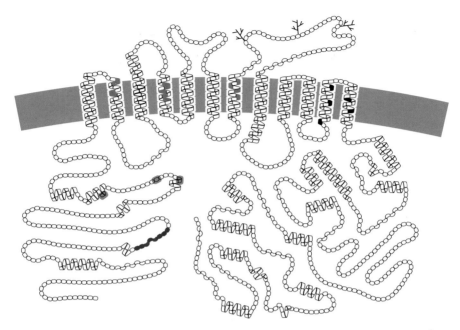

Figure 1 Model of NKCC1 based on its cDNA sequence and on hydropathy and secondary structural analyses. The proposed secondary structure with 12 transmembrane helices and large intracellular amino-terminal and carboxy-terminal domains is shared by the other members of the cation-chloride cotransporter superfamily listed in Table 1. Branched lines indicate potential glycosylation sites between putative transmembrane domains 7 and 8, as predicted for shark rectal gland NKCC1 (88). Known phosphothreonine residues within the amino-terminal domain (Thr-184, Thr-189, and Thr-202) (5, 54, 88) are indicated in green. Portions of transmembrane domains 2, 4, and 7 involved in the binding and/or transport of Na, K, and/or Cl (38--40) are indicated in red, and portions of transmembrane domains 11-12 involved in bumetanide binding are highlighted in black. The consensus binding site for type 1 protein phosphatase (4) is indicated in blue.

Figure 3 Phosphorylation of dog tracheal epithelial NKCC1 protein in response to secretagogues. Primary cultures of dog tracheal epithelial cells grown on collagen-coated Transwell supports were loaded with ^{32}P, then incubated for 10 min without added agonist (lane 1), with 5-μM basolateral isoproterenol (lane 2), or with 10-μM apical UTP (lane 3). Plasma membranes were then isolated from each sample, solubilized, and subjected to immunoprecipitation using a monoclonal antibody to human colonic NKCC1 (T4)(56). The immunoprecipitated material was run on an SDS-polyacrylamide gel, and proteins were transferred to a polyvinylidine fluoride (PVDF) membrane for autoradiography and subsequent Western blotting with antibody T4. The upper portion of the figure is the autoradiogram; NKCC1 protein on these gels runs as a broad band centered at ~170 kDa. The lower portion of the figure shows the ~170 kDa region of the Western blot subsequently performed on the same transfer. In this experiment, relative amounts of ^{32}P incorporation (per unit protein) into the ~170-kDa Na-K-Cl cotransporter protein are lane 1, 1.0; lane 2, 2.3; lane 3, 3.2. Reproduced from Reference 33 with copyright permission from the Am. Soc. Biochem. Mol. Biol. Inc.

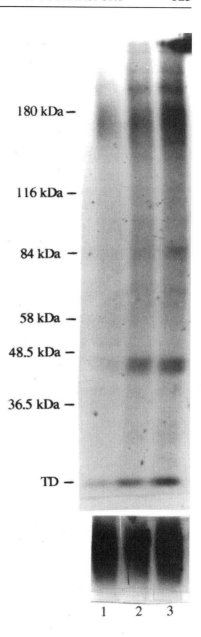

In that much or all of Na-K-Cl cotransport activation in response to secretagogues is an indirect response dependent on apical Cl efflux, likely candidates for the intracellular mediator leading to NKCC1 phosphorylation and cotransport activation included cell shrinkage and reduced $[Cl]_i$. Both have been shown to occur, at least transiently, during stimulated secretion in secretory epithelia (18, 55, 81), and both cell shrinkage and reduced $[Cl]_i$ are well documented as independent activators of NKCC1 activity in many epithelial and non-epithelial cells (1, 8, 21, 31–33, 36, 37, 48, 52, 55, 61, 67, 68, 79, 82, 88). Furthermore, both cell shrinkage and reduced $[Cl]_i$ have been shown to result in NKCC1 phosphorylation in a number of cell types (33, 48, 51, 52, 54, 55, 67), including dog tracheal epithelial cells (see Figure 4). In shark rectal gland epithelium, specific [³H]benzmetanide binding and NKCC1 phosphorylation increased proportionally with increasing degrees of hypertonic cell shrinkage (54), and in tracheal epithelial cells exposed to apical nystatin and varying apical $[Cl]_o$ in order to vary $[Cl]_i$, the levels of basolateral Na-K-Cl cotransport activity and NKCC1 phosphorylation increased proportionally with decreasing apical [Cl] (33). However, the evidence to date strongly suggests it is reduced $[Cl]_i$, rather than cell shrinkage, that is the major stimulus for basolateral Na-K-Cl cotransport activation in secretagogue-treated secretory epithelia. In shark rectal gland epithelium, a 45% reduction in cell water content was needed to mimic the effect of VIP and forskolin on the cotransporter (55), whereas these secretagogues produced only a very modest (and not statistically significant) decrease in cell water content, despite a nearly 50% decrease in $[Cl]_i$ under the same conditions (55). In rat parotid acini, where carbachol-stimulated salt and fluid secretion are accompanied by an increase in $[Ca^{2+}]_i$ and decreases in both cell volume and $[Cl]_i$, Robertson & Foskett (79) showed that only the rise in $[Ca^{2+}]_i$ and the fall in $[Cl]_i$ were required for the increase in basolateral Na influx that is an essential component of net secretion. In this tissue, basolateral Na influx is mediated by both Na/H exchange and Na-K-Cl cotransport. The findings of Robertson & Foskett (79) suggest that both Na influx pathways are similarly regulated (i.e. by $[Cl]_i$) in response to carbachol, although $[Cl]_i$-independent regulation of the cotransporter by a product of the cytochrome P450 pathway of arachidonic acid metabolism has also been proposed in this tissue (13). In addition, recent studies of Gillen & Forbush (23) showed that HEK-293 cells expressing the K-Cl cotransporter KCC1 had higher levels of endogenous Na-K-Cl (NKCC1) cotransport activity than control HEK-293 cells, a finding that could be accounted for by a lower level of $[Cl]_i$ in the cells expressing KCC1. There was also a steep relationship between Na-K-Cl cotransport activity and $[Cl]_i$ around the physiological range of the latter (23), highly consistent with $[Cl]_i$ serving as a physiological regulator of NKCC1 activity.

In addition to phosphorylation/dephosphorylation, NKCC1 in intestinal epithelia also appears to be regulated through its interactions with cytoskeletal and/or accessory proteins. In confluent monolayers of two different intestinal epithelial cell lines, T84 and HT29 subclone Cl.19A, stabilization of F-actin with phalloidin or its derivative phallicidin blocks cAMP-induced F-actin redistribution at the basal pole of the cells and attenuates cAMP-stimulated Cl secretion. The latter effect is due to inhibition of basolateral Na-K-Cl cotransport activity, as other

Figure 4 Phosphorylation of dog tracheal NKCC1 protein in response to reduced $[Cl]_i$ and hypertonic cell shrinkage in the absence of secretagogues. Primary cultures of dog tracheal epithelial cells grown on collagen-coated Transwell supports were loaded with ^{32}P, then incubated for 20 min with 350 units/ ml apical nystatin (to increase apical Cl permeability) and 124 mM apical [Cl]. Following this, the cells were incubated an additional 20 min in the continued presence of apical nystatin and 124 mM apical [Cl] (control, lane 1), 32 mM apical [Cl] (nitrate substitution, which results in loss of cell [Cl] without concurrent cell shrinkage, lane 2), or 124 mM apical [Cl] plus 50 mM sucrose apically and basolaterally (hypertonic cell shrinkage, lane 3). Plasma membranes were then isolated, solubilized, and subjected to immunoprecipitation and SDS-polyacrylamide gel electrophoresis followed by autoradiography and Western blotting with antibody T4 as described in the legend to Figure 3. The upper portion of the figure shows the autoradiogram; the lower portion shows the ~170 kDa region of the Western blot subsequently performed on the same PVDF transfer of the gel. In this experiment, relative amounts of ^{32}P incorporation (per unit protein) into the ~170 kDa Na-K-Cl cotransporter protein are: lane 1, 1.0; lane 2, 3.7; lane 3, 5.2. Reproduced from Reference 33 with copyright permission from the Am. Soc. Biochem. Mol. Biol. Inc.

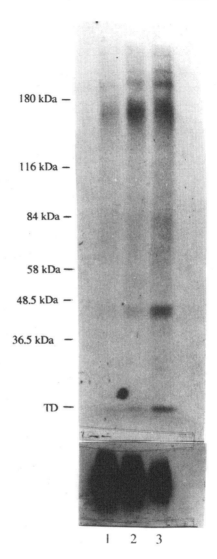

transport pathways involved in secretion (apical Cl channels, basolateral K channels and Na/K pumps) are not significantly affected by this F-actin stabilization (59,62). In T84 cells, the F-actin stabilizer jasplakinolide also inhibited cAMP-dependent and $[Ca^{2+}]_i$-dependent stimulation of transepithelial Cl secretion and Na-K-Cl cotransport, whereas cytochalasin D, which disrupts actin filaments, stimulated cotransport under basal conditions, without activating apical Cl efflux (60). A similar stimulatory effect of cytochalasin B on Na-K-Cl cotransport has been noted in Ehrlich ascites tumor cells (43). These findings suggest that reorganization of basal F-actin that occurs in response to secretagogues is necessary for Na-K-Cl cotransporter activation in these epithelial cells and that the local concentration of short actin filaments, a form of F-actin thought to be important as a regulator of some Na and K channels (41, 78, 85), may be involved in cotransport activation. It is noteworthy that while phalloidin treatment of HT29 subclone Cl.19A monolayers dramatically reduced cAMP-stimulated cotransporter activity, it did not affect cAMP-stimulated [^{3}H]bumetanide binding (62). As the level of such binding appears to be correlated with the phosphorylation state of NKCC1 (54), this suggests the possibility that regulation of cotransport activity by F-actin occurs subsequent to NKCC1 phosphorylation, perhaps at the level of ion translocation (30). However, in T84 monolayers phalloidin did not prevent cotransport activation by hypertonic cell shrinkage or by isosmotic replacement of extracellular [Cl] by gluconate (61), which would also be expected to cause cell shrinkage, and as such the role of the actin cytoskeleton in NKCC1 regulation appears more complex.

NKCC1 in T84 cells also appears to be associated with two proteins of 160 and 130 kDa, respectively, that coprecipitate with NKCC1 when the latter is isolated by immunoprecipitation using an anti-cotransporter monoclonal antibody (9). These accessory proteins may modulate the putative interaction of NKCC1 with F-actin in T84 cells. When these cells were stimulated with cAMP-dependent secretagogues prior to NKCC1 isolation, the levels of the 160 and 130 kDa proteins (but not that of NKCC1) detectable at the basolateral cell surface by biotinylation increased ~sixfold, an effect that was abolished by pre-treating the cells with phalloidin (9).

PROTEIN KINASE(S) INVOLVED IN NKCC1 PHOSPHORYLATION

Studies of Lytle (51, 52) in avian erythrocytes have provided evidence for the presence of a cotransporter kinase (CT-kinase) that phosphorylates and activates NKCC1 in response to a variety of stimuli of Na-K-Cl cotransport. In duck red blood cells, Na-K-Cl cotransport activation by norepinephrine (cAMP), fluoride, cell shrinkage, and the protein phosphatase inhibitor calyculin-A are all inhibited by the protein kinase inhibitor staurosporine with a similar IC$_{50}$ and, more importantly, each stimulus promotes phosphorylation of NKCC1 at the same sites as deduced from two-dimensional phosphopeptide maps (Figure 5) (51). This is consistent with recent findings in shark rectal gland that multiple stimuli of Na-K-Cl cotransport, including cAMP, cell shrinkage, and reduced [Cl]$_i$, are not additive (86). Thus CT-kinase may represent the final common step in cotransporter activation via a number of different signal transduction pathways. While the identity of CT-kinase remains unknown, kinetic studies have shown it to be inhibited

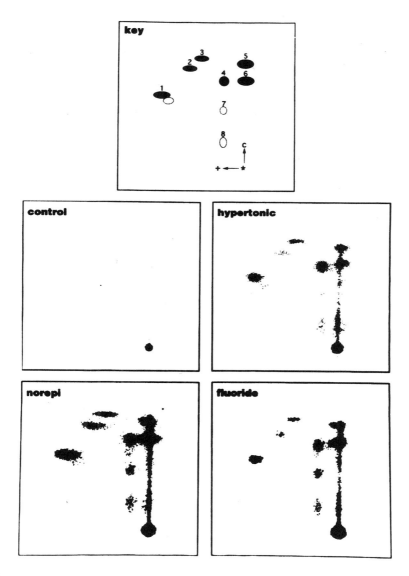

Figure 5   Two-dimensional phosphopeptide maps of duck erythrocyte NKCC1 activated by hypertonicity (100 mM sucrose added), norepinephrine (10 μM), or fluoride (10 mM). Cells were first incubated with ^{32}P, then incubated with or without the above stimuli and lysed. Membranes were then subjected to SDS-polyacrylamide gel electrophoresis and NKCC1 protein isolated from gel slices was treated with trypsin. Tryptic peptides were separated in two dimensions (51) and analyzed by autoradiography. Top panel (key) schematically shows the positions of major phosphopeptides and direction of peptide migrations (arrow) away from the origin (*). Spots containing lesser and/or variable amounts of ^{32}P are denoted by unfilled circles. Reproduced from Lytle (51) with copyright permission from the Am. Soc. Biochem. Mol. Biol. Inc.

by cell swelling and N-ethylmaleimide (NEM), as well as by staurosporine (51, 52). These latter properties suggest that NKCC1 may not be the only substrate for CT-kinase, but that the K-Cl cotransporter KCC1 may also be a substrate. Considerable evidence has been provided, at least in red blood cells, that KCC1 is inactivated by phosphorylation (15, 42). Furthermore, in red blood cells, Na-K-Cl and K-Cl cotransporters exhibit reciprocal behavior in that the latter is inhibited by norepinephrine and calyculin A, and stimulated by cell swelling, NEM, and staurosporine (6, 15, 35, 50), with a $K_{1/2}$ for staurosporine similar to that for inhibition of Na-K-Cl cotransport in red blood cells (52) and airway epithelial cells under conditions of reduced $[Cl]_i$ (29). Erythrocyte K-Cl cotransport may also be inhibited by reduced $[Cl]_i$ (26). Because NKCC1 and KCC1 appear to have reciprocal functions with respect to cell volume regulation, the hypothesis that activation of CT-kinase by cell shrinkage phosphorylates both proteins (thus activating Na-K-Cl cotransport and inhibiting K-Cl cotransport) and that inhibition of CT-kinase by swelling has the converse effect is an attractive one.

In a recent report, Klein and coworkers (47) used an in-the-gel kinase assay to identify a 45-kDa protein kinase from extracts of aortic endothelial cells that phosphorylated an amino-terminal (amino acids 1–278) but not a carboxy-terminal (amino acids 759–1212) NKCC1 fusion protein. This 45-kDa kinase was activated by cell shrinkage and tumor necrosis factor, the latter a known activator of c-jun N-terminal kinase (JNK) in endothelial cells. Klein et al (47) also showed that immunoprecipitates of JNK from shrunken but not euvolemic endothelial cells phosphorylated NKCC1 in gel kinase assays. Whether JNK is a true regulator of Na-K-Cl cotransport activity and whether it is in fact CT-kinase will require confirmation in intact cells.

Although the predicted amino acid sequence of NKCC1 contains consensus phosphorylation motifs for known protein kinases, including protein kinase C, casein kinase II, and (in mammalian but not shark forms) PKA (11, 76, 88, 90), there is no direct evidence that the cotransporter is in fact phosphorylated by any of these kinases. Although norepinephrine, acting via cAMP, stimulates Na-K-Cl cotransport and produces NKCC1 phosphorylation in avian erythrocytes, kinetic evidence suggests that this is not due to direct phosphorylation of NKCC1 or even direct activation of CT-kinase by PKA, but is more likely due to inhibition of the protein phosphatase that dephosphorylates NKCC1, probably a type 1 protein phosphatase (52). The latter effect could also potentially account for observations that PKA activation stimulates a component of Na-K-Cl cotransport in airway epithelial cells in the absence of apical Cl efflux or a decrease in $[Cl]_i$ (28, 32, 34). In aortic endothelial cells, which express NKCC1 (90), the time course of Na-K-Cl cotransport activation by cell shrinkage correlates closely with that of myosin light chain (MLC) phosphorylation, and the MLC kinase inhibitor ML-7 inhibits both processes with similar dose responses (48). However, NKCC1 phosphorylation, which is increased by cell shrinkage, was not affected by ML-7 under these conditions (48), indicating that MLC kinase does not directly phosphorylate the cotransporter and may modulate its activity by modifying cytoskeletal protein(s) (e. g. myosin) that potentially interact with NKCC1.

Because there is no evidence to date for NKCC1 phosphorylation on tyrosine residues in response to known stimuli of Na-K-Cl cotransport (51, 54), it is unlikely that one or more cell volume-sensitive tyrosine kinases (46, 64) directly phosphorylate and regulate NKCC1. However, such kinases may indirectly regulate the cotransporter by phosphorylating CT-kinase, a protein phosphatase that dephosphorylates NKCC1, and/or component(s) of the actin-based cytoskeleton. In ferret erythrocytes, stimulation of Na-K-Cl cotransport by arsenite, a sulfhydryl reagent, is blocked by treating the cells with the tyrosine kinase inhibitors genistein and PP1 (17). The latter compound is a relatively selective inhibitor of the Src kinase family, members of which have been shown to exhibit changes in activity in response to cell shrinkage and to phosphorylate the actin-binding protein cortactin (46).

CONCLUSION

Major challenges for investigators studying regulation of Na-K-Cl cotransport include the identification and characterization of the putative CT-kinase, of other protein kinases and/or phosphatases that regulate its activity in response to changes in cell volume, $[Cl]_i$, and other modulatory influences, and of the protein phosphatase(s) that dephosphorylate the cotransporter protein. It is anticipated that additional members of the cation-chloride cotransporter superfamily will be identified, and comparison of structural and functional properties of these with those of known superfamily members, both directly and through chimera approaches and site-directed mutagenesis, should further enhance our understanding of the function and regulation of these proteins at a molecular level.

ACKNOWLEDGMENTS

Original scientific work of the authors was supported by NIH/NIDDK grant DK-47661 (to BF III), and a grant-in-aid from the American Heart Association of Metropolitan Chicago (to MH). We thank Dr. Chris Lytle for many helpful discussions, Dr. Inaki Gimenez for helpful comments on the manuscript, and Drs. Lytle and Eric Delpire for allowing us to reproduce figures from their original work.

Visit the Annual Reviews home page at www.AnnualReviews.org.

LITERATURE CITED

1. Altamirano AA, Breitwieser GE, Russell JM. 1995. Effects of okadaic acid and intracellular Cl on Na-K-Cl cotransport. *Am. J. Physiol.* 269:C878–83
2. Attaphitaya S, Park K, Melvin JE. 1999. Molecular cloning and functional expression of a rat Na/H exchanger (NHE5) highly expressed in brain. *J. Biol. Chem.* 274:4383–88
3. Baird NR, Orlowski J, Szabo EZ, Zaun HC, Schultheis PJ, et al. 1999. Molecular cloning, genomic organization, and functional expression of Na/H exchanger isoform 5 (NHE5) from human brain. *J. Biol. Chem.* 274:4377–82
4. Behnke R, Bieswal F, Forbush B III. 1999. A protein phosphatase binding site in the N-terminus of the Na-K-Cl cotransport protein (NKCC1) is important in determining the activation state of the transporter. *FASEB J.* 13:A397 (Abstr.)
5. Behnke RD, Forbush B III. 1998. Stimulatory phosphorylation sites on the shark rectal gland Na-K-Cl cotransporter. *FASEB J.* 12:A1013 (Abstr.)
6. Bize I, Dunham PB. 1994. Staurosporine, a protein kinase inhibitor, activates K-Cl cotransport in LK sheep erythrocytes. *Am. J. Physiol.* 266:C759–70
7. Boucher RC, Hviid Larsen E. 1988. Comparison of ion transport by cultured secretory and absorptive canine airway epithelia. *Am. J. Physiol.* 254:C535–47
8. Breitwieser GE, Altamirano AA, Russell JM. 1990. Osmotic stimulation of Na-K-Cl cotransport in squid giant axon is [Cl]$_i$-dependent. *Am. J. Physiol.* 258:C749–53
8a. Crouch JJ, Sakaguchi N, Lytle C, Schulte BA. 1997. Immunohistochemical localization cotransporter (NKCC1) in gerbil inner ear. *J. Histochem. Cytochem.* 45:773–78
9. D'Andrea L, Lytle C, Matthews JB, Hofman P, Forbush B III, Madara JL. 1996. Na:K:Cl cotransporter (NKCC) of intestinal epithelial cells. Surface expression in response to cAMP. *J. Biol. Chem.* 271:28969–76
10. Delpire E, Gullans SR. 1994. Cell volume and K transport during differentiation of mouse erythroleukemia cells. *Am. J. Physiol.* 266:C515–23
10a. Delpire E, Lu J, England R, Dull C, Thorne T. 1999. Deafness and imbalance associated with inactivation of the secretory Na-K-2Cl co-transporter. *Nat. Genet.* 22:192–95
11. Delpire E, Rauchman MI, Beier DR, Hebert SC, Gullans SR. 1994. Molecular cloning and chromosome localization of a putative basolateral Na-K-2Cl cotransporter from mouse inner medullary collecting duct (mIMCD-3) cells. *J. Biol. Chem.* 269: 25677–83
12. Dharmsathaphorn K, McRoberts JA, Masui H, Mandel KG. 1985. Vasoactive intestinal peptide-induced Cl secretion by a colonic epithelial cell line. Direct participation of a basolaterally localized Na,K,Cl cotransport system. *J. Clin. Invest.* 75:462–71
12a. Dixon MJ, Gazzard J. Chaudhry SS, Sampson N, Schulte BA, Steel KP. 1999. Mutation of the Na-K-Cl co-transporter gene *Slc12a2* results in deafness in mice. *Hum. Mol. Genet.* 8:1579–84
13. Evans RL, Turner RJ. 1997. Upregulation of Na-K-2Cl cotransporter activity in rat parotid acinar cells by muscarinic stimulation. *J. Physiol.* 499:351–59
14. Eveloff JL, Calamia J. 1986. Effect of osmolality on cation fluxes in medullary thick ascending limb cells. *Am. J. Physiol.* 250:F176–80
14a. Flagella M, Clarke LL, Miller ML, Erway LC, Giannella RA, et al. 1999. Mice lacking the basolateral Na-K-2Cl cotransporter have impaired epithelial chloride secretion and are profoundly deaf. *J. Biol. Chem.* 274:26946–55

15. Flatman PW, Adragna NC, Lauf PK. 1996. Role of protein kinases in regulating sheep erythrocyte K-Cl cotransport. *Am. J. Physiol.* 271:C255–63

16. Flatman PW, Creanor J. 1999. Regulation of Na-K-2Cl cotransport by protein phosphorylation in ferret erythrocytes. *J. Physiol.* 517:699–708

17. Flatman PW, Creanor J. 1999. Stimulation of Na-K-2Cl cotransport by arsenite in ferret erythrocytes. *J. Physiol.* 519: 143–52

18. Foskett JK. 1990. $[Ca^{2+}]_i$ modulation of Cl content controls cell volume in single salivary acinar cells during fluid secretion. *Am. J. Physiol.* 259:C998–1004

19. Gamba G, Miyanoshita A, Lombardi M, Lytton J, Lee W-S, et al. 1994. Molecular cloning, primary structure, and characterization of two members of the mammalian electroneutral sodium-(potassium)-chloride cotransporter family expressed in kidney. *J. Biol. Chem.* 269:17713–22

20. Gamba G, Saltzberg SN, Lombardi M, Miyanoshita A, Lytton J, et al. 1993. Primary structure and functional expression of a cDNA encoding the thiazide-sensitive, electroneutral sodium-chloride cotransporter. *Proc. Natl. Acad. Sci. USA* 90:2749–53

21. Geck P, Pfeiffer B. 1985. Na^+ K^+ 2Cl cotransport in animal cells—its role in volume regulation. *Ann. NY Acad. Sci.* 456:166–82

22. Gillen CM, Brill S, Payne JA, Forbush B III. 1996. Molecular cloning and functional expression of the K-Cl cotransporter from rabbit, rat, and human. A new member of the cation-chloride cotransporter family. *J. Biol. Chem.* 271:16237–44

23. Gillen CM, Forbush B III. 1999. K-Cl cotransporter (KCC1) expressed in HEK 293 cells: regulation and functional interaction with the Na-K-Cl cotransporter. *Am. J. Physiol.* 276:C328–36

24. Greger R. 1985. Ion transport mechanisms in thick ascending limb of Henle's loop of mammalian nephron. *Physiol. Rev.* 65:760–97

25. Greger R, Schlatter E, Wang F, Forrest JN Jr. 1984. Mechanism of NaCl secretion in rectal gland tubules of spiny dogfish (*Squalus acanthias*). III. Effects of stimulation of secretion by cyclic AMP. *Pflügers Arch.* 402:376–84

26. Guizouarn H, Motais R. 1999. Swelling activation of transport pathways in erythrocytes: effects of Cl, ionic strength, and volume changes. *Am. J. Physiol.* 276: C210–20

27. Haas M. 1989. Properties and diversity of (Na-K-Cl) cotransporters. *Annu. Rev. Physiol.* 51: 443–57

28. Haas M. 1994. The Na-K-Cl cotransporters. *Am. J. Physiol.* 267:C869–85

29. Haas M. 1995. Activation of Na-K-Cl cotransport in airway epithelial cells by apical UTP, cell shrinkage, and reduced $[Cl]_i$: role of protein phosphorylation. *FASEB J.* 9:599 (Abstr.)

30. Haas M, Forbush B III. 1998. The Na-K-Cl cotransporters. *J. Bioenerg. Biombr.* 30:161–72

31. Haas M, Johnson LG, Boucher RC. 1990. Regulation of Na-K-Cl cotransport in cultured canine airway epithelia: a [^{3}H]bumetanide binding study. *Am. J. Physiol.* 259:C557–69

32. Haas M, McBrayer DG. 1994. Na-K-Cl cotransport in nystatin-treated tracheal cells: regulation by isoproterenol, apical UTP, and $[Cl]_i$. *Am. J. Physiol.* 266: C1440–52

33. Haas M, McBrayer D, Lytle C. 1995. $[Cl]_i$-dependent phosphorylation of the Na-K-Cl cotransport protein of dog tracheal epithelial cells. *J. Biol. Chem.* 270:28955–61

34. Haas M, McBrayer DG, Yankaskas JR. 1993. Dual mechanisms for Na-K-Cl cotransport regulation in airway epithelial cells. *Am. J. Physiol.* 264:C189–200

35. Haas M, McManus TJ. 1985. Effect of norepinephrine on swelling-induced potassium transport in duck red cells:

evidence against a volume-regulatory decrease under physiological conditions. *J. Gen. Physiol.* 85:649–67

36. Haas M, Schmidt WF III, McManus TJ. 1982. Catecholamine-stimulated ion transport in duck red cells: gradient effects in electrically neutral (Na-K-2Cl) co-transport. *J. Gen. Physiol.* 80: 125–47

36a. Hiki K, D'Andrea RJ, Furze J, Crawford J, Woollatt E, et al. 1999. Cloning, characterization, and chromosomal location of a novel human K^+-Cl^- cotransporter. *J. Biol. Chem.* 274:10661–67

37. Hoffmann EK, Sjoholm C, Simonsen LO. 1983. NaCl cotransport in Ehrlich ascites tumor cells activated during volume regulation (regulatory volume increase). *J. Membr. Biol.* 76:269–80

38. Isenring P, Forbush B III. 1997. Ion and bumetanide binding by the Na-K-Cl cotransporter. Importance of transmembrane domains. *J. Biol. Chem.* 272: 24556–62

39. Isenring P, Jacoby SC, Chang J, Forbush B III. 1998. Mutagenic mapping of the Na-K-Cl cotransporter for domains involved in ion transport and bumetanide binding. *J. Gen. Physiol.* 112:549–58

40. Isenring P, Jacoby SC, Forbush B III. 1998. The role of transmembrane domain 2 in cation transport by the Na-K-Cl cotransporter. *Proc. Natl. Acad. Sci. USA* 95:7179–84

41. Ismailov II, Berdiev BK, Shlyonsky VG, Fuller CM, Prat AG, et al. 1997. Role of actin in regulation of epithelial sodium channels by CFTR. *Am. J. Physiol.* 272:C1077–86

42. Jennings ML, Al-Rohil N. 1990. Kinetics of activation and inactivation of swelling-stimulated K/Cl transport. *J. Gen. Physiol.* 95:1021–40

43. Jessen F, Hoffmann EK. 1992. Activation of the Na/K/Cl cotransport system by reorganization of the actin filaments in Ehrlich ascites tumor cells. *Biochim. Biophys. Acta* 1110:199–201

44. Kaplan MR, Plotkin MD, Brown D,

Hebert SC, Delpire E. 1996. Expression of the mouse Na-K-2Cl cotransporter, mBSC2, in the terminal IMCD, the glomerular and extraglomerular mesangium and the glomerular afferent arteriole. *J. Clin. Invest.* 98:723–30

45. Kaplan MR, Plotkin MD, Lee W-S, Xu Z-C, Lytton J, Hebert SC. 1996. Apical localization of the Na-K-Cl cotransporter, rBSC1, on rat thick ascending limbs. *Kidney Int.* 49:40–47

46. Kapus A, Szaszi K, Sun J, Rizoli S, Rotstein OD. 1999. Cell shrinkage regulates Src kinases and induces tyrosine phosphorylation of cortactin, independent of the osmotic regulation of Na/H exchangers. *J. Biol. Chem.* 274:8093–102

47. Klein JD, Lamitina ST, O'Neill WC. 1999. JNK is a volume-sensitive kinase that phosphorylates the Na-K-2Cl cotransporter in vitro. *Am. J. Physiol.* 277: C425–31

48. Klein JD, O'Neill WC. 1995. Volume-sensitive myosin phosphorylation in vascular endothelial cells:correlation with Na-K-2Cl cotransport. *Am. J. Physiol.* 269:C1524–31

49. Larson M, Spring KR. 1984. Volume regulation by *Necturus* gallbladder: basolateral KCl exit. *J. Membr. Biol.* 81:219–32

50. Lauf PK, Bauer J, Adragna NC, Fujise H, Zade-Oppen AMM, et al. 1992. Erythrocyte K-Cl cotransport: properties and regulation. *Am. J. Physiol.* 263: C917–32

51. Lytle C. 1997. Activation of the avian erythrocyte Na-K-Cl cotransport protein by cell shrinkage, cAMP, fluoride, and calyculin-A involves phosphorylation at common sites. *J. Biol. Chem.* 272: 15069–77

52. Lytle C. 1998. A volume-sensitive protein kinase regulates the Na-K-2Cl cotransporter in duck red cells. *Am. J. Physiol.* 274:C1002–10

53. Lytle C, Forbush B III. 1992. Na-K-Cl cotransport in the shark rectal gland. II.

Regulation in intact tubules. *Am. J. Physiol.* 262:C1009–17

54. Lytle C, Forbush B III. 1992. The Na-K-Cl cotransport protein of shark rectal gland. II. Regulation by direct phosphorylation. *J. Biol. Chem.* 267:25438–43

55. Lytle C, Forbush B III. 1996. Regulatory phosphorylation of the secretory Na-K-Cl cotransporter: modulation by cytoplasmic Cl. *Am. J. Physiol.* 270:C437–48

56. Lytle C, Xu J-C, Biemesderfer D, Forbush B III. 1995. Distribution and diversity of Na-K-Cl cotransport proteins:a study with monoclonal antibodies. *Am. J. Physiol.* 269:C1496–505

57. Lytle C, Xu J-C, Biemesderfer D, Haas M, Forbush B III. 1992. The Na-K-Cl cotransport protein of shark rectal gland. I. Development of monoclonal antibodies, immunoaffinity purification, and partial biochemical characterization. *J. Biol. Chem.* 267:25428–37

58. Masuzawa T, Ohta T, Kawamura M, Nakahar N, Sato F. 1984. Immunohistochemical localization of Na K-ATPase in the choroid plexus. *Brain Res.* 302:357–62

59. Matthews JB, Awtrey CS, Madara JL. 1992. Microfilament-dependent activation of Na/K/2Cl cotransport by cAMP in intestinal epithelial monolayers. *J. Clin. Invest.* 90:1608–13

60. Matthews JB, Smith JA, Hrnjez BJ. 1997. Effects of F-actin stabilization or disassembly on epithelial Cl secretion and Na-K-2Cl cotransport. *Am. J. Physiol.* 272:C254–62

61. Matthews JB, Smith JA, Mun EC, Sicklick JK. 1998. Osmotic regulation of intestinal epithelial Na-K-Cl cotransport:role of Cl and F-actin. *Am. J. Physiol.* 274:C697–706

62. Matthews JB, Smith JA, Tally KJ, Awtrey CS, Nguyen H, et al. 1994. Na-K-Cl cotransport in intestinal epithelial cells:influence of chloride efflux and F-actin on regulation of cotransporter activ-

ity and bumetanide binding. *J. Biol. Chem.* 269:15703–9

63. Mount DB, Hoover RS, Hebert S.C. 1997. The molecular physiology of electroneutral cation-chloride cotransport. *J. Membr. Biol.* 158:177–86

63a. Mount DB, Mercado A, Song L, Xu J, George AL Jr, et al. 1999. Cloning and characterization of KCC3 and KCC4, new members of the cation-chloride cotransporter gene family. *J. Biol. Chem.* 274:16355–62

64. Musch MW, Hubert EM, Goldstein L. 1999. Volume expansion stimulates $p72^{syk}$ and $p56^{lyn}$ in skate erythrocytes. *J. Biol. Chem.* 274:7923–28

65. Nauntofte B. 1992. Regulation of electrolyte and fluid secretion in salivary acinar cells. *Am. J. Physiol.* 263:G823–37

66. Neilsen S, Maunsbach AB, Ecelbarger CA, Knepper MA. 1998. Ultrastructural localization of Na-K-2Cl cotransporter in thick ascending limb and macula densa of rat kidney. *Am. J. Physiol.* 275:F885–93

67. O'Donnell ME, Martinez A, Sun D. 1995. Endothelial Na-K-Cl cotransport regulation by tonicity and hormones: phosphorylation of cotransport protein. *Am. J. Physiol.* 269:C1513–23

68. O'Neill WC, Steinberg DF. 1995. Functional coupling of Na-K-2Cl cotransport and Ca^{2+}-dependent K channels in vascular endothelial cells. *Am. J. Physiol.* 269:C267–74

69. Palfrey HC, Feit PW, Greengard P. 1980. cAMP-stimulated cation cotransport in avian erythrocytes:inhibition by "loop" diuretics. *Am. J. Physiol.* 238:C139–48

70. Palfrey HC, O'Donnell ME. 1992. Characteristics and regulation of the Na/K/2Cl cotransporter. *Cell. Physiol. Biochem.* 2:293–307

71. Palfrey HC, Silva P, Epstein FH. 1984. Sensitivity of cAMP-stimulated salt secretion in shark rectal gland to "loop" diuretics. *Am. J. Physiol.* 246:C242–46

72. Panet R, Markus M, Atlan H. 1994.

Bumetanide and furosemide inhibited vascular endothelial cell proliferation. *J. Cell. Physiol.* 158:121–27

73. Payne JA. 1997. Functional characterization of the neuronal-specific K-Cl cotransporter:implications for [K]$_o$ regulation. *Am. J. Physiol.* 273:C1516–25

74. Payne JA, Forbush B III. 1994. Alternatively spliced isoforms of the putative renal Na-K-Cl cotransporter are differentially distributed within the rabbit kidney. *Proc. Natl. Acad. Sci. USA* 91:4544–48

75. Payne JA, Stevenson TJ, Donaldson LF. 1996. Molecular characterization of a putative K-Cl cotransporter in rat brain. A neuronal-specific isoform. *J. Biol. Chem.* 271:16245–52

76. Payne JA, Xu J-C, Haas M, Lytle CY, Ward D, Forbush B III. 1995. Primary structure, functional expression, and chromosomal localization of the bumetanide-sensitive Na-K-Cl cotransporter in human colon. *J. Biol. Chem.* 270:17977–85

77. Plotkin MD, Kaplan MR, Peterson LN, Gullans SR, Hebert SC, Delpire E. 1997. Expression of the Na-K-2Cl cotransporter BSC2 in the nervous system. *Am. J. Physiol.* 272:C173–83

78. Prat AG, Bertorello AM, Ausiello DA, Cantiello HF. 1993. Activation of epithelial Na channels by protein kinase A requires actin filaments. *Am. J. Physiol.* 265:C224–33

79. Robertson MA, Foskett JK. 1994. Na transport pathways in secretory acinar cells: membrane cross talk mediated by [Cl]$_i$. *Am. J. Physiol.* 267:C146–56

80. Russell JM. 1983. Cation-coupled chloride influx in squid axon. Role of potassium and stoichiometry of the transport process. *J. Gen. Physiol.* 81:909–25

81. Shorofsky SR, Field M, Fozzard HA. 1984. Mechanism of Cl secretion in canine trachea: changes in intracellular

Cl activity with secretion. *J. Membr. Biol.* 81:1–8

82. Sun A, Grossman EB, Lombardi M, Hebert SC. 1991. Vasopressin alters the mechanism of apical Cl entry from Na:Cl to Na:K:2Cl cotransport in mouse medullary thick ascending limb. *J. Membr. Biol.* 120:83–94

83. Tanimura A, Kurihara K, Reshkin SJ, Turner RJ. 1995. Involvement of direct phosphorylation in the regulation of the rat parotid Na-K-2Cl cotransporter. *J. Biol. Chem.* 270:25252–58

84. Torchia J, Lytle C, Pon DJ, Forbush B III, Sen AK. 1992. The Na-K-Cl cotransporter of avian salt gland. Phosphorylation in response to cAMP-dependent and calcium-dependent secretogogues. *J. Biol. Chem.* 267:25444–50

85. Wang W-H, Cassola A, Giebisch G. 1994. Involvement of actin cytoskeleton in modulation of apical K channel activity in rat collecting duct. *Am. J. Physiol.* 267:F592–98

86. Warth R, Bleich M, Thiele I, Lang F, Greger R. 1998. Regulation of the Na$^+$2Cl$^-$K$^+$ cotransporter in in vitro perfused rectal gland tubules of *Squalus acanthias. Pflügers Arch.* 436:521–28

87. Willumsen NJ, Davis CW, Boucher RC. 1989. Cellular Cl transport in cultured cystic fibrosis airway epithelium. *Am. J. Physiol.* 256:C1045–53

88. Xu J-C, Lytle C, Zhu TT, Payne JA, Benz E Jr, Forbush B III. 1994. Molecular cloning and functional expression of the bumetanide-sensitive Na-K-Cl cotransporter. *Proc. Natl. Acad. Sci. USA* 91:2201–5

89. Yang T, Huang YG, Singh I, Schnermann J, Briggs JP. 1996. Localization of bumetanide- and thiazide-sensitive Na-K-Cl cotransporters along the rat nephron. *Am. J. Physiol.* 271:F931–39

90. Yerby TR, Vibat CRT, Sun D, Payne JA, O'Donnell ME. 1997. Molecular characterization of the Na-K-Cl cotransporter of bovine aortic endothelial cells. *Am. J. Physiol.* 273:C188–97

Annu. Rev. Physiol. 2000. 62:535–72

CHLORIDE SECRETION BY THE INTESTINAL EPITHELIUM: Molecular Basis and Regulatory Aspects

Kim E. Barrett and Stephen J. Keely

Department of Medicine, University of California, San Diego, School of Medicine, San Diego, California 92103; e-mail: kbarrett@ucsd.edu

Key Words CFTR, secretagogues, fluid and electrolyte transport, growth factors, membrane transporters

■ **Abstract** Chloride secretion is the major determinant of mucosal hydration thoughout the gastrointestinal tract, and chloride transport is also pivotal in the regulation of fluid secretion by organs that drain into the intestine. Moreover, there are pathological consequences if chloride secretion is either reduced or increased such as in cystic fibrosis and secretory diarrhea, respectively. With the molecular cloning of many of the proteins and regulatory factors that make up the chloride secretory mechanism, there have been significant advances in our understanding of this process at the cellular level. Similarly, emerging data have clarified the intercellular relationships that govern the extent of chloride secretion. The goal of our article is to review this area of investigation, with an emphasis on recent developments and their implications for the physiology and pathophysiology of chloride transport.

INTRODUCTION

Secretion of water and electrolytes by the gastrointestinal tract is central to its physiological functions. The intestine and the organs that drain into it, secrete approximately eight liters of fluid per day (1). This fluid secretion provides an appropriate medium for digestive processes to occur, in that digestive enzymes must be able to diffuse to their substrates and act upon them in an aqueous environment. Similarly, the water-soluble products of digestion of proteins and carbohydrates require an aqueous medium in which to diffuse to the absorptive surface of intestinal epithelial cells. While much of this fluid is provided for in the secretions of the stomach, as well as the pancreatic and biliary systems, the intestine itself supplies a significant proportion of the daily fluid load to subserve these functions (1). Moreover, intestinal secretory processes may have additional more specialized functions. For example, the ability of the proximal duodenum to sustain high levels of bicarbonate secretion protects it from the aggressive action of gastric acid and pepsin (2). Similarly, the ability of various segments of

0066–4278/00/0315–0535$12.00

the intestine to undergo bursts of secretion in response to mechanical stimulation of the mucosa is important in lubricating the epithelial surface, thereby protecting the mucosa from physical damage as a food bolus passes along the length of the intestinal tract (3, 4). The importance of intestinal secretory mechanisms is underscored by the pathological consequences of their absence or dysregulation. For example, defective duodenal bicarbonate secretion is associated with the development of peptic ulcer disease, whereas a congenital deficiency in intestinal chloride secretion, occurring in cystic fibrosis, is accompanied by intestinal obstruction and malabsorption (5–8).

In health, absorption of fluid predominates such that the eight liters of endogenous secretions plus an average of one liter of oral intake are largely absorbed (1). Throughout the gastrointestinal tract, fluid transport is dependent on active transport processes for electrolytes and other solutes. Water flows in accordance with the osmotic gradients that result from active transport, although the precise route(s) for transepithelial water movement remains somewhat unclear. A classical view held that water moves paracellularly according to a standing gradient set up in the lateral spaces of absorptive enterocytes (9, 10). More recent evidence, however, suggests that transcellular transport of water may also occur in the gastrointestinal tract. For example, Wright and co-workers have championed the view that the sodium-glucose cotransporter, SGLT-1, is an obligate water influx site, and takes water into the cell in a vectorial fashion with each cycle of coupled sodium and glucose uptake (11). This property may be shared by other sodium-coupled nutrient transporters (12). Similarly, there is also biochemical evidence that intestinal epithelia may express members of the aquaporin family of molecular water channels, particularly AQP8, although this remains controversial, and evidence for a functional role for such aquaporins in intestinal water transport is still lacking (13). Whatever the route by which water traverses the epithelium, it remains well-accepted that the net movement of fluid is driven by active absorptive and secretory mechanisms for osmotically active solutes present in the luminal contents and interstitial fluid, respectively.

Although secretion of bicarbonate and potassium occurs along the length of the intestine, the predominant electrolyte driving fluid secretion is chloride. Chloride secretion is accompanied by paracellular movement of sodium, and the resulting luminal accumulation of sodium chloride provides the osmotic basis for water movement. A portion of bicarbonate secretion is also secondary to active secretion of chloride, which recycles into the cell through apical anion exchangers in exchange for bicarbonate (14). Thus the focus of this review is on chloride secretion. Coverage of this topic is timely in light of several advances that have occurred in our understanding of chloride secretion in recent years. First, intestinal cell lines have been developed that faithfully recapitulate the chloride secretory mechanism of the intact intestine, therefore permitting a detailed examination of the intracellular biochemical mechanisms intrinsic to the epithelium that regulate this process (15, 16). Second, there has been an explosion in the identification, at a molecular level, of the proteins inserted in the membranes of epithelial cells that allow for the concerted movement of chloride and other ions across these hydrophobic barriers, thereby subserving the vectorial transport of chloride across the epithelium as a whole (1). Finally, the discipline of molecular genetics has yielded great insights into disease states such as cystic fibrosis and congenital chloride diarrhea where chloride secretion by the intestine is abnormal (1, 17). Thus the goal of this review is to discuss what is currently known of the molecular basis of chloride transport across the intestinal epithelium and how this process is regulated by both intracellular and extracellular influences. Bicarbonate secretion by the intestinal tract will be alluded to in passing, but the reader is also directed to several recent articles that address this topic more specifically (1, 5, 18).

CELLULAR AND MOLECULAR BASIS OF INTESTINAL CHLORIDE SECRETION

Epithelial Biology Pertinent to Intestinal Secretion

The intestine is lined by a continuous monolayer of columnar epithelial cells (19). These cells arise from anchored stem cells localized near the base of intestinal crypts and are subject to constant renewal. In the mammalian intestine, and under normal circumstances, the epithelium turns over once every 4–7 days (20, 21). Under pathological conditions, the rate of epithelial proliferation may be enhanced, sometimes with consequent effects on the expression of differentiated functions by epithelial cell subpopulations (20).

The anchored stem cells give rise to a proliferative zone in the intestinal crypts that is responsible for populating the entire crypt and villus (20). Some cells migrate to the base of the crypt and give rise to Paneth cells, which secrete antimicrobial peptides and other products thought to be important in maintaining the sterility of the crypt (21, 22). However, the majority of proliferating cells migrate upward along the crypt-villus (or in the colon, crypt-surface) axis, where they give rise to the other differentiated cell types of the mature intestine, namely columnar secretory and absorptive epithelial cells, mucus-secreting goblet cells, and enteroendocrine cells, which secrete products that regulate epithelial function and act as sensors for luminal composition (21). As cells exit the crypt region, they cease proliferating and begin a process of differentiation and maturation. Secretory and absorptive processes of intestinal epithelial cells are thought largely to be restricted to crypt and villus epithelial cells, respectively, although recent data indicate under certain circumstances villus cells can secrete and perhaps crypt cells can absorb (23–26). However, it remains useful to consider that there is spatial segregation of absorptive and secretory functions, which is lent further weight by the observation that the expression of transport proteins, such as the cystic fibrosis transmembrane conductance regulator (CFTR) and the Na/K/2Cl cotransporter (NKCC1), both required for chloride secretion, appears mostly restricted to cells located in the crypt (27). Conversely, intestinal epithelial cell differentiation is accompanied by the cessation of expression of the named proteins, and concomitant upregulation of expression of other transporters and membrane proteins needed for an absorptive phenotype, such as the apical isoforms of the sodium proton exchanger (NHE2 and NHE3), SGLT-1, and brush border hydrolases (28–30).

Another feature of the intestinal epithelium central to its ability to perform vectorial solute transport, including the secretion of chloride, is its ability to form an electrically resistive monolayer, thereby restricting back-diffusion of transported ions. This property is conferred by the tight junctions located near the apical pole of epithelial cells (31). Significant progress has been made in defining the molecular constituents of such junctional complexes and the basis for their regulation (31). Several transmembrane sealing proteins have been identified that form the actual site of junctional occlusion between cells via homotypic interactions, including occludin, members of the claudin family, and a recently discovered claudin-related protein, paracellin (32–34). This last junctional component is thought to confer the cation-selective properties displayed by tight junctions in many organs including the intestine (33). Furthermore, it is now recognized that tight junctions are not static structures but can be regulated in an active fashion (31). In keeping with this, several additional proteins are associated with the tight junction at its cytoplasmic face, including those that link the junction functionally to the cytoskeleton, and a variety of kinases and other signaling intermediates that mediate regulatory changes in junction integrity (1, 31, 34).

Chloride secretion and trans-epithelial transport processes in general are possible because the intestinal epithelium is functionally polarized, with segregation of specific membrane transport proteins to either the apical or basolateral pole of the cell. Trafficking signals are incorporated in the primary structure of specific membrane transport proteins, which are then interpreted by sorting machinery within the cell and directed to the appropriate membrane domain to provide for vectorial transport function. While progress in this area of cell biology has been significant, the details of the sorting machinery that decode what appears to be a whole catalogue of sorting signals, and the specific signals that come into play in chloride-secreting epithelia, have yet to be elucidated fully (35, 36). Nevertheless, it appears at this point that many different sorting signals can work in concert in polarized cells, perhaps allowing for plasticity of the system and providing for the construction of a wide variety of complex transport mechanisms using a relatively small selection of constituent membrane transport proteins.

The Chloride Secretory Mechanism

The transepithelial chloride secretory mechanism, in common with other epithelial transport mechanisms, is made up of several transmembrane transport pathways, arranged asymmetrically in intestinal epithelial cells (and particularly in those located in the crypts, as discussed above). On the basis of several studies, the chloride secretory mechanism present in the intestine, as well in other epithelia, has been well characterized (Figure 1) (1). Chloride is taken up into the cell across the basolateral membrane via NKCC1, in an electroneutral manner ($1Na^+:1K^+:2Cl^-$), with accumulation of chloride, driven in particular by the large inwardly directed sodium concentration gradient established by the basolateral Na,K-ATPase (secondary active Cl^- transport). Also at the basolateral membrane are at least two types of potassium channel (defined functionally) that allow for potassium recycling and thus prevent cellular depolarization, preserving the electrical driving force for chloride exit from the cell. Therefore, chloride accumulates in the cell above its electrochemical equilibrium so that when apical chloride channels are opened, chloride flows out of the cell and net transcellular movement of this ion occurs. A major portion of chloride movement across the apical membrane is via the cAMP-dependent CFTR chloride channel. However,

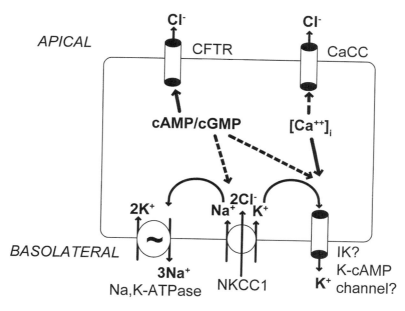

Figure 1 Model of the chloride secretory mechanism in intestinal epithelial cells. Secretion can be stimulated by increases in either cyclic nucleotides (cAMP/cGMP) or cytosolic calcium ($[Ca^{2+}]_i$). Major targets for regulation by these intracellular messengers are indicated with solid arrows, with additional postulated sites of action indicated with broken arrows. The identity of basolateral potassium channel(s) involved in either cyclic nucleotide- or calcium-mediated chloride secretion remains unknown. Abbreviations: CFTR, cystic fibrosis transmembrane conductance regulator; CaCC, calcium-activated chloride channel; NKCC1, sodium/potassium/2 chloride cotransporter type 1; IK, intermediate conductance potassium channel; K-cAMP channel, putative potassium channel regulated by cAMP. For further details, see text.

recent data also point to the existence of at least one additional class of chloride channels, namely calcium-activated chloride channels (CaCC), probably expressed in the apical membrane of intestinal epithelial cells. These channels would mediate chloride secretory responses to agonists that raise cytosolic calcium (37–39).

The primary points for regulation of the overall chloride secretory mechanism are most likely the apical chloride channel(s) and basolateral potassium channels, although more recent data also implicate the NKCC1 cotransporter as an additional locus of both positive and negative regulation of transport.

Mechanisms of Transporter Regulation

In this section we review general mechanisms by which transport pathways are regulated in epithelia. This information is then applied to the specific transport pathways that make up the chloride secretory mechanism.

General Aspects   Four major mechanisms appear to regulate epithelial transport in the intestine, as well as other epithelia (1). These are portrayed schematically in Figure 2, using individual facets of the chloride secretory process as examples. First, transport proteins (channels, pumps, and cotransporters or exchangers) can be acted upon directly by cellular factors that result in a change in transport function. Examples include the role of the cytoplasmic H^+ modifier of sodium-hydrogen exchangers (40), or, for the case of chloride secretion, the action of calcium on both basolateral potassium and apical chloride channels, which increases their open probability. Second, transport is regulated by covalent modifications of transport proteins. For example, CFTR is phosphorylated by both protein kinase A (PKA) and protein kinase C (PKC), with resulting changes in channel function (41, 42). Third, transport protein activity is acutely regulated by the number of copies in the plasma membrane, which changes by net insertion or net retrieval. In the first case, vesicles containing preformed transport protein molecules, often localized immediately below the relevant membrane domain, are stimulated to fuse with the plasma membrane in an agonist-sensitive fashion and thereby increase the number of transporters present in the membrane and their transport V_{max} (43, 44). Conversely, channels and other transporters can be retrieved from the plasma membrane by endocytosis. This can limit or terminate secretory responses, and information is now emerging on signaling mechanisms that promote endocytic retrieval (44). For chloride secretion, regulation by alterations in the rate of transporter insertion and/or retrieval has been reported both for NKCC1 and CFTR (44–46). However, the findings with CFTR are controversial, and it seems likely that the relative contribution of channel insertion into the membrane to chloride secretion may vary among different tissues (47, 48).

Finally, transporter abundance can be regulated by changes in the rates of transcription and/or translation of the relevant transport proteins. This regulation differs from those outlined in the foregoing discussion, in that it occurs at the

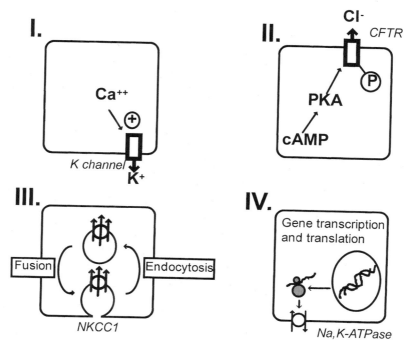

Figure 2 Modes of regulation of membrane transport pathways, exemplified by components of the chloride secretory mechanism. (I) Some transport pathways can be regulated via direct interactions of cytoplasmic factors with the transport protein. For example, basolateral potassium channels are regulated by calcium. (II) Some transport pathways are regulated by covalent modifications. For example, CFTR is activated by cAMP-dependent phosphorylation mediated by PKA. (III) Some transport pathways are regulated by insertion of preformed protein stored in submembrane vesicles (fusion) or by retrieval of such transporters from the membrane by endocytosis back into a vesicular compartment. NKCC1 appears to be regulated in this fashion. (IV) Regulation of transport proteins at the level of gene transcription and translation is also likely, as shown for Na,K-ATPase, although the significance of this mechanism for intestinal chloride secretion has yet to be demonstrated.

level of de novo protein synthesis and thus has slower kinetics. However, relatively little is known regarding transcriptional control of the proteins involved in chloride secretion, in contrast to the body of data supporting the concept that intestinal sodium channels, for example, are transcriptionally regulated in response to alterations in salt intake (49–51). For these reasons, the information below focuses predominantly on acute regulation of transport proteins involved in the chloride secretory mechanism.

Basolateral Pathways   This section summarizes the basolateral transport pathways required for chloride secretion. We review their molecular characteristics and the ways in which each is regulated.

Na,K-ATPase   The energetic requirements for active chloride secretion are provided for by the activity of a Na,K-ATPase or Na pump. This transports three sodium ions out of the cell across the basolateral membrane in exchange for two potassium ions, and at the cost of hydrolysis of one molecule of ATP (52, 53). The activity of this pump therefore maintains a low intracellular sodium concentration and a high intracellular potassium concentration. The K^+ concentration difference (diffusion potential) and the stoichiometry of the pump render the interior of the cell electronegative with respect to the extracellular fluid. The cell-negative membrane voltage is important in providing a driving force for chloride exit.

Na,K-ATPase is a heterodimer of α and β subunits. All the ion transport characteristics of the pump appear to be embodied in the α subunit (54), whereas the β subunit may be important for directing delivery of the pump to the plasma membrane and for stabilizing the pump at that site. Several isoforms of both α and β subunits have been described, but in the intestine, the pumps appear to be composed predominantly of α_1 and β_1 heterodimers (55).

Little is known regarding the acute regulation of Na,K-ATPase activity in intestinal epithelial cells other than the fact that the pump has an obligate requirement for magnesium ions and is inhibited by cardiac glycosides such as ouabain (54). Indeed, chloride secretion, in common with most active transport mechanisms in the intestine, can be fully inhibited by ouabain, indicating the central role played by the maintenance of a low intracellular sodium concentration and a cell-negative membrane voltage in intestinal transport processes. It is presumed that the pump is always operative, although upregulation at the transcriptional level, as described in epithelial tissues in response to growth factors such as epidermal growth factor (EGF), has been reported (56). This could presumably increase the capacity for chloride secretion were it not for the fact that EGF also evokes negative signaling cascades in chloride secretory cells (see below).

NKCC1   The Na/K/2Cl cotransporter that serves as the chloride uptake step in intestinal secretory epithelia has been cloned, and it is the NKCC1 isoform of this protein that appears to mediate secretory function (57). [Of note, a related protein, NKCC2, with opposite cellular polarity, is central to sodium chloride reabsorption in the thick ascending limb of the loop of Henle in the kidney (58).] In fact, NKCC1 appears to be expressed in most cell types, although its specialized role in chloride secretory epithelia is perhaps underscored by the knowledge that 10- to 30-fold higher levels of expression of NKCC1 are seen in secretory epithelial cells, compared with other cell types (57). NKCC1 is expressed throughout the gastrointestinal system, with most prominent expression in the colon and an abrupt cessation of expression at the top of the crypts along the crypt-villus axis (57, 59). It is characteristically inhibited by loop diuretic drugs such as bumetanide (57).

NKCC1 is referred to as a secondary active transporter because it takes advantage of the ionic gradients established by an active transport pathway (the Na,K-ATPase) to enable movement of an energetically unfavored ion against its concentration gradient by coupling transport to an ion whose movement is favored. Because two chloride ions are transported in combination with two cations, transport by NKCC1 is electroneutral and thus is unaffected by the membrane voltage. However, the low intracellular sodium concentration allows NKCC1 to accumulate chloride in secretory epithelial cells above the concentration predicted from electrochemical equilibrium.

A classical view of epithelial chloride secretion originally held that NKCC1 was not a primary target for intracellular regulatory mechanisms in epithelial cells, but rather responded to the ionic gradients across the cell membrane. However, this view has been overturned by the molecular characterization of this protein. It is now apparent that the activity of NKCC1 is stimulated by intracellular kinase cascades and phosphorylation, although the identity of the kinase(s) responsible for covalent modification of the cotransporter is still the subject of speculation (60–62). What is known, however, is that phosphorylation of the protein can be markedly stimulated by a decrease in intracellular chloride, via a kinase presumed to be sensitive to chloride activity, to changes in cell volume, or to both (62). In essence, the chloride sensitivity of cotransporter function provides a mechanism where chloride loss across the apical membrane of epithelial cells can be matched by an increased rate of chloride entry, thereby allowing sustained chloride secretion. This apparent communication between apical and basolateral membranes, to allow for maximal transport rates, provides an excellent example of how chloride secretion reflects a tightly integrated process at the level of the intact epithelial cell.

NKCC1 is of further interest because its activity in intestinal epithelial cells appears to be also regulated by membrane insertion and retrieval, at least under some conditions (59). For example, chloride secretory responses to agonists that elevate intracellular cAMP (although interestingly, not to those agents acting through cytoplasmic calcium) can be reduced by agents that affect the integrity of the cytoskeleton (63). Matthews and co-workers showed that the cAMP-dependent secretory response was associated with an enhanced rate of bumetanide-sensitive rubidium uptake across the basolateral membrane, a measure of NKCC1 activity (43, 64). This increase in functional activity was accompanied by an increase in bumetanide binding to the basolateral membrane, although it remains unresolved to what degree this reflects insertion of NKCC1 molecules into the plasma membrane versus a conformational change in the protein that increases its turnover number and allows for more efficient bumetanide binding (44, 65). Conversely, some treatments cause an increase in endocytosis of NKCC1 into epithelial cells, thereby reducing cotransporter density. Specifically, the phorbol ester PMA causes internalization of NKCC1, an effect that appears to be mediated by PKCε (44, 65).

K channels   The molecular characterization of potassium channels involved in the chloride secretory mechanism has lagged behind that of the other proteins discussed in this section. However, at least two types of potassium channels involved in chloride secretion have been identified on functional grounds (66–68). One is activated by increases in cytosolic calcium and is relatively insensitive to the channel blocker barium. The channel is, however, blocked by clotrimazole and charybdotoxin and can be opened directly by 1-ethyl-2-benzimidazolinone (69–71). Data also suggest that this channel is activated by the calcium-dependent agonist, carbachol, via a G protein and perhaps an increase in the sensitivity of the channel to cytosolic calcium (72). Emerging data suggest that the recently characterized hIK1 potassium channel may be a candidate for this conductance, based on its electrophysiological properties, sensitivity to submicromolar calcium concentrations, and pharmacology (69–71). However, no direct assessment of the role of this channel in calcium-mediated chloride secretion has been reported. There is even less information on the molecular basis of a second potassium channel, relatively sensitive to barium, presumed to participate in chloride secretion and activated by increases in cAMP (66, 68). Finally, Devor and co-workers have functionally described a potassium channel present in T_{84} cells that is activated by arachidonic acid (73). This finding may be relevant to the observation that certain chloride secretagogues appear to act, at least in part, by stimulating the release of this fatty acid from membrane phospholipids (74).

In contrast to the Na,K-ATPase and NKCC1 discussed above, basolateral potassium channels (or at least that conductance that is activated in response to changes in calcium) have long been thought to be direct loci whereby the regulation of the overall process of chloride secretion is accomplished. Thus a classical view of calcium-dependent chloride secretion held that a basolateral potassium channel was the only site of regulation for this process (75, 76). In this scenario, potassium channel opening would cause cell hyperpolarization and hence promote chloride efflux across the fraction of chloride channels found open in the apical membrane at any given time. This model for calcium-dependent chloride secretion, which contrasts with cAMP-induced secretion that is thought to be regulated at the level of an apical chloride channel (CFTR), is supported by some experimental data (75), but it now appears to be an oversimplification (72). Although it is clear that calcium-dependent chloride secretion is dependent on potassium channel opening, there may also be apical chloride exit pathways, other than CFTR, that are direct targets of calcium-mediated signaling events. In any case, a primary effect of calcium on a potassium channel versus cAMP on a chloride channel does provide at least a partial explanation for the finding that treatment of intestinal epithelial cells with combinations of agonists acting through calcium and cAMP leads to synergistic, or greater than additive, effects on secretion (77, 78). Calcium- and cAMP-dependent chloride secretion would thus have different rate-limiting steps (the opening of chloride and potassium channels, respectively). Thus when both messengers are elevated simultaneously, both rate-limiting steps are removed and synergism can result.

Apical Pathways   In this section we discuss apical channels in intestinal epithelial cells that mediate chloride exit. Given the available data we focus on CFTR, but also discuss emerging data that support a role for an additional family of calcium-activated chloride channels.

CFTR   The main pathway for apical chloride exit in intestinal epithelial cells is embodied in the CFTR chloride channel. Since the cloning of this protein in 1989 (79), there has been a veritable explosion of information regarding its structure and function and the functional consequences of various mutations (80, 81). CFTR is a large protein with a number of distinct functional domains (Figure 3) and occurs as dimers in the membrane (82). In addition to 12 membrane-spanning regions that are presumed to form the pore of the channel, the protein also contains 2 nucleotide-binding folds (with structures reminiscent of those found in several ATPase pumps), as well as a large regulatory domain that contains consensus sequences for phosphorylation by several protein kinases. In the intestine, CFTR is expressed predominantly in the apical membrane of the crypt cells, although a small number of cells with very high expression of the channel are also detected scattered through the villus epithelium (at least in rats and humans) (27, 83). The function of these latter cells remains unclear.

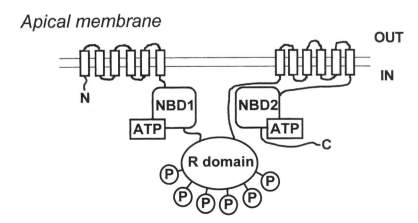

Figure 3   Proposed domain structure of CFTR. The protein is comprised of 12 transmembrane regions that form the channel pore, 2 nucleotide binding domains (NBD) that bind and hydrolyse ATP, and a regulatory (R) domain that can be phosphorylated by several protein kinases, including PKA and PKC.

CFTR is regulated in a two-step process that involves covalent modification of the R domain by cAMP-dependent PKA, followed by nucleotide binding and hydrolysis in the nucleotide-binding domains (82, 84–86). Both steps are required for channel opening. The unusual (for a channel) requirement for nucleotide hydrolysis has led some authors to speculate that CFTR function, and thus the overall process of chloride secretion, is to some extent dependent on the cellular energy charge (87). PKA activity results in the ordered phosphorylation of a number of sites in the R domain, although none of these has been shown to be essential for channel activity since the channel remains functional even when all are mutated (42, 81, 88–90). Presumably, either other phosphorylation sites play a role in channel regulation or some sites are inhibitory (90). The efficiency of CFTR phosphorylation may be enhanced by the fact that the channel may exist in a localized domain that contains other signaling proteins, such as the type II isoform of PKA that can be anchored to specific membrane domains via A-kinase anchoring proteins (84), as well as phosphatases that serve to reverse channel activation (91, 92). In particular, protein phosphatases of types 2C and 2A may be important in CFTR regulation although multiple phosphatases are likely required for complete channel inactivation (91, 92).

In addition to primary regulation by PKA-mediated phosphorylation, there are additional levels of regulation for the CFTR chloride channel. One is provided for by the cAMP-dependent delivery of preformed CFTR from subapical membrane vesicles, thereby increasing channel density at the apical membrane (46, 93). This finding has not been reproduced in all chloride secretory cell types, however (47), suggesting that the relative contribution of channel trafficking to rates of chloride secretion may be tissue specific. The molecular details of how this trafficking event occurs are also still rather sketchy, although the signaling pathway apparently involves well-known components of the vesicular trafficking pathway in other tissues such as syntaxin isoforms (94). Regulation of CFTR by other protein kinases has also been proposed. For example, it has been suggested that, while phosphorylation of CFTR by PKC alone may not necessarily result in channel opening, activity of this kinase (specifically the ε isoform) nevertheless may be permissive for, or may potentiate, activation of the channel by PKA (95, 96). Thus the prostanoid $PGF_{2}\alpha$ can activate CFTR at lower levels of cAMP than those required for forskolin stimulation, a discrepancy that has been ascribed to the fact that this prostaglandin activates both PKA and PKC (97). Other authors have provided evidence that tyrosine kinases might regulate CFTR. For example, addition of the non-receptor tyrosine kinase c-Src to excised membrane patches increases the current attributable to CFTR in patch-clamp studies, and correspondingly, the gradual loss of the fast gating mode of CFTR upon patch excision may be due to the activity of membrane-associated tyrosine phosphatases (98). A tyrosine-based motif in the C terminus of the CFTR molecule has also been implicated in directing CFTR endocytosis from the plasma membrane (99). Finally, CFTR is also activated secondary to increases in cGMP in intestinal epithelial cells (100). This may reflect cross-activation of PKA by the high levels of cGMP induced by certain agonists, and/or a direct effect of a type II cGMP-dependent protein kinase on the CFTR molecule (100–102).

CaCC   Controversy persists with respect to whether other apical chloride channels are involved in chloride secretory responses in the intestine. Several authors have reported that intestinal epithelial cells in situ, or cultured intestinal epithelial cells growing as confluent monolayers, exhibit minimal if any calcium-activated chloride conductances (8, 103, 104). Moreover, intestinal tissues either from patients with cystic fibrosis or from mice with a targeted deletion of the CFTR gene have neither cAMP nor calcium-mediated chloride secretory responses, compared with the restriction of the transport defect to cAMP-mediated transport alone in the airways (8, 105). On the basis of these data, it was suggested that chloride secretory responses evoked in normal intestinal tissues by agonists that mobilize intracellular calcium are in fact driven primarily by the opening of a basolateral potassium channel, with chloride then able to exit the cell across the small fraction of CFTR chloride channels open at any given time. However, there are also suggestions that calcium-activated chloride channels may indeed be functionally significant in the intestine (106, 107). Importantly, calcium-activated chloride secretion can be independent of CFTR, in that treatment of intestinal epithelial cells with antisense oligonucleotides to the channel, a maneuver sufficient to abolish cAMP-stimulated secretion, is without effect on calcium-mediated responses (108). Similarly, emerging data suggest that the ability to display a calcium-mediated chloride secretory response, and the magnitude of that response, are actually mitigating factors in the mouse model of cystic fibrosis (8, 109). Thus prolonged survival and less severe gastrointestinal symptoms in a subset of CFTR knockout mice were correlated with expression of this alternative secretory pathway (109).

A resolution of the controversy surrounding the mechanism of calcium-mediated chloride secretion still awaits. However, the recent cloning of a rapidly growing family of chloride channels designated CaCCs may shed light on this area. Several such proteins have now been identified, with four human isoforms known (CM Fuller, personal communication). At least one of these channels (hCaCC1) is expressed in intestinal tissues and cell lines, where it can be activated by increases in cytosolic calcium concentration (39). In fact, the activation of these channels is complex, integrating several intracellular inputs. For example, when bovine CaCC is examined in lipid bilayers under basal conditions, the channel is activated only by calcium concentrations that exceed those to be expected in either resting or activated cells (37, 110). However, if the channel is phosphorylated by the calmodulin-dependent protein kinase CaMKII, the dependency of channel opening on calcium concentration becomes bell-shaped, with channel opening now occurring within the range of calcium concentrations in activated cells and channel closure occurring at supraphysiological calcium concentrations (110). Interestingly, an intracellular mediator identified as a possible endogenous negative regulator of calcium-dependent chloride secretion, inositol 3,4,5,6, tetrakisphosphate [Ins(3,4,5,6)P_4] shifts the calcium dose-response curve farther to the left, so that the channel is now open at calcium concentrations below those seen under basal conditions and closes at calcium concentrations achieved in stimulated epithelial cells (111). The existence of a negative signaling mechanism(s) that may limit the activity of CaCC channels could provide some explanation for why these channels have often proven elusive to detect in intestinal tissues. Finally, CaCC activation, at least when the channel is exogenously expressed, can also be accomplished by activating PKC with phorbol ester treatment or by the addition of the Src-related soluble tyrosine kinase, p56[lyk]. Pharmacologically, the channel is inhibited by DIDS (4,4'diisothiocyanatostilbene-2,2'disulfonic acid), DTT (dithiothreitol), and (for some isoforms) niflumic acid (39, 110).

Cell-Cell Interactions Involved in Transport Regulation

Chloride secretion is a property intrinsic to a subset of the epithelial cells lining the gastrointestinal tract, predominantly localized to the crypt region. However, the extent of chloride secretion is governed by specific cell-cell interactions and via the release of soluble mediators (discussed in greater detail below). In this section, some of the broad classes of regulatory interactions of different cell types with the epithelium are introduced to provide a context for further discussion.

Gastrointestinal physiologists have long recognized several classes of regulatory interactions among the cell types in the gastrointestinal tract that govern intestinal function (Figure 4) (1). The chloride secretory mechanism is an excellent example of these interactions because it is subject to influences from all major regulatory systems. Early work in this area recognized regulation of the epithelium by endocrine, neurocrine, and paracrine mediators (1). Thus hormones secreted by other parts of the gastrointestinal system and organs that drain into it, synaptic release of neurotransmitters from nerve terminals of the enteric nervous system, and mediators released from cell types (either endocrine or other) in close proximity to secreting epithelial cells can all contribute to the control of chloride secretion. We now also appreciate that interactions with various effector cell types of the mucosal immune system, as well as autocrine regulatory influences derived from epithelial cells themselves, contribute to modulating intestinal secretion. For example, mediators released by resident mast cells are capable of initiating chloride secretory responses not only to classical immune agonists, such as an antigen to which the subject has previously been sensitized, but also to secretagogues such as bile acids, not classically considered to be immune cell activators (114–116). Finally, intestinal epithelial cells are active in the production of a wide range of growth factors, including ligands for the EGF receptor and related receptors (20, 117, 118). Because they also bear receptors for these ligands, cell-cell interactions at the level of the epithelium itself, either by juxtacrine signaling from membrane-tethered ligands, or in an autocrine fashion, almost certainly alter ion transport responses, although in ways that have not been elucidated fully in the setting of the intact intestine (117).

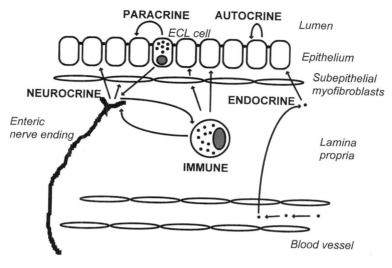

Figure 4   Mechanisms for the regulation of intestinal chloride secretion at the intact tissue level. Mediators released from enteric nerve endings can act directly on epithelial cells or can exert indirect prosecretory actions via effects on other cells in the mucosa, including immunocytes and subepithelial myofibroblasts (neurocrine regulation). Immune effector cells can similarly have both direct and indirect effects on epithelial cells (immune regulation). Enterochromaffin-like (ECL) cells respond to changes in luminal contents and release mediators that influence local epithelial cells (paracrine regulation); this mode of regulation is also used by subepithelial myofibroblasts. Epithelial cells themselves also release substances that modify epithelial function (autocrine regulation). Finally, blood-borne hormones from distant sites (indicated by the small dots) can also diffuse into the mucosa and regulate epithelial cell function (endocrine regulation). For further details, see text.

There is also significant cross-talk between the regulatory mechanisms described above; one system may be recruited by another to augment the overall secretory response. For example, a reflex loop involving sensory nerve endings, the release of neuropeptides and other neurotransmitters, and the release of mast cell mediators can clearly contribute to the secretory response produced by certain bacterial enterotoxins (e.g. that produced by *Clostridium difficile*) or perhaps by intense mechanical stimulation of the intestinal wall (3, 4, 119). Conversely, activation of mast cells by exogenous antigens appears to recruit secondarily the enteric nervous system to propagate the effect of mast cell mediators on chloride secretion (120). Finally, secretory responses to inflammatory mediators and cytokines, such as interleukin 1 (IL-1), occur in part via prostaglandin synthesis by the subepithelial layer of myofibroblasts (121–123). These prostanoids can then act on the epithelium in a paracrine fashion to promote chloride secretion. Thus the chloride secretory mechanism is the target of a tightly integrated network of regulatory influences. This complex control mechanism underscores the physiological importance of this response and allows for fine-tuning of fluid and electrolyte secretory responses under a variety of physiological (e.g. post-prandial) or pathophysiological (e.g. during infection) circumstances.

AGONISTS AND ANTAGONISTS OF CHLORIDE SECRETION AND THEIR MECHANISMS OF ACTION

In this section we do not attempt to provide a comprehensive catalogue of all mediators with reported chloride secretory actions. Rather, we focus on those mediators that are most likely to have physiological roles in the regulation of secretion in vivo. Our coverage is slanted toward recent findings. For an exhaustive listing of putative chloride secretagogues see Reference 124.

Mediators are categorized according to the major regulatory system whereof they are derived. However, it is important to recognize that these categories are not absolute, and some substances could be listed under more than one heading.

Secretagogues

This section discusses substances capable of stimulating a chloride secretory response. They can be neurotransmitters, immune mediators, endocrine hormones, and paracrine agents.

Neurotransmitters   Two most prominent transmitters in activating intestinal chloride secretion, acetylcholine and vasoactive intestinal polypeptide (VIP), are interesting in that they mediate their effects through divergent intracellular signaling events. VIP binds to its cognate receptor on the basolateral membrane of epithelial cells, which is linked to a G protein of the G_s class. This, in turn, results in the activation of adenylyl cyclase, elevated cAMP, activation of CFTR and perhaps other membrane transport proteins, and a sustained effect on chloride secretion in continued presence of the agonist (1). In contrast, acetylcholine (or carbachol) binds to an m_3 muscarinic receptor on the basolateral membrane that is linked to a G_q G protein (76, 125, 126). Via activation of phospholipase C and phosphatidylinositol hydrolysis to yield the calcium-mobilizing messenger $Ins(1,4,5)P_3$, this results in an elevation in intracellular calcium concentration. In turn, calcium activates potassium and/or CaCC chloride channels to evoke a chloride secretory response that is considerably more transient than that stimulated by VIP (76, 125, 126). In part, the transient nature of the calcium-dependent response may relate to the concomitant generation of negative signals that limit secretion, as discussed in greater detail below (126). It is also of interest that secretory responses to VIP and acetylcholine are synergistic, as might be predicted from the fact that they utilize different signaling events to produce their effects on transport (76). In fact, the response to acetylcholine may be transient by design (to provide for minute-to-minute fine-tuning of the secretory response in a delimited fashion) unless the effect is coordinated with that of VIP, or another cAMP-dependent secretagogue. It is likely that the ability of the intestine to call upon rapidly increased rates of chloride secretion, such as those activated by synergistic interactions of the type discussed here, may play a role as a primitive host defense mechanism designed to flush the intestinal lumen of potentially injurious substances and/or invading pathogens.

Evidence also supports a role for the sensory neurotransmitter, substance P, in the activation of chloride secretion. However, in contrast to the effects of VIP and acetylcholine discussed above, there is little evidence to suggest that the effects of substance P are mediated via direct interactions of this neuropeptide with secretory epithelial cells. Rather, substance P appears to mediate its effects via the activation of secondary cell types, including other nerve endings and mucosal mast cells (119, 127, 128).

Immune Mediators   Various cell types, both resident and infiltrating, which make up the mucosal immune system, alter rates of intestinal chloride secretion via the release of soluble mediators (129, 130). Several immunologic mediators interact directly with intestinal epithelial cells to activate secretion, and some are highlighted here together with their presumed mechanism of action.

Histamine, released from mast cells in response to antigenic stimulation or to other non-immunologic mast cell activators, binds to histamine H_1 receptors on the basolateral membranes of secretory epithelial cells to evoke chloride secretion via a calcium-dependent mechanism (131). Like acetylcholine, histamine also acts synergistically with mediators that induce elevations in cAMP (131). However, in contrast to cholinergic stimulation, histaminergic stimulation appears to be far less effective in generating negative second messengers, such as $Ins(3,4,5,6)P_4$, that can block the ability of the epithelium to respond to a second calcium-dependent agonist (132). This implies that histamine-dependent activation of epithelial chloride secretion may be permissive for ongoing responsiveness, whereas cholinergic stimulation is not, unless coordinated with cAMP. This may be relevant in intestinal inflammation, where histamine is likely to be only one of several immunologically derived mediators released in the vicinity of the epithelium. Furthermore, in addition to its direct effects on epithelial cells, in the intact intestine of some animals, histamine may exert additional effects on secretion via indirect pathways, including the activation of enteric nerves via histamine H_2 receptors and the stimulation of prostaglandin production by subepithelial myofibroblasts (122, 133). However, these indirect effects may be species-specific in that evidence exists to suggest that the secretory effects of histamine in the human colon do not involve neuronal activity (134).

Immunologic effector cells also release other products with effects on chloride secretion. In particular, adenosine, released from activated mast cells and acting through A_{2b} receptors that may be localized to both apical and basolateral poles of epithelial cells, induces chloride secretion via a mechanism that involves, at least in part, the cAMP-dependent activation of CFTR (135–137). However, as discussed above for $PGF_2\alpha$, it is likely that additional intracellular messengers contribute to the effect of adenosine because high levels of secretion can be stimulated with little or no discernable change in cAMP (135). Some studies from our own laboratory suggest that one candidate for this accessory messenger is arachidonic acid, which is liberated in response to the same concentrations of adenosine that evoke chloride secretion and is known to be capable of activating a subpopulation of potassium channels present on the basolateral membrane (73, 74). The bilateral expression of adenosine receptors in epithelial cells is also likely to be of pathophysiological significance. Thus, in addition to mast cells, neutrophils secrete a precursor of adenosine, 5'AMP, that can be converted to adenosine by a 5' nucleotidase expressed on the apical membrane (138). This mechanism may be pertinent to the diarrhea seen in ulcerative colitis and other inflammatory bowel diseases, where neutrophils are known to migrate into the intestinal lumen forming crypt abscesses.

Some immune mediators may evoke chloride secretion via mechanisms that are either largely or wholly indirect. For example, a variety of reactive oxygen species, platelet activating factor, lipoxygenase metabolites of arachidonic acid, and certain cytokines including IL-1, all induce chloride secretion that is sensitive to inhibition by non-steroidal anti-inflammatory drugs that act as cyclooxygenase inhibitors (1). Thus the ability of these compounds to evoke secretion is presumed to be secondary to the generation of prostaglandins. In fact, prostaglandins, especially of the E series, are potent chloride secretagogues likely to be active under both physiological and pathophysiological circumstances (139). These mediators are thought to induce their effects on epithelial cells via elevations in cAMP, although the bewildering spectrum of prostanoid receptors, many of which are present in intestinal epithelial cells, makes data in this area difficult to interpret (140).

Endocrine Mediators Like other facets of the gastrointestinal response to food intake (141), the intestinal secretory mechanism is presumed to be regulated by hormones that integrate changes in secretory rates with events taking place at remote locations in the system (e.g. coordinating upregulation of downstream intestinal secretion when food is present in the stomach). However, in the large body of literature in which digestive hormones have been shown to have effects on intestinal secretory responses, their concentrations were supraphysiologic (124). Thus the precise role of endocrine pathways in regulating chloride secretion in the intestine and the mechanisms of any such effects remain unresolved. A possible exception to this statement is the putative hormone uroguanylin, which may serve to coordinate intestinal chloride secretion with renal fluid and electrolyte homeostasis (142). The mechanism of action of uroguanylin is discussed below.

Paracrine Mediators In contrast to the lack of knowledge regarding endocrine regulators of chloride secretion, there is substantial understanding of how peptides and other mediators may be responsible for regulating chloride secretion on a local level. One major class of paracrine regulators are the prostanoids. Another important mediator of chloride secretion is 5-hydroxytryptamine (5-HT), released from enterochromaffin cells located within the epithelial layer (143). This mediator has a variety of targets, including $5HT_2$ receptors on epithelial cells whose activation evokes chloride secretion via a calcium-dependent mechanism. In vivo, however, 5HT also induces release of acetylcholine and non-adrenergic, non-cholinergic neurotransmitters (most likely VIP) from enteric nerve endings, via $5HT_3$ and $5HT_{3/4}$ receptors, respectively. These effects may be quantitatively more important in the overall secretory response. In this regard, enterochromaffin cells can act as sensors for the luminal environment and, by releasing 5-HT, promote appropriate changes in luminal composition or tonicity (143).

Guanylin is a recently discovered gastrointestinal peptide that appears to be synthesized predominantly by specialized enteroendocrine cells within the epithelial layer (142, 144). Guanylin is an unusual endogenous secretagogue in that its receptors are localized solely to the apical pole of the cell (144, 145). The response to guanylin is also distinctive in that it does not utilize the classical cAMP- or calcium-dependent pathways to activate chloride secretion. Instead, the receptor for guanylin is a membrane-bound guanylyl cyclase (GC-C), and ligand binding results in an intracellular accumulation of cGMP (144, 145). Secretory responses to cGMP are reminiscent of those evoked by cAMP in terms of their magnitude and kinetics, and are neither additive nor synergistic with cAMP-mediated responses, indicating that there are at least some signaling elements (or CFTR as the final target) in common (146). There is some indication that cGMP may exert secretory effects via cross-activation of the cAMP-dependent protein kinase, although the involvement of a cGMP-dependent kinase (PKG) has also been implicated (100–102). The stimuli that promote the release of guanylin, and thus the secretory response, are unknown, although there is a suggestion that expression of both guanylin and its receptor is downregulated by a low-salt diet, perhaps implying a role in salt homeostasis (147). Similarly, the related renal peptide uroguanylin, which also activates the guanylin receptor (although how this ligand gains access to the intestinal lumen is unknown), has been implicated as a mediator that may balance the salt-handling capabilities of the intestine and kidneys (142).

Exogenous Agents   This section reviews luminal substances that share the ability to stimulate chloride secretion of those mediators discussed above. Some are significant only under pathological circumstances (e.g. toxins) but are of interest because they provide insight into the regulation of secretion.

Bacteria and Bacterial Toxins   The reserve secretory capacity of the intestine has often been considered a defensive mechanism designed to flush the lumen free of microorganisms that might otherwise invade the mucosa and cause disseminated disease. Several bacteria express enterotoxins that can have profound effects on chloride secretion. The prototypic example of such a toxin is that elaborated by *Vibrio cholerae,* which remains a major cause of life-threatening diarrhea, particularly in developing countries. Cholera toxin has a subunit structure consisting of five binding or B subunits and one active or A subunit. The B subunits are responsible for binding the toxin to GM_1 gangliosides expressed on the apical membrane of intestinal epithelial cells. This allows the A subunit to be transported into the cell, whereupon it follows a directed pathway to the basolateral pole of the cell and there irreversibly activates the adenylyl cyclase signaling mechanism (148). This causes a profound increase in cAMP and an irreversible stimulation of chloride secretion. Cholera toxin also has indirect effects on secretion, most of which are ascribable to the recruitment of the enteric nervous system and are mediated in part by 5-HT (149, 150). In addition, cholera toxin reduces sodium chloride absorption via cAMP-dependent inhibitory effects on NHE. Figure 5 summarizes pathways thought to be important in the pathogenesis of diarrhea associated with cholera infection. Despite the significant fluid losses that can occur in this disease (up to 20 l per day), the disease is usually self-limiting, and patients can do well if adequate hydration can be maintained during the acute phase of the illness (including with use of oral rehydration solutions that exploit the persistent sodium-glucose absorptive mechanism).

Enterotoxigenic strains of *Escherichia coli* can also activate excessive chloride secretion via specific toxins. One of these, ST_b, or heat-labile toxin of *E. coli,* is similar in its mechanism of action to cholera toxin in that an active subunit is internalized in epithelial cells and causes a large increase in cAMP levels. However, the secretory mechanisms of ST_b and cholera toxin are not wholly overlapping: While both toxins appear to activate the enteric nervous system in stimulating chloride secretion, ST_b does so without causing a detectable release of 5-HT (Figure 5) (150). Enterotoxigenic strains of *E. coli* also elaborate a heat-stable toxin, ST_a, which has been implicated as a frequent cause of traveler's diarrhea (151). ST_a binds to the guanylin receptor and causes an elevation in cGMP (Figure 5) (146, 152); indeed, the existence of guanylin was first postulated on the basis that there was likely to be an endogenous ligand for the high-affinity apical ST_a receptor (144). Guanylin and ST_a are also structurally related, although the latter molecule contains an additional disulfide bond that appears to render the molecule less sensitive to luminal proteolysis. As such, ST_a could be considered to be a super-agonist that subverts a pathway normally involved in the regulation of intestinal fluid and electrolyte transport (153).

Another microorganism that is a frequent cause of diarrhea, particularly associated with the use of antibiotics, is *C. difficile.* This microorganism also elaborates two toxins that may exert direct effects on the barrier function of the intestinal epithelium. This occurs via changes in intracellular calcium, as well as the modulation of low-molecular-weight G proteins that normally maintain tight junction integrity, such as Rho (154–156). As described for cholera toxin, *C.*

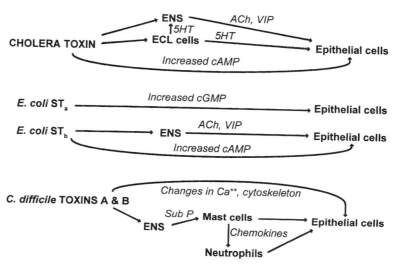

Figure 5 Comparison of mechanisms contributing to the initiation of epithelial chloride secretion in response to various bacterial toxins. The effects of cholera toxin are mediated via direct actions on epithelial cells that increase cellular cAMP, as well as by indirect effects involving the release of 5-hydroxytryptamine (5-HT) from enterochromaffin-like (ECL) cells. Cholera toxin and 5-HT also activate enteric nerve endings to release vaso-active intestinal polypeptide (VIP) and acetylcholine (ACh), which in turn act on epithelial cells to evoke chloride secretion. *E. coli* heat-stable enterotoxin (ST_a) appears to act pre-dominantly via direct effects on epithelial receptors that result in an increase in cGMP. *E. coli* heat-labile enterotoxin (ST_b), in contrast, has a mechanism of action similar to that utilized by cholera toxin, although ST_b does not appear to evoke 5-HT release from ECL cells. Finally, the toxins elaborated by *C. difficile* (A and B) have direct effects on epithelial cells (mediated by changes in cytoplasmic calcium and the cytoskeleton), as well as effects that are mediated indirectly via release of substance P (Sub P) from enteric nerve endings, activation of mucosal mast cells, and recruitment of neutrophils via the release of che-mokines and other chemotactic mediators. ENS, enteric nervous system. For further details, see text.

difficile toxins A and B also evoke secretory responses via indirect pathways (Figure 5). Sensory nerve endings containing substance P are activated by the toxin, and the release of this neurotransmitter goes on to result in mast cell acti-vation (119, 128). This further amplifies the secretory response via the mecha-nisms described above, as does the ensuing inflammation, with neutrophil influx, that is brought about by the release of inflammatory cytokines and other mediators from mast cells and other cell types at the site of infection (128).

Finally, we are beginning to learn how some invasive bacteria that do not elaborate any known enterotoxins may nevertheless evoke chloride secretory responses. *Salmonella* species have often been studied as a prototype of such effects. Invasion of epithelial cells by *Salmonella* results in the upregulation of a large number of chemokines as well as adhesion molecules, which in turn can stimulate the transmigration of neutrophils with accompanying effects on secretion (157–159). *Salmonella* infection also induces the upregulation of cyclooxygenase-2 in infected epithelial cells, and the prostaglandins produced by such cells are then candidates to evoke autocrine stimulation of secretory function (160). Finally, recent data indicate that infection with *Salmonella* may upregulate the ability of the epithelium to respond to certain neuropeptide stimuli of secretion, such as galanin (161, 162). However, this is not a finding that applies universally to responsiveness to all chloride secretagogues (K Barrett, L Bertelsen & S Resta-Lenert, unpublished observations) and so the mechanism of this effect remains to be elucidated.

Bile Acids   Bile acids, which are produced in large quantities by the liver, are key contributors to lipid digestion and absorption (163). Normally, the majority of the intestinal bile acid load is actively re-absorbed and recycled by the terminal ileum, leaving little of this pool to spill over to the colon (163). However, if ileal function is compromised (either by resection or disease), then appreciable quantities of bile acids may enter the colon, where they are known to exert secretory effects (163). Thus bile acids are luminally active secretagogues that may assume significance in certain gastrointestinal disease states.

Bile acids have been studied extensively with respect to their ability to evoke colonic chloride and fluid secretion. At least part of their activity appears to be the result of a direct effect on intestinal epithelial cells, in which they elevate cytoplasmic calcium (164). Subepithelial mast cells may also contribute to the secretory effect. Bile acids are known stimuli of mast cell mediator release (165), and the secretory response to bile acids in the colon can be correlated with mast cell density and with histamine release, and is at least in part inhibited by H_1 antihistamines and inhibitors of prostaglandin production (116). Moreover, intestinal tissues from mast cell–deficient mice have markedly diminished and delayed chloride secretory responses to bile acid stimulation (116). Bile acids may also recruit neural pathways in mediating their secretory effects (166).

It is unclear whether the effects described above are limited to the colon, and if so, why the small intestine, which is exposed to a very large bile acid load on a daily basis, is resistant to the secretory effect of these biological detergents. It is possible that ileal responses are limited by specialized permeability characteristics of the epithelial cells in this site, although this is pure speculation. Alternatively, responses to bile acids might tonically be limited by intracellular inhibitory mechanisms (see below). Finally, it remains possible that bile acids do cause significant secretion in the small intestine and that they are even important physiological regulators of this process, but that diarrheal symptoms do not normally ensue because of the large capacity of the colon for absorption of fluid following re-uptake of the bile acids from the lumen (1).

Inhibitors of Chloride Secretion

In common with many biological processes, stimuli of chloride secretion in the intestine are counterbalanced by inhibitors of this process. Information emerging over the last few years indicates that a number of mechanisms, some of which are intrinsic to the epithelium, accomplish this inhibitory purpose.

Neuropeptides Certain neuropeptides are able to antagonize the pro-secretory actions of hormones and neurotransmitters. For example, in common with its inhibitory profile toward other gastrointestinal secretory processes such as gastric acid secretion, somatostatin can reverse active chloride secretion, at least in experimental models (167–170). The mechanism is thought to involve the activation of an inhibitory G_i protein and a consequent fall in intracellular cAMP levels, via the SST2 isoform of the somatostatin receptor family (168–171). The physiological significance of this finding is, however, unclear. Nevertheless, the ability of somatostatin to reduce active chloride secretion finds clear clinical application in the use of the analogue octreotide acetate (Sandostatin), which is indicated in the treatment of severe and/or refractory secretory diarrhea (172).

Two related peptides, neuropeptide Y and peptide YY, also inhibit chloride secretion (173). They are released post-prandially and have been postulated to play a role in the ileal brake mechanism and perhaps in signaling satiety (173, 174). Both peptides have antisecretory properties versus a variety of secretagogues in both cell lines and intact intestinal tissue, perhaps by inhibiting chloride and potassium channels (175–178). However, as for somatostatin, the physiological implications, if any, of these observations remain unclear.

Growth Factors Ongoing studies from our and other laboratories have revealed that a number of peptide growth factors, including epidermal growth factor (EGF), transforming growth factor-α, insulin, insulin-like growth factors, and heregulin, may all inhibit calcium-dependent chloride secretion without themselves serving as agonists of the process (179–183). These growth factors have in common the ability to bind to basolateral membrane receptors with intrinsic tyrosine kinase activity (184). They likely also share a common mechanism of action whereby they inhibit chloride secretion, as exemplified by the studies discussed below for EGF.

Addition of EGF to monolayers of T_{84} intestinal epithelial cells results in the rapid activation of the tyrosine kinase activity of the EGF receptor, and recruitment of the heterodimeric enzyme, phosphatidylinositol 3-kinase (PI 3-kinase) (180, 185). This enzyme is thus brought into proximity to its lipid substrates in the plasma membrane, resulting in the formation of phosphatidylinositol PtdIns(3,4)P_2 and PtdIns(3,4,5)P_3 (180). These lipids appear to inhibit a basolaterally localized potassium channel, likely thereby reducing active chloride secretion by allowing potassium accumulation in the cytosol and thus reducing the driving force for chloride exit across the apical membrane (181). The importance of PI 3-kinase in this inhibitory effect is demonstrated by the fact that inhibition induced by EGF or other growth factors can be reversed by a variety of PI 3-kinase inhibitors (180, 186). However, the precise mechanism whereby products of this lipid kinase go on to inhibit basolateral potassium channels or other components of the secretory mechanism remains a topic for investigation (186). Preliminary data from our laboratory, however, implicate the novel PKC isoform, PKCε, as a downstream effector in this signaling cascade (Y Chow, J Uribe & K Barrett, unpublished observations).

Agents that Act as Both Activators and Inhibitors of Secretion   We have additionally identified stimuli of chloride secretion that also have the capability to act as inhibitors of this process. The prototypic agonist of this type is the acetylcholine analogue, carbachol, which, as discussed above, induces chloride secretion via binding to an m_3 muscarinic receptor, activation of G_q, mobilization of intracellular calcium, and consequent stimulatory effects on basolateral potassium channels and perhaps on an apical CaCC (76). However, the secretory response to carbachol is transient, and cells are then rendered refractory to activation by a second calcium-dependent agonist such as histamine or thapsigargin (132, 187).

We showed that the inhibitory effect of carbachol is likely attributable to a sustained elevation in the 3,4,5,6 isomer of inositol tetrakisphosphate ($Ins(3,4,5,6)P_4$), a molecule that we have subsequently shown to exert a direct inhibitory effect on the open probability of CaCC (111, 187). This inhibitory effect of $Ins(3,4,5,6)P_4$, hitherto considered to be an "orphan messenger" whose levels were modulated in stimulated cells without a relationship to a known function, is highly specific for this isomer. Thus the inhibitory effect is not reproduced by other isomers of $InsP_4$, including its enantiomer, $Ins(1,4,5,6)P_4$, nor by inositol trisphosphate or the presumed precursor of $InsP_4$, $InsP_5$, even at much higher concentrations (111). The interaction of $Ins(3,4,5,6)P_4$ with calcium-activated chloride channels has been observed in several other systems, including pancreatic epithelial cells that lack functional CFTR, and thus may be a general phenomenon in secretory epithelia (188–190). The ability of cholinergic agonists to increase levels of this messenger in a sustained fashion may also account, at least in part, for the ability of carbachol to inhibit subsequent chloride secretory responses to substance P in piglet jejunum, whereas the reverse effect (i.e. an ability of substance P to reduce responsiveness to carbachol) was not observed (191). In this regard, it is important to note that not all calcium-dependent chloride secretagogues appear to evoke this inhibitory mechanism. For example, histamine does not evoke a sustained increase in $Ins(3,4,5,6)P_4$ in T_{84} cells, nor does it inhibit subsequent responsiveness of the cells to calcium-mediated stimuli of chloride secretion (132). In contrast, preliminary data suggest that inhibitory signaling is evoked in T_{84} cells by uridine triphosphate (UTP), a calcium-dependent agonist of chloride secretion that has been proposed as a pharmacological means to exploit the calcium-mediated chloride secretory mechanism for therapeutic effect in cystic fibrosis (192, 193).

The ability of carbachol to limit chloride secretion may involve recruitment of tyrosine kinase–mediated signaling pathways involving the EGF receptor. Treatment of T_{84} cells with carbachol evokes a rapid transactivation of the EGF receptor with resulting phosphorylation and increased kinase activity, via a mechanism that appears to involve intracellular calcium, CaMKII, the calcium-dependent tyrosine kinase Pyk-2, and the non-receptor tyrosine kinase c-Src (185, 194, 195). Downstream of the EGF receptor, carbachol evokes recruitment of components of the mitogen-activated protein (MAP) kinase cascade and activation of the ERK isoforms of MAP kinase. Inhibitors of either EGF receptor kinase activity or MAP kinase activation can potentiate and prolong chloride secretory responses to carbachol (185).

The inhibition of chloride secretion by EGF and carbachol involves different targets (potassium versus chloride channels), and the ability of carbachol to reduce chloride secretion does not appear to involve PI 3-kinase activity (180, 181). This then raises the question of how signaling is diversified at the level of the EGF receptor in response to bona fide ligand binding versus transactivation from the muscarinic receptor. It is of interest that EGF, but not carbachol, recruits another member of the EGF receptor/ErbB receptor family, ErbB2, to EGF receptor immunoprecipitates (182). Moreover, only EGF recruits the p85 regulatory subunit of PI 3-kinase to ErbB2 (182). Thus EGF may mediate its inhibitory effects on chloride secretion by formation of EGF receptor/ErbB2 heterodimers, whereas the inhibitory effects of carbachol are mediated, at least in part, via EGF receptor homodimers (Figure 6). Ongoing work in our laboratory is defining the basis for this differential signaling at a molecular level. In any event, it would appear that the overall long-term effects of agonists such as carbachol on chloride secretion may actually be inhibitory, unless the response is coordinated with one evoked via the cAMP-dependent pathway, where there is the potential for synergistic interactions.

SUMMARY AND CONCLUSIONS

Integrated Regulation of Chloride Secretion

We are some way from a complete understanding of the contributions of the diverse regulatory factors discussed above to the control of chloride secretion under any given circumstance. What does appear clear is that these various regulatory strata can be brought into play to subserve the need for minute-by-minute as well as longer term demands for changes in the rate of chloride, and thus fluid, secretion. For example, experimental stroking of the mucosal surface, a stimulus that is presumed to mimic the passage of the food bolus along the gastrointestinal tract, evokes a reflex stimulation of secretion involving enteric nerves and the release of neurotransmitters such as acetylcholine, and a transient, self-limited response ensues (3, 4). This may serve to lubricate the epithelium just as the bolus

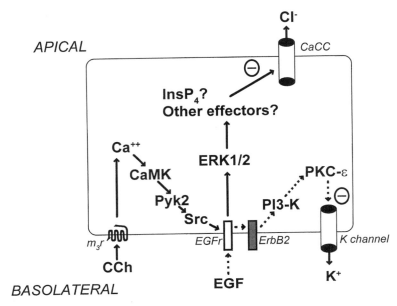

Figure 6 Negative signaling mechanisms that limit the extent of calcium-dependent chloride secretion in intestinal epithelial cells. The signaling cascade evoked by carbachol (CCh), which involves transactivation of the epidermal growth factor (EGF) receptor and targets an apical calcium-activated chloride channel (CaCC), is depicted with solid arrows. The signaling cascade evoked by EGF itself, which involves phosphatidylinositol 3-kinase (PI3-K) and targets a basolateral potassium channel, is depicted with broken arrows. Abbreviations: m_3r, m_3 muscarinic receptor; CaMK, calcium-calmodulin kinase; Pyk-2, calcium-activated tyrosine kinase; ERK 1/2, extracellular signal-regulated kinases 1 and 2 (isoforms of mitogen-activated protein kinases); InsP$_4$, inositol (3,4,5,6) tetrakisphosphate; PKC, protein kinase C. For further details, see text.

passes, without turning on excessive and ongoing secretion that might result in an inappropriate loss of fluid and electrolytes. Conversely, the barrage of mediators released in the setting of intestinal invasion by pathogens, including those from both immune and neural sources, may orchestrate a massive chloride secretory response on the basis of synergistic interactions between mediators (120). This may be appropriate in an infection in that it could help to flush away the offending microorganism from the body, but may also be a liability in inflammation of non-infectious origin, where a similar secretory response can result in massive diarrhea. Finally, in addition to the regulatory mechanisms that govern chloride secretion described here, which are largely intrinsic to the epithelium and the underlying mucosa, it is clear that intestinal transport responses are also governed by organ-level control mechanisms such as blood flow and motility (1). The latter is exploited in the clinical setting by opiate drugs that desynchronize propulsive motility, thereby allowing for longer contact time of the intestinal contents with absorptive epithelial cells. Thus, they can act as effective anti-diarrheals by balancing excessive secretion with a greater opportunity for absorptive fluxes (197).

Implications for Pathophysiological Chloride Secretion

Secretory Diarrhea   Active and excessive chloride secretion can clearly contribute to secretory diarrhea. This has been discussed above in the context of microbial and immune regulation of chloride secretion, and is not reiterated here. Suffice to say, however, that a reduction in chloride secretion is one therapeutic strategy for the treatment of such disease states (197).

Cystic Fibrosis   The converse of disease that results from excessive chloride secretion, the manifestations of cystic fibrosis are thought to result, at least primarily, from a failure to secrete sufficient amounts of chloride and thus a failure to hydrate mucosal surfaces adequately (198). In the gastrointestinal tract, this can lead to intestinal obstruction, maldigestion from a lack of pancreatic enzymes, malabsorption, biliary abnormalities, and pancreatitis (199, 200). It remains controversial whether all components of the gastrointestinal system express a calcium-mediated chloride secretory mechanism that might serve as an alternative pathway to bypass the secretory defect in cystic fibrosis. It is certainly possible that previous failures to identify such a pathway in intestinal tissue might in fact be a reflection of the functional expression of negative signaling events of the types discussed above, rather than a lack of the required transport machinery. If this is the case, further elucidation of such negative signaling events should eventually enable us to circumvent them, which in turn could optimize therapies for cystic fibrosis that target the calcium-dependent secretory mechanism.

Conclusions

It is hopefully apparent from the foregoing that the overall extent of chloride secretion in the intestinal epithelium is the integrated product of a multitude of regulatory influences, at both the intra- and extracellular levels. Further elucidation of the details of these regulatory influences should ultimately improve therapies for diseases of epithelial dysfunction, such as secretory diarrhea and cystic fibrosis.

ACKNOWLEDGMENTS

Studies from the authors' laboratory have been supported by grants from the National Institutes of Health to KEB [DK28305, DK35108 (Project 5) and DK53480] and by a Career Development Award from the Crohn's and Colitis Foundation of America to SJK. We thank our colleagues Lone Bertelsen, Sean

Calandrella, Yip Chuen Chow, Silvia Resta-Lenert, Jane Smitham, and Jorge Uribe for helpful and stimulating discussions on the topic of chloride secretion, as well as contributions to some of the studies we discuss here. We are also grateful to Glenda Wheeler-Loessel for assistance with manuscript preparation.

Visit the Annual Reviews home page at www.AnnualReviews.org.

LITERATURE CITED

1. Montrose MH, Keely SJ, Barrett KE. 1999. Secretion and absorption: small intestine and colon. See Ref. 201, pp. 320–55

2. Hogan DL, Ainsworth MA, Isenberg JI. 1994. Review article: gastroduodenal bicarbonate secretion. Aliment. Pharmacol. Ther. 8:475

3. Cooke HJ. 1994. Neuroimmune signalling in regulation of intestinal ion transport. Am. J. Physiol. 266:G167

4. Sidhu M, Cooke HJ. 1995. Role for 5-HT and ACh in submucosal reflexes mediating colonic secretion. Am. J. Physiol. 269:G346–51

5. Isenberg JI, McQuaid KR, Laine L, Walsh JH. 1995. Acid-peptic disorders. In Textbook of Gastroenterology, ed. T Yamada, pp. 1347–430. Philadelphia: Lippincott. 2nd ed.

6. O'Loughlin EV, Hunt DM, Gaskin KJ, Stiel D, Bruszuszcak IM, et al. 1991. Abnormal epithelial transport in cystic fibrosis jejunum. Am. J. Physiol. 260: G758–63

7. Kerem E, Corey M, Kerem B, Rommens J, Markiewicz D, et al. 1990. Association between the deltaF508 mutation and phenotypes in cystic fibrosis. N. Engl. J. Med. 323:1517–22

8. Grubb BR, Gabriel SE. 1997. Intestinal physiology and pathology in gene-targeted mouse models of cystic fibrosis. Am. J. Physiol. 273:G258–66

9. Pappenheimer JR, Reiss KZ. 1987. Contribution of solvent drag through intercellular junctions to absorption of nutrients by the small intestine of the rat. J. Membr. Biol. 100:123–36

10. Fromter E, Diamond J. 1972. Route of passive ion permeation in epithelia. Nature 235:9

11. Loo DDF, Zeuthen T, Chandy G, Wright EM. 1996. Cotransport of water by the Na^+/glucose cotransporter. Proc. Natl. Acad. Sci. USA 93:13367–70

12. Wright EM, Loo DDF, Turk E, Hirayama BA. 1996. Sodium cotransporters. Curr. Opin. Cell Biol. 8:468–73

13. Koyama Y, Yamamoto T, Tani T, Nihei K, Kondo D, et al. 1999. Expression and localization of aquaporins in rat gastrointestinal tract. Am. J. Physiol. 276: C621–27

14. Hogan DL, Crombie DL, Isenberg JI, Svendsen P, Schaffalitzky de Muckadell OB, et al. 1997. CFTR mediates cAMP- and Ca^{2+}-activated duodenal epithelial HCO_3^- secretion. Am. J. Physiol. 272:G872–78

15. Gelbmann CM, Barrett KE. 1996. In vitro models of epithelial pathophysiology. In Experimental Models of Mucosal Ulceration and Inflammation, ed. TS Gaginella, pp. 111–31. Boca Raton, FL: CRC Press

16. Dharmsathaphorn K, Madara JL. 1990. Established intestinal cell lines as model systems for electrolyte transport studies. In Methods of Enzymology: Biomembranes and Biological Transport, Vol. 5: Cellular and Subcellular Transport: Epithelial Cells, ed. S Fleischer, B Fleischer, pp. 354–89. San Diego: Academic

17. Moseley RH, Hoglund P, Wu GD, Silberg DG, Haila S, et al. 1999. Downregulation in adenoma gene encodes a chloride transporter defective in congenital chloride diarrhea. *Am. J. Physiol.* 276:G185–92

18. Walker MM, Crabtree JE. 1998. *Helicobacter pylori* infection and the pathogenesis of duodenal ulceration. *Ann. NY Acad. Sci.* 859:96–111

19. Madara JL. 1999. Epithelia: biologic principles of organization. See Ref. 201, pp. 141–56

20. Podolsky DK. 1993. Regulation of intestinal epithelial proliferation: a few answers, many questions. *Am. J. Physiol.* 264:G179–86

21. Karam SM. 1999. Lineage commitment and maturation of epithelial cells in the gut. *Front. Biosci.* 4:D286–98

22. Ouellette A. 1997. Paneth cells and innate immunity in the crypt microenvironment. *Gastroenterology* 113:1779–84

23. Welsh MJ, Smith PL, Fromm M, Frizzell RA. 1982. Crypts are the site of intestinal fluid and electrolyte secretion. *Science* 218:1219

24. Kockerling A, Fromm M. 1993. Origin of cAMP-dependent Cl$^-$ secretion from both crypts and surface epithelia of rat intestine. *Am. J. Physiol.* 264:C1294–301

25. Stewart SP, Turnberg LA. 1989. A microelectrode study of reponses to secretagogues by epithelial cells on villus and crypt of rat small intestines. *Am. J. Physiol.* 257:G334

26. Singh SK, Binder HJ, Boron WF, Giebel JP. 1995. Fluid absorption in isolated perfused colonic crypts. *J. Clin. Invest.* 96:2373

27. Strong TV, Boehm K, Collins FS. 1994. Localization of cystic fibrosis transmembrane conductance regulator mRNA in the human gastrointestinal tract by in situ hybridization. *J. Clin. Invest.* 93:347–54

28. Hoogerwerf WA, Tsao SC, Devuyst O, Levine SA, Yun CH, et al. 1996. NHE2 and NHE3 are human and rabbit intestinal brush-border proteins. *Am. J. Physiol.* 270:G29–41

29. Hwang ES, Hirayama BA, Wright EM. 1991. Distribution of the SGLT1 Na$^+$/glucose cotransporter and mRNA along the crypt-villus axis of rabbit small intestine. *Biochem. Biophys. Res. Commun.* 181:1208–17

30. Traber PG, Wang W, Yu L. 1992. Differential regulation of cytochrome P-450 genes along rat intestinal crypt-villus axis. *Am. J. Physiol.* 263:G215–23

31. Anderson JM, Van Itallie CM. 1995. Tight junctions and the molecular basis for regulation of paracellular permeability. *Am. J. Physiol.* 269:G467–75

32. Tsukita S, Furuse M. 1999. Occludin and claudins in tight-junction strands: leading or supporting players? *Trends Cell Biol.* 9:268–73

33. Simon DB, Lu Y, Choate KA, Velazquez H, Al-Sabban E, et al. 1999. Paracellin-1, a renal tight junction protein required for paracellular Mg^{2+} resorption. *Science* 285:103–6

34. Fanning AS, Mitic LL, Anderson JM. 1999. Transmembrane proteins in the tight junction barrier. *J. Am. Soc. Nephrol.* 10:1337–45

35. Yeaman C, Grindstaff KK, Nelson WJ. 1999. New perspectives on mechanisms involved in generating epithelial cell polarity. *Physiol. Rev.* 79:73–98

36. Caplan MJ. 1997. Ion pumps in epithelial cells: sorting, stabilization, and polarity. *Am. J. Physiol.* 272:G1304–13

37. Cunningham SA, Awayda MS, Bubein JK, Ismailov II, Arrate MP, et al. 1995. Cloning of an epithelial chloride channel from bovine trachea. *J. Biol. Chem.* 270:31016–26

38. Gruber AD, Schreur KD, Ji HL, Fuller CM, Pauli BU. 1999. Molecular cloning and transmembrane structure of hCLCA2 from human lung, trachea, and mammary gland. *Am. J. Physiol.* 276:C1261–70

39. Gruber AD, Elble RC, Ji HL, Schreur

KD, Fuller CM, et al. 1998. Genomic cloning, molecular characterization, and functional analysis of human CLCA1, the first human member of the family of Ca^{2+}-activated Cl^- channel proteins. *Genomics* 54:200–14

40. Levine SA, Montrose MH, Tse CM, Donowitz M. 1993. Kinetics and regulation of three cloned mammalian Na^+/H^+ exchangers stably expressed in a fibroblast cell line. *J. Biol. Chem.* 268:25527–35

41. Berger HA, Anderson MP, Gregory RJ, Thompson S, Howard PW, et al. 1991. Identification and regulation of the cystic fibrosis transmembrane conductance regulator-generated chloride channel. *J. Clin. Invest.* 88:1422–31

42. Berger HA, Travis SM, Welsh MJ. 1993. Regulation of the cystic fibrosis transmembrane conductance regulator Cl^- channel by specific protein kinases and protein phosphatases. *J. Biol. Chem.* 268:2037–47

43. Matthews JB, Awtrey CS, Madara JL. 1992. Microfilament-dependent activation of $Na^+/K^+/2Cl^-$ cotransport by cAMP in intestinal epithelial monolayers. *J. Clin. Invest.* 90:1608–13

44. Matthews JB, Smith JA, Nguyen H. 1995. Modulation of intestinal chloride secretion at basolateral transport sites: opposing effects of cyclic adenosine monophosphate and phorbol ester. *Surgery* 118:147–53

45. Bradbury NA, Cohn JA, Venglarik CJ, Bridges RJ. 1994. Biochemical and biophysical identification of cystic fibrosis transmembrane conductance regulator chloride channels as components of endocytic clathrin-coated vesicles. *J. Biol. Chem.* 269:8296–302

46. Howard M, Jilling T, DuVall M, Frizzell RA. 1996. cAMP-regulated trafficking of epitope-tagged CFTR. *Kidney Int.* 49:1642–48

47. Loffing J, Moyer BD, McCoy D, Stanton BA. 1998. Exocytosis is not involved in activation of Cl^- secretion via CFTR in Calu-3 airway epithelial cells. *Am. J. Physiol.* 275:C913–20

48. Guggino WB. 1998. Focus on "Exocytosis is not involved in activation of Cl^- secretion via CFTR in Calu-3 airway epithelial cells." *Am. J. Physiol.* 275: C911–12

49. Binder HJ, McGlone F, Sandle GI. 1989. Effects of corticosteroid hormones on the electrophysiology of rat distal colon: implications for Na^+ and K^+ transport. *J. Physiol.* 410:425–41

50. Rajendran VM, Kashgarian M, Binder HJ. 1989. Aldosterone induction of electrogenic sodium transport in the apical membrane vesicles of rat distal colon. *J. Biol. Chem.* 264:18638–44

51. Turnamian SG, Binder HJ. 1989. Regulation of active sodium and potassium transport in the distal colon of the rat. Role of the aldosterone and glucocorticoid receptors. *J. Clin. Invest.* 84:1924–29

52. Kaplan JH. 1983. Sodium ions and the sodium pump: transport and enzymatic activity. *Am. J. Physiol.* 245:G327–33

53. Kirk KL, Halm DR, Dawson DC. 1980. Active sodium transport by turtle colon via an electrogenic Na-K exchange pump. *Nature* 287:237–39

54. Pressley TA. 1996. Structure and function of the Na,K pump: ten years of molecular biology. *Miner. Electrolyte Metab.* 22:264–71

55. Fuller PJ, Verity K. 1990. Colonic sodium-potassium adenosine triphosphate subunit gene expression: ontogeny and regulation by adrenocortical steroids. *Endocrinology* 127:32–38

56. Danto SI, Borok Z, Zhang XL, Lopez MZ, Patel P, et al. 1998. Mechanisms of EGF-induced stimulation of sodium reabsorption by alveolar epithelial cells. *Am. J. Physiol.* 275:C82–92

57. Payne JA, Forbush B III. 1995. Molecular characterization of the epithelial Na-

K-Cl cotransporter isoforms. *Curr. Opin. Cell Biol.* 7:493–503

58. Isenring P, Jacoby SC, Payne JA, Forbush B III. 1998. Comparison of Na-K-Cl cotransporters. NKCC1, NKCC2, and the HEK cell Na-K-Cl cotransporter. *J. Biol. Chem.* 273:11295–301

59. D'Andrea L, Lytle C, Matthews JB, Hofman P, Forbush B III. 1996. Na:K:2Cl cotransporter (NKCC) of human intestinal epithelial cells. Surface expression in response to cAMP. *J. Biol. Chem.* 271:28969–76

60. Torchia J, Lytle C, Pon DJ, Forbush B, Sen AK. 1992. The Na-K-Cl cotransporter of avian salt gland. Phosphorylation in response to cAMP-dependent and calcium-dependent secretogogues. *J. Biol. Chem.* 267:25444–50

61. Lytle C, Forbush B. 1992. The Na-K-Cl cotransport protein of shark rectal gland. II. Regulation by direct phosphorylation. *J. Biol. Chem.* 267:25438–43

62. Lytle C, Forbush III B. 1996. Regulatory phosphorylation of the secretory Na-K-Cl cotransporter: modulation by cytoplasmic Cl. *Am. J. Physiol.* 270:C437–48

63. Shapiro M, Matthews J, Hecht G, Delp C, Madara JL. 1991. Stabilization of F-actin prevents cAMP-elicited Cl⁻ secretion in T₈₄ cells. *J. Clin. Invest.* 87:1903–9

64. Matthews JB, Smith JA, Hrnjez BJ. 1997. Effects of F-actin stabilization or disassembly on epithelial Cl⁻ secretion and Na-K-2Cl cotransport. *Am. J. Physiol.* 272:C254–62

65. Song JC, Hrnjez BJ, Farokhzah OC, Matthews JB. 1999. Protein kinase Cε selectively regulates basolateral membrane endocytosis in polarized human intestinal epithelia: role of F-actin and MARCKS. *Am. J. Physiol.* In press

66. McRoberts JA, Beuerlein G, Dharmsathaphorn K. 1985. Cyclic AMP and Ca²⁺-activated K⁺ transport in a human colonic epithelial cell line. *J. Biol. Chem.* 260:14163

67. Lomax RB, Warhurst G, Sandle GI. 1996. Characteristics of two basolateral potassium channel populations in human colonic crypts. *Gut* 38:243–47

68. Greger R, Bleich M, Warth R. 1997. New types of K⁺ channels in the colon. *Wien. Klin. Wochenschr.* 109:497–98

69. Jensen BS, Strobaek D, Christophersen P, Jorgensen TD, Hansen C, et al. 1998. Characterization of the cloned human intermediate-conductance Ca²⁺-activated K⁺ channel. *Am. J. Physiol.* 275:C848–56

70. Vandorpe DH, Shmukler BE, Jiang L, Lim B, Maylie J, et al. 1998. cDNA cloning and functional characterization of the mouse Ca²⁺-gated K⁺ channel, mIK1. Roles in regulatory volume decrease and erythroid differentiation. *J. Biol. Chem.* 273:21542–53

71. Ishii TM, Silvia C, Hirschberg B, Bond CT, Adelman JP, et al. 1997. A human intermediate conductance calcium-activated potassium channel. *Proc. Natl. Acad. Sci. USA* 94:11651–56

72. Devor DC, Duffey ME. 1992. Carbachol induces K⁺, Cl⁻, and nonselective cation conductances in T₈₄ cells: a perforated patch-clamp study. *Am. J. Physiol.* 263:C780–87

73. Devor DC, Frizzell RA. 1998. Modulation of K⁺ channels by arachidonic acid in T₈₄ cells. II. Activation of a Ca(²⁺)-independent K⁺ channel. *Am. J. Physiol.* 274:C149–60

74. Barrett KE, Bigby TD. 1993. Involvement of arachidonic acid in the chloride secretory response of intestinal epithelial cells. *Am. J. Physiol.* 264:C446–52

75. Devor DC, Simasko SM, Duffey ME. 1990. Carbachol induces oscillations of membrane potassium conductance in a colonic cell line, T₈₄. *Am. J. Physiol.* 258:G318–26

76. Dharmsathaphorn K, Pandol SJ. 1986. Mechanisms of chloride secretion induced by carbachol in a colonic epithelial cell line. *J. Clin. Invest.* 77:348–54

77. Cartwright CA, McRoberts JA, Mandel KG, Dharmsathaphorn K. 1985. Synergistic action of cyclic adenosine monophosphate- and calcium-mediated secretion in a colonic epithelial cell line. *J. Clin. Invest.* 76:1837–42

78. Vajanaphanich M, Schultz C, Tsien RY, Traynor-Kaplan AE, Pandol SJ, Barrett KE. 1993. Cross-talk between calcium and cAMP-dependent intracellular signalling pathways: implications for synergistic secretion in T$_{84}$ colonic epithelial cells and rat pancreatic acinar cells. *J. Clin. Invest.* 96:386–93

79. Riordan JR, Rommens JM, Kerem B, Alon N, Rozmahel R, et al. 1989. Identification of the cystic fibrosis gene: cloning and characterization of complementary DNA. *Science* 245:1066–73

80. Fuller CM, Benos DJ. 1992. CFTR! *Am. J. Physiol.* 263:C267–86

81. Sheppard DN, Welsh MJ. 1999. Structure and function of the CFTR chloride channel. *Physiol. Rev.* 79:S23–45

82. Welsh MJ, Smith AE. 1993. Molecular mechanisms of CFTR chloride channel dysfunction in cystic fibrosis. *Cell* 73:1251–54

83. Ameen NA, Ardito T, Kashgarian M, Marino CR. 1995. A unique subset of rat and human villus cells express the cystic fibrosis transmembrane conductance regulator. *Gastroenterology* 108:1016–23

84. Singh AK, Tasken K, Walker W, Frizzell RA, Watkins SC, et al. 1998. Characterization of PKA isoforms and kinase-dependent activation of chloride secretion in T$_{84}$ cells. *Am. J. Physiol.* 275:C562–70

85. Picciotto MR, Cohn JA, Bertuzzi G, Greengard P, Nairn AC. 1992. Phosphorylation of the cystic fibrosis transmembrane conductance regulator. *J. Biol. Chem.* 267:12742–52

86. Reddy MM, Quinton PM. 1996. Hydrolytic and nonhydrolytic interactions in the ATP regulation of CFTR Cl$^-$ conductance. *Am. J. Physiol.* 271:C35–42

87. Bell CL, Quinton PM. 1993. Regulation of CFTR Cl$^-$ conductance in secretion by cellular energy levels. *Am. J. Physiol.* 264:C925–31

88. Gadsby DC, Nairn AC. 1999. Regulation of CFTR Cl$^-$ ion channels by phosphorylation and dephosphorylation. *Adv. Second Messenger Phosphoprotein Res.* 33:79–106

89. Gadsby DC, Nairn AC. 1999. Control of CFTR channel gating by phosphorylation and nucleotide hydrolysis. *Physiol. Rev.* 79:S77–107

90. Wilkinson DJ, Strong TV, Mansoura MK, Wood DL, Smith SS, et al. 1997. CFTR activation: additive effects of stimulatory and inhibitory phosphorylation sites in the R domain. *Am. J. Physiol.* 273:L127–33

91. Luo J, Pato MD, Riordan JR, Hanrahan JW. 1998. Differential regulation of single CFTR channels by PP2C, PP2A, and other phosphatases. *Am. J. Physiol.* 274:C1397–410

92. Travis SM, Berger HA, Welsh MJ. 1997. Protein phosphatase 2C dephosphorylates and inactivates cystic fibrosis transmembrane conductance regulator. *Proc. Natl. Acad. Sci. USA* 94:11055–60

93. Jilling T, Kirk KL. 1997. The biogenesis, traffic, and function of the cystic fibrosis transmembrane conductance regulator. *Int. Rev. Cytol.* 192:193–241

94. Naren AP, Nelson DJ, Xie W, Jovov B, Pevsner J, et al. 1997. Regulation of CFTR chloride channels by syntaxin and Munc18 isoforms. *Nature* 390:302–5

95. Liedtke CM, Cole TS. 1998. Antisense oligonucleotide to PKC-epsilon alters cAMP-dependent stimulation of CFTR in Calu-3 cells. *Am. J. Physiol.* 275:C1357–64

96. Jia Y, Mathews CJ, Hanrahan JW. 1997. Phosphorylation by protein kinase C is required for acute activation of cystic fibrosis transmembrane conductance reg-

ulator by protein kinase A. *J. Biol. Chem.* 272:4978–84

97. Yurko-Mauro KA, Reenstra WW. 1998. Prostaglandin F2–alpha stimulates CFTR activity by PKA- and PKC-dependent phosphorylation. *Am. J. Physiol.* 275:C653–60

98. Fischer H, Machen TE. 1996. The tyrosine kinase p60[c-Src] regulates the fast gate of the cystic fibrosis transmembrane conductance regulator chloride channel. *Biophys. J.* 71:3073–82

99. Prince LS, Peter K, Hatton SR, Zaliauskiene L, Cotlin LF, et al. 1999. Efficient endocytosis of the cystic fibrosis transmembrane conductance regulator requires a tyrosine-based signal. *J. Biol. Chem.* 274:3602–9

100. French PJ, Bijman J, Edixhoven M, Vaandrager AB, Scholte BJ, et al. 1995. Isotype-specific activation of cystic fibrosis transmembrane conductance regulator-chloride channels by cGMP-dependent protein kinase II. *J. Biol. Chem.* 270:26626–31

101. Vaandrager AB, Smolenski A, Tilly BC, Houtsmuller AB, Ehlert EM, et al. 1998. Membrane targeting of cGMP-dependent protein kinase is required for cystic fibrosis transmembrane conductance regulator Cl⁻ channel activation. *Proc. Natl. Acad. Sci. USA* 95:1466–71

102. Forte LR, Thorne PK, Eber SL, Krause WJ, Freeman RH, et al. 1992. Stimulation of intestinal Cl⁻ transport by heat-stable enterotoxin: activation of cAMP-dependent protein kinase by cGMP. *Am. J. Physiol.* 263:C607–15

103. Anderson MP, Sheppard DN, Berger HA, Welsh MJ. 1992. Chloride channels in the apical membrane of normal and cystic fibrosis airway and intestinal epithelia. *Am. J. Physiol.* 263:L1–14

104. Morris AP, Cunningham SA, Benos DJ, Frizzell RA. 1992. Cellular differentiation is required for cAMP but not Ca^{2+}-dependent Cl⁻ secretion in colonic epithelial cells expressing high

levels of cystic fibrosis transmembrane conductance regulator. *J. Biol. Chem.* 267:5575–83

105. Berschneider HM, Knowles MR, Azizkhan RG, Boucher RC, Tobey NA, et al. 1988. Altered intestinal chloride transport in cystic fibrosis. *FASEB J.* 2:2625–29

106. McEwan GTA, Hirst BH, Simmons NL. 1994. Carbachol stimulates Cl⁻ secretion via activation of two distinct apical Cl⁻ pathways in cultured human T_{84} intestinal epithelial monolayers. *Biochem. Biophys. Acta* 1220:241–47

107. Merlin D, Jiang L, Strohmeier GR, Nusrat A, Alper SL, et al. 1998. Distinct Ca^{2+}- and cAMP-dependent anion conductances in the apical membrane of polarized T_{84} cells. *Am. J. Physiol.* 275:C484–95

108. Wagner JA, McDonald TV, Nghiem PT, Lowe AW, Schulman H, et al. 1992. Antisense oligodeoxynucleotides to the cystic fibrosis transmembrane conductance regulator inhibit cAMP-activated but not calcium-activated chloride currents. *Proc. Natl. Acad. Sci. USA* 89:6785–89

109. Rozmahel R, Wilchanski M, Matin A, Plyte S, Oliver M, et al. 1996. Modulation of disease severity in cystic fibrosis transmembrane conductance regulator deficient mice by a secondary genetic factor. *Nat. Genet.* 12:280–87

110. Fuller CM, Ismailov II, Keeton DA, Benos DJ. 1994. Phosphorylation and activation of a bovine tracheal ion channel by Ca^{2+}/calmodulin-dependent protein kinase II. *J. Biol. Chem.* 269:26642–50

111. Ismailov II, Fuller CM, Berdiev BK, Shlyonsky VG, Benos DJ, et al. 1996. A biologic function for an "orphan" messenger: D-myo-inositol (3,4,5,6) tetrakis-phosphate selectively blocks epithelial calcium-activated chloride channels. *Proc. Natl. Acad. Sci. USA* 93:10505–9

112. Ling BN, Webster CL, Eaton DC. 1992.

Eicosanoids modulate apical Ca^{2+}-dependent K^+ channels in cultured rabbit principal cells. *Am. J. Physiol.* 263:F116–26

113. Bell CL, Quinton PM. 1992. T_{84} cells: anion selectivity demonstrates expression of Cl^- conductance affected in cystic fibrosis. *Am. J. Physiol.* 262:C555–62

114. Barrett KE. 1988. Immune-related intestinal secretion: control of colonic chloride secretion by inflammatory mediators. In *Inflammatory Bowel Disease: Current Status and Future Approach,* ed. RP MacDermott, pp. 377–82. Amsterdam: Elsevier

115. Barrett KE. 1993. Positive and negative regulation of chloride secretion in T_{84} cells. *Am. J. Physiol.* 265:C859–68

116. Gelbmann CM, Schteingart CD, Thompson SM, Hofmann AF, Barrett KE. 1995. Mast cells and histamine contribute to bile-acid stimulated secretion in the mouse colon. *J. Clin. Invest.* 95:2831–39

117. Uribe JM, Barrett KE. 1997. Non-mitogenic actions of growth factors: an integrated view of their role in intestinal physiology and pathophysiology. *Gastroenterology* 112:255–68

118. Suemori S, Ciacci C, Podolsky DK. 1987. Regulation of transforming growth factor expression in rat intestinal epithelial cell lines. *J. Clin. Invest.* 87:2216–21

119. Castagliuolo I, LaMont JT, Letourneau R, Kelly C, O'Keane JC, et al. 1994. Neuronal involvement in the intestinal effects of *Clostridium difficile* toxin A and *Vibrio cholerae* enterotoxin in rat ileum. *Gastroenterology* 107:657–65

120. Perdue MH, McKay DM. 1994. Integrative immunophysiology in the intestinal mucosa. *Am. J. Physiol.* 267:G151–65

121. Bern MJ, Sturbaum CW, Karayalcin SS, Berschneider HM, Wachsman JT, et al. 1989. Immune system control of rat and rabbit colonic electrolyte transport. Role of prostaglandins and enteric nervous system. *J. Clin. Invest.* 83:1810–20

122. Berschneider HM, Powell DW. 1992. Fibroblasts modulate intestinal secretory responses to inflammatory mediators. *J. Clin. Invest.* 89:484–89

123. Valentich JD, Powell DW. 1994. Intestinal subepithelial myofibroblasts and mucosal immunophysiology. *Curr. Opin. Gastroenterol.* 10:645–51

124. Barrett KE, Dharmsathaphorn K. 1991. Secretion and absorption: small intestine and colon. In *Textbook of Gastroenterology,* ed. T Yamada, pp. 265–94. Philadelphia: Lippincott

125. Vajanaphanich M, Schultz C, Tsien RY, Traynor-Kaplan AE, Pandol SJ, et al. 1995. Cross-talk between calcium and cAMP-dependent intracellular signalling pathways: implications for synergistic secretion in T_{84} colonic epithelial cells and rat pancreatic acinar cells. *J. Clin. Invest.* 96:386–93

126. Barrett KE. 1997. Integrated regulation of intestinal epithelial transport: intercellular and intracellular pathways. 1996 Bowditch Lecture. *Am. J. Physiol.* 272: C1069–76

127. Frieling T, Dobreva G, Weber E, Becker K, Rupprecht C, et al. 1999. Different tachykinin receptors mediate chloride secretion in the distal colon through activation of submucosal neurones. Naunyn-Schmiedebergs *Arch. Pharmacol.* 359: 71–79

128. Wershil BK, Castagliuolo I, Pothoulakis C. 1998. Direct evidence of mast cell involvement in *Clostridium difficile* toxin A-induced enteritis in mice. *Gastroenterology* 114:956–64

129. McKay DM, Perdue MH. 1993. Intestinal epithelial function: The case for immunophysiological regulation. Implications for disease (second of two parts), *Dig. Dis. Sci.* 38:1735–45

130. McKay DM, Perdue MH. 1993. Intestinal epithelial function: the case for immunophysiological regulation. Cells and mediators (first of two parts). *Dig. Dis. Sci.* 38:1377–87

131. Wasserman SI, Barrett KE, Huott PA,

Beuerlein G, Kagnoff M, et al. 1988. Immune-related intestinal Cl⁻ secretion. I. Effect of histamine on the T_{84} cell line. *Am. J. Physiol.* 254:C53–62

132. Kachintorn U, Vajanaphanich M, Barrett KE, Traynor-Kaplan AE. 1993. Elevation of inositol tetrakisphosphate parallels inhibition of calcium-dependent chloride secretion in T_{84} colonic epithelial cells. *Am. J. Physiol.* 264:C671–76

133. Wang YZ, Cooke HJ. 1990. H2 receptors mediate cyclical chloride secretion in guinea pig distal colon. *Am. J. Physiol.* 258:G887–93

134. Keely SJ, Stack WA, O'Donoghue DP, Baird AW. 1995. Regulation of ion transport by histamine in human colon. *Eur. J. Pharmacol.* 279:203–9

135. Barrett KE, Cohn JA, Huott PA, Wasserman SI, Dharmsathaphorn K. 1990. Immune-related intestinal chloride secretion. II. Effect of adenosine on T_{84} cell line. *Am. J. Physiol.* 258:C902–12

136. Barrett KE, Huott PA, Shah SS, Dharmsathaphorn K, Wasserman SI. 1989. Differing effects of apical and basolateral adenosine on the colonic epithelial cell line, T_{84}. *Am. J. Physiol.* 256:C197–203

137. Strohmeier GR, Reppert SM, Lencer WI, Madara JL. 1995. The A_{2b} adenosine receptor mediates cAMP responses to adenosine receptor agonists in human intestinal epithelia. *J. Biol. Chem.* 270:2387–94

138. Madara JL, Patapoff TW, Gillece-Castro B, Colgan S, Parkos C, et al. 1993. 5'-AMP is the neutrophil derived paracrine factor that elicits chloride secretion from T_{84} intestinal epithelial cell monolayers. *J. Clin. Invest.* 91:2320–25

139. Weymer A, Huott P, Liu W, McRoberts JA, Dharmsathaphorn K. 1985. Chloride secretory mechanism induced by prostaglandin E₁ in a colonic epithelial cell line. *J. Clin. Invest.* 76:1828–36

140. Ding M, Kinoshita Y, Kishi K, Nakata H, Hassan S, et al. 1997. Distribution of prostaglandin E receptors in the rat gastrointestinal tract. *Prostaglandins* 53:199–216

141. Raybould HE, Pandol SJ. 1999. The integrated response of the gastrointestinal tract to a meal. See Ref. 201, pp. 2–10

142. Forte LR, Hamra FK. 1996. Guanylin and uroguanylin: intestinal peptide hormones that regulate epithelial transport. *News Physiol. Sci.* 11:17–24

143. Brown DR. 1996. Mucosal protection through active intestinal secretion: neural and paracrine modulation by 5-hydroxytryptamine. *Behav. Brain Res.* 73:193–97

144. Currie MG, Fok KF, Kato J, Moore RJ, Hamra FK, et al. 1992. Guanylin: an endogenous activator of intestinal guanylate cyclase. *Proc. Natl. Acad. Sci. USA* 89:947–51

145. Forte LR, Eber SL, Turner JT, Freeman RH, Fok KF, et al. 1993. Guanylin stimulation of Cl⁻ secretion in human intestinal T_{84} cells via cyclic guanosine monophosphate. *J. Clin. Invest.* 91:2423–28

146. Huott PA, Liu W, McRoberts GA, Giannella RA, Dharmsathaphorn K. 1988. The mechanism of *E. coli* heat stable enterotoxin in a human colonic cell. *J. Clin. Invest.* 82:514–23

147. Li Z, Knowles JW, Goyeau D, Prabakhar S, Short DB, et al. 1996. Low salt intake down-regulates the guanylin signaling pathway in rat distal colon. *Gastroenterology* 111:1714–21

148. Lencer WI, Moe S, Rufo PA, Madara JL. 1995. Transcytosis of cholera toxin subunits across model human intestinal epithelia. *Proc. Natl. Acad. Sci. USA* 92:10094–98

149. Jodal M, Lundgren O. 1995. Neural reflex modulation of intestinal epithelial transport. In *Regulatory Mechanisms in Gastrointestinal Function*, ed. TS Gaginella, pp. 99–144. Boca Raton, FL: CRC Press

150. Turvill JL, Mourad FH, Farthing MJG. 1998. Crucial role for 5-HT in cholera toxin but not *Escherichia coli* heat-labile

enterotoxin-intestinal secretion in rats. *Gastroenterology* 115:883–90

151. Bishai WR, Sears CL. 1993. Food poisoning syndromes. *Gastroenterol. Clin. N. Am.* 22:579–608

152. Cohen MB, Jensen NJ, Hawkins JA, Mann EA, Thompson MR, et al. 1993. Receptors for *Escherichia coli* heat-stable enterotoxin in human intestine and in a human intestinal cell line (Caco-2). *J. Cell. Physiol.* 156:138–44

153. Carpick BW, Gariepy J. 1993. The *Escherichia coli* heat-stable enterotoxin is a long-lived superagonist of guanylin. *Infect. Immun.* 61:4710–15

154. Hecht G, Pothoulakis C, LaMont JT, Madara JL. 1988. *Clostridium difficile* toxin A perturbs cytoskeletal structure and tight junction permeability of cultured human intestinal epithelial monolayers. *J. Clin. Invest.* 82:1516–24

155. Nusrat A, Giry M, Turner JR, Colgan SP, Parkos CA, et al. 1995. Rho protein regulates tight junctions and perijunctional actin organization in polarized epithelia. *Proc. Natl. Acad. Sci. USA* 92:10629–33

156. Dillon ST, Rubin EJ, Yakubovich M, Pothoulakis C, LaMont JT, et al. 1995. Involvement of Ras-related Rho proteins in the mechanisms of action of *Clostridium difficile* toxin A and toxin B. *Infect. Immun.* 63:1421–26

157. Eckmann L, Kagnoff MF, Fierer J. 1993. Epithelial cells secrete the chemokine interleukin-8 in response to bacterial entry. *Infect. Immun.* 61:4569–74

158. Jung HC, Eckmann L, Yang SK, Panja A, Fierer J, et al. 1995. A distinct pattern of proinflammatory cytokines is expressed in human colon epithelial cells in response to bacterial invasion. *J. Clin. Invest.* 95:55–65

159. McCormick BA, Parkos CA, Colgan SP, Carnes DK, Madara JL. 1998. Apical secretion of a pathogen-elicited epithelial chemoattractant activity in response to surface colonization of intestinal epithelia by *Salmonella typhimurium*. *Infect. Immun.* 160:455–66

160. Eckmann L, Stenson WF, Savidge TC, Lowe DC, Barrett KE, et al. 1997. Role of intestinal epithelial cells in the host secretory response to infection by invasive bacteria. Bacterial entry induces epithelial prostaglandin H synthase-2 expression and prostaglandin E_2 and F_{2alpha} production. *J. Clin. Invest.* 100: 296–309

161. Marrero JA, Matkowskyi KA, Danilovich A, Koutsouris A, Hecht G, et al. 1999. *Salmonella* infection causes increased fluid secretion in mouse colon by activating NF-κB and increasing galanin-1 receptor (GAL1R) expression. *Gastroenterology* 116:A860 (Abstr.)

162. Benya RV, Marrero JA, Ostrovskiy DA, Koutsouris A, Hecht G. 1999. Human colonic epithelial cells express galanin-1 receptors, which when activated cause Cl^- secretion. *Am. J. Physiol.* 276:G64–72

163. Moseley RH. 1999. Bile secretion. See Ref. 201, pp. 380–403

164. Dharmsathaphorn K, Huott PA, Vongkovit P, Beuerlein G, Pandol S, et al. 1989. Cl^- secretion induced by bile salts. A study of the mechanism of action based on a cultured colonic epithelial cell line. *J. Clin. Invest.* 84:945–53

165. Quist RG, Ton-Nu H-T, Lillienau J, Hofmann AF, Barrett KE. 1991. Activation of mast cells by bile acids. *Gastroenterology* 101:446–56

166. Jodal M. 1990. Neuronal influence on intestinal transport. *J. Intern. Med. Suppl.* 732:125–32

167. Levitt DG, Bond JH, Levitt MD. 1980. Use of a model of small bowel mucosa to predict passive absorption. *Am. J. Physiol.* 239:G23

168. Warhurst G, Barbezat GO, Higgs NB, Reyl-Desmars F, Lewin MJM, et al. 1995. Expression of somatostatin receptor genes and their role in inhibiting Cl^-

secretion in HT-29cl.19A colonocytes. *Am. J. Physiol.* 269:G729–36

169. Warhurst G, Higgs NB, Fakhoury H, Warhurst AC, Garde J, et al. 1996. Somatostatin receptor subtype 2 mediates somatostatin inhibition of ion secretion in rat distal colon. *Gastroenterology* 111:325–33

170. McKeen ES, Feniuk W, Humphrey PP. 1995. Somatostatin receptors mediating inhibition of basal and stimulated electrogenic ion transport in rat isolated distal colonic mucosa. Naunyn-Schmiedebergs *Arch. Pharmacol.* 352:402–11

171. Warhurst G, Turnberg LA, Higgs NB, Tonge A, Grundy J, et al. 1993. Multiple G-protein-dependent pathways mediate the antisecretory effects of somatostatin and clonidine in the HT29–19A colonic cell line. *J. Clin. Invest.* 92:603–11

172. Gaginella TS, O'Dorisio TM, Fassler JE, Mekhjian HS. 1990. Treatment of endocrine and nonendocrine secretory diarrheal states with sandostatin. *Metab. Clin. Exp. 39. Suppl.* 2:172–75

173. Playford RJ, Cox HM. 1996. Peptide YY and neuropeptide Y: two peptides intimately involved in electrolyte homeostasis. *Trends Pharmacol. Sci.* 17:436–38

174. Palmiter RD, Erickson JC, Hollopeter G, Baraban SC, Schwartz MW. 1998. Life without neuropeptide Y. *Rec. Progr. Horm. Res.* 53:163–99

175. Strabel D, Diener M. 1995. The effect of neuropeptide Y on sodium, chloride and potassium transport across the rat distal colon. *Br. J. Pharmacol.* 115:1071–79

176. Bouritius H, Oprins JC, Bindels RJ, Hartog A, Groot JA. 1998. Neuropeptide Y inhibits ion secretion in intestinal epithelium by reducing chloride and potassium conductance. *Pflügers Arch.* 435:219–26

177. Eto B, Boisset M, Anini Y, Voisin T, Desjeux JF. 1997. Comparison of the antisecretory effect of endogenous forms of peptide YY on fed and fasted rat jejunum. *Peptides* 18:1249–55

178. Eto B, Boisset M, Eden P, Balasubramaniam A, Desjeux JF. 1995. Effects of peptide YY and its analogues on chloride ion secretion in fed and fasted rat jejunum. *Peptides* 16:1403–9

179. Uribe JM, Gelbmann CM, Traynor-Kaplan AE, Barrett KE. 1996. Epidermal growth factor inhibits calcium-dependent chloride secretion in T$_{84}$ human colonic epithelial cells. *Am. J. Physiol.* 271: C914–22

180. Uribe JM, Keely SJ, Traynor-Kaplan AE, Barrett KE. 1996. Phosphatidylinositol 3-kinase mediates the inhibitory effect of epidermal growth factor on calcium-dependent chloride secretion. *J. Biol. Chem.* 271:26588–95

181. Barrett KE, Smitham J, Traynor-Kaplan AE, Uribe JM. 1998. Inhibition of Ca^{2+} dependent Cl$^-$ secretion in T$_{84}$ cells: membrane target(s) of inhibition are agonist-specific. *Am. J. Physiol.* 274:C958–65

182. Keely SJ, Barrett KE. 1999. ErbB2 and ErbB3 receptors mediate inhibition of calcium-dependent chloride secretion in colonic epithelial cells. *J. Biol. Chem.* In press

183. Chang N, Uribe JM, Barrett KE. 1996. Inhibition of calcium-dependent chloride secretion by insulin and insulin-like growth factor. *Gastroenterology* 110: A317 (Abstr.)

184. Playford RJ, Hanby AM, Gschmeissner S, Peiffer LP, Wright NA, et al. 1996. The epidermal growth factor receptor (EGF-R) is present on the basolateral, but not the apical, surface of enterocytes in the human gastrointestinal tract. *Gut* 39: 262–66

185. Keely SJ, Uribe JM, Barrett KE. 1998. Carbachol stimulates transactivation of epidermal growth factor receptor and MAP kinase in T$_{84}$ cells: implications for carbachol-stimulated chloride secretion. *J. Biol. Chem.* 273:27111–17

186. Toker A, Cantley LC. 1997. Signalling through the lipid products of phospho-

inositide-3-OH kinase. *Nature* 387:673–76

187. Vajanaphanich M, Schultz C, Rudolf MT, Wasserman M, Enyedi P, et al. 1994. Long-term uncoupling of chloride secretion from intracellular calcium levels by Ins(3,4,5,6)P$_4$. *Nature* 371:711–14

188. Xie W, Kaetzel MA, Bruzik KS, Dedman JR, Shears SB, et al. 1996. Inositol 3,4,5,6 tetrakisphosphate inhibits the calmodulin-dependent protein kinase II-activated chloride conductance in T$_{84}$ cells. *J. Biol. Chem.* 271:14092–97

189. Ho MW, Shears SB, Bruzik KS, Duszyk M, French AS. 1997. Ins(3,4,5,6)P$_4$ specifically inhibits a receptor-mediated Ca^{2+}-dependent Cl$^-$ current in CFPAC-1 cells. *Am. J. Physiol.* 272:C1160–68

190. Xie W, Solomons KR, Freeman S, Kaetzel MA, Bruzik KS, et al. 1998. Regulation of Ca^{2+}-dependent Cl$^-$ conductance in a human colonic epithelial cell line (T$_{84}$): cross-talk between Ins(3,4,5,6)P$_4$ and protein phosphatases. *J. Physiol.* 510:661–73

191. Blumenthal JAS, Onorato JJ, Carey HV. 1998. Muscarinic inhibition of substance P induced ion secretion in piglet jejunum. *Can. J. Physiol. Pharmacol.* 76:169–75

192. Smitham JE, Barrett KE. 1998. Differential effects of uridine triphosphate on intestinal chloride secretion depending on the side of addition: implications for cystic fibrosis therapy. *Gastroenterology* 114:A417 (Abstr.)

193. Parr CE, Sullivan DM, Paradiso AM, Lazarowski ER, Burch LH, et al. 1994. Cloning and expression of a human P$_{2U}$ nucleotide receptor, a target for cystic fibrosis pharmacotherapy. *Proc. Natl. Acad. Sci. USA* 91:3275–79

194. Keely SJ, Barrett KE. 1999. Carbachol stimulates p60^{src} in T$_{84}$ epithelial cells: implications for carbachol-stimulated chloride secretion. *Gastroenterology* 116:A859 (Abstr.)

195. Keely SJ, Calandrella SO, Barrett KE. 1999. Elevations in intracellular calcium are sufficient to evoke antisecretory signaling via the epidermal growth factor receptor and ERK in T$_{84}$ cells. *Gastroenterology* 116:A858 (Abstr.)

196. Deleted in proof

197. Barrett KE, Dharmsathaphorn K. 1991. Pharmacological approaches to the therapy of diarrheal diseases. In *Diarrheal Diseases,* ed. M Field, pp. 501–15. New York: Elsevier

198. Frizzell RA. 1993. The molecular physiology of cystic fibrosis. *News Physiol. Sci.* 8:117–20

199. Scheich AM, Grand RJ. 1999. Disorders of epithelial transport in the small intestine. See Ref. 201, pp. 1677–96

200. Cohn JA, Friedman KJ, Noone PG, Knowles MR, Silverman LM, et al. 1998. Relation between mutations of the cystic fibrosis gene and idiopathic pancreatitis. *N. Engl. J. Med.* 339:653–58

201. Yamada T, Alpers DH, Laine L, Owyang C, Powell DW, eds. 1999. *Textbook of Gastroenterology, 3rd ed.* Philadelphia: Lippincott, Williams & Wilkins

Annu. Rev. Physiol. 2000. 62:573–94

Structure and Regulation of Amiloride-Sensitive Sodium Channels

Diego Alvarez de la Rosa, Cecilia M. Canessa, Gregor K. Fyfe, and Ping Zhang

Department of Cellular and Molecular Physiology, Yale University School of Medicine, 333 Cedar Street, New Haven, Connecticut, 06520–8026; e-mail: cecilia.canessa@yale.edu

Key Words   ENaC, ASIC, DRASIC, BNaC, degenerins, sodium reabsorption, Liddle's syndrome

■ **Abstract**   Amiloride-sensitive Na^+ channels constitute a new class of proteins known as the ENaC-Deg family of ion channels. All members in this family share a common protein structure but differ in their ion selectivity, their affinity for the blocker amiloride, and in their gating mechanisms. These channels are expressed in many tissues of invertebrate and vertebrate organisms where they serve diverse functions varying from Na^+ absorption across epithelia to being the receptors for neurotransmitters in the nervous system. Here, we review progress made during the last years in the characterization, regulation, and cloning of new amiloride-sensitive Na^+ channels.

INTRODUCTION

The name of the ENaC-Deg family derives from the first two members of this family of ion channels: the epithelial Na^+ channel (ENaC) and the degenerins (Deg). In the early 1990s, Chalfie et al described a group of genes in *Caenorhabtidis elegans* that when mutated induced degeneration of a set of specific neurons involved in touch perception, hence the name degenerins (Mec-4, Mec-10, and Deg-1) (1–3). The phenotype induced by the mutated degenerins suggested that they were ion channels, although they did not share homology with any of the families of channels then known. More recently, many other members have been added to this rapidly expanding family of proteins from vertebrates and invertebrates. The newly described channels are expressed in non-epithelial tissues, mainly in neurons but also in other cell types, suggesting that they participate in a variety of functions.

ENaC is the prototype and the best characterized channel in the ENaC-Deg superfamily of ion channels. Although sodium channels in epithelia were identified and functionally characterized many years ago, initially using the short-

0066–4278/00/0315–0573$12.00

circuit current technique of Ussing and later with noise analysis and patch clamp techniques, their molecular structure is a recent discovery. The structure was elucidated by expression cloning and functional complementation in *Xenopus* oocytes using mRNA extracted from rat distal colon (4–6). Three homologous subunits were identified, α, β, and γ, that together form functional channels. Since then, ENaC has been cloned from many other species including human (7), chicken (8), bovine (9), and frog (10).

Epithelial sodium channels mediate Na^+ absorption in most epithelia with high electrical resistance. ENaC is expressed at the apical surface of cells lining the cortical and collecting tubules of the kidney, the distal colon, ducts of secretory glands, the respiratory airways, and in amphibian skin (11, 12). Na^+ channels are directly involved in the maintenance of extracellular volume and blood pressure, and indirectly in the homeostasis of K^+ and H^+ ions. The reabsorption of Na^+ in the cortical collecting tubule generates a lumen-negative potential that facilitates the secretion of K^+ and H^+ by the distal nephron. Blocking ENaC with amiloride or inactivation by mutations in the channel protein leads to Na^+ wasting, hyperkalemia, and metabolic acidosis. Many regulatory mechanisms such as the renin-angiotensin-aldosterone axis, antidiuretic hormone, and catecholamines modulate the activity of ENaC channels (13). The importance of ENaC in sodium homeostasis is not restricted to the conservation of total body sodium; ENaC also plays a crucial role in the intake of salt. Humans, and mammals in general, pursue and enjoy the taste of salt in food. The sensory transduction of salty taste is also mediated by ENaC channels expressed in the fungiform papillae located in the dorsal epithelium of the anterior tongue (14). Moreover, modifications of salt taste acuity are mediated by many of the hormones and dietary changes that regulate ENaC in the kidney.

Sodium channels are expressed all along the respiratory tract, from the epithelium of the nose to the alveoli (15). In the lung, ENaC activity is necessary for fluid handling, in particular at birth, when the transition from a liquid-filled to air-filled lung occurs (16, 17). Consistent with the importance of ENaC function in the reabsorption of fluid from the airways, the levels of expression of the subunits are markedly increased in the fetal lung at the end of gestation (18).

The composition of the fluid produced by secretory organs such as salivary glands, sweat glands, and pancreas is also modified by ENaC channels located along the secretory ducts that reabsorp most of the luminal sodium. Aldosterone in these tissues also stimulates the activity of ENaC to enhance Na^+ retention.

In amphibia, the skin plays an important role in the absorption of sodium and maintenance of extracellular volume. The abundance of Na^+ channels in the amphibian skin made it a useful model for studying the properties of ENaC for many years. In contrast, mammalian skin does not have vectorial transport activity; however, the epidermis expresses high levels of the three subunits of ENaC channels. The functional role of ENaC channels in the epidermis remains unclear (19).

MOLECULAR STRUCTURE OF ENaC CHANNELS

ENaC channels are heteromultimeric proteins formed by the association of three homologous subunits: α, β, and γ. α subunits alone can generate channels, but β or γ subunits cannot form functional channels by themselves. Nonetheless, they impart specific properties to the hetero-oligomeric complex. For instance, α in combination with either β or γ forms channels with distinct affinities for the blocker amiloride, distinct single channel kinetics, and ion selectivity, indicating that different combinations of subunits allow functional diversity (20, 21). The ability to form heteromultimeric channels with unique functional properties is also observed with the neuronal members of the family as we discuss further below.

The subunits of ENaC are glycoproteins of 60 to 75 kDa. The hydropathy profile of the amino acid sequence, gene fusion experiments, identification of glycosylation sites (22, 23), and partial proteolysis (24) have confirmed a simple structure characterized by two transmembrane segments, a large extracellular domain with multiple N-glycosylation sites, and the amino and carboxytermini in the cytoplasmic side.

The Ion Pathway

Much work has been devoted to elucidate the domains in the subunits that participate in forming the ion pathway. Several lines of evidence indicate that the properties of the channel pore are conferred by the second hydrophobic domain. This region is highly conserved among even the most distant members of the ENaC-Deg family from *C. elegans* to human. It includes a typical α-helix, long enough to traverse the plasma membrane, and a less structured segment of hydrophobic residues preceding the α-helix that has been postulated to form a hairpin similar to the pore region of K^+ channels (P region). The segment has been extensively examined by mutagenesis of all of its residues (24–27). The main conclusions derived from these studies are that residues in the second hydrophobic domain from all three subunits affect the amiloride affinity and ion selectivity.

As is the case for many channel blockers, characterization of the kinetics of block at the single channel level is a powerful tool to probe the nature of the ion pore. Experimental results supporting the notion that amiloride blocks the outer pore include the voltage dependence of block, the k_{on} increases, and k_{off} decreases linearly at hyperpolarizing membrane voltages. Analysis of the voltage-dependence indicates that amiloride senses 20% of the membrane electrical field (21, 28). Therefore, residues in the initial segment of the second hydrophobic domain must be located within the membrane electrical field. Another result that speaks in favor of amiloride blocking the mouth of the pore is that the affinity for amiloride decreases by increasing concentrations of extracellular Na^+, indicating a competitive interaction between transported Na^+ ions and amiloride. In addition, some of the mutations in the initial part of the second hydrphobic domain that affect amiloride K_i also decrease the single channel conductance (26).

Other parts of the protein may also participate in amiloride binding. The region in the α subunit, made up of residues 278–283 (WYRFHY), has been identified as part of the amiloride-binding site. Kieber-Emmons et al developed an antibody that recognizes the amiloride molecule (29). The structure of the variable region of this antibody was elucidated and thought to be analogous to the amiloride-binding site in the channel protein, making possible the identification of the six-amino acid domain in αENaC. Deletion of these residues changed the K_i for amiloride to 26.5 μM (30). Because the amiloride molecule is composed of two modules, a pyrazine ring and a guanidinium moiety, it is possible that the M2 contributes to the guanidinium site, whereas the extracellular domain of α participates in the binding of the pyrazine ring.

ENaC is highly selective for Na^+ and with the exception of Li^+ (Li^+/Na^+:1.5/1.0), which is more permeant than Na^+, no other monovalent cations permeate the channel. Mutagenesis of residues in the second hydrophobic domain (αS589D in the rat cDNA sequence) markedly alters the selectivity, making the channels permeable to K^+ and even to divalent cations such as Ca^{2+} (27).

A model consistent with all the data is depicted in Figure 1. The channel is predicted to have a narrow pore formed by the initial segment of the second hydrophobic domain of all subunits. It is more likely that the backbone and not

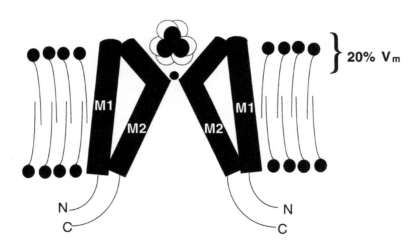

Figure 1 Model of ENaC channels. The subunits have two transmembrane domains with the amino and carboxy termini in the cytoplasmic side. The second hydrophobic domain from each subunit participates in the ion pathway. Only two subunits are shown. The entrance of the pore can accomodate the guanidinium group of amiloride that penetrates 20% of the transmembrane electrical field. The pore becomes narrow such that only dehydrated Na^+ and Li^+ ions can permeate. Position S589 in the α subunit may correspond to the narrowest region.

the side chains of the residues are facing the lumen of the pore (31). The guanidinium moiety of amiloride can penetrate the entrance of the pore and block the channel. The only permeant ions are small monovalent cations that interact with the walls of the initial segment of the second hydrophobic domain to strip the water of hydration. No negatively charged residues participate in attracting or binding of ions to the entrance of the pore. The narrowest region of the ion pathway may be located at the level of residues S589 in the α subunits (27). Selectivity is achieved by exclusion of ions by size after removal of the hydration water. This model is similar to the original one proposed by Palmer prior to the cloning of ENaC (32).

Stoichiometry and Subunit Composition

Several recent papers have addressed the important issue of subunit composition and stoichiometry of ENaC and related channels. Not all groups agree on the number of subunits that form functional channels. Some propose that there are four subunits arranged around a central pore (33, 34), whereas others contend that ENaC is a much larger complex formed by nine subunits (35).

Firsov et al (33) used several lines of evidence to determine the subunit composition of ENaC channels. They expressed subunits tagged in the extracellular domain with an epitope that could be recognized by a radioiodinated monoclonal antibody specific for the epitope. Oocytes injected with $\alpha\beta\gamma^F$ or $\alpha\beta^F\gamma$ (F stands for FLAG epitope) bound the same number of antibodies, but this number doubled with injection of $\alpha\beta^F\gamma^F$ or when oocytes were injected with $\alpha^F\beta\gamma$. These results suggest that channels have an equal number of β and γ subunits and twice the number of α subunits; the most likely stoichiometry would be $\alpha_2\beta_1\gamma_1$.

The number of subunits in ENaC channels has been calculated using mutants with lower affinity to amiloride than the wild-type channel (αS583C, βG525C, and γG542C). Injection into oocytes of varying ratios of wild-type and mutant cRNAs results in the expression of two populations of channels, one with amiloride sensitivity equal to wild-type channels and the other with low sensitivity to amiloride. The proportion of channels that are sensitive or resistant to amiloride can be correlated to the ratio of cRNA injected for the wild-type and mutant subunits by applying an analysis originally used by MacKinnon to calculate the stoichiometry of the Shaker K^+ channel (for details of the analysis see reference 36). Two groups working independently used this experimental approach and arrived at the conclusion that ENaC is a tetrameric channel $\alpha_2\beta_1\gamma_1$ (33, 34).

In contrast, Snyder et al proposed that ENaC is formed by nine subunits, with a stoichiometry of $\alpha_3\beta_3\gamma_3$ (35). They also used the mutant γ_{G537C}, in which cysteine 537 can be modified by the reagent MTSET ([2-(tri-methylammonium-Oethyl]methanethiosulfonate bromide). Modification by MTSET produces inhibition of the current of mutant channels but not of wild-type channels. The experimental approach consisted of coexpressing several combinations of wild-type γ and the mutant γG537C and measuring the fraction of current blocked by

MTSET. The reagent MTSET decreased ENaC currents in a much larger proportion than the fraction of injected mutant subunits. The result suggested that modification of γ_{G537C} produced a dominant effect and that there was more than one γ subunit per channel. Analysis of the results according to MacKinnon's method gave a number of three γ subunits per channel. Similar experiments, using αS583C and βG525C mutants, indicated the presence of three α and three β subunits per channel. Therefore, the model proposed by Snyder et al consists of nine subunits $\alpha_3\beta_3\gamma_3$.

Using a different experimental approach, sedimentation of channel complexes in sucrose gradients, Snyder et al estimated the molecular mass of ENaC from which can be calculated the number of subunits per channel complex. ENaC sedimented in two regions in the sucrose gradients corresponding to M_r of 240 (unassembled subunits) and 950 (channel complexes). According to their calculations, the 950-kDa complexes are formed by nine subunits (37). However, Coscoy et al (38) reported that FaNaCh, another member of the ENaC-Deg family expressed in the ganglion of *Helix aspersa,* sedimented in the fraction corresponding to M_r 333 $\pm$ 24. Since the molecular mass of individual subunits is around 80 kDa, the most likely number of subunits in FaNaCh is four. Given the strong structural similarities between ENaC and FaNaCh, they proposed a tetrameric structure for all members of the ENaC-Deg family of cation channels.

It is evident from the summary of these studies that a definitive answer has not yet been reached. Until the structure of ENaC has been imaged at high enough resolution to discern the number of subunits, further studies using new approaches are necessary to resolve the controversy on the stoichiometry of the subunits.

REGULATION OF ENAC BY INTERACTING PROTEINS

In addition to the classical pathways that regulate ENaC activity such as aldosterone and vasopressin, recent work has shown that ENaC is also regulated by mechanisms working in entirely different ways than hormonal pathways (Figure 2). The following proteins have been shown to directly or indirectly interact with ENaC and modulate its activity. The mechanisms of action of these recently discovered regulatory proteins are still poorly understood and are areas of active investigation.

Channel Activated Protease: CAP1

The notion that luminal proteases can modulate the activity of ENaC has long been entertained by groups studying sodium reabsorption by tight epithelia. In 1983, Garty & Edelman showed that exposing the luminal side of toad urinary bladders to trypsin produced an irreversible reduction ($\sim$50%) in sodium transport (39). The authors concluded that trypsin inactivated the amiloride-sensitive sodium conductance by direct proteolysis of apical sodium channels. More

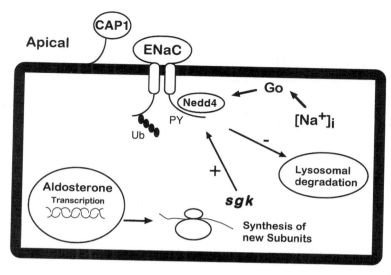

Figure 2 Mechanisms that regulate ENaC in principal cells from the distal tubule of the kidney. CAP1 tethered to the membrane activates channels in the apical membrane. Nedd4 binds to the proline-rich motifs (PY) located in the carboxy termini and ubiquitinates the amino termini of the subunits to promote endocytosis and degradation in lysosomes. Increases in intracellular Na^+ concentration $[Na^+]_i$ are transmitted via heterotrimeric G_o proteins to Nedd4 to promote removal of channels. Aldosterone binds to its receptor, which translocates into the nucleus to activate transcription of AIP such as the subunits of ENaC and *sgk*. *sgk* may activate ENaC by direct phosphorylation of the channel or indirectly by phosphorylation of other proteins.

recently, Lewis et al, experimenting with rabbit urinary bladders, tested serine proteases–kallikrein, urokinase, and plasmin–normally present in segments of the distal nephron. These proteases induced a 67% decrease in the amiloride-sensitive sodium transport rate, and the effect could be inhibited by amiloride (40, 41). The interpretation of these experiments was that proteases cleaved the channels at a site near the ion pore that accounted for the decrease in ENaC activity and, in many cases, loss of ion selectivity of the channels.

In contrast to these results, Chraïbi et al recently found that trypsin produces the opposite effect on ENaC expressed in *Xenopus* oocytes. When 2 µg/ml of trypsin was added to the bathing solution, up to a 20-fold increase in amiloride-sensitive current was produced in oocytes expressing various combinations of rat and *Xenopus* subunits of ENaC (42). The activated current exhibited the same ion selectivity and amiloride affinity as the nonstimulated channels. This effect was independent of activation of G proteins or changes in intracellular calcium, which led the authors to conclude that trypsin activated ENaC by direct prote-olysis of the extracellular domain and that such a modification increased the open probability of the channels.

Recently, Vallet et al cloned a serine protease from the A6 cell line (derived from *Xenopus laevis* kidney) that when co-expressed with ENaC in oocytes increased the amiloride-sensitive current by twofold (43). The new protease, called CAP1 (channel activating protease), is related to trypsin, prostatin, kalli-krein, and hepsin. The gene is expressed in *Xenopus* kidney, lung, intestine, and skin. An interesting feature in the amino acid sequence of CAP1 is the presence of a consensus sequence for the addition of a glycosylphospatidylinositol (GPI). Since proteins containing GPI are targeted to the apical membrane, the catalytic site of CAP1 could be exposed to the extracellular side allowing for modification of apical sodium channels. Modulation of the activity of channels by direct pro-teolysis of the extracellular domain is a unique and novel way to modify the activity of ion channels. However, none of these studies has yet provided data to show that the subunits of ENaC are cleaved by CAP1 or trypsin; another more indirect pathway could account for the observations.

A potential goal in cloning CAP1 was to isolate cDNAs induced by aldoste-rone. It turned out, however, that the mRNA levels of CAP1 were not altered by aldosterone, indicating that it is not CAP1 that mediates the activation of ENaC by the hormone. The functional significance of CAP1 in the regulation of ENaC in the kidney or in other organs has not yet been elucidated.

Nedd4

Nedd4 is a ubiquitin ligase originally cloned from embryonic brain (44). It is abundant in brain but is also expressed in other organs including lung, kidney, and colon (45). There are three distinct domains in the Nedd4 protein. The amino terminus has a Ca^{2+} and phospholipid binding domain (CaLB) that mediates the redistribution of Nedd4 from the cytosol to the plasma membrane in response to increases in intracellular Ca^{2+} (46). In the middle of the protein there are three to four WW domains, small globular domains composed of 40 semiconserved amino acids, that participate in protein-protein interactions. Functionally, WW domains have been proposed to operate in a manner similar to the SH3 domains in that they bind polyproline ligands (47). The carboxy terminus of Nedd4 con-tains the catalytic domain that functions as a ubiquitin ligase.

It has been proposed that the WW domains of Nedd4 bind the proline-rich motifs (XPPXY) present in the carboxy termini of the three subunits of ENaC (48) and that binding to the channel allows subsequent ubiquitination of several lysine residues in the amino termini of the α and γ subunits but not in the β subunit. Although α and γ subunits are ubiquitinated by Nedd4, only ubiquitin-ation of α subunits is functionally important (49). By analogy to certain membrane proteins with rapid turnover, ubiquitination of ENaC could serve as a signal for retrieval of channels from the plasma membrane and their subsequent degradation in lysosomes. In fact, co-injection of Nedd4 and ENaC in *Xenopus* oocytes decreases the amiloride-sensitive current of wild-type ENaC channels but not channels lacking the proline-rich motifs (50, 51).

If Nedd4 were to decrease the number of channels at the cell surface, it would be an attractive candidate as a mediator of inhibitory processes such as the effects of increasing intracellular Na^+. The rate of Na^+ entry across the apical membrane is regulated to match the basolateral extrusion rate and thereby to maintain cell volume and intracellular Na^+ concentration (Na^+_i). In salivary glands, increased Na^+_i inhibits ENaC by a mechanism that involves α subunits of the guanine nucleotide-binding G_o protein (52). The intermediate steps of the pathway are not known. Dinudom et al, seeking evidence linking Nedd4 to this pathway, showed that the inhibitory effect of increasing Na^+_i in salivary cells could be abolished by blocking the activity of Nedd4 either with anti-Nedd4 antibodies or by injecting fusion proteins containing WW domains (53, 54). Similar results were obtained in oocytes where increasing concentrations of Na^+_i produced a reduction of the amiloride-sensitive current in oocytes expressing wild-type ENaC but not in oocytes expressing the carboxy-terminal truncated channels (55).

Recently, Lu et al showed that the WW domains of Nedd4 bind with high affinity to peptides containing serines or threonines, but only when the peptides are phosphorylated at the serine or threonine residues (56). The amino acid sequences of the peptides recognized by the WW domains of Nedd4 were different from the previously reported proline-rich peptides, which also can interact with Nedd4 in vitro but with low affinity. Some of the known substrates for Nedd4 are proteins such as uracil permease and Cdc25C that do not contain the typical proline-rich motifs but have serine and threonine residues that undergo phosphorylation. The findings of Lu are consistent with Nedd4 mediating the ubiquitination of proteins by binding to sequences containing phosphoserine or phosphothreonine different from the bona fide proline-rich motifs, and thus raise questions about ENaC being a substrate for Nedd4.

Even if Nedd4 turns out not to bind ENaC, all the currently available data can still be explained because the proline-rich domains of ENaC also contain endocytic signals for removal of channels from the plasma membrane (57). Therefore, deletions or disruptions of these sequences would retain channels in the plasma membrane explaining all the mutagenesis performed in vitro and also the phenotype of the mutations found in patients with hypertension.

CFTR

Most of the interest on the interaction between CFTR and ENaC comes from the observation made in airways of patients with cystic fibrosis that amiloride-sensitive Na^+ absorption is larger than in normal individuals. There are other instances where ion channels are regulated by a member of the ABC transporter superfamily. The pancreatic β cell K_{ATP} channel consists of two types of subunits: an inward rectifying K^+ channel subunit ($K_{IR6.2}$) and a sulfonylurea receptor subunit (SUR1) that assemble in a 4:4 stoichiometry to form an octameric channel (58). Many functional differences can be detected in $K_{IR6.2}$ channels expressed alone or in combination with SUR1.

The question arises whether CFTR and ENaC have a similar type of interaction. However, all attempts to demonstrate protein-protein interactions between the two channels such as co-immunoprecipitations and the two-hybrid system in yeast (59) have not supported this model. Another line of research has focused on the intracellular trafficking of CFTR. In normal cells, vesicles containing CFTR and ENaC may interact to regulate the delivery of their cargo to the plasma membrane. In the absence of CFTR, more ENaC will reach the cell surface thereby increasing the amiloride-sensitive conductance.

Stutts et al have observed that protein kinase A (PKA) added to excised patches containing ENaC increased the open probability of the channels and that the effect was markedly reduced when CFTR was co-expressed with ENaC (60). According to this model, when CFTR is present, PKA cannot effectively phosphorylate ENaC.

Regulation of ENaC by Aldosterone

Aldosterone is the most potent stimulus for sodium reabsorption in the cortical collecting tubule and the distal colon. Its natriferic action is mediated by activation of ENaC channels expressed in the apical membrane and Na^+/K^+-ATPase in the basolateral membrane. Although the molecular mechanisms used by aldosterone to activate ENaC have remained elusive, significant progress has been made recently. Upon entering a cell, aldosterone binds to the mineralocorticoid receptor in the cytosol; the activated receptor translocates to the nucleus, where it represses the transcription of some genes and induces the transcription of others (aldosterone-induced protein; AIPs) (61). Some of the AIPs are the subunits of the Na^+/K^+-ATPase and of ENaC, but most are still unknown.

The time course of aldosterone action on epithelial tissues has two phases: The early response takes place in the first 0.5 to 3 h and is characterized by a 2- to 3-fold increase in sodium reabsorption. The mRNA levels of the subunits of ENaC increase little or not at all during the early phase. The late response takes place after $\sim$ 3 h and is characterized by a progressive and large increase, up to 20-fold after 24 h, in the rate of sodium reabsorption. This large increase in ENaC activity is not associated with a parallel increase in transcription of the subunits. In most tissues the increase in mRNA levels are moderate and vary according to unique patterns for each of the aldosterone target tissues. For instance, rats treated with aldosterone for more than 24 h or placed on a low salt diet for several days respond with a small induction of αENaC mRNA but no change of β and γ mRNAs in the kidney. The distal colon, which constitutively expresses α mRNA, responds with a strong induction of β and γ but little change of α mRNA (62). The heterogeneity of the response, even among the classical aldosterone responsive epithelia, indicates that there is not a single mechanism of aldosterone action but that the response is tissue specific.

Therefore, the conventional notion that aldosterone increases Na absorption by inducing synthesis of channels may explain the response in distal colon but not in other issues such as the kidney. These observations suggest that the aldosterone response is mediated by modification of pre-existing channels, either by increasing the open probability or by redistributing channels from intracellular compartments to the plasma membrane.

Several groups using different approaches, such as cell-attached patches of apical membranes of principal cells of rat cortical collecting tubules (63) or noise analysis on A6 cells grown on permeable supports (64, 65), have found that the major effect of both acute and chronic aldosterone treatment was an increase in the number of active ENaC channels and not a change in open probability as previously described in A6 cells (66).

Most recently, two groups working independently have identified a gene whose mRNA is induced very rapidly after aldosterone stimulation in A6 cells and in rabbit cortical collecting tubule cells (67, 68). The experimental approach consisted of subtracting the genes expressed in control cells from a library of aldosterone-stimulated cells. Differentially expressed genes are those induced by aldosterone. One such aldosterone-regulated early gene is *sgk* (serum- and glucocorticoid-regulated kinase). The *sgk* gene was originally cloned by two other groups, first by Webster et al in 1993 as a gene induced by glucocorticoids in a mammary tumor cell line (69), then by Waldegger et al in 1997 as a gene induced in liver cells by changes in cell volume (70). The deduced amino acid sequence indicates that it is a novel member of the serine/threonine protein kinase gene family. Expression of *sgk* has been detected in many tissues, not just exclusively in epithelia regulated by aldosterone. Both the mRNA and the protein levels of *sgk* increase rapidly after aldosterone stimulation in cortical collecting tubule cells and, when co-expressed with ENaC in *Xenopus* oocytes, *sgk* increases the amiloride-sensitive current five- to sevenfold. How *sgk* activates ENaC has not been determined, but among the possibilities are a direct phosphorylation of the channel. Shimkets et al showed that the β and γ subunits are phosphorylated in their carboxy termini and that the level of phosphorylation is increased by aldosterone stimulation (71). On the other hand, the effect could be indirect, and the *sgk* substrate could be any of the proteins so far identified as modulators of ENaC such as Nedd4, a methyl transfere (72), a channel-associated G protein, another kinase, or components of the plasma membrane-trafficking machinery.

ENAC AND GENETIC DISEASES

Gain-of-Function Mutations: Hypertensive Syndromes

The disease known as Liddle's syndrome was first described in 1963 by Liddle, who studied many members of a large family that presented with early onset of hypertension, variable degrees of hypokalemia and metabolic alkalosis, and had low aldosterone and plasma renin levels. Hypertension in these patients responded well to restriction of dietary salt and to the diuretics amiloride and triamterene, both inhibitors of the epithelial sodium channel. This led to the suspicion that ENaC was the best candidate gene for the disease. Most recently, linkage studies in the original kindred described by Liddle (18 subjects) demonstrated linkage of hypertension to a segment of chromosome 16, which contains the β and γ subunits of the amiloride-sensitive epithelial sodium channel (73, 74). Examination of these two genes in several other Liddle's syndrome kindreds demonstrated several mutations in the β and γ subunits that either deleted most of the carboxy terminus or introduced point mutations in a short carboxy-terminal proline-rich sequence (75, 76). To assess the functional effect of the mutations found in patients with hypertension, the cDNAs of the β and γ subunits were mutated in vitro and expressed in *Xenopus* oocytes for analysis. In all cases the mutant channels exhibited three- to fivefold larger current without changes in any of the other channel properties (77). Furthermore, it was found that the increase in activity was produced by expression of a larger number of channels at the plasma membrane. The effect was mediated by the carboxy-terminal proline-rich motifs that contain the binding sites for Nedd4 (78). Two observations still need to be explained: (*a*) To date, no Liddle's patients have been found to carry mutations in the proline-rich motif of the α subunit; (*b*) expression of α subunits with deletion of the carboxy terminus does not increase the current of ENaC channels. These findings suggest that the proline-rich domain of α may not bind Nedd4. Alternatively, it has been shown that the carboxy termini of β and γ, but not α, contain sequences that conform to known signals for clathrin-mediated endocytosis. Removal of these signals would result in slow endocytosis and accumulation of channels at the cell surface (56).

Loss-of-Function Mutations: Hypotensive Syndromes

The syndrome characterized by hypotension, renal salt wasting, hyperkalemia, and failure to respond to mineralocorticoids is known as pseudohypoaldosteronism (PHA). Some patients with the autosomal recessive inheritance of this syndrome, known as pseudohypoaldosteronism type 1 (PHA1), have been found to carry mutations in one or another of the α, β, or γ subunits of ENaC. Some of the mutations introduce premature stop codons or splice variants that result in nonfunctional truncated subunits (79, 80). Other mutations introduce single amino acid substitutions or deletions of a few residues in the extracellular domain of the γ subunit. The mechanisms by which these mutations inactivate ENaC have not been examined in all cases. Some of the mutations such as β_{G37S} have been characterized. Surprisingly, when channels containing the mutation β_{G37S} were expressed in oocytes, the level of current was only moderately smaller than in oocytes expressing wild-type channels. It has been suggested that this mutation might be temperature sensitive because at 37°C it will induce a significant decrease in current, thereby explaining the phenotype of patients with PHA1;

however, at room temperature, at which the in vitro experiments were performed, the effect is only partial (81).

The importance of ENaC in the absorption of salt and fluid by epithelia has been confirmed by the generation of knockout mice with inactivated subunits of ENaC. Homozygous animals βENaC(-/-) and γENaC(-/-) developed hyperkalemia, lost weight, and died with metabolic abnormalities attributed to the inability of the kidneys to retain sodium and excrete potassium (82, 83). In contrast, homozygous αENaC(-/-) animals had normal lung development but died from pulmonary edema shortly after birth (17). The phenotype of the αENaC(-/-) mice indicates that the activity of ENaC is necessary to clear fluid from the lungs. Because γENaC(-/-) and βENaC(-/-) newborns were able to clear fluid from the lungs, although at a slower rate than normal pups, it seems that small levels of activity provided by the remaining intact subunits (αβ or αγ channels) are enough to maintain normal respiratory function but not sufficient to absorb sodium in the kidney.

These experiments also point out important differences between human and mouse pulmonary physiology. The human lung can function in the absence of any ENaC activity possibly because it expresses other pathways for sodium reabsorption. In contrast, sodium reabsorption in the mouse lung, at least at birth, is dependent on ENaC activity.

NEURONAL CHANNELS

In recent years, the ENaC-Deg family has expanded rapidly with the cloning of many new members. Initially it was thought that the channels were exclusively expressed in the nervous system, but most recently they have been found in many epithelial and non-epithelial tissues such as in testis, spleen, placenta, lung, in cell lines such as HEK-293, and even in *Xenopus* oocytes (84).

The biophysical characterization of these channels is still in progress and in many cases has been hampered by the lack of functional expression. Some groups have tried to overcome this difficulty by introducing mutations in the proteins or by using harsh maneuvers such as decreasing the pH of the testing solutions as low as 4.0. In most cases, the functional significance of these channels and the stimuli that normally activate them remain unknown. Nomenclature is also a source of confusion because several names have been given to the same cDNA sequences by various groups. With these words of caution, we summarize the present state of the field.

Proton-Gated Cation Channels: ASIC

Proton-gated channels expressed in sensory neurons are believed to mediate the pain induced by acidosis that occurs in ischemic, damaged, or inflamed tissue. Acid solutions evoke two distinct inward currents in neurons from the dorsal root ganglia and certain neurons in the brain: a rapidly inactivating Na^+ current and a sustained, slowly inactivating cation current (85). The molecular identity of these channels is unknown. Recently, several channels have been cloned from the central and peripheral nervous systems that are activated by extracellular protons and might be the mediators of the currents previously described. ASIC (for acid-sensing ion channel) was originally found to be expressed in brain (86), and DRASIC (for dorsal root acid-sensing ion channel) was found to be expressed in dorsal root ganglia (87). DRASIC channels have been renamed ASIC3 because they are expressed not only in dorsal root ganglia but also in many other tissues. In addition, several splice variants, ASIC-α and ASIC-β from ASIC, have been found in dorsal root ganglia (88). ASIC-α has the coding sequence of ASIC but different 5' and 3' untranslated regions. In contrast, the first N-terminal 172 amino acids of ASIC-β are unique (89). The mRNAs of these channels were originally reported to be expressed exclusively in neurons; however, most recently they have been found in many non-neuronal tissues (90, 91).

The most salient characteristic of these channels is that they are activated by extracellular protons. The half-maximal pH for activation is quite different for each channel: for ASIC1 it is pH 6.0, and for ASIC3 it is as low as pH 4.0. ASIC1 currents inactivate rapidly, whereas ASIC3 exhibit sustained currents in the continous presence of protons. All are cation channels permeable to Na^+, K^+, and Ca^{2+} and are blocked by relatively high doses of amiloride (K_i 10–20 µM).

Any of the proton-gated channels could be a good candidate to mediate acid taste because on the surface of the tongue the pH levels can become very acidic. However, using reverse transcription and polymerase chain reaction from RNA extracted from rat lingual epithelium, Kretz et al amplified the three subunits of ENaC but none of the ASICs (92), indicating that they do not participate in mediating the acid taste.

Brain Na Channels: BNaC

Two closely related proteins, BNaC1 and BNaC2 (brain Na channel), 68% identical, have been cloned from human brain (93). A third clone corresponding to a splice variant of BNaC1 has also been identified. The first 236 amino acids of the splice variant of BNaC2 are unique, whereas the rest of the protein is identical to BNaC2. BNaC channels are also called MDEG for mammalian degenerins; however, this is a misnomer because the BNaCs lack the hallmark sequences of the degenerins, and in the phylogenetic tree they are located in a branch distant from the degenerins (Figure 3). BNaC1 and BNaC2 are co-expressed in most neurons of the brain; in addition, BNaC2 is also present in choroid plexus. Expression of BNaC1 in oocytes or in HEK-293 cells does not induce currents, suggesting that an agonist or other subunits are needed to open these channels.

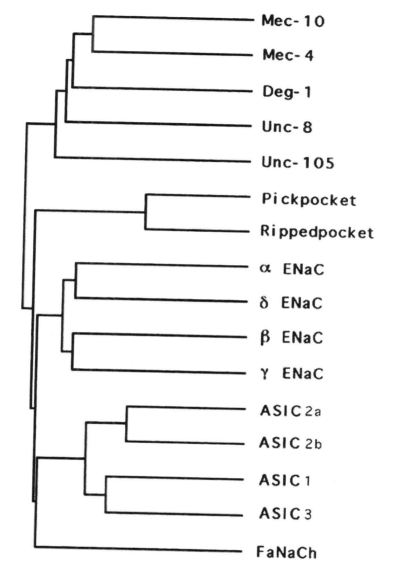

Figure 3 Members of the ENaC-Deg family of ion channels. A homology tree based on amino acid sequences shows that the channels from invertebrates cloned thus far can be divided into two major groups: the first group contains the degenerins from *C. elegans* that are expressed in neurons (Mec-10, Mec-4, and Deg-1) and in muscle (Unc-8 and Unc-105). The second group contains *Drosophila* channels: *Pickpocket* and *Rippedpocket*. Channels from vertebrates are divided also in two groups: the subunits of ENaC expressed in epithelial cells and the neuronal channels that encompass ASIC1, ASIC2 (BNaC), and ASIC3 (DRASIC). The FaNaCh channel expressed in ganglia of *Helix aspersa* is distantly related to the mammalian group.

The notion that BNaC could be the mammalian homologue of the degenerins prompted investigators to introduce into the cDNA one of the mutations known to activate the degenerins from *C. elegans*. For that purpose, glycine 430 in BNaC was replaced by residues with bulky side chains. These mutations transformed BNaC into constitutively active channels, thus making possible the characterization of its properties. The selectivity of the channels was $Na^+ > Li^+ > K^+$, and they were blocked by amiloride with a K_i between 1.7 and 13 µM. Channel open probability was strongly voltage-dependent with activation at depolarizing voltages (94). Later, it was found that BNaC channels could also be activated by high concentration of extracellular protons, although the pH required for activation was very low, pH < 5.0. Due to its sensitivity to protons, this channel was later renamed ASIC2 (95–97).

ASIC1 and ASIC2 can associate to form heteromultimeric channels that exhibit properties different from the homomeric channels (98). This result, together with the finding that ASIC1 and ASIC2 are co-expressed in many tissues, suggests that functional heterogeneity can arise by various combinations of the ASIC subunits.

FMRFamide Peptide-Gated Sodium Channel: FaNaCh

FaNaCh is one of the recently cloned channels from the ENaC-Deg family. It is the receptor for the peptide Phe-Met-Arg-Phe-NH2 (FMRFamide) and related neuropeptides found in ganglia of mollusks (99). The amino acid sequence of FaNaCh is distant from that of all the mammalian channels, as well as from the degenerins. It forms a new branch in the phylogenetic tree that separated early in evolution from the other channels. When FaNaCh was expressed in *Xenopus* oocytes, it reproduced the native properties of channels from *Helix aspersa* neurons: opening with the application of FMRFamide (EC_{50} of 2 µM), rapid desensitization, high Na^+ selectivity, and block by amiloride (K_i 0.6 µM). So far, no mammalian homologue has been found.

Drosophila Channels

Two genes of the ENaC-Deg family have been cloned from *Drosophila* (100): *pickpocket* (PPK) and *ripped pocket* (RPK). These names are not descriptive of a phenotype derived from mutations in the genes of *Drosophila*. PPK is expressed in a subset of peripheral neurons that are involved in a variety of mechanosensory functions in insects, suggesting that it may be a mechanosensitive channel. When expressed in *Xenopus* oocytes, PPK does not generate currents, as is the case for many of the members of the ENaC-Deg family. RPK was found in early stages of embryos with an expression pattern different from PPK. There is no overlap of expression of the two messages in tissues, indicating that they are not subunits of the same channel. RPK by itself generates small amiloride-sensitive Na^+ currents when injected in oocytes; the current is markedly increased by introducing the gain-of-function mutation from the degenerins (A524V). Given the advantages and relative ease of performing genetic studies in *Drosophila,* it is expected that in the near future these genes will provide valuable information on the their functional role, as has been the case for the degenerins in *C. elegans.*

ACKNOWLEDGMENTS

We thank Dr. Robert Berliner for his comments on the manuscript. This work was supported by the National Institutes of Health grant (HL 56163).

Visit the Annual Reviews home page at www.AnnualReviews.org.

LITERATURE CITED

1. Driscoll M, Chalfie M. 1991. The mec-4 is a member of a family of Caenorhabditis elegans genes that can mutate to induce neuronal degeneration. *Nature* 349:588–93
2. Mingxia H, Chalfie M. 1994. Gene interactions affecting mechanosensory transduction in Caenorhabditis elegans. *Nature* 367:467–70
3. Chalfie M, Wollinsky E. 1990. The identification and suppression of inherited neurodegeneration in Caenorhabditis elegans. *Nature* 345:410–16
4. Canessa CM, Horisberger J-D, Rossier BC. 1993. Epithelial sodium channel related to proteins involved in neurodegeneration. *Nature* 361:467–70
5. Lingueglia E, Voilley N, Waldmann R, Lazdunski M, Barbry P. 1993. Expression cloning of an epithelial amiloride-sensitive Na⁺ channel: a new channel type with homologies to Caenorhabditis elegans degenerins. *FEBS Lett.* 318:95–99
6. Canessa CM, Schild L, Buell G, Thorens B, Gautschi I, et al. 1994. Amiloride-sensitive epithelial Na⁺ channel is made of three homologous subunits. *Nature* 367:463–66
7. McDonald FJ, Price MP, Snyder PM, Welsh MJ. 1995. Cloning and expression of the beta- and gamma-subunits of the human epithelial sodium channel. *Am. J. Physiol.* 268:C1157–63
8. Goldstein O, Asher C, Garty H. 1997. Cloning and induction by low NaCl intake of avian intestine Na⁺ channel subunits. *Am. J. Physiol.* 272:C270–77
9. Fuller CM, Awayda MS, Arrate MP, Bradford AL, Morris RG, et al. 1995. Cloning of a bovine renal epithelial Na⁺ channel subunit. *Am. J. Physiol.* 269:C641–54; [published erratum. *Am. J. Physiol.* 1997. 72:C, following table of contents]
10. Puoti A, May A, Canessa CM, Horisberger JD, Schild L, et al. 1995. The highly selective low-conductance epithelial Na channel of Xenopus laevis A6 kidney cells. *Am. J. Physiol.* 269:C188–97
11. Duc C, Farman N, Canessa CM, Bonvalet J-P, Rossier BC. 1994. Cell specific expression of epithelial sodium channel α, β and γ subunits in aldosterone responsive epithelia from the rat: localization by in situ hybridization and immunocytochemistry. *J. Cell Biol.* 127:1907–21
12. Renard S, Voilley N, Bassilana F, Lazdunski M, Barbry P. 1995. Localization and regulation by steroids of the alpha, beta and gamma subunits of the amiloride-sensitive Na⁺ channel in colon, lung and kidney. *Pflügers Arch.* 430:299–307

13. Seldin DW, Giebisch G, eds. 1992. *The Kidney Physiology and Pathophysiology,* Vol. 1, 2, 3. New York: Raven. 2003 pp. 2nd ed.

14. Lindemann B. 1996. Taste reception. *Physiol. Rev.* 76:719–66

15. Farman N, Talbot CR, Boucher RC, Fay M, Canessa C, et al. 1997. Non-coordinated expression of α, β, and γ subunit mRNAs of the epithelial sodium channel along the respiratory tract. *Am. J. Physiol.* 272:C131–41

16. O'Brodovich H, Hannam V, Seear M, Mullen JB. 1990. Amiloride impairs lung water clearance in newborn guinea pigs. *J. Appl. Physiol.* 68:1758–62

17. Hummler E, Barker P, Gatzy J, Beermann F, Verdumo C, et al. 1996. Early death due to defective neonatal lung liquid clearance in αENaC-deficient mice. *Nat. Genet.* 12:325–28

18. Tchepichev S, Ueda J, Canessa C, Rossier BC, O'Brodovich H. 1995. Lung epithelial subunits are differentially regulated during development and by steroids. *Am. J. Physiol.* 269:C805–12

19. Roudier-Pujol C, Rochat A, Escoubet B, Eugene E, Barrandon Y, et al. 1996. Differential expression of epithelial sodium channel subunit mRNA in rat skin. *J. Cell Sci.* 109:379–85

20. McNicholas CM, Canessa CM. 1997. Diversity of channels generated by different combinations of epithelial sodium channel subunits. *J. Gen. Physiol.* 109:681–92

21. Fyfe GK, Canessa CM. 1998. Subunit composition determines the single channel kinetics of the epithelial sodium channel. *J. Gen. Physiol.* 112:423–32

22. Canessa CM, Merillat A-M, Rossier BC. 1994. Membrane topology of the epithelial sodium channel α-subunit: identification of N-linked glycosylation sites and of start and stop transfer signals used in intact cells. *Am J. Physiol.* 267:C1682–90

23. Snyder P, McDonald FJ, Stokes JB, Welsh MJ. 1994. Membrane topology of the amiloride-sensitive epithelial sodium channel. *J. Biol. Chem.* 269:24379–82

24. Renard S, Lingueglia E, Voilley N, Lazdunski M, Barbry P. 1994. Biochemical analysis of the membrane topology of the amiloride-sensitive Na$^+$ channel. *J. Biol. Chem.* 269:12981–86

25. Waldman R, Champigny G, Lazdunski M. 1995. Functional degenerin-containing chimeras identify residues essential for amiloride-sensitive Na$^+$ channel function. *J. Biol. Chem.* 270:11735–37

26. Schild L, Schneeberger E, Gautschi I, Firsov D. 1997. Identification of amino acid residues in the α, β, and γ subunits of the epithelial sodium channel (ENaC) involved in amiloride block and ion permeation. *J. Gen. Physiol.* 109:15–26

27. Kellenberger S, Gautschi I, Schild L. 1999. A single point mutation in the pore region of the epithelial Na$^+$ channel changes ion selectivity by modifying molecular sieving. *Proc. Natl. Acad. Sci. USA* 96:4170–75

28. Li JH-Y, Cragoe EJ, Lindemann B. 1987. Structure-activity relationship of amiloride analogs as blockers of epithelial Na channels: II. side-chain modifications. *J. Membr. Biol.* 95:171–85

29. Kieber-Emmons T, Lin C, Prammer KV, Villalobos A, Kosari F, et al. 1995. Defining topological similarities among ion transport proteins with anti-amiloride antibodies. *Kidney Int.* 48:956–64

30. Ismailov II, Kieber-Emmons T, Lin C, Berdiev BK, Shlyonsky VG, et al. 1997. Identification of an amiloride binding domain within the α-subunit of the epithelial Na$^+$ channel. *J. Biol. Chem.* 272:1075–83

31. Kellenberger S, Hoffman-Pochon N, Gautschi I, Schneberger E, Schild L. 1999. On the molecular basis of ion permeation in the epithelial Na$^+$ channel. *J. Gen. Physiol.* 114:13–30

32. Palmer LG. 1987. Ion selectivity of epithelial Na channels. *J. Membr. Biol.* 96:97–106

33. Firsov D, Gautschi I, Merillat A-M, Rossier BC, Schild L. 1998 The heterotetrameric architecture of the epithelial sodium channel (ENaC). *EMBO J.* 17:344–52

34. Kosari F, Sheng S, Li J, Mak D-O, Foskett JK, et al. 1998. Subunit stoichiometry of the epithelial sodium channel. *J. Biol. Chem.* 273:13469–74

35. Snyder PM, Cheng C, Prince LS, Rogers JC, Welsh MJ. 1998. Electrophysiological and biochemical evidence that DEG/ENaC cation channels are composed of nine subunits. *J. Biol. Chem.* 273:681–84

36. MacKinnon R. 1991. Determination of the subunit stoichiometry of a voltage-activated potassium channel. *Nature* 350:232–35

37. Cheng C, Prince LS, Snyder PM, Welsh MJ. 1998. Assembly of the epithelial Na$^+$ channel evaluated using sucrose gradient sedimentation analysis. *J. Biol. Chem.* 273:22693–700

38. Coscoy S, Lingueglia E, Lazdunski M, Barbry P. 1998. The Phe-Met-Arg-Phe-amide-activated sodium channel is a tetramer. *J. Biol. Chem.* 14:8317–22

39. Garty H, Edelman IS. 1983. Amiloride-sensitive trypsinization of apical sodium channels. *J. Gen. Physiol.* 81: 785–803

40. Lewis SA, Alles WP. 1986. Urinary kallikrein: a physiological regulator of epithelial Na$^+$ absorption. *Proc. Natl. Acad. Sci. USA* 83: 5345–48

41. Lewis SA, Clausen C, Wills NK. 1991. Urinary proteases degrade epithelial sodium channels. *J Membr. Biol.* 122: 77–88

42. Chraïbi A, Vallet V, Firsov D, Kharoubi Hess S, Horisberger J-D. 1998. Protease modulation of the activity of the epithelial sodium channel expressed in Xenopus oocytes. *J. Gen. Physiol.* 111:127–38

43. Vallet V, Chraibi A, Gaeggeler H-P, Horisberger J-D, Rossier BC. 1998. An epithelial serine protease activates the amiloride-sensitive sodium channel. *Nature* 389:607–10

44. Kumar S, Tomooka Y, Noda M. 1992. Identification of a set of genes with developmentally down-regulated expression in the mouse brain. *Biochem. Biophys. Res. Commun.* 185:1155–61

45. Staub O, Yeger H, Plant PJ, Kim H, Ernst S, et al. 1997. Immunolocalization of the ubiquitin-protein ligase Nedd4 in tissues expressing the epithelial Na$^+$ channel (ENaC). *Am. J. Physiol.* 41:C1871–80

46. Plant PJ, Yeger H, Staub O, Howard P, Rotin D. 1997. The C2 domain of the ubiquitin protein ligase Nedd4 mediates Ca^{2+}-dependent plasma membrane localization. *J. Biol. Chem.* 272:32329–36

47. Sudol M. 1996. Structure and function of the WW domain. *Prog. Biophys. Mol. Biol.* 65:113–32

48. Staub O, Dho S, Henry PC, Correa J, Ishikawa T, McGlade J, et al. 1996. WW domains of Nedd4 bind to the proline-rich PY motifs in the epithelial Na$^+$ channel deleted in Liddle's syndrome. *EMBO J.* 15:2371–80

49. Staub O, Gautschi I, Ishikawa T, Bretschopf K, Ciechanover A, et al. 1997. Regulation of stability and function of the epithelial Na$^+$ channel (ENaC) by ubiquitination. *EMBO J.* 16:6325–36

50. Goulet CC, Volk KA, Adams CM, Prince LS, Stokes JB, et al. 1998. Inhibition of the epithelial Na$^+$ channel by interaction of Nedd4 with a PY motif deleted in Liddle's syndrome. *J. Biol. Chem.* 273:30012–17

51. Abriel H, Liffing J, Rebhun JF, Pratt JH, Schild L, et al. 1999. Defective regulation of the epithelial Na$^+$ channel by Nedd4 in Liddle's syndrome. *J. Clin. Invest.* 103:667–73

52. Komwatana P, Dinudom A, Young JA, Cook DI. 1996. Cytosolic Na$^+$ controls

an epithelial Na^+ channel via the G_o guanine nucleotide-binding regulatory protein. *Proc. Natl. Acad. Sci. USA* 93:8107–11

53. Dinudom A, Harvey KF, Komwatana P, Young JA, Kumar S, Cook DI. 1998. Nedd4 mediates control of an epithelial Na^+ channel in salivary duct cells by cytosolic Na^+. *Proc. Natl. Acad. Sci. USA.* 95:71690–93

54. Harvey KF, Dinudom A Komwatana P, Jolliffe CN, Day ML, et al. 1999. All three WW domains of murine Nedd4 are involved in the regulation of epithelial sodium channels by intracellular Na^+. *J. Biol. Chem.* 274:12525–30

55. Kellenberger S, Gautschi I, Rossier BC, Schild L. 1998. Mutations causing Liddle syndrome reduce sodium-dependent downregulation of the epithelial sodium channel in the Xenopus oocyte expression system. *J. Clin. Invest.* 101:2741–50

56. Lu PJ, Zhou XZ, Shen M, Lu KP. 1999. Function of WW domains as phosphoserine- or phosphothreonine-binding modules. *Science* 283:1325–28

57. Shimkets RA, Lifton RP, Canessa CM. 1997. The activity of the epithelial sodium channel is regulated by clathrin-mediated endocytosis. *J. Biol. Chem.* 272:25537–41

58. Shyng S, Nichols CG. 1997. Octameric stoichiometry of the K_{ATP} channel complex. *J. Gen. Physiol.* 110:655–64

59. Kunzelmann K, Kiser GL, Schreiber R, Riordan JR. 1997. Inhibition of the epithelial Na^+ currents by intracellular domains of the cystic fibrosis transmembrane conductance regulator. *FEBS Lett.* 400:341–44

60. Stutts MJ, Rossier BC, Boucher RC. 1997. Cystic fibrosis transmembrane regulator inverts protein kinase A-mediated regulation of epithelial sodium channel kinetics. *J. Biol. Chem.* 272:14037–40

61. Verrey F. 1995. Transcriptional control of sodium transport in tight epithelia by adrenal steroids. *J. Membr. Biol.* 144:93–110

62. Asher C, Wald H, Rossier BC, Garty H. 1996. Aldosterone-induced increase in the abundance of Na^+ channel subunits. *Am. J. Physiol.* 271:C605–11

63. Pacha J, Frindt G, Antonian L, Silver RB, Palmer LG. 1993. Regulation of Na channels on the rat cortical collecting tubule by aldosterone *J. Gen. Physiol.* 102:25–42

64. Blazer-Yost BL, Liu X, Helman SI. 1998. Hormonal regulation of ENaCs: insulin and aldosterone. *Am. J. Physiol.* 274: C1373–79

65. Helman SI, Liu X, Baldwin K, Blazer-Yost BL, Els WJ. 1998 Time-dependent stimulation by aldosterone of blocker-sensitive ENaCs in A6 epithelia. *Am. J. Physiol.* 274:C947–57

66. Kemendy AE, Kleyman TR, Eaton DC. 1992. Aldosterone alters the open probability of amiloride-blockable sodium channels in A6 epithelia. *Am. J. Physiol.* 263:C825–37

67. Chen S-Y, Bhargava A, Mastroberardino L, Meijer OC, Wang J, et al. 1999. Epithelial sodium channel regulated by aldosterone-induced protein sgk. *Proc. Natl. Acad. Sci. USA* 96:2514–19

68. Naray-Fejes-Tóth A, Canessa C, Cleaveland ES, Aldrich G, Fejes-Tóth G. 1999. SGK is an aldosterone-induced kinase in the renal collecting duct: effects on epithelial Na channels. *J. Biol. Chem.* 274:16973–78

69. Webster MK, Goya L, Ge Y, Maiyar AC, Firestone GL. 1993. Characterization of sgk, a novel member of the serine/threonine protein kinase gene family which is transcriptionally induced by glucocorticoids and serum. *Mol. Cell Biol.* 13:2031–40

70. Waldegger S, Bath P, Raber G, Lang F, 1997. Cloning and characterization of a putative serine/threonine protein kinase transcriptionally modified during anisotonic and isotonic alterations of cell

volume. *Proc. Natl. Acad. Sci. USA* 94:4440–45

71. Shimkets RA, Lifton RP, Canessa CM. 1998. In vivo phosphorylation of the epithelial sodium channel. *Proc. Natl. Acad. Sci. USA* 95:3301–5

72. Rokaw MD, Wang J-M, Edinger RS, Weisz OA, Hui D, et al. 1998. Carboxymethylation of the β subunit of xENaC regulates channel activity. *J. Biol. Chem.* 273:28746–51

73. Shimkets RA, Warnock DG, Bositis CM, Nelson-Williams C, Hansson JH, et al. 1994. Liddle's syndrome: heritable human hypertension caused by mutations in the β subunit of the epithelial sodium channel. *Cell* 79:407–18

74. Hansson JH, Nelson-Williams C, Suzuki H, Schild L, Shimkets R, et al. 1995. Hypertension caused by a truncated epithelial sodium channel gamma subunit: genetic heterogeneity of Liddle's syndrome. *Nat. Genet.* 11:76–80

75. Hansson JH, Schild L, Lu Y, Wilson T, Gautschi I, et al. 1995. A de novo missense mutation of the beta subunit of the epithelial sodium channel causes hypertension and Liddle syndrome, identifying a proline-rich segment critical for regulation of channel activity. *Proc. Natl. Acad. Sci. USA* 92:11495–99

76. Tamura H, Schild L, Enomoto N, Matsui N, Marumo F, et al. 1996. Liddle disease caused by a missense mutation of beta subunit of the epithelial sodium channel gene. *J. Clin. Invest.* 97:1780–84

77. Schild L, Canessa CM, Shimkets RA, Gautschi I, Lifton RP, et al. 1995. A mutation in the epithelial sodium channel causing Liddle disease increases channel activity in the Xenopus laevis oocyte expression system. *Proc. Natl. Acad. Sci. USA* 92:56699–703

78. Schild L, Lu Y, Gautschi I, Scheeberger E, Lifton RP, et al. 1996. Identification of a PY motif in the epithelial Na channel subunits as a target sequence for muta-

tions causing channel activation found in Liddle syndrome. *EMBO J.* 15:2381–87

79. Chang SS, Grunder S, Hanukoglu A, Rosler A, Mathew PM, et al. 1996. Mutations in subunits of the epithelial sodium channel cause salt wasting with hyperkalaemic acidosis, pseudohypoaldosteronism type 1. *Nat. Genet.* 12:248–53

80. Strautnieks SS, Thompson RJ, Gardiner RM, Chung E. 1996. A novel splice site mutation in the γ subunit of the epithelial sodium channel gene in three pseudohypoaldosteronism type 1 families. *Nat. Genet.* 13:248–50

81. Gründer S, Firsov D, Chang SS, Fowler Jaeger N, Gautsch I, et al. 1997. A mutation causing pseudohypoaldosteronism type 1 identifies a conserved glycine that is involved in the gating of the epithelial sodium channel. *EMBO J.* 16:899–907

82. Barker PM, Nguyen MS, Gatzy JT, Grubb B, Norman H, et al. 1998. Role of γENaC subunit in lung liquid clearance and electrolyte balance in newborn mice. *J. Clin. Invest.* 102:1634–40

83. McDonald FJ, Yang B, Hrstka RF, Drummond HA, Tarr DE, et al. 1999. Disruption of the β subunit of the epithelial Na⁺ channel in mice: hyperkalemia and neonatal death associated with a pseudohypoaldosteronism phenotype. *Proc. Natl. Acad. Sci. USA* 96:1727–31

84. Cesare P, Young J, Wafford K, Clark S, England S, et al. 1999. Endogenous proton-gated cation channels in cell lines and Xenopus oocytes. *J. Physiol.* 518:116P (Abstr.)

85. Beva S, Yeats J. 1991. Protons activate a cation conductance in a subpopulation of rat dorsal root ganglion neurones. *J. Physiol.* 433:145–61

86. Waldmann R, Champigny G, Bassilana F, Heurteaux C, Lazdunski M. 1997. A proton-gated cation channel involved in acid-sensing. *Nature* 386:173–77

87. Waldmann R, Bassilana F, de Weille J, Champigny G, Heurteaux C, Lazdunski

M. 1997. Molecular cloning of a non-inactivating proton-gated Na$^+$ channel specific for sensory neurons. *J. Biol. Chem.* 272: 20975–78

88. Lingueglia E, de Wielle JR, Bassilana F, Heurteaux C, Sakai H, et al. 1997. A modulatory subunit of acid sensing ion channels in brain and dorsal root ganglion cells. *J. Biol. Chem.* 272:29778–83

89. Chen C-C, England S, Akopian AN, Wood JN. 1998. A sensory neuron-specific, proton-gated ion channel. *Proc. Natl. Acad. Sci. USA* 95:1040–45

90. Ishibashi K, Marumo F. 1998. Molecular cloning of a Deg/ENaC sodium channel cDNA from human testis. *Biochem. Biophys. Res. Commun.* 245:589–93

91. Babinski K, Lê K-T, Séguéla P. 1999. Molecular cloning and regional distribution of a human proton receptor subunit with biphasic functional properties. *J. Neurochem.* 72:51–57

92. Kretz O, Barbry P, Bock R, Lindemann B. 1999. Differential expression of RNA and protein of the three pore-forming subunits of the amiloride-sensitive epithelial sodium channel in taste buds on the rat. *J. Histochem. Cytochem.* 47:51–64

93. Price MP, Snyder PM, Welsh MJ. 1996. Cloning and expression of a novel human brain Na$^+$ channel. *J. Biol. Chem.* 271:7879–82

94. Garcia-Añoveros J, Derfler B, Neville-Golden J, Hyman BT, Corey DP. 1997. BNaC1 and BNaC2 constitute a new family of human neuronal sodium channels related to degenerins and epithelial sodium channels. *Proc. Natl. Acad. Sci. USA* 94:1459–64

95. Waldmann R, Champigny G, Voilley N, Lauritzen I, Lazdunski M. 1996. The mammalian degenerin MDEG, an amiloride-sensitive cation channel activated by mutations causing neurodegeneration in Caenorhabditis elegans. *J. Biol. Chem.* 271:10433–36

96. Adams CM, Price MP, Snyder PM, Welsh MJ. 1999. Tetraethylammonium block of the BNC1 channel. *Biophys. J.* 76:1377–83

97. Bassilana F, Champigny G, Waldmann R, de Weille JR, Heurteaux C, et al. 1997. The acid-sensitive ionic channel subunit ASIC and the mammalian degenerin MDEG form a heteromultimeric H$^+$-gated Na$^+$ channel with novel properties. *J. Biol. Chem.* 272:28819–22

98. Adams CM, Snyder PM, Price MP, Welsh MJ. 1998. Protons activate brain Na$^+$ channel 1 by inducing a conformational change that exposes a residue associated with neurodegeneration. *J. Biol. Chem.* 273:30204–7

99. Lingueglia EL, Champigny G, Lazdunski, Barbry P. 1995. Cloning of the amiloride-sensitive FMRFamide peptide-gated sodium channel. *Nature* 378:730–33

100. Adams CM, Anderson MG, Motto DG, Price MP, Anderson WA, et al. 1998. Ripped pocket and pickpocket, novel Drosophila DEG/ENaC subunits expressed in early development and in mechanosensory neurons. *J. Cell. Biol.* 140:143–52

Annu. Rev. Physiol. 2000. 62:595–620

BRANCHING MORPHOGENESIS DURING KIDNEY DEVELOPMENT

M. Pohl, R. O. Stuart, H. Sakurai, and S. K. Nigam

Departments of Pediatrics and Medicine, Division of Nephrology/Hypertension, University of California, San Diego, 9500 Gilman Drive, La Jolla, California 92093–0693; e-mail: snigam@ucsd.edu

Key Words tubulogenesis, ureteric bud, MDCK, IMCD, three-dimensional culture

■ **Abstract** Epithelial tissues such as kidney, lung, and breast arise through branching morphogenesis of a pre-existing epithelial structure. They share common morphological stages and a need for regulation of a similar set of developmental decisions—where to start; when, where, and in which direction to branch; and how many times to branch—decisions requiring regulation of cell proliferation, apoptosis, invasiveness, and cell motility. It is likely that similar molecular mechanisms exist for the epithelial branching program. Here we focus on the development of the collecting system of the kidney, where, from recent data using embryonic organ culture, cell culture models of branching morphogenesis, and targeted gene deletion experiments, the outlines of a working model for branching morphogenesis begin to emerge. Key branching morphogenetic molecules in this model include growth factors, transcription factors, distal effector molecules (such as extracellular matrix proteins, integrins, proteinases and their inhibitors), and genes regulating apoptosis and cell proliferation.

INTRODUCTION

Epithelial tissues such as the kidney, lung, and gut serve as structural and functional interfaces between the internal compartments of the organism and the environment. Teleologically, the processes underlying kidney development can be viewed as ways to establish a selectively permeable conduit (between the extracellular space and the space external to the organism) together with maximization of surface area relative to organ size in order to efficiently accomplish vectorial transport of solutes. The strategy adopted during the development of many epithelial tissues is branching morphogenesis. In most cases the tubular network arises through branching, proliferation, and remodeling of an initial epithelial evagination. In the kidney, this is the ureteric bud, which, through iterative branching tubulogenesis, gives rise to the collecting system. Before discussing molecules and cellular mechanisms in detail, we provide a conceptual overview.

0066–4278/00/0315–0595$12.00

OVERVIEW OF A WORKING MODEL

Metanephric kidney development begins with a hollow epithelial tube, known as the Wolffian duct, interacting with a group of non-epithelial cells, the metanephric mesenchyme (MM) (1–8). The first phase in the development of the branching collecting system involves the outgrowth of an initial epithelial structure called the ureteric bud (UB), the induction of which depends on the decision of a group of Wolffian duct cells nearest the MM to sprout (Figure 1A, see color insert). These cells go on to form the entire urinary collecting system from the bladder trigone through the collecting tubules.

The UB grows into the MM, leading to a period characterized by the many iterations of branching morphogenesis. Complex molecular interactions ensue between the UB and the MM, during which the MM is committed to a pathway of epithelial differentiation (ultimately leading to the formation of the epithelial glomerulus through the distal tubule of the nephron) and the UB is induced to branch into epithelial tubules that will form the collecting system (Figure 1B) (1–8). At each round of dichotomous branching, the number of UB tips doubles; each of these tips is then available for the induction of additional nephrons through epithelialization of the surrounding MM. The precise mechanisms responsible for UB branching in vivo remain to be elucidated; however, data from organ culture and cell culture models suggest that a variety of soluble growth factors are involved.

Apart from the decision to branch, the direction in which the developing structure will grow must be continually specified. One hypothesis explaining this vectoriality of branching is that UB branches are sensitive to morphogenetic gradients of soluble factors. That is, they grow toward (or away from) a source of growth factors. These gradients may arise from growth factor production by mesenchymal and stromal cells as well as from selective binding and processing by the extracellular matrix (ECM) of factors that enhance and inhibit tubule formation and/or branching. Cells of the branching UB may also produce autocrine factors, which, in response to mesenchymal factors, regulate its own branching. Data from in vitro models support these notions and suggest mechanisms to generate complex local (and possibly global) gradients of growth factors that can help establish the directionality of new branches. Recent data from culture of isolated UB tissue also suggest that intimate contact with the mesenchyme guides UB branching and influences branch elongation (Figure 1C), either through direct cell-cell contact or through very short-acting soluble factors. The MM may also provide a stop signal for branching.

A program for branching morphogenesis necessarily consists of effector mechanisms that must overcome various barriers created by surrounding cells and matrix in order for UB cells to migrate and form branching tubules. In organ culture, embryonic lung and kidney appear morphologically to extend new branches by the budding of entire groups of epithelial cells, which proliferate and appear to push in a given direction. The problem can be conceptualized as a changing figure (the developing branching structure) in a changing ground (the surrounding matrix and mesenchyme). During this process, extensive remodeling of the basement membrane and selective modulation of cellular adhesion to the ECM occur. Regulation probably lies in the changing sets of distal effector molecules. These include matrix proteins, matrix-degrading proteinases that are secreted by various cells, as well as cell adhesion molecules expressed on cell surfaces. Thus the branching UB shapes the surrounding matrix and mesenchyme, which in turn shape the UB as it further develops. In other words, the figure (branching UB) continually changes the ground (surrounding cells and matrix), and the ground changes the figure as the collecting system forms.

Programmed cell death (apoptosis) is likely to be critical in determination of morphology of the ultimate collecting system. Selective death of cell populations could potentially sculpt structures and/or provide space for organ expansion. In addition, the formation of lumens involves a process of gradual cavitation, which is likely to involve selective death of some cells in the developing structure and enhanced proliferation of other cells.

Between the action of morphogenetic growth factors that cause branching by altering the expression of distal effector molecules (such as proteinases, matrix, and cell adhesion molecules) lies signal transduction and transcriptional activity. Considerable information has accumulated on the intracellular signaling pathways involved in the action of growth factors such as the hepatocyte growth factor, which induces branching morphogenesis of mature renal epithelial cells in three-dimensional culture, although it is not yet clear whether these same signaling pathways are involved in UB branching morphogenesis. Insight into the role of various transcription factors in renal development has been generated by various targeted gene deletion experiments in the mouse. It has, however, been difficult in most cases to ascertain a direct connection between transcription factor activity and branching per se. Establishing links between branching morphogenetic growth factors, the intracellular signals they transmit, the ensuing binding of transcription factors, and the resulting expression of distal effector molecules is a major focus of current research employing various experimental systems to model branching morphogenesis.

EXPERIMENTAL SYSTEMS FOR THE STUDY OF BRANCHING MORPHOGENESIS

In the embryonic kidney, the intimate interactions between the developing ureteric tree and the mesenchymal and stromal cells that surround it, as well as the matrix secreted by all these cells, make it difficult to determine the contribution of specific molecules to branching morphogenesis. A perturbation, such as a gene deletion in a mouse or neutralization of a secreted molecule in embryonic kidney organ culture (with an antibody), that has a direct effect upon mesenchymal development can also have a profound effect on UB branching, even if this is an indirect effect. On histological sectioning, defects in UB branching are easy to detect, and it is often assumed that this implies a direct effect upon the UB. Spatiotemporal expression patterns can provide support for or against such a hypothesis but are limited by being circumstantial in nature. Therefore, while studies of intact embryos and whole embryonic kidney in organ culture will always be important, in order to delineate specific roles for a molecule in branching morphogenesis, it is equally important to demonstrate the role of such a molecule in a system in which branching of cells or tissue can be analyzed in comparative isolation.

In general, several kinds of model systems have been used to study branching morphogenesis (indirectly and directly) (7, 9): (*a*) whole embryonic kidney organ culture, exploiting the in vitro growth of explanted fetal kidneys; (*b*) genetically engineered (knockout and transgenic) mice; (*c*) so-called three-dimensional cell culture models that rely on the branching of embryonic and adult renal cell lines in ECM-preparations (Figure 2*A–C,* see color insert); and (*d*) isolated UB culture (Figure 2*D–F*).

Organ Culture

The classical experiments of Grobstein and colleagues established an in vitro organ culture system for kidney development that has continued to allow testing individual influences on the process of nephron formation, and indirectly, branching morphogenesis (6). Developing metanephroi are harvested from mouse (or rat) embryos on day 11 (or 13) of gestation and are cultured in defined medium for several days, during which they grow and differentiate further. Although this system does not allow for the study of the first step of kidney development, the induction of the UB, it provides a powerful approach to study processes leading to nephron formation and branching, although, once again, direct versus indirect effects on branching are difficult to distinguish.

Genetically Engineered Mice

Results from genetically engineered mice, primarily knockouts, have the great advantage of being able to unambiguously demonstrate the role of a particular gene in at least some aspect of kidney development when such a phenotype occurs. As with organ culture, however, when branching is affected, it is difficult to determine whether the phenotype is due to defective branching per se or to an indirect effect evoked by abnormal mesenchymal or stromal development. Furthermore, disruption of many genes that seem likely to be important in branching morphogenesis fail to result in abnormalities, presumably due to compensation by genes with similar activities, a phenomenon often referred to as redundancy.

Cell Culture Models

To gain greater insight into the fundamental cellular processes involved in branching, in vitro tubulogenesis models have been employed in which epithelial cells of kidney origin cultured in three-dimensional gels are observed to form branching tubular structures in response to various soluble factors. In 1991, branching tubule formation of Madin-Darby canine kidney (MDCK) cells was observed in three-dimensional collagen type I matrices in response to stimulation with conditioned medium from Swiss 3T3-fibroblasts; the key morphogenetic factor was subsequently shown to be hepatocyte growth factor (HGF) (10, 11). This model has been used to further elucidate the role of soluble factors and ECM components in tubulogenesis (12, 13). Two other renal cell lines also form tubules in three-dimensional cultures: murine inner medullary collecting duct (mIMCD) cells (isolated from adult SV40 transgenic mice) that undergo branching in response to HGF and all tested ligands for the epidermal growth factor (EGFR) (14, 15); and UB cells, which originate from SV40-transgenic mouse on embryonic day 11.5 (e11.5) (Figure 2A–C) (16). The latter have the advantage of being derived from the embryonic kidney and address the criticism that the MDCK and mIMCD cell lines arise from mature renal epithelia, which do not normally branch. In fact, using the UB cell system, it has been shown that about half the branching activity made by the MM can not be accounted for by HGF or EGFR ligands (see below). Furthermore, the key factor(s) necessary for the formation of branching UB cell tubules (cultured in vitro) with lumens remains to be identified. Other important differences between the UB and the MDCK cell system are beginning to emerge, at least some of which presumably reflect authentic differences in the behavior of embryonic UB tissue and mature renal epithelium.

Isolated Ureteric Bud Culture

For many years the isolated MM has been cultured under the influence of other inductive tissues, typically the spinal cord. However, until recently, the UB had been largely resistant to isolated in vitro growth and morphogenesis over an extended period, so that the development of the renal collecting duct system, which is the focus of this review, could be evaluated only in whole rudiment culture. Recently, in vitro growth and sustained branching of isolated rat UBs from e13 have been achieved by using a putative MM cell-derived conditioned medium, previously shown to induce UB cell branching in three-dimensional culture (referred to as BSN-CM) in combination with GDNF (Figure 2D), thereby allowing investigation of UB branching morphogenesis independent of mutual interactive processes with the MM (17). ECM requirements for isolated UB tissue morphogenesis appear similar to those for cultured UB cell branching tubule formation in three-dimensional gels. Together, these in vitro models have begun to shed new light on roles of growth factors, ECM composition, and on ECM degrading enzymes and their inhibitors. They also help clarify the contributions of cell contact versus soluble factors in establishing the architecture of the ureteric tree and collecting system.

Ideally, the following criteria should be met to invoke the direct involvement of a molecule in branching morphogenesis in the kidney: (a) It should be expressed in a spatiotemporal fashion such that enhancing or neutralizing its activity in whole embryonic kidney organ culture would result in abnormal nephrogenesis and aberrant branching. (*b*) Altering its expression in genetically engineered animals should result in a kidney phenotype with altered branching patterns. (*c*) Increasing or decreasing its activity in a cell culture model should affect branching morphogenesis. (*d*) Upon potentiating or perturbing its activity in the isolated UB culture system, early or later branching events should be altered. (One might also add the criterion that the phenotypic change is reversed by readdition of the protein factor and/or re-expression of the gene product.) To date, no molecule satisfies all these criteria, although it should be noted that the UB cell culture model and the isolated UB tissue culture system are relatively new, and comparatively few molecules have been studied. Nevertheless, the absence of an example that fulfills all these requirements highlights the difficulty in unambiguously demonstrating a role for a particular molecule in branching morphogenesis during collecting system development. What follows is an account of those molecules that fulfill (or seem most likely to fulfill) several of these criteria with the aim of incorporating them into a working model of collecting system development.

INDUCTION OF URETERIC BUD OUTGROWTH

The first step in the development of the mammalian metanephros is the formation of the UB out of the caudal Wolffian duct (Figure 1*A*). Normal differentiation of intermediate mesoderm (which gives rise to the MM, UB, Wolffian duct, and much gonadal tissue) has been shown in targeted gene deletion experiments to depend on several transcription factors. When the transcription factors LIM1 or PAX-2 are homozygously mutated, the Wolffian duct either does not (LIM1) or only incompletely (PAX-2) forms, which leads to renal agenesis (18, 19). Needless to say, with an absent or compromised Wolffian duct, UB outgrowth is not possible, although in the case of LIM1 the exact reason could not be investigated, due to the early death of the embryos around e10. In the setting of a normal Wolffian duct, UB induction occurs by interaction with the surrounding mesenchyme. This process depends on the expression of the Wilms' tumor suppressor gene *WT-1* and the peptide growth factor GDNF in the mesenchyme. In mice carrying null mutations for either of those molecules, the UB does not form in spite of a normally developed Wolffian duct; consequently those mice suffer from renal agenesis (20–23).

WT-1, a zinc finger–containing transcription factor, is normally expressed in the uninduced mesenchyme, and in the case of the null mutants, this cell population undergoes apoptosis at e11, suggesting a role for this gene in the survival of the mesenchyme surrounding the Wolffian duct (20). GDNF is expressed in and secreted by the MM at e11 and acts on c-ret, a receptor tyrosine kinase, which is expressed by the Wolffian duct and later in the developing UB, especially in the tips of the branches (24–26). For activation by GDNF, c-ret requires a glycosyl phosphatidylinositol (GPI)-linked co-receptor, the GDNF family receptor α1

(GFR1), which is found on cells of the UB (27–29). If any one of these molecules, WT1, GDNF, c-ret, or GFR1, is functionally deleted, renal agenesis ensues due to failure of UB outgrowth. Interestingly, whereas WT1 null mutations show complete penetrance, mice carrying null mutations in GDNF, c-ret, or GFR1, occasionally develop hypoplastic kidneys, suggesting an existing but insufficient compensatory pathway for UB induction and branching morphogenesis (21, 30–32). In addition to gene targeting studies, organ culture experiments have clearly shown the unique significance of the GDNF:c-ret axis for the induction of the UB. Exogenous GDNF induces multiple and dystopic UBs from the Wolffian duct, provokes supernumerary UB branches, acts as a chemoattractant on the branches, and appears to increase proliferation and expression of Wnt-11 at the UB tips (28, 33). Wnt-11 is exclusively expressed on the leading edges of the UB and its derived branches in all stages of collecting system development, although its function in this process has not yet been shown (34). Two other members of the GDNF family, persephin and neurturin, also have effects similar to GDNF in vitro (35, 36). Neurturin is expressed by the UB itself and may therefore account for some of the phenotypic variability in *GDNF –/–* mice. Given the similar phenotype of mice carrying WT1 or GDNF null mutations, it is tempting to assume a requirement of WT1 for GDNF expression, but to date this has not been shown, and indeed, GDNF mRNA (but not protein) has been detected in *WT1 –/–* MM (37).

A number of other gene deletion phenotypes, as well as naturally occurring mutations, are also associated with variable failure of UB outgrowth, including the limb-deformity gene (*ld*) (38), the *homeobox-A11/D11* double knockout (39), and the Danforth Short-tail mutation (40). The exact interactions between the gene products associated with these genes and the GDNF:c-ret axis remain to be elucidated. Interestingly, at least for the transcription factor ld, a functional link appears likely as the MM in ld-deficient mice retains the ability to differentiate, when induced by wild-type UB (38), and the expression of ld in the UB appears dependent on c-ret signaling (41). Overall, the gene deletion data clearly demonstrate a critical role for GDNF signaling in initial UB outgrowth. However, experiments that result in complete renal agenesis necessarily can not shed much light on the role of GDNF signaling in subsequent branching events.

VECTORIAL BRANCHING OF THE DEVELOPING URETERIC TREE

The number of branching events has consequences for total nephron number, which in humans has been related to the development of essential hypertension and the progression of renal disease (42). Loss of one initial branching event could mean halving the total number of nephrons, and a subtle decrease (less than 1%) in branching efficiency can likewise, over many iterations of branching, potentially reduce nephron number by half or more. A knockout mouse with an unambiguous isolated defect in the number of branching events, directionality, or elongation has yet to be described. Of course, this may simply reflect the difficulty of quantitative morphometric analyses of branching events in the intact embryonic kidney. A priori, there appear to be four not entirely exclusive possible core developmental mechanisms for explaining the vectoriality of the developing collecting system. (*a*) Vectorial branching morphogenesis can be regulated through long-range morphogenetic (or chemoattractive/repulsive) gradients (such as retinoids in limb patterning); (*b*) It can be regulated through short-range soluble factor paracrine-autocrine relay (such as TGF-β in early development); (*c*) Branching morphogenesis can be regulated through direct cell-cell contact with the MM (as in Eph-Ephrin or Notch-Delta signaling in the nervous system); (*d*) It could be an intrinsic property of UB tissue itself, and directionality is conferred by the provision of growth stimulating soluble factors by the MM.

Data from various model systems (see below) seem to support several of these mechanisms. With branching morphogenesis so essential to nephrogenesis and occurring over the bulk of metanephrogenesis, even as the spatiotemporal expression patterns of many candidate morphogenetic molecules change markedly, there is a certain teleologic sense to this answer. Further, it is not likely that all branching events are the same, but instead fall into functionally different periods, an idea supported by the fact that distinct subsets of genes are expressed during different periods of branching in the UB cell culture model (43).

Mediators of Isolated Ureteric Bud Branching Morphogenesis

Maintenance of the embryonic kidney in culture has long been possible. Both branching morphogenesis of the UB and epithelialization of the MM are observed in this setting. Nevertheless, earlier work appeared to indicate that branching morphogenesis of the UB, and even its survival, was absolutely dependent on contact with mesenchyme (6). However, the fact that exogenously added soluble growth factors or soluble factors produced by the isolated MM can induce adult and embryonic epithelial cells, ultimately derived from the UB, to branch continued to suggest that soluble factors could activate the UB branching program in the absence of MM contact (Figure 2A). Recently, it has become possible to culture the isolated UB in the presence of appropriate ECM, GDNF, and a conditioned medium derived from what appear to be e11.5 MM cells (BSN-CM). That the isolated UB is observed to undergo impressive branching morphogenesis in the absence of any interaction with the MM (other than indirectly via soluble factors present in BSN-CM) demonstrates that at least a portion of the program for branching morphogenesis is intrinsic to the UB and can be initiated and maintained by soluble factors (17) (Figure 2D). Nevertheless, the branching of the UB in this setting is absolutely dependent on GDNF and a currently unidentified factor(s) present in BSN-CM, suggesting that a similar dependence on soluble factors occurs in vivo. GDNF was previously shown to be involved in UB outgrowth, but in this model system, it also appears necessary for continued branching. The key activity in BSN-CM does not appear to be any of a number of known growth factors tested or a mixture of them.

Role of Mesenchymal Contact

While the UB does not require contact with the MM for early branching, its morphogenetic potential appears to be open to modulation by such contact. Recombination experiments in which the cultured isolated UB that has undergone extensive branching in the presence of soluble factors is placed next to freshly obtained MM demonstrate a strong tendency for the UB branches to elongate into the MM (Figure 2*E,F*) (17). Thus the MM appears to provide vectorial guidance and modulate branch length in this model. Whether this tendency to elongate within the MM is a function of actual cell-cell signaling or is mediated via soluble factors (possibly acting over a short range) remains to be elucidated. Furthermore, because many iterations of branching can be induced in this system, it has been hypothesized that the MM provides a key stop signal for branching (17). It is interesting to note that BSN-CM consistently upregulates the expression of the ephrins A5 and B2 in UB cells, when cultured in three-dimensional gels over 7 days (43). Ephrins are membrane-bound molecules that can transmit signals to Eph-receptor tyrosine kinase family members only in the membrane-linked state (44). Ephrin:Eph signaling has been shown to be critical in two developmental processes with at least superficial resemblance to branching morphogenesis of the collecting system: regulation of axonal guidance in the CNS (45) and patterning of the embryonic vascular system (46). The Eph:ephrin interaction has also recently been implicated in epithelial morphogenesis. The *Caenorhabditis elegans* gene *vab-1* has recently been shown to encode an Eph-like protein (most similar to Eph-A3). Worms carrying null mutations in this protein display defective migration of epidermal cells during epidermal enclosure of neuroblasts, and it is thought that *vab-1* expression provides a repulsive signal that prevents migrating epidermal cells from invading the neuroblasts (47).

Growth Factors Modulating Branching Morphogenesis of Epithelial Cells in Three-Dimensional Culture

The one or more growth factors required for branching morphogenesis, presumably through long- and short-range gradients, has been the focus of much effort. As whole-organ culture models do not allow testing growth factor effects on the UB independent of the mesenchyme, the most direct evidence for the involvement of growth factors in the branching process has been gained from studies employing cell culture models. All three renal cell lines (MDCK, mIMCD, and UB cells), modeling the process of in vitro UB branching morphogenesis, react to HGF in three-dimensional culture by undergoing a range of changes (that vary depending upon cell type), including increased motility, extending cellular processes, forming branching multicellular cords and even tubules with lumens (11–16, 48). The case for HGF is most persuasive for MDCK-cells, which, in three-dimensional collagen-culture and serum grow as cysts unless HGF is added, whereupon they form tubules with lumens (11, 12, 49). HGF is the only known tubulogenic factor for MDCK cells, whereas mIMCD and UB cells, which respond to HGF by forming cell processes and multicellular structures, are also responsive to EGFR ligands and other soluble factors (14–16). C-met, a receptor tyrosine kinase, has been identified as the transmembrane receptor for HGF and is expressed in the branching epithelia of several developing organs, including the kidney, whereas HGF is expressed in the respective mesenchyme (50, 51). Interestingly, even though neutralization of HGF has been shown to inhibit nephrogenesis in organ culture (50, 52), neither c-met nor HGF null mutant mice show impaired renal development through e14–16, at which time they die, either from liver or from placenta failure (53–55). This result could be interpreted in several ways: (*a*) The HGF:c-met axis is unimportant for nephrogenesis; (*b*) it becomes important in kidney development only after day 16 of gestation; or (*c*) in the kidney, there are sufficient compensatory factors or mechanisms to overcome the effects of loss of the HGF:c-met axis in early embryogenesis. The in vitro cell culture data seem most consistent with this latter possibility.

Based on results obtained from in vitro branching assays using the mIMCD and UB cell line, it seems likely that in the embryonic development there is redundancy in the effects of certain growth factors. While mIMCD cells respond to HGF and can be induced to form tubules with lumens, they are also responsive to EGFR ligands. In co-culture experiments where the embryonic kidney or MM is placed atop the gel and at a distance from the branching cells, neutralization of HGF only slightly diminishes branching of mIMCD cells (14, 15). However, the same co-culture experiment done with MDCK cells gives very different results in that HGF neutralization alone abolishes most branching (15). Embryonic renal epithelial cells from *c-met* knockout mice form cellular processes and cords in response to TGFα, an EGFR ligand (56). In fact, EGFR knockout mice with certain genetic backgrounds suffer collecting system abnormalities and develop renal failure (57).

In retrospect, the perhaps excessive focus on HGF may have been a result of the unique properties of the MDCK cell, itself an adult cell. In an effort to create a more developmentally relevant system, a UB cell line derived from the e11.5 kidney was stimulated with conditioned medium (in the presence of no or minimal serum) that appears to be derived from e11.5 MM (16, 43). The UB cells formed cellular processes, multicellular cords, and tubules with lumens (Figure 2*A–C*). Neutralization experiments such as those described above indicate that, whereas EGFR ligands and HGF may be important for initial cellular process formation, about half the activity necessary for the formation of multicellular cords can not be accounted for by these factors, and some other factors are necessary for the formation of branching tubules with lumens (16). In fact, EGFR ligands, HGF, insulin-like growth factor (IGF)-I, fibroblast growth factor (FGF)-2 or GDNF, or a combination thereof, could not induce branching tubules with lumens, just as none of those growth factors (or their mixture) was able to induce isolated UB tissue branching in vitro, even when combined with GDNF (17). The findings are consistent with a view that the aforementioned growth factors have a less specific effect on branching morphogenesis of the UB cells, possibly being more important for cell motility, survival, proliferation, or later steps in branching morphogenesis during collecting system development. It is also possible that these growth factors are important in establishing and maintaining the differentiated state, not only with respect to structure but also with respect to the proper expression of water channels and transporters upon which the functional segmentation of the collecting system depends. It is noteworthy that certain EGFR knockout mice have defects in collecting duct morphology (57).

The data from mIMCD cells support the notion of redundancy of branching morphogenetic factors in that both EGFR ligands and HGF can induce branching (14). Consistent with this argument, targeted deletions of IGF-I, the IGF-II receptor, FGF-2, and HGF do not show kidney-specific phenotypes (53–55, 58–60). FGF-7 mutant kidneys appear to branch less efficiently in that they are smaller and contain fewer UB branches in otherwise similarly developed animals, but earlier branching events (before e13.5 in mouse) are not affected (61). A possible explanation for growth factor redundancy lies in the convergence of effector pathways. Recently, epimorphin was shown to be required for branching morphogenesis and regulation of cyst and branching duct formation in mammary gland cells in vitro. Interestingly, the effects were comparable, regardless of whether HGF, epidermal growth factor (EGF), keratinocyte growth factor, or FGF-2 was used to stimulate the process and, indeed, all these factors promoted only proliferation, but not branching, in the absence of epimorphin (62). Compared to the situation in the adult, functional redundancy intuitively seems more important in the embryo, where defective branching potentially leads to dire consequences for organogenesis. It is also worth noting that the UB cell culture and the isolated UB tissue culture system presumably model early UB branching; if HGF and EGFR-ligands are largely involved in later branching and differentiation events in the developing collecting system, their contribution might be missed. In both the UB cell culture and isolated UB tissue culture models, addition of only BSN-CM, the MM cell conditioned medium (along with GDNF in the case of isolated UB tissue), resulted in impressive branching (Figure 2A,D). Thus identification of the key activities in BSN-CM will be of considerable interest in furthering our understanding of the role of soluble factors in collecting system development.

In addition to the identification of branching promoting factors, at least one factor (TGF-β) has been found to have an inhibitory effect on branching. In MDCK cells, the process of HGF-induced branching tubulogenesis is very sensitive to TGF-β, and even early cell process formation is inhibited (12). With mIMCD cells the result is more interesting. Under conditions of tubulogenesis, TGF-β1, 2, and 3 all inhibit branching without affecting tubulogenesis, thus generating longer tubular structures with a reduced number of branch points (63). Bone morphogenetic protein (BMP) 2 and 7, also members of the TGF-β superfamily, have been reported to inhibit branching of mIMCD cells (BMP7 only at high concentrations) (64). This raises the possibility that a branching tubulogenesis-promoting growth factor can, in combination with a factor that selectively inhibits branching, regulate the number of branching events. It has been postulated that bipolar gradients of such branch promoting and branch inhibiting factors can lead to vectorial branching of the developing collecting system (Figure 3, see color insert) (4, 5). TGF-β not only directly inhibits branching in this model (in part by altering proteinase expression) but also reduces the expression of HGF by 3T3 cells, the fibroblast cell line that was the source of HGF in the original MDCK cell experiments (63). The role for TGF-β1, 2, and possibly for activin, another member of the TGF-β family, in the regulation of epithelial branching morphogenesis is supported by results from studies in kidney organ culture (65). Indeed, pointing to the similarity of the branching algorithms in different epithelial organs, TGF-β1 has similar effects in lung and mammary gland development (66, 67), and functional deletion of the TGF-β type II receptor results in stimulation of branching in both organs (68, 69). It appears that the TGF-β signaling acts in concert with, but antagonistically to, EGFR signaling in patterning of pulmonary branch morphology (70, 71), a situation that remarkably mirrors results obtained with mIMCD cells (14, 63).

EFFECTOR MECHANISMS: PROTEINASES, ECM, AND CELL ADHESION MOLECULES

Whatever the nature of the branching stimulus might be, there is a need for extensive matrix remodeling and cell migration for branching to become manifest. In this context, it has been argued that branching morphogenesis of the UB should be accompanied by differential expression of branch inhibiting and facilitating ECM components at various points on the developing branching ureteric tree (e.g. existing stalks versus branch points versus leading edges of new sprouts) (4, 5, 49). Changes in ECM composition would then be accompanied and accomplished by differential expression of matrix receptors (integrins, CD44), as well as ECM degrading proteinases (Figure 3). Changes in the ECM milieu might be expected to facilitate cell migration outright and at the same time influence gene expression via outside-in signaling through integrins or other cell adhesion molecules.

Extracellular Matrix Degrading Enzymes

Several proteinases and proteinase-inhibitors have been found to be associated with branching morphogenesis in different model systems. Growth factors like EGFR ligands and TGF-β regulate the expression of collagenase I, TIMP-I, urokinase, and urokinase-receptor in mIMCD-cells, presumably shaping the developing structure by altering the local proteinase/proteinase-inhibitor ratio (14, 63). In addition, 1,10-orthophenanthroline, a synthetic inhibitor of metalloproteinases, inhibits branching morphogenesis in mIMCD and UB cells, and MDCK cell tubulogenesis and UB cell branching morphogenesis in three-dimensional matrices are inhibited by addition of exogenous TIMP-2 (14, 72; H Sakurai, M Pohl, SK Nigam, unpublished observations). Organ culture experiments show reduced branching in the presence of TIMP-1 or TIMP-2 (73, 74). Together, these data indicate the involvement of metalloproteinases (MMPs) and their inhibitors in extracellular remodeling during branching.

On the other hand, it has proven difficult to demonstrate the importance and origin of individual MMPs in that process. Both physiological and most synthetic MMP-inhibitors are able to inactivate more than one MMP and lead to a broader loss of MMP-activity than the functional deletion of individual MMPs. Recently, blocking gelatinase B-antibodies and antisense inhibition of MT1-MMP have been reported to perturb kidney development in organ culture (74, 75), although in mice carrying null mutations for gelatinase B, a renal phenotype has not been reported (76, 77). Therefore, the soluble MMPs seem to overlap considerably with respect to their function. In addition, the sources of MMPs are potentially multiple. Mainly produced by the mesenchyme, they can be stored in the ECM and can also be produced by the UB and mIMCD cells themself in the presence of tubulogenic soluble factors (H Sakurai, M Pohl, SK Nigam, unpublished observations).

There are indications that the membrane-bound MT1-MMP, together with its inhibitors TIMP-2 and -3, plays an important role in the regulated local remodeling of the ECM during UB branching morphogenesis (43, 72, 75; H Sakurai, M Pohl, SK Nigam, unpublished observations). It is therefore tempting to speculate that soluble MMPs from potentially multiple sources are locally activated by MT1-MMP, a process probably regulated by TIMP-2 (78). TIMP-3, which binds to the ECM (79), could serve to protect the ECM close to the established branches and clefts from degradation. Local activation would establish gradients of MMPs with higher active concentrations at the tip than in the cleft. The concentrations of the inhibitors would then be expected to decrease toward the tip, effectively concentrating the active MMPs at the place of cell outgrowth (Figure 3).

Extracellular Composition

It is apparent that not only the ECM-degrading enzymes, but also the composition of the ECM itself and the cell matrix-interaction, potentially influence UB branching morphogenesis. Different matrices, such as collagen type I or the basement membrane preparation Matrigel, lead to morphologically different growth in three-dimensional gel cultures (12, 16). Hyaluronan in the ECM seems to increase cell survival and support branch formation via its receptor CD44, which is upregulated by growth promoting conditions in UB cells and localizes to the tips of cellular processes in three-dimensional culture (43; M Pohl, H Sakurai, RO Stuart, SK Nigam, unpublished observations). Individual components of the ECM seem to act as facilitatory and inhibitory factors for branching morphogenesis in MDCK branching (12). The significance of the ECM environment becomes clear through the fact that the UB in the absence of mesenchyme can be cultured only in the appropriate matrix milieu (17). This implies the requirement of cell adhesion molecules as receptors for various ECM molecules.

Integrins

Integrins appear to play a key role in branching morphogenesis through their interaction with different components of the ECM. A detailed catalogue of the integrin matrix interactions is beyond the scope of this review, and only a few examples are discussed here. The $\alpha_6\beta_1$ integrin binds to laminin (80); the $\alpha_3\beta_1$ integrin binds to collagen, laminin, and fibronectin (81); and the $\alpha_8\beta_1$ integrin appears to bind fibronectin, vitronectin, and tenascin (82). During the development of the collecting system the laminin α_1- and α_5-chains are found in the basement membrane of the branching murine UB at day 13 of gestation (83). Laminin α_2 seems exclusively expressed by the mesenchymal cells, but, nevertheless, weak staining (with immunohistochemical methods) is found in the basement membranes of the UB-derived structures (83).

Perturbing the expression of integrin-$\alpha_2\beta_1$ in MDCK-cells inhibits in vitro tubulogenesis (84). The integrin subunits α_3, α_6, and β_1 are expressed on the cell surface of the branching UB, and their blockade by antibodies in organ culture or in the case of α_3, in a targeted mutation, leads to smaller kidneys with fewer collecting ducts than in the control conditions (85, 86). The integrin α_v subunit is found on most cell types, including the UB and collecting ducts during metanephrogenesis, and its blockade leads to disorganization of the UB branches in organ culture (87). Most strikingly, when mice carry null mutations of the α_8 integrin subunit, kidneys either do not develop at all or are severely abnormal, although the expression of the $\alpha_8\beta_1$ integrin is restricted to the mesenchyme surrounding the UB and its developing branches (88). Therefore, $\alpha_8\beta_1$ integrin likely is involved in the early epithelial-mesenchymal interaction. On the other hand, some of the mutant mice develop smaller but sufficiently functioning kidneys to stay alive after birth, indicating that compensatory mechanisms must exist. As demonstrated by the isolated UB culture (at least with respect to early branching morphogenesis), compensating mechanisms are not necessarily mesenchymal cell dependent, but can be fulfilled to a certain extent by an artificial ECM environment (17). It will be important to study the role of these and other integrins in the three-dimensional UB cell culture system, isolated UB tissue culture, and other systems that are being developed in order to more directly attribute roles to specific integrins in various aspects of branching.

Proteoglycans

After growing into the MM, the UB becomes T-shaped, dichotomously branching for the first time before undergoing the many iterations of branching necessary for collecting system development. When the generation of heparan sulfate is impaired by targeted null mutation of the heparan sulfate 2-sulfotransferase, UB development is arrested at the point of the first branching event (89). This is particularly interesting because HGF is known to require binding to heparan sulfate (90), and TGF-β to betaglycan (91), for its proper function, and it may be that proteoglycans serve to locally concentrate these and other growth factors necessary for branching and outgrowth (92–94). Indeed, following the invasion of the MM, mesenchymal condensation does not occur in the heparan sulfate-deficient mice, expression of Wnt-11 is not detectable, and both c-ret and GDNF expression decreases rapidly (89). Given the fact that more general inhibition of heparan and chondroitin/dermatan sulfate production selectively inhibits UB branching morphogenesis without affecting mesenchymal differentiation (95), it would appear that some proteoglycans have a specific role in the cascade leading to branching and elongation of the UB, which could partly lie in their potential to bind soluble growth factors. Apart from HGF and TGF-β, FGFs are known to be adherent to proteoglycans (91, 93, 96). Therefore, cell surfaces with fewer proteoglycans are probably less sticky for these and other growth factors and not able to locally achieve appropriate concentrations necessary for proper branching; proteoglycans could serve to store growth factors in sufficient amounts near the cell membrane, ready to release them to or to interact with local receptors with higher affinity (94). The fact that branching morphogenesis of the isolated UB requires only soluble factors and the appropriate ECM environment supports the potential importance of the growth factor binding and cell adhesion capacity for this process.

Other Cell Adhesion Molecules

In addition to integrins and proteoglycans, the cell adhesion molecule L1, a member of the immunoglobulin superfamily, has been found to stain exclusively UB-derived structures at least until e15 (in the mouse), when multiple branching events have already occurred (97). Antibody inhibition of L1 resulted in a decrease of UB branching without loss of its capacity to induce proximal nephron formation, suggesting an important role in the process (97). L1 is known to form homodimers, but is also thought to dimerize with integrins, proteoglycans, GPI-linked cell adhesion molecules, and FGF receptors during neurite outgrowth, transmitting signals into the cell, where L1 binds to ankyrin and the actin-cytoskeleton (98). If its binding partners in the UB are similar, it could therefore play a role in modifying or regulating outside-in signaling from growth factors or the ECM.

Interplay of Growth Factors and Distal Effector Molecules

A complicated interplay of growth factors, matrix proteins, cell adhesion molecules, MMPs, and TIMPs is likely to be responsible for effecting the characteristic morphological changes seen in the developing collecting system (Figure 3). Additional complexity is illustrated by the example of HGF, which can be activated by urokinase (99), possibly produced at the branch tip. This conceivably can generate high local concentrations of HGF, which may bind tightly to local heparan sulfate–containing proteoglycans (96), creating a sustained local reservoir of HGF. Higher concentrations of HGF (acting through its receptor c-met) in turn may lead to alteration in the expression of MMPs, TIMPs, integrins, matrix proteins and, indeed, to generation of more urokinase (100). As the proteinases and new matrix proteins are secreted, they will change the physical and biochemical properties of the matrix, further altering its affinity for growth factors. Differences in the amounts and localization of growth factors will again affect the subset of MMPs, TIMPs, integrins, and matrix proteins expressed locally. The process could go through many such cycles, resulting in very different locally expressed subsets of these proteins, as an initial filopodial structure becomes a sprout and eventually a stable stalk in the developing tree. Analysis of the expression of large numbers of genes in various stages of branching tubulogenesis of UB cells supports such a dynamic model (43).

EFFECTOR MECHANISMS: CELL SURVIVAL VERSUS APOPTOSIS

Another essential mechanism of tissue remodeling for which examples abound is the process of apoptosis. As UB cells undergo branching morphogenesis in three-dimensional culture, both pro- and antiproliferative genes are expressed (43). In embryonic kidney, an interesting molecular mechanism has been postulated for the action of angiotensin on the angiotensin type-2 receptor (AT2R). Targeted deletion of the AT2R in the mouse leads to a spectrum of kidney phenotypes ranging from normal kidneys to complete renal agenesis. In the wild-type animal, much of the tissue that expresses the AT2R undergoes apoptosis. However, homozygous mutant mesenchyme fails to commit to apoptosis, presumably presenting a physical barrier to UB branching morphogenesis and subsequent induction of nephrons (101). Consequently, the phenotype may result from a variable encasement of the UB in mesenchymal tissues. It is important to remember that the final form of the urinary collecting system does not resemble a collection of evenly weighted, dichotomously branched tubes (1). Earlier generations of UB branches have been merged/resorbed to form large structures such as the renal pelvis and calyces. Such an arrangement could be generated by differential growth rates (or total time of growth) of various generations of the UB; however, it is likely that, here too, apoptosis plays a role.

SIGNAL TRANSDUCTION AND REGULATION OF GENE EXPRESSION

Regulation of Gene Expression

The effects of morphogenetic growth factor and ECM signals, which are transmitted through cell membrane–spanning proteins such as the receptor tyrosine kinases and integrins, converge at the level of gene expression. At the present

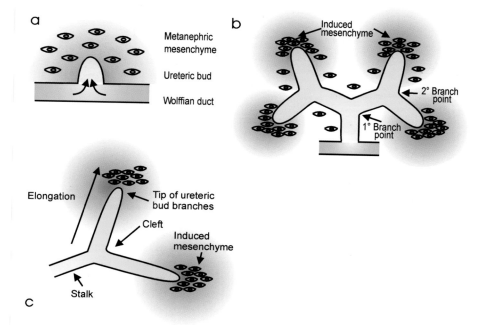

Figure 1 Ureteric bud development. (*a*) At embryonic day 11 (e11) the murine ureteric bud (UB) evaginates from the caudal Wolffian duct and invades the surrounding metanephric mesenchyme (MM). (*b*) It then branches dichotomously, and (*c*) its branches elongate, both processes occurring as a result of interaction (direct and indirect) with the MM, which condenses around the tips of the UB branches.

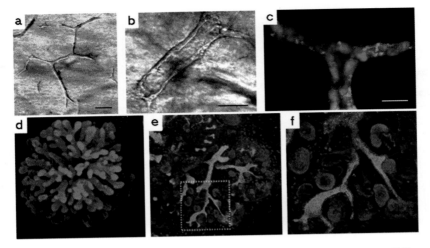

Figure 2 Model systems for investigating ureteric bud branching. (*a–c*) Cells derived from the ureteric bud (UB) of SV40 transgenic mice at e11.5 form multicellular branching tubules reminiscent of the developing collecting system when cultured in the appropriate extracellular matrix (ECM) and grown in the presence of conditioned medium from a metanephric mesenchyme (MM) derived embryonic cell line (BSN-CM). (*d*) UB tissue, dissected from the rat on e13 and devoid of mesenchymal cells, branches repetitively over several days, when cultured with GDNF, BSN-CM, and a permissive ECM environment. (*e, f*) When subsequently recombined with isolated MM, the UB branches appear to elongate and acquire directionality. Scale bars correspond to 50 μm.

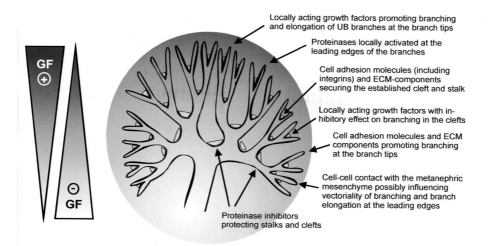

Figure 3 Model for ureteric bud branching morphogenesis. After induction of the ureteric bud (UB), in which the GDNF:c-ret axis appears to play a critcal role, UB branching may be guided by gradients of branching promoting (GF +) and inhibiting growth factors (GF -). Promoting factors might include HGF, EGFR ligands, GDNF and factor(s) in BSN-CM, whereas TGF-β family members may inhibit branching. Distal effector molecules probably include facilitating and inhibiting extracellular matrix (ECM) components together with signal transducing-cell adhesion molecules such as integrins, Ll or CD44, membrane-bound proteinase activators such as MT1-MMP and active proteinases (e.g. gelatinase B), as well as proteinase inhibitors such as TIMP-3, which binds to the ECM and could protect the matrix around the stalks from degradation. In this model, the local concentrations of such distal effector molecules would likely have a differential distribution in order to favor outgrowth at the tips, establishing branch points and refining shape at the stalks. As the isolated UB tissue culture system suggests, cell-cell contact with the metanephric mesenchyme may be necessary for vectoriality and/or elongation (adapted from Reference 8).

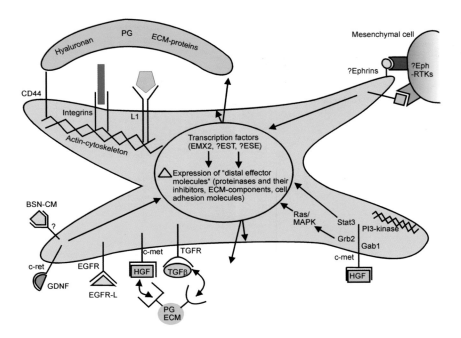

Figure 4 How soluble factors might alter gene expression in ureteric bud branching. Growth factors that regulate in vitro branching morphogenesis (GDNF, EGFR ligands, HGF, and factors in BSN-CM and TGF-β family members) signal to the nucleus, altering transcriptional activity of distal effector molecules. C-met-bound HGF promotes motility via PI3-kinase, requires Stat3 for its tubulogenic action, and increases growth via the Ras/MAPK pathway. Transcription factors, probably including EMX2, and possibly members of the ETS and ESE families, may regulate expression of distal effector molecules [proteinases and their inhibitors, cell adhesion molecules such as L1, integrins, CD44, and extracellular matrix (ECM) components]. The ECM in turn can act on cell adhesion molecules connected to the actin-cytoskeleton, sequester and therefore concentrate growth factors locally, probably by their affinity to proteoglycans (PG). A possible mechanism for cell-cell interaction with the metanephric mesenchyme is the Ephrin:Eph-receptor tyrosine kinase (-RTK) pathway, which may influence the vectoriality of branching.

time, however, there are no known master regulators of epithelial branching morphogenesis per se. Nearly every phenotype in published knockout experiments is the result of disruption of genes important early in renal development (*PAX-2, WT-1, LIM1, GDNF,* and other genes) prior to UB branching. An interesting exception is the transcription factor EMX2, which appears to be important for events linked to the first UB branching event. In mice carrying null mutations for EMX2, the UB is induced and invades the MM, but never reaches the T-shaped form, and the expression of *PAX-2, LIM1, GDNF,* and *c-ret* subsequently decreases from initially normal levels (102). Considered together with the fact that EMX2 is exclusively expressed by the Wolffian duct and the developing UB during early metanephrogenesis (102), the data suggest that EMX2 plays a role in the genetic regulation of UB branching morphogenesis (Figure 4, see color insert).

It is the intermediate events, between the initial outgrowth of the bud and the period of intensive repetitive branching, that are of primary interest here, because these signaling events presumably lead to the activation of transcription factors that regulate the expression of distal effector molecules such as MMPs, TIMPs, integrins, and ECM molecules, which are essential for proper branching. Homeobox genes may play a key role in this process, since collecting system development presents at least two types of patterning problems: regulation of branching events in the developing tree and structural (and thus functional) segmentation along the tree. In this regard, it is interesting to note that during UB cell branching in three-dimensional culture, a number of Hox genes are upregulated (43).

In another instance of branching morphogenesis, *Drosophila* tracheal system development, the details are somewhat clearer and may bear on branching morphogenesis of the mammalian UB. Briefly stated, the *Drosophila* tracheal system is a complex set of branching tubes. Branching morphogenesis of this system is dependent on the action of the genes *trachealess* and *tango* (103), both of which code for basic helix-loop-helix (bHLH)-period, aryl hydrocarbon receptor, single-minded (PAS) domain containing transcription factors. Recently, the clock gene, *Timeless,* (also coding for a bHLH-PAS protein) was isolated in a broad-based screen for differentially expressed genes in UB cell branching morphogenesis. Selective downregulation of *Timeless* mRNA expression markedly inhibited branching morphogenesis of the UB in both whole embryonic kidney explants and in the isolated UB (Z Li, RO Stuart, J Qiao, A Pavlova, M Pohl, SK Nigam, unpublished observations). Thus *Timeless,* a known circadian rhythm gene, appears to have an additional function either generally in the cellular response to growth factor stimulation or in the regulation (and possibly timing) of branching. In addition, spatiotemporal expression patterns of classes of transcription factors largely or exclusively expressed in epithelia raise the possibility that they may play a role in branching morphogenesis. These include the ETS transcription factor family and the related ESE (epithelial-specific ETS) family. Expression of ETS-1 is initially found in all developing murine organs but is mainly associated with organs undergoing branching morphogenesis in later fetal stages (104). ESE-

1 is an ETS-related transcription factor exclusively expressed in epithelial cells, including fetal lung and kidney, and is thought to be involved in epithelial differentiation (105). Interestingly, in *Drosophila* an ETS transcription factor, pointed ETS, has been found to be required for secondary branching and expression of terminal branch markers in the lung (106). Therefore, in addition to EMX2, which seems to be required for branching of the UB, these transcription factors are possible candidates for regulating UB branching morphogenesis (Figure 4).

Signal Transduction

Signal transduction mechanisms as they might relate to branching morphogenesis have been most extensively studied in the MDCK cell model of tubulogenesis and scattering. In this model, it has been shown that HGF, through its receptor c-met, produces three distinct effects—scattering, growth, and tubulogenesis—each apparently involving different intracellular pathways (Figure 4). Scattering of MDCK cells requires both the binding of phosphatidylinositol (PI)-3-kinase to the cytoplasmic tail of c-met and the involvement of the small GTP-binding protein Rac (107, 108). In mIMCD cells, PI-3-kinase has been shown to be important for tubulogenesis (48). Growth stimulation of MDCK cells relies on activation of a Ras-MAP kinase pathway, mediated by Grb2 (109), and tubulogenesis requires binding of STAT3 to c-met (110). The adaptor protein Gab1 can also bind to c-met, increasing the tubulogenic and scattering response, and is therefore thought to be part of the tubulogenic pathway (111). Multiple phosphorylation cascades modulate this pathway (112). In order to form tubules out of spherical cysts, cells form cellular processes, then multicellular cords, which subsequently cavitate and finally reorganize themselves to form continuous lumens. During this process, cell junctions and cell polarity are first lost and later reestablished in the tubule (13, 112). Although these dynamics have not been studied in tubulogenesis, in scattering, junctional disassembly and cell dissociation appear to require a degradation step mediated by the cytosolic proteasome, which may target junctional proteins, cell adhesion molecules, or modulators of these molecules (113).

FUTURE DIRECTIONS

The working model for branching morphogenesis of the urinary collecting system, which emerges from the various experimental systems described above, is quite different from one that might have been proposed several years ago. We now appreciate the fact that initial UB branching morphogenesis can occur in the absence of contact with the MM in response to GDNF plus (an) additional factor(s) present in BSN-CM. The role of the MM may then be more limited to production of soluble factors important for UB survival and branching and to promotion of elongation through either cell-cell contact or soluble factors. Of course, a detailed molecular description of this is largely lacking. Despite advances, many elements of the model for branching morphogenesis remain conceptualized only in broad strokes, with just a few details filled in. But some key molecules (e.g. GDNF and c-ret) are now known, and as we have discussed, a variety of likely candidate transcription factors and distal effector molecules have been identified, even if their precise role in the cellular processes necessary for branching morphogenesis remains to be elucidated. Application of new methods and reagents to whole embryonic kidney organ culture, the development of genetic models and more authentic cell culture models for UB branching morphogenesis, and isolated UB culture will surely help to connect the signaling pathways initiated by soluble factors to changes in transcription factor activity and expression of subsets of distal effector molecules necessary for branching morphogenesis. It will also be important to understand autocrine, paracrine, and other mechanisms that regulate this iterative process. In addition, little is known about the structural and functional segmentation of the collecting system during final differentiation, but it is possible that growth factors such as EGF play a role.

It is interesting to note that while the epithelial UB is branching into the surrounding mesenchyme, ultimately resulting in the formation of the post-filtration kidney, vessel development is occurring on the pre-filtration front via an angiogenic process mediated by mesenchymal signals that is conceptually similar to epithelial branching morphogenesis. Thus, on both sides of the mesenchyme similar morphogenetic events are taking place, a key distinction being that one cell type is epithelial and the other endothelial. Nevertheless, the similarities between the two cell types are well known. Even if not simultaneous, coordination of the two processes (and perhaps vasculogenesis in the mesenchyme itself) would seem to make certain teleological sense because the ultimate functioning of the kidney depends on the vascular side interfacing with the tubular side, thereby connecting the blood and extracellular compartment to the outside world. The fact that we often focus upon angiogenesis or branching tubulogenesis does not necessarily mean that these two processes are completely independent, and in future studies it may be worth considering their coordination, which is presumably mediated by the mesenchyme and/or mesenchyme-derived tissue.

ACKNOWLEDGMENTS

SK Nigam is supported by National Institutes of Health grant PO1 Dk54711–01, RO Stuart by the National Institute of Diabetes and Kidney Diseases grant D6 02392, and M Pohl by the Deutsche Forschungsgemeinschaft. We thank Jizeng Qiao, Dylan Steer, and Roy Zent for critical discussion of the manuscript.

Visit the Annual Reviews home page at www.AnnualReviews.org.

LITERATURE CITED

1. Al-Awqati Q, Goldberg MR. 1998. Architectural patterns in branching morphogenesis in the kidney. *Kidney Int.* 54:1832–42
2. Kanwar YS, Carone FA, Kumar A, Wada J, Ota K, Wallner EI. 1997. Role of extracellular matrix, growth factors and protooncogenes in metanephric development. *Kidney Int.* 52:589–606
3. Lechner MS, Dressler GR. 1997. The molecular basis of embryonic kidney development. *Mech. Dev.* 62:105–20
4. Nigam SK. 1995. Determinants of branching tubulogenesis. *Curr. Opin. Nephrol. Hypert.* 4:209–14
5. Sakurai H, Nigam SK. 1998. In vitro branching tubulogenesis: implications for developmental and cystic disorders, nephron number, renal repair, and nephron engineering. *Kidney Int.* 54:14–26
6. Saxen L. 1987. *Organogenesis of the Kidney.* Cambridge, UK: Cambridge Univ. Press
7. Stuart RO, Nigam SK. 1999. Developmental biology of the kidney. In *The Kidney.* ed. BM Brenner. Philadelphia: Saunders. In press
8. Horster M, Huber S, Tschöp J, Dittrich G, Braun G. 1997. Epithelia nephrogenesis. *Pflügers Arch.* 434:647–60.
9. Sakurai H, Nigam SK. 1999. Molecular and cellular mechanism of kidney development. In *The Kidney: Physiology and Pathophysiology,* ed. D Seldin, G Giebisch. Philadelphia: Lippincott-Raven. In press
10. Montesano R, Schaller G, Orci L. 1991. Induction of epithelial tubular morphogenesis in vitro by fibroblast-derived soluble factors. *Cell* 66:697–711
11. Montesano R, Matsumoto K, Nakamura T, Orci L. 1991. Identification of a fibroblast-derived epithelial morphogen as hepatocyte growth factor. *Cell* 67:901–8
12. Santos OF, Nigam SK. 1993. HGF-induced tubulogenesis and branching of epithelial cells is modulated by extracellular matrix and TGF-β. *Dev. Biol.* 160:293–302
13. Pollack AL, Runyan RB, Mostov KE. 1998. Morphogenetic mechanisms of epithelial tubulogenesis: MDCK cell polarity is transiently rearranged without loss of cell-cell contact during scatter factor/hepatocyte growth factor-induced tubulogenesis. *Dev. Biol.* 204:64–79
14. Sakurai H, Tsukamoto T, Kjelsberg CA, Cantley LG, Nigam SK. 1997. EGF receptor ligands are a large fraction of in vitro branching morphogens secreted by embryonic kidney. *Am. J. Physiol.* 273:F463–72
15. Barros EJ, Santos OF, Matsumoto K, Nakamura T, Nigam SK. 1995. Differential tubulogenic and branching morphogenetic activities of growth factors: implications for epithelial tissue development. *Proc. Natl. Acad. Sci. USA* 92:4412–16
16. Sakurai H, Barros EJ, Tsukamoto T, Barasch J, Nigam SK. 1997. An in vitro tubulogenesis system using cell lines derived from the embryonic kidney shows dependence on multiple soluble growth factors. *Proc. Natl. Acad. Sci. USA* 94:6279–84
17. Qiao J, Sakurai H, Nigam SK. 1999. Branching morphogenesis independent of mesenchymal-epithelial contact in the developing kidney. *Proc. Natl. Acad. Sci. USA* 96:7330–35
18. Torres M, Gomez-Pardo E, Dressler GR, Gruss P. 1995. *Pax-2* controls multiple steps of urogenital development. *Development* 121:4057–65
19. Shawlot W, Behringer RR. 1995. Requirement for *Lim1* in head-organizer function. *Nature* 374:425–30
20. Kreidberg JA, Sariola H, Loring JM, Maeda M, Pelletier J, et al. 1993. WT-1

is required for early kidney development. *Cell* 74:679–91

21. Moore MW, Klein RD, Farinas I, Sauer H, Armanini M, et al. 1996. Renal and neuronal abnormalities in mice lacking GDNF. *Nature* 382:76–79

22. Pichel JG, Shen L, Sheng HZ, Granholm AC, Drago J, et al. 1996. Defects in enteric innervation and kidney development in mice lacking GDNF. *Nature* 382:73–76

23. Sanchez MP, Silos-Santiago I, Frisen J, He B, Lira SA, Barbacid M. 1996. Renal agenesis and the absence of enteric neurons in mice lacking GDNF. *Nature* 382:70–73

24. Hellmich HL, Kos L, Cho ES, Mahon KA, Zimmer A. 1996. Embryonic expression of glial cell-line derived neurotrophic factor (GDNF) suggests multiple developmental roles in neural differentiation and epithelial-mesenchymal interactions. *Mech. Dev.* 54:95–105

25. Pachnis V, Mankoo B, Costantini F. 1993. Expression of the *c-ret* proto-oncogene during mouse embryogenesis. *Development* 119:1005–17

26. Vega QC, Worby CA, Lechner MS, Dixon JE, Dressler GR. 1996. Glial cell line-derived neurotrophic factor activates the receptor tyrosine kinase RET and promotes kidney morphogenesis. *Proc. Natl. Acad. Sci. USA* 93:10657–61

27. Jing S, Wen D, Yu Y, Holst PL, Luo Y, et al. 1996. GDNF-induced activation of the ret protein tyrosine kinase is mediated by GDNFR-α, a novel receptor for GDNF. *Cell* 85:1113–24

28. Sainio K, Suvanto P, Davies J, Wartiovaara J, Wartiovaara K, et al. 1997. Glial-cell-line-derived neurotrophic factor is required for bud initiation from ureteric epithelium. *Development* 124:4077–87

29. Treanor JJ, Goodman L, de Sauvage F, Stone DM, Poulsen KT, et al. 1996. Characterization of a multicomponent receptor for GDNF. *Nature* 382:80–83

30. Cacalano G, Farinas I, Wang LC, Hagler K, Forgie A, et al. 1998. GFRα1 is an essential receptor component for GDNF in the developing nervous system and kidney. *Neuron* 21:53–62

31. Enomoto H, Araki T, Jackman A, Heuckeroth RO, Snider WD, et al. 1998. GFRα1-deficient mice have deficits in the enteric nervous system and kidneys. *Neuron* 21:317–24

32. Schuchardt A, D'Agati VD, Pachnis V, Costantini F. 1996. Renal agenesis and hypodysplasia in *ret-k*-mutant mice result from defects in ureteric bud development. *Development* 122:1919–29

33. Pepicelli CV, Kispert A, Rowitch DH, McMahon AP. 1997. GDNF induces branching and increased cell proliferation in the ureter of the mouse. *Dev. Biol.* 192:193–98

34. Kispert A, Vainio S, Shen L, Rowitch DH, McMahon AP. 1996. Proteoglycans are required for maintenance of *Wnt-11* expression in the ureter tips. *Development* 122:3627–37

35. Davies JA, Millar CB, Johnson EM Jr, Milbrandt J. 1999. Neurturin: an autocrine regulator of renal collecting duct development. *Dev. Genet.* 24:284–92

36. Milbrandt J, de Sauvage FJ, Fahrner TJ, Baloh RH, Leitner ML, et al. 1998. Persephin, a novel neurotrophic factor related to GDNF and neurturin. *Neuron* 20:245–53

37. Donovan MJ, Natoli TA, Sainio K, Amstutz A, Jaenisch R, et al. 1999. Initial differentiation of the metanephric mesenchyme is independent of WT1 and the ureteric bud. *Dev. Genet.* 24:252–62

38. Maas R, Elfering S, Glaser T, Jepeal L. 1994. Deficient outgrowth of the ureteric bud underlies the renal agenesis phenotype in mice manifesting the *limb deformity* (*ld*) mutation. *Dev. Dyn.* 199:214–28

39. Davis AP, Witte DP, Hsieh-Li HM, Potter SS, Capecchi MR. 1995. Absence of radius and ulna in mice lacking *hoxa-11* and *hoxd-11*. *Nature* 375:791–95

40. Mesrobian HG, Sulik KK. 1992. Characterization of the upper urinary tract anatomy in the Danforth spontaneous murine mutation. *J. Urol.* 148:752–55

41. Ehrenfels CW, Carmillo PJ, Orozco O, Cate RL, Sanicola M. 1999. Perturbation of RET signaling in the embryonic kidney. *Dev. Genet.* 24:263–72

42. Mackenzie HS, Lawler EV, Brenner BM. 1996. Congenital oligonephropathy: The fetal flaw in essential hypertension? *Kidney Int. Suppl.* 55:S30–34

43. Pavlova A, Stuart RO, Pohl M, Nigam SK. 1999. Evolution of gene expression patterns in a model of branching morphogenesis. *Am. J. Physiol.* 277:F650–63

44. Holder N, Klein R. 1999. Eph receptors and ephrins: effectors of morphogenesis. *Development* 126:2033–44

45. Gao PP, Yue Y, Zhang JH, Cerretti DP, Levitt P, Zhou R. 1998. Regulation of thalamic neurite outgrowth by the Eph ligand ephrin-A5: implications in the development of thalamocortical projections. *Proc. Natl. Acad. Sci. USA* 95:5329–34

46. Wang HU, Chen ZF, Anderson DJ. 1998. Molecular distinction and angiogenic interaction between embryonic arteries and veins revealed by ephrin-B2 and its receptor Eph-B4. *Cell* 93:741–53

47. George SE, Simokat K, Hardin J, Chisholm AD. 1998. The VAB-1 Eph receptor tyrosine kinase functions in neural and epithelial morphogenesis in C. elegans. *Cell* 92:633–43

48. Cantley LG, Barros EJ, Gandhi M, Rauchman M, Nigam SK. 1994. Regulation of mitogenesis, motogenesis, and tubulogenesis by hepatocyte growth factor in renal collecting duct cells. *Am. J. Physiol.* 267:F271–80

49. Stuart RO, Barros EJ, Ribeiro E, Nigam SK. 1995. Epithelial tubulogenesis through branching morphogenesis: relevance to collecting system development. *J. Am. Soc. Nephrol.* 6:1151–59

50. Santos OF, Barros EJ, Yang XM, Mat-sumoto K, Nakamura T, et al. 1994. Involvement of hepatocyte growth factor in kidney development. *Dev. Biol.* 163:525–29

51. Sonnenberg E, Meyer D, Weidner KM, Birchmeier C. 1993. Scatter factor/hepatocyte growth factor and its receptor, the c-met tyrosine kinase, can mediate a signal exchange between mesenchyme and epithelia during mouse development. *J. Cell Biol.* 123:223–35

52. Woolf AS, Kolatsi-Joannou M, Hardman P, Andermarcher E, Moorby C, et al. 1995. Roles of hepatocyte growth factor/scatter factor and the met receptor in the early development of the metanephros. *J. Cell Biol.* 128:171–84

53. Bladt F, Riethmacher D, Isenmann S, Aguzzi A, Birchmeier C. 1995. Essential role for *c-met* receptor in the migration of myogenic precursor cells into the limb bud. *Nature* 376:768–71

54. Schmidt C, Bladt F, Goedecke S, Brinkmann V, Zschiesche W, et al. 1995. Scatter factor/hepatocyte growth factor is essential for liver development. *Nature* 373:699–702

55. Uehara Y, Minowa O, Mori C, Shiota K, Kuno J, et al. 1995. Placental defect and embryonic lethality in mice lacking hepatocyte growth factor/scatter factor. *Nature* 373:702–5

56. Kjelsberg C, Sakurai H, Spokes K, Birchmeier C, Drummond I, et al. 1997. Met -/- kidneys express epithelial cells that chemotax and form tubules in response to EGF receptor ligands. *Am. J. Physiol.* 272:F222–28

57. Threadgill DW, Dlugosz AA, Hansen LA, Tennenbaum T, Lichti U, et al. 1995. Targeted disruption of mouse EGF receptor: effect of genetic background on mutant phenotype. *Science* 269:230–34

58. DeChiara TM, Efstratiadis A, Robertson EJ. 1990. A growth-deficiency phenotype in heterozygous mice carrying an insulin-like growth factor II gene disrupted by targeting. *Nature* 345:78–80

59. Liu JP, Baker J, Perkins AS, Robertson EJ, Efstratiadis A. 1993. Mice carrying null mutations of the genes encoding insulin-like growth factor I (*Igf-1*) and type 1 IGF receptor (*Igf1r*). *Cell* 75:59–72

60. Ortega S, Ittmann M, Tsang SH, Ehrlich M, Basilico C. 1998. Neuronal defects and delayed wound healing in mice lacking fibroblast growth factor 2. *Proc. Natl. Acad. Sci. USA* 95:5672–77

61. Qiao J, Uzzo R, Obara-Ishihara T, Degenstein L, Fuchs E, Herzlinger D. 1999. FGF-7 modulates ureteric bud growth and nephron number in the developing kidney. *Development* 126:547–54

62. Hirai Y, Lochter A, Galosy S, Koshida S, Niwa S, Bissell MJ. 1998. Epimorphin functions as a key morphoregulator for mammary epithelial cells. *J. Cell Biol.* 140:159–69

63. Sakurai H, Nigam SK. 1997. Transforming growth factor-β selectively inhibits branching morphogenesis but not tubulogenesis. *Am. J. Physiol.* 272:F139–46

64. Piscione TD, Yager TD, Gupta IR, Grinfeld B, Pei Y, et al. 1997. BMP-2 and OP-1 exert direct and opposite effects on renal branching morphogenesis. *Am. J. Physiol.* 273:F961–75

65. Ritvos O, Tuuri T, Eramaa M, Sainio K, Hilden K, et al. 1995. Activin disrupts epithelial branching morphogenesis in developing glandular organs of the mouse. *Mech. Dev.* 50:229–45

66. Daniel CW, Silberstein GB, Van Horn K, Strickland P, Robinson S. 1989. TGF-β 1-induced inhibition of mouse mammary ductal growth: developmental specificity and characterization. *Dev. Biol.* 135:20–30

67. Serra R, Pelton RW, Moses HL. 1994. TGF-β 1 inhibits branching morphogenesis and N-myc expression in lung bud organ cultures. *Development* 120:2153–61

68. Joseph H, Gorska AE, Sohn P, Moses HL, Serra R. 1999. Overexpression of a kinase-deficient transforming growth factor-β type II receptor in mouse mammary stroma results in increased epithelial branching. *Mol. Biol. Cell* 10:1221–34

69. Zhao J, Sime PJ, Bringas P Jr, Gauldie J, Warburton D. 1998. Epithelium-specific adenoviral transfer of a dominant-negative mutant TGF-β type II receptor stimulates embryonic lung branching morphogenesis in culture and potentiates EGF and PDGF-AA. *Mech. Dev.* 72:89–100

70. Chinoy MR, Zgleszewski SE, Cilley RE, Blewett CJ, Krummel TM, et al. 1998. Influence of epidermal growth factor and transforming growth factor beta-1 on patterns of fetal mouse lung branching morphogenesis in organ culture. *Pediatr. Pulmonol.* 25:244–56

71. Wappner P, Gabay L, Shilo BZ. 1997. Interactions between the EGF receptor and DPP pathways establish distinct cell fates in the tracheal placodes. *Development* 124:4707–16

72. Kadono Y, Shibahara K, Namiki M, Watanabe Y, Seiki M, Sato H. 1998. Membrane type 1-matrix metalloproteinase is involved in the formation of hepatocyte growth factor/scatter factor-induced branching tubules in Madin-Darby canine kidney epithelial cells. *Biochem. Biophys. Res. Commun.* 251:681–87

73. Barasch J, Yang J, Qiao J, Tempst P, Erdjument-Bromage H, et al. 1999. Tissue inhibitor of metalloproteinase-2 stimulates mesenchymal growth and regulates epithelial branching during morphogenesis of the rat metanephros. *J. Clin. Invest.* 103:1299–307

74. Lelongt B, Trugnan G, Murphy G, Ronco PM. 1997. Matrix metalloproteinases MMP2 and MMP9 are produced in early stages of kidney morphogenesis but only MMP9 is required for renal organogenesis in vitro. *J. Cell Biol.* 136:1363–73

75. Ota K, Stetler-Stevenson WG, Yang Q,

Kumar A, Wada J, et al. 1998. Cloning of murine membrane-type-1–matrix metalloproteinase (MT-1–MMP) and its metanephric developmental regulation with respect to MMP-2 and its inhibitor. *Kidney Int.* 54:131–42

76. Liu Z, Shipley JM, Vu TH, Zhou X, Diaz LA, et al. 1998. Gelatinase B-deficient mice are resistant to experimental bullous pemphigoid. *J. Exp. Med.* 188:475–82

77. Vu TH, Shipley JM, Bergers G, Berger JE, Helms JA, et al. 1998. MMP-9/gelatinase B is a key regulator of growth plate angiogenesis and apoptosis of hypertrophic chondrocytes. *Cell* 93:411–22

78. Will H, Atkinson SJ, Butler GS, Smith B, Murphy G. 1996. The soluble catalytic domain of membrane type 1 matrix metalloproteinase cleaves the propeptide of progelatinase A and initiates autoproteolytic activation. Regulation by TIMP-2 and TIMP-3. *J. Biol. Chem.* 271:17119–23

79. Leco KJ, Khokha R, Pavloff N, Hawkes SP, Edwards DR. 1994. Tissue inhibitor of metalloproteinases-3 (TIMP-3) is an extracellular matrix-associated protein with a distinctive pattern of expression in mouse cells and tissues. *J. Biol. Chem.* 269:9352–60

80. Sonnenberg A, Modderman PW, Hogervorst F. 1988. Laminin receptor on platelets is the integrin VLA-6. *Nature* 336:487–89

81. Takada Y, Murphy E, Pil P, Chen C, Ginsberg MH, Hemler ME. 1991. Molecular cloning and expression of the cDNA for α_3 subunit of human $\alpha_3\beta_1$ (VLA-3), an integrin receptor for fibronectin, laminin, and collagen. *J. Cell Biol.* 115:257–66

82. Schnapp LM, Hatch N, Ramos DM, Klimanskaya IV, Sheppard D, Pytela R. 1995. The human integrin $\alpha_8\beta_1$ functions as a receptor for tenascin, fibronectin, and vitronectin. *J. Biol. Chem.* 270:23196–202

83. Sorokin LM, Pausch F, Durbeej M, Ekblom P. 1997. Differential expression of five laminin α (1–5) chains in developing and adult mouse kidney. *Dev. Dyn.* 210:446–62

84. Saelman EU, Keely PJ, Santoro SA. 1995. Loss of MDCK cell $\alpha_2\beta_1$ integrin expression results in reduced cyst formation, failure of hepatocyte growth factor/scatter factor-induced branching morphogenesis, and increased apoptosis. *J. Cell Sci.* 108:3531–40

85. Falk M, Salmivirta K, Durbeej M, Larsson E, Ekblom M, et al. 1996. Integrin $\alpha_6\beta_1$ is involved in kidney tubulogenesis in vitro. *J. Cell Sci.* 109:2801–10

86. Kreidberg JA, Donovan MJ, Goldstein SL, Rennke H, Shepherd K, et al. 1996. Alpha 3 beta 1 integrin has a crucial role in kidney and lung organogenesis. *Development* 122:3537–47

87. Wada J, Kumar A, Liu Z, Ruoslahti E, Reichardt L, et al. 1996. Cloning of mouse integrin α_V cDNA and role of the α_V-related matrix receptors in metanephric development. *J. Cell Biol.* 132:1161–76

88. Muller U, Wang D, Denda S, Meneses JJ, Pedersen RA, Reichardt LF. 1997. Integrin $\alpha_8\beta_1$ is critically important for epithelial-mesenchymal interactions during kidney morphogenesis. *Cell* 88:603–13

89. Bullock SL, Fletcher JM, Beddington RS, Wilson VA. 1998. Renal agenesis in mice homozygous for a gene trap mutation in the gene encoding heparan sulfate 2-sulfotransferase. *Genes Dev.* 12:1894–906

90. Deakin JA, Lyon M. 1999. Differential regulation of hepatocyte growth factor/scatter factor by cell surface proteoglycans and free glycosaminoglycan chains. *J. Cell Sci.* 112:1999–2009

91. Lopez-Casillas F, Wrana JL, Massague J. 1993. Betaglycan presents ligand to the TGF-β signaling receptor. *Cell* 73:1435–44

92. Carey DJ. 1997. Syndecans: multifunctional cell-surface co-receptors. *Biochem. J.* 327:1–16

93. Schlessinger J, Lax I, Lemmon M. 1995. Regulation of growth factor activation by proteoglycans: What is the role of the low affinity receptors? *Cell* 83:357–60

94. Taipale J, Keski-Oja J. 1997. Growth factors in the extracellular matrix. *FASEB J.* 11:51–59

95. Davies J, Lyon M, Gallagher J, Garrod D. 1995. Sulphated proteoglycan is required for collecting duct growth and branching but not nephron formation during kidney development. *Development* 121:1507–17

96. Lyon M, Deakin JA, Mizuno K, Nakamura T, Gallagher JT. 1994. Interaction of hepatocyte growth factor with heparan sulfate. Elucidation of the major heparan sulfate structural determinants. *J. Biol. Chem.* 269:11216–23

97. Debiec H, Christensen EI, Ronco PM. 1998. The cell adhesion molecule L1 is developmentally regulated in the renal epithelium and is involved in kidney branching morphogenesis. *J. Cell Biol.* 143:2067–79

98. Kamiguchi H, Lemmon V. 1997. Neural cell adhesion molecule L1: signaling pathways and growth cone motility. *J. Neurosci. Res.* 49:1–8

99. Naldini L, Vigna E, Bardelli A, Follenzi A, Galimi F, Comoglio PM. 1995. Biological activation of pro-HGF (hepatocyte growth factor) by urokinase is controlled by a stoichiometric reaction. *J. Biol. Chem.* 270:603–11

100. Ried S, Jager C, Jeffers M, Vande Woude GF, Graeff H, et al. 1999. Activation mechanisms of the urokinase-type plasminogen activator promoter by hepatocyte growth factor/scatter factor. *J. Biol. Chem.* 274:16377–86

101. Nishimura H, Yerkes E, Hohenfellner K, Miyazaki Y, Ma J, et al. 1999. Role of the angiotensin type 2 receptor gene in congenital anomalies of the kidney and urinary tract, CAKUT, of mice and men. *Mol. Cell* 3:1–10

102. Miyamoto N, Yoshida M, Kuratani S, Matsuo I, Aizawa S. 1997. Defects of urogenital development in mice lacking *Emx2*. *Development* 124:1653–64

103. Metzger RJ, Krasnow MA. 1999. Genetic control of branching morphogenesis. *Science* 284:1635–39

104. Kola I, Brookes S, Green AR, Garber R, Tymms M, et al. 1993. The Ets1 transcription factor is widely expressed during murine embryo development and is associated with mesodermal cells involved in morphogenetic processes such as organ formation. *Proc. Natl. Acad. Sci. USA* 90:7588–92

105. Oettgen P, Alani RM, Barcinski MA, Brown L, Akbarali Y, et al. 1997. Isolation and characterization of a novel epithelium-specific transcription factor, ESE-1, a member of the *ets* family. *Mol. Cell. Biol.* 17:4419–33

106. Samakovlis C, Hacohen N, Manning G, Sutherland DC, Guillemin K, Krasnow MA. 1996. Development of the *Drosophila* tracheal system occurs by a series of morphologically distinct but genetically coupled branching events. *Development* 122:1395–407

107. Ridley AJ, Comoglio PM, Hall A. 1995. Regulation of scatter factor/hepatocyte growth factor responses by Ras, Rac, and Rho in MDCK cells. *Mol. Cell. Biol.* 15:1110–22

108. Royal I, Fournier TM, Park M. 1997. Differential requirement of Grb2 and PI3-kinase in HGF/SF-induced cell motility and tubulogenesis. *J. Cell. Physiol.* 173:196–201

109. Ponzetto C, Zhen Z, Audero E, Maina F, Bardelli A, et al. 1996. Specific uncoupling of GRB2 from the Met receptor. Differential effects on transformation and motility. *J. Biol. Chem.* 271:14119–23

110. Boccaccio C, Ado M, Tamagnone L, Bardell A, Michieli P, et al. 1998. Induction of epithelial tubules by growth factor

HGF depends on the STAT pathway. *Nature* 391:285–88

111. Weidner KM, Di Cesare S, Sachs M, Brinkmann V, Behrens J, Birchmeier W. 1996. Interaction between Gab1 and the c-Met receptor tyrosine kinase is responsible for epithelial morphogenesis. *Nature* 384:173–76

112. Santos OF, Moura LA, Rosen EM, Nigam SK. 1993. Modulation of HGF-induced tubulogenesis and branching by multiple phosphorylation mechanisms. *Dev. Biol.* 159:535–48

113. Tsukamoto T, Nigam SK. 1999. Cell-cell dissociation upon epithelial cell scattering requires a step mediated by the proteasome. *J. Biol. Chem.* 274:24579–84

Annu. Rev. Physiol. 2000. 62:621–47

INTRARENAL DOPAMINE: A Key Signal in the Interactive Regulation of Sodium Metabolism

Anita C. Aperia

Karolinska Institutet, Department of Woman and Child Health, Stockholm, Sweden

Key Words Na^+, K^+ ATPase, hypertension, G protein-coupled receptors, ANP, Na^+, H^+ exchanger

■ **Abstract**   The kidney regulates sodium metabolism with extraordinary precision and sensitivity. This is accomplished by an intricate interaction between signals from extrarenal and intrarenal sources and between anti-natriuretic and natriuretic factors. Dopamine, produced in renal proximal tubule cells, plays a central role in this interactive network. Natriuretic hormones that are released from extrarenal sources, such as atrial natriuretic peptide, mediate some of their effects via renal dopamine receptors. On the level of the tubules, dopamine acts by opposing the effects of anti-natriuretic factors, such as angiotensin II and α-adrenergic receptors. Sodium retention leads to an increase in renal dopamine tonus, and the natriuretic effects of dopamine are more prominent under this condition. Inhibition or down-regulation of dopamine receptors significantly attenuates the natriuretic response to salt loading. Renal dopamine is modulated by the supply of filtered L-DOPA and the metabolism of dopamine via catechol-*O*-methyldopamine. The importance of dopamine as a natriuretic hormone is reflected by its capacity to inhibit the majority of renal tubule sodium transporters. Notably, the activity of Na^+, K^+ ATPase is inhibited in most tubule segments by dopamine. Recent studies have elucidated many of the signaling pathways for renal dopamine receptors. Novel principles for homologous and heterologous sensitization of dopamine receptors have been detected that may explain some of the interaction between dopamine and other first messengers that modulate renal tubule sodium transport. A broad understanding of the renal dopamine system has become increasingly important, since there is now strong evidence from both clinical and experimental studies that dysregulation of the renal dopamine system plays a role in many forms of multigenetic hypertension.

DOPAMINE, AN INTRARENAL HORMONE

The catecholamines dopamine, norepinephrine, and epinephrine are synthesized from the same precursors, the amino acid tyrosine and its hydroxylated product L-DOPA. Originally only norepinephrine and epinephrine were considered to be of functional importance. In the late 1950s the view emerged that dopamine, the

0066–4278/00/0315–0621$12.00

intermediate in catecholamine synthesis, may also have a transmitter role (1). Since that time dopamine has received enormous attention because of its important role in the regulation of behavior and motor function.

The role of dopamine as a regulator of renal function was first recognized in the early 1970s, when it was found that dopamine increased the glomerular filtration rate and sodium excretion (2). These observations led to extensive clinical use of dopamine to improve renal function in critically ill patients.

It soon became apparent that dopamine had a natriuretic effect, independent of the increase in glomerular filtration rate (GFR) (3). Studies on renal dopamine content and on the relationship between the amount of dopamine filtered and the amount of dopamine and dopamine metabolites excreted in urine first suggested that dopamine was formed in the kidney (4). This was confirmed by studies on the rate of dopamine formation from L-DOPA in slices and isolated proximal tubules (5, 6). For some time there was controversy whether the renal effects of endogenous dopamine were mediated via renal nerves or via locally produced dopamine. However, it was soon concluded that the natriuretic effects of dopamine were mainly mediated via locally produced dopamine. Today dopamine is generally recognized as an intrarenal natriuretic hormone with both autocrine and paracrine effects.

In 1986 it was reported that locally formed dopamine regulates the activity of the enzyme responsible for active sodium transport, Na^+, K^+ ATPase, in the rat renal proximal tubule (7). This was the first demonstration of short-term regulation of this important enzyme by a first messenger. Since then, numerous studies have unequivocally shown that dopamine inhibits both Na^+, K^+ ATPase and several other tubule sodium transporting pathways (for review, see 8). Other research has shown that most of the hormonal factors that have an effect on sodium excretion, will, in a variety of ways, interact with dopamine. Taken together, these observations have led to the concept that the intrarenal dopamine system is one of the major mechanisms by which sodium metabolism is regulated.

Sodium retention is common in hypertension, and treatment with natriuretic drugs generally lowers the blood pressure in patients with this disease. The function of the renal dopamine system in hypertension has been extensively studied in both patients and experimental animals, and there are strong indications that alterations in this system play a pathophysiological role in many forms of hypertension (for reviews, see 9, 10). Hence, factors that regulate the renal dopamine tonus have become important issues for research because they may be potential targets for antihypertensive therapy.

The goal of this review is to present the experimental evidence that has led to the conclusion that dopamine is a major regulator of sodium metabolism, to present some novel aspects on dopamine signaling pathways and the regulation of the renal dopamine receptor, to discuss the role of the renal dopamine system in the pathophysiology of hypertension, and to present the potential regulatory sites in the renal dopamine system.

HEMODYNAMIC EFFECTS

Low doses of dopamine, i.e. less than 5 μg · kg^{-1} · min^{-1}, have a vasodilating effect that is more pronounced in the kidney than in most other organs (2). Dopamine increases both renal blood flow and GFR. The effects on GFR are, however, not consistent (10). This may be due to the fact that even moderate doses of dopamine can also activate α − and β − adrenergic receptors. Studies on a single nephron level have shown that a dose of dopamine of 1 μg · kg^{-1} · min^{-1} causes a large increase in single nephron GFR and a more pronounced dilatation in preglomerular than in postglomerular arterioli (11). The vascular effects of dopamine are, in contrast to the tubule effects, elicited by dopamine released from renal nerves and by circulating dopamine.

DOPAMINE REGULATION OF SODIUM EXCRETION AND TUBULE TRANSPORTERS

Numerous studies show that dopamine causes a large increase in urinary sodium excretion that is mainly dependent on inhibition of tubule sodium reabsorption. This natriuretic effect, which is due to inhibition of both proximal and distal tubule sodium reabsorption (12), was first observed in studies where exogenous dopamine was administered. Since then, numerous studies have confirmed that administration of dopamine causes natriuresis by inhibiting tubule sodium reabsorption. The natriuretic effect of intrarenal dopamine was first demonstrated by the intravenous administration of a dopamine precursor to humans and of inhibitors of dopamine synthesis to humans and dogs (13–15). A recent elegant study by Wang et al provided direct evidence for a natriuretic effect of endogenous dopamine (16). By injecting rats with an antisense oligodeoxynucleotide into the renal interstitium, the expression of the dopamine 1 receptor was reduced by 35% to 46%. This procedure decreased urinary sodium excretion in rats on both normal and high-sodium diets.

It is important to note that the natriuretic effect of dopamine is prominent following salt loading and small or negligible following salt depletion (17, 18). This has implications for the regulation of GFR. Because dopamine inhibits proximal tubule sodium reabsorption, one expects that it should via the tubular glomerular feedback system, thus decrease the GFR. However, during volume loading and salt loading there is hardly any tubular glomerular feedback response. Studies on a tubule level have shown that dopamine inhibition of Na$^+$, K$^+$ ATPase is much more pronounced in proximal tubules from salt-loaded rats than from euvolemic rats (19, 20).

The importance of dopamine as a natriuretic hormone is reflected by its capacity to inhibit sodium transporters in almost the entire nephron (21). Dopamine inhibits the activity of Na$^+$, K$^+$ ATPase in the proximal tubule, the thick ascending limb of Henle, the distal tubule, and the collecting duct. Dopamine also has profound effects on sodium entry into tubule cells. It inhibits the activity of Na^+H^+ exchanger and the sodium phosphate cotransporter in the proximal tubule, the sodium chloride cotransporter in thick ascending limb (TAL), and the arginine vasopressin (AVP)-stimulated sodium transporter in the collecting duct. These dual effects on sodium in and out transport permit the tubule cells to decrease the reabsorption of sodium with little or no change in intracellular sodium concentration.

Na^+, K^+ ATPase

The energy for transcellular sodium transport is generated by Na^+, K^+ ATPase, which is located in the basolateral membrane in all tubule cells. Most tubule cells have a high abundance of Na^+, K^+ ATPase. In fact, the turnover of Na^+, K^+ ATPase is responsible for approximately 70% of renal oxygen consumption (22).

The main ligands of Na^+, K^+ ATPase are Na^+, K^+, and ATP. Because intracellular concentration of sodium is low, Na^+, K^+ ATPase is generally not saturated with regard to this ligand. Any increase in intracellular sodium concentration will therefore lead to activation of Na^+, K^+ ATPase. It was long believed that this was the only way by which this important enzyme was regulated. Studies on the effect of dopamine on renal tubule Na^+, K^+ ATPase changed that view (7). Dissected tubule segments turned out to be an ideal model for studies of hormonal regulation of Na^+, K^+ ATPase. They consist of homogenous cells with a high Na^+, K^+ ATPase activity, and the cells can be permeabilized under microscopic supervision to clamp intracellular sodium concentration. By use of this preparation, it was shown that activation of dopamine receptors can inhibit the activity of Na^+, K^+ ATPase in proximal tubules (23–25), in the thick ascending loop of Henle (26), and in the collecting duct (27). Furthermore, the model could be used to identify new dopamine signaling pathways, such as activation of protein kinase C and generation of arachidonic acid metabolites. Studies of dopamine regulation of renal tubule Na^+, K^+ ATPase led to the first demonstration of protein kinase A-(PKA) and protein kinase C (PKC) mediated phosphorylation of the catalytic subunit of Na^+, K^+ ATPase (28) and identification of PKA and PKC sites of phosphorylation. Site-directed mutagenesis studies have demonstrated that phosphorylation of the rat renal Na^+, K^+ ATPase catalytic subunit may directly inhibit enzyme activity (29) and cause a transient increase in intracellular sodium (30).

It now appears likely that dopamine regulation of Na^+, K^+ ATPase activity involves more steps than phosphorylation of only a single site of the catalytic subunit of this enzyme. There is evidence that dopamine-induced phosphorylation may also lead to internalization and subsequent inhibition of the enzyme (31). The mechanisms by which dopamine modifies the conformation and activity of Na^+, K^+ ATPase may be species dependent, since direct phosphorylation of Na^+, K^+ ATPase by PKC occurs with much higher stoichiometry in rat than in pig and dog (32).

The observation that dopamine regulates renal tubule Na^+, K^+ ATPase, has stimulated researchers to examine the effect of dopamine on Na^+, K^+ ATPase in basal ganglia (33, 33a), retina (34), vascular tissue (35, 36), and intestine (37). In all these tissues an inhibitory effect of dopamine on Na^+, K^+ ATPase has been observed.

Na^+, H^+–Exchanger

More than one third of sodium uptake in the proximal tubule cell occurs via the $Na^+ H^+$ exchanger. Dopamine inhibits the activity of the proximal tubule Na^+, H^+ exchanger (38–40). This effect, which may be mediated via the dopamine D1 receptor and adenylate cyclase stimulation, has been demonstrated in both intact cells and in brush border vesicles from proximal tubules. Dopamine antagonizes the stimulatory effect of α-adrenergic receptors and angiotensin on this transporter (41).

Na^+–Phosphate Cotransporter

Dopamine has, in addition to its natriuretic effect, a phosphaturic effect. The proximal tubule is the major site for phosphate reabsorption in the nephron. The rate-limiting step in this process is the Na^+-Pi cotransporter, located in the apical membrane. Locally formed dopamine inhibits the proximal tubule Na^+-Pi cotransporter (42–44) and increases phosphate excretion (45, 46). Dopamine inhibition may be mediated via both D1- and D2-type receptors. The D1 receptor may use the cAMP pathway to inhibit the Na^+-Pi cotransporter. There is also some evidence that other pathways may be involved. Dopamine opposes the stimulatory effect of serotonin on the Na^+-Pi cotransporter (47).

Other Sodium Transporters

Dopamine, applied from the luminal side, inhibits NaCl transport in the medullary thick ascending limb of Henle (48). The response is blocked by a selective D1 antagonist.

Dopamine inhibits vasopressin-dependent sodium transport in the collecting duct. The effect appears to be mediated by a D4-like receptor (49). The most likely target for this effect is the epithelial sodium channel. In the central nervous system, dopamine inhibits tetratoxin-sensitive sodium channels via D1-like receptors and activation of adenylate cyclase (50).

SIGNALING PATHWAYS

Expression of Dopamine Receptors

The dopamine receptors belong to the G protein-coupled receptor (GPCR) family. The diverse physiological actions of dopamine are mediated by at least five receptor subtypes, D1–D5. For reviews on dopamine receptors see References 10, 51.

The dopamine receptors can be divided into two subclasses: D1-like and D2-like. The D1-like receptors (D1 and D5) are characterized by their capacity to activate adenylate cyclase, and the D2-like receptors (D2, D3, and D4) by their capacity to inhibit adenylate cyclase. The D1 type but not the D2 type of receptor is intronless. The question whether the D2 type of receptors can be modified by alternative splicing has not been resolved

Information about the expression of dopamine receptors in the kidney has been obtained by use of a variety of techniques, including radioligand binding studies, immunohistochemistry, and PCR performed on renal tissue or specific nephron segments. The D1type receptor is present in most tubular segments (52–54) and is colocalized with D2 type receptors in the proximal tubule. The D3 receptor is the predominant member of the D2 type of receptor expressed in the kidney (55). There is evidence suggesting that D4 receptors are expressed in the collecting duct (56).

In situ hybridization studies of renal dopamine receptor mRNA have generally given negative results, but the much more sensitive RT-PCR technique has demonstrated the presence of D1, D3, and D4 mRNA in single tubule segments. Immunoreactive signals for renal dopamine receptors have been generally robust. This apparent discrepency in the expression between receptor messenger and receptor protein suggests that the turnover of the renal dopamine receptors is slow.

The interaction between dopamine and other catecholamines and their cognate receptors occurs within the membrane (57). Transmembrane domain 6, 5, and 3 of the receptor appear to be of particular importance for ligand binding.

It is generally agreed that among the two types of D1-like receptors, the original D1 receptor (also referred to as D1A in the kidney), plays an important role in mediating the natriuretic effects of dopamine. It is, however, possible that synergism between D1A and a D2-like receptor is required to achieve the full natriuretic effect (58, 59). Studies on whether D1 and D2 receptors interact with regard to the regulation of proximal tubule Na^+,K^+ATPase have given controversial results (24, 60). To resolve the question whether D1 alone can inhibit Na^+,K^+ATPase, studies will need to be carried out in the presence of D2 antagonists, since dopamine is normally present in proximal tubule cells. In the central nervous system, opposite effects of D1- and D2-like receptors are commonly observed. There is currently no indication that this should be the case in the kidney.

Intracellular Messengers

The renal dopamine receptors use a variety of intracellular pathways to produce their physiological tasks (Figure 1). The classical signaling pathway for the D1-like receptors leads to activation of adenylate cyclase, increased levels of cAMP, and PKA activation. PKA may either directly phosphorylate a target protein, such as a sodium transporting protein, or initiate a cascade of phosphorylation events

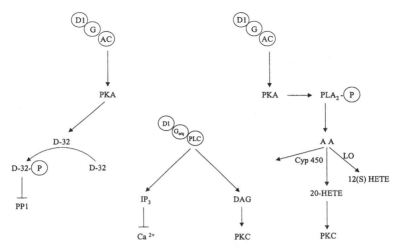

Figure 1   The renal D1 receptors may use several different intracellular signal pathways. They may couple to Gs proteins, activate adenylate cyclase, release cAMP, and activate PKA. This may lead to one of the following effects: PKA may directly phosphorylate a target protein, such as a sodium transporter. PKA may phosphorylate DARPP32 (D-32), which in its phosphorylated state is an inhibitor of protein phosphatase1. PKA may phosphorylate PLA$_2$, which leads to release of arachidonic acid and its metabolism into several unsaturated fatty acids that may activate PKC. Note that activation of classical PKC isoforms is, in the presence of these unsaturated fatty acids, independent of calcium release. D1 can also couple to PLC, which should lead to activation of PKC and release of calcium from the IP$_3$ stores.

by phosphorylation and activation of the dopamine and cAMP-regulated phosphoprotein DARPP32. In its phosphorylated state, DARPP32 is a potent inhibitor of protein phosphatase 1A (61) and is dephosphorylated and inactivated by the calcium-dependent protein phosphatase calcineurin. DARPP32 is highly enriched in the medium spiny neurons in the striatum, where it is of central importance for regulation of the efficacy of dopaminergic neurotransmission (62). In the kidney, DARPP32 is expressed in the proximal convoluted tubule and thick ascending limb of Henle (63). Phosphorylated, but not dephosphorylated, DARPP32 has been shown to inhibit the activity of Na$^+$,K$^+$ATPase in single TAL segments (64, 64a).

José and collaborators demonstrated in 1989 that the D1-like receptor could couple to phospholipase C (PLC) in renal tubule cells (65). This finding has since been confirmed in other studies (66, 67). The coupling occurs between the D1A receptor and PLC. What makes the D1A receptor select between adenylate cyclase or PLC coupling? There is no evidence that there are different classes of D1A receptors. The fact that D1A receptors can be actively recruited to the plasma membrane (described below) raises the question whether the interaction between the D1 receptor and a certain G protein may be related to the mechanism by which the receptor is transported to and inserted into the membrane.

Dopamine-mediated activation of PLC in the proximal tubule leads to the translocation of both classical and novel forms of PKC isoforms to the plasma membrane (68), where they initiate phosphorylation reactions that modulate the activity of the Na^+, K^+ ATPase and other integral membrane proteins.

Many of the physiological effects that follow activation of D1 receptors in proximal convoluted tubule (PCT) and cortical collecting duct (CCD) are mediated by phospholipase A2 (PLA_2) and subsequent release of arachidonic acid and its metabolites (69). It is suggested that this pathway is initiated by D1-dependent PKA phosphorylation of PLA_2. The predominant arachidonic acid metabolite in the mature kidney is the CYP 450 product 20HETE (70). Interestingly, the metabolic pathways for arachidonic acid in the renal tubules are developmentally regulated and appear to be altered in hypertension (71, 72). In proximal tubules from infant rat kidneys the lipoxygenase product 12(S)HETE is the predominant arachidonic acid metabolite (D Li, manuscript submitted). Whether these developmentally regulated switches in pathways have significant effects on dopamine regulation of sodium metabolism remains to be elucidated.

The unsaturated fatty acids, which are the metabolites of arachidonic acid, may exert their effects by direct interaction with a target protein that has a lipid binding site or they may, as 20HETE, activate classical and novel forms of PKC isoforms (73, 74). Activation of classical PKC isoforms by 20HETE, in contrast to activation of classical PKC isoforms by diacylglycerol, is calcium independent (74). Hence dopamine acting on PLA_2 may exert PKC-mediated effects in the absence of increased calcium concentration. This may be important for the physiological response, since the effects of PKA and PKC activation on the regulation of Na^+, K^+ ATPase activity are highly dependent on the intracellular calcium concentration (75, 76).

Homologous and Heterologous Sensitization of D1 Receptor

Studies of the expression of D1 receptors have been greatly facilitated by the development of a highly specific and well characterized antibody that recognizes the third extracellular loop of the D1A receptor (52). Immunohistochemical studies of D1A localization indicate that under basal conditions the majority of the D1A-like receptors are located intracellularly in the kidney (52), the heart (77), and in striatal neurons (A Aperia, unpublished observations). This prompted us to examine the function of these intracellular silent receptors in tubule cells.

It is generally agreed that GPCRs cycle between the plasma membrane and the cytoplasm. Information about the mechanisms by which receptors are internalized and desensitized is extensive thanks to the elegant work by Lefkowitz and coworkers (78). Internalization involves several steps of phosphorylation mediated by relatively specific receptor kinases, as well as by PKA and steps of protein-protein interaction, where arrestin plays an important role. The internalized receptors are inserted in vesicles or endosomes that have an acidic environment.

It has long been assumed that the recycling of these endosomes and vesicles and the insertion of the receptors in the plasma membrane are constitutive processes. Internalization of GPCR often occurs within a minute of ligand binding. The rapid desensitization of GPCR is undoubtedly of great importance in neurons, where signals of short duration are generally required. In the renal tubule cells, however, a sustained response is often needed. Inhibition of sodium reabsorption in response to a positive salt balance should last longer than seconds.

We studied the possibility that there is a regulated recruitment of renal D1A receptors to the plasma membrane using different approaches: confocal laser scanning microscopy of a proximal tubule-like cell line and LLCPK cells, and subcellular fractionation of rat outer renal cortex (79). With both methods, we found that exposure to increased availability of dopamine caused a recruitment of the D1A receptor to the plasma membrane. The effect was seen following incubation with dopamine, fenoldopam (a D1A agonist), the dopamine precursor L-DOPA, or by inhibition of the dopamine metabolizing enzyme catechol-O-methyltransferase (COMT). The effect was abolished by inhibition of the vesicular proton pump, which is responsible for the intracellular acidic environment. In a recently completed study we also observed that atrial natriuretic peptide (ANP) has the capacity to recruit D1A receptors to the plasma membrane in LLCPK cells and in rat renal cortical slices (80). The response was mimicked by cGMP, an ANP second messenger. ANP-mediated recruitment of D1A receptors also appeared to require dopamine binding to D1 receptors and PKA activation. The finding that ANP recruits the cytoplasmically located D1A receptors to the plasma membrane may offer an explanation for the ANP–dopamine interaction described below.

The heterologous receptor sensitization of D1A receptors by ANP may provide a novel principle for synergistic and additive effects between different GPCRs that modulate sodium metabolism and blood pressure. We have observed that neuropeptide Y, which has a synergistic effect on the activation of Na^+, K^+ATPase mediated by α-adrenergic receptors, prevents renal tubule α- adrenergic receptors from being desensitized (80). Our current hypothesis of how receptor recruitment may occur is illustrated in Figure 2.

Recent evidence suggests that active recruitment of receptors to the plasma membrane may also occur in neurons. Insulin has been shown to recruit GABA receptors to the plasma membrane in hippocampal neurons (81). During basal conditions, neuronal opiod receptors are located intracellularly but can be recruited to the plasma membrane by salt loading (82).

INTRARENAL DOPAMINE, A COMMON REGULATOR OF TUBULE SODIUM TRANSPORT

The finely tuned regulation of renal sodium excretion requires extensive interaction between the autocrine, paracrine, and endocrine factors. Dopamine plays a central role in this interactive process. Intrarenal dopamine can act in connection

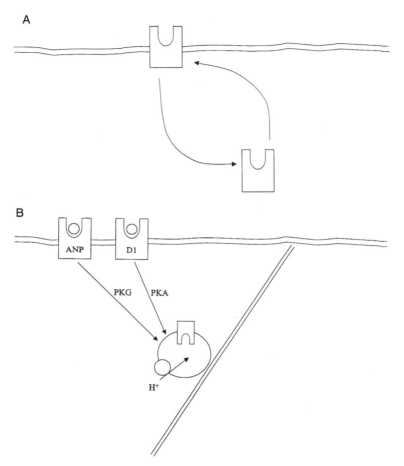

Figure 2   (*A*) G protein-coupled receptors cycle between the plasma membrane and the cytoplasm. The equilibrium between internalization (desensitization), and recruitment (sensitization) varies in different cell types. Although rapid agonist-induced desensitization is common in certain cell types and for certain receptors, rapid agent-induced recruitment is the case for the proximal tubule D1 receptor. Agent-induced recruitment creates a positive feedback and a sustained physiological response, which is beneficial in cells responsible for regulation of total body homeostasis. (*B*) Heterologous and homologous recruitment of D1 receptors to the plasma membrane is mediated by cGMP and/or cAMP. Recruitment is dependent on an acid environment created by the vesicular proton pump. Evidence from ongoing studies indicates that microtubules, which are abundantly expressed in proximal tubule cells, are required for recruitment.

with other natriuretic hormones and can oppose the effects of anti-natriuretic hormones (83). The manner by which dopamine interacts with other hormones can be divided into two categories: (*a*) short-term synergistic or antagonistic effects: e.g. dopamine interacting synergistically with ANP and antagonistically with α-adrenergic receptors and vasopressin; (*b*) long-term effects: e.g. dopamine down-regulation of the expression of angiotensin receptors and up-regulation of prostaglandin synthesis.

Dopamine Interaction with ANP

Between 1985 and 1992 several laboratories unanimously reported that the natriuretic effect of ANP required the presence of dopamine receptors (84–87). Furthermore, the inhibitory effect of dopamine on the Na^+,H^+ exchanger in the proximal tubule was potentiated by ANP (88). For unknown reasons, these interesting observations have not been followed up, and the mechanisms behind the ANP-dopamine interaction remain unknown. The finding described above, that ANP can recruit intracellularly located D1 receptors to the plasma membrane, would offer an explanation for how this peptide hormone facilitates the renal effects of dopamine.

The described interaction between circulating ANP and locally formed dopamine should contribute to a well-balanced regulation of sodium metabolism by allowing for adjustment between extrarenal salt and volume sensors and local renal sensors.

Dopamine Interaction with α — Adrenergic Receptors

In one of the first review articles on the role of peripheral dopamine in the pathophysiology of hypertension, Kuchel (89) wrote " . . . dopamine is the predominant catecholamine in fish but under salt-poor terrestrial conditions, when sodium retention becomes a main concern, dopamine takes a backseat to norepinephrine and other sodium retaining factors. These natriuretic and anti-natriuretic forces operate in a dynamic equilibrium and are linked, possibly in the form of a cascade." This visionary statement was soon supported by experimental data. First, Ibarra et al (90) demonstrated that dopamine inhibited Na^+,K^+ ATPase activity at saturating sodium concentrations, but not at low sodium concentration. In contrast, activation of α-adrenergic receptors stimulated Na^+,K^+ ATPase activity at low sodium concentrations, but not at saturating sodium concentration (5). The stimulatory effect of adrenergic receptors at low sodium concentrations was blocked by dopamine, as well as by one of its first messengers, cAMP. Conversely the inhibitory effect of dopamine at saturating sodium concentrations was blocked by the calcium-dependent protein phosphatase activated by an α-adrenergic receptor calcineurin (91). These data fitted well with the concept proposed by Kuchel. A model for the bidirectional regulation of tubule sodium transport by dopamine and α-adrenergic receptors is shown in Figure 3. Second, Baum & Quigley, who studied isolated perfused rabbit proximal tubules, found

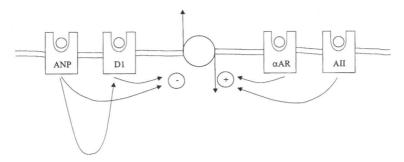

Figure 3 Bidirectional regulation of Na^+, KK^+ ATPase by anti-natriuretic and natriuretic factors. The equilibrium between these opposite forces is influenced by salt homeostasis. The effect of the anti-natriuretic forces is predominant in salt-depleted conditions but can be opposed by high levels of anti-natriuretic factors. The effect of natriuretic forces is predominant in conditions of salt excess but can be opposed by high levels of anti-natriuretic factors. Dopamine plays a central role in this bidirectional regulation by opposing the stimulatory effects of α-adrenergic and angiotensin receptors on salt reabsorption. Furthermore, the effects of ANP, which also opposes adrenergic and angiotensin stimulation, are at least partially mediated via dopamine receptors.

that dopamine antagonized the stimulation in transport produced by norepinephrine, but had little effect in the absence of a norepinephrine tonus (92). Third, Lederer et al found, in studies of opossum kidney (OK) cells, that the dopamine regulation of the proximal sodium phosphate transporter was potentiated by treatment with α-adrenergic receptor antagonists (93).

Dopamine Interaction with Vasopressin

It is well documented that the water permeability of the collecting ducts is bidirectionally regulated and that the water permeation effect of arginine vasopressin can be opposed by several hormonal factors, including dopamine (94). D2-like receptors are expressed in the collecting duct, and Sun & Schafer (49) have shown that a member of the D2 family, most likely a D4 receptor, inhibits AVP-dependent sodium and water transport and osmotic water permeability in isolated perfused rat cortical collecting ducts. Those results may have implications for understanding conditions with inappropriate water retention.

Dopamine Interaction with Angiotensin

The bidirectional regulation of tubule sodium transport involves both catecholamines and peptide hormones. There is evidence that dopamine opposes the anti-natriuretic effect of angiotensin on both short- and long-term bases (95, 96). Angiotensin II, in the dose range of 10^{-11} to 10^{-10} M, stimulates the activity of proximal tubule Na^+, K^+ ATPase (21). This effect is completely abolished in the presence of dopamine or its messenger cAMP. Dopamine may also have a more sustained effect on renal angiotensin tonus. Harris and coworkers found that dopamine, acting via D1-like receptors, decreased angiotensin 1 receptor mRNA and protein expression in the proximal tubule (96). The dopamine precursor L-DOPA had a similar effect.

Dopamine Interaction with Prostaglandins

Prostaglandin E2, produced in the collecting duct, has a diuretic and natriuretic effect. The mechanism of action is not completely understood, but it is generally believed that prostaglandin exerts its diuretic effect by counteracting the effects of arginine vasopressin. The natriuretic effect may be accomplished by inhibition of several sodium transporters, including $Na^+, K^+ATPase$. Dopamine has been reported to increase the urinary excretion of prostaglandins. This prompted Healy and collaborators to study the effect of dopaminergic agents on prostaglandin production in rat inner medullary collecting duct cells (97, 98). They found that dopamine, through a D2-like receptor, possibly a novel type of receptor in the D2 family, significantly enhanced the production of prostaglandin E2 within 10 min. This effect appeared to be mediated via PLA_2.

DOPAMINE METABOLISM

Renal dopamine metabolism has been extensively reviewed by Lee (99). The formation of dopamine has been studied in renal cortical tissue, renal tubules, and dispersed cells. The renal proximal tubule-like cell lines, LLCPK cells (79), and OK cells (100), which have dopamine synthesizing and metabolizing enzymes, have also been used as models for studies of the renal dopamine metabolism. The synthesis of dopamine differs in kidney and brain. In the brain, dopamine synthesizing neurons contain tyrosine hydroxylase (TH), which converts tyrosine to L-DOPA, which then, via aromatic acid decarboxylate (AADC), is decarboxylated to dopamine. The main source of renal dopamine is the proximal tubule, which lacks TH but has a high concentration of AADC. The dopamine precursor, L-DOPA, is freely filtered. L-DOPA is taken up by the proximal tubule cell via a sodium-dependent transporter in the apical membrane (101).

The L-DOPA supply to the proximal tubule influences the renal dopamine tonus. Acute administration of L-DOPA or γ–glutamyltranspeptidase (gludopa) results in a natriuresis (102), which is dopamine dependent and is accompanied by inhibition of the activity of renal tubule $Na^+, K^+ATPase$ activity (103). Armando and coworkers have shown that 3-O-methyldopa can also be converted into dopamine in the proximal tubule (104). It is possible that other compounds also serve as precursors of dopamine formed in the proximal tubule because the amount of filtered L-DOPA may not be sufficient to explain the renal production of dopamine, as judged by urinary excretion of dopamine and its metabolites.

Inside the proximal tubule cell, L-DOPA is rapidly decarboxylated to dopamine by AADC. AADC activity is up-regulated with a high-salt diet and down-regulated with a low-salt diet (20). The activity of AADC is high in the proximal tubules and almost negligible in the medulla.

Dopamine is very unstable in a nonacidic environment and would be rapidly metabolized in the proximal tubule cell if it were not protected. Remarkably little is known about the mechanisms by which dopamine is stored in proximal tubule cells. Nor is there any report on the presence of dopamine-containing vesicles or vesicular monoamino transporters in the proximal tubule cells. Alternative routes for the handling of proximal tubule dopamine are shown in Figure 4.

Dopamine can be both deaminated to DOPAC by monaminooxidases (MAO) and methylated to 3-methoxytyramine (3-MT) by catechol-O-methyltransferase (COMT) in renal tubule cells. COMT will methylate DOPAC to homovanillic acid (HVA). The activities of MAO and COMT are high in renal tissue compared with activity in other peripheral tissues. There are at least two isoforms of MAO present in the kidney, MAO-A and MAO-B. MAO-A is more important than MAO-B for deamination of renal dopamine (105, 106). Dopamine deamination by MAO in renal tubule cells and isolated tubular segments is a time-dependent process that occurs early after the decarboxylation of dopamine. In rat renal cortical slices incubated with L-DOPA, deamination by MAO was found to be the major metabolic pathway for renal dopamine. A scheme for the metabolism of dopamine in proximal tubule cells is shown in Figure 5.

In the intact kidney, COMT appears to play an important role for the physiological regulation of the renal dopamine tonus. Inhibition of COMT leads to a dopamine-dependent inhibition of tubule Na^+,K^+ATPase activity and to a profound dopamine-dependent natriuresis (103, 107). In contrast, MAO inhibition has little effect on urinary sodium excretion (P Hansell, personal communication).

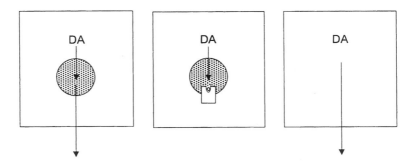

Figure 4   Alternative routes for dopamine transport out of the proximal tubule cell. Because dopamine is stable only in an acidic environment, it is highly likely that it is taken up by vesicles expressing an inwardly directed proton pump. The possibility that dopamine binds to its D1 receptor already in these vesicles (2) and that the ligand receptor complex is recruited to the plasma membrane cannot be ruled out.

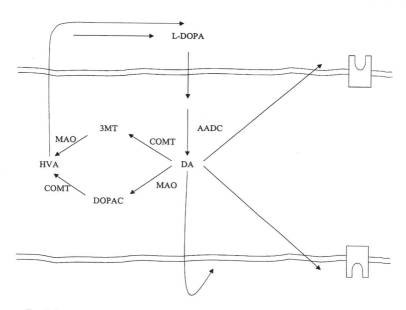

Figure 5   Scheme for dopamine metabolism in proximal tubule cells.

The COMT-induced natriuresis is much more pronounced than the natriuresis that accompanies the administration of L-DOPA (103). These findings raise the question whether the intracellular localization of COMT is such that it plays the most important physiological role for the regulation of the renal dopamine system and that MAO may be more of a housekeeping enzyme.

Dopamine formed in the proximal tubule can exit the cell either apically or basolaterally. Soares-da-Silva and coworkers have provided evidence that the basolateral outward transporter is dependent on sodium and pH and is developmentally regulated (108). Dopamine excreted in the urine is mainly derived from intrarenally formed dopamine. In clinical studies the urinary excretion of dopamine and its metabolite, HVA, is generally used as an index for renal dopamine production.

DYSFUNCTION OF THE RENAL DOPAMINE SYSTEM IN HYPERTENSION

For some years the prevailing theory on the nature of hypertension held that it was due to an excess of factors that produced vasoconstriction and sodium retention in the kidney. Obvious candidates for the factors involved were angiotensin and norepinephrine. This theory has been challenged by demonstrations that low levels of vasodilatory and natriuretic factors also predispose to hypertension. A more likely hypothesis is therefore that hypertension may be caused by a change in balance between vasodilatory and natriuretic factors, on one hand, and vaso-constrictive and anti-natriuretic factors, on the other hand. This theory would better fit with the concept that the cause of hypertension is, with few exceptions, multi-factorial. An abundance of circumstantial evidence (some of which has been presented above) suggests that dopamine plays a central role as a counter-regulator of the hypertensive effects of angiotensin and norepinephrine and that a regularly functioning renal dopamine system is essential for maintaining normal arterial blood pressure throughout life (for review, see 59, 109, 110).

Functional studies of the renal dopamine system in humans have, for natural reasons, been limited to determinations of urinary dopamine excretion. As stated above, the urinary excretion of dopamine may be used as an index of renal dopa-mine production. Numerous studies, performed with different ethnic groups, have confirmed that the dopaminuric response to sodium loading, seen in healthy indi-viduals, may be blunted in patients with hypertension (111–113). Attenuation of the dopaminuric response has also been observed in hypertensive individuals (114) and in young normotensive individuals with a family history of hyperten-sion (115, 116). Renal dopamine production increases in response to high protein intake. This response is blunted in prehypertensive individuals (117). Taken together these clinical studies indicate that an inability to decrease dopamine availability may contribute to the development of salt-sensitive hypertension.

Clinical studies have also provided genetic evidence for the role of dopamine as a counter-regulator of hypertension (118). A few cases of dopamine beta hydroxylase deficiency have been described. These patients have low norepi-nephrine/ epinephrine levels and increased dopamine levels, as measured in blood and cerebrospinal fluid. The most prominent symptom is orthostatic hypotension. Individuals that have an AADC deficiency also suffer from hypotension.

Experimental evidence for a role of dopamine in hypertension has been obtained from studies on rats strains that are genetically predisposed to develop hypertension and from transgenic mice lacking subtypes of dopamine receptors. The first demonstration of defective function of renal dopamine receptors in these genetically altered rats was made in 1989 by Kinoshita et al (119). They showed that in contrast to the normotensive WKY rats, SHR rats express only low-affinity dopamine receptors in the proximal tubule and that this defect is accompanied by an inability of the proximal tubule D1 receptor to activate adenylate cyclase. Subsequent studies from several laboratories have confirmed and extended this finding (9, 120–122). A coupling defect between the renal D1-like receptor and PLC and an inability to inhibit the activity of Na^+, K^+ ATPase have been described IN SHR rats by Lokhandwala and coworkers (123, 123a, 124). A blunted capacity to activate adenylate cyclase and inhibit Na^+, K^+ ATPase was observed in the Dahl salt-sensitive rat, which develops hypertension when chal-lenged with a high salt load (125). The defect coupling of the D1 receptor in the hypertensive-prone rats appears to be organ-segment specific. In a recent study, José and coworkers (126) examined proximal tubule cells from nephrectomized hypertensive individuals and noted that they exhibit a similar coupling defect of the D1 receptor. This finding may shed light on one of the more important contributing defects in salt-dependent hypertension. It will be of great interest to find out whether the uncoupling of the D1 receptor from its effector enzymes may be related to a defect in the cycling and recruitment of D1 receptors described above. Defect coupling of dopamine receptors is not the only cellular abnormality observed in SHR and Dahl salt-sensitive rats. This is not surprising if we consider hypertension as a change in the balance between natriuretic/vasoconstrictive and anti-natriuretic/vasodilating factors.

Further evidence for an involvement of dopamine as a counter-regulator of hypertension has been obtained from studies on mice lacking either the D1 or the D3 receptor. Mice lacking one or both D1 receptor alleles have a blunted response to sodium loading and develop diastolic hypertension (127). Disruption of the D3 receptor gene results in a blunted natriuretic response to sodium loading and hypertension (128). This effect is at least partially due to the loss of inhibition of renin production normally exerted by the renal D3 receptor (129).

DOPAMINE IN THE DEVELOPING KIDNEY

Components of the dopamine system are already expressed in the immature kidney. Both AADC and COMT are expressed from at least day 20 in embryonic rats (130, 131). DARPP32 is present from embryonic day 18 (132). Interestingly, DARPP32 expression is mainly seen in the ureteric buds, i. e. the epithelium that induces nephron formation. The dopamine content of the neonatal rat kidney is relatively high, and the dopamine/norepinephrine ratio is higher in 3-day old rats than in 20-, 40- or 80-day old rats (130, 133, 134). There is evidence from functional studies in lambs and infant rats that the renal response to dopamine is blunted with regard to natriuresis and inhibition of Na^+, K^+ ATPase. This raises the question whether dopamine has a role other than regulating salt metabolism in the late embryonic and infant kidney. In other tissues, dopamine has been demonstrated to activate transcriptional factors and be important for development (135, 136).

POTENTIAL THERAPEUTIC STRATEGIES

Because dopamine acts both as a neurotransmittor and an intrarenal natriuretic hormone, it is important that drugs developed to enhance the renal dopamine tonus are mainly targeting the kidney. Gludopa (137) is potentially such a drug. Gludopa is converted to L-DOPA by γ–glutamyltranspeptidase (γ–GT), an enzyme that is almost exclusively located in the apical membrane of proximal tubule cells (138). Gludopa has a natriuretic effect in both humans and rats. In hypertensive individuals, acute administration of gludopa results in a pronounced natriuresis associated with a fall in blood pressure (139, 140). Unfortunately, it is not yet possible to prove the long-term benefit of gludopa treatment in hypertensive individuals. This may be due in part to poor bioavailability of the drug.

Gludopa-like drugs may also be used as phosphaturics. It was recently shown in rats that gludopa inhibited the sodium phosphate cotransporter of the apical membrane in the proximal tubule apical membrane, which resulted in a substantial increase in urinary phosphate excretion, as well as a decrease in serum phosphate concentration (44). It may also be possible to use COMT inhibitors to enhance the renal dopaminergic tonus, since the COMT inhibitor nitecapone (141), which acts only on peripheral COMT, had a profound natriuretic effect that is considerably more pronounced than that of gludopa.

The observation that oxidative stress may decrease the number of proximal tubule functional D1 receptors (142) implies that it may be worthwhile to test antioxidant drugs on the effect of functioning D1 receptors. This would be of particular interest in situations where there is a reason to assume that the number of functioning D1 receptors present in the plasma membrane is decreased and/or that the coupling to G proteins is defective.

The recent observation that the availability of D1 receptors in the plasma membrane may be regulated by hormones other than dopamine could open up new therapeutic possibilities. ANP, which targets D1 receptors to the plasma membrane and appears to have many of its renal effects mediated via the D1 receptor, may be of particular interest in this respect.

PERSPECTIVES

Phylogenetically, dopamine is probably the first functioning catecholamine. It is therefore likely that many of the principles by which dopamine accomplishes its physiological task can be applied to many other first messengers that couple to GPCR. Future studies on the interaction between dopamine and its receptors, on how dopamine synergizes with other natriuretic factors, and on how dopamine opposes the effects of anti-natriuretic factors will provide further insights into principles for regulation of cell function and homeostasis.

Studies on the spatial localization of the dopamine receptor have revealed that recruitment (sensitization) as well as internalization (desensitization) of GPCR to and from the plasma membrane are regulated processes. Most likely the equilibrium between these processes differs markedly depending on cell type. It seems plausible that in the renal tubules, which modulate responses that should last for minutes or even hours, a sensitization response is generally biologically more appropriate than a rapid desensitization response. Studies on the sensitization of renal dopamine receptors should further elucidate the mechanisms by which hormones control salt homeostasis and may give an insight into the pathophysiology of sodium homeostasis in various forms of hypertension.

The role of dopamine in the embryonic and infant kidney needs to be further clarified. Whether intrarenal dopamine induces transcriptional factors and is important for growth and development remains to be studied.

The renal dopamine system is sensitized by high salt intake and volume expansion. Further studies on how salt intake influences renal dopamine availability and the inhibitory effect of dopamine on Na^+, K^+ ATPase and other sodium transporters may offer insight into the function of intrarenal sodium sensors.

Appropriate regulation of renal dopamine tonus is one important requisite for the maintenance of sodium homeostasis and normal blood pressure. Further studies need to be done on which factors determine the dopamine availability in the nephron. Such studies may lead to the development of new therapeutic strategies in conditions of salt retention and hypertension. Identification of the various steps of crucial importance for the regulation of the renal dopamine tonus should provide us with new tools for early genetic diagnosis of individuals that are predisposed to developing hypertension.

Visit the Annual Reviews home page at www.AnnualReviews.org.

LITERATURE CITED

1. Carlsson A, Lindqvist M, Magnusson T, Waldeck B. 1958. On the presence of 3-hydroxytyramine in brain. *Science* 127:471

2. Goldberg LI. 1972. Cardiovascular and renal actions of dopamine: potential clinical applications. *Pharmacol. Rev.* 24(1): 1–29

3. McGrath BP, Bode K, Luxford A, Howden B, Jablonski P. 1985. Effects of dopamine on renal function in the rat isolated perfused kidney. *Clin. Exp. Pharmacol. Physiol.* 12:343–52

4. Ball SG, Oates NS, Lee MR. 1978. Urinary dopamine in man and rat: effects of inorganic salts on dopamine excretion. *Clin. Sci. Mol. Med.* 55:167–73

5. Baines AD, Drangova R. 1984. Dopamine production by the isolated perfused rat kidney. *Can. J. Physiol. Pharmacol.* 62(3):272–76

6. Baines AD, Drangova R, Hatcher C. 1985. Dopamine production by isolated glomeruli and tubules from rat kidneys. *Can. J. Physiol. Pharmacol.* 63(2):155–58

7. Aperia A, Bertorello A, Seri I. 1987. Dopamine causes inhibition of Na^+, K^+ ATPase activity in rat proximal convoluted tubule segments. *Am. J. Physiol.* 252:F39–45

8. Aperia A. 1994. Dopamine action and metabolism in the kidney. *Curr. Opin. Nephrol. Hypertens.* 3:39–45

9. José PA, Eisner GM, Drago J, Carey RM, Felder RA. 1996. Dopamine receptor signaling defects in spontaneous hypertension. *Am. J. Hypertens.* 9:400–5

10. José PA, Eisner GM, Felder RA. 1998. Renal dopamine receptors in health and hypertension. *Pharmacol. Ther.* 80(2): 149–82

11. Seri I, Aperia A. 1988. Contribution of dopamine2 receptors to the dopamine-induced increase in glomerular filtration rate. *Am. J. Physiol.* 254:F196–20

12. Hughes J, Beck T, Rose C Jr, Carey RM. 1988. The effect of selective dopamine-1 stimulation on renal and adrenal function in man. *J. Clin. Endocrinol. Metab.* 66:518–25

13. Siragy HM, Felder RA, Howell NL, Chevalier RL, Peach MJ, Carey RM. 1989. Evidence that intrarenal dopamine acts as

a paracrine substance at the renal tubule. *Am. J. Physiol.* 257:F469–77

14. Ball SG, Lee MR. 1977. The effect of carbidopa administration on urinary sodium excretion in man. Is dopamine an intrarenal natriuretic hormone? *Br. J. Clin. Pharmacol.* 4:115–19

15. Frederickson ED, Bradley T, Goldberg LI. 1985. Blockade of renal effects of dopamine in the dog by the DA$_1$ antagonist SCH 23390. *Am. J. Physiol.* 249:F236–40

16. Wang ZQ, Felder RA, Carey RM. 1999. Selective inhibition of the renal dopamine subtype D$_{1A}$ receptor induces antinatriuresis in conscious rats. *Hypertension* 33:504–10

17. Wang ZQ, Siragy HM, Felder RA, Carey RM. 1997. Intrarenal dopamine production and distribution in the rat: physiological control of sodium excretion. *Hypertension* 29:228–34

18. Hansell P, Fasching A. 1991. The effect of dopamine receptor blockade on natriuresis is dependent on the degree of hypervolemia. *Kidney Int.* 39(2):253–58

19. Bertorello A, Hökfelt T, Goldstein M, Aperia A. 1988. Proximal tubule Na-KATPase activity is inhibited during high salt diet: evidence for DA-mediated effect. *Am. J. Physiol.* 254:F795–801

20. Seri I, Kone BC, Gullans SR, Aperia A, Brenner BM, Ballermann BJ. 1990. Influence of Na$^+$ intake on dopamine-induced inhibition of renal cortical Na$^+$, K$^+$ATPase. *Am. J. Physiol.* 258:F52–60

21. Aperia A, Holtbäck U, Syrén M-L, Svensson L-B, Fryckstedt J, Greengard P. 1994. Activation/deactivation of renal Na$^+$, K$^+$-ATPase: A final common pathway for regulation of natriuresis. *FASEB J.* 8:436–39

22. Clausen T, van Hardeveld C, Everts ME. 1991. Significance of cation transport in control of energy metabolism and thermogenesis. *Physiol. Rev.* 71(3):733–63

23. Baines AD, Ho P, Drangova R. 1992. Proximal tubular dopamine production

regulates basolateral Na-K-ATPase. *Am. J. Physiol.* 262:F566–71

24. Chen C, Lokhandwala MF. 1993. Inhibition of Na$^+$/K$^+$ATPase activity in rat renal proximal tubules by dopamine involved DA-1 receptor activation. *Naunyn Schmiedebergs Arch. Pharmacol.* 347:289–95

25. Seri I, Kone BC, Gullans SR, Aperia A, Brenner BM, Ballermann BJ. 1988. Locally formed dopamine inhibits Na-KATPase activity in rat renal cortical tubule cells. *Am. J. Physiol.* 255:F666–73

26. Fryckstedt J, Aperia A. 1992. Sodium-dependent regulation of sodium, potassium-adenosine-tri-phosphatase (Na$^+$, K$^+$-ATPase) activity in medullary thick ascending limb of Henle segments. Effect of cyclic-adenosine-monophosphatase guanosine-nucleotide-binding-protein activity and arginine vasopressin. *Acta Physiol. Scand.* 144:185–90

27. Takemoto F, Cohen HT, Satoh T, Katz AI. 1992. Dopamine inhibits Na/K-ATPase in single tubules and cultured cells from distal nephron. *Pflügers Arch.* 421:302–6

28. Bertorello A, Aperia A, Walaas I, Nairn AC, Greengard P. 1991. Phosphorylation of the catalytic subunit of Na$^+$/K$^+$-ATPase inhibits the activity of the enzyme. *Proc. Natl. Acad. Sci. USA* 88:11359–62

29. Fisone G, Cheng S X-J, Nairn AC, Czernik AJ, Hemmings HC Jr, Höög J-O, et al. 1994. Identification of the phosphorylation site for cAMP-dependent protein kinase on Na$^+$/K$^+$ATPase and effects of site-directed mutagenesis. *J. Biol. Chem.* 269 (12): 9368–73

30. Belusa R, Wang Z, Matsubara T, Sahlgren B, Dulubova I, et al. 1997. Mutation of the site of protein kinase C phosphorylation on rat α1 Na$^+$/K$^+$ATPase alters regulation of intracellular Na$^+$, pH and

influences cell shape and adhesiveness. *J. Biol. Chem.* 272:20179–84

31. Chibalin AV, Ogimoto G, Pedemonte CH, Pressley TA, Katz AI, et al. 1999. Dopamine-induced endocytosis of Na^+/K^+ ATPase is initiated by phosphorylation of Ser-18 in the rat alpha subunit and is responsible for the decreased activity in epithelial cells. *J. Biol. Chem.* 274(4):1920–27

32. Feschenko MS, Sweadner KJ. 1995. Structural basis for species-specific differences in the phosphorylation of Na,K-ATPase by protein kinase C. *J. Biol. Chem.* 270:14072–77

33. Bertorello A, Aperia A. 1990. Inhibition of proximal tubule Na^+/K^+ ATPase activity requires simultaneous activation of DA1 and DA2 receptors. *Am. J. Physiol.* 259:F924–28

33a. Bertorello AM, Hopfield JF, Aperia A, Greengard P. 1990. Inhibition by dopamine (Na^+, K^+)ATPase activity in neostriatal neurons through D1 and D2 dopamine receptor synergism. *Nature* 347:386–88

34. Shulman LM, Fox DA. 1996. Dopamine inhibits mammalian photoreceptor Na^+,K^+-ATPase activity via a selective effect on the $\alpha3$ isozyme. *Proc. Natl. Acad. Sci. USA* 93:8034–39

35. Rashed SMK, Songu-Mize E. 1996. Regulation of Na^+,K^+-ATPase activity by dopamine in cultured rat aortic smooth muscle cells. *Eur. J. Pharmacol.* 305:223–30

36. Borin ML. 1997. Dual inhibitory effects of dopamine on Na^+ homeostasis in rat aorta smooth muscle cells. *Am. J. Physiol.* 272:C428–38

37. Vieira-Coelho MA, Lucas Teixeira VA, Finkel Y, Soares-da-Silva P, Bertorello AM. 1998. Dopamine-dependent inhibition of jejunal Na^+,K^+-ATPase during high-salt diet in young but not in adult rats. *Am. J. Physiol.* 275:G1317–23

38. Felder CC, Campbell T, Albrecht F, José PA. 1990. Dopamine inhibits Na^+,H^+

exchanger activity in renal BBMV by stimulation of adenylate cyclase. *Am. J. Physiol.* 259:F297–303

39. Felder CC, Albrecht FE, Campbell T, Eisner GM, José PA. 1993. Cyclic AMP independent G protein linked inhibition of Na^+/H^+ exchange activity in renal cortical brush border membranes by dopamine-1 agonists. *Am. J. Physiol.* 264:F1032–37

40. Jadhav AL, Liu Q. 1992. DA1 receptor mediated regulation of Na^+-H^+ antiport activity in rat renal cortical brush border membrane vesicles. *Clin. Exp. Hypertens.* A14:653–66

41. Gesek FA, Schoolwerth AC. 1990. Hormonal interactions with the proximal Na^+-H^+ exchanger. *Am. J. Physiol.* 258:F514–21

42. Perrichot R, Garcia-Ocana A, Couette S, Comoy E, Amiel C, Friedlander G. 1995. Locally formed dopamine modulates renal Na-P_i co-transport through DA_1 and DA_2 receptors. *Biochem. J.* 312:433–37

43. Baines AD, Drangova R. 1997. Regulation of sodium transport by endogenous dopamine production in proximal tubular and OK cells. *Clin. Exp. Hypertens.* 19(1–2):87–91

44. de Toledo F, Thompson MA, Bolliger C, Tyce GM, Dousa TP. 1999. γ-L-DOPA inhibits Na^+-phosphate cotransport across renal brush border membranes and increases renal excretion of phosphate. *Kidney Int* 55:1832–42

45. Debska-Slizien A, Ho, P, Drangova R, Baines AD. 1994. Endogenous renal dopamine production regulates phosphate excretion. *Am. J. Physiol.* 266: F858–67

46. LeClaire MM, Berndt TJ, Knox FG. 1998. Effect of renal interstitial infusion of L-dopa on sodium and phosphate excretions. *J. Lab. Clin. Med.* 132:308–12

47. de Toledo FGS, Beers KW, Berndt TJ, Thompson MA, Tyce GM, et al. 1997.

Opposite paracrine effects of 5-HT and dopamine on Na$^+$-Pi cotransport in opossum kidney cells. *Kidney Int.* 52:152–56

48. Grider J, Kilpatrick E, Ott C, Jackson B. 1998. Effect of dopamine on NaCl transport in the medullary thick ascending limb of the rat. *Eur. J. Pharmacol.* 342:281–84

49. Sun D, Schafer JA. 1996. Dopamine inhibits AVP-dependent Na$^+$ transport and water permeability in rat CCD via a D4-like receptor. *Am. J. Physiol.* 271: F391–400

50. Cantrell AR, Smith RD, Goldin AL, Scheuer T, Catterall WA. 1997. Dopaminergic modulation of sodium current in hippocampal neurons via cAMP-dependent phosphorylation of specific sites in the sodium channel alpha subunit. *J. Neurosci.* 17(19):7330–38

51. Missale C, Nash SR, Robinson SW, Jaber M, Caron MG. 1998. Dopamine receptors: from structure to function. *Physiol. Rev.* 78(1): 189–225

52. O'Connell DP, Botkin SJ, Ramos SI, Sibley DR, Ariano MA, et al. 1995. Localization of dopamine D$_{1A}$ receptor protein in rat kidneys. *Am. J. Physiol.* 268(6):F1185–97

53. O'Connell DP, Aherne AM, Lane E, Felder RA, Carey RM. 1998. Detection of dopamine receptor D$_{1A}$ subtype-specific mRNA in rat kidney by in situ amplification. *Am. J. Physiol.* 274:F232–41

54. Amenta F, Barili P, Bronzetti E, Ricci A. 1999. Dopamine D1-like receptor subtypes in the rat kidney: a microanatomical study. *Clin. Exp. Hypertens.* 21(1–2):17–23

55. O'Connell DP, Vaughan CJ, Aherne AM, Botkin SJ, Wang Z-Q, et al. 1998. Expression of the dopamine D3 receptor protein in the rat kidney. *Hypertension* 32:886–95

56. Sun D, Wilborn TW, Schafer JA. 1998. Dopamine D4 receptor isoform mRNA

and protein are expressed in the rat cortical collecting duct. *Am. J. Physiol.* 275:F742–51

57. Ji TH, Grossman M, Ji I. 1998. G protein-coupled receptors. I. Diversity of receptor-ligand interactions. *J. Biol. Chem.* 273(28):17299–302

58. Eklöf AC. 1997. The natriuretic response to a dopamine DA1 agonist requires endogenous activation of dopamine DA2 receptors. *Acta Physiol. Scand.* 160(4): 311–14

59. José PA, Asico LD, Eisner GM, Pocchiari F, Semeraro C, Felder RA. 1998. Effects of costimulation of dopamine D$_1$- and D$_2$–like receptors on renal function. *Am. J. Physiol.* 275(4):R986–94

60. Bertorello A, Aperia A. 1990A. Inhibition of proximal tubule Na$^+$,K$^+$-ATPase activity requires simultaneous activation of DA1 and DA2 receptors. *Am. J. Physiol.* 259:F924–28

61. Hemmings HC Jr, Greengard P, Lim Tung HY, Cohen P. 1984. DARPP-32, a dopamine-regulated neuronal phosphoprotein, is a potent inhibitor of protein phosphatase-1. *Nature* 310:503–8

62. Fienberg AA, Hiroi N, Mermelstein PG, Song WJ, Snyder GL, et al. 1998. DARPP-32: regulator of the efficacy of dopaminergic neurotransmission. *Science* 281:838–42

63. Meister B, Fryckstedt J, Schalling M, Cortés R, Hökfelt T, Aperia A, et al. 1989. Dopamine- and cAMP-regulated phosphoprotein (DARPP-32) and dopamine DA1 agonist sensitive Na$^+$,K$^+$-ATPase in renal tubule cells. *Proc. Natl. Acad. Sci. USA* 86:8068–72

64. Aperia A, Fryckstedt J, Svensson L-B, Hemmings HC Jr, Nairn AC, Greengard P. 1991. Phosphorylated M_r32,000 dopamine- and cAMP-regulated phosphoprotein inhibits Na$^+$,K$^+$-ATPase activity in renal tubule cells. *Proc. Natl. Acad. Sci. USA* 88:2798–801

64a. Aperia A, Fryckstedt J, Holtbäck U, Belusa R, Cheng X-J, et al. 1996. Cellular mechanisms for bi-directional regulation of tubular sodium reabsorption. *Kidney Int.* 49 (6): 1743–47

65. Felder CC, Blecher M, José PA. 1989. Dopamine-1 mediated stimulation of phospholipase C activity in rat renal cortical membranes. *J. Biol. Chem.* 264:8739–45

66. Vyas SJ, Jadhav AL, Eichberg J, Lokhandwala MF. 1992. Dopamine receptor-mediated activation of phospholipase C is associated with natriuresis during high salt intake. *Am. J. Physiol.* 262:F494–98

67. Yu PY, Eisner GM, Yamaguchi I, Mouradian MM, Felder RA, José PA. 1996. Dopamine D_{1A} receptor regulation of phospholipase C isoform expression. *J. Biol. Chem.* 271:19503–8

68. Yao LP, Li XX, Yu PY, Xu J, Asico LD, José PA. 1998. Dopamine D1 receptor and protein kinase C isoforms in spontaneously hypertensive rats. *Hypertension* 32(6):1049–53

69. Satoh T, Cohen HT, Katz AI. 1993. Intracellular signaling in the regulation of renal Na-K-ATPase. II. Role of eicosanoids. *J. Clin. Invest.* 91:409–15

70. Lin F, Abraham NG, Schwartzman ML. 1994. Cytochrome P450 arachidonic acid omega-hydroxylation in the proximal tubule of the rat kidney. *Ann. NY Acad. Sci.* 744:11–24

71. Omata K, Abraham NG, Escalante B, Schwartzman ML. 1992. Age-related changes in renal cytochrome P-450 arachidonic acid metabolism in spontaneously hypertensive rats. *Am. J. Physiol.* 262:F8–16

72. Ma YH, Schwartzman ML, Roman RJ. 1994. Altered renal P-450 metabolism of arachidonic acid in Dahl salt-sensitive rats. *Am. J. Physiol.* 267:R579–89

73. Shinomura T, Asaoka Y, Oka M, Yoshida K, Nishizuka Y. 1991. Synergistic action of diacylglycerol and unsaturated fatty acid for protein kinase C activation: its possible implications. *Proc. Natl. Acad. Sci. USA* 88:5149–53

74. Nowicki S, Chen S, Aizman O, Cheng X, Li D, et al. 1997. 20-Hydroxyeicosatetraenoic acid (20 HETE) activates protein kinase C. Role in regulation of rat renal Na^+,K^+-ATPase. *J. Clin. Invest.* 99:1224–30

75. Gao J, Mathias RT, Cohen IS, Baldo GJ. 1992. Isoprenaline, Ca^{2+} and the Na^+,K^+ pump in guinea-pig ventricular myocytes. *J. Physiol.* 449:689–704

76. Cheng SXJ, Aizman O, Nairn AC, Greengard P, Aperia A. 1999. [Ca2+]i determines the effects of PKA and PKC on activity of rat renal Na^+,K^+-ATPase. *J. Physiol.* 518:37–46

77. Ozono R, O'Connell DP, Wang ZQ, Moore AF, Sanada H, et al. 1997. Localization of the dopamine D1 receptor protein in the human heart and kidney. *Hypertension* 30:725–29

78. Lefkowitz RJ. 1998. G protein-coupled receptors. III. New roles for receptor kinases and β-arrestins in receptor signaling and desensitization. *J. Biol. Chem.* 273(30):18677–80

79. Brismar H, Asghar M, Carey RM, Greengard P, Aperia A. 1998. Dopamine-induced recruitment of dopamine D1 receptors to the plasma membrane. *Proc. Natl. Acad. Sci. USA* 95:5573–78

80. Holtbäck U, Brismar H, DiBona GF, Fu M, Greengard P, Aperia A. 1999. Receptor recruitment: a novel mechanism for interactions between G protein-coupled receptors. *Proc. Natl. Acad. Sci. USA.* 96:7271–75

81. Wan Q, Xiong ZG, Man HY, Ackerley CA, Braunton J, et al. 1997. Recruitment of functional GABA(A) receptors to postsynaptic domains by insulin. *Nature* 388(6643):686–90

82. Shuster SJ, Riedl M, Li X, Vulchanova L, Elde R. 1999. Stimulus-90 dependent translocation of kappa opioid receptors to

the plasma membrane. *J. Neurosci.* 19(7): 2658–64

83. Aperia A, Fryckstedt J, Holtbäck U, Belusa R, Cheng X-J, et al. 1996. Cellular mechanisms for bi-directional regulation of tubular sodium reabsorption. *Kidney Int.* 49(6):1743–47

84. Marin-Grez M, Briggs JP, Schubert G, Schnermann J. 1985. Dopamine receptor antagonists inhibit the natriuretic response to atrial natriuretic factor (ANF). *Life Sci.* 36:2171–76

85. Petterson A, Hedner J, Hedner T. 1986. The diuretic effect of atrial natriuretic peptide (ANP) is dependent on dopaminergic activation. *Acta Physiol. Scand.* 126:619–21

86. Katoh T, Sophasan S, Kurokawa K. 1989. Permissive role of dopamine in renal action of ANP in volume-expanded rats. *Am. J. Physiol.* 257:F300–9

86. Israel A, Torres M, Barbella Y. 1989. Evidence for a dopaminergic mechanism for the diuretic and natriuretic action of centrally administered atrial natriuretic factor. *Cell. Mol. Neurobiol.* 9(3): 369–78

87. Hedge SS, Chen C-J, Lokhandwala MF. 1991. Involvement of endogenous dopamine and DA-1 receptors in the renal effects of atrial natriuretic factor in rats. *Clin. Exp. Hyper. Theory Pract.* A13(3):357–69

88. Winaver J, Burnett JC, Tyce GM, Dousa TP. 1990. ANP inhibits Na($^+$)-H$^+$ antiport in proximal tubular brush border membrane: role of dopamine. *Kidney Int.* 38(6):1133–40

89. Kuchel OG, Kuchel GA. 1991. Peripheral dopamine in pathophysiology of hypertension. Interaction with aging and lifestyle. *Hypertension* 18:709–21

90. Ibarra F, Aperia A, Svensson L-B, Eklöf A-C, Greengard P. 1993. Bidirectional regulation of Na$^+$,K$^+$-ATPase activity by dopamine and an α-adrenergic ago-nist. *Proc. Natl. Acad. Sci. USA* 90:21–24

91. Aperia A, Ibarra F, Svensson L-B, Klee C, Greengard P. 1992. Calcineurin mediates α-adrenergic stimulation of Na$^+$, K$^+$-ATPase activity in renal tubule cells. *Proc. Natl. Acad. Sci. USA* 89:7394–97

92. Baum M, Quigley R. 1998. Inhibition of proximal convoluted tubule transport by dopamine. *Kidney Int.* 54(5):1593–600

93. Lederer ED, Sohi SS, McLeish KR. 1998. Dopamine regulates phosphate uptake by opossum kidney cells through multiple counter-regulatory receptors. *J. Am. Soc. Nephrol.* 9(6):975–85

94. Muto S, Tabei K, Asano Y, Imai M. 1985. Dopaminergic inhibition of the action of vasopressin on the cortical collecting tubule. *Eur. J. Pharmacol.* 114(3):393–97

95. Chen CJ, Apparsundaram S, Lokhandwala MF. 1991. Intrarenally produced angiotensin II opposes the natriuretic action of the dopamine-1 receptor agonist fenoldopam in rats. *J. Pharmacol. Exp. Ther.* 256:486–91

96. Cheng H-F, Becker BN, Harris RC. 1996. Dopamine decreases expression of type-1 angiotensin II receptors in renal proximal tubule. *J. Clin. Invest.* 97(12):2745–52

97. Huo T, Healy DP. 1991. Prostaglandin E$_2$ production in rat IMCD cells I. Stimulation by dopamine. *Am. J. Physiol.* 261:F647–54

98. Huo T, Grenader A, Blandina P, Healy DP. 1991. Prostaglandin E$_2$ production in rat IMCD cells II. Possible role for locally formed dopamine. *Am. J. Physiol.* 261:F655–62

99. Lee MR. 1993. Dopamine and the kidney: ten years on. *Clin. Sci.* 84:357–75

100. Guimaraes JT, Vieira-Coelho MA, Serrao MP, Soares-da-Silva P. 1997. Opossum kidney (OK) cells in culture synthesize and degrade the natriuretic hormone dopamine: a comparison with

rat renal tubular cells. *Int. J. Biochem. Cell Biol.* 29(4):681–88

101. Soares-da-Silva P, Fernandes MH, Pinto-do-O PC. 1994. Cell inward transport of L-DOPA and 3-O-methyl-L-DOPA in rat renal tubules. *Br. J. Pharmacol.* 112(2):611–15

102. Worth DP, Harvey JN, Brown, Worral A, Lee MR. 1986. Domperidone treatment in man inhibits the fall in plasma renin activity induced by intravenous γ-L-glutamyl-L-dopa. *Br. J. Clin. Pharmacol.* 21:497–502

103. Eklöf A-C, Holtbäck U, Sundelöf M, Chen S, Aperia A. 1997. Inhibition of COMT induces dopamine-dependent natriuresis and inhibition of proximal tubular Na^+,K^+-ATPase. *Kidney Int.* 52:742–47

104. Ibarra FR, Aguirre J, Nowicki S, Barontini M, Arrizurieta EE, Armando I. 1996. Demethylation of 3-O-methyldopa in the kidney: a possible source for dopamine in urine. *Am. J. Physiol.* 270:F862–68

105. Pestana M, Soares-da-Silva P. 1994. Effect of type A and B monoamine oxidase selective inhibition by Ro 41–1049 and Ro 19–6327 on dopamine outflow in rat kidney slices. *Br. J. Pharmacol.* 113(4):1269–74

106. Guimaraes JT, Soares-da-Silva P. 1998. The activity of MAO A and B in rat renal cells and tubules. *Life Sci.* 62(8):727–37

107. Hansell P, Odlind C, Mannisto PT. 1998. Different renal effects of two inhibitors of catechol-O-methylation in the rat: entacapone and CGP 28014. *Acta Physiol. Scand.* 162(4):489–94

108. Soares-da-Silva P, Serrao MP, Vieira-Coelho MA. 1998. Apical and basolateral uptake and intracellular fate of dopamine precursor L-dopa in LLC-PK1 cells. *Am. J. Physiol.* 274:F243–51

109. Kuchel O. 1990. Dopamine and hypertension. *Curr. Opin. Cardiol.* 5:594–600

110. Hussain T, Lokhandwala MF. 1998. Renal dopamine receptor function in

hypertension. *Hypertension* 32(2):187–97

111. Critchley JAJH, Lee MR. 1986. Salt-sensitive hypertension in West Africans: an uncoupling of the renal sodium-dopamine relation. *Lancet* ii:460

112. Harvey JN, Casson IF, Clayden AD, Cope GF, Perkins CM, Lee MR. 1984. A paradoxical fall in urine dopamine output when patients with essential hypertension are given added dietary salt. *Clin. Sci.* 67:83–88

113. Sowers JR, Zemel MB, Zemel P, Beck FWJ, Walsh MF, Zawada ET. 1988. Salt sensitivity in blacks: Salt intake and natriuretic substances. *Hypertension* 12:485–90

114. Imura O, Shimamoto K. 1990. Suppressed dopaminergic activity and water-sodium handling in the kidneys at the prehypertensive stge of essential hypertension. *J. Auton. Pharmacol.* 10 (Suppl. 1):S73–77

115. Saito I, Takeshita E, Saruta T, Nagano S, Sekihara T. 1986. Urinary dopamine excretion in normotensive subjects with or without family history of hypertension. *J. Hypertens.* 4:57–60

116. Rudberg S, Lemne C, Persson B, Krekula A, de Faire U, Aperia A. 1997. The dopaminuric response to high salt diet in insulin-dependent diabetes mellitus and in family history of hypertension. *Pediatr. Nephrol.* 11:169–73

117. Clark BA, Rosa RM, Epstein FH, Young JB, Landsberg L. 1992. Altered dopaminergic responses in hypertension. *Hypertension* 19:589–94

118. Kuchel O. 1995. Genetic determinants of dopaminergic activity: potential role in blood pressure regulation. *Hypertens. Res.* 18(Suppl.) I:S1–10

119. Kinoshita S, Sidhu A, Felder RA. 1989. Defective dopamine-1 receptor adenylate cyclase coupling in the proximal convoluted tubule from the spontaneously

hypertensive rat. *J. Clin. Invest.* 84: 1849–56

120. Gesek FA, Schoolwerth AC. 1991. Hormone responses of proximal Na⁺-H⁺ exchanger in spontaneously hypertensive rats. *Am. J. Physiol.* 3:96S-99

121. Horiuchi A, Albrecht F, Eisner GM, José PA, Felder RA. 1992. Renal dopamine receptors and pre- and post-cAMP mediated sodium transport defect in the spontaneously hypertensive rat. *Am. J. Physiol.* 263:F1105–11

122. Sidhu A, Vachvanichsanong P, José PA, Felder RA. 1992. Persistent defective coupling of dopamine-1 receptors to G proteins after solubilization from kidney proximal tubules of hypertensive rats. *J. Clin. Invest.* 89:789–93

123. Chen C, Lokhandwala MF. 1992. An impairment of renal tubular DA-1 receptor function as the causative factor for diminished natriuresis to volume expansion in spontaneously hypertensive rats. *Clin. Exp. Hypertens.* 14:615–28

123a. Chen CJ, Vyas SJ, Eichberg J, Lokhandwala MF. 1992. Diminished phospholipase C activation by dopamine in spontaneously hypertensive rats. *Hypertension* 19:102–8

124. Chen C, Beach RE, Lokhandwala MF. 1993. Dopamine fails to inhibit renal tubular sodium pump in hypertensive rats. *Hypertension* 21:364–72

125. Nishi A, Eklöf A-C, Bertorello AM, Aperia A. 1993. Dopamine regulation of renal Na⁺,K⁺-ATPase activity is lacking in Dahl salt-sensitive rats. *Hypertension* 21:767–71

126. Sanada H, José PA, Hazen-Martin D, Yu PY, Xu J, et al. 1999. Dopamine-1 receptor coupling defect in renal proximal tubule cells in hypertension. *Hypertension* 33(4):1036–42

127. Albrecht FE, Drago J, Felder RA, Printz MP, Eisner GM, et al. 1996. Role of the D₁A dopamine receptor in the pathogenesis of genetic hypertension. *J. Clin. Invest.* 97(10):2283–88

128. Asico LD, Ladines C, Fuchs S, Accili D, Carey RM, et al. 1998. Disruption of the dopamine D₃ receptor gene produces renin-dependent hypertension. *J. Clin. Invest.* 102(3):493–98

129. Yamaguchi I, Yao L, Sanada H, Ozono R, Mouradian MM, et al. 1997. Dopamine D₁A receptors and renin release in rat juxtaglomerular cells. *Hypertension* 29(4):962–68

130. Meister B, Fried G, Holgert H, Aperia A, Hökfelt T. 1992. Ontogeny of aromatic L-amino acid decarboxylase-containing tubule cells in rat kidney. *Kidney Int.* 42:617–23

131. Meister B, Bean AJ, Aperia A. 1993. Catechol-*O*–methyltransferase mRNA in the kidney and its appearance during ontogeny. *Kidney Int.* 44:726–33

132. Fryckstedt J, Aperia A, Snyder G, Meister B. 1993. Distribution of dopamine- and cAMP-dependent phosphoprotein (DARPP-32) in the developing and mature kidney. *Kidney Int.* 44:495–502

133. Segar JL, Smith FG, Guillery EN, José PA, Robillard JE. 1992. Ontogeny of renal response to specific dopamine DA1–receptor stimulation in sheep. *Am. J. Physiol.* 263:R868–73

134. Fukuda Y, Bertorello A, Aperia A. 1991. Ontogeny of the regulation of Na⁺,K⁺-ATPase activity in the renal proximal tubule cell. *Pediatr. Res.* 30:131–34

135. Sarasa M, Climent S. 1991. Cardiac differentiation induced by dopamine in undifferentiated cells of early chick embryo. *Dev. Biol.* 148:243–48

136. Robertson GS, Vincent SR, Fibiger HC. 1992. D1 and D2 dopamine receptors differentially regulate c-*fos* expression in striatonigral and striatopallidal neurons. *Neuroscience* 49(2):285–96

137. Wilk S, Mizoguchi H, Orlowski M. 1978. A kidney-specific dopamine pre-

cursor. *J. Pharmacol. Exp. Ther.* 206: 227–32

138. Shimada H, Endou H, Sakai F. 1982. Distribution of y-glutamyl transpeptidase and glutaminase isozymes in the rabbit nephron. *Jpn. J. Pharmacol.* 32:121–29

139. Lee MR. 1987. Dopamine, the kidney and essential hypertension studies with gludopa. *Clin. Exp. Ther. Prac.* A9(5,6): 977–86

140. Lee MR. 1990. Five years' experience with γ-L-glutamyl-L-dopa: a relatively renal specific prodrug in man. *J.*

Autonom. Pharmacol. 10(Suppl. 1): S103–8

141. Männistö PT, Ulmanen I, Lundström K, Taskinen J, Tenhunen J, et al. 1992. Characteristics of catechol *O*-methyltransferase (COMT) and properties of selective COMT inhibitors. *Prog. Drug Res.* 39:291–350

142. White BH, Sidhu A. 1998. Increased oxidative stress in renal proximal tubules of the spontaneously hypertensive rat: a mechanism for defective dopamine D_{1A} receptor/G-protein coupling. *J. Hypertens.* 16(11):1659–65

Annu. Rev. Physiol. 2000. 62:649–71

ENDOTHELIAL SIGNAL INTEGRATION IN VASCULAR ASSEMBLY

Thomas O. Daniel[1] and Dale Abrahamson[2]

*[1]Center for Vascular Biology, Departments of Medicine and Cell Biology,
Vanderbilt University Medical Center, Nashville, Tennessee 37232;
e-mail: tom.daniel@mcmail.vanderbilt.edu; [2]Department of Cell Biology,
University of Kansas Medical Center, Kansas City, Kansas 66160–7420*

Key Words   angiogenesis, vasculogenesis, endothelial targeting, differentiation

■ **Abstract**   Regulated assembly of a highly specialized interconnecting network
of vascular endothelial and supportive cells is fundamental to embryonic development
and organogenesis, as well as to postnatal tissue repair in metazoans. This review
advances an "endotheliocentric" model that defines tasks required of endothelial cells
and describes molecular controls that regulate steps in activation, assembly, and maturation of new vessels. In addition to the classical assembly mechanisms—angiogenesis and vasculogenesis—endothelial cells are also recruited into vascular structures
from the circulatory system in adult animals and from resident mesenchymally derived
progenitors during organogenesis of kidney and other organs. Paracrine signaling
cascades regulated by hypoxia initiate a sequentially coordinated series of endothelial
responses, including matrix degradation, migration, proliferation, and morphogenetic
remodeling. Surface receptors on committed endothelial lineage progenitors transduce
cues from extracellular-matrix–associated proteins and cell-cell contact to direct
migration, matrix attachment, proliferation, targeting and cell-cell assembly, and vessel maturation. Through their capacity to spatially segregate and temporally integrate
a diverse range of extracellular signals, endothelial cells determine their migratory
paths, cellular partners, and life-or-death responses to local cues.

INTRODUCTORY COMMENTS

Toward an Integrated Model for Vascular Assembly

Endothelial cells are the central cellular organizational unit of vascular structures.
Their lineage commitment, expansion, organization, and assembly into ordered
and tissue-specific interconnecting vascular structures are required for organogenesis and successful embryonic development. In mature subjects, expansion,
contraction, and remodeling of microvascular structures underlie wound healing,
reproductive tissue cycles, tumorigenesis, and a number of other pathological
conditions involving inflammation (1). Endothelial cells are integrators, trans-

0066–4278/00/0315–0649$12.00   **649**

ducers, and effectors of local environmental signals (2). Their tightly balanced proliferation, migration, and morphogenic responses to angiogenic or angiostatic stimuli are context appropriate in two critical features: (*a*) they maintain integrity of the vascular barrier function, and (*b*) they conform with fidelity (under physiological situations) to the architectural cues of adjacent nonvascular tissue structures to integrate critical functions of such tissues as the mammalian kidney.

This review considers spatial and temporal problems faced by endothelial cells as they assemble and remodel vascular structures, from an "endotheliocentric" vantage. Maintenance of vascular integrity requires that endothelial cells spatially and temporally segregate responses to local cues in the context of cell-cell and cell-matrix attachments. Indeed, endothelial shape and tractional forces that influence it are critical determinants of gene expression, signaling, and apoptosis (3). Although useful in integrating recently obtained information, the model is, at some level, a conceptual artifice that underplays many crucial features of vascular development and neovascularization, summarized in recent reviews (4–6). The timing and morphological features of vascularization failure in mouse embyros that are null for molecules regulating vascular development have provided some insight into the necessity for specific receptors, their ligands, matrix-interactive proteinases, and cell-cell–targeting machinery. The pattern of vascularization failure in homozygous animals that are null for intermediaries is evolving as a gold standard to define molecular features, yet considerable overlap in the morphological characteristics exists, and specifics of organogenesis and vascular bed–specific neovascularization may not be uncovered until conditional gene deletion strategies are expanded. In this review, we highlight recent advances that provide insight into emerging pictures of integrated response.

PROCESSES OF ENDOTHELIAL INCORPORATION

Endothelial Progenitor Spatio-Temporal Tasks

Schematically represented in Figure 1 is the process of vasculogenic assembly, in which individual endothelial progenitor cells display markers of lineage commitment and assemble vessels de novo. This contrasts with so-called angiogenic assembly (Figure 2), in which new vessels arise from existing vessels through endothelial branching, sprouting, migration, proliferation, and anastomotic interconnection with endothelial cells residing in existing vessels (4). Compelling evidence defines a common role for vascular endothelial growth factor (VEGF) to support both processes through its actions on endothelial cells and progenitors (7, 8), and recent definition of hypoxia-sensitive transcriptional mechanisms that regulate VEGF production in tissue sites underserved by vascular supply are emerging (9) (see below). Yet requirements of integrated endothelial-cell function in the neovascularization process extend far beyond roles for VEGF and its recep-

**Specification/
Differentiation**   *EC Commitment*   **Expansion/Extension/
Interconnection**

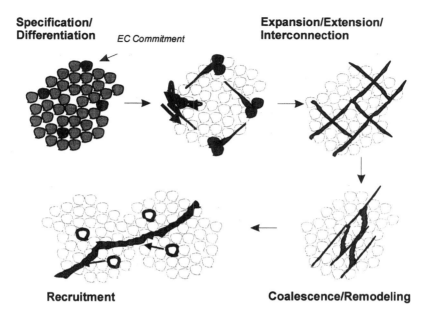

Recruitment   **Coalescence/Remodeling**

Figure 1 Vasculogenesis. Early flk-1 (+) angioblasts in the paraxial mesoderm are specified, expand in clusters, and extend long projecting processes that interconnect to form a
network or primary vascular plexus. Through coalescence of this network, a linear structure
evolves that undergoes remodeling to form a single central lumen within the developing
aorta. Supportive smooth muscle cells are recruited and coordinately participate in vessel
maturation and morphogenesis. A similar process evolves through the primary plexus stage
in the extraembryonic circulation, where hemangioblasts migrate and expand in clusters
(blood islands) that contain central hematopoietic progenitors and peripheral angioblasts.

tors, obligating additional cellular processes, including cell-cell discrimination,
recruitment, and remodeling.

A developmental progression of endothelial events was chronicled in the 1930s
(10). It is now possible to frame endothelial cellular events within the context of
molecular mediators that are likely to contribute. During angiogenesis, endothelial
cells in existing vessels are initially activated by a net imbalance favoring angiogenic over angiostatic factors (2). Activated endothelial cells break down and
penetrate existing subendothelial basement membrane through actions of proteinases, such as matrix metaloproteinase (MMP)-9 (11). Long, filopodial-like cellular processes migrate, tracking along fibrillar extracellular-matrix components,
through migratory responses that are mediated by α_v and α_5 integrins (12). These
endothelial processes contact and discriminate among inappropriate cell partners,
such as fibroblasts and inflammatory cells, to approach an existing vessel.
Through currently unknown mechanisms, a collaborator endothelial cell is acti-

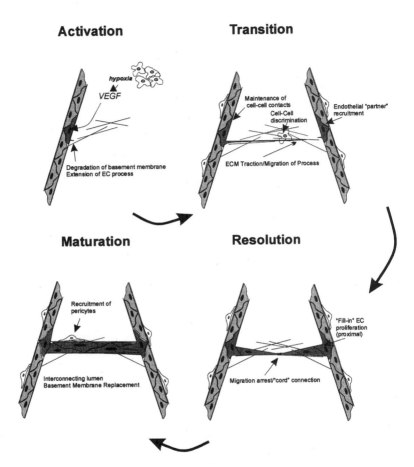

Figure 2   Endotheliocentric stages in angiogenesis. Expansion of new vessels from existing vascular networks proceeds in response to tissue hypoxia, a primary stimulus for VEGF production and release. A receptive endothelial cell responds (Activation) by degrading subjacent basement membrane, extending an elongating cellular process by traction upon fibrillar connective tissue elements, while maintaining integrity of the existing vessel on the trailing end. The extending process discriminates inappropriate partner cells, approaches an existing vessel, and through unknown means (likely release of chemokine or other soluble factor), signals a collaborating partner endothelial cell to penetrate basement membrane, and extend a cell process (Transition). A stable interconnecting cord-like scaffold is formed (Resolution), about which proliferation, migration, and morphogenesis ensue to create an interconnecting lumen. Pericytes are recruited and basement membrane elaborated (Maturation). Adapted, with modern interpretation, from Clark & Clark (10).

vated to project a reciprocating process through its basement membrane. Cell-cell recognition machinery, likely involving Eph/ephrin juxtacrine signaling (13), initiates molecular coupling events that proceed through establishment of VE-cadherin–containing junctional complexes, connexin-integrated gap junctions, and focal contacts (14). Morphogenetic events then establish a lumen interconnecting with existing vessels, basement membrane is reestablished, and pericytes are recruited as critical elements of vessel maturation and maintenance (6). Coordinated recruitment of pericytes and smooth muscle cells provides not only structural support but also paracrine signals implicated in endothelial maturation and vessel integrity such as angiopoetins (5) and transforming growth factor (TGF) β (15).

These spatial problems require integration of signals linked with and regulated by endothelial cell-cell and cell-matrix interactions. Each interval step of the process of vascular assembly appears critical to the next, based on embryonic vascularization defects in animals homozygous for targeted gene deletions. Distinctions in the timing and morphology of defective vascularization in gene knockout mice illustrate the sequential features of the process during early development, at a time when much of the vascularization process is temporally compressed and synchronized (Table 1).

An additional mechanism for incorporation of endothelial cells into new vessels has recently been described (Figure 3). Endothelial progenitor cells (EPCs) are also recruited to sites of neovascularization in mature mammals from a cir-

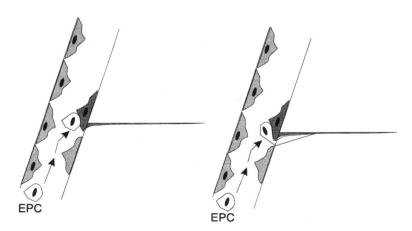

Figure 3 Circulating endothelial progenitor cell (EPC) incorporation: targeting to sites of neovascularization. With the demonstration that marrow-derived EPCs are incorporated into new vessels, questions arise about the mechanisms responsible for their targeting. If activation (Figure 2) at local sites recruits substantial numbers of EPCs from the circulation, their recruitment may depend upon their cell-cell interactions at the lumen interface with activated endothelial cells.

TABLE 1 Molecular identity of genes necessary for embryonic vascularization

Molecular class	Embryonic stage lethality	(Vascular phenotype extraembryonic/intraembryonic)
Transcription factors		
HIF1α or ARNT (HIF1β)	≤$E_{10.5}$	Defective yolk sac vascularization with intact EC differentiation, fusion but maturation failure (38, 103, 104)
MEF2C	≤$E_{9.5}$	Normal EC differentiation, with failure to organize a primitive vascular network. Failure of SMC differentiation defective yolk sac vessels with failure of anterior cardinal vein and dorsal aortae formation (106)
LKLF	$E_{12.5-14.5}$	Normal vasculogenesis and angiogenesis, failure of vessel wall stabilization (107)
TEL	$E_{10.5-11.5}$	Normal EC differentiation with defective yolk sac angiogenesis and normal hematopoiesis (36)
Ets2	<$E_{12.5}$	Defective trophoblast migration/differentiation with persistent ECM and defective MMP-9, 3, and 13 production (35)
Transcription factor interactor		
PVHL	$E_{10.5-12.5}$	Extraembryonic vasculogenesis failure after $E_{9.5}$ (105)
Receptor tyrosine kinases		
VEGFR1 (flk1)	$E_{8.5-9.5}$	Endothelial and hemangioblast migration and differentiation failure (29, 41)
VEGFR2 (flt1)	$E_{8.5-9.5}$	Endothelial cell differentiation intact. Vascular channels disorganized, overpopulated with angioblasts (42)
VEGFR3	$E_{9.5}$	Vasculogenesis/angiogenesis intact; large vessel disorganization with lumen defects (44)
Tie1	$E_{13.5-14.5}$	Defective vascular integrity/endothelial survival in angiogenesis, edema, and hemorrhage (57, 108)
Tie2	$E_{10.5}$	Defects in organization, remodeling, sprouting; heart trabeculations (56)
EphB2/EphB3	$E_{10.5}$	Defects in sprouting, vessel remodeling, and organization (63)
PDGFβR	P_1	Failure of mesangial recruitment, glomerular development (24, 109)

Other receptors		
Endoglin (HHT1)	$\leq E_{11.5}$	Normal vasculogenesis; defects in SMC recruitment/endothelial remodeling (110)
Other membrane proteins		
VE Cadherin$^{-/-}$	$E_{10.5}$	Defective anterior large vessels and failure to establish yolk sac vascular plexus (111)
Integrin $\alpha_v$$^{-/-}$	$E_{10.5} \rightarrow P_1$	Vasculogenesis and early angiogenesis intact. Placental (labyrinthine) defects. Intracerebral, intestinal hemorrhage (112)
Ligands		
VEGF$^{+/-}$	$E_{11.5}$	Rudimentary dorsal aorta, reduced ventricular mass (39, 40)
VEGF$^{-/-}$	$E_{10.5}$	No dorsal aorta; defective hematopoiesis (39, 40)
Ephrin-B2$^{-/-}$	$E_{11.5}$	Failure of extraembryonic vessel fusion/remodeling (64)
Angiopoietin 1$^{-/-}$	$E_{10.5}$	Defective organization, remodeling (113)
Angiopoietin 2$^{-/-}$	$E_{12.5} \rightarrow P_1$	Defects in vessel integrity, hemorrhage (5)
JAG1$^{dDSL/dDSL}$	$E_{10.5}$	Normal vasculogenesis, with dysmorphic, small vessels; failure to remodel primary plexus in yolk sac and embryo (114)
TGFβ 1$^{-/-}$	$E_{10.5}$	Failure to remodel the primary vascular plexus of yolk sac and cranial vessels (47)
PDGF BB$^{-/-}$	P_1	Failure of glomerular development (25)
Protease/coagulation factor		
[Tissue Factor (TF)$^{-/-}$]	$E_{8.5}$	Extraembryonic vascular failure with failure of SMC/pericyte recruitment (115)

655

culating, marrow-derived population of progenitor cells (16, 17). This population of circulating EPCs is mobilized by regional ischemia or administration of either GM-CSF or VEGF, and increased numbers of marrow-derived EPCs are incorporated into neovascularization sites after VEGF administration (18, 19). At present, incorporation of these circulating EPCs into sites of neovascularization appears to obligate some yet undefined targeting machinery to recruit circulating cell participation. Such a function may be served by Eph/ephrin or other juxtacrine-targeting interactions, as defined below. Finally, vascular remodeling and formation of networks may also involve formation of pillars within existing vascular lumen space, to create bissected "hallways" and new capillary networks (20, 21).

During organogenesis, mesenchymally derived EPCs within fields of differentiating mesenchyme contribute to vascularization of such organs as mammalian kidney (22, 23). These cells assimilate into new vessels through coordinated recruitment to vascularization sites, such as the developing glomerulus, through a process that shares features with both vasculogenesis and angiogenesis (Figure 5, see color insert). In addition to endothelial-endothelial assembly, endothelial cells actively participate in recruitment of supportive pericytes and equivalent mesangial cells through expression of growth factors such as platelet-derived growth factor (PDGF) BB. Developmental vascularization fails, as demonstrated by glomerulogenesis defects and cerebral circulation defects, in mice null for PDGF B (an endothelial product) or PDGF β receptors (expressed on pericytes) (24–26).

Embyronic Origins and Commitment of Endothelial Cells

Vascular development in mouse embryos initiates around embryonic day 7 (E7.5). At that time, intraembryonic angioblasts, the earliest EPCs, arise as individual cells from paraxial- and lateral-plate mesoderm under the influence of inducing factors (8, 27, 28). Those that contribute to yolk sac vasculature migrate through the primitive streak into the extraembryonic tissues and assemble first into mesodermal-cell aggregates that contain both endothelial and hematopoietic precursors (4). Common lineage is defined by shared expression of CD34, CD31, and Flk-1, a VEGF receptor that is required for development of both lineages during mouse development (29). During maturation of these blood islands these lineages segregate, with endothelial precursors lining spaces containing the hematopoietic progenitors. In contrast, angioblast precursors of intraembryonic vessels arise in paraxial mesoderm as individual cells expressing Flk-1 and SCL/TAL-1, an HLH transcription factor (30). There they proliferate locally, extending sprouts that interconnect into a loose meshwork and undergo both cranio-caudal and dorso-ventral progression into a primary vascular plexus of cells expressing PECAM, CD34, and the angiopoeitin receptor, Tie-2, in that progression. This network subsequently fuses and remodels through morphogenesis into the earliest intraembryonic vessels (Figure 1) (30).

Specification of Endothelial Lineages Although Flk-1 and SCL/TAL1 are among the earliest markers for cells with endothelial potential, the signals and transcriptional controls regulating specialization and specification as distinct from hematopoietic lineages are not yet clear. In vitro differentiation of embryonic stem cells suggests that Flk-1$^+$ cell populations destined for endothelial differentiation subsequently express in sequence VE-cadherin, PECAM, and CD34 and that the earliest marker for hematopoietic cells not expressed on the common endothelial lineage precursor is α_4 integrin (31, 32).

Among other early molecular controls regulating specification of angioblasts, several transcription factors have been evaluated in developmental systems. Ets-1 and Ets-2 are expressed in early vascular sites, and putative Ets-1–interacting *cis* elements have been identified in genes expressed in endothelium, including MMP-1, MMP-3, MMP-9, and u-PA (33). Ets-1 expression is induced in angiogenic endothelial cells adjacent to imposed wounds in vivo and in vitro (34). Homozygous null mutations in Ets-2 are embryonic lethal, as a consequence of impaired trophoblast development in ectoplacental cone formation, with suppressed expression of MMP-9 (gel B) (35).

The Ets-related helix-loop-helix factor TEL is implicated in a number of leukemias through genetic rearrangements that create fusion proteins with PDGF receptor (PDGFR), Abl, AML-1, and others. Yet, TEL-null embryos die between E10.5 and E11.5 with failure of yolk sac angiogenesis, apparently the consequence of failure to maintain and mature the yolk sac vessels, whereas intraembryonic vasculature appears normal (36). Surprisingly, hematopoietic lineages derived from explanted yolk sacs are unaffected. Prominent mesenchymal-cell apoptosis suggests TEL plays a critical role in endothelial survival.

Regulation of Endothelial Activation

Hypoxia and Molecular Controls for VEGF Expression   The hypoxia-inducible factor (HIF)-basic helix-loop-helix-PAS family of transcription factors has recently surfaced as a control system that regulates VEGF expression. The product of a tumor suppressor gene responsible for von Hippel Lindau disease, *VHL,* is implicated in this hypoxia-sensitive regulation (9). The *VHL* protein product, pVHL, associates with HIF-1α and HIF-2α and appears to target them for ubiquitination and rapid degradation under normoxic conditions (37). In hypoxic cells, HIF-1α is stabilized by an undefined oxygen-sensitive sensor mechanism, permitting it to form an active complex with HIF-1β [aryl hydrocarbon receptor nuclear translocator (ARNT)] that induces VEGF transcription. In VHL-deficient cells, VEGF production is constitutively elevated as a consequence of HIF-α subunit stabilization, even under normoxic conditions. ARNT$^{-/-}$ embryonic stem cells fail to induce VEGF expression in response to hypoxia, and null embryos die before E10.5 with failure to develop yolk sac vessels, similar to the defects in VEGF$^{-/-}$ embryos (38). Thus ARNT deficiency reduces VEGF levels sufficiently to impose vascular consequences. The molecular identity of the oxygen sensor and how it may be modified in settings where neovascularization is impaired are critical issues yet to be defined.

VEGF and Its Receptors Under influence of VEGF supplied by adjacent cells, the Flk-1 (VEGFR2)-positive angioblast or hemangioblast population expands during development, extending sprouts that initiate formation of the primary vascular plexus (8). It now appears that VEGF administration and VEGF produced in response to ischemic injury can also induce release of marrow-derived endothelial progenitor cells (EPCs) that may be recruited to neovascular sites in mature animals (Figure 3) (19). Tight regulation of VEGF availability appears to determine vascular progenitor survival, proliferation, and migration. The critical nature of this signal is highlighted by effects of deficiency of a single *VEGF-A* allele to cause developmental failure in both embryonic and extraembryonic circulation (39, 40). Flk-1 (VEGR2) expression and activation are critical for early vasculogenesis. Flk-1 null mice die between E8.5 and E9.5, with defects in blood island formation and lack of organized blood vessels in either the yolk sac or embryo proper (41).

Although a second VEGF receptor, VEGFR1 (Flt-1), is also required for early embryonic vascular development, null animals do develop blood islands, but they include abnormally mixed angioblasts, which suggests overexuberant proliferation (42). Flt-1 may play a role in sequestering and damping VEGF responses through Flk-1, because it has higher affinity and its ectodomain is sufficient to mediate normal vascular development (43). Although VEGFR-3 has high affinity for the VEGF-C isoform implicated in lymphangiogenesis, mice null for functional VEGFR-3 show failure of embryonic vascularization as well (44).

VEGF has also been shown to be functionally linked to eNOS activity. VEGF, but not fibroblast growth factor (FGF), stimulates accumulation of eNOS- and nitric oxide–dependent in vitro assembly of endothelial capillary-like structures (45). Consistent with a downstream role for nitric oxide in VEGF action, dietary supplementation with L-arginine promotes angiogenesis in a hind-limb ischemia model, and ischemia-induced angiogenesis is impaired in eNOS$^{-/-}$ mice (46).

Transforming Growth Factor β Signaling   Strong genetic evidence supports the function of TGFβ family proteins and their receptors in vascularization and vessel integrity. TGFβ1-null mice have a vascular embryonic lethal phenotype, depending on genetic background (47). Moreover, distinct subsets of families with hereditary hemorrhagic telangiectasia (HHT) have mutations in genes encoding TGFβ receptors or homologous proteins. Familial mutations in endoglin, a type-III TGFβ receptor homolog, or activin-like kinase (ALK)-1, a type-I TGFβ receptor, are implicated in the angiodysplastic lesions in these patients (48, 49). A single mutant allele of either gene is sufficient to evoke the angiodysplasia typical of this disease.

TGFβ ligands are bound initially by type-II receptors, which recruit and phosphorylate type-I receptors, such as ALK-1, that signal specific downstream

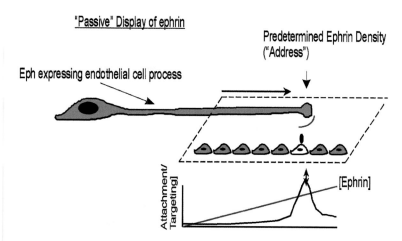

Figure 4 A model for Eph/ephrin function in vascular cell assembly. Developmental vascularization failure in ephrin-B2 (64) or combined EphB2/B3 null (63) embryos implicates a critical role for temporally synchronized function of these molecules. Membrane-bound Eph receptors/ephrin counter-receptors expressed on endothelial surfaces must engage through inter-endothelial cell-cell contact to signal reciprocating participation in vascular assembly. During a critical phase of Transition (Figure 2), cell processes discriminate their targets to establish intercellular contacts and cords. EphB receptors read specific ephrin densities to regulate integrin-mediated attachment (13). In this model schema, a migrating process identifies its target based on an address specified by the ephrin density, here displayed in a migratory field of cells expressing a linear gradient of increasing densities (left to right). While such spatial gradients have been demonstrated in fields of axonal targeting, such as retina (61), perivascular spatial patterning is not currently as well resolved.

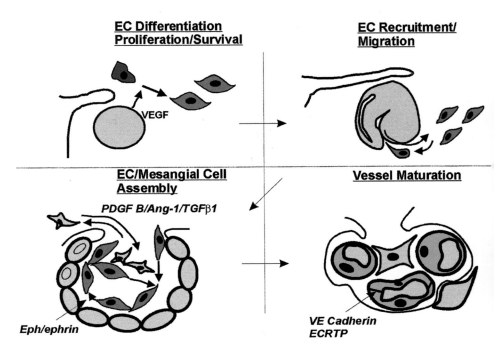

EC Differentiation Proliferation/Survival

VEGF

EC Recruitment/ Migration

EC/Mesangial Cell Assembly

PDGF B/Ang-1/TGFβ1

Eph/ephrin

Vessel Maturation

VE Cadherin
ECRTP

Figure 5 Glomerular vascularization progression. Glomerular development progresses through recruitment of endothelial progenitors from mesenchyme adjacent sites where the ureteric bud induces epithelial transition. Through VEGF release, these EPCs are recruited into the vascular cleft of the developing glomerular epithelial structures, in conjunction with recruitment of mesangial cell progenitors, which serve as the local pericytes and structural supports for glomerular capillary loops. Key roles for VEGF in endothelial recruitment (96) and PDGF in mesangial recruitment (24, 25) have been demonstrated (96); participation of Eph/ephrin, angiopoietin-1 (ang-1) ECRPT, and VE cadherin is speculative but consistent with expression patterns and functions in other contexts.

responses (50). Endoglin does not bind ligand independently, but does associate with type-II receptors to which TGFβ1 and TGFβ3 have bound, to form serine/threonine kinase signaling complexes (51). Endoglin also associates with type-I receptors for bone morphogenetic protein (BMP)-7 and activin-A, which suggests it functions as an accessory protein of multiple receptor complexes within this TGFβ superfamily (51). Among the seven type-I TGFβ receptors, involvement of ALK-1 in HHT and ALK-5 as an important intermediary of TGFβ1 signaling appears most important in mediating endothelial responses to TGFβ, yet required to assemble the cardiac valves (52). Confirmation of a vascular role for endoglin was recently provided by the phenotype of null mice, with failure of extraembryonic endothelial development into syncytiotrophoblasts and placental failure (53).

Although endothelial responses to TGFβ and related ligands are critically defined by their expression of specific receptors, many regulatory aspects of TGFβ expression and processing are interactive with endothelial proteases, integrins (54), and extracellular matrix proteins such as thrombospodin-1 (55). Synthesized as a single propeptide chain from which an N-terminal latency-associated peptide (LAP) is cleaved, TGFβ1 is inactive in this small latent complex. LAP-binding proteins are disulfide linked and appear to target TGFβ1 to potential sites of action. Protease release from this complex, through plasmin or other proteases that cleave LAP in conjunction with its interaction with mannose-6-phosphate/insulin-like growth factor (IGF)-II receptors, has, until recently, appeared to be the likely physiological mechanism of activation.

New evidence defines the capacity for thrombospondin-1 (TSP-1) to bind LAP and change the conformation of associated TGFβ1 to promote its activation (55). Moreover, TSP-1–null mice have a phenotype strikingly similar to that of TGFβ1-null animals. Interactions between $\alpha_v\beta_6$ integrin and LAP have also been shown to activate TGFβ in specific cell presentation contexts (54). It appears likely that TGFβ plays an angiomodulatory role at several steps during angiogenesis, with the most notable net effect exerted on the maturation phase required to stabilize vascular structures.

Angiopoietins and Tie-2 Receptor   A third receptor-ligand system is critically important in embryonic vascular development. Initially identified as orphan receptor tyrosine kinases restricted to endothelial expression, Tie-1 and Tie-2 functions were evaluated by gene deletion and dominant negative transgenic experiments (5). Mouse embryos null for a functional angiopoietin receptor, Tie-2, and its structural homolog, Tie-1, display vascular lethal outcomes. Tie-2–null or –dominant-negative animals die before E10.5 with malformation of vascular networks (56). In contrast, the majority of Tie-1–null mice survive to die immediately after birth from respiratory failure and edema attributed to lack of vessel integrity (57).

Among at least four different angiopoietins identified to date, Ang-1 is an activator of the Tie-2 kinase, whereas Ang-2 binds without activating (58). Knockout embryos lacking angiopoietin 1 expression display a picture quite similar to the Tie-2–null embryos, with failure of normal endothelial cell adherence and interaction with subjacent supporting cells and extracellular matrix (59). Similarly, endocardial cell attachment and subjacent myocardial trabeculations are disordered in both Tie-2– and Ang-1–null embryos. Transgenic mice overexpressing Ang-2 during embryogenesis display vascular lethal phenotypes similar to those of either Tie-2– or Ang-1–null mice (58). Based on endothelium-restricted expression of Tie-2 and the dominant smooth muscle cell expression of angiopoietins, it appears that recruitment of smooth muscle cells or pericytes into proximity with endothelial cells of newly formed vessels is required for Tie-2 activation. Local overexpression of Ang-2, as a Tie-2 receptor antagonist, appears to disrupt developmental vessel maturation as effectively as Tie-2 deficiency. This argues for a delicately balanced role for Tie-2 signaling in the maturation phase (Figures 1 and 2) and suggests that important biological functions attend both receptor activation and subsequent antagonism. Temporally staged expression of Ang-1, then Ang-2, during the progression of ovarian follicle vascularization and regression provides support for this sequential process (58).

Regulation of Endothelial Targeting

In both vasculogenic (Figure 1) and angiogenic (Figure 2) neovascularization, a critical task required of migrating or extending endothelial cells is the recognition and recruitment of appropriate partners for anastomosis and interendothelial self-assembly.

Eph/Ephrin Interactions   The Eph/ephrin receptor/counter-receptor system has been identified as an important mediator of early developmental patterning (60) and neural targeting (61, 62). This system participates importantly in vascular development (5, 63, 64). Gradients of membrane-bound ephrins appear to explicitly direct the targeting of axons through spatially defined migratory fields. These Eph/ephrin receptors are candidates to signal interendothelial cell-cell recognition.

Function in the vasculature was first recognized when the tumor necrosis factor (TNF)α-inducible ephrin-A1 (B61) was shown to mediate corneal angiogenesis responses through EphA2 (65). More recently, homozygous deletion of ephrin-B2 was shown to cause failure of extraembryonic vascularization at a stage when vascular plexus fusion is normally seen between an arterial limb plexus expressing ephrin-B2 and a venous limb plexus expressing its receptor, EphB4 (64). This was a striking observation because it demonstrated endothelial "chimerism" in Eph/ephrin expression that defined anatomical and biochemical distinctions in commitment to venous or arterial function before competency of vascular flow. Subsequent experiments have expanded evidence of endothelial heterogeneity. Mice null for both EphB2 and EphB3 also display variable penetrance of embryonic vascularization defects, manifest at the same developmental stage (>E9.5). Yet the expression pattern shows endothelial bed–selective differences that are not limited to the arterovenous border (63). Cultured endothelial cells derived from distinct vascular beds also display differential attachment and self-assembly responses to specific ephrins A or ephrins B (66).

One model for how endothelial cell-cell contact could participate in cell-cell fusion functions to provide cell recognition addresses has been advanced by function linkage between EphB1 activation and $\alpha_v\beta_3$ integrin. Shown in Figure 4 (see color insert), EphB1 functions as a molecular switch, not only distinguishing whether it is engaging ephrin counter-receptor, but also reading the oligomerized form of ephrin-B1 to relay different signals that control integrin-mediated cell attachment and migration (13). At a biochemical level, the composition of EphB1 signaling complexes is also critically regulated by the state of ephrin oligomerization (67). Thus EphB1 receptors are poised to discriminate spatial signals on cell surfaces to regulate movement and attachment.

As outlined above, juxtacrine cell-cell discrimination is a critical task facing endothelial cells during neovascularization, whether vasculogenic (Figure 1), angiogenic (Figure 2), or through recruitment of EPCs from a circulating pool (Figure 3). The Eph/ephrin system also meets another expectation imposed on cell-cell recognition, that of reciprocity. Reciprocal signaling has been demonstrated, transduced through ephrin-B counter-receptors upon engagement of the EphB2 ectodomain (68, 69). Thus, this system provides an ideal early recognition "molecular sensor" capable of "reading" counter-receptor density like an address to direct cell-cell assembly of appropriate collaborative cell partners through correct targeting (70).

Extracellular Matrix and Matrix-Associated Matricellulins in Angiogenesis

An exceptionally strong body of evidence implicates $\alpha_v\beta_3$ and $\alpha_v\beta_5$ integrins in neovascularization responses to defined stimuli, such as VEGF and FGF, as well as in tumor-responsive neovascularization (12, 71). It appears that integrins not only provide structural links to extracellular matrix for attachment and motility, they also bind metalloproteinases or inactive fragments to regulate endothelial invasiveness (72).

Recent findings further highlight the intimate interaction between matrix-associated proteins that have been described as matricellulins, SPARC and thrombospondin-1 (TSP-1), and specific angiomodulatory growth factors. For example, SPARC and peptides derived from selected domains inhibit VEGF stimulation by direct binding to VEGF and by reducing the association of VEGF with endothelial cell surface receptors (73). This provides a mechanism for matrix sequestration and inactivation of secreted VEGF. In addition, SPARC is a counter-adhesive protein that reduces endothelial spreading and acts to dissolve focal adhesions between endothelial cells and extracellular matrix (74).

As noted above, TSP-1 is an important regulator of TGFβ activity. It controls conversion of the latent TGFβ complex to active forms, by binding through a defined peptide loop, KRFK, to the LAP component (55). It apparently sequesters LAP and dissociates it from TGFβ in an activation step. This biochemical mechanism has been confirmed by the striking phenotype similarity of TSP-1–null mice to those with inactivated TGFβ1. It is noteworthy that TSP-1 also has intrinsic antiangiogenic activity, mediated through its binding to CD36 through a different domain (75). Thus, these matricellulins display independent functions resident within modular domains, including those that sequester and alter activity of matrix-associated growth factors such as VEGF and TGFβ.

VASCULAR DEVELOPMENT OF THE MAMMALIAN KIDNEY

Although the kidneys are among the most richly vascularized organs in mammals, mechanisms regulating the development of the renal vascular system are only now beginning to be understood. The permanent, metanephric kidney originates at ~E10 in mice, ~E11 in rats, and ~5 weeks gestation in humans, when the ureteric bud projects dorsolaterally from the nephric duct into a group of metanephric blastemal mesenchymal cells (Figure 5, *upper left panel*; see color insert) (76). Reciprocal inductive signals emitted by cells of the ureteric bud and metanephric mesenchyme, respectively, lead to repeated branching of the bud (which ultimately forms the collecting system of the kidney) and aggregation of mesenchymal cells at each branch tip.

Each of these mesenchymal aggregates subsequently converts into a cluster (vesicle) of epithelial cells that ultimately differentiate into the glomerular and tubular epithelial cells of individual nephrons (76–78). Early in nephron development, a vascular cleft forms near the base of each vesicle to produce a comma-shaped nephric figure (Figure 5, *upper right panel*). Vascular elements assemble within this cleft, which give rise to the glomerular capillary tufts and mesangial cells (76, 79). Concurrent with these events, the epithelial cells above the vascular cleft ultimately produce the proximal convoluted tubule, Henle's loop, and distal tubular segments of the nephron, which connects to the branching collecting system.

The glomerular and peritubular capillaries form rapidly. The period from initial nephron induction to glomerular filtration and tubular reabsorption is only a few days in the mouse. The first nephrons and glomeruli induced to form in the mouse (at ~E11) occupy the juxtamedullary region of the fully developed kidney cortex, whereas the last nephrons that form (~postnatal day 7) are found in the outer cortex immediately beneath the capsule. This unique centrifugal pattern for nephrogenesis makes the kidney particularly attractive for studying a number of spatio-temporal developmental events, including formation of the vascular system.

Along with VEGF, all of its receptor tyrosine kinases are expressed in the embryonic kidney, as are many of the other growth factor receptor and signaling systems important for vascular assembly and referred to earlier. Because mice with targeted null mutations for VEGF, Flk-1, and Flt-1 die before the kidney develops, the exact roles for these signaling molecules in renal vascular development specifically are not fully understood. A cascade of overlapping events appears to govern the orderly formation and stabilization of glomerular and peritubular capillaries, and VEGF and its receptors are clearly among dominant regulators of this process.

VEGF is expressed in glomerular visceral epithelial cells (developing podocytes), which are located beneath the vascular cleft of comma-shaped nephric figures, and it continues to be expressed by podocytes of later-stage glomeruli and into adulthood (80–83). Likewise, the VEGF receptors Flk-1/KDR and Flt-1 are found in glomerular and other kidney endothelial cells in both fetal and adult humans (80, 81). By using in situ hybridization (84), lacZ reporter gene expression (85), and protein immunolocalization in the embryonic mouse (23), Flk-1 has been observed in metanephric angioblasts, developing microvessels, and glomerular endothelium of immature kidneys.

The expression of VEGF by podocytes and of the VEGF receptor Flk-1 by adjacent endothelial cells clearly implicates this ligand-receptor system in juxtacrine regulation of glomerular vascularization. As a test for this, injection of anti-VEGF antibodies into newborn mouse kidney cortex results in the formation of avascular glomeruli [resembling those that develop under normoxic conditions in organ culture (see below)], providing further evidence that VEGF is crucial for glomerular endothelialization (86). The sustained expression of both VEGF and Flk-1 in fully mature glomeruli of adult kidneys is unusual, however, because fully developed glomeruli are remarkably stable vascular structures. The data therefore suggest that both VEGF and Flk-1 are needed for maintenance of the extensively fenestrated phenotype of the highly differentiated glomerular endothelium (87, 88).

As explained above, the roles for TGFβ1 and its receptors in blood vessel development have been difficult to unravel, and it now appears that TGFβ1 may exert its angiogenic effects in vivo indirectly by stimulating VEGF production (89, 90). When neutralizing anti-TGFβ1 antibodies are infused into newborn rat kidneys, early glomeruli lack endothelial cells, a consequence similar to that seen after injection of anti-VEGF, except that the endothelium in more mature glomeruli is also affected as it fails to flatten and form fenestrae (91). Overall, however, kidney VEGF levels are unchanged after infusion of anti-TGFβ1 antibodies, so exactly how TGFβ1 mediates glomerular vascularization remains undefined.

Several morphological investigations reviewed in detail previously (76, 92) considered the two likely origins of endothelial cells in the embryonic kidney: (*a*) in situ differentiation of mesenchymal endothelial precursors (angioblasts) into vascular endothelial cells (vasculogenesis) or (*b*) ingress of angiogenic sprouts from preformed vessels outside the metanephros (angiogenesis). Evidence in support of this second possibility came from observations that, despite the organotypic tubulogenesis and glomerulogenesis that occurs when fetal rodent kidneys are maintained under standard organ culture conditions, the glomeruli that form in vitro are avascular (93, 94). Additionally, when fetal mouse kidneys are grafted onto avian chorioallantoic membranes, glomeruli within grafts contain endothelial cells of host (avian) lineages (95).

More recently, however, new evidence indicates that kidney microvessels may instead originate from intrinsic kidney angioblasts. For example, when fetal kidneys are cultured under hypoxic conditions, there is an upregulation of VEGF, and under these conditions, renal microvessels do assemble in vitro (96). As referred to above, this finding is consistent with activation of VEGF transcription by ARNT/HIF-1α heterodimers, which are stabilized specifically in hypoxia. Additionally, this points to an ability by the kidney to form vessels from its own internal resources and fits with immunolocalization and reporter gene expression data showing that dispersed mesenchymal cells in the metanephric cortex that express Flk-1 are candidate angioblasts (23, 85). On the other hand, when embryonic kidneys are cultured under routine normoxic conditions, there is a marked downregulation of Flk-1 expression in vitro (85). When these cultured kidneys are then grafted into anterior eye chambers, however, Flk-1 expression resumes, and endothelial cells, which are derived exclusively from the engrafted kidney, constitute an extensive microvasculature that forms in oculo (85). In aggregate, these data demonstrate that (*a*) both VEGF and Flk-1 expression are necessary for renal microvessel formation and (*b*) the kidney is capable of establishing its own microvascular network independent of external vessels, presumably through activation of resident angioblasts.

Whereas an abundant amount of data shows that complementary expression of VEGF and its receptors is likely to be a major controlling element for initial glomerular endothelial-cell development, most experimental evidence in cultured endothelial cells indicates that this signaling system results mainly in increased mitotic and cell motility behavior. Although enhanced mitosis and motility would be crucially important for seeding and maintenance of a renal angioblast stem cell population in vivo, different activities need to be invoked for the actual targeting of differentiating endothelial cells into glomeruli and the capillary nets that surround renal tubules. As suggested previously, the Eph/ephrin families of cell surface receptor-ligand pairs, which are capable of inducing endothelial network formation in vitro, are probably more important than VEGF and its receptors for endothelial-cell targeting and aggregation in vivo. When the distributions of EphB1 and ephrin-B1 were evaluated in the embryonic kidney, both members of this receptor-ligand pair were identified in metanephric angioblasts and on endothelial cells of developing and maturing glomeruli (66). These patterns were in fact indistinguishable from those seen for cells bearing Flk-1 (66) and Tie-1 (97). Although it is too soon to know for certain whether all of these membrane proteins colocalize exactly to the same cells, the possibility seems highly likely. Taken together with the evidence reviewed earlier on the respective roles for VEGF and its receptors and the Eph/ephrin families, these data from the developing kidney suggest that VEGF/Flk-1 mediates renal angioblast activation and, at least for glomerular endothelial cells, may also be necessary for maintenance of the differentiated state. The expression of Eph/ephrin by these same cells may direct partnering between activated angioblasts and the subsequent formation of spatially restricted vascular networks.

Once the basic vascular framework is established, additional signaling systems are required for modulating endothelial-cell mitotic activity and stabilizing the network. Among the more promising candidates for this role is ECRPTP/DEP-1, a type-III receptor protein tyrosine phosphatase. Cells expressing ECRTP/DEP-1 have the same distribution pattern in developing kidney as those expressing the endothelial lineage restricted protein, vascular endothelial-cadherin, and this receptor phosphatase accumulates at points of inter-endothelial contact in vessels and in cultured endothelial cells (98). Although not implicated directly in endothelial differentiation, PDGF B functions as an attractant signal to recruit pericytes and other myofibroblasts to developing vessels. In the immature kidney, PDGF B is expressed by epithelial cells of early nephrons, whereas PDGFRβ is found on interstitial cells and undifferentiated mesenchyme (99). As glomeruli develop, both PDGF B and PDGFRβ are concentrated on mesangial cells, which suggests a paracrine and then autocrine signaling system for mesangial cell recruitment and maintenance.

In mice with targeted mutations of either PDGF B (25) or PDGFRβ (24), glomerular mesangial cells are absent, and the glomeruli that form are characterized by a large, irregular capillary loop. Although PDFGFA and PDGFRα are coordinately expressed in collecting-duct epithelium and vascular smooth muscle, respectively, indicating an involvement in recruitment of renal arterial adventitial cells (99–101), no renal arteriolar defects are apparent in null mutants (24, 102).

CONCLUSION

With further molecular definition of the endotheliocentric responses that direct proliferation, migration, cell-cell discrimination, and assembly of vascular structures, we anticipate further understanding of the molecular code read by endothelial cells as they assemble and remodel the interconnecting vascular network that is so integral to tissue structure and function.

ACKNOWLEDGMENTS

This effort was supported by PHS awards RO1-DK47078, RO1-DK38517, NCI Center Grant CA68485, and the TJ Martell Foundation (TOD), and PHS awards RO1-DK52483 and DK34972 (DRA).

Visit the Annual Reviews home page at www.AnnualReviews.org.

LITERATURE CITED

1. Folkman J. 1995. Angiogenesis in cancer, vascular, rheumatoid and other disease. *Nat. Med.* 1:27–31
2. Hanahan D. 1997. Signalling vascular morphogenesis and maintenance. *Science* 277:48–50
3. Chen CS, Mrksich M, Huang S, Whitesides GM, Ingber DE. 1997. Geometric of cell life and death. *Science* 276:1425–28
4. Risau W. 1997. Mechanisms of angiogenesis. *Nature* 386:671–74
5. Gale NW, Yancopoulos GD. 1999. Growth factors acting via endothelial cell-specific receptor tyrosine kinases: VEGFs, angiopoietins, and ephrins in vascular development. *Genes Dev.* 13:1055–66
6. Darland DC, D'Amore PA. 1999. Blood vessel maturation: vascular development comes of age. *J. Clin. Invest.* 103:157–58
7. Ferrara N, Davis-Smyth T. 1997. The biology of vascular endothelial growth factor. *Endocr. Rev.* 18:4–25
8. Drake CJ, Little CD. 1995. Exogenous vascular endothelial growth factor induces malformed and hyperfused vessels during embryonic neovascularization. *Proc. Natl. Acad. Sci. USA* 92:7657–61
9. Kaelin WGJ. 1999. Cancer. Many vessels, faulty gene. *Nature* 399:203–4
10. Clark ER, Clark EL. 1939. Microscopic observations on the growth of blood capillaries in the living mammal. *Am. J. Anat.* 64(2):251–301
11. Werb Z, Vu TH, Rinkenberger JL, Coussens LM. 1999. Matrix-degrading proteases and angiogenesis during development and tumor formation. *Acta Pathol. Microbiol. Immunol. Scand.* 107:11–18
12. Eliceiri BP, Cheresh DA. 1999. The role of alpha$_V$ integrins during angiogenesis:

insights into potential mechanisms of action and clinical development. *J. Clin. Invest.* 103:1227–30
13. Huynh-Do U, Stein E, Lane AA, Liu H, Cerretti DP, Daniel TO. 1999. Surface densities of ephrin-B1 determine EphB1-coupled activation of cell attachment through $\alpha_v\beta_3$ and $\alpha_5\beta_1$ integrins. *EMBO J.* 18:2165–73
14. Lampugnani MG, Corada M, Caveda L, Breviario F, Ayalon O, et al. 1995. The molecular organization of endothelial cell to cell junctions: differential association of plakoglobin, β-catenin, and α-catenin with vascular endothelial cadherin (VE-cadherin). *J. Cell Biol.* 129:203–17
15. Folkman J, D'Amore PA. 1996. Blood vessel formation: What is its molecular basis? *Cell* 87:1153–55
16. Asahara T, Murohara T, Sullivan A, Silver M, van der Zee R, et al. 1997. Isolation of putative progenitor endothelial cells for angiogenesis. *Science* 275:964
17. Isner JM, Asahara T. 1999. Angiogenesis and vasculogenesis as therapeutic strategies for postnatal neovascularization. *J. Clin. Invest.* 103:1231–36
18. Takahashi T, Kalka C, Masuda H, Chen D, Silver M, et al. 1999. Ischemia- and cytokine-induced mobilization of bone marrow-derived endothelial progenitor cells for neovascularization. *Nat. Med.* 5:434–38
19. Asahara T, Takahashi T, Masuda H, Kalka C, Chen D, et al. 1999. VEGF contributes to postnatal neovascularization by mobilizing bone marrow-derived endothelial progenitor cells. *EMBO J.* 18:3964–72
20. Burri PH. 1992. Intussusceptive microvascular growth, a new mechanism of capillary network formation. *Exerc. Sci.* 61:32–39
21. Patan S, Haenni B, Burri PH. 1996.

Implementation of intussusceptive microvascular growth in the chicken chorioallantoic membrane (CAM): 1. Pillar formation by folding of the capillary wall. *Microvasc. Res.* 51:80–98

22. Noden DM. 1989. Embryonic origins and assembly of blood vessels. *Am. Rev. Respir. Dis.* 140:1097–103

23. Robert B, St John PL, Hyink DP, Abrahamson DR. 1996. Evidence that embryonic kidney cells expressing flk-1 are intrinsic, vasculogenic angioblasts. *Am. J. Physiol.* 271:F744–53

24. Soriano P. 1994. Abnormal kidney development and hematological disorders in platelet-derived growth factor β-receptor knock out mice. *Genes Dev.* 8:1888–96

25. Leveen P, Pekny M, Gebre-Medhin S, Swolin B, Larsson E, Betsholtz C. 1994. Mice deficient for PDGF B show renal, cardiovascular, and hematological abnormalities. *Genes Dev.* 8:1875–87

26. Lindahl P, Johansson BR, Leveen P, Betsholtz C. 1997. Pericyte loss and microaneurysm formation in PDGF-B-deficient mice. *Science* 277:242–45

27. Hatzopoulos AK, Folkman J, Vasile E, Eiselen GK, Rosenberg RD. 1998. Isolation and characterization of endothelial progenitor cells from mouse embryos. *Development* 125:1457–68

28. Coffin JD, Harrison J, Schwartz S, Heimark R. 1991. Angioblast differentiation and morphogenesis of the vascular endothelium in the mouse embryo. *Dev. Biol.* 148:51–62

29. Shalaby F, Ho J, Stanford WL, Fischer K-D, Schuh AC, et al. 1997. A requirement for Flk1 in primitive and definitive hematopoiesis and vasculogenesis. *Cell* 89:981–90

30. Drake CJ, Brandt SJ, Trusk TC, Little CD. 1997. TAL1/SCL is expressed in endothelial progenitor cells/angioblasts and defines a dorsal-to-ventral gradient of vasculogenesis. *Dev. Biol.* 192:17–30

31. Ogawa M, Kizumoto M, Nishikawa S, Fujimoto T, Kodama H, Nishikawa SI.

1999. Expression of alpha4-integrin defines the earliest precursor of hematopoietic cell lineage diverged from endothelial cells. *Blood* 93:1168–77

32. Nishikawa SI, Nishikawa S, Hirashima M, Matsuyoshi N, Kodama H. 1998. Progressive lineage analysis by cell sorting and culture identifies FLK1 + VE-cadherin + cells at a diverging point of endothelial and hemopoietic lineages. *Development* 125:1747–57

33. Oda N, Abe M, Sato Y. 1999. ETS-1 converts endothelial cells to the angiogenic phenotype by inducing the expression of matrix metalloproteinases and integrin beta3. *J. Cell Physiol.* 178:121–32

34. Tanaka K, Oda N., Iwasaka C, Abe M, Sato Y. 1998. Induction of Ets-1 in endothelial cells during reendothelialization after denuding injury. *J. Cell Physiol.* 176:235–44

35. Yamamoto H, Flannery ML, Kupriyanov S, Pearce J, McKercher SR, et al. 1998. Defective trophoblast function in mice with a targeted mutation of Ets2. *Genes Dev.* 12:1315–26

36. Wang LC, Kuo F, Fujiwara Y, Gilliland DG, Golub TR, Orkin SH. 1997. Yolk sac angiogenic defect and intra-embryonic apoptosis in mice lacking the Ets-related factor TEL. *EMBO J.* 16:4374–83

37. Maxwell PH, Wiesener MS, Chang GW, Clifford SC, Vaux EC, et al. 1999. The tumour suppressor protein VHL targets hypoxia-inducible factors for oxygen-dependent proteolysis. *Nature* 399:271–75

38. Maltepe E, Schmidt JV, Baunoch D, Bradfield CA, Simon MC. 1997. Abnormal angiogenesis and responses to glucose and oxygen deprivation in mice lacking the protein ARNT. *Nature* 386:403–7

39. Ferrara N, Carver-Moore K, Chen H, Dowd M, Lu L, et al. 1996. Heterozygous embryonic lethality induced by tar-

geted inactivation of the VEGF gene. *Nature* 380:439–42

40. Carmeliet P, Ferreira V, Breier G, Pollefeyt S, Kieckens L, et al. 1996. Abnormal blood vessel development and lethality in embryos lacking a single VEGF allele. *Nature* 380:435–39

41. Shalaby F, Rossant J, Yamaguchi TP, Gerstenstein M, Wu XF, et al. 1995. Failure of blood-island formation and vasculogenesis in Flk-1 deficient mice. *Nature* 376:62–66

42. Fong GH, Rossant J, Gertsenstein M, Breitman ML. 1995. Role of the *flt-1* receptor tyrosine kinase in regulating the assembly of vascular endothelium. *Nature* 376:66–70

43. Hiratsuka S, Minowa O, Kuno J, Noda T, Shibuya M. 1998. Flt-1 lacking the tyrosine kinase domain is sufficient for normal development and angiogenesis in mice. *Proc. Natl. Acad. Sci. USA* 95:9349–54

44. Dumont DJ, Jussila L, Taipale J, Lymboussaki A, Mustonen T, et al. 1998. Cardiovascular failure in mouse embryos deficient in VEGF receptor-3. *Science* 282:946–49

45. Woodard A, Garc C, Leong M, Madri J, Sessa W, Languino L. 1998. The synergistic activity of α_v β_3 integrin and PDGF receptor increases cell migration. *J. Cell Sci.* 111:469–78

46. Murohara T, Asahara T, Silver M, Bauters C, Masuda H, et al. 1998. Nitric oxide synthase modulates angiogenesis in response to tissue ischemia. *J. Clin. Invest.* 101:2567–78

47. Dickson MC, Martin JS, Cousins FM, Kulkarni AB, Karlsson S, Akhurst RJ. 1995. Defective haematopoiesis and vasculogenesis in transforming growth factor-β1 knock out mice. *Development* 121:1845–54

48. McAllister KA, Grogg KM, Johnson DW, Gallione CJ, Baldwin MA, et al. 1994. Endoglin, a TGF-beta binding protein of endothelial cells, is the gene for hereditary haemorrhagic telangiectasis type 1. *Nat. Genet.* 8:345–51

49. Johnson DW, Berg JN, Baldwin MA, Gallione CJ, Marondel I, et al. 1996. Mutations in the activin receptor-like kinase 1 gene in hereditary haemorrhagic telangiectasia type 2. *Nat. Genet.* 13: 189–95

50. Massague J. 1998. TGF-beta signal transduction. *Annu. Rev. Biochem.* 67: 753–91

51. Barbara NP, Wrana JL, Letarte M. 1999. Endoglin is an accessory protein that interacts with the signaling receptor complex of multiple members of the transforming growth factor- beta superfamily. *J. Biol. Chem.* 274:584–94

52. Brown CB, Boyer AS, Runyan RB, Barnett JV. 1999. Requirement of type III TGF-beta receptor for endocardial cell transformation in the heart. *Science* 283:2080–82

53. Li DY, Sorensen LK, Brooke BS, Urness LD, Davis EC, et al. 1999. Defective angiogenesis in mice lacking endoglin. *Science* 284:1534–37

54. Munger JS, Huang X, Kawakatsu H, Griffiths MJ, Dalton SL, et al. 1999. The integrin $\alpha_v\beta_6$ binds and activates latent TGF beta 1: a mechanism for regulating pulmonary inflammation and fibrosis. *Cell* 96:319–28

55. Crawford SE, Stellmach V, Murphy-Ullrich JE, Ribeiro SM, Lawler J, et al. 1998. Thrombospondin-1 is a major activator of TGF-beta1 in vivo. *Cell* 93:1159–70

56. Dumont DJ, Gradwohl G, Fong G-H, Puri MC, Gertsenstein M, et al. 1994. Dominant-negative and targeted null mutations in the endothelial receptor tyrosine kinase, *tek,* reveal a critical role in vasculogenesis of the embryo. *Genes Dev.* 8:1897–909

57. Sato TN, Tozawa Y, Deutsch U, Wolburg-Buchholz K, Fujiwara Y, et al. 1995. Distinct roles of the receptor tyro-

sine kinases Tie-1 and Tie-2 in blood vessel formation. *Nature* 376:70

58. Maisonpierre PC, Suri C, Jones PF, Bartunkova S, Wiegand SJ, et al. 1997. Angiopoietin-2, a natural antagonist for Tie2 that disrupts in vivo angiogenesis. *Science.* 277:55–60

59. Davis S, Yancopoulos GD. 1999. The angiopoietins: yin and yang in angiogenesis. *Curr. Top. Microbiol. Immunol.* 237:173–85

60. Gale NW, Holland SJ, Valenzuela DM, Flenniken A, Pan L, et al. 1996. Eph receptors and ligands comprise two major specificity subclasses and are reciprocally compartmentalized during embryogenesis. *Neuron* 17:9–19

61. Nakamoto M, Cheng H-J, Friedman GC, McLaughlin T, Hansen MJ, et al. 1996. Topographically specific effects of ELF-1 on retinal axon guidance in vitro and retinal axon mapping in vivo. *Cell* 86:755–66

62. Henkemeyer M, Orioli D, Henderson JT, Saxton TM, Roder S, et al. 1996. Nuk controls pathfinding of commissural axons in the mammalian central nervous system. *Cell* 86:35–46

63. Adams RH, Wilkinson GA, Weiss C, Diella F, Gale NW, et al. 1999. Roles of ephrin B ligands and EphB receptors in cardiovascular development: demarcation of arterial/venous domains, vascular morphogenesis, and sprouting angiogenesis. *Genes Dev.* 13:295–306

64. Wang HU, Chen ZF, Anderson DJ. 1998. Molecular distinction and angiogenic interaction between embryonic arteries and veins revealed by ephrin-B2 and its receptor Eph-B4. *Cell* 93:741–53

65. Pandey A, Shao H, Marks RM, Polverini PJ, Dixit VM. 1995. Role of B61, the ligand for the Eck receptor tyrosine kinase, in TNF-α-induced angiogenesis. *Science* 268:567–69

66. Daniel TO, Stein E, Cerretti DP, St. John PL, Robert BL, Abrahamson DR. 1996. ELK and LERK-2 in developing kidney and microvascular endothelial assembly. *Kidney Int.* 50:73–81 (Suppl.)

67. Stein E, Lane AA, Cerretti DP, Schoecklmann HO, Schroff AD, et al. 1998. Eph receptors discriminate specific ligand oligomers to determine alternative signaling complexes, attachment, and assembly responses. *Genes Dev.* 12:667–78

68. Holland SJ, Gale NW, Mbamalu G, Yancopoulos GD, Henkemeyer M, Pawson T. 1996. Bidirectional signaling through the EPH-family receptor Nuk and its transmembrane ligands. *Nature* 383:722–25

69. Bruckner K, Pasquale EB, Klein R. 1997. Tyrosine phosphorylation of transmembrane ligands for EPH receptors. *Science* 275:1640–43

70. Sperry RW. 1963. Chemoaffinity in the orderly growth of nerve fiber patterns and connections. *Proc. Natl. Acad. Sci. USA* 50:703–10

71. Freidlander M, Brooks PC, Shaffer RW, Kincaid CM, Varner JA, Cheresh DA. 1995. Definition of two angiogenic pathways by distinct αV integrins. *Science* 270:1500–2

72. Brooks PC, Silletti S, von Schalscha TL, Friedlander M, Cheresh DA. 1998. Disruption of angiogenesis by PEX, a noncatalytic metalloproteinase fragment with integrin binding activity. *Cell* 92:391–400

73. Kupprion C, Motamed K, Sage EH. 1998. SPARC (BM-40, osteonectin) inhibits the mitogenic effect of vascular endothelial growth factor on microvascular endothelial cells. *J. Biol. Chem.* 273:29635–40

74. Motamed K, Sage EH. 1998. SPARC inhibits endothelial cell adhesion but not proliferation through a tyrosine phosphorylation-dependent pathway. *J. Cell Biochem.* 70:543–52

75. Dawson DW, Pearce SF, Zhong R, Silverstein RL, Frazier WA, Bouck NP. 1997. CD36 mediates the In vitro inhib-

itory effects of thrombospondin-1 on endothelial cells. *J. Cell Biol.* 138:707–17

76. Saxen L. 1987. *Organogenesis of the Kidney.* Cambridge, UK: Cambridge Univ. Press

77. Kanwar YS, Carone FA, Kumar A, Wada J, Ota K, Wallner EI. 1997. Role of extracellular matrix, growth factors and proto-oncogenes in metanephric development. *Kidney Int.* 52:589–606

78. Vainio S, Muller U. 1997. Inductive tissue interactions, cell signaling, and the control of kidney organogenesis. *Cell* 90:975–78

79. Abrahamson DR. 1991. Glomerulogenesis in the developing kidney. *Semin. Nephrol.* 11:375–89

80. Simon M, Grone H-J, Johren O, Kullmer J, Plate HK, et al. 1995. Expression of vascular endothelial growth factor and its receptors in human renal ontogenesis and in adult kidney. *Am. J. Physiol.* 268: F240–50

81. Kaipainen A, Korhonen J, Pajusola K, Aprelikova O, Persico MG, et al. 1993. The related FLT4, FLT1, and KDR receptor tyrosine kinases show distinct expression patterns in human fetal endothelial cells. *J. Exp. Med.* 178:2077–88

82. Breier G, Albrecht U, Sterrer S, Risau W. 1992. Expression of vascular endothelial growth factor during embryonic angiogenesis and endothelial cell differentiation. *Development* 114:521–32

83. Dumont DJ, Fong GH, Puri MC, Gradwohl G, Alitalo K, Breitman ML. 1995. Vascularization of the mouse embryo: a study of flk-1, tek, tie, and vascular endothelial growth factor expression during development. *Dev. Dynam.* 203:80–92

84. Oelrichs RB, Reid HH, Bernard O, Ziemiecki A, Wilks AF. 1993. NYK/FLK-1: a putative receptor protein tyrosine kinase isolated from E10 embryonic neuroepithelium is expressed in endothelial cells of the developing embryo. *Oncogene* 8:11–18

85. Robert B, St. John PL, Abrahamson DR. 1998. Direct visualization of renal vascular morphogenesis in flk1 heterozygous mutant mice. *Am. J. Physiol.* 275:F164–72

86. Kitamoto Y, Tokunaga H, Tomita K. 1997. Vascular endothelial growth factor is an essential molecule for mouse kidney development: glomerulogenesis and nephrogenesis. *J. Clin. Invest.* 99:2351–57

87. Roberts WG, Palade GE. 1997. Neovasculature induced by vascular endothelial growth factor is fenestrated. *Cancer Res.* 57:765–72

88. Risau W, Esser S, Engelhardt B. 1998. Differentiation of blood-brain barrier endothelial cells. *Pathol. Biol.* 46:171–75

89. Frank S, Hubner G, Breier G, Longaker MT, Greenhalgh DG, Werner S. 1995. Regulation of vascular endothelial growth factor expression in cultured keratinocytes. Implications for normal and impaired wound healing. *J. Biol. Chem.* 270:12607–13

90. Pertovaara L, Kaipainen A, Mustonen T, Orpana A, Ferrara N, et al. 1994. Vascular endothelial growth factor is induced in response to transforming growth factor-beta in fibroblastic and epithelial cells. *J. Biol. Chem.* 269:6271–74

91. Liu A, Dardik A, Ballerman BJ. 1999. Neutralizing TGF-â1 antibody infusion in neonatal rat delays in vivo glomerular capillary formation. *Kidney Int.* 56:1334–48

92. Hyink DP, Abrahamson DR. 1995. Origin of the glomerular vasculature in the developing kidney. *Semin. Nephrol.* 15:300–14

93. Bernstein J, Cheng F, Roszka J. 1981. Glomerular differentiation in metanephric culture. *Lab. Invest.* 45:183

94. Ekblom P. 1989. Developmentally regu-

lated conversion of mesenchyme to epithelium. *FASEB J.* 3:2141–50

95. Sariola H, Ekblom P, Lehtonen E, Saxen L. 1983. Differentiation and vascularisation of the metanephric kidney grafted on the chorioallantoic membrane. *Dev. Biol.* 96:427–35

96. Tufro-McReddie A, Norwood VF, Aylor KW, Botkin SJ, Carey RM, Gomez RA. 1997. Oxygen regulates vascular endothelial growth factor-mediated vasculogenesis and tubulogenesis. *Dev. Biol.* 183:139–49

97. Loughna S, Landels E, Woolf AS. 1996. Growth factor control of developing kidney endothelial cells. *Exp. Nephrol.* 4:112–18

98. Takahashi T, Takahashi K, Mernaugh R, Drozdoff V, Sipe C, et al. 1999. Endothelial localization of receptor tyrosine phosphatase, ECRTP/DEP-1, in devel-

oping and mature renal vasculature. *Kidney Int.* 10:2135–45

99. Alpers CE, Seifert RA, Hudkins KL, Johnson RJ, Bowen-Pope DF. 1992. Developmental patterns of PDGF B-chain, PDGF-receptor, and α-actin expression in human glomerulogenesis. *Kidney Int.* 42:390–99

100. Gesualdo L, Pinzani M, Floriano JJ, Hassan MO, Nagy NU, et al. 1991. Platelet-derived growth factor expression in mesangial proliferative glomerulonephritis. *Lab Invest.* 65:160–67

101. Floege J, Hudkins KL, Seifert RA, Francki A, Bowen-Pope DF, Alpers CE. 1997. Localization of PDGF alpha-receptor in the developing and mature human kidney. *Kidney Int.* 51:1140–50

102. Bostrom H, Willetts K, Pekny M, Leveen P, Lindahl P, et al. 1996. PDGF-A signaling is a critical event in lung alveolar myofibroblast development and alveogenesis. *Cell* 85:863–73

Annu. Rev. Physiol. 2000. 62:673–95

MECHANISMS OF GUANYLIN ACTION VIA CYCLIC GMP IN THE KIDNEY

Leonard R. Forte, Roslyn M. London, William J. Krause, and Ronald H. Freeman

Harry S. Truman Memorial Veterans Hospital and the Departments of Pharmacology, Pathology and Anatomical Sciences and Physiology, School of Medicine, Missouri University, Columbia, Missouri 65212; e-mail: lrf@missouri.edu

Key Words   uroguanylin, lymphoguanylin, *E. coli* heat-stable enterotoxin, guanylate cyclase, intestine

■ **Abstract**   Guanylin, uroguanylin, and lymphoguanylin are small peptides that activate cell-surface guanylate cyclase receptors and influence cellular function via intracellular cGMP. Guanylins activate two receptors, GC-C and OK-GC, which are expressed in intestine and/or kidney. Elevation of cGMP in the intestine elicits an increase in electrolyte and water secretion. Activation of renal receptors by uroguanylin stimulates urine flow and excretion of sodium, chloride, and potassium. Intracellular cGMP pathways for guanylins include activation of PKG-II and/or indirect stimulation of PKA-II. The result is activation of CFTR and/or ClC-2 channel proteins to enhance the electrogenic secretion of chloride and bicarbonate. Similar cellular mechanisms may be involved in the renal responses to guanylin peptides. Uroguanylin serves as an intestinal natriuretic hormone in postprandial states, thus linking the digestive and renal organ systems in a novel endocrine axis. Therefore, uroguanylin participates in the complex physiological processes underlying the saliuresis that is elicited by a salty meal.

BACKGROUND

Studies of cellular mechanisms underlying a cholera-like disease caused by *Escherichia coli* and other enteric microbes unexpectedly led to the discovery of uroguanylin, a novel peptide hormone that regulates urinary sodium chloride excretion by direct actions on the kidney. Uroguanylin was first isolated from opossum urine as 13-, 14-, and 15-amino acid peptides; the T84 intestinal cell cGMP bioassay was used to detect and purify the active peptides by gel filtration, preparative isoelectric focusing, and reverse phase (RP)-HPLC methods (1). T84 cells express high levels of a membrane receptor guanylate cyclase (GC), which is activated by peptide toxins secreted by strains of *E. coli* that cause a cholera-like diarrhea. Heat-stable enterotoxin (stable toxin; ST) peptides stimulate cGMP production in target enterocytes lining the small and large intestine, thus increasing secretion of chloride, bicarbonate, sodium, and fluid into the intestinal lumen (2, 3). Bacterial STs were the first peptides shown to activate membrane receptor GC signaling molecules in vertebrates, thereby revealing a novel signaling pathway for hormonal regulation of cell function via intracellular cGMP. Although discovery of this cGMP signaling mechanism for *E. coli* ST was reported in 1978 by Hughes et al (2) and Field et al (3), the first of the endogenous ST-like peptides to be identified in mammals was isolated more than a decade later by Currie et al (4). This 15-residue peptide was purified from rat intestine and named guanylin, denoting its receptor, *guanyl* cyclase, and *in*testinal origin. However, guanylin and uroguanylin were not the first endogenous cGMP-regulating peptides to be identified in mammals. Shortly following the demonstration that *E. coli* ST activates intestinal receptor GCs as a means of stimulating intestinal anion secretion (2, 3), deBold and coworkers prepared extracts from heart atria that elicited a dramatic diuresis and natriuresis when injected into rats (5). Atriopeptin-A [atrial natriuretic peptide (ANP)] was subsequently purified from atria and shown to be a small peptide containing a single disulfide bond (6, 7). Atriopeptin-B (BNP) and atriopeptin-C (CNP) were isolated from porcine brain a few years later, thus constituting a family of three endogenous peptides that influence cellular function by regulating cGMP production in target cells in the kidney, blood vessels, adrenal cortex, and other organs (8, 9). With the identification of a third guanylin, lymphoguanylin, both families of cGMP-regulating peptide hormones now contain three structurally distinct peptides (10). This review focuses on the cell and molecular biology of guanylin, uroguanylin, and lymphoguanylin with emphasis on their mechanism(s) of action in the kidney, where they serve to regulate urinary sodium chloride excretion, thus influencing sodium balance.

The physiological control of sodium balance in the body is a complex process involving the regulation of renal blood flow, glomerular filtration rate, and filtered load as well as a myriad of tubular functions for reabsorptive and/or secretory modes of transport. Following a salty meal, sodium chloride is absorbed by the digestive tract, which leads to a prolonged natriuresis that is crucial for maintaining body sodium balance. Physiological mechanisms contributing to increased sodium excretion following salt ingestion are numerous and redundant. Discovery of uroguanylin provides a novel endocrine link between the intestine and kidney by means of circulating uroguanylin (1, 29). An intestinal natriuretic factor was postulated to exist in the digestive system by Carey and colleagues, who offered this substance as an explanation for the dramatic natriuresis elicited by oral salt loads (11, 12). Their experiments were direct and elegant demonstrations in humans and experimental animals that oral salt intake increases urinary sodium excretion to a far greater extent than does intravenous salt. It was reasoned that one or more organs of the digestive system, perhaps the stomach and upper small intestine, have the capability to detect salt and release a natriuretic hormone into the circulation. The intestinal natriuretic hormone would stimulate urinary sodium excretion to help maintain sodium balance. When uroguanylin was isolated in

1992, we soon realized that this peptide has key properties required of such an intestinal natriuretic hormone (11, 12). Uroguanylin is a highly effective natriuretic and diuretic peptide produced by and secreted from intestine mucosa under the influence of dietary sodium chloride (1,13–15). Thus an endocrine axis linking the digestive system with the kidney via uroguanylin is now considered as a possible physiological mechanism contributing to the maintenance of sodium balance in postprandial states.

GUANYLATE CYCLASE RECEPTORS

Two different kinds of GCs produce cGMP for intracellular signaling. Cytosolic GCs are heterodimers containing heme that serve as intracellular receptors for the membrane-permeable signaling molecule, nitric oxide, and were first described by White & Aurbach (16). Plasma membrane GCs are receptors for endogenous peptide hormones including the atriopeptins and guanylins. The cell-surface GC receptor-enzymes were described by Hardman & Sutherland (17). Membrane GCs have four domains consisting of N-terminal, ligand-binding regions, single membrane-spanning domains, kinase-like domains, and highly conserved catalytic regions at the C termini of the proteins (reviewed in 18). The first GC identified in vertebrates by molecular cloning is a receptor for ANP and BNP (GC-A), whereas a second receptor GC, GC-B, interacts specifically with CNP. Two additional GC-receptor cDNAs have been cloned from intestine (GC-C) and kidney (OK-GC) that are cell-surface receptors for guanylin peptides (19, 20). Four additional membrane GCs have been identified by molecular cloning of cDNAs from either sensory tissues or intestine, but these GCs have no known peptide agonist(s) and are classified as orphan receptors (18). *Caenorhabditis elegans,* a relatively simple invertebrate, has a total of about 26 genes for membrane receptor GCs (21). The genome expansion that occurred during the evolution of vertebrates predicts that mammalian genomes may contain as many as 100 genes encoding different molecular forms of cell-surface receptor GCs. Thus, several more receptor GCs are likely to be identified as various genome sequences are completed and mammalian GC genes are characterized at the molecular level. Four mammalian GC genes have been identified as cell-surface receptors for atriopeptins and guanylins, and four other GCs are presently considered orphan receptors. Elucidating the full repertoire of receptor GCs found in the body is a straightforward project, but a considerably more difficult and greater challenge awaits those who set out to identify peptide hormones that regulate the enzymatic activities of membrane GCs. No more than one tenth of membrane GCs have been identified, leaving about 90 GCs as unidentified molecules. Assuming that one half of these GCs are receptors for peptides and that four receptor GC genes exist for each peptide family, then approximately 10 different families of cGMP-regulating peptides may exist that have not yet been identified. Completion of genome projects will provide the experimental means to identify both novel peptide hormones and their cognate GC receptors. Reverse endocrinology will be the game of the day when a full GC gene list is reported for mouse or human genomes. Each membrane GC is a candidate orphan receptor that could be regulated by presently unknown families of peptide hormones. We suggest that the totality of cellular cGMP signaling via membrane GCs controlled by various peptides will be equivalent in diversity and physiological significance to cGMP signaling via nitric oxide GC pathways. Moreover, each cellular function controlled by nitric oxide via cGMP is likely to have a counterpart and complementary mechanism mediated through cell-surface receptor GCs for atriopeptins, guanylins, and other peptide hormones that await discovery.

DISCOVERY OF GUANYLIN PEPTIDES

Guanylin was the first endogenous ST-like peptide that was isolated and sequenced. This 15-residue peptide was purified from rat jejunum (4). A receptor GC that is activated by *E. coli* ST and located in the brush border membranes (BBM) of renal proximal tubules provided a physiological rationale for the presence of a guanylin-like peptide in urine of opossums (22–25). This finding prompted a search for endogenous ST-like peptides that could regulate the enzymatic activity of membrane GCs located in the kidney and other extra-intestinal tissues, such as testes, liver, and airway epithelium. It was initially thought that an opossum homologue of guanylin might be present in tubular filtrate to regulate the activity of BBM-localized GCs in kidney cells and that these peptides could be excreted in urine in biologically active forms. Figure 1 depicts the stimulation of cGMP production in cultured opossum kidney (OK) cells by treatment with extracts of urine and intestinal mucosa. Extracts of urine yielded three biologically active peptides when subjected to purification by gel filtration, preparative isoelectric focusing, and RP-HPLC. The primary structure of each peptide was elucidated by N-terminal sequence analysis and electrospray mass spectrometry (1). Active peptides in opossum urine are 13-, 14- and 15-residue forms of the same guanylin/ST-like peptide. However, peptides isolated from opossum urine were unlike rat or human guanylin in several key residues, suggesting that a novel peptide was abundant in urine. This conclusion was verified when the opossum version of guanylin was subsequently isolated from both intestinal mucosa and urine (1). The dominant urinary peptide was named uroguanylin, indicating its biological source, urine, and peptide family relationship. Various forms of uroguanylin were then isolated from human and rat urine (26, 27), rat intestine (28), and opossum and human plasma (29, 30). Uroguanylin is clearly the major biologically active peptide in urine because guanylin is either undetectable (in human and rat urine) or found at much lower concentrations than uroguanylin in opossum urine (1, 26, 27). A third member of the guanylin family of peptides was identified recently by molecular cloning of cDNAs from lymphoid, cardiovascular-renal, reproductive, and central nervous organ systems that encode a uroguanylin-like

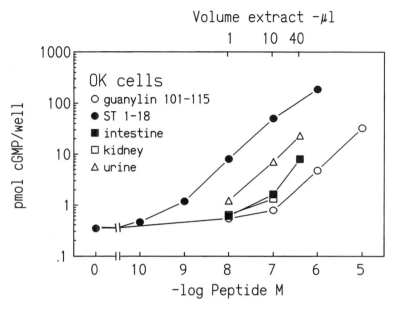

Figure 1 Stimulation of cGMP production by extracts of opossum urine and intestine in the opossum kidney cell line. OK cells were grown to confluence in 24-well dishes and then exposed for 40 min to rat guanylin, *E. coli* ST, or the indicated volumes of extracts prepared from urine and intestinal mucosa, as described previously (1). The cellular cGMP

peptide that we call lymphoguanylin (10). This structurally unique peptide was synthesized as a 15-residue molecule containing a single intramolecular disulfide and shown to be biologically active in T84 and OK cell cGMP bioassays. Surprisingly, the expression of lymphoguanylin mRNA is greatest in the renal cortex and myocardium. Thus, lymphoguanylin may have a physiological role in an intrarenal pathway for regulation of kidney function via cGMP. Lymphoguanylin could be a counterpart in the guanylins to a form of atriopeptin-A (i.e. urodilatin), which is produced locally in the kidney (31). A potential link between the heart and kidney via lymphoguanylin may also be present in the opossum. To summarize, both the atriopeptin and guanylin families of cGMP-regulating hormones have at least three different peptides derived from six different genes, and these peptide hormones selectively regulate the enzymatic activities of membrane GCs in target tissues. Two receptors, GC-C and OK-GC, are cell-surface targets for guanylins, whereas two different membrane GCs, GC-A and GC-B, are membrane receptors for atriopeptins.

STRUCTURES OF GUANYLIN PEPTIDES

Complementary DNAs encoding the precursors of guanylin, uroguanylin, and lymphoguanylin have been isolated revealing that the active peptides are found at C-terminal ends of 100–116 amino acid proteins (10, 28, 29, 32–34). Proguanylin and prouroguanylin are secreted polypeptides that possess little or no intrinsic biological activity until the prohormones are cleaved by converting enzymes to form the biologically active peptides that bind to and activate receptor GC molecules (14, 29, 35, 36). Prouroguanylin and proguanylin have been purified from the intestinal mucosa of opossums, and the N terminus of each polypeptide was sequenced, thus revealing the cleavage sites for production of the mature prohormones (14). The signal peptides are cleaved between serine and valine residues of opossum preprouroguanylin and preproguanylin. Cleavage of signal peptides occurs in rat and human preproguanylin between glycine and valine residues and between serine and valine in preprouroguanylin (28, 34, 37). Primary structures for the biologically active forms of guanylin, uroguanylin, and lymphoguanylin in the mammalian species elucidated thus far are shown in Figure 2, for comparison with the ST peptides produced by *E. coli, Vibrio cholerae, Citrobacter freundi,* and *Yersinia enterocolitica* . Guanylin peptides can be clas-

GUANYLIN
```
  Opossum              S H T C E I C A F A A C A G C
  Human                P G T C E I C A Y A A C T G C
  Rat/Mouse            P N T C E I C A Y A A C T G C
  Porcine/Guinea pig   P S T C E I C A Y A A C A G C
```

UROGUANYLIN
```
  Opossum              Q E D C E L C I N V A C T G C
  Human                N D D C E L C V N V A C T G C L
  Rat/Mouse            T D E C E L C I N V A C T G C
  Guinea pig           N D E C E L C V N I A C T G C
  Porcine              G D D C E L C V N V A C T G C S
  Bovine               N D D C E L C V N V A C T G C S
```

LYMPHOGUANYLIN
```
  Opossum              Q E E C E L C I N M A C T G Y
```

ST PEPTIDES
```
  E. coli-h                N S S N Y C C E L C C N P A C T G C Y
  E. coli-p/C. freundi     N T F Y C C E L C C N P A C A G C Y
  V. cholerae                  L I D C C E I C C N P A C F G C L N
  Y. enterocolitica    ... S S D W D C C D V C C N P A C A G C
```

Figure 2 Primary structures of biologically active peptides belonging to the guanylin family of cGMP-regulating peptides. The primary structures of these peptides were taken from publications cited in this review and from public data bases including GenBank. The bovine uroguanylin sequence was obtained in this laboratory from a cDNA clone isolated

sified into three groups according to the number of intramolecular disulfide bonds in the peptide molecules; lymphoguanylin has only one disulfide bond, guanylin and uroguanylin exhibit two disulfides, and bacterial STs have three. Disulfide bonds in guanylin and uroguanylin are formed between the first to third and second to fourth cysteines in each peptide (1, 4). ST molecules have the same disulfide pairings as guanylins plus an additional disulfide bond. This feature may contribute to the higher binding affinities and potencies of ST peptides for activation of intestinal receptor-GCs compared with those of guanylin and uroguanylin (1, 4, 38). Lymphoguanylin is strikingly different because this peptide has three cysteines; thus only one disulfide bond can be formed. Lymphoguanylin containing a single disulfide between the first and third cysteines was synthesized and, surprisingly, activated the receptors in T84 and OK cells (10).

INTESTINAL NATRIURETIC HORMONES

Activation of renal receptor GCs by *E. coli* ST in vivo markedly increases urinary cGMP excretion, reflecting a stimulation of cGMP production in uroguanylin target cells located in convoluted and straight portions of proximal tubules in opossum kidney (22, 23). In the isolated perfused kidney of rats, uroguanylin and ST elicit substantial increases in urine flow and in sodium, chloride, and potassium excretion (39, 40). Guanylin is apparently less potent than either uroguanylin or ST as a natriuretic and diuretic agonist in perfused kidneys; however, guanylin does cause a substantial increase in urinary potassium excretion, which suggests a different profile of biological activity for this peptide in the kidney. Lymphoguanylin was tested in the perfused kidney and also found to stimulate urine flow and increase sodium and potassium excretion (41). Administration of uroguanylin or ST to mice in vivo also increases the urinary output of sodium, potassium, and water, whereas guanylin is relatively ineffective at the doses tested (42). We conclude that guanylin peptides elicit these responses by direct actions on the kidney through interaction with one or more specific receptor GC signaling molecules in target cells. *E. coli* ST can be considered a potent uroguanylin-like agonist that mimics the physiological actions of uroguanylin and guanylin in both the renal and gastrointestinal (GI) organ systems (1–4, 38–42). The natriuretic and diuretic responses to uroguanylin in vivo are biological activities consistent with this peptide to serve as an intestinal natriuretic hormone.

For uroguanylin (or guanylin) to serve in an endocrine axis linking the intestine and kidney, these peptides should be produced in the stomach and/or intestine and secreted into the bloodstream under regulation by dietary salt. Uroguanylin and guanylin are produced in extraordinarily high concentrations in the intestinal mucosa, with their mRNAs exhibiting levels equivalent to those of highly abundant housekeeping proteins (28–30, 32–37). The remarkable levels of these peptides within the intestine (where they stimulate chloride and bicarbonate secretion) may be required to support the local actions of guanylin and uroguanylin (43,

44). Both peptides are found in multiple cell types in the intestinal mucosa, but localization of uroguanylin within enterochromaffin (enteroendocrine) cells provides an appropriate cell type, where secretion of uroguanylin into the circulation can be achieved in response to dietary salt (45–49). Both the biologically active forms of uroguanylin and inactive prouroguanylin have been isolated from plasma and identified by their unique properties and N-terminal sequence analyses (29, 30). Proguanylin has also been isolated from hemodialysates used in the treatment of patients with chronic renal failure (50). Biologically active forms of guanylin have not been isolated from plasma. Values for plasma proguanylin are reported to be in the 30–40 pM range, whereas plasma uroguanylin/prouroguanylin is about 5–7 pM in plasma of normal humans, which suggests that proguanylin is far more abundant than the sum of uroguanylin plus prouroguanylin in the circulation (51–54). Proguanylin and prouroguanylin levels are markedly increased with the severity of renal disease, which correlates positively with the magnitude of increases in both propeptides (53). Plasma uroguanylin levels are substantially reduced in renal failure, whereas prouroguanylin is markedly increased, which results in a major shift in the ratio of prouroguanylin to uroguanylin in the circulation. Thus guanylin and uroguanylin/prouroguanylin are probably cleared from plasma by the kidney because reduced functioning renal mass and decreased glomerular filtration rates are associated with massive increases in plasma proguanylin and prouroguanylin. Moreover, functioning kidneys may be required for conversion of plasma prouroguanylin to bioactive uroguanylin, perhaps via uroguanylin converting enzymes in the kidney.

A prominent question is how does plasma uroguanylin/prouroguanylin serve as a putative intestinal natriuretic hormone in the face of considerably higher circulating levels of proguanylin? Perhaps circulating proguanylin also participates in the regulation of urinary sodium excretion by an endocrine mechanism. However, evidence is mounting in favor of uroguanylin functioning in this capacity because guanylin is relatively ineffective compared with the natriuretic efficacy of uroguanylin (40, 42). Moreover, uroguanylin is the only biologically active peptide found in urine even though circulating proguanylin levels greatly exceed the plasma concentrations of uroguanylin and prouroguanylin (1, 26, 27). This finding suggests that proguanylin is degraded by tubular proteases after filtration. Guanylin is uniquely sensitive to inactivation by hydrolysis of the peptide C terminal to aromatic amino acids found only in guanylin and not in the uroguanylin and ST peptides (13, 14, 55). This observation is consistent with the possible degradation of proguanylin by one or more chymotrypsin-like proteases located on the BBM of cells lining the proximal renal tubule. Inactivation of proguanylin that enters the tubular filtrate at glomeruli may be a physiologically protective mechanism that prevents plasma proguanylin from acting on receptor GCs that have localized to apical membranes of target cells along the nephron. It is likely that filtered proguanylin is cleaved and inactivated by proteases located in the initial portion of proximal tubules, which prevents the accumulation of biologically active guanylin in tubular filtrate, thus allowing filtered uroguanylin access to the receptors located in parts of the nephron distal to this segment. In this way, circulating uroguanylin could serve as the primary intestinal natriuretic hormone in a novel endocrine axis linking the digestive and renal organ systems to influence sodium homeostasis in the postprandial state. This feature may be one of the physiological factors required as a selective pressure for evolution of the distinct uroguanylin and guanylin structures. It is speculated that a uroguanylin-like gene is ancestral to the uroguanylin and guanylin genes. Following gene duplication during vertebrate evolution (56–59), the guanylin gene may have accumulated mutations that resulted in changes in the coding region so that tyrosine or phenylalanine residues occur in the bioactive guanylin molecule at the position where asparagine residues occurs in the uroguanylin and ST molecules (Figure 2). Because of this simple change in primary structure, guanylin can be rapidly degraded in the renal tubule or in the upper small intestine, where high concentrations of chymotrypsin-like proteases are found. This structural difference between the uroguanylin and guanylin peptides is likely to be of considerable physiological importance and may limit the biological activity of guanylin in both the kidney and upper small intestine. In these organs, it is likely that uroguanylin has a dominant role in regulating cellular function via the cGMP signaling pathway.

Recent experimental evidence reveals that high salt diets significantly stimulate uroguanylin, cGMP, and sodium excretion in human urine (60). Quantitative increases in uroguanylin excretion were significantly correlated with the magnitude of increases in urinary sodium and cGMP. This effect of dietary salt is consistent with the postulate that uroguanylin influences urinary salt excretion as an endocrine factor. It is likely that increased urinary uroguanylin elicited by high salt diets is due to increases in plasma uroguanylin and prouroguanylin that are subsequently filtered and then appear in the urine. Specialized cells in GI mucosa that produce uroguanylin are enterochromaffin cells in the duodenum and stomach (61–64). These specialized enterocytes can secrete into both the blood and the intestinal lumen. It should be stressed that other cell types in the intestinal mucosa also produce uroguanylin. The stomach and upper small intestine are reasonable segments of the digestive tract for sodium-modulated secretion of uroguanylin into the systemic circulation. If uroguanylin is indeed an intestinal natriuretic hormone, then oral administration of sodium chloride should stimulate increases in both plasma and urinary levels of uroguanylin to a substantially greater extent than that achieved by intravenous salt (11, 12). Experiments in the human and in experimental animals should be done to further test the hypothesis that uroguanylin released from the GI tract acts directly on the kidney to stimulate urine sodium excretion following a salty meal. Major questions that should be addressed in future studies could focus on both the cellular and molecular mechanisms involved in the regulation of uroguanylin secretion from the GI tract. For example, how do uroguanylin-secreting cells in the GI tract and/or other organs of the digestive system detect sodium chloride in the diet? Are neural, endocrine and/or paracrine pathways involved in salt detecting mechanisms that influence uroguanylin secretion? Answers to some of these important questions should provide a new level of understanding concerning the role of uroguanylin in complex physiological mechanisms that collectively work to maintain body sodium homeostasis.

CELL AND MOLECULAR MECHANISMS

The first cell-surface receptor for guanylin peptides that was identified at the molecular level is GC-C (19). Expression of GC-C cDNAs in vitro produces a membrane GC that is activated by ST. GC-C is expressed throughout the GI mucosa, and this receptor GC is clearly an important target for enteric guanylin and uroguanylin secreted into the intestinal lumen, as well as serving pathophysiologically as a receptor for ST peptides secreted by diarrhea-inducing microbes. However, GC-C may not participate in cGMP signaling in renal target cells responsible for the diuretic and natriuretic responses of the kidney to uroguanylin (39–42). Studies in transgenic GC-C$^{-/-}$ mice reveal that intestinal fluid secretion responses to ST are greatly diminished (65, 66). However, the saliuresis elicited by uroguanylin and ST in vivo is retained in the absence of GC-C (67). Accordingly, GC-C does not appear to serve as a major receptor GC for uroguanylin in the kidney. A cGMP signaling pathway for uroguanylin was first identified in OK and potoroo (PtK-2) cell lines (22–24). Therefore, we postulated prior to the discovery of guanylin and uroguanylin that receptor GCs found in OK cells could function in the control of kidney transport mechanisms. Recently, cDNAs for receptor GCs found in OK cells were isolated by molecular cloning (20). OK-GC cDNAs encode a 1049–amino acid mature protein belonging to the growing family of membrane GC proteins. Expression of OK-GC cDNAs in COS-1 or HEK-293 cells produced a 160-kDa membrane GC, which is activated by uroguanylin, guanylin, and E. coli ST. OK-GC mRNA transcripts of ~3.8 kb are most abundant in kidney cortex and intestinal mucosa, but mRNAs are also expressed in renal medulla and in the heart and urinary bladder. OK-GC differs from GC-C most strikingly between their ligand-binding domains, with the OK-GC protein exhibiting about 57–59% identity with rat, human, and porcine forms of intestinal GC-C (Figure 3) (19, 68, 69). OK-GC and GC-C proteins share >90% identity when their cyclase catalytic domains are compared, indicating that these two GC signaling molecules constitute a subclass of uroguanylin/guanylin/ST receptors within the family of membrane GC proteins. Limited similarity in the ligand-binding domains compared with those of eutherian GC-Cs suggests that OK-GC may be a novel receptor GC for guanylin and ST peptides, which plays a physiological role in renal cGMP signaling. A eutherian homolog of opossum OK-GC in renal tubules of GC-C$^{-/-}$ mice could be responsible for the apparently normal natriuretic and diuretic responses to uroguanylin and ST observed in these animals (67). A counterpart to OK-GC in renal tubules of GC-C$^{-/-}$ mice can be identified by cloning to address an important question con-

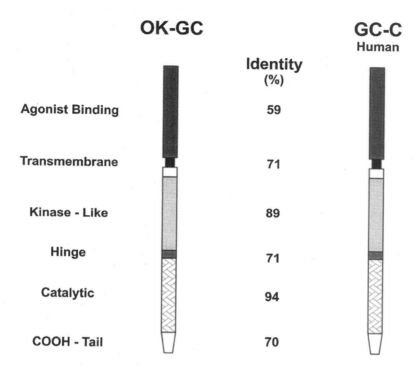

Figure 3 Comparison of the primary domains between opossum OK-GC and human

cerning the molecular identity of uroguanylin receptors in eutherian mammals that are responsible for the diuretic, natriuretic, and kaliuretic responses of the kidney to guanylin peptides in vivo. Identification of an opossum homolog for GC-C can also test the hypothesis that at least two receptor GCs for guanylin and uroguanylin are present in both eutherian and metatherian mammals.

Locating specific cells with receptors for guanylin and ST peptides in the kidney will advance our understanding of the actions of uroguanylin and ST on kidney function. In particular, the nephron localization of uroguanylin target cells will help define potential cellular mechanisms of uroguanylin action that result in the stimulation of sodium, chloride, potassium, and water excretion in vivo. Tubular epithelial cells expressing high levels of specific binding sites have been labeled with ^{125}I-ST, which is a high-affinity radioligand for membrane receptors in both the opossum kidney and mammalian intestine (23, 25, 70, 71). Receptor autoradiography in situ reveals that ^{125}I-ST binds to receptors located on proximal tubular cells with the highest apparent receptor density observed on cells of straight compared with convoluted portions of proximal tubules in opossum kidney. Proximal tubular localization of receptors that are labeled by ^{125}I-ST in vitro also occurs in mesonephros early during organogenesis, as well as in the meta-nephric kidney later in life (25). Uroguanylin, guanylin, and unlabeled ST all compete effectively for membrane sites labeled with ^{125}I-ST, indicating that ^{125}I-ST binds to all of the detectable receptors for guanylin peptides identified by this method. No receptors for ^{125}I-ST were detected in glomeruli in these experiments. It is likely that OK-GC accounts for some of the binding sites for ^{125}I-ST observed in proximal tubules, but it is also possible that other receptor GCs labeled by ^{125}I-ST in situ are expressed in opossum kidney. In situ receptor autoradiography is useful for detection of uroguanylin/ST receptors expressed at high density, such as those found in the intestine of mammals or in the kidney of opossums. How-ever, this assay may not detect all of the functional receptors for uroguanylin in the kidney or in other putative target tissues. For example, rat and mouse kidneys respond to uroguanylin and ST with large increases in urinary sodium, potassium, and water excretion (39–42), but we have not readily detected renal receptor GCs in these species using in situ binding assays (LR Forte, RM London & WJ Krause, unpublished data). Thus future experiments need to address a basic question con-cerning the nephron locations for all of the functional receptor GCs for uroguan-ylin and guanylin expressed in the kidney. A complete catalog of guanylin/uroguanylin receptor GCs, together with elucidation of the nephron or other locations of receptors, is needed to address fundamental questions about the cel-lular mode of action of guanylin peptides.

INTRACELLULAR SIGNALING PATHWAYS

Many questions remain concerning the cellular mechanisms of action of guanylin peptides in the kidney. As previously summarized, the type and location of tubular target cells and the molecular nature and properties of receptor GC signaling molecules are important subjects for future investigations. However, the intra-cellular cGMP signal transduction pathways may also have a few unusual twists because of the possibility that novel mechanisms operate in the kidney similar to those found in the intestine. Finally, the tubular transporters that are regulated by cGMP under the influence of guanylin peptides remain to be identified. Nature is frugal in the use and reuse of molecular mechanisms for control within different tissues and organs of the body. Therefore, it is highly likely that much if not all of the postulated intracellular signaling pathways that are involved in the control of intestinal fluid secretion by guanylin hormones will ultimately be instructive in guiding future studies of the kidney as a target for the guanylins. Sketches of cellular and molecular mechanisms of guanylin action in the kidney are drawn from studies of ST, guanylin, and uroguanylin action on intracellular cGMP sig-naling pathways of intestine.

After *E. coli* ST was shown to cause a cholera-like form of diarrhea through activation of BBM GCs in the intestinal mucosa (2, 3), it was quickly demon-strated that ST via cGMP greatly stimulates the electrogenic secretion of chloride and bicarbonate anions (reviewed in 72). In addition, ST peptides also appear to inhibit net sodium absorption by the intestine, which could be secondary to the increased secretion of anions or may represent another discrete, but undefined action of ST via cGMP in the intestine. The remarkable stimulation of intestinal fluid secretion is a main cause of the increased fecal excretion of electrolytes and water underlying diarrhea. ST peptides released by enteric bacteria stimulate intestinal fluid secretion beyond the capacity of the colon to reabsorb and conserve the secreted fluid. The net effect of ST is a marked loss of electrolytes and water from the body, which can have disastrous results, especially in young children. It may be useful at this point to consider that both the kidney and intestinal epithelia absorb as well as secrete ions, water, and small molecules. Although the kidney does not exhibit net secretion of sodium, chloride, and water at rates greater than filtered loads, this remarkable organ does have the capacity to secrete sodium, chloride, and water in localized segments of renal tubules utilizing cellular mechanisms that are shared between the intestine and the kidney. Thus stimulation of electrogenic anion secretion in certain uroguanylin target cells along the nephron may help explain the natriuretic, kaliuretic, and diuretic responses of kidney to uroguanylin, guanylin, lymphoguanylin, and *E. coli* ST (39–42). Net fluid and sodium excretion in the urine is always substantially less than filtered loads, whereas the intestine has the capacity to secrete and ultimately excrete far greater quantities of salt and water than are ingested orally. If uroguanylin acts similarly in the kidney and intestine with respect to the cellular mechanisms that are shared between the two organs, then enhanced secretion of sodium, chloride, and water could appear as an inhibition of salt reabsorption. Inhibition of tubular sodium reabsorption is a more commonly accepted mechanism of action for natriuretic and diuretic agents in the kidney. Stimulation of chloride secretion in proximal tubules and/or thick limbs of the loop of Henle by the guanylins could enhance the delivery of solute to the collecting tubules, thus stimulating potassium secretion and eliciting the characteristic kaliuresis produced by uroguanylin, guanylin, and ST (39–42). Therefore, stimulation of salt and water secretion by guanylin regulatory peptides may simply appear as diminished reabsorption of sodium chloride in an organ that does not exhibit net secretion of salt and water at rates exceeding filtered loads. We believe that this possibility should be considered as future experiments are designed to explore the tubular mechanisms underlying the saliuretic, kaliuretic, and diuretic actions of guanylin peptides on kidney function. An alternate possibility is that stimulation of cGMP production by guanylins inhibits sodium reabsorption in the kidney similar to the cellular actions of atriopeptin-A via cGMP that inhibit tubular sodium reabsorption and increase urinary sodium excretion (18).

The cellular mechanism of action of guanylin and uroguanylin as regulators of intestinal secretion has been fleshed out considerably in recent years. A major receptor GC in the GI tract is GC-C (19), as defined recently in studies of intestinal secretion responses of GC-C$^{-/-}$ mice to ST (65, 66). Intragastric administration of ST to suckling mice markedly stimulates fluid accumulation in the upper small intestine of normal animals, but GC-C$^{-/-}$ mice have no detectable fluid secretion responses to ST. Thus, GC-C is considered to be an important signaling molecule in a pathway that regulates intestinal fluid secretion. However, additional guanylin/ST receptors are found in the intestine because specific binding of ^{125}I-ST is detected in BBM isolated from the intestine of GC-C$^{-/-}$ animals (66). Recent experiments reveal that when the duodenum from GC-C$^{-/-}$ mice is mounted in Ussing chambers and exposed to luminal agonists, a substantial increase in short-circuit current (Isc) is still observed, indicating that a novel receptor regulates electrogenic transport in the intestinal mucosa (73). Transport regulation experiments employing the classical Ussing chamber methods are beginning to provide insight into the biological actions of guanylins when GC-C is not expressed in the intestine. Moreover, this finding clearly shows that the suckling mouse bioassay method is quite insensitive and does not detect key physiological responses to guanylin peptides in the GI mucosa. Use of the in vitro Ussing chamber approach with investigations designed to carefully examine the other major segments of small and large intestine from GC-C$^{-/-}$ and wild-type animals should provide new information concerning the physiological actions of guanylin peptides mediated by a presently unidentified receptor.

Intracellular cGMP influences transepithelial Cl$^-$ and HCO$_3$$^-$ secretion by two distinctly different mechanisms in the intestine (Figure 4). The cGMP-dependent protein kinase-II (PKG-II), which is highly abundant in the BBM of cells lining the small intestine, appears to be a key receptor for cGMP in the upper intestinal tract (74, 75; reviewed in 76). Disabling the genes encoding PKG-II results in a loss of fluid secretion responses to *E. coli* ST measured in vivo using the suckling mouse bioassay (77). Also, a marked decrease in Isc responses to ST was found in intestinal mucosa mounted in Ussing chambers. However, the Isc responses to ST in vitro are not completely lost even in the small intestine of PKG-II$^{-/-}$ mice, suggesting that alternate signaling pathways for cGMP in addition to PKG-II probably exist in some discrete guanylin target cells. Other major intracellular receptors for cGMP have been postulated to be either PKA-II, which can bind cGMP and is activated by high levels of cGMP in vivo, and/or a cGMP-regulated cAMP phosphodiesterase (PDE). It was previously shown in cultured cell models derived from the colon (i.e. T84, CaCO2) that cGMP produced by GC-C activates transepithelial Cl$^-$ secretion via binding to and cross-activation of PKA-II rather than by activation of PKG-II, which is not expressed in these intestinal cells (78, 79). This intracellular signaling model for cGMP directly via PKA-II is consistent with the very low expression levels of PKG-II found in the colon compared with levels of PKG-II in the small intestine (76). A third cGMP signaling mechanism for regulation of intestinal PKA-II is through cGMP binding to regulatory sites on cGMP-regulated PDE enzymes in guanylin target cells, with subsequent inhibition of cAMP hydrolysis causing increased intracellular cAMP and activation of PKA-II (Figure 4). Thus cGMP could have direct or indirect actions that result in the activation of PKA-II in guanylin target cells. If guanylin peptides can regulate intestinal secretion by at least three different signal transduction mechanisms in different target cells of intestinal mucosa, it seems clear that multiple intracellular signaling mechanisms could also exist in various target cells for guanylin peptides found in the renal tubules. The PKG-II, PKA-II, and cGMP-regulated PDE receptors for cGMP are also found in the kidney. However, co-localization of specific receptor GCs that are activated by uroguanylin, guanylin, and lymphoguanylin, together with the intracellular receptors for cGMP in cells along the nephron, has not been accomplished and remains an important task.

A prime substrate for PKG-II or PKA-II is the apical membrane-localized cystic fibrosis transmembrane conductance regulator (CFTR) molecule that is

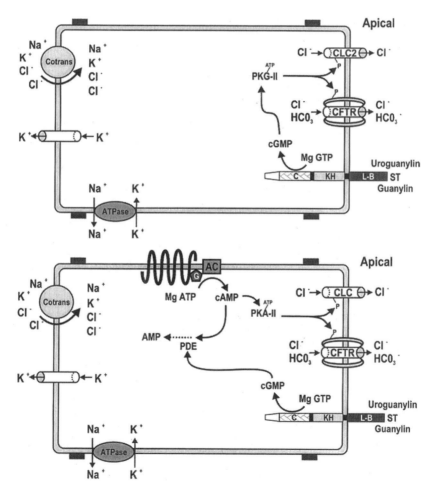

Figure 4 Models for the intracellular cGMP signal transduction pathways of guanylin target cells in epithelia. Abbreviations are defined in the text.

found in the intestine, kidney, airway, and other epithelia that have receptor GCs for guanylin peptides (reviewed in 80). CFTR is a member of the ABC protein family that transports small molecules across cell membranes through an ATP-dependent mechanism. This protein is also capable of transporting anions in a selective, chloride channel-like manner. Disordered chloride transport in the genetic disease of cystic fibrosis, and the channel-like activity of CFTR places this protein in both the cGMP and cAMP pathways that control Cl^- and HCO_3^- secretion across apical plasma membranes. Transgenic $CFTR^{-/-}$ mice have marked reductions in the intestinal secretion responses to ST, guanylin, and other anion secretogogues (44, 81). Of interest is the finding that duodenum and jejunum segments of small intestine from $CFTR^{-/-}$ animals retain substantial Isc responses to uroguanylin, although the anion secretion responses are substantially less than normal (44). In contrast, guanylin elicits very small increases in Isc in the colon of $CFTR^{-/-}$ mice (81). These findings are consistent with the conclusion that CFTR is a target substrate for phosphorylation by either PKA-II or PKG-II enzymes under the influence of cGMP derived from receptor GCs that are activated by guanylin peptides.

A candidate for another functional Cl^- channel in the small intestine of $CFTR^{-/-}$ animals is ClC-2, a member of the rapidly growing ClC family of Cl^- channel proteins (reviewed in 82). ClC-2 cDNAs were recently isolated from mouse intestine, and ClC-2 was shown to be highly expressed in the upper small intestine of $CFTR^{-/-}$ mice (83). Expression of ClC-2 in the small intestine provides an alternate anion conductance mechanism that may be regulated by uroguanylin via cGMP in vivo. This finding may explain the observation that proximal small intestine of $CFTR^{-/-}$ animals has a relatively normal morphology and function compared with that of the colon, which exhibits a much greater impairment of function. ClC-2 may act in the small intestine complementary to CFTR, thus preserving relatively normal fluid secretion in the absence of CFTR in $CFTR^{-/-}$ mice. Thus secretion of chloride across the apical plasma membranes of uroguanylin target cells in small intestine may occur through ClC-2 channels under regulation by cGMP and guanylin hormones. Continued expression of ClC-2 in the upper small intestine of $CFTR^{-/-}$ mice may account for the substantial Isc responses to uroguanylin that are observed in segments of small intestine taken from these animals (44). cGMP regulates the conductance of chloride through ClC-2 channels in the apical membranes of a subset of target cells for guanylin peptides that may not express CFTR. A postulated mechanism invokes two distinct types of chloride-secreting cells in the duodenum and jejunum, one with a cell type that has GC-C and CFTR and a second that has GC-C or another guanylin receptor GC such as an eutherian homolog of OK-GC together with ClC-2. This type of cellular mechanism could account for the electrogenic anion secretion that is present in the small intestine of $CFTR^{-/-}$ mice (44).

The possibility that CFTR may also be a target for regulation by guanylin peptides via cGMP in the kidney should be entertained because CFTR is quite clearly present in renal tubules (84, 85). Although patients with CF disease do not appear to have marked disturbances in renal function per se, it is possible that the kidney has compensatory mechanisms that work to complement the loss of CFTR function similar to that proposed for the upper small intestine via ClC-2 channels described above. A key question is whether the tubular target cells containing OK-GC or other guanylin receptor GC proteins also express CFTR. An important question that can be answered using $CFTR^{-/-}$ mice is whether CFTR is required for either some or all of the physiological responses of the kidney to guanylin peptides in vivo. Clearly, this experiment would allow insight into the possible participation of CFTR in cGMP signaling pathways used by guanylin peptides in the regulation of kidney function. Co-localization studies, as well, could determine which types of tubular cells contain both the OK-GC receptor and CFTR proteins. If the natriuretic, kaliuretic, or diuretic responses to uroguanylin, guanylin, and ST are impaired in the kidneys of $CFTR^{-/-}$ animals, as found in the intestine (44, 81), then location of renal cells containing both the guanylin receptors and CFTR would help explain this phenomenon.

It is a reasonable speculation that uroguanylin regulates both CFTR and ClC types of anion channel activities in renal and intestinal epithelia. Figure 4 illustrates two potential signal transduction pathways that could occur in different cells along the nephron that have receptor GC proteins and respond to guanylin peptides with increased cGMP production. One possible mechanism mirrors that of the small intestine, where cGMP binds to and activates the apical membrane-bound PKG-II, which then phosphorylates CFTR with channel opening and flow of chloride and/or bicarbonate anions through the channel to exit the cell. In this fashion, guanylin peptides could enhance sodium chloride secretion, which may underlie the saliuretic and diuretic actions of uroguanylin and ST (39–42). A second type of guanylin target cell in the kidney could resemble those in the colon, where PKG-II does not appear to be present and does not regulate electrogenic anion secretion mediated by cGMP. In this putative cGMP signaling mechanism, either direct or indirect activation of PKA-II by cGMP is postulated to regulate CFTR activity and chloride secretion. Participation of ClC-2 or other ClC proteins in the transport of chloride by renal tubular cells under regulation by uroguanylin is also possible, but this type of mechanism has not been demonstrated thus far. A major goal is to define the nephron locations and catalog the different phenotypes of guanylin target cells, which may possess different subtypes of receptor GCs together with variable sets of intracellular cGMP signaling machinery (PKG, PKA, PDE) and multiple transport pathways, such as CFTR and ClC-2. Enough complexity of cellular machinery is currently known to reasonably construct several models of guanylin target cells. Determination of the types and locations of guanylin target cells that are likely arrayed at multiple positions along the longitudinal axis of the nephron will be required to gain insights into the cellular and molecular mechanisms underlying the renal actions of uroguanylin, guanylin, and lymphoguanylin in vivo.

In searching for novel receptors that interact with guanylin peptides, it should be remembered that truly selective receptor GCs with high affinity for guanylin, uroguanylin, or lymphoguanylin may exist, but this type of receptor has not been discovered. Precedence for selective receptors clearly exists in the other family of cGMP-regulating peptides because GC-A receptors are indeed selective for atriopeptins-A and -B over atriopeptin-C, whereas GC-B is highly selective for atriopeptin-C and has poor affinity for the other atriopeptins (18). Moreover, a truncated and nonselective cell-surface receptor for atriopeptins has been identified, cloned, and described as a putative clearance receptor (86). This clearance receptor is often the most abundant binding site for atriopeptins on cells within target tissues. The existence of a guanylin/ST clearance receptor could markedly change our perception of the nephron distribution of guanylin target cells in opossum kidney; for example, ^{125}I-ST labels binding sites of high density located on the apical side of cells in both convoluted and straight segments of renal proximal tubules (22, 25). The ^{125}I-ST-labeled receptors are likely GC proteins such as the OK-GC receptor GC because BBMs isolated from opossum kidney have relatively high GC activity that is stimulated by ST peptides (22, 23). However, an alternate possibility is that some of the binding sites for ^{125}I-ST are actually uroguanylin/guanylin clearance receptors rather than OK-GC signaling molecules. It would greatly affect our current concepts pertaining to the distribution of uroguanylin target cells along the nephron in mammalian kidney if the dominant ^{125}I-ST binding sites of proximal tubules are actually a clearance form of receptor that lacks GC signaling activity. Future studies designed to catalog the full repertoire of receptors for guanylin peptides of mammals should bear this in mind because strategies for homology cloning of the GC types of receptors will likely be unsuccessful in cloning novel clearance receptors that possess neither kinase-homology nor catalytic domains. Identification of clearance receptors for guanylins would require either a classical approach from protein structure to cDNA cloning or use of conserved regions within the ligand-binding and/or transmembrane domains of GC proteins to employ powerful homology cloning methods in the isolation of cDNAs encoding putative guanylin clearance receptors (19, 20).

CONCLUSION

The rapid emergence of information regarding a novel cGMP signaling pathway that influences fluid and electrolyte transport in the kidney, intestine, and other epithelia by the guanylin family of peptide hormones has created a new area within the field of endocrinology. Isolation of guanylin and uroguanylin, together with molecular cloning techniques that have identified lymphoguanylin as well as the GC-C and OK-GC receptors for guanylin peptides, has energized this field. The excitement generated by discovery of hormones and receptors by classical means may never be the same when the information becomes "siliconized" after various genome projects are completed in the very near future. On the other hand, a large number of orphan receptor GCs will be identified, and the classical methods of molecular endocrinology will still be required to elucidate the primary structures of many, presently unknown, peptide hormones that regulate cGMP production via cell-surface receptor GC signaling molecules. At that time, it will become quite clear that cGMP signaling through membrane GCs located on the surface of cells is equivalent in physiological significance to the cGMP derived from nitric oxide–dependent GC molecules located within cells.

Visit the Annual Reviews home page at www.AnnualReviews.org.

LITERATURE CITED

1. Hamra FK, Forte LR, Eber SL, Pidhorodeckyj NV, Krause WJ, et al. 1993. Uroguanylin: structure and activity of a second endogenous peptide that stimulates intestinal guanylate cyclase. *Proc. Natl. Acad. Sci. USA* 90:10464–68

2. Hughes JM, Murad F, Chang B, Guerrant RL. 1978. Role of cyclic GMP in the action of heat-stable enterotoxin of *Escherichia coli. Nature* 271:755–56

3. Field, M, Graf LH Jr, Laird WJ, Smith PL. 1978. Heat-stable enterotoxin of *Escherichia coli:* in vitro effects on guanylate cyclase activity, cyclic GMP concentration, and ion transport in small intestine. *Proc. Natl. Acad. Sci. USA* 75:2800–4

4. Currie MG, Fok KF, Kato J, Moore RJ, Hamra FK, et al. 1992. Guanylin: an endogenous activator of intestinal guanylate cyclase. *Proc. Natl. Acad. Sci. USA* 89:947–51

5. de Bold, AJ, Borenstein HB, Veress AT, Sonnenberg H. 1981. A rapid and potent natriuretic response to intravenous injection of atrial myocardial extract in rats. *Life Sci.* 28:89–94

6. Flynn, TG, de Bold ML, de Bold AJ. 1983. The amino acid sequence of an atrial peptide with potent diuretic and natriuretic properties. *Biochem. Biophys. Res. Commun.* 117:859–65

7. Currie MG, Geller DM, Cole BR, Siegel NR, Fok, KF, et al. 1984. Purification and sequence analysis of bioactive atrial peptides (atriopeptins). *Science* 223:76–69

8. Sudoh T, Kangawa K, Minamino N, Matsuo H. 1988. A new natriuretic peptide in porcine brain. *Nature* 332:78–81

9. Sudoh T, Minamino N, Kangawa K, Matsuo H. 1990. C-type natriuretic peptide (CNP): a new member of natriuretic peptide family identified in porcine brain. *Biochem. Biophys. Res. Commun.* 168: 863–70

10. Forte LR, Eber SL, Fan X, London RM, Wang Y, et al. 1999. Lymphoguanylin: cloning and characterization of a unique member of the guanylin peptide family. *Endocrinology* 140:1800–6

11. Lennane RJ, Peart WS, Carey RM, Shaw J. 1975. Comparison of natriuresis after oral and intravenous sodium loading in sodium-depleted rabbits: evidence for a gastrointestinal or portal monitor of sodium intake. *Clin. Sci. Mol. Med.* 49:433–36

12. Carey RM. 1978. Evidence for a splanchnic sodium input monitor regulating renal sodium excretion in man: lack of dependence upon aldosterone. *Circ. Res.* 43:19–23

13. Hamra FK, Krause WJ, Smith CE, Freeman RH, Currie MG, Forte LR. 1996. Opossum colonic mucosa of the opossum contains uroguanylin and guanylin peptides. *Am. J. Physiol.* 270:G708–16

14. Hamra FK, Fan X, Krause WJ, Freeman RH, Chin DT, et al. 1996. Prouroguanylin and proguanylin: purification from colon, structure, and modulation of bio-

activity by proteases. *Endocrinology* 137:257–65

15. Kinoshita H, Fujimoto S, Nakazato M, Yokota N, Date Y, et al. 1997. Urine and plasma levels of uroguanylin and its molecular forms in renal diseases. *Kidney Int.* 52:1028–34

16. White AA, Aurbach GD. 1969. Detection of guanyl cyclase in mammalian tissues. *Biochim. Biophys. Acta* 191:686–87

17. Hardman JG, Sutherland EW. 1969. Guanyl cyclase, an enzyme catalyzing the formation of guanosine 3′,5′-monophosphate from guanosine triphosphate. *J. Biol. Chem.* 244:6363–70

18. Schulz S, Waldman SA. 1999. The guanylyl cyclase family of natriuretic peptide receptors. *Vitam. Horm.* 57:123–51

19. Schulz S, Green CK, Yuen PST, Garbers DL. 1990. Guanylyl cyclase is a heat-stable enterotoxin receptor. *Cell* 63:941–48

20. London RM, Eber SL, Visweswariah SS, Krause WJ, Forte LR. 1999. Structure and activity of OK-GC: a kidney receptor-guanylate cyclase activated by guanylin peptides. *Am. J. Physiol.* 276:F882–91

21. Bargmann CI. 1998 .Neurobiology of the *Caenorhabditis elegans* genome. *Science* 282:2028–33

22. Forte LR, Krause WJ, Freeman RH. 1989. *Escherichia coli* enterotoxin receptors: localization in opossum kidney, intestine and testis. *Am. J. Physiol.* 257: F874–81

23. Forte LR, Krause WJ, Freeman RH. 1988. Receptors and cGMP signaling mechanism for *E. coli* enterotoxin in opossum kidney. *Am. J. Physiol.* 255: F1040–46

24. White AA, Krause WJ, Turner JT, Forte LR. 1989. Opossum kidney contains a functional receptor for the *Escherichia coli* heat-stable enterotoxin. *Biochem. Biophys. Res. Commun.* 159:363–67

25. Krause WJ, Freeman RH, Forte LR. 1990. Autoradiographic demonstration

of specific binding sites for *E. coli* enterotoxin in various epithelia of the North American opossum. *Cell Tissue Res.* 260:387–94

26. Kita T, Smith CE, Fok KF, Duffin KL, Moore WM, et al. 1994. Characterization of human uroguanylin: member of the guanylin peptide family. *Am. J. Physiol.* 266:F342–48

27. Fan X, Hamra FK, London RM, Eber SL, Krause WJ, et al. 1997. Structure and activity of uroguanylin isolated from urine and intestine of rats. *Am. J. Physiol.* 273:E957–64

28. Li Z, Perkins AG, Peters MF, Campa MJ, Goy MF. 1997. Purification, cDNA sequence, and tissue distribution of rat uroguanylin. *Regul. Pept.* 68:45–56

29. Fan X, Hamra FK, Freeman RH, Eber SL, Krause WJ, et al. 1996. Uroguanylin: cloning of preprouroguanylin cDNA, mRNA expression in the intestine and heart and isolation of uroguanylin and prouroguanylin from plasma. *Biochem. Biophys. Res. Commun.* 219:457–62

30. Hess R, Kuhn M, Schulz-Knappe P, Raida M, Fuchs M, et al 1995. GCAP-II: isolation and characterization of the circulating form of human uroguanylin. *FEBS Lett.* 374:34–38.

31. Schulz-Knappe P, Forssmann K, Herbst F, Hock D, Popkorn R, Forssmann WG. 1988. Isolation and structural analysis of "urodilatin," a new peptide of the cardiodilatin-(ANP)-family, extracted from human urine. *Klin. Wochenschr.* 66:752–59

32. Wiegand RC, Kato J, Currie MG. 1992. Rat guanylin cDNA: characterization of the precursor of the endogenous activator of intestinal guanylate cyclase. *Biochem. Biophys. Res. Commun.* 185:812–17

33. Wiegand RC, Kato J, Huang MD, Fok KF, Kachur JF, Currie MG. 1992. Human guanylin: cDNA isolation, structure and activity. *FEBS Lett.* 311:150–54

34. Hill O, Cetin Y, Cieslak A, Magert HJ, Forssmann WG. 1995. A new human

guanylate cyclase-activating peptide (uroguanylin): precursor cDNA and colonic expression. *Biochim. Biophys. Acta* 1253:146–49

35. DeSauvage FJ, Keshav S, Kuang WJ, Gillet N, Henzel W, et al. 1992. Precursor structure, expression, and tissue distribution of human guanylin. *Proc. Natl. Acad. Sci. USA* 89:9089–93

36. Schulz S, Chrisman TD, Garbers DL. 1992. Cloning and expression of guanylin—its existence in various mammalian tissues. *J. Biol. Chem.* 267:16019–21

37. Miyazato M, Nakazato M, Matsukura S, Kangawa K, Matsuo H. 1996. Uroguanylin gene expression in the alimentary tract and extra-gastrointestinal tissues. *FEBS Lett.* 398:170–74

38. Forte LR, Eber SL, Turner JT, Freeman RH, Fok KF, et al. 1993. Guanylin stimulation of Cl⁻ secretion in human intestinal T$_{84}$ cells via cyclic GMP. *J. Clin. Invest.* 91:2423–28

39. Lima AAM, Monteiro HSA, Fonteles MC. 1992. The effects of *Escherichia coli* heat-stable enterotoxin in renal sodium tubular transport. *Pharmacol. Toxicol.* 70:163–67

40. Fonteles MC, Greenberg RN, Monteiro HSA, Currie MG, Forte LR. 1998. Natriuretic and kaliuretic activities of guanylin and uroguanylin in the isolated perfused rat kidney. *Am. J. Physiol.* 275:F191–97

41. Fonteles MC, Carvalho AF, Coelho GR, Monteiro HAS, Forte LR. 1999. Natriuretic activity of lymphoguanylin in the isolated perfused rat kidney. *FASEB J.* 13:A727 (Abstr.)

42. Greenberg RN, Hill M, Crytzer J, Krause WJ, Eber SL, et al. 1997. Comparison of effects of uroguanylin, guanylin, *Escherichia coli* heat-stable enterotoxin STa in mouse intestine and kidney: evidence that uroguanylin is an intestinal natriuretic hormone. *J. Invest Med.* 45:276–82

43. Guba M, Kuhn M, Forssmann WG, Clas-

sen M, Gregor M, et al. 1996. Guanylin strongly stimulates rat duodenal HCO$_3^-$ secretion: proposed mechanism and comparison with other secretagogues. *Gastroenterology* 111:1558–68

44. Joo NS, London RM, Kim HD, Forte LR, Clarke LL. 1998. Regulation of intestinal Cl⁻ and HCO$_3^-$ secretion by uroguanylin. *Am. J. Physiol.* 274: G633–44

45. Cetin Y, Kuhn M, Kulaksiz H, Adermann K, Bargsten G, et al. 1994. Enterochromaffin cells of the digestive system: cellular source of guanylin, a guanylate cyclase-activating peptide. *Proc. Natl. Acad. Sci. USA* 91:2935–39

46. Cohen MB, Witte DP, Hawkins JA, Currie MG. 1995. Immunohistochemical localization of guanylin in the rat small intestine and colon. *Biochem. Biophys. Res. Commun.* 209:803–8

47. Perkins A, Goy MF, Li Z. 1997. Uroguanylin is expressed by enterochromaffin cells in the rat gastrointestinal tract. *Gastroenterology* 113:1007–14

48. Magert HJ, Reinecke M, David I, Raab HR, Adermann K, et al. 1998. Uroguanylin: gene structure, expression, processing as a peptide hormone, and co-storage with somatostatin in gastrointestinal D-cells. *Regul. Pept.* 73:165–76

49. Nakazato M, Yamaguchi H, Date Y, Miyazato M, Kangawa K, et al. 1998. Tissue distribution, cellular source and structural analysis of rat immunoreactive uroguanylin. *Endocrinology* 139:5247–54

50. Kuhn M, Raida M, Adermann K, Schulz-Knappe P, Gerzer R, et al. 1993. The circulating bioactive form of human guanylin is high molecular weight peptide (10.3 kDa). *FEBS Lett.* 318:205–9

51. Kuhn M, Kulaksiz H, Cetin Y, Frank M, Nold R, et al. 1995. Circulating and tissue guanylin immunoreactivity in intestinal secretory diarrhoea. *Eur. J. Clin. Invest.* 25:899–905

52. Nakazato M. Yamaguchi H, Shiomi K, Date Y, Fujimoto S, et al. 1994. Identi-

fication of 10-kDa proguanylin as a major guanylin molecule in human intestine and plasma and its increase in renal insufficiency. *Biochem. Biophys. Res. Commun.* 205:1966–75

53. Nakazato M, Yamaguchi H, Kinoshita H, Kangawa K, Matsuo H, et al. 1996. Identification of biologically active and inactive human uroguanylins in plasma and urine and their increases in renal insufficiency. *Biochem. Biophys. Res. Commun.* 220:586–93

54. Kinoshita H, Fujimoto S, Fukae H, Yokota N, Hisanaga S, et al. 1999. Plasma and urine levels of uroguanylin, a new natriuretic peptide, in nephrotic syndrome. *Nephron* 81:160–64

55. Carpick BW, Gariepy J. 1993. The *Escherichia coli* heat-stable enterotoxin is a long-lived superagonist of guanylin. *Infect. Immun.* 61: 4710–15

56. Hill O, Kuhn M, Zucht HD, Cetin Y, Kulaksiz H, et al. 1995. Analysis of the human guanylin gene and the processing and cellular localization of the peptide. *Proc. Natl. Acad. Sci. USA* 92:2046–50

57. Miyazato M, Nakazato M, Matsukura S, Kangawa K, Matsuo H. 1997. Genomic structure and chromosomal localization of human uroguanylin. *Genomics* 43: 359–65

58. Magert HJ, Hill O, Zucht HD, Martin S, Meyer M, et al. 1999. Porcine guanylin and uroguanylin: cDNA sequences, deduced amino acid sequences, and biological activity of the chemically synthesized peptides. *Biochem. Biophys. Res. Commun.* 259:141–48

59. Sciaky D, Kosiba JL, Cohen MB. 1994. Genomic sequence of the murine guanylin gene. *Genomics* 24:583–87

60. Kinoshita H, Fujimoto S, Nakazato M, Yokota N, Date Y, et al. 1997. Urine and plasma levels of uroguanylin and its molecular forms in renal diseases. *Kidney Int.* 52:1028–34

61. Whitaker TL, Witte DP, Scott MC, Cohen MB. 1997. Uroguanylin and guanylin: distinct but overlapping patterns of messenger RNA expression in mouse intestine. *Gastroenterology* 113: 1000–6

62. Perkins A, Goy MF, Li Z. 1997. Uroguanylin is expressed by enterochromaffin cells in the rat gastrointestinal tract. *Gastroenterology* 113:1007–14

63. Nakazato M, Yamaguchi H, Date Y, Miyazato M, Kangawa K, et al. 1998. Tissue distribution, cellular source and structural analysis of rat immunoreactive uroguanylin. *Endocrinology* 139:5247–54

64. Date Y, Nakazato M, Yamaguchi H, Kangawa K, Kinoshita Y, et al. 1999. Enterochromaffin-like cells, a cellular source of uroguanylin in rat stomach. *Endocrinology* 140:2398–404

65. Schulz S, Lopez MJ, Kuhn M, Garbers DL. 1997. Disruption of the guanylyl cyclase-C gene leads to a paradoxical phenotype of viable but heat-stable enterotoxin-resistant mice. *J. Clin. Invest.* 100:1590–95

66. Mann EA, Jump ML, Wu J, Yee E, Giannella RA. 1997. Mice lacking the guanylyl cyclase C receptor are resistant to STa-induced intestinal secretion. *Biochem. Biophys. Res. Commun.* 239:463–66

67. Carrithers SL, Hill MJ, Johnson BR, O'Hara SM, Jackson BA, et al. 1999. Renal effects of uroguanylin and guanylin in vivo. *J. Med. Biol. Res.* 32:In press

68. De Sauvage FJ, Camerato TR, Goeddel DV. 1991. Primary structure and functional expression of the human receptor for *Escherichia coli* heat-stable enterotoxin. *J. Biol. Chem.* 266:17912–18

69. Wada A, Hirayama T, Kitao S, Fujisawa J, Hidaka Y, et al. 1994. Pig intestinal membrane-bound receptor (guanylyl cyclase) for heat-stable enterotoxin: cDNA cloning functional expression, and characterization. *Microbiol. Immunol.* 38:535–41

70. Krause WJ, Cullingford GL, Freeman

RH, Eber SL, Richardson KC, et al. 1994. Distribution of heat-stable enterotoxin/guanylin receptors in the intestinal tract of man and other mammals. *J. Anat.* 184:407–17

71. Fan X, Wang Y, London RM, Eber SL, Krause WJ, et al. 1997. Signaling pathways for guanylin and uroguanylin in the digestive, renal, central nervous, reproductive and lymphoid systems. *Endocrinology* 138:4636–48

72. Forte LR. 1999. Guanylin regulatory peptides: structures, biological activities mediated by cyclic GMP and pathobiology. *Regul. Pept.* 81:25–39.

73. Giannella RA, Mann EA. 1999. Consequences of ablation of the guanylate cyclase C (GC-C) gene. *FASEB J.* 13:A725 (Abstr.)

74. Vaandrager AB, Tilly BC, Smolenski A, Schneider-Rasp S, Bot AGM, et al. 1997. cGMP Stimulation of cystic fibrosis transmembrane conductance regulator Cl⁻ channels co-expressed with cGMP-dependent protein kinase type II but not type Iβ. *J. Biol. Chem.* 272:4195–200.

75. French PJ, Bijman J, Edixhoven M, Vaandrager AB, Scholte BJ, et al. 1995. Isotype-specific activation of cystic fibrosis transmembrane conductance regulator-chloride channels by cGMP-dependent protein kinase II. *J. Biol. Chem.* 270:26626–31

76. Lohmann SM, Vaandrager AB, Smolenski A, Walter U, De Jonge HR. 1997. Distinct and specific functions of cGMP-dependent protein kinases. *Trends Biochem. Sci.* 22:307–12

77. Pfeifer A, Aszodi A, Seidler U, Ruth P, Hofmann F, et al. 1996. Intestinal secretory defects and dwarfism in mice lacking cGMP-dependent protein kinase II. *Science* 274:2082–86

78. Forte LR, Thorne PK, Eber SL, Krause WJ, Freeman RH, et al. 1992. Stimulation of intestinal Cl⁻ transport by heat-stable enterotoxin: activation of cAMP-dependent protein kinase by cGMP. *Am. J. Physiol.* 263:C607–15

79. Chao AC, deSauvage FJ, Dong YJ, Wagner JA, Goeddel DV, et al. 1994. Activation of intestinal CFTR Cl⁻ channels by heat-stable enterotoxin and guanylin via cAMP-dependent protein kinase. *EMBO J.* 13:1065–72

80. Sheppard DN, Welsh MJ. 1999. Structure and function of the CFTR chloride channel. *Physiol. Rev.* 79:S23–45

81. Cuthbert AW, Hickman ME, MacVinish LJ, Evans MJ, Colledge WH, et al. 1994. Chloride secretion in response to guanylin in colonic epithelia from normal and transgenic cystic fibrosis mice. *Br. J. Pharmacol.* 112:31–36

82. Jentsch TJ, Friedrich T, Schriever A, Yamada H. 1999. The ClC chloride channel family. *Pflügers Arch.* 437:783–95

83. Joo NS, Clarke LL, Hee BH, Forte LR, Kim HD. 1999. Cloning of ClC-2 chloride channel from murine duodenum and its presence in CFTR knockout mice. *Biochim. Biophys. Acta* 1446:431–37

84. Morales MM, Carroll TP, Morita T, Schwiebert EM, Devuyst O, et al. 1996. Both the wild type and a functional isoform of CFTR are expressed in kidney. *Am. J. Physiol.* 270:F1038–48

85. Todd-Turla KM, Rusvai E, Naray-Fejes-Toth A, Fejes-Toth G. 1996. CFTR expression in cortical collecting duct cells. *Am. J. Physiol.* 270:F237–44

86. Fuller F, Porter JG, Arfsten AE, Miller J, Schilling JW, et al. 1988. Atrial natriuretic peptide clearance receptor. *J. Biol. Chem.* 263:9395–401

Annual Review of Physiology 1999. 62:697–722

THE HUMAN LANGUAGE FACULTY AS AN ORGAN

Stephen R. Anderson[1] and David W. Lightfoot[2]

[1]*Department of Linguistics, Yale University, New Haven, CT 06520-8236; e-mail: stephen.anderson@yale.edu;* [2]*Department of Linguistics, University of Maryland, College Park, MD 20742; e-mail: dlight@deans.umd.edu*

Key Words poverty of stimulus, Universal Grammar, cognitive module, functional organ

■ **Abstract** Developments in the study of language and cognition give increasing credibility to the view that human knowledge of natural language results from—and is made possible by—a biologically determined capacity specific both to this domain and to our species. The functional properties of this capacity develop along a regular maturational path, such that it seems more appropriate to speak of knowledge of our own language as growing rather than as being learned. That our learning of language results from a specific innate capacity rather than by general mechanisms of induction is supported by the extent to which we can be shown to know things that we could not have learned from observation of any plausible available teaching. The domain-specificity of the language faculty is supported by the many dissociations that can be observed between control of language structure and other cognitive functions. Finally, the species-specificity of the human language faculty is supported by the observation that (absent severe pathology) every human child exposed in even limited ways to the triggering experience of linguistic data develops a full, rich capacity that is essentially homogeneous with that of the surrounding community. Efforts to teach human language to other species, however, have uniformly failed. These considerations make it plausible that human language arises in biologically based ways that are quite comparable to those directing other aspects of the structure of the organism. The language organ, in this sense, can be interpreted in a functional sense, and not as implying an anatomical location comparable to that of, say, the kidney.

INTRODUCTION

> "[H]uman cognitive systems, when seriously investigated, prove to be no less marvelous and intricate than the physical structures that develop in the life of the organism. Why, then, should we not study the acquisition of a cognitive structure such as language more or less as we study some complex bodily organ?" (Noam Chomsky; 1:10)

0066–4278/00/0315–0697/$12.00   **697**

The study of language and cognition during the past several decades has given increasing credibility to the view that human knowledge of natural language results from—and is made possible by—a biologically determined capacity specific both to this domain and to our species. The functional properties of this capacity develop along a regular maturational path, such that it seems more appropriate to speak of our knowledge of our language as growing rather than as being learned. As with the visual system, much of the detailed structure that we find seems to be wired in, although triggering experience is necessary to set the system in operation and to determine some of its specific properties.

The proposition that our learning of language results from a specific innate capacity rather than inductively from observation of the language around us is supported by the extent to which we can be shown to know things that we could not have learned from such observation or any plausible available teaching. The degree of deep similarity among the world's languages provides support for the notion that they are the product of a common human faculty rather than mere artifacts. The manual languages, which develop in Deaf communities independently of one another or of the language of the surrounding hearing community, share in these fundamental properties, and we must conclude that they are neither the result of simple shared history nor necessary consequences of the articulatory/acoustic/auditory modality of spoken language. The development of structurally deficient pidgins into the essentially normal linguistic systems found in creoles, as a result of transmission through the natural language learning process in new generations of children, provides additional evidence for the richness of that process.

The domain-specificity of the language faculty is supported by the many dissociations that can be observed between control of language structure and other cognitive functions. Focal brain lesions can also result in quite specific language impairments in the presence of otherwise normal cognitive abilities, and vice versa. The proposal that the human language faculty is a product of our genetically determined biological nature is further supported by evidence that certain language deficits show a clear distribution within families that epidemiological and other studies show to be just what would be predicted of relatively simple heritable traits.

Finally, the species-specificity of the human language faculty is supported by the observation that (absent severe pathology) every human child exposed in even limited ways to the triggering experience of linguistic data develops a full, rich capacity that is essentially homogeneous with that of the surrounding community. Efforts to teach human languages to individuals of other species, however, even those closest to ours, have uniformly failed. While a certain capacity for arbitrary symbolic reference can be elicited in certain higher apes (and perhaps even in other animals such as parrots), syntactic systems even remotely comparable to those of human languages seem to be quite outside the capacity of non-human animals, despite intensive highly directed training.

These considerations make it plausible that human language arises in biologically based ways that are quite comparable to those directing other aspects of the structure of the organism. However, the language organ is not to be interpreted as having an anatomical location comparable to that of, say, the kidney. Our understanding of the localization of cognitive function in brain tissue is much too fragmentary and rudimentary. Certain cortical and subcortical areas can be shown to subserve functions essential to language in the sense that lesions in these regions disrupt language functioning (sometimes in remarkably specific ways), but an inference from this evidence to a claim that "language is located in Broca's (and/or Wernicke's) area" is unwarranted. The linguistic capacity that develops naturally in every normal human being appears to be best understood in functional rather than literal anatomical terms.

LANGUAGE DEVELOPMENT AS GROWTH

The apparently common-sense notion that an adult speaker's knowledge of his/her language arises by simple learning, that is as a direct generalization of experience, turns out to pose a logical paradox. We begin with two brief examples that illustrate this point, and then explore the consequences of this for the mechanisms that must in fact underlie the development of linguistic knowledge in normal human speakers.

We Know More Than We Learn

A striking property of language acquisition is that children attain knowledge that, quite literally, infinitely surpasses their actual experience. On the basis of quite limited experience, a productive system, a grammar, arises in each speaker that not only encompasses (a principled subset of) the actual facts to which they have been exposed but also permits the production and comprehension of an unlimited range of novel utterances in the language. There must, therefore, be much more to language acquisition than mimicking what is heard in childhood, and there is more to it than the simple transmission of a set of words and sentences from one generation of speakers to the next.

Two Grammatical Puzzles Consider some subtleties that people are usually not consciously aware of. The verb *is* may be used in its full form or its reduced form: English speakers can say either *Kim is happy* or *Kim's happy*. However, certain instances of *is* never reduce: for example, the underlined items in *Kim is happier than Tim is* or *I wonder where the concert is on Wednesday*. Most speakers are not aware of this, but we all know subconsciously not to use the reduced form in such cases. How did we come to know this? As children we were not instructed to avoid the reduced form in certain places. Yet, all children typically attain the ability to use the forms in the adult fashion, and this ability is quite independent of intelligence level or educational background. Children attain it early in their linguistic development. More significantly, children do not try out the non-occurring forms as if testing a hypothesis in the way that they experiment by using forms like *goed* and *taked*. The ability emerges perfectly and as if by magic.

Another example: Pronouns like *she, her, he, him, his* sometimes may refer back to a noun previously mentioned in a sentence (1a–c). However, one can only understand 1d as referring to two men, Jay and somebody else; here the pronoun may not refer to Jay, unlike 1a–c.

1. a. Jay hurt his nose.
   b. Jay's brother hurt him.
   c. Jay said he hurt Ray.
   d. Jay hurt him.

As adults we generalize that a pronoun may refer to another noun within the same sentence except under very precise conditions (as in 1d). But then, how did we all acquire the right generalization, particularly knowledge of the exception?

To extend this point, consider some more complex examples, as in 2:

2. a. When Jay entered the room, he was wearing a yellow shirt.
   b. Jay was wearing a yellow shirt when he entered the room.
   c. When he entered the room, Jay was wearing a yellow shirt.
   d. He was wearing a yellow shirt when Jay entered the room.
   e. His brother was wearing a yellow shirt when Jay entered the room.

In all of the sentences in 2 the pronoun (*he* or *his*) may refer to some other individual, not mentioned. It may also refer to Jay, in all cases, that is, except 2d, where the wearer of the yellow shirt can only be understood to be someone other than Jay. Again, all speakers are in essential agreement on this point, when these facts are pointed out to them, but we may legitimately be puzzled at the source of this knowledge. It is quite unlikely to have come from any explicit instruction. As far as we know, these points about the interpretation of pronouns had not been systematically noted, even by grammarians, prior to the late 1960s (2–5).

As adults we generalize that a pronoun may refer to another noun within the same sentence except under very precise conditions (as in 1d or 2d). But then, how did we all acquire the right generalization, particularly knowledge of the exceptions? In the case of 2d, we might be tempted to say that it is only natural that a pronoun should not be able to refer to an individual mentioned only later in the sentence, but the evidence of 2c,e shows that such "backwards anaphora" is in fact possible under some circumstances.

Where Does This Knowledge Come From?   In approaching both of these problems, recall the nature of our childhood experience. We were exposed to a haphazard set of linguistic expressions. We heard various sentences containing both the full verb *is* and its reduced form *'s;* we also heard sentences containing pronouns, in some of which the pronoun referred to another noun in the same sentence, and in others to a person not mentioned there. The problem is that, because we were not informed about what cannot occur, our childhood experience provided no evidence for the except clause(s), the cases in which the contracted form is impossible or where a pronoun and a noun in the same sentence may not corefer. That is, we had evidence for generalizations like "*is* may be pronounced [z]"[1] and "pronouns may refer to an individual named by a noun in the same sentence," but no evidence for where these generalizations break down.

As children, we come to know the generalizations and their exceptions, and we come to this knowledge quickly and uniformly. Yet our linguistic experience is not rich enough to determine the limits to the generalizations. We call this the problem of the poverty of the stimulus. Children have no data showing them that *is* may not be reduced in some contexts, and they have no data showing that *him* may not refer to Jay in 1d. These two small illustrations are examples of the form that the poverty-of-stimulus problem takes in language. It may look as if children are behaving magically, but there is no magician and magic is no answer.

There are two easy solutions to the poverty-of-stimulus problem, but neither is adequate. One is to say that children do not overgeneralize because they are reliable imitators. That is, children do not produce the reduced *'s* in the wrong place or use a pronoun in 1d or 2d wrongly to refer to Jay because they never hear language being used in this way. In other words, children acquire their native language simply by imitating the speech of their elders. We know this cannot be literally true because everybody constantly says things that they have never heard. We express thoughts with no conscious or subconscious consideration of whether we are imitating somebody else's use of language. This is true of the most trivial speech: In saying *I want to catch the 3:25 PM bus, which leaves from outside Border's bookstore,* one is using a sentence that one has almost certainly not heard.

The alternative of saying that we form new sentences by analogy with specific sentences we have heard before simply conceals the problem because it does not account for the fact that some possible analogies are good and others are not. Why, that is, does not the existence of the contracted *'s* in *Tim's happy* provide an analogical foundation for a similar reduced form in *Kim's happier than Tim is*? Why do the sentences 2a–c,e not provide an analogical basis for co-reference between *Jay* and *he* in 2d? The point is that language learners arrive at certain very specific generalizations, and fail to arrive at certain other logically possible ones, in ways that cannot be founded on any independent general notion of induction or analogy.

An alternative approach is to claim that children learn not to say the deviant forms because they are corrected by their elders. Alas, this view offers no better insight for several reasons. First, it would take an acute observer to detect and

---

[1] We follow the convention in linguistics of enclosing phonetic representations in square brackets.

correct the error. Second, where linguistic correction is offered, young children are highly resistant and often ignore or explicitly reject the correction. Third, in the examples discussed, children do not overgeneralize, and therefore parents have nothing to correct; this will become clearer when we discuss experimental work with young children.

So the first easy solution to the poverty-of-stimulus problem is to deny that it exists, to hold that the environment is rich enough to provide evidence for where the generalizations break down. But the problem is real, and this solution does not address it.

The second easy answer would be to deny that there is a problem because there would be nothing to be learned if we could maintain that a person's language is fully determined by genetic properties. Yet this answer also cannot be right because people speak differently, and many of the differences are environmentally induced. There is nothing about a person's genetic inheritance that makes her a speaker of English; if she had been raised in a Dutch home, she would have become a speaker of Dutch.

The two easy answers either attribute everything to the environment or everything to the genetic inheritance. Neither position is tenable. Instead, language emerges through an interaction between our genetic inheritance and the linguistic environment to which we happen to be exposed. English-speaking children learn from their environment that the verb *is* may be pronounced [ɪz] or [z], and native principles prevent the reduced form from occurring in the wrong places. Likewise, children learn from their environment that *he, his,* etc are pronouns, while native principles entail where pronouns may not refer to a preceding noun. The interaction of the environmental information and the native principles accounts for how the relevant properties emerge in an English-speaking child.

We sketch some relevant principles below. It is worth pointing out that we are doing a kind of Mendelian genetics here in the most literal sense. In the mid-nineteenth century, Mendel postulated genetic "factors" to explain the variable characteristics of his pea plants, without the slightest idea of how these factors might be biologically instantiated. Similarly, linguists seek to identify information that must be available independently of experience in order for a grammar to emerge in a child. We have no idea whether this information is encoded directly in the genome or results from epigenetic, developmental properties of the organism; it is, in any case, native. As a shorthand device for these native properties, we shall write of the linguistic genotype, that part of our genetic endowment that is relevant for our linguistic development. Each individual's genotype determines the potential range of functional adaptations to the environment (6:36), and we assume that the linguistic genotype (what linguists call Universal Grammar) is uniform across the species (in the absence of fairly severe and specific pathology). That is, linguistically we all have the same potential for functional adaptations, and any of us may grow up to be a speaker of Catalan or Hungarian, depending entirely on our circumstances and not at all on variation in our genetic make-up.

It is important to understand that Universal Grammar in this sense is not to be confused with the grammar of any particular language: To say that would be close to the second fallacious approach to the problem of the poverty of the stimulus discussed above. Rather, Universal Grammar can be seen as the set of principles by which the child can infer, on the basis of the limited data available in the environment, the full grammatical capacity that we think of as a mature speaker's knowledge of a language.

Because children are capable of acquiring any language to which they happen to be exposed between infancy and puberty, the same set of genetic principles that accounts for the emergence of English (using genetic now in the extended sense we have indicated) must also account for the emergence of Dutch, Vietnamese, Hopi, or any other of the thousands of languages spoken by human beings. This plasticity imposes a strong empirical demand on hypotheses about the linguistic genotype; the principles postulated must be open enough to account for the variation among the world's languages. The fact that people develop different linguistic capacities depending on whether they are brought up in Togo, Tokyo, or Toronto provides a delicate tool to refine claims about the nature of the native component.

We conclude that there is a biological entity, a finite mental organ, that develops in children along one of a number of paths. The range of possible paths of language growth is determined in advance of any childhood experience. The language organ that emerges, the grammar, is represented in the brain and plays a central role in the person's use of language. We have gained some insight into the nature of people's language organs by considering a wide range of phenomena: the developmental stages that young children go through, the way language breaks down in the event of brain damage, the manner in which people analyze incoming speech signals, and more. At the center is the biological notion of a language organ, a grammar.

The Nature of Grammars

Children acquire a productive system, a grammar, in accordance with the requirements of the genotype. If asked to say quite generally what is now known about the linguistic genotype, we would say that it yields finite grammars, because they are represented in the finite space of the brain, but that they range over an infinity of possible sentences. Finite grammars consist of a set of operations allowing for infinite variation in the expressions that are generated. The genotype is plastic, consistent with speaking Japanese or Quechua. It is modular and uniquely computational.

By modular we mean that the genotype consists of separate subcomponents, each of which has its own distinctive properties, that interact to yield the properties of the whole. These modules are, in many cases, specific to language. Research has undermined the notion that the mind possesses only general principles of intelligence that hold of all kinds of mental activity. One module of innate linguistic capacity contains abstract structures that are compositional (consisting of units made up of smaller units) and fit a narrow range of possibilities. Another module encompasses the ability to relate one position to another within these structures by movement, and those movement relationships are narrowly defined. Yet another module is the mental lexicon, a list of word-forms and their crucial properties.

These modules may or may not be separately represented in neural tissue. For example, Grodzinsky (7) recently argued that movement relations—and not other aspects of syntactic form—are computed by specific tissue within the classical Broca's area. The claim of modularity does not in any sense rest on such physical separation, however. It refers, rather, to the fact that various aspects of linguistic knowledge are logically and functionally independent of one another, yielding the full complexity of human language through the interaction of individually rather simple systems.

To see the kind of compositionality involved, consider how words combine. Words are members of categories like noun (N), verb (V), preposition (P), adjective/adverb (A). If two words combine, then the grammatical properties of the resulting phrase are determined by one of the two words, which we call the head: We say that the head projects the phrase. If we combine the verb *visit* with the noun *Chicago,* the resulting phrase *visit Chicago* has verbal and not nominal properties. It occurs where verbs occur and not where nouns occur: *I want to visit Chicago,* but not **the visit Chicago*² nor **we discussed visit Chicago.* So the expression *visit Chicago* is a verb phrase (VP), where the V *visit* is the head projecting the VP. This can be represented as a labeled bracketing (3a) or as a tree diagram (3b). The verb is the head of the VP and the noun is the complement.

3. a. [$_{VP}$ [$_V$ visit] [$_N$ Chicago]]

b.

In general, two categories merge to form a new category. So an inflectional element like *will* might combine with the VP *visit Chicago,* to yield the more complex expression *will visit Chicago,* with a structure [$_{IP}$ [$_I$ will] [$_{VP}$ visit Chicago]]. The auxiliary, inflectional *will* heads the new phrase and projects to a phrasal category IP. This means that *visit Chicago* is a unit (VP), which acts as the complement of *will,* but *will visit* is not a unit; that is, there is no single node that dominates *will visit* and nothing else in this example.

The units defined by these trees are the items that the computational operations manipulate; they are the items that move and delete and to which reference

---

²Following a standard convention in linguistics, we indicate phrases or sentences that are not grammatical in English with a preceding *.

(including co-reference) can be assigned. Non-units are not available to these operations.

One of the computational operations involved is that of overt movement to account for the fact that in the surface forms of many sentences, elements occur in positions other than those with which their syntactic function is naturally assigned. We describe such displaced elements with the metaphor of movement. This does not, of course, entail a claim that speakers go through some process of re-adjustment of structure in producing or understanding the relevant sentences. It is only a way of characterizing explicitly the relation between the sentential position in which a word or phrase appears and that with which its grammatical functions are associated. For example, an expression like *What city will the student visit?* (where *what city* is understood as the complement of *visit*) can be described by a structure along the lines of 4. Here we need more structure to enable the subject *the student* to combine with *will* and its complement VP to form a full IP, and then to enable *what city* to merge with the rest of the clause. *Will* is a head (labeled C for complementizer), which in such question constructions precedes the rest of the IP, and *what city* is a specifier to that head. We indicate the positions from which these elements have moved with empty pairs of brackets.

4.

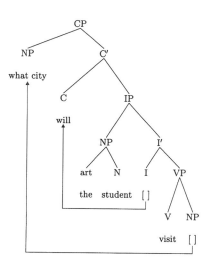

The syntactic component of a speaker's knowledge of a language, then, can be represented by a system of rules that describes (or generates) the set of structures (similar to that in 4) occurring in sentences of the language and characterizing the range of possible structural relations between moved elements and their functional positions, etc. Other aspects of a full grammar provide explicit accounts of the relation between this kind of syntactic organization and the way the words of sentences are constructed and pronounced, etc. The set of possible grammars of this type is narrowly limited by the principles of Universal Grammar, which require that systems within this range (and no others) are in principle attainable by the specific principles available to the child, with differences among them corresponding to differences in the Primary Linguistic Data available in the child's experience.

Back to the Puzzles

Let us return now to the problems raised above, beginning with that of *'s,* the reduced form of *is.* In a sentence like *Kim's happy,* the auxiliary element *'s* is grammatically the head of the IP, taking the adjective phrase *happy* as its complement. In pronunciation, however, it forms part of a single unbroken unit with the preceding word *Kim,* as the apostrophe in the conventional spelling *'s* suggests, despite the fact that the sequence *Kim —'s* does not constitute a phrase syntactically.

We thus see that the correspondence between syntactic phrases and units of sound (phonological words and phrases) is not a strict isomorphism. The relation is not, however, simply arbitrary and unconstrained. In particular, every syntactic phrase, if pronounced at all, must correspond to at least one phonological word, even though not every *syntactic* word constitutes a full phonological word of its own. This condition on the relation between syntactic and phonological form seems not to be a fact about English per se, but rather about language in general.

In the case that interests us, reduced forms of auxiliaries such as *'s* (as well as *'ve, 're,* and the reduced forms of *am, will, would, shall,* and *should*) do not have enough phonological substance to be words on their own, and thus necessarily combine with a word on their left to make up a single phonological word in the pronunciation of sentences in which they occur. In terms of pronunciation, that is, *Kim's* in *Kim's happy* is just as indissoluble a unit as *birds* in *Birds fly.*

Even though *'s* in *Kim's happy* is not itself a phonological word, this does not compromise the principle that every syntactic phrase corresponds to at least one phonological word, however, since *'s* is not itself a phrase and the phrase of which it is the head, *'s happy,* is represented by the word *happy.* Consider the case of the underlined *is* in *Kim's happier than Tim* <u>is</u>, though. In this structure the underlined *is* is the only representative of its phrase (which consists of *is* and understood, but unpronounced, *happy*). If this *is* were to be replaced with the non-word *'s,* the result would be a syntactic phrase that corresponded to no phonological word. It is this that is responsible for the fact that we cannot say **Kim's happier than Tim's.* Poets make linguistic jokes from these principles: the Gershwins were famous for contraction jokes such as that in *Girl Crazy* (1930) where a chorus begins *I'm bidin' my time /'Cause that's the kind of guy I'm.*

A sentence-internal understood element can have similar effects, as in *I wonder where$_x$ the concert is* [ ]$_x$ *on Wednesday.* Here *where$_x$* has moved from the position indicated as [ ]$_x$, but is still understood there. This shows that the reduced *is* has to be combined with a word that stands in a certain kind of structural relationship to it: It forms a phrase together with its complement, and this phrase is represented by at least that complement as a phonological word even though *'s* itself would not suffice to supply a well-formed phonological correspondent to a syntactic phrase. *On Wednesday* is not the complement of *is* in this example. In 5a, *happy* is the complement of *is* and therefore reduced *'s* may attach to the preceding word without leaving the phrase it heads stranded. The same is true for the first *is* of 5b. However, *Tim* is not the complement of the underlined *is* in 5b; in this case, the subject *Tim* and the copula verb *is* have permuted. As a result, the underlined *is* is the only overt representative of its phrase, and cannot be reduced.

5. a. Kim's happy.
   b. Kim is happier than <u>is</u> Tim.

So now we have an answer to the problem sketched at the outset: A reduced *is* may not be the only phonological material representing the syntactic phrase of which it is the head. This follows from principled restrictions that are in fact quite general. In natural languages, syntactic phrases must be represented, if at all, by at least one phonological word, and reduced auxiliary verbs do not consist of enough material to satisfy this requirement. One productive approach is to treat reduced *is* as a clitic. Clitics are little words that occur in many, perhaps all languages, and have the property of not being able to stand alone. In some languages, these elements attach systematically to the word to their left; in others, to the right, and in others the direction of attachment depends on details of the syntactic and/or phonological structure. What is consistently the case, however, is that syntactic elements that do not constitute words in their own right must attach to some other word as clitics in order to be pronounced at all, and also that these clitics cannot be the only overt representative of a syntactic phrase.

Part of what a child growing a grammar needs to do is to determine the clitics in his or her linguistic environment, knowing in advance of any experience that these are small, unstressed items attached phonologically to an adjacent word in ways that may be contrary to the syntactic relations they bear to surrounding material. This predetermined knowledge—the nature of clitics and the fact that they cannot by themselves satisfy the requirement that phrases be represented by at least one phonological word—is contributed by the linguistic genotype and is part of what the child brings to language acquisition. The environment provides examples such as *Pat's happy, Bob's happy, and Alice's happy too.* The child can observe that the three instances of *'s* in these cases vary in their pronunciation ([s] after *Pat,* [z] after *Bob,* and [ɪz] after *Alice*). This variation is quite systematic, and in fact follows the same principles as those that determine the form of the plural ending in *cats, knobs, palaces:* a fact confirming that *'s* forms part of a single phonological unit with the preceding word just as the plural ending does, and thus must be a clitic.

Under this approach, the child is faced with a chaotic environment and scans it, looking for clitics among many other things, of course (8). This is the answer that we provide to our initial problem, and it is an answer of the right shape. It makes a general claim at the genetic level (clitics and their behavior are predefined) and postulates that the child arrives at a plausible analysis on exposure to a few simple expressions. The analysis that the child arrives at predicts no reduction for the underlined *is* in *Kim is happier than Tim is̲, I wonder where the concert is̲ on Wednesday,* and countless other cases, and the child needs no correction in arriving at this system. The very fact that *'s* is a clitic, a notion defined in advance of any experience, dictates that it may not occur in certain contexts. It is for this reason that the generalization that *is* may be pronounced as *'s* breaks down at certain points and does not hold across the board.

Consider now the second problem, the reference of pronouns. An initial definition might propose that pronouns refer to a preceding noun, but the data of 1 and 2 show that this is both too strong and too weak. It is too strong because, as we saw in 1d, *him* may not refer to Jay; in 1b *him* may refer to Jay but not to Jay's brother. The best account of this complex phenomenon seems to be to invoke a native principle that says that pronouns may not refer back to a local nominal element, where local means contained in the same clause or in the same NP.

In 6 we give the relevant structure for the corresponding sentences of 1. In 6b the NP *Jay's brother* is local to *him*, and so *him* may not refer back to that NP: We express this by indexing them differently. On the other hand, *Jay* is contained inside the NP and therefore is not available to *him* for indexing purposes, so those two nouns do not need to be indexed differently—they may refer to the same person and they may thus be co-indexed. Again we see the constituent structure illustrated earlier playing a central role in the way in which the indexing computations are carried out. In 6d *Jay* is local to *him* and so the two elements may not be co-indexed; they may not refer to the same person. In 6c *Jay* is not local to *he* because the two items are not contained in the same clause: *Jay* and *he* may thus refer either to the same person or to different people. In 6a *his* is contained inside a NP and may not be co-indexed with anything else within that NP; what happens outside the NP is not systematic; so *his* and *Jay* may co-refer and do not need to be indexed differently.

6. a. $[_{IP}$ Jay$_i$ hurt $[_{NP}$ his$_{i/j}$ nose$]]$
    b. $[_{IP}$ $[_{NP}$ Jay$_i$'s brother$]_k$ hurt him$_{i/j/*k}]$
    c. $[_{IP}$ Jay$_i$ said $[_{IP}$ he$_{i/j}$ hurt Ray$]]$
    d. $[_{IP}$ Jay$_i$ hurt him$_{j/*i}]$

The proposal that pronouns refer to a preceding noun is shown to be too weak because sometimes, as in 2c,e, the pronoun refers to a following noun. In this case, the relevant principle seems to be that such "backwards anaphora" is not possible if the pronoun not only precedes the noun, but is also higher (in a precise sense whose details are not relevant to our present concerns) in the syntactic structure than the noun that serves as its antecedent. In 2c, the pronoun precedes

Jay, but this is acceptable because the pronoun appears within a subordinate clause. In 2e, the pronoun is subordinated because it appears as a possessor within a larger NP. In 2d, however, the pronoun appears as subject of the main clause and is thus (in the relevant structural sense) syntactically higher than the following noun, which therefore cannot serve as its antecedent.

We could have illustrated these points equally well with data from French or from Dutch, or from many other languages, because the principles apply quite generally, to pronouns in all languages. If we assume a native principle, available to the child independently of any actual experience, language acquisition is greatly simplified. Now the child does not need to learn why the pronoun may refer to Jay in 6a or 6b,c but not in 6d; in 2a–c, e but not in 2d, etc. Rather, the child raised in an English-speaking setting has only to learn that *he, his, him* are pronouns, i.e. elements subject to our principles. This can be learned by exposure to a simple sentence like 1d (structurally 6d), uttered in a context where *him* refers to somebody other than Jay.

One way of thinking of the contribution of the linguistic genotype is to view it as providing invariant principles and option-points or parameters. There are invariant principles that clitics attach phonologically to adjacent words, that a (non-null) syntactic phrase must correspond to at least one phonological word, that pronouns cannot be locally co-indexed, and that they cannot both precede and be structurally higher than a full NP with which they are co-referential. Meanwhile, there are also options: Direct objects may precede the verb in some grammars (German, Japanese) and may follow it in others (English, French); some clitics attach to the right and some to the left. These are parameters of variation, and the child sets these parameters one way or another on exposure to her particular linguistic experience. As a result, a grammar emerges in the child, part of the linguistic phenotype. The child has learned that *'s* is a clitic and that *he* is a pronoun; the genotype ensures that *'s* cannot be the only phonological material corresponding to a syntactic phrase and that *he* is never used in a structurally inappropriate context.

The Acquisition Problem

In the preceding sections we have looked at some specific acquisition problems and considered what ingredients are needed for their solution. Now let us stand back and think about these matters more abstractly.

The child acquires a finite system, a grammar that generates structures corresponding more or less to utterances of various kinds. Some structural principle prevents forms like **Kim's happier than Tim's* from occurring in the speech of English speakers, as we have seen. Children are not exposed to pseudo-sentences like this and informed systematically that they are not to be produced. Speakers come to know subconsciously that they cannot be said, and this knowledge emerges somehow, even though it is not part of the environmental input to the child's development. It is not enough to say that people do not utter such forms because they never hear them: People say many things that they have not heard, as we have noted. Language is not learned simply by imitating or repeating what has been heard.

The Poverty of the Stimulus   This poverty-of-stimulus problem defines our approach to language acquisition. Over the last 40 years, much of the linguistic literature has focused on areas where the best description cannot be derived directly from the data to which the child has access or is under-determined by those data, as in the examples with the clitic *'s* and the pronouns discussed above. If the child's linguistic experience does not provide the basis for establishing a particular aspect of linguistic knowledge, another source must exist for that knowledge.

This is not to say that imitation plays no role but only that it does not provide a sufficient explanation. This is worth emphasizing because antagonists some-times caricature this approach to language acquisition as "denying the existence of learning," when in fact we merely deny that learning is the whole story, a very different matter. The quotation is from a remarkable article in *Science* (9), in which the authors assert that "Noam Chomsky, the founder of generative lin-guistics, has argued for 40 years that language is unlearnable" and that they, on the other hand, have "rediscovered" learning!

Caricatures of this type show up in the writing of people who claim that all information is derived from the environment and that there is no domain-specific genetic component to language acquisition. These people deny the poverty-of-stimulus problems, claiming that children may derive all relevant information from their linguistic environment. Bates & Elman provide a recent and particu-larly clear and striking instance of this line, claiming that artificial neural networks can learn linguistic regularities from imperfect but "huge computerized corpora of written and spoken language."

Nobody denies that the child must extract information from the environment; it is no revelation that there is learning in that technical sense. Our point is that there is more to language acquisition than this. Children react to evidence in accordance with specific principles.

The problem demanding explanation is compounded by other factors. Despite variation in background and intelligence, people's mature linguistic capacity emerges in fairly uniform fashion, in just a few years, without much apparent effort, conscious thought, or difficulty; and it develops with only a narrow range of the logically possible errors. Children do not test random hypotheses, gradually discarding those leading to incorrect results and provoking parental correction. In each language community the non-adult sentences formed by very young chil-dren seem to be few in number and quite uniform from one child to another, which falls well short of random hypotheses. Normal children attain a fairly rich system of linguistic knowledge by five or six years of age and a mature system by puberty. In this regard, language is no different from, say, vision, except that vision is taken for granted, and ordinary people give more conscious thought to language.

These, then, are the salient facts about language acquisition or, more properly, language growth. The child masters a rich system of knowledge without significant instruction and despite an impoverished stimulus; the process involves only a narrow range of errors and takes place rapidly, even explosively between two and three years of age. The main question is how children acquire so much more than they experience.

A grammar represents what a speaker comes to know, subconsciously for the most part, about his or her native language. It represents the fully developed linguistic capacity and is therefore part of an individual's phenotype. It is one expression of the potential defined by the genotype. Speakers know what an infinite number of sentences mean and the various ways in which they can be pronounced and rephrased. Most of this largely subconscious knowledge is represented in a person's grammar. The grammar may be used for various purposes, from everyday events like expressing ideas, communicating, or listening to other people, to more contrived functions like writing elegant prose or lyric poetry, or compiling and solving crossword puzzles, or writing an article about the language organ.

We do not want to give the impression that all linguists adopt this view of things. In fact, people have studied language with quite different goals in mind, ranging from the highly specific (to describe Dutch in such a way that it can be learned easily by speakers of Indonesian), to more general goals, such as showing how a language may differ from one historical stage to another (comparing, for example, Chaucerian and present-day English). However, the research paradigm we sketch has been the focus of much activity over the last 40 years, and it construes a grammar as a biological object, the language organ.

The Analytical Triplet   A grammar, for us, is a psychological entity, part of the psychological state of somebody who knows a language. For any aspect of linguistic knowledge, three intimately related items are included in a full account of this state. First, there is a formal and explicit characterization of what a mature speaker knows; this is the grammar, which is part of that speaker's phenotype. Since the grammar is represented in the mind/brain, it must be a finite system that can relate sound and meaning for an infinite number of sentences.

Second, also specified are the relevant principles and parameters common to the species and part of the initial state of the organism; these principles and parameters make up part of the theory of grammar or Universal Grammar, and they belong to the genotype.

The third item is the trigger experience, which varies from person to person and consists of an unorganized and fairly haphazard set of utterances, of the kind that any child hears (the notion of a trigger is from ethologists' work on the emergence of behavioral patterns in young animals). The universal theory of grammar and the variable trigger together form the basis for attaining a grammar; grammars are attained on the basis of a certain trigger and the genotype.

In 7 we give the explanatory schema, using general biological terminology in 7a and the corresponding linguistic terms in 7b. The triggering experience causes the genotype to develop into a phenotype; exposure to a range of utterances from, say, English allows the Universal Grammar capacity to develop into a particular mature grammar. One may think of the theory of grammar as making available a set of choices; the choices are taken in the light of the trigger experience or the Primary Linguistic Data, and a grammar emerges when the relevant options are resolved. A child develops a grammar by setting the open parameters of Universal Grammar in the light of her particular experience.

7. a. linguistic triggering experience (genotype → phenotype)
    b. Primary Linguistic Data (Universal Grammar → grammar)

Each of the items in the triplet—trigger, Universal Grammar, and grammar—must meet various demands. The trigger, or Primary Linguistic Data, must consist of only the kinds of things that children routinely experience and includes only simple structures. The theory of grammar, or Universal Grammar, is the one constant and must hold universally such that any person's grammar can be attained on the basis of naturally available trigger experiences. The mature grammar must define an infinite number of expressions as well formed, and for each, it must specify at least the sound and the meaning. A description always involves these three items, and they are closely related; changing a claim about one of the items usually involves changing claims about the other two.

The grammar is one subcomponent of the mind that interacts with other cognitive capacities or modules. Like the grammar, each of the other modules is likely to develop in time and to have distinct initial and mature states. So the visual system recognizes triangles, circles, and squares through the structure of the circuits that filter and re-compose the retinal image (10). Certain nerve cells respond to only a straight line sloping downward from left to right within a specific, narrow range of orientations, other nerve cells to lines sloped in different directions. The range of angles that an individual neuron can register is set by the genetic program, but experience is needed to fix the precise orientation specificity (11). In the mid-1960s, Hubel, Wiesel, and their colleagues devised an ingenious technique to identify how individual neurons in an animal's visual system react to specific patterns in the visual field (including horizontal and vertical lines, moving spots, and sharp angles). They found that particular nerve cells were set within a few hours of birth to react to only certain visual stimuli and, furthermore, that if a nerve cell is not stimulated within a few hours, it becomes totally inert in later life. In several experiments on kittens, it was shown that if a kitten spent its first few days in a deprived optical environment (a tall cylinder painted with only vertical stripes), only the neurons stimulated by that environment remained active; all other optical neurons became inactive because the relevant synapses degenerated, and the kitten never learned to see horizontal lines or moving spots in the normal way.

Therefore, we see learning as a selective process: Parameters are provided by the genetic equipment, and relevant experience fixes those parameters (12, 13). A certain mature cognitive structure emerges at the expense of other possible structures that are lost irretrievably as the inactive synapses degenerate. The view that there is a narrowing down of possible connections out of an overabundance of initially possible ones is now receiving more attention in the light of Hubel & Wiesel's Nobel Prize winning success. For the moment, this seems to be a more likely means to fine tune the nervous system as learning takes place, as opposed to the earlier view that there is an increase in the connections among nerve cells.

So human cognitive capacity is made up of identifiable properties that are genetically prescribed, each developing along one of various pre-established routes, depending on the particular experience encountered during the individual's early life. These genetic prescriptions may be extremely specialized, as Hubel & Wiesel showed for the visual system. They assign some order to our experience. Experience elicits or triggers certain kinds of specific responses but it does not determine the basic form of the response.

This kind of modularity is very different from the view that the cognitive faculties are homogeneous and undifferentiated, that the faculties develop through general problem-solving techniques. In physical domains, nobody would suggest that the visual system and the system governing the circulation of the blood are determined by the same genetic regulatory mechanisms. Of course, the possibility should not be excluded that the linguistic principles postulated here may eventually turn out to be special instances of principles holding over domains other than language, but before that can be established, much more must be known about what kinds of principles are needed for language acquisition to take place under normal conditions. The same is, of course, true for other aspects of cognitive development. Only on such a basis can meaningful analogies be detected. Meanwhile, "we are led to expect that each region of the central nervous system has its own special problems that require different solutions. In vision we are concerned with contours and directions and depth. With the auditory system, on the other hand, we can anticipate a galaxy of problems relating to temporal interactions of sounds of different frequencies, and it is difficult to imagine that the same neural apparatus deals with all of these phenomena . . . for the major aspects of the brain's operation no master solution is likely" (14:28).

Real-Time Acquisition of Grammars   In the domain of language, our colleagues at the University of Maryland have shown that the sophisticated distinctions we discussed at the beginning of this article do not result from learning and that the hypothesized genetic constraints seem to be at work from the outset. The experimenters constructed situations in which the overriding temptation for children would be to violate the relevant constraints. The fact that children conform to the hypothesized constraints, resisting preferences they show in other contexts, is taken to be evidence that the constraints under investigation are active for them, and that this is true at the earliest stage at which they might be manifested (15).

Crain & Thornton (16) developed an elicitation task that encouraged children to ask questions such as *Do you know what that's up there,* to determine if these were compatible with their grammars. They hypothesized that children would generally show a preference for the reduced *'s* form whenever this was consistent with their grammars. This preference would be revealed in a frequency count of legitimate forms, like *Do you know what that's doing up there?* Comparing the frequency of the reduced forms in the contexts where adults find reduced forms unacceptable with that of non-adult reduced forms more generally would indicate whether children's grammars contained the hypothetical genetic constraint. If the genetic constraint is at work, there should be a significant difference in frequency.

The target productions were evoked by the following protocols in which Thornton & Crain provided children with a context designed to elicit questions.

8. Protocols for cliticization:
    a. Experimenter: Ask Ratty if he knows what that is doing up there.
       Child: Do you know what that's doing up there?
       Rat: It seems to be sleeping.
    b. Experimenter: Ask Ratty if he knows what that is up there.
       Child: Do you know what that is up there?
       Rat: A monkey.

In 8a, the child is invited to produce a sentence where *what* is understood as the object of doing: *do you know what$_x$ that is doing [ ]$_x$ up there?* Since the resulting phrase of which *is* is head, [$_{VP}$ is [$_{VP}$ doing [ ]$_x$]], contains at least one phonological word in addition to *is* itself, *is* can be replaced with the clitic form *'s* without resulting in an ill-formed correspondence between syntactic and phonological structure. However, in 8b, the child produces a sentence where *what* is understood as the complement of *is,* but is not pronounced in that position: *do you know what$_x$ that is [ ]$_x$ up there?* (cf *That is a bottle up there*). As a result, the phrase of which *is* is the head ([$_{VP}$ is [ ]$_x$]) corresponds only to a phonological word to the extent that *is* itself is a word and not merely a clitic. This fact prevents the *is* from cliticizing in adult speech; no adult would use the reduced form to produce *Do you know what that's up there* (cf. *That's a bottle up there*).

Thornton & Crain found that young children behaved just like adults, manifesting the hypothetical genetic constraint. The children tested ranged in age from 2 years, 11 months to 4 years, 5 months, with an average age of 3 years, 8 months. In the elicited questions there was not a single instance of the reduced form where it is impossible in adult speech. Children produced elaborate forms like those of 9, but never with *'s,* the reduced form of *is.*

9. a. Do you know what that black thing on the flower is? (4 years, 3 months)
    b. Squeaky, what do think that is? (3 years, 11 months)

    c. Do you know what that is on the flower? (4 years, 5 months)

    d. Do you know what that is, Squeaky? (3 years, 2 months)

There is, of course, much more to be said about grammars and their acquisition, and there is an enormous technical literature (16). Meanwhile, we have an approach to the riot of differences that we find in the languages of the world and even within languages. As children, our linguistic experience varies tremendously; no two children experience the same set of sentences, let alone the same pronunciations. Nonetheless, the approach we have sketched enables us to understand the universality of our development: why we categorize the linguistic world so similarly and can talk to each other despite the enormous variation in our childhood experience.

THE ORGANIC BASIS OF LANGUAGE

Human knowledge of natural language results from, and is made possible by, a richly structured and biologically determined capacity specific to this domain. It appears, furthermore, that much of this capacity is also specific to humans, lacking significant parallels even in those species closest to us, including the higher apes. This conclusion follows from the failures of a half century of intensive efforts to teach human languages to individuals of other species, especially chimpanzees and other primates.

The failure of initial attempts to teach spoken languages to non-human primates was initially attributed to deficiencies in these animals' vocal apparatus, and attention shifted in the 1960s to studies based on manual languages such as American Sign Language (ASL) (17). Research has demonstrated, as we note below, that ASL and other natural signed languages have the structural properties of spoken languages (see 18, 19) and are well within the dexterity of chimpanzees and other primates. Despite this, however, the animals in these experiments have never been shown to acquire even the rudiments of the syntactic organization of natural languages (20–22). This conclusion has been repeatedly challenged by members of the ape language research community, especially in connection with experiments involving bonobos (*pan paniscus*) (23), but the fact remains that nothing resembling the natural human capacity for free, recursive syntactic combination has been shown in any serious scientific work to date.

In contrast to the failure of these attempts to instill in primates a syntactic ability comparable to that which appears naturally and spontaneously in every remotely normal human child, a certain capacity for arbitrary symbolic reference has undoubtedly been elicited in some higher apes (24–30) and perhaps even in other animals such as parrots (31). Such use of arbitrary symbols does not, apparently, occur in nature in non-human species, and the demonstration that in some cases it is nonetheless within their cognitive capacities is extremely interesting and important. It does not, however, compromise the conclusion that the syntactic properties of human language are provided to our language organ as a consequence of our specific genotype and as such are well outside the capacity of non-humans. This should hardly come as a great surprise, since every species has unique systems and capacities that are determined by its specific genotype and inaccessible in the absence of the appropriate biology. It is not far-fetched to compare the situation regarding language in other primates with the fact that humans, even with intensive training, are incapable of free flight.

The functional properties of our language capacity develop along a regular maturational path, such that it seems more appropriate to see our linguistic knowledge as growing rather than being learned. As with the visual system, much of the detailed structure we find is wired in, though triggering experience is necessary to set the system in operation and to determine some of its specific properties. In this respect, human language shows fascinating and detailed analogies (as well, of course, as significant dis-analogies) with the development of song in birds (32, 33), a system that is uncontroversially attributed to properties of the animal's specific biology and not to some system of generalized learning or the like.

The notion that the world's languages are the product of a common human faculty, rather than mere culturally determined accidents, is supported by the deep similarity that evidently exists among them, as the research of the past 40 years or so has made clear. A particularly striking instance of the commonality of the human language faculty is supplied by the manual languages that develop in Deaf communities independently of one another or of the language of the surrounding hearing community and that share fully in these fundamental properties. We must conclude that the profound structural similarities between signed and spoken languages (34–36), including not only the basic principles of their organization but the specific path of their development, the brain regions associated with their control, and many others, are neither the result of simple shared history nor necessary consequences of the articulatory/acoustic/auditory modality of spoken language, but rather derive from shared biology.

The notion that human language acquisition is primarily a matter of cultural transmission, rather than biologically driven maturation in the presence of relevant experience, is also controverted by instances of the development of structurally deficient pidgins into the essentially normal linguistic systems found in creoles. The deep reorganization of pidgins into creoles, which takes place as an essentially automatic result of transmission through the natural language learning process in new generations of children, provides additional support for the richness of the genotypic system involved in linguistic development (8, 37, 38).

The language faculty has properties typical of a bodily organ, a specialized structure that carries out a particular function. Some organs, like the blood and the skin, interact with the rest of the body across a widespread, complex interface, and all organs are integrated into a complex whole. Often the limits to an organ are unclear, and anatomists do not worry about whether the hand is an organ or whether this designation should be reserved for one of its fingers. It is clear that the body is not made up of cream cheese, and the same seems to be true of the brain.

The language organ is not (at least in the present state of our knowledge) comparable to, say, the kidney, in having a clear and specifiable anatomical location. Our understanding of the localization of cognitive function in brain tissue is currently too fragmentary and rudimentary to allow for clear claims of this sort. While certain areas of the brain (both cortical and subcortical) can be shown to subserve functions essential to language, in the sense that lesions in these areas disrupt language functioning (sometimes in remarkably specific ways) (39), the inferences from this evidence to claims that e.g. "language is located in Broca's (and/or Wernicke's) area" is quite unwarranted. Indeed, even the overall localization of language function in the left cortical hemisphere has been seen in recent years to be a significant oversimplification (40). But in fact, even if it were to become clear that there is no clear segregation between language-related and non-language-related brain tissue, it would still be useful and important to treat the language capacity as a discrete and specifiable human biological system in functional, if not anatomical terms, on the basis of arguments of the sort we have adduced above.

The domain-specificity of the language faculty is supported by the extensive literature documenting dissociations between control of language structure and of other aspects of cognition. Where a system operates and is subject to discrete impairment independently of other systems, it is a candidate for modular status. Thus in the domain of senses, one can be deaf without being blind, and vice versa, which supports (though it does not by itself require) the claim that hearing and sight are the products of distinct systems. Smith (41) provides an excellent discussion of this point. He discusses the case of a linguistic savant Christopher, whose hand-eye coordination is severely impaired and whose psychological profile shows "moderate to severe disability in performance tasks, but results close to normal in verbal tasks." Despite low general intelligence, not only is his language essentially unimpaired, but in fact he has an astonishing capacity to pick up languages; see Reference 42 for more extensive documentation and analysis.

In contrast, the phenomenon known as specific language impairment (SLI) (for an overview, see 43) represents an apparently genetically determined condition in which language ability is impaired in fairly precise ways in the presence of otherwise normal abilities in other domains: Most SLI children are cognitively normal but fail to develop age-appropriate linguistic capacities (44). The homogeneity of the cases that have been grouped together under this diagnosis is quite controversial, but in support of the biological nature of the faculty in question, the distribution of SLI in some well-studied populations has been shown (in both epidemiological and genetic studies (45) to be that of a relatively simple Mendelian trait (46, 47), perhaps even one with a specific, identifiable chromosomal location. Researchers have postulated a range of grammatical deficits associated with this genetic abnormality (48–50) (see 51 for a useful overview).

Smith (41) points to other dissociations: "Just as intelligence and language are dissociable, so also is it possible to separate linguistic ability and Theory of Mind, with autistic subjects lacking in the latter but [potentially, especially in the case of Asperger's Syndrome; see (52)] with language being retained within normal limits. Some Down Syndrome children provide a contrary scenario, with their Theory of Mind being intact, but their linguistic ability moderately to severely degraded."

Similarly we find sub-modular dissociations within the language organ, suggesting that grammars have their own internal modules. Smith points to dissociations between the lexicon and the computational system. Christopher's talent for learning second languages "is restricted largely to mastery of the morphology and the lexicon, whilst his syntactic ability rapidly peaks and then stagnates [. . . A] reverse dissociation [is] found in the case of children with Spinal Muscular Atrophy, who seem to develop a proficient syntactic rule system but have correspondingly greater difficulty with lexical development (see 53)." Edwards & Bastiaanse (54) address this issue for some aphasic speakers, seeking to distinguish deficits in the computational system from deficits in the mental lexicon.

We also know that focal brain lesions can result in quite specific language impairments in the presence of normal cognitive abilities and vice versa (55). Friedmann & Grodzinsky (56) argue that agrammatic aphasics may be unable to compute certain abstract structural elements (functional categories), whereas Grodzinsky (7) identifies much of agrammatism with a disorder specifically impairing the computation of movement relations, localized in the classical Broca's area. Ingham (57) describes a young child in similar terms, arguing that she lacked one particular functional category.

This modular view runs contrary to a long tradition, often associated with Jean Piaget, which claims that language is dependent on prior cognitive capacities and is not autonomous and modular (58, 59). Such a claim is undermined by the kinds of dissociations that have been observed, however. Bellugi et al (60) have shown, for example, that Williams Syndrome children consistently fail to pass seriation and conservation tests but nonetheless use syntactic constructions whose acquisition is supposedly dependent on those cognitive capacities. Clahsen & Almazan (61) demonstrate that Williams Syndrome children have good control of the rule-governed aspects of syntax and word formation but are severely impaired in certain irregular, memory-based functions, whereas SLI children display an essentially symmetrical pattern of affected and spared abilities. More generally, language and other cognitive abilities dissociate in development just as they do in acquired pathology (62).

CONCLUSION

Recent theoretical developments have brought an explosive growth in what we know about human languages. Linguists can now formulate interesting hypotheses and account for broad ranges of facts in many languages with elegant abstract principles. They understand certain aspects of language acquisition in young children and can model some aspects of speech comprehension.

Work on human grammars has paralleled work on the visual system and has reached similar conclusions, particularly with regard to the existence of highly specific computational mechanisms. In fact, language and vision are the areas of cognition about which most is known. Much remains to be done, but we can show how children attain certain elements of their language organs by exposure to only an unorganized and haphazard set of simple utterances; for these elements we have a theory that meets basic requirements. Eventually, the growth of language in a child will be viewed as similar to the growth of hair: Just as hair emerges with a certain level of light, air, and protein, so, too, a biologically regulated language organ necessarily emerges under exposure to a random speech community.

From the perspective sketched here, our focus is on grammars, not on the properties of a particular language or even of general properties of many or all languages. A language (in the sense of a collection of things people within a given speech community can say and understand) is on this view an epiphenomenon, a derivative concept, the output of certain people's grammars (perhaps modified by other mental processes). A grammar is of clearer status: the finite system that characterizes an individual's linguistic capacity and that is represented in the individual's mind/brain. No doubt the grammars of two individuals whom we regard as speakers of the same language will have much in common, but there is no reason to worry about defining much in common or about specifying precise conditions under which the outputs of two grammars could be said to constitute one language. Just as it is unimportant for most work in molecular biology whether two creatures are members of the same species [as emphasized, for example by Monod (63, Chpt. 2) and by Dawkins (64)], so too the notion of a language is not likely to have much importance if our biological perspective is taken and if we explore individual language organs, as in the research program we have sketched here.

Visit the Annual Reviews home page at www.AnnualReviews.org.

LITERATURE CITED

1. Chomsky N. 1975. *Reflections on Language*. New York: Pantheon
2. Ross JR. 1967. On the cyclic nature of English pronominalization. In *To Honor Roman Jakobson*. The Hague: Mouton
3. Langacker RW. 1969. Pronominalization and the chain of command. In *Modern Studies in English*, ed. D Reibel, S Schane. Englewood Cliffs, NY: Prentice-Hall
4. Reinhart T. 1976. *The Syntactic Domain of Anaphora*. PhD thesis. Massachusetts Institute of Technology
5. McCawley JD. 1999. Why surface syntactic structure reflects logical structure as much as it does, but only that much. *Language* 75:34–62
6. Dobzhansky T. 1970. *Genetics of the Evolutionary Process*. New York: Columbia Univ. Press
7. Grodzinsky Y. 2000. The neurology of syntax: language use without Broca's area. *Behav. Brain Sci.* 23(1): In press

8. Lightfoot DW. 1999. *The Development of Language: Acquisition, Change and Evolution.* Oxford, UK: Blackwell

9. Bates EA, Elman JL. 1996. Learning rediscovered. *Science* 274:1849–50

10. Hubel D, Wiesel T. 1962. Receptive fields, binocular interaction and functional architecture in the cat's visual cortex. *J. Physiol.* 160:106–54

11. Sperry R. 1968. Plasticity of neural maturation. *Dev. Biol. Suppl.* 2:306–27

12. Piattelli-Palmarini M. 1986. The rise of selective theories: a case study and some lessons from immunology. In *Language Learning and Concept Acquisition: Foundational Issues,* ed. W Demopoulos, A Marras. Norwood, NJ: Ablex

13. Piattelli-Palmarini M. 1989. Evolution, selection, and cognition: from "learning" to parameter setting in biology and the study of language. *Cognition* 31:1–44

14. Hubel D. 1978. Vision and the brain. *Bull. Am. Acad. Arts Sci.* 31 (7):28

15. Crain S. 1991. Language acquisition in the absence of experience. *Behav. Brain Sci.* 14:597–612

16. Crain S, Thornton R. 1998. *Investigations in Universal Grammar: A Guide to Experiments on the Acquisition of Syntax and Semantics.* Cambridge, MA: MIT Press

17. Gardner RA, Gardner BT. 1969. Teaching sign language to a chimpanzee. *Science* 165:664–72

18. Perlmutter DM. 1991. The language of the deaf. *NY Rev. Books* March 28, 1991:65–72

19. Klima ES, Bellugi U. 1979. *The Signs of Language.* Cambridge, MA: Harvard Univ. Press

20. Terrace HS, Pettito LA, Sanders RJ, Bever TG. 1979. Can an ape create a sentence? *Science* 206:891–902

21. Petitto LA, Seidenberg M. 1979. On the evidence for linguistic abilities in signing apes. *Brain Lang.* 8:162–83

22. Wallman J. 1992. *Aping Language.* Cambridge, UK: Cambridge Univ. Press

23. Savage-Rumbaugh ES, Murphy J, Sevcick RA, Brakke KE, Williams SL, Rumbaugh DL. 1993. Language comprehension in ape and child. *Monog. Soc. Res. Child Dev.* 58:1–221

24. Premack D. 1980. Representational capacity and accessibility of knowledge: the case of chimpanzees. In *Language Learning: The Debate Between Jean Piaget and Noam Chomsky,* ed. M Piattelli-Palmarini, pp. 203–30. London: Routledge & Kegan Paul

25. Premack D. 1990. Words: What are they, and do animals have them? *Cognition* 37.3:197–212

26. Premack D, Woodruff G. 1978. Chimpanzee problem-solving: a test for comprehension. *Science* 202:532–35

27. Savage-Rumbaugh ES. 1986. *Ape Language: From Conditioned Response to Symbol.* New York: Columbia Univ. Press

28. Savage-Rumbaugh ES, McDonald K, Sevcick RA, Hopkins WD, Rupert E. 1986. Spontaneous symbol acquisition and communicative use by pygmy chimpanzees (*Pan paniscus*). *J. Exp. Psych.: Gen.* 115:211–35

29. Seidenberg M, Petitto LA. 1986. Communication, symbolic communication, and language: comment on Savage-Rumbaugh et al. (1987). *J. Exp. Psych.: Gen.* 116:279–87

30. Savage-Rumbaugh ES. 1987. Communication, symbolic communication, and language: reply to Seidenberg & Petitto. *J. Exp. Psych.: Gen.* 116:288–92

31. Pepperberg IM. 1999. *In Search of King Solomon's Ring: Studies to Determine the Communicative and Cognitive Capacities of Grey Parrots.* Cambridge, MA: Harvard Univ. Press

32. Marler P. 1970. Birdsong and human speech: Could there be parallels? *Am. Sci.* 58:669–74

33. Marler P. 1991. Song-learning behavior: the interface with neuroethology. *Trends Neurosci.* 14:199–206

34. Newport EL. 1999. Reduced input in the acquisition of signed languages: contributions to the study of creolization. In *Language Creation and Change: Creolization, Diachrony and Development*, ed. M DeGraff. Cambridge, MA: MIT Press

35. Supalla S. 1990. *Segmentation of manually coded English: problems in the mapping of English in the visual/gestural mode.* PhD thesis. Univ. Ill.

36. Anderson SR. 1993. Linguistic expression and its relation to modality. In *Phonetics and Phonology 3: Current Issues in ASL Phonology,* ed. GR Coulter. San Diego: Academic

37. Bickerton D. 1999. How to acquire language without positive evidence: what acquisitionists can learn from creoles. In *Language Creation and Change: Creolization, Diachrony and Development*, ed. M DeGraff. Cambridge, MA: MIT Press

38. Lefebvre C. 1998. *Creole Genesis and the Acquisition of Grammar.* Cambridge, UK: Cambridge Univ. Press

39. Mayeux R, Kandel ER. 1991. Disorders of language: the aphasias. In *Principles of Neural Science,* ed. ER Kandel, JH Schwartz, TM Jessel, pp. 839–51. New York: Elsevier

40. Kosslyn SM, Gazzaniga MS, Galaburda AM, Rabin C. 1999. Hemispheric specialization. In *Fundamental Neuroscience*, ed. MJ Zigmond, FE Bloom, SC Landis, JL Roberts, LR Squire. San Diego: Academic

41. Smith NV. 1999. Dissociation and modularity. In *Mind, Brain and Language: Multidisciplinary Perspectives*, ed. MT Banich, M Mack. Hillsdale, NJ: Erlbaum

42. Smith NV, Tsimpli IM. 1995. *The Mind of a Savant: Language-Learning and Modularity.* Oxford, UK: Blackwell

43. Joanisse M, Seidenberg M. 1998. Specific language impairment: a deficit in grammar or processing? *Trends Cognitive Sci.* 2:240–47

44. Bishop DVM. 1997. *Uncommon Understanding: Development and Disorders of Language Comprehension in Children.* London: Psychology

45. Tomblin JB. 1997. Epidemiology of specific language impairment. In *The Inheritance and Innateness of Grammars,* ed. M Gopnick. New York: Oxford Univ. Press

46. Gopnik M. 1990. Feature blindness: a case study. *Lang. Acquisition* 1(2):139–64

47. Gopnik M, Crago M. 1991. Familial aggregation of a developmental language disorder. *Cognition* 39:1–50

48. Clahsen H, Bartke S, Gollner S. 1997. Formal features in impaired grammars: a comparison of English and German SLI children. *Essex Res. Rept. in Linguist.* 14:42–75

49. Gopnik M. 1997. Language deficits and genetic factors. *Trends Cogn. Sci.* 1:5–9

50. van der Lely HKJ. 1996. Specifically language impaired and normally developing children: verbal passive vs. adjectival passive sentence interpretation. *Lingua* 98:243–72

51. Levy Y, Kaye J. 1999. Language breakdown and linguistic theory: a tutorial overview. *Lingua* 107:95–113

52. Frith U. 1991. *Autism and Asperger Syndrome.* Cambridge, UK: Cambridge Univ. Press

53. Sieratzki J, Woll B. 1999. Toddling into language: precocious language development in motor-impaired children with Spinal Muscular Atrophy. *Cognition.* In press

54. Edwards S, Bastiaanse R. 1998. Diversity in the lexical and syntactic abilities of fluent aphasic speakers. *Aphasiology* 12.2:99–117

55. Caplan D. 1987. *Neurolinguistics and Linguistic Aphasiology.* Cambridge, UK: Cambridge Univ. Press

56. Friedmann N, Grodzinsky Y. 1997. Tense and agreement in agrammatic produc-

tion: pruning the syntactic tree. *Brain Lang.* 56:397–425

57. Ingham R. 1998. Tense without agreement in early clause structure. *Lang. Acquisition* 7:51–81

58. Piaget J, Inhelder B. 1968. *The Psychology of the Child.* London: Routledge

59. Piattelli-Palmarini M, ed. 1980. *Language and Learning: The Debate Between Jean Piaget and Noam Chomsky.* London: Routledge & Kegan Paul

60. Bellugi U, Marks S, Bihrle A, Sabo H. 1993. Dissociation between language and cognitive functions in Williams Syndrome. In *Language Development in Exceptional Circumstances,* ed D Bishop, K Mogford. Hillsdale, NJ: Erlbaum

61. Clahsen H, Almazan M. 1998. Syntax and morphology in Williams Syndrome. *Cognition* 68:167–98

62. Curtiss S. 1988. Abnormal language acquisition and the modularity of language. In *Linguistics: The Cambridge Survey,* Vol. II, ed. FJ Newmeyer. Cambridge, UK: Cambridge Univ. Press

63. Monod J. 1972 *Chance and Necessity.* London: Collins

64. Dawkins R. 1976. *The Selfish Gene.* Oxford, UK: Oxford Univ. Press

Annu. Rev. Physiol. 2000. 62:723–53

NEURAL ADAPTATION IN THE GENERATION OF RHYTHMIC BEHAVIOR

K. G. Pearson

Department of Physiology, University of Alberta, Edmonton, Canada T6G 2H7;
e-mail: keir.pearson@ualberta.ca

Key Words   motor pattern generation, walking, motor learning, neuronal plasticity, neuromodulation

■ **Abstract**   Motor systems can adapt rapidly to changes in external conditions and to switching of internal goals. They can also adapt slowly in response to training, alterations in the mechanics of the system, and any changes in the system resulting from injury. This article reviews the mechanisms underlying short- and long-term adaptation in rhythmic motor systems. The neuronal networks underlying the generation of rhythmic motor patterns (central pattern generators; CPGs) are extremely flexible. Neuromodulators, central commands, and afferent signals all influence the pattern produced by a CPG by altering the cellular and synaptic properties of individual neurons and the coupling between different populations of neurons. This flexibility allows the generation of a variety of motor patterns appropriate for the mechanical requirements of different forms of a behavior. The matching of motor output to mechanical requirements depends on the capacity of pattern-generating networks to adapt to slow changes in body mechanics and persistent errors in performance. Afferent feedback from body and limb proprioceptors likely plays an important role in driving these long-term adaptive processes.

INTRODUCTION

An obvious feature of animal movement is its enormous flexibility. Movements adapt quickly to changes in the environment, and similar goals can be achieved by many different strategies. New movements can be learned, whereas established movements can be refined by training and adapt to changes in body mechanics. Finally, purposeful movements can often be reestablished after injury of the nervous system. This flexibility depends on two processes. The first is the ability of the nervous system to precisely regulate complex patterns of activity in numerous muscles according to the demands of the task and the mechanics of the motor system. The second is a capacity of pattern-generating networks to adapt slowly in response to persistent changes in use, modifications of elements within the system, and maintained alterations in external conditions.

0066–4278/00/0315–0723$12.00

In general we have only a rudimentary understanding of the neuronal mechanisms for motor pattern generation, and even less knowledge about the cellular and synaptic processes producing short- and long-term adaptations of motor patterns. Reaching for an object is a good example. We know that this task requires activation of muscles throughout the arm and that the pattern of activation of the muscles depends on the speed and direction of movement, the initial position of the arm, and the mechanical properties of the arm (1–4). In monkeys the activity of neurons in the central nervous system has been correlated with many of these parameters (5–7). However, knowledge of the activity patterns in central neurons and patterns of electrical activity in muscles has not yet led to a clear understanding of the mechanisms coordinating the activation of different arm muscles to produce the appropriate motor pattern for a specific reaching movement (8). Knowledge of these mechanisms is a prerequisite for understanding the cellular and synaptic processes involved in the adaptive modification and learning of reaching movements (9–11)

Greater gains have been made in investigations of rhythmic motor systems, particularly in lower vertebrates and invertebrates. In many systems in these animals it has been possible to establish details of neuronal circuits responsible for generating rhythmic motor patterns (12–14). Knowledge of the connectivity and the cellular and synaptic properties of neurons in rhythm-generating networks has provided insight into mechanisms for modifying the functioning of these systems for different tasks (15–17). We also know that many rhythmic motor systems adapt in response to training, changes in body mechanics, alterations in external conditions, and injury of the nervous system. Thus the neuronal analysis of rhythmic behaviors holds considerable promise for gaining an understanding of the mechanisms for long-term adaptive plasticity in motor systems.

The purpose of this article is to review our current understanding of adaptive processes in rhythmic motor systems. Rapid, task-dependent modification of pattern-generating networks is referred to as short-term adaptation. Slower, more persistent changes occurring as a result of training, chronic alterations in sensory input, and injury are referred to as long-term adaptation. No attempt has been made to exhaustively describe all examples of short- and long-term adaptation, although references to a wide range of studies are listed in tables contained herein. The review focuses on key contemporary issues, with examples drawn mainly from walking systems of vertebrates.

SHORT-TERM ADAPTATION OF RHYTHMIC MOTOR PATTERNS

In the analysis of short-term adaptation of rhythmic motor systems, a distinction has been made between modifications that are limited to a single cycle and those that persist over many cycles. The former includes immediate alterations of the motor pattern in response to a sensory stimulus and is often termed phase-dependent modulation because the response varies depending on the time of stimulus occurrence in the rhythmic cycle. Phase-dependent modulation of pattern generating networks by visual, cutaneous, and proprioceptive signals has been reviewed extensively over the past five years (18–23) and therefore is not considered in this article. Instead we focus on alterations in rhythmic motor patterns that persist for many cycles in response to changes in either external conditions or internal goals. This type of alternation is sometimes referred to as state-dependent modulation.

Numerous studies have now documented short-term (state-dependent) adaptation of rhythmic behaviors (Table 1). The common feature of all these studies is a description of modifications in the rhythmic motor pattern when the behavior, or the form of the behavior, is altered. The behavior receiving considerable attention in recent years has been walking. Modifications of the rhythmic patterns of activity associated with different forms of walking have been described in mammals (humans and cats), birds, amphibians, and arthropods. Because the recent investigations on walking in vertebrates have provided excellent examples of the short-term adaptation of rhythmic motor patterns and raised important conceptual issues regarding the organization and functioning of pattern generating networks, the following discussion concentrates mainly on these studies. Short-term adaptation of respiration and other rhythmic behaviors has been reviewed elsewhere (15, 16, 63, 64).

Short-Term Adaptation of Vertebrate Walking

It seems obvious that the degree of similarity of motor patterns for two walking tasks would depend on the similarity of the two tasks. Indeed in cats, increasing the speed of walking or walking with a crouched posture produces alterations in the magnitude of activity in certain muscles but only relatively minor changes in the overall temporal pattern of activity (29, 33). A transition from trotting to galloping produces further modifications in burst amplitudes and the elimination of a burst activity in at least one muscle, semitendinosus (34). The basic pattern of alternation in the activity of muscles producing flexion and extension movements at the hip, knee, and ankle is maintained (31, 32). However, this reciprocal pattern in flexor and extensor muscles is not fully preserved when the animals walk up and down steep slopes. The loss of the reciprocity is seen most clearly for the hip and knee flexor muscles. On a flat surface, the hip flexor, iliopsoas, becomes active just before the onset of swing and remains active throughout the first half of the swing phase. On steep downhill slopes, however, it is strongly active during most of the stance phase and less active during swing (32). Similarly, the knee flexor semitendinosus, which is only active briefly before the onset of swing and onset of stance during walking on a horizontal surface, becomes co-active with extensors during most of the stance phase when an animal walks up a steep slope (31). Other major changes in the motor pattern compared with

TABLE 1   Task-dependent modification of rhythmic motor programs

Behavior	Animal	Tasks	References
Walking	Human	Forward/backward	24, 25
	Cat	Forward/backward	26–28
	Cat	Upright/crouching	29
	Cat	Upslope/downslope	30–32
	Cat	Slow/fast	33, 34
	Cat	Walking/paw-shake	35
	Rat	Walking/swimming	36
	Chick	Walking/swimming	37
	Salamander	Forward/backward	38
	Crayfish	Forward/backward	39
	Cockroach	Upright/inverted	40
	Locust	Upright/vertical/inverted	41
	Stick insect	Forward/backward	42
Scratching	Cat	Gentle/strong	43
	Turtle	Rostral/pocket/caudal	44
Swimming	Lamprey	Forward/backward	45
	Tadpole	Swimming/struggling	46, 47
	Crayfish	Forward/backward	48
	Tritonia	Swimming/withdrawal	49
Feeding	Rabbit	Soft food/hard food	50
	Lobster	Hungry/satiated	51
	Aplysia	Ingestion/rejection	52
	Helisoma	Ingestion/rejection	53
	Pleurobranchia	Ingestion/regurgitation	54
Respiration	Human/cat	Wakefulness/Sleep	55
	Monkey	Breathing/vocalization/swallowing	56
	Cat	Breathing/coughing/vomiting	57, 58
	Crab	Forward/reverse	59, 60
Flight	Locust	Straight/turning	61, 62

walking on a horizontal surface are the loss of activity in hip extensors during walking down a slope, large increases in amplitude and duration of activity in the knee flexor semitendinosus during upslope and downslope walking, and large increases in the magnitude of hip, knee, and ankle extensors during upslope walking.

Substantial differences in motor patterns have also been found during forward and backward walking in cats (26–28), humans (24), and salamanders (38). In cats, there are large differences in the timing and magnitude of burst activity in many muscles of the hind legs, particularly in bifunctional muscles (ST, RF, and SMa in Figure 1). However, the basic alternating pattern between flexors and extensors is generally maintained. Analysis of the activity in 15 hind leg muscles has revealed that only two muscles, extensor digitoris brevis and flexor digitorum longus, switch from one synergy to the other [a synergy being defined as the set of muscles active simultaneously during one phase of the step cycle (28)]. Both muscles are primarily active in association with flexors during forward walking, but become mainly active with extensors during backward walking. Even larger differences have been noted in the motor patterns during forward and backward walking in humans and salamanders. There is little resemblance between the electromyogram (EMG) waveforms during forward and backward walking in humans, and cross-correlation analysis has revealed that the pattern of muscle synergies differs drastically (24). In the salamander there is also a large difference in the pattern of muscle synergies and in the amplitude and envelope of activity of individual muscles during forward and backward walking (38). For example, all muscles studied are co-active during the swing phase of backward walking, but during forward walking there is never a period when all the muscles are active simultaneously.

The flexibility of spinal pattern-generating networks has also been revealed by comparisons of the motor pattern for walking with those associated with a variety of other rhythmic leg movements. A good example is a recent study of walking, air-stepping, and swimming in chicks (37). Each behavior is associated with a distinctly different motor pattern in six major muscles of each leg. However, with one exception, muscles that are recruited together in walking are also recruited together in swimming and air-stepping. Thus the main differences in the motor patterns for these three behaviors are changes in the timing and duration of activity within either a flexor or an extensor synergy. The one exceptional muscle, femorotibialis, is active twice per cycle during walking. The first burst is absent during air-stepping, and the second burst shifts from the flexor synergy in walking to straddle the flexor and extensor synergies in air-stepping and swimming. Thus no muscle switches completely from the flexor to extensor synergy or vice versa. A clear example of a complete switch in muscle activity from one synergy to another is during paw-shaking in the cat (35). During this behavior the knee extensor muscle, vastus lateralis, is co-activated with hip and ankle flexors, whereas during walking it is an element of the extensor synergy.

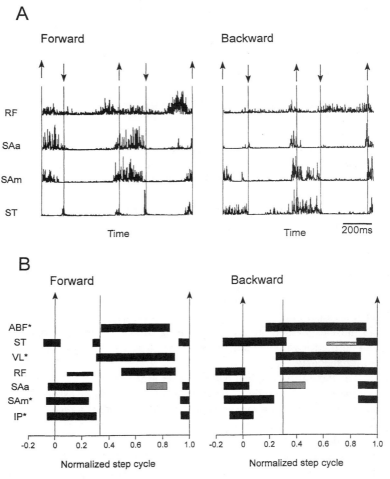

Figure 1 Short-term adaptation of the motor pattern for forward and backward walking in the cat. (A) Rectified and filtered electromyograms (EMGs) from bifunctional thigh muscles during forward (*left*) and backward (*right*) walking. (B) Summary of average time of EMG activity in hindleg muscles during forward (*left*) and backward (*right*) walking. Asterisks (*) indicate unifunctional muscles, and shaded bars indicate bursts that do not occur on every cycle. Note the greater difference in the timing of activity in the bifunctional muscles. Abbreviations: RF, rectus femoris; SAm, medial sartorius; SAa, anterior sartorius; ST, semiteninosus; ABF, anterior biceps femoris; VL, vastus lateralis; IP, iliopsoas (modified from 27).

Mechanisms of Short-Term Adaptation of Vertebrate Walking

How are neuronal networks reorganized to generate the different motor patterns associated with the different forms of walking? One extreme possibility is that the motor pattern for each form is produced by a different neuronal network. However, this seems unlikely since, with the possible exception of forward and backward swimmeret movements in the crayfish (48), there is no clear example of this in other motor systems (16, 65). It is much more likely that the different motor patterns are generated by the same interneuronal system, although not every element in this system needs to be active during all forms of the task. An influential idea has been that the central pattern-generating networks (CPGs) for walking consist of a set of unit burst generators, with each burst generator being responsible for activating muscles controlling movement in one direction at a joint [66; see review by Stein & Smith (67) for detailed discussion of this and related concepts]. In his original proposal, Grillner (66) suggested that alterations in the sign of coupling (excitation or inhibition) between unit burst generators could be the basis for the production of different motor patterns associated with different forms of walking.

The evidence that the CPGs for walking in vertebrates can be reduced to a small number of functional units, each regulating a movement in one direction at a single joint, is not compelling. Nevertheless, some observations are consistent with this view. In decerebrate and spinal cats (i.e. spinal cord transected at the thoracic level), rhythmic bursts can occur in ankle flexors in the absence of bursts in ankle extensors and vice versa (68, 69). My colleagues and I have also occasionally observed rhythmic bursting in hip flexors during periods of maintained tonic activity in ankle extensors (KG Pearson et al, unpublished observations). A recent study in the mudpuppy has found that bursts in elbow flexors can occur in the absence of bursts in elbow extensors and vice versa, and described a method for physically isolating the neuronal systems generating the flexor and the extensor bursts (70). However, whether bursts in elbow motoneurons can occur independently of bursts in motoneurons controlling movements at the shoulder and wrist has not been established. The notion that spinal CPGs can be decomposed into unit burst generators also receives support from investigations on scratching in the turtle (71–73). In this system, a hip flexor rhythm can be generated in the absence of hip extensor activity without the loss of the knee extensor rhythm. Furthermore, separate sites for the generation of the hip flexor and hip extensor bursts have been identified by transections of the spinal cord at different levels. From all these observations it is reasonable to conclude that the CPGs for walking consist of a set of interacting unit burst generations even though these units have not yet been fully defined.

An admirable application of the unit burst generator concept has been to explain the modifications in the basic muscle synergies when cats walk up and down slopes (32). For example, during downslope walking the generation of bursts of activity in the hip flexor, iliopsoas, during the stance phase is explained by the opening of an excitatory pathway from the knee extensor burst generator to the hip flexor burst generator. A switch in the influence from the knee extensor burst generator from excitatory to inhibitory explains the loss of activity in the hip extensors in this situation. During upslope walking, the double bursting of the biarticular muscle, semitendinosus, is explained by excitatory connections to the knee flexor burst generator from the hip flexor, knee extensor, and ankle flexor generators. These three burst generators are considered to inhibit the knee flexor generator during walking on a horizontal surface.

Although these postulated alterations in the coupling between burst generators easily account for the modification in synergies between upslope and downslope walking, they fail to explain large changes in the intensity profile of the bursts that occur in most muscles throughout the hind legs. Nor do they account for the numerous shifts in the timing of the onset and termination of burst activity. These alterations are much more apparent than modifications in synergies. The concept of flexible coupling between unit burst generators has also been unable to readily account for most of the modifications in the motor patterns during forward and backward walking in cats, humans, and salamanders (24, 28, 38) and for the different patterns of activity associated with walking, air-stepping, and swimming in chicks (37). Thus altering patterns of muscle synergies by changing the coupling between a small number of burst generators does not appear to be the primary mechanism responsible for enabling the high degree of flexibility in the stepping of single limbs. This conclusion cannot be generalized to all rhythmic movements of the legs of vertebrates. The different forms of scratching in the turtle, and the differences in the motor patterns for walking and paw-shaking in the cat, do appear to depend primarily on the ability of some muscles to switch from one synergy to another.

The complexity of the differences in motor patterns within each of the basic synergies for the different forms of walking suggests that the flexibility in motor pattern generation depends to a large extent on an ability to independently regulate the activity of individual muscles. Independence is indicated by the fact that the activity in some muscles can increase while the activity in synergists either remains unchanged or decreases. Moreover, changes in the timing of burst activity (duration and the time of burst onset and termination) in synergists are often unrelated. Macpherson (74) has thoughtfully discussed the notion that the flexibility of motor behavior depends on specific regulation of individual muscles for the systems producing voluntary limb movements and postural adjustments. In general, it has proven difficult to identify fixed synergies regulating these movements, and those that have been defined probably depend on experimental constraints.

Thus an important question in the analysis of walking in vertebrates is what mechanisms are utilized to control the timing and intensity of activity in individual muscles? One mechanism in walking systems could be to modify descending command signals to individual pools of motoneurons from supraspinal regions.

However, if this were the mechanism for controlling activity in each group of motoneurons it would not provide a satisfactory solution because the commands themselves would have to be specifically regulated. A more likely possibility is that descending commands establish the level of activity in the CPGs and set the properties of neurons and the strengths of neuronal connections to produce the synergies appropriate for the general form of the behavior. The detailed structure of the activity patterns in individual groups of motoneurons is then established by the pattern of afferent input from the body and limbs. This general mechanism was suggested by Grillner (66) to underlie the changes in motor output associated with turning and changes in speed. Results from recent investigations on the afferent regulation of extensor activity during stance in walking cats are generally consistent with this notion (75–78). Furthermore, the constructive role of afferent feedback in the generation and patterning of rhythmic motor activity has now been demonstrated in a number of other rhythmic motor systems (37; reviewed in 21 and 65).

For afferent signals to regulate the level of activity in individual muscles, or a group of close synergists, there must be specificity in the organization of afferent pathways, and some of these pathways must bypass the spinal CPGs. Indeed, many studies have shown this to be the case. First, the monosynaptic pathways from group Ia afferents to limb motoneurons bypass the spinal CPGs (there is no evidence that motoneurons are elements in CPGs in vertebrate walking systems). Second, the group Ia pathways from each muscle are organized to control activity in the homonymous muscle and closely related muscles (79, 80). Third, stimulation of group I afferents from ankle and hip extensor muscles during fictive locomotion in decerebrate cats produced significantly different responses in ankle motoneurons (81). Finally, cutaneous afferents from different regions of the leg have highly specific effects on the activity of different groups of motoneurons during fictive locomotion (23, 82, 83).

Despite the fact that we do not have a detailed understanding of how signals from sensory afferents and from supraspinal structures modify the CPGs for stepping in vertebrates, it is possible to speculate with some confidence about the cellular and synaptic processes that might be involved. Information on this point is drawn from the large number of studies of pattern-generating networks in lower vertebrates and invertebrates. Because the connectivity and the cellular and synaptic properties of the neurons in these systems have been well defined, the mechanisms responsible for their modification can be examined in detail (15–17, 47, 84). These mechanisms include recruitment and de-recruitment of neurons into and out of neuronal circuits (16), differential regulation of transmission along parallel antagonistic pathways connecting two groups of neurons (85, 86), and the modification of synaptic and cellular properties by neuromodulators (17). The extent to which neuromodulators acting via second messenger systems are involved in modifying motor pattern generation in the walking systems of vertebrates is an open question. The rapidity and short durations of some of these modifications, such as those occurring when a cat walks up a steep slope for a few steps, suggests that these modifications depend on the conventional action of fast-acting neurotransmitters. However, this is not necessarily always the case since neuromodulators in some systems can have very rapid actions (87). In addition, marked changes in locomotor patterns following the administration of serotonergic and noradrenergic drugs in chronic spinal cats (88–90) indicate that descending aminergic pathways may be involved in modifying the pattern of motor activity in some situations. Neuromodulators, such as serotonin, may also regulate the activity of motoneurons by controlling inward calcium movement that underlies the generation of plateau potentials (91–93).

An important fact to emerge from recent investigations on the organization of interneuronal inputs to motoneurons is that the action of many pre-motor interneurons is not always appropriate for state of activation of the motoneurons. For instance, excitatory input from some interneurons can be accompanied by a simultaneous increase in input from inhibitory interneurons and/or a decrease in excitation from other excitatory interneurons (85, 86, 94–99). A functional consequence of this type of organization is that a common input to the different groups of pre-motor interneurons can produce a variety of effects in motoneurons depending on the excitability of each group of interneurons, even to the extent of reversing the motoneuronal response (95, 96). Differential regulation of transmission in parallel excitatory and inhibitory pathways from flexor and extensor half-centers of the spinal CPG to motoneurons has been postulated to be responsible for cutaneous modulation of fictive locomotor patterns in the cat (100). The adjustment of respiratory drive to phrenic motoneurons for different behaviors such as coughing, vocalization, and defecation may also depend on the differential regulation of simultaneous excitatory and inhibitory synaptic inputs (99). Finally, broadly distributed sensory inputs acting via parallel, antagonistic interneuronal pathways have been proposed as the mechanism for the production of different motor patterns for different forms of scratching in the turtle (101).

Summary

Rapid changes in behavior depend on the ability of the nervous system to quickly modify the functioning of the neuronal networks generating the pattern of activity in numerous muscles. The general form of a rhythmic behavior is established by the characteristics of central inputs to local CPGs. Each form is associated with a characteristic temporal sequence of muscle activation and intensity profile of muscle activity. Specific details of the timing and magnitude of activity in individual muscles depend to some extent on afferent feedback from peripheral receptors. Recruitment and de-recruitment of neurons into and out of pre-motoneuronal networks, differential regulation of transmission via parallel antagonistic pathways, and modification of cellular and synaptic properties of interneurons and motoneurons by neuromodulators are some of the mechanisms underlying short-term adaptive changes.

LONG-TERM ADAPTATION OF RHYTHMIC MOTOR PATTERNS

Because some rhythmic movements are essential for survival, respiratory and locomotor movements being the most obvious, there must be mechanisms to ensure that they develop normally and function optimally for a lifetime. Over a lifetime there are substantial changes to body, limbs, and muscles and presumably to the neuronal elements responsible for the production of the rhythmic motor patterns. Since any change in the mechanical and/or neuronal properties of the system has the potential for modifying the behavior, a priori we must expect the existence of mechanisms for compensating for progressive changes in any element of the system. Furthermore, mechanisms must exist for refining the functioning of rhythmic motor systems with training, e.g. learning to walk, and for learning a new rhythmic behavior, e.g. learning to skate. Rhythmic and other motor systems also have the capacity for some functional recovery following damage to the central nervous system, and in some instances recovery can be enhanced by training (102–104). An interesting issue, therefore, is whether the mechanisms underlying functional recovery are related to those that are involved in the day-to-day maintenance of the system.

This section reviews some instances of long-term adaptation in rhythmic motor systems and considers the mechanisms that may underlie this plasticity. As in the previous section, the discussion focuses mainly on long-term adaptation in the walking systems of vertebrates.

Adaptation in Response to Training and Altered External Conditions

Long-term adaptation of rhythmic behavior in response to training and altered conditions has been described in numerous animals, with the majority of investigations limited to the behaviors of walking and respiration (Table 2). Good examples come from recent studies on walking in humans. The ability of very young infants to step regularly on a moving treadmill can be facilitated by daily training (110, 111), and after-effects lasting for up to an hour are produced in normal adults following a period of walking on circular and split treadmills (105, 106, 108). The after-effects of walking on treadmills are most likely due to persistent alteration in feedback from leg proprioceptors since the adaptive changes are specifically related to the characteristics of the leg movements and not to more global variables such as altered visual and vestibular input. The walking system of humans is also modified by weightlessness during prolonged space flight and full recovery takes up to a week following the return to earth (109).

Fewer studies have been done on animal walking, but one notable recent observation is that stepping movements in chronic decerebrate cats adapt slowly to persistent changes in the speeds of different treadmills supporting different limbs (113). Modification in cerebellar function has been implicated in this adaptive

TABLE 2 Long-term adaptation of rhythmic motor systems with training and altered external conditions

Behavior	Animal	Condition	References
Walking	Human	Circular treadmill	105, 106
	Human	Split treadmill	107, 108
	Human	Post-spaceflight	109
	Human infant	Training on treadmill	110, 111
	Cat	Operant conditioning on treadmill	112
	Cat (decerebrate)	Split treadmill	113, 114
Respiration	Human	Exercise conditioning	115, 116
	Goat	Exercise conditioning	117
	Goat/rat/dog/cat	Repeated hypoxia	118–121
	Aplysia	Conditioning to sea water concentration	122
	Aplysia	Conditioning to pH	123
	Lymnaea	Conditioning to touch	124
Feeding	Aplysia	Operant conditioning	125–128

change because adaptation is abolished by the injection of drugs into the cerebellum that block the production of nitric oxide (114). Nitric oxide is involved in the long-term depression in the parallel fiber-Purkinje cell connection in the cerebellum, and long-term depression in the cerebellum is considered to be an important mechanism for long-term adaptive plasticity in vertebrate motor systems (129, 130).

A general issue arising from recent work on long-term adaptation of rhythmic motor systems is whether the adaptive changes involve modification of neuronal elements in CPGs. An alternative may be changes in the command and/or modulatory inputs to CPGs. A recent approach to address this issue has been to examine the changes produced by operant conditioning of rhythmic behaviors in invertebrates (124–128). The relative simplicity of these systems allows the examination of elements within the CPG following conditioning. One mode of respiration in the pond-dwelling snail, Lymnaea, is swimming to the surface of water and rhythmically breathing air for short bouts (aerial respiration). The respiratory rate of breathing can be reduced by a tactile stimulus delivered to the open pulmonary orifice as the animal attempts to breath (131). Comparison of the cellular and synaptic properties of neurons in the respiratory CPG has shown that some properties are altered by the operant conditioning (124). These include a reduced frequency of spontaneous tonic activity in one neuron in the CPG and a reduction in the strength of excitatory coupling between some pairs of neurons in the CPG.

These changes are appropriate for the reduction in breathing rate in conditioned animals. It is interesting that these changes are not identical in all animals, suggesting that individual animals may use different neuronal pathways to modify their behavior.

Long-term changes in elements of a CPG have also been found following in vitro operant conditioning of the feeding system of *Aplysia* (126–128). In the isolated feeding system the probability of an ingestion-like pattern occurring spontaneously can be increased by stimulating a sensory nerve from the esophagus (this stimulus is equivalent to a reward) contingent with the occurrence of the pattern. This increase in the probability is not accompanied by changes in the probability of occurrence of a second, rejection-like pattern. The selectivity of the conditioned response implies that the conditioned changes in the neuronal circuits do not occur in shared elements. Indeed, recent studies have demonstrated that operant conditioning of the ingestion pattern increases the excitability of a neuron (B51) in the ingestion pattern-generating network by decreasing the threshold for the induction of plateau potentials (127). Neuron B51 has no significant role in the generation of the rejection-like pattern. The properties of neurons shared by both pattern-generating networks appear to be unaffected by the conditioning procedure.

Adaptation in Response to Altered Sensory Feedback and Muscle Denervation

In walking systems, as well as many other rhythmic motor systems, phasic sensory feedback has an important role in establishing features of the motor pattern (65). One function is to detect critical events in the movement sequence and to use this information to initiate subsequent events. For example, the transition from stance to swing during treadmill walking in decerebrate and spinal cats is initiated by sensory signals generated near the end of the stance phase (75, 77). Another function is to regulate ongoing motoneuronal activity according to concomitant mechanical events. Stance-phase activity in walking humans, cats, insects, and crustaceans is controlled to a large extent by feedback from leg proprioceptors (78, 132; reviewed in 65). Proprioceptors can also provide information about changes in movements due to persistent changes in external conditions and in the mechanical properties of the system, and this information can be used to adapt the motor output to compensate for the altered conditions/mechanics.

Numerous studies have demonstrated long-term adaptation of a rhythmic behavior following a sudden change in afferent signals (Table 3). In most cases these adaptations, which occur over periods of hours to days, are appropriate for reducing the deficit produced by the altered afferent signals. Direct evidence for plasticity in afferent systems regulating spinal pattern-generating networks has been obtained in recent investigations on the afferent control of stepping following denervation of hind leg muscles (137–139). Increasing the loading of an ankle extensor muscle, medial gastrocnemius (MG), by denervating synergist muscles

TABLE 3 Long-term adaptation of rhythmic motor systems with altered sensory feedback and muscle denervation

Behavior	Animal	Condition	References
Walking	Cat	Deafferentation	133–135
	Cat	Muscle dennervation	136–140
	Ferret	Cutaneous stimulation	141
Swimmimg	Chick	Cutaneous stimulation	142–143
Respiration	Cat	Carotid nerve stimulation	144
	Rat	Cervical dorsal rhizotomy	145
Flight	Locust	Partial deafferentation	146–148

(lateral gastrocnemius and soleus) results in an increase in the effectiveness of MG group I afferents in regulating the duration of extensor bursts. Normally, stimulation of these afferents during walking in decerebrate animals has only a weak effect on extensor burst duration. However, in animals in which the MG has been subjected to increased loading for three to seven days, stimulation of the MG group I afferents has a powerful effect on extensor burst duration, often maintaining extensor activity for the duration of long stimulus trains (137). This increase in effectiveness is appropriate for compensating for the loss of afferent feedback from the denervated synergists. The enhanced effectiveness of the group I afferents persists in some animals after transection of the spinal cord and the induction of stepping with L-DOPA (138). Thus at least one site for this plasticity is in the spinal cord, but exactly what changes occur in the spinal cord remain to be established. Enhanced transmission from group I afferents to spinal interneurons is a likely possibility, since monosynaptic field potentials evoked by stimulation of MG group I afferents in the intermediate regions of the spinal cord are increased in amplitude following chronic overuse of the MG muscle (149).

Chronic loading of the MG muscle also results in a progressive increase in the magnitude of the MG bursts (Figure 2) (139). This increase in the level of MG activity is associated with a progressive reduction in the exaggerated ankle flexion produced immediately following denervation of synergist muscles. The interesting feature of this adaptive response is a difference in the rate of increase in the initial and late components of the MG bursts (Figure 2C). The increase in the late component occurs relatively quickly and is most likely due to an increase in the gain of afferent pathways contributing to the generation of the MG bursts. The increase in the initial component of the MG bursts occurs more slowly. The initial component begins before ground contact and establishes the stiffness at the ankle

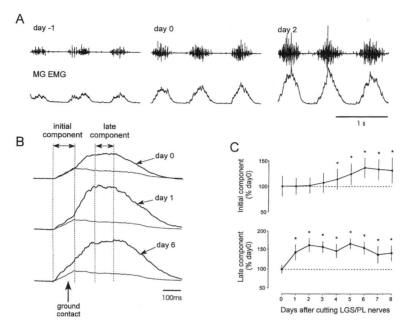

Figure 2   Long-term adaptation of activity in the medial gastrocnemius (MG) muscle of the cat following transection of the nerves innervating synergist muscles (lateral gastrocnemius, LG; soleus, SOL; and plantaris, PL). (*A*) EMGs in MG before (day −1), 5 hours after (day 0), and 2 days after (day 2) the nerve transections during walking at 0.6m/s. (*B*) Averages of rectified and filtered EMG bursts in MG 5 hours (day 0), 1 day (day 0), and 6 days (day 6) after cutting the LG and SOL (LGS) and PL nerves. The thin traces show the averaged EMG before the nerve transections. In the first few days the increase in the magnitude of MG bursts occurs mainly after ground contact (late component). By day 6 there is also a significant increase in the initial component (onset prior to ground contact). (*C*) Plots showing (for another animal) the different time course of the increase in the initial and late components of the MG EMGs following transection of the LGS and PL nerves. Error bars – standard deviations. Asterisks indicate significant increases compared to day 0 (modified from 139).

joint during the early part of stance. The increase in this component is primarily responsible for functional recovery. The mechanisms underlying the increase in the initial component of the MG bursts are unknown. One attractive possibility is that an error signal generated by increased feedback from the abnormally stretched MG muscle recalibrates the magnitude of a feedforward motor command generating the initial component (139). Consistent with this possibility is that the adaptive changes in the MG burst do not occur when normal sensory feedback is eliminated by immobilization of the leg. The notion that feedback signals act to recalibrate a central command is analogous to the scheme proposed by Kawato (150) for feedback-error learning in the acquisition of inverse models of the controlled elements in a motor system.

The complexity of adaptive processes in the walking system of the cat is well illustrated by the effects produced by chronic denervation of the ankle flexor muscles, tibialis anterior (TA) and extensor digitorum longus (EDL), in intact and chronic spinal cats (140). Within a few days of denervation, cats adapt their locomotor behavior so that stepping of the partially denervated hind leg returns close to normal. However, when these animals are spinalized and trained to step with their hind legs on a treadmill, the stepping movements of the denervated leg are disorganized and very different from the movements in trained spinal animals with normal innervation of hind leg muscles. The disorganized stepping movements persist for at least one month. If, however, the ankle flexors are denervated after spinalization and step training, the disorganized movements do not occur. These observations indicate that the adaptive processes in the intact animal involve a modification of spinal circuitry but not in a manner that allows this circuitry by itself to generate a normal stepping pattern. The maladaptive alterations in the spinal circuitry appear to be compensated by corrective supraspinal signals. Thus complete functional adaptation in this situation depends on changes occurring at spinal and supraspinal levels.

The issue of the relative importance of spinal versus supraspinal systems in mediating long-term adaptive responses in the walking system of the cat has also been addressed in investigations on functional recovery following dorsal root transections (133–135). The results of these studies provide evidence that the relative importance of spinal versus supraspinal systems in functional recovery depends on the type of modification used to induce adaptive changes. Unilateral transection of dorsal roots in adult cats results in an immediate abnormality of stepping in the ipsilateral hind leg. Subsequently, functional recovery of stepping occurs over a period of a few weeks. The characteristics of recovery following complete deafferentation differ from those following partial deafferentation (spared-root preparation with one root left intact) in a manner that suggests that animals adopt a new motor strategy for stepping after complete deafferentation but return to using the normal motor pattern following partial deafferentation (135). The development of the new strategy, termed behavioral substitution, following complete deafferentation involves modification of signals in descending pathways since the recovered stepping movements are permanently abolished (one year) by an ipsilateral thoracic hemisection of the spinal cord (133). Hemisection following the recovery of stepping after partial deafferentation has only a transient effect on stepping (134). The latter observation, together with the recovery of normal motor patterns in spared-root preparations, indicates that recovery in spared-root preparations depends on local modification of lumbosacral pattern generating networks and/or modification of the influence of afferent signals on these networks. Consistent with this conclusion is sprouting of undamaged afferents but not descending fibers in spared-root preparations (151).

Adaptation in Response to Injury of the Central Nervous System

It is well known that a certain amount of functional recovery of movement can occur after injury to the nervous system. The extent of recovery depends on the site and extent of the injury and on rehabilitative procedures (102, 152). In some cases normal motor patterns can be re-established, while in others new movement strategies are learned to replace lost strategies (102, 103, 153, 154).

Numerous investigations have described functional improvement in walking after damage to the nervous system, with the majority focusing on improvements following injury to the spinal cord (Table 4). The obvious clinical relevance has been the driving force behind these investigations. In general, we have a very poor understanding of the mechanisms underlying functional recovery of walking after damage to the central nervous system. Since most of what we do know has come from studies on cats with injury to the spinal cord, the following section focuses on this topic.

Recovery of stepping in the hind legs of cats has been examined after complete transection of the spinal cord (89, 90, 104, 163, 171, 172), following hemisection of the spinal cord (173–177) and after transection of descending tracts (153, 154, 165–167). Perhaps the most significant finding to come from these studies is that recovery of stepping following complete cord transection is facilitated by daily training sessions. With only relatively minor exceptions the motor pattern and leg kinematics are very similar to those in the normal animal (163). This similarity indicates that recovery depends on the re-activation of the neuronal circuits involved in generating the motor pattern in normal animals. Re-activation clearly depends on afferent feedback from the hind legs because weight support and movement of the legs are necessary. One possibility is that afferent pathways

TABLE 4   Adaptation of stepping following injury of the central nervous system

Animal	Site of Injury	References
Human	Cerebral hemispheres	155–157
	Spinal cord	158–161
Cat	Cerebellum	162
	Spinal cord	104, 163, 164
	Dorsal lateral funiculi	153, 165, 166
	Ventral funiculi	154, 165, 167
Chick	Spinal cord	168
Rat	Spinal cord	169, 170

influencing the spinal pattern generators are strengthened and these pathways eventually substitute for the lost descending pathways involved in the initiation and maintenance of stepping. This has been proposed as one of the mechanisms involved in the functional recovery of posture and stepping following hemisection of the cord where extensive sprouting of the sensory afferents in segments distal to the hemisection has been observed (176). As yet, however, sprouting of afferent fibers has not been reported in chronic spinal cats that have regained their ability to step with their hind legs. Another possibility is that repetitive signals from sensory afferents enhance the excitability of the spinal pattern generating networks. In this case the adaptive changes would be in the CPGs and not in the activating pathways.

Associated with spinal cord injury are marked alterations in the pharmacology of many transmitter systems (178–180). Some of these alterations are consistent with changes in the effects of various pharmacological agents on stepping in spinal animals, such as an association between enhanced effects of the α_2-noradrenergic receptor agonist clonidine in chronic spinal cats and the upregulation of α_2 receptors (89). However, as yet there have been no detailed reports of pharmacological changes in the spinal cord that can be directly associated with enhancement of stepping with training. Preliminary reports have suggested that step training reduces the efficacy of inhibitory systems in the spinal cord in cats and rats (181, 182). These preliminary findings are consistent with a report that stepping in adult chronic spinal cats can be improved by the administration of the GABA receptor antagonist bicuculline (183).

The physiological changes in the functioning of interneuronal systems in the spinal cord that must accompany step training in spinal animals are completely unknown. This is due largely to our poor understanding of the organization of the neuronal systems generating locomotor activity and in part to the absence of any studies comparing neuronal events associated with locomotor activity in trained and untrained animals. A potentially fruitful approach may be to examine alterations in the effectiveness of afferent pathways involved in the generation and regulation of the motor pattern for stepping. This approach has demonstrated modifications in afferent pathways regulating stance duration following peripheral nerve injury (137) and indicates that the modifications, at least partially, arise from alterations of synaptic transmission in the spinal cord (138).

The discovery that regular training leads reliably to stepping in spinal cats has strongly influenced the development of rehabilitative strategies for enhancing stepping in humans with spinal cord injury. Daily locomotor training in incomplete paraplegic patients beginning after a post-trauma period often results in significant improvements in locomotor function (159, 184, 185). Improved performance is associated with an increase in the level of EMG activity in leg extensor muscles (186), and the magnitude of activity is larger than can be voluntarily recruited from resting positions (159). These observations indicate that training specifically influences the locomotor pattern-generating network. This conclusion is supported by the fact that a locomotor pattern can be induced in complete paraplegic patients when leg movements are externally assisted (184, 187).

The critical parameters in the training schedules that are necessary for improved locomotion in paraplegic patients have not been well defined. However, one important factor is the degree of weight support. In the initial stages of training the patients must be partially supported by a harness, and the degree of support can be progressively decreased with time (161, 188). Furthermore, during step training the EMG mean amplitude in lower leg muscles is directly related to the load carried by the leg (160). Taken together, these two sets of observations indicate that feedback from load-sensitive receptors has a significant role in the generation of motor output in spinal cord–injured patients and is likely involved in modifying neuronal circuits in a manner that improves locomotor ability.

The extent to which training enhances the recovery of locomotion after injuries to regions of the central nervous system other than the spinal cord has not been established in animal experiments. However, training is likely to be a factor because procedures similar to those used in spinal cord-injured patients enhance the recovery of stepping in stroke patients (155–157).

Recently considerable effort has also been directed toward the study of the adaptation of walking following partial lesions of the spinal cord, a situation that more closely resembles the majority of spinal cord injuries in humans. The descending pathways that normally initiate and maintain locomotor activity are located in the ventro-lateral regions of the spinal cord (189). Damage of these pathways results in severe impairment of stepping in the hind legs (154, 167). Stepping eventually returns within a few weeks, and in animals with moderate lesions the motor patterns and kinematics of movement in the hind legs following recovery are close to normal. The major residual deficits in these animals are alterations in the coordination of stepping in the fore- and hind legs and the absence of adaptive modifications of extensor activity when the animals walk up inclines (154). The latter is likely due to loss of descending signals to extensor motoneurons from vestibulo- and reticulospinal pathways. The fact that the recovered motor pattern in the hind legs resembles the normal motor pattern indicates that spared axons in the ventral pathways and/or axons in the dorsal region of the cord can substitute for the lesioned axons.

Adaptive changes in the walking system of the cat have also been revealed by the analysis of the EMG and kinematic patterns following bilateral lesions of the dorsolateral funiculi (DLF) (153). Immediately after these lesions, animals have difficulty supporting their hindquarters and walking. These deficits were attributed to the loss of input to spinal pattern generators from the cortico- and rubrospinal tracts. Weight support and stepping improve over a period of about two weeks, but full recovery occurs only in animals with incomplete lesions of the DLF. This is another example indicating that functional restoration depends in part on modification of the actions of spared axons in descending pathways.

Currently we possess little information on the physiological and anatomical bases for the reorganization of descending pathways after partial injuries to the spinal cord. The early work by Goldberger and colleagues (151, 176) demonstrated that at least some descending axons have the capacity to sprout following complete deafferentation of the lumbosacral segments of cats, and an increase in the number of synaptic terminals of descending axons is considered important in reestablishing respiratory drive to ipsilateral phrenic motoneurons following hemisection of the spinal cord in rats and guinea pigs (190). The extent to which the reorganization of descending pathways regulating stepping is simply the result of spinal cord trauma or a specific process depending on use remains to be resolved.

Summary

A number of conclusions can be drawn from recent investigations on long-term adaptive mechanisms in rhythmic motor systems. The first is that adaptive changes can occur in the neuronal elements of the CPG associated with the rhythmic behavior. This has been demonstrated most clearly for adaptations produced by operant conditioning of respiration and feeding in mollusks. An important point, however, is that when a CPG is used to generate motor patterns for multiple behaviors the modifications are likely confined to those elements specifically involved in the altered behavior. This is the case in the feeding system of *Aplysia*. The second conclusion is that many long-term adaptive changes are driven by alterations in afferent feedback. Modifications of stepping in humans after walking on split and circular treadmills, adaptive changes in motor patterns for walking in cats following muscle denervation, and step-training in chronic spinal cats are some examples. It remains to be established whether the adaptive changes in walking behavior depend on alterations in the strength of transmission in afferent pathways regulating the CPGs or whether persistent alterations in the afferent signals modify elements in the CPGs. A third conclusion is that descending pathways involved in the initiation, maintenance, and coordination of rhythmic movements can be reorganized to compensate for loss of descending axons due to damage to the spinal cord. Sprouting of terminal processes of descending axons may be a factor in the reorganization of descending pathways.

An interesting issue is whether anatomical changes, such as terminal sprouting, are also involved in the long-term adaptation of rhythmic behavior in normal animals. This must be considered likely since significant modifications of synaptic morphology occur in the phrenic nucleus of rats within hours of reversibly blocking descending respiratory drive (191), and sprouting of axonal processes has been linked to adaptive plasticity in the head-orientation system of the owl (192).

CONCLUSIONS

The emphasis of recent research on rhythmic motor systems has been on their flexibility. A major effort has been directed toward determining how the pattern-generating networks are modified to produce different patterns for different forms of a specific task and for different behaviors using the same sets of muscles. Considerable insight has come from investigations of invertebrate and a few simpler vertebrate systems. These studies have revealed numerous processes contributing to short-term adaptation of rhythmic motor systems. Far less is known about short-term adaptive mechanisms in mammalian motor systems, but plausible ideas have come from the analysis of the simpler systems. An important fact to emerge from the recent analysis of walking systems in vertebrates is that the magnitude and timing of activity in individual muscles, or a group of close synergists, can be independently regulated according to the mechanical requirements of the task (28, 34, 67). This has also been found in the systems controlling arm movements in humans (3, 4) and in the systems controlling posture in humans and cats (74). In walking systems, afferent signals generated by receptors in the moving limbs make a substantial contribution to the patterning of activity in individual muscles. Thus modification of these signals by a change in body mechanics, e.g. a change in posture, is probably a major factor in the short-term adaptation of the motor pattern for walking.

Afferent feedback also has an important role in driving long-term adaptation of many rhythmic behaviors. For instance, use of the limbs is necessary for the improvement of walking in infants (110, 111), functional recovery following muscle denervation (139) and spinal cord transection (104, 193) in cats, and the improvement in stepping in partial paraplegic patients (159). The ability of afferent signals to modify the functioning of pattern-generating networks is likely related to the need for adaptive mechanisms for maintaining motor patterns appropriate for the mechanics of the system. Over the course of a lifetime the mechanics of motor systems can change considerably yet behavior remains relatively constant. Exactly how afferent feedback is utilized to calibrate motor output according to body mechanics is unknown. An attractive concept is that persistent errors in behavior are detected by proprioceptors and these error signals recalibrate the magnitude of feedforward commands (150). Thus one possibility is that a persistent alteration in afferent signals results in long-term changes in central commands from CPGs to motoneurons. Data consistent with this notion have recently been obtained in the walking system of the cat (139). This type of mechanism is likely to be of major importance in the learning of new movements, particularly during early postnatal development (11, 110, 111, 194).

ACKNOWLEDGMENTS

I thank DJ Bennett, R Harris-Warrick, T Lamb, JE Misiaszek, PSG Stein, and JF Yang for their valuable comments on a draft of this review. This work was supported by a grant from the Medical Research Council of Canada.

Visit the Annual Reviews home page at www.AnnualReviews.org.

LITERATURE CITED

1. Flanders M, Soechting JF. 1990. Arm muscle activation for static forces in three-dimensional space. *J. Neurophysiol.* 64:1818–37

2. Buneo CA, Soechting JF, Flanders M. 1994. Muscle activation patterns for reaching: the representation of distance and time. *J. Neurophysiol.* 71:1546–58

3. Flanders M, Pellegrini JJ, Geisler SD. 1996. Basic features of phasic activation for reaching in vertical planes. *Exp. Brain Res.* 110:67–79

4. Herrmann U, Flanders M. 1998. Directional tuning of single motor units. *J. Neurosci.* 18:8402–16

5. Georgopoulos AP, Kettner RE, Schwartz AB. 1988. Primate motor cortex and free arm movements to visual targets in three-dimensional space. II. Coding of the direction of movement by a neuronal population. *J. Neurosci.* 8:2929–37

6. Kalaska JF, Crammond DJ. 1992. Cerebral cortical mechanisms of reaching movements. *Science* 255:1517–23

7. Kalaska JF, Scott SH, Cisek P, Sergio LE. 1997. Cortical control of reaching movements. *Curr. Opin. Neurobiol.* 7:849–59

8. Georgopoulos AP. 1996. On the translation of directional motor cortical commands to activation of muscles via spinal interneuronal systems. *Cogn. Brain Res.* 3:151–55

9. Shadmehr R, Mussa-Ivaldi FA. 1994. Adaptive representation of dynamics during learning of a motor task. *J. Neurosci.* 14:3208–24

10. Conditt MA, Gandolfo F, Mussa-Ivaldi FA. 1997. The motor system does not learn the dynamics of the arm by rote memorization of past experience. *J. Neurophysiol.* 78:554–60

11. Konczak J, Borutta M, Dichgans J. 1997. The development of goal-directed reaching in infants. II. Learning to produce task-adequate patterns of joint torque. *Exp. Brain Res.* 113:465–74

12. Arshavsky YI, Deliagina TG, Orlovsky GN. 1997. Pattern generation. *Curr. Opin. Neurobiol.* 7:781–89

13. Stein PSG, Grillner S, Selverston AI, Stuart DG, eds. 1997. *Neurons, Networks, and Motor Behavior.* Cambridge, MA: MIT Press

14. Calabrese RL. 1998. Cellular, synaptic, network, and modulatory mechanisms involved in rhythm generation. *Curr. Opin. Neurobiol.* 8:710–17

15. Morton DW, Chiel HJ. 1994. Neural architectures for adaptive behavior. *Trends Neurosci.* 17:413–20

16. Dickinson PS. 1995. Interactions among neural networks for behavior. *Curr. Opin. Neurobiol.* 5:792–98

17. Harris-Warrick RM, Baro DJ, Coniglio LM, Johnson BR, Levini RM, et al. 1997. Chemical modulation of crustacean stomatogastric pattern generator networks. See Ref. 13, pp. 209–15

18. Drew T, Jiang W, Kably B, Lavoie S. 1996. Role of the motor cortex in the control of visually triggered gait modifications. *Can. J. Physiol. Pharmacol.* 74:426–42

19. Rossignol S. 1996. Control of stereotypic limb movements. In *Handbook of Physiology, Section 12. Exercise: Regulation and Integration of Multiple Systems,* ed. LB Rowell, JT Sheperd, pp. 173–216. Bethesda: Am. Physiol. Soc.

20. Pearson KG. 1995. Proprioceptive regulation of locomotion. *Curr. Opin. Neurobiol.* 5:786–91

21. Pearson KG, Ramirez JM. 1997. Sensory modulation of pattern-generating circuits. See Ref. 13, pp. 225–36

22. Büschges A, El Manira A. 1998. Sensory pathways and their modulation in the

control of locomotion. *Curr. Opin. Neurobiol.* 8:733–39

23. Burke RE. 1999. Use of state-dependent modulation of spinal reflexes as a tool to investigate the organization of spinal interneurons. *Exp. Brain Res.* 128:263–77

24. Grasso R, Bianchi L, Lacquaniti F. 1998. Motor patterns for human gait: backward versus forward locomotion. *J. Neurophysiol.* 80:1868–85

25. Carpenter MG, Bellos A, Patla AE. 1998. Is backward stepping over obstacles achieved through a simple temporal reversal of forward stepping. *Int. J. Neurosci.* 93:189–96

26. Buford JA, Smith JL. 1990. Adaptive control of backward quadriped walking. II. Hindlimb muscle synergies. *J. Neurophysiol.* 64:756–66

27. Pratt CA, Buford JA, Smith JL. 1996. Adaptive control of backward quadrupedal walking. V. Mutable activation of bifunctional thigh muscles. *J. Neurophysiol.* 75:832–42

28. Trank TV, Smith JL. 1996. Adaptive control of backward quadrupedal walking. VI. Metatarsophalangeal joint dynamics and motor patterns of digit muscles. *J. Neurophysiol.* 75:678–94

29. Trank TV, Chen C, Smith JL. 1996. Forms of forward quadrupedal locomotion. I. A comparison of posture, hindlimb kinematics, and motor patterns for normal and crouched walking. *J. Neurophysiol.* 76:2316–26

30. Smith JL, Carlson-Kuhta P. 1995. Unexpected motor patterns for hindlimb muscles during slope walking in the cat. *J. Neurophysiol.* 74:2211–15

31. Carlson-Kuhta P, Trank TV, Smith JL. 1998. Forms of forward quadrupedal locomotion. II. A comparison of posture, hindlimb kinematics, and motor patterns for upslope and level walking. *J. Neurophysiol.* 79:1687–701

32. Smith JL, Carlson-Kuhta P, Trank TV. 1998. Forms of forward quadrupedal

locomotion. III. A comparison of posture, hindlimb kinematics, and motor patterns for downslope and level walking. *J. Neurophysiol.* 79:1702–16

33. Pierotti DJ, Roy RR, Gregor RJ, Edgerton VR. 1989. Electromyographic activity of cat hindlimb flexors and extensors during locomotion at varying speeds and inclines. *Brain Res.* 481:57–66

34. Smith JL, Chung SH, Zernicke RF. 1993. Gait-related motor patterns and hindlimb kinetics for the cat trot and gallop. *Exp. Brain Res.* 94:308–22

35. Smith JL, Hoy MG, Koshland GF, Phillips DM, Zernicke RF. 1985. Intralimb coordination of the paw-shake response: a novel mixed synergy. *J. Neurophysiol.* 54:1271–81

36. Roy RR, Hutchison DL, Pierotti DJ, Hodgson JA, Edgerton VR. 1991. EMG patterns of rat ankle extensors and flexors during treadmill locomotion and swimming. *J. Appl. Physiol.* 70:2522–29

37. Johnston RM, Bekoff A. 1996. Patterns of muscle activity during different behaviors in chicks: implications for neural control. *J. Comp. Physiol. A* 179:169–84

38. Ashley-Ross MA, Lauder GV. 1997. Motor patterns and kinematics during backward walking in the pacific giant salamander: evidence for novel motor output. *J. Neurophysiol.* 78:3047–60

39. Ayers JL, Davis WJ. 1977. Neuronal control of locomotion in the lobster *Homarus americanus*. I. Motor programs for forward and backward walking. *J. Comp. Physiol. A* 115:1–27

40. Larsen GS, Frazier SF, Fish SE, Zill SN. 1995. Effects of load inversion in cockroach walking. *J. Comp. Physiol. A* 176:229–38

41. Duch C, Pfluger HJ. 1995. Motor patterns for horizontal and upside-down walking and vertical climbing in the locust. *J. Exp. Biol.* 198:1963–76

42. Graham D, Epstein S. 1985. Behaviour and motor output for an insect walking

on a slippery surface. II. Backward walking. *J. Exp. Biol.* 118:287–96

43. Kuhta PC, Smith JL. 1990. Scratch responses in normal cats: hindlimb kinematics and muscle synergies. *J. Neurophysiol.* 64:1653–67

44. Robertson GA, Mortin LI, Keifer J, Stein PSG. 1985. Three forms of the scratch reflex in the spinal turtle: central generation of motor patterns. *J. Neurophysiol.* 53:1517–34

45. Matsushima T, Grillner S. 1992. Neural mechanisms of intersegmental coordination in lamprey: local excitability changes modify the phase coupling along the spinal cord. *J. Neurophysiol.* 67:373–88

46. Soffe SR. 1993. Two distinct rhythmic motor patterns are driven by common premotor and motor neurons in a simple vertebrate spinal cord. *J. Neurosci.* 13:4456–69

47. Soffe SR. 1997. The pattern of sensory discharge can determine the motor response in young Xenopus tadpoles. *J. Comp. Physiol.* A 180:711–15

48. Heitler WJ. 1985. Motor programme switching in the crayfish swimmeret system. *J. Exp. Biol.* 114:521–50

49. Getting PA, Dekin MS. 1985. Mechanisms of pattern generation underlying swimming in Tritonia. IV. Gating of central pattern generator. *J. Neurophysiol.* 53:466–80

50. Hidaka O, Morimoto T, Masuda Y, Kato T, Matsuo R, Inoue T, Kobayashi M, Takada K. 1997. Regulation of masticatory force during cortically induced rhythmic jaw movements in the anesthetized rabbit. *J. Neurophysiol.* 77:3168–79

51. Clemens S, Meyrand P, Simmers J. 1998. Feeding-induced changes in temporal patterning of muscle activity in the lobster stomatogastric system. *Neurosci. Lett.* 254:65–68

52. Morton DW, Chiel HJ. 1993. The timing of activity in motor neurons that produce radula movements distinguishes inges-

tion from rejection in *Aplysia*. *J. Comp. Physiol.* A 173:519–36

53. Quinlan EM, Murphy AD. 1996. Plasticity in the multifunctional buccal central pattern generator in *Helisoma* illuminated by the identification of phase 3 interneurons. *J. Neurosci.* 75:561–74

54. McClellan AD. 1982. Movements and motor patterns of the buccal mass of *Pleurobranchea* during feeding, regurgitation and rejection. *J. Exp. Biol.* 98:195–211

55. Dempsey JA, Forster HV. 1982. Mediation of ventilatory adaptations. *Physiol. Rev.* 62:262–346

56. Larson CR, Yajima Y, Ko P. 1994. Modification in activity of medullary respiratory-related neurons for vocalization and swallowing. *J. Neurophysiol.* 71:2294–304

57. Oku Y, Tanaka I, Ezure K. 1994. Activity of bulbar respiratory neurons during fictive coughing and swallowing in the decerebrate cat. *J. Physiol.* 480:309–24

58. Grelot L, Milano S, Portillo F, Miller AD. 1993. Respiratory interneurons of the lower cervical (C4-C5) cord: Membrane potential changes during fictive coughing, vomiting, and swallowing in decerebrate cat. *Pflügers Arch.* 425:313–20

59. Simmers AJ, Bush BMH. 1983. Motor programme switching in the ventilatory system of *Carcinus maenas:* the neuronal basis of bimodal scaphognathite beating. *J. Exp. Biol.* 104:163–81

60. DiCaprio R. 1990. An interneurone mediating motor programme switching in the ventilatory system of the crab. *J. Exp. Biol.* 154:517–36

61. Zarnack W, Möhl B. 1977. Activity of the direct downstroke flight muscles of *Locusta migratoria* (L.) during steering behaviour in flight. I. Patterns of time shift. *J. Comp. Physiol.* A 118:215–33

62. Shoemaker KL, Robertson RM. 1998. Flight motor patterns of locusts respond-

ing to thermal stimuli. *J. Comp. Physiol. A* 183:477–88

63. Feldman JL. 1986. Neurophysiology of respiration in mammals. In *Handbook of Physiology; Section 1: The Nervous System*, Vol. IV, ed. FE Bloom, pp. 463–524. Bethesda: Am. Physiol. Soc.

64. Feldman JL, Smith JC. 1989. Cellular mechanisms underlying modulation of breathing pattern in mammals. *Ann. NY Acad. Sci.* 563:114–30

65. Pearson KG. 1993. Common principles of motor control in vertebrates and invertebrates. *Annu. Rev. Neurosci.* 16:265–97

66. Grillner S. 1981. Control of locomotion in bipeds, tetrapods and fish. In *Handbook of Physiology. Sect 1, Vol 2. The Nervous System, Motor Control*, ed. VB Brooks, pp. 1179–236. Bethesda: Am. Physiol. Soc.

67. Stein PSG, Smith JL. 1997. Neural and biomechanical control strategies for different forms of vertebrate hindlimb motor tasks. See Ref. 13, p. 61

68. Duysens J. 1977. Reflex control of locomotion as revealed by stimulation of cutaneous afferents in spontaneously walking premammillary cats. *J. Neurophysiol.* 40:737–51

69. Grillner S, Zangger P. 1979. On the central generation of locomotion in the low spinal cat. *Exp. Brain Res.* 34:241–61

70. Cheng JG, Stein RB, Jovanovic K, Yoshida K, Bennett DJ, Han YC. 1998. Identification, localization, and modulation of neural networks for walking in the mudpuppy (*Necturus maculatus*) spinal cord. *J. Neurosci.* 18:4295–304

71. Mortin LI, Stein PSG. 1989. Spinal cord segments containing key elements of the central pattern generators for three forms of scratch reflex in the turtle. *J. Neurosci.* 9:2285–96

72. Stein PSG, Victor JC, Field EC, Currie SN. 1995. Bilateral control of hindlimb scratching in the spinal turtle: Contralateral spinal circuitry contributes to the normal ipsilateral motor pattern of fictive

rostral scratching. *J. Neurosci.* 15:4343–55

73. Stein PSG, McCullough ML, Currie SN. 1998. Reconstruction of flexor/extensor alternation during fictive rostral scratching by two-site stimulation in the spinal turtle with a transverse spinal hemisection. *J. Neurosci.* 18:467–79

74. Macpherson JM. 1991. How flexible are muscle synergies? In *Motor Control: Concepts and Issues*, ed. DR Humphrey, HJ Freund, pp. 33–47. New York: Wiley & Sons

75. Whelan PJ, Hiebert GW, Pearson KG. 1995. Stimulation of the group I extensor afferents prolongs the stance phase in walking cats. *Exp. Brain Res.* 103:20–30

76. McCrea DA, Shefchyk SJ, Stephens MJ, Pearson KG. 1995. Disynaptic group I excitation of synergist ankle extensor motoneurones during fictive locomotion. *J. Physiol.* 487:527–39

77. Hiebert GW, Whelan PJ, Prochazka A, Pearson KG. 1996. Contributions of hindlimb flexor muscle afferents to the timing of phase transitions in the cat step cycle. *J. Neurophysiol.* 75:1126–37

78. Hiebert GW, Pearson KG. 1999. The contribution of sensory feedback to the generation of extensor activity during walking in the decerebrate cat. *J. Neurophysiol.* 81:758–70

79. Eccles JC, Eccles RM, Lundberg A. 1957. The convergence of monosynaptic excitatory afferents on to many different species of alpha motoneurones. *J. Physiol.* 137:22–50

80. Eccles RM, Lundberg A. 1958. Integrative patterns of Ia synaptic action on motoneurones of hip and knee muscles. *J. Physiol.* 144:271–98

81. Guertin P, Angel M, Perreault M-C, McCrea DA. 1995. Ankle extensor group I afferents excite extensors throughout the hindlimb during fictive locomotion in the cat. *J. Physiol.* 487:197–209

82. Degtyarenko AM, Simon ES, Burke RE. 1996. Differential modulation of disy-

naptic cutaneous inhibition and excitation in ankle flexor motoneurons during fictive locomotion. *J. Neurophysiol.* 76: 2972–85

83. Degtyarenko AM, Simon ES, Norden-Krichmar T, Burke RE. 1998. Modulation of oligosynaptic cutaneous and muscle afferent reflex pathways during fictive locomotion and scratching in the cat. *J. Neurophysiol.* 79:447–63

84. Katz PS. 1995. Intrinsic and extrinsic neuromodulation of motor circuits. *Curr. Opin. Neurobiol.* 5:799–808

85. Nagayama T, Hisada M. 1987. Opposing parallel connections through crayfish local nonspiking interneurons. *J. Comp. Neurol.* 257:347–58

86. Wolf H, Büschges A. 1995. Nonspiking local interneurons in insect leg motor control. II. Role of nonspiking local interneurons in the control of leg swing during walking. *J. Neurophysiol.* 73: 1861–75

87. Nagy F, Cardi P. 1994. A rhythmic modulatory gating system in the stomatogastric nervous system of *Homarus gammarus.* II. Modulatory control of the pyloric CPG. *J. Neurophysiol.* 71:2490–502

88. Barbeau H, Rossignol S. 1990. The effects of serotonergic drugs on the locomotor pattern and on cutaneous reflexes in the adult chronic spinal cat. *Brain Res.* 514:55–67

89. Chau C, Barbeau H, Rossignol S. 1998. Early locomotor training with clonidine in spinal cats. *J. Neurophysiol.* 79:392–409

90. Chau C, Barbeau H, Rossignol S. 1998. Effects of intrathecal α1- and α2-noradrenergic agonists and norepinephrine on locomotion in chronic spinal cats. *J. Neurosci.* 79:2941–63

91. Hounsgaard J, Hultborn H, Jespersen B, Kiehn O. 1988. Bistability of alpha-motoneurones in the decerebrate cat and in the acute spinal cat after intravenous 5-hydroxytrytophan. *J. Physiol.* 405: 345–67

92. Bennett DJ, Hultborn H, Fedirchuck B, Gorassini M. 1998. Synaptic activation of plateaus in hindlimb motoneurons of decerebrate cats. *J. Neurophysiol.* 80: 2023–37

93. Lee RH, Heckman CJ. 1998. Distablility in spinal motoneurons in vivo: systematic variations in persistent inward currents. *J. Neurophysiol.* 80:583–93

94. Robertson GA, Stein PSG. 1988. Synaptic control of hindlimb motoneurones during three forms of the fictive scratch reflex in the turtle. *J. Physiol.* 404:101–28

95. Skorupski P. 1992. Synaptic connections between nonspiking afferent neurons and motor neurons underlying phase-dependent reflexes in crayfish. *J. Neurophysiol.* 67:664–79

96. Driesang RB, Büschges A. 1996. Physiological changes in central neuronal pathways contributing to the generation of a reflex reversal. *J. Comp. Physiol. A* 179:45–58

97. Stein W, Sauer AE. 1998. Modulation of sensorimotor pathways associated with gain changes in a posture-control network of an insect. *J. Comp. Physiol. A* 183:489–502

98. Murayama M, Takahata M. 1998. Neuronal mechanisms underlying the facilitatory control of uropod steering behaviour during treadmill walking in crayfish. I. Antagonistically regulated background excitability of uropod motoneurones. *J. Exp. Biol.* 201:1283–94

99. Parkis MA, Dong XW, Feldman JL, Funk GD. 1999. Concurrent inhibition and excitation of phrenic motoneurons during inspiration: phase-specific control of excitability. *J. Neurosci.* 19:2368–80

100. Perret C. 1983. Centrally generated pattern of motoneuron activity during locomotion in the cat. In *Neural Origin of Rhythmic Movements,* ed. A Roberts, B

Roberts, pp. 405–22. Cambridge, UK: Cambridge Univ. Press

101. Berkowitz A, Stein PSG. 1994. Activity of descending propriospinal axons in the turtle hindlimb enlargement during two forms of fictive scratching: phase analyses. *J. Neurosci.* 14:5105–19

102. Taub E, Miller NE, Novack TA, Cook EW, Fleming WC, et al. 1993. Technique to improve chronic motor deficit after stroke. *Arch. Phys. Med. Rehabil.* 74:347–54

103. Friel KM, Nudo RJ. 1998. Recovery of motor function after focal cortical injury in primates: compensatory movement patterns used during rehabilitative training. *Somatosen. Mot. Res.* 15:173–89

104. De Leon RD, Hodgson JA, Roy RR, Edgerton VR. 1998. Locomotor capacity attributable to step training versus spontaneous recovery after spinalization in adult cats. *J. Neurophysiol.* 79:1329–40

105. Gordon CR, Fletcher WA, Melvill Jones G, Block EW. 1995. Adaptive plasticity in the control of locomotor trajectory. *Exp. Brain Res.* 102:540–45

106. Weber KD, Fletcher WA, Gordon CR, Jones GM, Block EW. 1998. Motor learning in the "podokinetic" system and its role in spatial orientation during locomotion. *Exp. Brain Res.* 120:377–85

107. Prokop T, Berger W, Zijlstra W, Dietz V. 1995. Adaptational and learning processes during human split-belt locomotion: interaction between central mechanisms and afferent input. *Exp. Brain Res.* 106:449–56

108. Jensen L, Prokop T, Dietz V. 1998. Adaptational effects during human split-belt walking: influence of afferent input. *Exp. Brain Res.* 118:126–30

109. Layne CS, McDonald PV, Bloomberg JJ. 1997. Neuromuscular activation patterns during treadmill walking after space flight. *Exp. Brain Res.* 113:104–16

110. Vereijken B, Thelen E. 1997. Training infant treadmill stepping: the role of indi-

vidual pattern stability. *Dev. Psychobiol.* 30:89–102

111. Yang JF, Stephens MJ, Vishram R. 1998. Infant stepping: a method to study the sensory control of human walking. *J. Physiol.* 507:927–37

112. Wetzel MC. 1982. Operant control and cat locomotion. *Am. J. Phys. Med.* 61:11–25

113. Yanagihara D, Udo M, Kondo I, Yoshida T. 1993. A new learning paradigm: adaptive changes in interlimb coordination during perturbed locomotion in decerebrate cats. *Neurosci. Res.* 18:241–44

114. Yanagihara D, Kondo I. 1996. Nitric oxide plays a key role in adaptive control of locomotion in cat. *Proc. Natl. Acad. Sci. USA* 93:13292–97

115. Wuyam B, Moosavi SH, Decety J, Adams L, Lansing RW, Guz A. 1995. Imagination of dynamic exercise produced ventilatory responses which were more apparent in competitive sportsmen. *J. Physiol.* 482:713–24

116. Turner DL, Bach KB, Martin PA, Olsen EB, Brownfield M, et al. 1997. Modulation of ventilatory control during exercise. *Resp. Physiol.* 110:277–85

117. Martin PA, Mitchell GS. 1993. Long-term modulation of the exercise ventilatory response in goats. *J. Physiol.* 470:601–17

118. Turner DL, Mitchell GS. 1997. Long-term facilitation of ventilation following repeated hypoxic episodes in awake goats. *J. Physiol.* 499:543–50

119. Bach KB, Mitchell GS. 1996. Hypoxia induced long-term facilitation of respiratory activity is serotonin dependent. *Resp. Physiol.* 104:251–60

120. Cao KY, Zwillich CW, Berthon-Jones M, Sullivan CE. 1992. Increased normoxic ventilation induced by repetitive hypoxia in conscious dogs. *J. Appl. Physiol.* 73:2083–88

121. Morris KF, Arata A, Shannon R, Lindsey BG. 1996. Long-term facilitation of phrenic activity in cats: responses and

short time scale correlations of medullary neurones. *J. Physiol.* 490:463–80

122. Levy M, Weller A, Susswein AJ. 1994. Learned changes in the rate of respiratory pumping in *Aplysia fasciata* in response to increases and decreases in seawater concentration. *Behav. Neurosci.* 108:161–70

123. Levy M, Susswein AJ. 1990. Learned changes of respiratory pumping rate in response to lowered pH in *Aplysia*. *Behav. Neural Biol.* 54:218–33

124. Spencer GE, Syed NI, Lukowiak K. 1999. Neural changes after operant conditioning of the aerial respiratory behavior in *Lymnaea stagnalis*. *J. Neurosci.* 19:1836–43

125. Susswein AJ, Schwarz M, Feldman E. 1986. Learned changes in feeding behavior in *Aplysia* in response to edible and inedible foods. *J. Neurosci.* 6:1513–27

126. Nargeot R, Baxter DA, Byrne JH. 1997. Contingent-dependent enhancement of rhythmic motor patterns: an in vitro analog of operant conditioning. *J. Neurosci.* 17:8093–105

127. Nargeot R, Baxter DA, Byrne JH. 1999. In vitro analog of operant conditioning in *Aplysia*. I. Contingent reinforcement modifies the functional dynamics of an identified neuron. *J. Neurosci.* 19:2247–60

128. Nargeot R, Baxter DA, Byrne JH. 1999. In vitro analog of operant conditioning in *Aplysia*. II. Modifications of the functional dynamics of an identified neuron contribute to motor pattern selection. *J. Neurosci.* 19:2261–72

129. Ito M. 1989. Long-term depression. *Annu. Rev. Neurosci.* 12:85–102

130. Linden DJ, Connor JA. 1995. Long-term synaptic depression. *Annu. Rev. Neurosci.* 18:319–58

131. Lukowiak K, Ringseis E, Spencer G, Wildering W, Syed N. 1996. Operant conditioning of aerial respiratory behav-

ior in *Lymnaea stagnalis*. *J. Exp. Biol.* 199:683–91

132. Yang JF, Stein RB, James KB. 1991. Contribution of peripheral afferents to the activation of the soleus muscle during walking in humans. *Exp. Brain Res.* 87:679–87

133. Goldberger ME. 1977. Locomotor recovery after unilateral hindlimb deafferentation in cats. *Brain Res.* 123:59–74

134. Goldberger ME. 1988. Partial and complete deafferentation of cat hindlimb: the contribution of behavioral substitution to recovery of motor function. *Exp. Brain Res.* 73:343–53

135. Goldberger ME. 1988. Spared root deafferentation of a cat's hindlimb: hierarchical regulation of pathways mediating recovery of motor behavior. *Exp. Brain Res.* 73:329–42

136. Wetzel MC, Gerlach RL, Stern LZ, Hannapel LK. 1973. Behavior and histochemistry of functionally isolated cat ankle extensors. *Exp. Neurol.* 39:223–33

137. Whelan PJ, Hiebert GW, Pearson KG. 1995. Plasticity of the extensor group I pathway controlling the stance to swing transition in the cat. *J. Neurophysiol.* 74:2782–87

138. Whelan PJ, Pearson KG. 1997. Plasticity in reflex pathways controlling stepping in the cat. *J. Neurophysiol.* 78:1643–50

139. Pearson KG, Fouad K, Misiaszek JE. 1999. Adaptive changes in motor activity associated with functional recovery following muscle deneration in walking cats. *J. Neurophysiol.* 82:370–81

140. Carrier L, Brustein E, Rossignol S. 1997. Locomotion of the hindlimbs after neurectomy of ankle flexors in intact and spinal cats: model for the study of locomotor plasticity. *J. Neurophysiol.* 77:1979–93

141. Lou JS, Bloedel JR. 1988. A new conditioning paradigm: conditioned limb movements in locomoting decerebrate ferrets. *Neurosci. Lett.* 84:185–90

142. Muir GD, Steeves JD. 1995. Phasic cuta-

neous input facilitates locomotor recovery after incomplete spinal injury in the chick. *J. Neurophysiol.* 74:358–68

143. Muir GD, Steeves JD. 1997. Sensorimotor stimulation improves locomotor recovery after spinal cord injury. *Trends Neurosci.* 20:72–78

144. Fregosi RF, Mitchell GS. 1994. Long-term facilitation of inspiratory intercostal nerve activity following carotid sinus nerve simulation in cats. *J. Physiol.* 477:469–79

145. Kinkead R, Zhan WZ, Prakash YS, Bach KB, Siech GC, Mitchell GS. 1998. Cervical dorsal rhizotomy enhances serotonergic innervation of phrenic motoneurons and serotonin-dependent long-term facilitation of respiratory motor output in rats. *J. Neurosci.* 18:8436–43

146. Büschges A, Ramirez JM, Pearson KG. 1992. Reorganization of sensory regulation of locust flight after partial deafferentation. *J. Neurobiol.* 23:31–43

147. Gee CE, Robertson RM. 1996. Recovery of the flight system following ablation of the tegulae in immature adult locusts. *J. Exp. Biol.* 199:1395–403

148. Wolf H, Büschges A. 1997. Plasticity of synaptic connections in sensory-motor pathways of the adult locust flight system. *J. Neurophysiol.* 78:1276–84

149. Fouad K, Pearson KG. 1997. Modification of group I field potentials in the intermediate nucleus of the cat spinal cord after chronic axotomy of an extensor nerve. *Neurosci. Lett.* 236:9–12

150. Kawato M. 1996. Learning internal models of the motor apparatus. In *The Acquisition of Motor Behavior in Verebrates*, ed. JR Bloedel, TJ Ebner, SP Wise, pp. 409–30. Cambridge, MA: MIT Press

151. Goldberger ME, Murray M. 1982. Lack of sprouting and its presence after lesions of the cat spinal cord. *Brain Res.* 241:227–39

152. Nudo RJ, Wise BM, SiFuentes F, Milliken GW. 1996. Neural substrates for the effects of rehabilitative training on motor recovery after ischemic infarct. *Science* 272:1791–94

153. Jiang W, Drew T. 1996. Effects of bilateral lesions of the dorsolateral funiculi and dorsal columns at the level of the low thoracic spinal cord on the control of locomotion in the adult cat. I. Treadmill walking. *J. Neurophysiol.* 76:849–66

154. Brustein E, Rossignol S. 1998. Recovery of locomotion after ventral and ventrolateral spinal lesion in the cat. I. Deficits and adaptive mechanisms. *J. Neurophysiol.* 80:1245–67

155. Richards CL, Malouin F, Wood-Dauphinee S, Williams JI, Bouchard JP, Brunet D. 1993. Task-specific physical therapy for optimization of gait recovery in acute stroke patients. *Arch. Phys. Med. Rehabil.* 74:611–20

156. Hesse S, Bertelt C, Jahnke MT, Schaffrin A, Baake P, et al. KH. 1995. Treadmill training with partial body weight support compared with physiotherapy in nonambulatory hemiplegic patients. *Stroke* 26:976–81

157. Visintin M, Barbeau H, Korner-Bitensky N, Mayo NE. 1998. Using a new approach to re-train gait in stroke patients through body weight support and treadmill stimulation. *Stroke* 29:1122–28

158. Nathan PW. 1994. Effects on movement of surgical incisions into the human spinal cord. *Brain* 117:337–46

159. Wernig A, Muller S, Nanassy A, Cagol E. 1995. Laufband therapy based on 'rules of spinal locomotion' is effective in spinal cord injured persons. *Eur. J. Neurosci.* 7:823–29

160. Harkema SJ, Hurley SL, Patel UK, Requejo PS, Dobkin BH, Edgerton VR. 1997. Human lumbosacral spinal cord interprets loading during stepping. *J. Neurophysiol.* 77:797–811

161. Dietz V, Wirz M, Colombo G, Curt A. 1998. Locomotor capacity and recovery of spinal cord function in paraplegic

patients: a clinical and electrophysiological evaluation. *Electroenceph. Clin. Neurophysiol.* 109:140–53

162. Yu J, Eidelberg E. 1983. Recovery of locomotor function in cats after localized cerebellar lesions. *Brain Res.* 273:121–31

163. Belanger M, Drew T, Provencher J, Rossignol S. 1996. A comparison of treadmill locomotion in adult cats before and after spinal transection. *J. Neurophysiol.* 76:471–91

164. De Leon RD, Hodgson JA, Roy RR, Edgerton VR. 1999. Retention of hindlimb stepping ability in adult spinal cats after cessation of step training. *J. Neurophysiol.* 81:85–94

165. Gorska T, Bem T, Majczynski H. 1990. Locomotion in cats with ventral spinal lesions: support patterns and duration of support phases during unrestrained walking. *Acta Neurobiol. Exp.* 50:191–200

166. Gorska T, Bem T, Majczynski H, Zmyslowski W. 1993. Unrestrained walking in cats with partial spinal cord lesions. *Br. Res. Bull.* 32:241–49

167. Bem T, Gorska T, Majczynski H, Zmyslowski W. 1995. Different patterns of fore-hindlimb coordination during overground locomotion in cats with ventral and lateral spinal lesions. *Exp. Brain Res.* 104:70–80

168. Muir GD, Katz SL, Gosline JM, Steeves JD. 1998. Asymmetric bipedal locomotion—an adaptive response to incomplete spinal injury in the chick. *Exp. Brain Res.* 122:275–82

169. Kunkel-Bagden E, Dai HN, Bregman BS. 1992. Recovery of function after spinal cord hemisection in newborn and adult rat: differential effects on reflex and locomotor function. *Exp. Neurol.* 116:40–51

170. Cheng H, Almstrøm S, Gimenez-Llort L, Chang R, Ogren SO, et al. 1997. Gait analysis of adult paraplegic rats after spinal cord repair. *Exp. Neurol.* 148:544–57

171. Lovely RG, Gregor RJ, Roy RR, Edger-ton VR. 1986. Effects of training on the recovery of full-weight bearing stepping in the adult spinal cat. *Exp. Neurol.* 92:421–35

172. Barbeau H, Rossignol S. 1987. Recovery of locomotion after chronic spinalization in the adult cat. *Brain Res.* 412:84–95

173. Kato M. 1989. Chronically isolated lumbar half spinal cord produced by hemisection and longitudinal myelotomy generates locomotor activities of the ipsilateral hindlimb of the cat. *Neurosci. Lett.* 98:149–53

174. Kato M. 1992. Walking of cats on a grid: performance of locomotor task in spinal intact and hemisected cats. *Neurosci. Lett.* 145:129–32

175. Masimichi K, Murakami S, Yasuda K, Hirayama H. 1984. Disrupting the fore- and hindlimb coordination during overground locomotion in cats with bilateral serial hemisection of the spinal cord. *Neurol. Res.* 2:27–47

176. Helgren ME, Goldberger ME. 1993. The recovery of postural reflexes and locomotion following low thoracic hemisection in adult cats involves compensation by undamaged primary afferent pathways. *Exp. Neurol.* 123:17–34

177. Kutz-Buschbeck JP, Boczek-Funcke A, Mautes A, Nacimiento W, Weinhardt C. 1996. Recovery of locomotion after spinal cord hemisection: an X-ray study of the cat hindlimb. *Exp. Neurol.* 137:212–24

178. Barbeau H, Bedard P. 1981. Denervation supersensitivity to 5-HT in rats following spinal transection and 5,7 dihydroxytryptamine injection. *Neuropharmacology* 20:611–16

179. Roudet C, Mouchet P, Feuerstein C, Savasta M. 1994. Normal distribution of α2-adrenoreceptors in the rat spinal cord and its modification after noradrenergic denervation: a quantitative autoradiographic study. *J. Neuro. Rehab.* 39:319–29

180. Giroux N, Aloyz RS, Rossignol S,

Reader TA. 1995. Serotonin 1a and α_1 and β_2-noradrenergic receptors in the spinal cord of spinalized cats. *Neurosci. Abst.* 21:926

181. Tillakaratne NJK, Hodgson JA, Roy RR, Tobin AJ, Edgerton VR. 1995. Spinally transected adult cats show changes in glutamate decarboxylase (GAD67 mRNA in lumbar spinal cord after locomotor of standing training. *Neurosci. Abst.* 21:380

182. Talmadge RJ, Roy RR, Edgerton VR. 1996. Alterations in the glycinergic neurotransmission system are associated with stepping behavior in neonatal spinal cord transected rats. *Neurosci. Abst.* 22:1397

183. Robinson GA, Goldberger ME. 1986. The development and recovery of motor function in spinal cats. II. Pharmacological enhancement of recovery. *Exp. Brain Res.* 62:387–400

184. Dobkin BH, Harkema S, Requejo PS, Edgerton VR. 1995. Modulation of locomotor-like EMG activity in subjects with complete and incomplete spinal cord injury. *J. Neuro. Rehab.* 9:183–90

185. Wickelgren I. 1998. Teaching the spinal cord to walk. *Science* 279:319–21

186. Dietz V, Colombo G, Jensen L, Baumgartner L. 1995. Locomotor capacity of spinal cord paraplegic patients. *Ann. Neurol.* 37:574–82

187. Dietz V, Colombo G, Jensen L. 1994. Locomotor activity in spinal man. *Lancet* 344:1260–62

188. Barbeau H, Rossignol S. 1994. Enhancement of locomotor recovery following spinal cord injury. *Curr. Opin. Neurol.* 7:517–24

189. Jordan LM. 1991. Brainstem and spinal cord mechanisms for the initiation of locomotion. In *Neurobiological Basis of Human Locomotion,* ed. M Shimamura, S Grillner, VR Edgerton, pp. 3–20. Tokyo: Jpn. Sci. Soc. Press

190. Sperry MA, Goshgarian HG. 1993. Ultrastructural changes in the rate phrenic nucleus developing within 2 h after cervical cord hemisection. *Exp. Neurol.* 120:233–44

191. Castro-Moure F, Goshgarian HG. 1997. Morphological plasticity induced in the phrenic nucleus following cervical cold block of descending respiratory drive. *Exp. Neurol.* 147:299–310

192. Feldman DE, Knudsen EI. 1997. An anatomical basis for visual calibration of the auditory space map in the barn owl's midbrain. *J. Neurosci.* 17:6820–37

193. Rossignol S, Chau C, Brustein E, Belanger M, Barbeau H, Drew T. 1996. Locomotor capacities after complete and partial lesions of the spinal cord. *Acta Neurobiol. Exp.* 56:449–63

194. Kuhtz-Buschbeck JP, Stolze H, Jöhnk K, Boczek-Funcke A, Illert M. 1998. Development of prehension movements in children: a kinematic study. *Exp. Brain Res.* 122:424–32

Annu. Rev. Physiol. 2000. 62:755–78

LIGAND-GATED ION CHANNEL INTERACTIONS WITH CYTOSKELETAL AND SIGNALING PROTEINS

Morgan Sheng and Daniel T. S. Pak

Department of Neurobiology, and Howard Hughes Medical Institute, Massachusetts General Hospital and Harvard Medical School, Boston, Massachusetts 02114; e-mail: sheng@helix.mgh.harvard.edu; e-mail: pak@helix.mgh.harvard.edu

Key Words NMDA receptors, AMPA receptors, GABA receptors, PDZ domains, scaffold protein

■ **Abstract** In recent years, it has become apparent that ligand-gated ion channels (ionotropic receptors) in the neuronal plasma membrane interact via their cytoplasmic domains with a multitude of intracellular proteins. Different classes of ligand-gated channels associate with distinct sets of intracellular proteins, often through specialized scaffold proteins containing PDZ domains. These specific interactions link the receptor channel to the cortical cytoskeleton and to appropriate signal transduction pathways in the cell. Thus ionotropic receptors are components of extensive protein complexes that are likely involved in the subcellular targeting, cytoskeletal anchoring, and localized clustering of the receptors at specific sites on the neuronal surface. In addition to structural functions, receptor-associated proteins can play important roles as activity modulators or downstream effectors of ligand-gated channels.

INTRODUCTION

Ligand-gated ion channels (or ionotropic receptors) undergo a conformational change upon the binding of a specific ligand (usually a neurotransmitter), which leads to opening of the intrinsic ion channel. Ligand-gated channels thus transduce a chemical signal into charge flux across the membrane. Because of their fascinating self-contained properties and because their gating has immediate electrical consequences, ligand-gated channels have been studied largely at the biophysical, pharmacological, and electrophysiological levels, both in situ and in heterologous expression systems. In recent years, however, it has become apparent that ionotropic receptors do not operate as free-floating entities in the plasma membrane, but rather that they interact with specific cytoplasmic proteins that link them to the cytoskeleton and to intracellular signal transduction pathways. Association with intracellular molecules is likely to be important for immobilization and clustering of the receptors, for correct targeting of receptors to specific subcellular sites, for the ability of receptors to funnel ionic and conformational signals to appropriate cytoplasmic effectors, and for modulation of the receptors by kinases, phosphatases, and other regulatory proteins. Thus the elucidation of interactions with intracellular proteins promises to reveal a great deal about the function, regulation, and cell biology of ligand-gated ion channels.

This review focuses on recent advances in our understanding of how postsynaptic ionotropic receptors of neurons [such as N-methyl-D-aspartate (NMDA)- and AMPA-type glutamate receptors, glycine, and GABA receptors] interact with cytoskeletal and signaling proteins. We do not cover nicotinic acetylcholine (ACh) receptors of the neuromuscular junction (NMJ), which have been recently reviewed (1). A major motivation for studying the protein associations of neuronal neurotransmitter-gated channels is that they are among the most precisely localized of membrane proteins, being clustered at specific postsynaptic sites. Another is that these neurotransmitter receptors can activate intracellular signaling pathways with a specificity that cannot be explained by ion flux alone. How are these receptors targeted to specific microdomains of the plasma membrane? How do they link to specific downstream effectors? Answers to these questions are gradually being revealed by characterization of the specific cytoplasmic proteins that bind to the intracellular domains of the ionotropic receptors.

N-METHYL-D-ASPARTATE RECEPTORS

The discovery of NMDA receptor interactions with intracellular proteins has been particularly influential in this field. There were several rationales for seeking NMDA receptor-interacting proteins. First, NMDA receptors are selectively concentrated in the postsynaptic density (PSD), a morphological and functional specialization of excitatory synapses (2, 3). Second, there is indirect evidence that NMDA receptor activity is regulated by interaction with the cytoskeleton (4, 5). Third, NMDA receptors are permeable to calcium ions and activate intracellular events that specifically lead to long-term potentiation (LTP) or long-term depression (LTD), neurotoxicity, and transcriptional responses in the nucleus (6). The identification of a large multiprotein complex associated with the cytoplasmic tails of NMDA receptor subunits has provided mechanistic insight into the above phenomena.

Interactions of the NR2 Subunit: The PSD-95 Complex

NMDA receptors include NR1 and a family of NR2 subunits, probably with a tetrameric stoichiometry (6, 7). The four NR2 subunits (NR2A–D) have long cytoplasmic tails [≤644 amino acid (aa) residues], the C termini of which end in the conserved sequence –ESDV (NR2A and NR2B) or –ESEV (NR2C and NR2D). A key finding was that this short C-terminal peptide motif mediates binding to the first two PDZ domains of PSD-95/synapse-associated protein

(SAP) 90, an abundant protein of the PSD (8, 9; reviewed in 10–12). PDZ domains have been discussed in depth recently (13–16), so they are not dwelled upon here; however, it is worth pointing out that it was the interaction of PSD-95 with NR2 subunits and with Shaker-type K^+ channels (ending in the sequence –ETDV) (17) that first revealed the function of PDZ domains as modular binding sites for specific C-terminal peptide sequences.

PSD-95/SAP90 is a member of the membrane-associated guanylate kinase (MAGUK) superfamily (18, 19). The PSD-95 subfamily of MAGUKs is characterized by three N-terminal PDZ domains, an SH3 domain, and a C-terminal guanylate kinase (GK)-like domain, each of which is now recognized as a protein interaction motif. Other members of the PSD-95 family in mammals include PSD-93/Chapsyn-110 (20, 21), SAP97/hDlg (22, 23), and SAP102 (24). All of the family members except SAP97 (which is predominantly presynaptic and axonal) (23) appear to be components of the PSD and to be associated with NMDA receptors in synapses. We discuss the NR2 interaction with PSD-95 in terms of its possible functional significance, which we have divided into four themes.

Localization/Targeting   A simple hypothesis based on the colocalization of PSD-95 and NMDA receptors in the PSD is that NR2 binding to PSD-95 is important for the postsynaptic localization of NMDA receptors. Genetic tests of such a concept were first performed in *Drosophila melanogaster,* which expresses a single homolog of the PSD-95 family, called discs large (Dlg) (25). Dlg is concentrated in the NMJ of *Drosophila,* a glutamatergic synapse (26), where it colocalizes with the Shaker K^+ channel and the Fasciclin II (Fas II) cell adhesion molecule, two transmembrane (TM) proteins that bind directly to the PDZ domains of Dlg. *dlg* mutants show loss of the normal synaptic localization of Shaker and Fas II (27–29). Moreover, the C termini of Fas II and Shaker (containing the PDZ-binding motifs) are sufficient to confer synaptic targeting on a heterologous protein in wild-type but not in *dlg* mutant flies (29). Taken together, these genetic studies indicate that Dlg is important in vivo for synaptic localization of its binding partners. The C termini of cloned *Drosophila* glutamate receptors do not have C-terminal motifs that bind the PDZ domains of Dlg, and it remains unclear how ionotropic glutamate receptors are targeted to the *Drosophila* NMJ. A general role for PDZ proteins in subcellular targeting of binding partners is supported by genetic analysis of other PDZ-containing proteins. For instance, InaD (a protein containing five PDZs) has been shown to be important in localizing its interacting proteins to the rhabdomere of *Drosophila* photoreceptors (30, 31), and the LIN-2/LIN-7/LIN-10 complex is required for localization of membrane receptors in neurons and epithelia of *Caenorhabditis elegans* (reviewed in 32).

By extrapolation from genetic studies of Dlg in *Drosophila,* the PSD-95 family of proteins in mammals may be involved in the targeting of its PDZ ligands (such as NMDA receptors) to the PSD. However, a disruption of the PSD-95 gene in mice (leading to near absence of PSD-95 protein) did not cause an obvious defect in synaptic localization of NMDA receptors (33). The lack of effect could be caused by functional redundancy of PSD-95 and its postsynaptic relatives (such as chapsyn-110/PSD-93 and SAP102). Alternatively, other mechanisms may exist for proper localization of NMDA receptors, for example via interactions with NR1 (see below). The importance of the NR2 cytoplasmic tail (which binds to PSD-95) for the synaptic targeting of NMDA receptors has also been studied in knockout mice. One study found a significant (but not complete) loss of synaptic localization of NR2B in mice deleted for the NR2B C-terminal tail, based on quantitative analysis of synaptic NMDA receptor activity and direct immuno-staining (34). These studies analyzed neonatal mice at a developmental stage when NR2B is the predominant NR2 subtype expressed. However, these results are complicated by the deleterious effects of this mutation on brain development and organismal survival (34). In contrast, another group performed similar experiments deleting the cytoplasmic tails of NR2A, NR2B, and NR2C but inferred normal synaptic localization of the mutant NMDA receptors by indirect analysis (35). Thus the case remains open as to whether the NR2 C-terminal interaction with PSD-95 is involved in localization of NMDA receptors at postsynaptic sites.

Scaffold for Assemby of a Signaling Complex Although the results of genetic experiments in mice are equivocal with respect to the importance of PSD-95 in NMDA receptor targeting, they do provide strong evidence that the NR2–PSD-95 interaction is involved in the signaling functions of NMDA receptors. The PSD-95 knockout had dramatic effects on NMDA receptor-dependent LTP in hippocampus (33). At all frequencies of synaptic stimulation tested, the magnitude of LTP in mutant mice was enhanced, even at low frequencies that in wild-type mice produced no LTP or even LTD. Thus PSD-95 somehow regulates the threshold between induction of LTP and LTD. Indeed, the mutant phenotype suggests that PSD-95 normally has a restraining influence on LTP, at least in the mature brain. Presumably this is because PSD-95 links NMDA receptors to downstream effectors that include negative regulators of synaptic transmission, such as protein phosphatases. Further evidence that NR2 interactions with cytoplasmic proteins are important for NMDA receptor signaling comes from mouse mutants that have targeted deletions of the cytoplasmic tails of NR2A, NR2B, and NR2C (35). These mutations essentially phenocopied the deletion of the entire respective genes (for NR2A and NR2C, without dramatically affecting NMDA receptor expression or channel activity). Although these findings indicate the importance of the NR2 C-terminal tails in NMDA receptor function, they do not necessarily imply that PSD-95 is the sole mediator of NMDA receptor intracellular signaling. These targeted mutations deleted the entire cytoplasmic tails (~400–600 aa) of the NR2 subunits, whereas only the last several amino acids are involved in binding to PSD-95. The function of the remaining bulk of the NR2 C-terminal tails remains uncertain, although CaMKII has been reported to bind to these regions at one or two sites, depending on the technique used (36, 37). Intriguingly, stimulation of NMDA receptors in forebrain slices increases the association of

CaMKII with NR2B and NR1 (36), suggesting a possible mechanism for the translocation of CaMKII to dendritic spines after NMDA receptor stimulation (38).

How is PSD-95 involved in NMDA receptor function? Recent findings indicate that, in addition to receptors and ion channels, PSD-95 binds to a variety of cytoplasmic proteins that are likely involved in NMDA receptor signal transduction (see Figure 1; reviewed in 39). These findings have led to the idea that PSD-95 serves as a scaffold to assemble a complex of specific signaling proteins associated with NMDA receptors. For example, neuronal nitric oxide synthase (nNOS), which itself contains a PDZ domain, has been shown to bind to PDZ1/2 of PSD-95 via a PDZ-PDZ interaction (40). A splice variant of nNOS that specifically lacks its PDZ domain no longer associates with PSD-95 in vitro and becomes mislocalized from membrane to cytosolic fractions in vivo (40). By binding to both nNOS and NR2 subunits, PSD-95 can bring nNOS into close proximity of the NMDA receptor channel. The selective stimulation of nNOS (a calcium-regulated enzyme) by activation of NMDA receptors (a calcium-permeant channel) can be neatly explained by the physical association of these

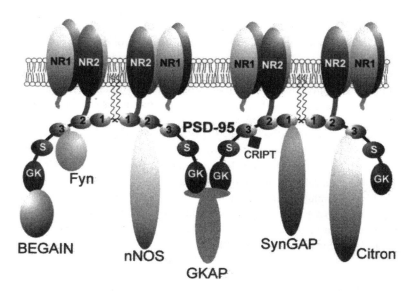

Figure 1 The *N*-methyl-D-aspartate receptor–postsynaptic density-95 complex. The C terminus of *N*-methyl-D-aspartate receptor NR2 subunits binds to the first two PDZ domains of postsynaptic density (PSD)-95. Major identified cytoplasmic components of the PSD-95 complex and their sites of binding are shown (see text for details). PSD-95 is shown multimerized via its N-terminal region, which is palmitoylated. Individual PDZ domains are labeled 1, 2, and 3. S, SH3 domain; GK, guanylate kinase-like domain; nNOS, nitric oxide synthase; GKAP, guanylate kinase-associated protein; SynGAP, synaptic GTPase-activating protein.

proteins mediated by PSD-95. Although attractive, such a molecular mechanism for functional coupling of nNOS and NMDA receptors remains to be tested directly. It is important to understand the mechanism of NMDA receptor-nNOS coupling because it may be involved in NMDA receptor-induced production of nitric oxide, which is implicated in glutamate excitotoxicity (41) and in activity-dependent synaptic plasticity (reviewed in 42).

Regulators or effectors of small GTPases (such as Ras and Rho) have been found to bind to PSD-95 and hence to be associated with the NMDA receptor complex in the PSD. A synaptic GTPase-activating protein for Ras, SynGAP, has a C terminus that interacts with all three PDZ domains of PSD-95 (43, 44). SynGAP is a PSD protein whose association with PSD-95 positions it appropriately to inactivate Ras, after Ras is activated by NMDA receptor stimulation (45). Interestingly, SynGAP enzymatic activity is repressed by CaMKII (44), another abundant PSD enzyme that has been implicated in synaptic plasticity and NMDA receptor signaling. The functional role of SynGAP in synaptic function and plasticity remains to be clarified.

The Rho/Rac subfamily of small GTPases may also be involved in NMDA receptor signaling, based on the observation that a Rho effector, citron, can bind preferentially to PDZ3 of PSD-95 (46, 47). Because Rho-type GTPases are involved in regulation of the cytoskeleton, activity-dependent modulation of postsynaptic actin might be mediated via a cascade involving NMDA receptors, Rho/Rac, PSD-95, and citron. Citron is localized predominantly to glutamatergic synapses of inhibitory neurons in the hippocampus, whereas the protein is found in both inhibitory and excitatory neurons in other brain regions (46). These data illustrate the principle that distinct protein complexes can be assembled around PSD-95 (and hence NMDA receptors) in different cell types.

Nonreceptor tyrosine kinases of the Src family are implicated in NMDA receptor modulation and downstream signaling; for example, NMDA receptor channel activity is regulated by tyrosine phosphorylation (48) and can be stimulated in heterologous cells by Src and the related kinase Fyn (49). Furthermore, induction of hippocampal LTP is associated with Src activation (50) and phosphorylation of NR2A/B subunits (51, 52). Recent evidence suggests that Fyn binds via its SH2 domain to PDZ3 of PSD-95 (53). This interaction appears to be of physiological importance because Fyn-deficient mice show greatly reduced levels of NR2A phosphorylation, indicating that Fyn is probably the major kinase that phosphorylates the NR2A subunit in vivo. Because PSD-95 enhances the phosphorylation of NR2A by Fyn in heterologous cells (53), it is likely that PSD-95 targets Fyn to its NMDA receptor substrate by formation of a ternary complex. Other tyrosine kinases of this family (Src, Yes, and Lyn) can also be coimmunoprecipitated with NMDA receptors (53, 54), perhaps via binding to PSD-95. The importance of PSD-95 in the association of nonreceptor tyrosine kinases with NMDA receptors should be testable in the PSD-95 knockout mice.

The GK-like domain of PSD-95 family proteins also functions as a site for protein-protein interactions. No catalytic activity has been found for this domain

(55), which shows homology to enzymes involved in GMP/GDP metabolism. The GK domain binds to an abundant family of proteins in the PSD, termed guanylate kinase-associated protein (GKAP)/SAPAP/DAP, whose function is unclear (56–59). In addition, the GK domain of PSD-95 family proteins binds to a novel protein of unknown function, BEGAIN (60), to a putative GTPase-activating protein for the small GTPase Rap (60; DTS Pak & M Sheng, unpublished observations), and to the microtubule-binding protein MAP1A (61; see below). The potential interactions among this set of GK-binding proteins and their physiological roles in NMDA receptor function remain to be determined.

Although the concept of PSD-95 as a scaffold for NMDA receptor signaling proteins is an attractive one, there is a paucity of direct evidence that PSD-95–associated proteins are relevant to NMDA receptor signal transduction. In some cases, such as nNOS, Src/Fyn, and SynGAP, the signaling molecules are involved in biochemical pathways known to be activated by, or to impinge upon, NMDA receptors. In other cases, the functional connection between NMDA receptors and the PSD-95–interacting protein is quite conjectural. That PSD-95 functions as a signaling scaffold is still largely extrapolated from other PDZ-based signaling complexes in genetically amenable organisms. Perhaps the best example is in *Drosophila,* where many components of the phototransduction cascade are organized around InaD, a scaffold protein containing 5 PDZ domains (30, 31, 62). Mutation of individual PDZs of InaD causes mislocalization of specific interacting proteins and disruption of normal light responses. PSD-95 needs to be analyzed in a similarly systematic fashion by genetic or dominant-negative approaches to confirm its function as a scaffold for proteins involved in NMDA receptor signaling. It should be borne in mind that PSD-95 might organize other membrane receptors in addition to NMDA receptors (such as adhesion receptors or receptor tyrosine kinases), and thus PSD-95–associated proteins may serve NMDA receptor-independent signaling functions. An example of a PSD-95–binding protein that might be unrelated to NMDA receptor signaling is adenomatosis polyposis coli (63), whose only known functions are in tumorigenesis and Wingless/Wnt signaling.

PSD-95 family MAGUKs contain an SH3 domain, a well-known protein-binding module (64). To date, however, no binding partner has been identified for the SH3 domain of PSD-95, except a kainate receptor subunit in vitro (65). Almost certainly, other cytoplasmic binding partners of PSD-95 remain to be identified. These could be novel proteins or established players in NMDA receptor signaling and/or synaptic plasticity, such as tyrosine phosphatases, serine/threonine phosphatases, and serine/threonine kinases. These proteins could bind directly to the various domains of PSD-95, or they could associate with PSD-95 indirectly via intermediary proteins. Thus the known PSD-95–based protein complex linked to NMDA receptors will undoubtedly grow in size and complexity in the coming years.

Anchoring to the Cytoskeleton Although anchoring to the cytoskeleton is probably involved in the subcellular localization of a ligand-gated channel, it will be considered here separately from subcellular targeting (which is the endpoint of a complex series of sorting and anchoring mechanisms). By binding to cytoskeletal elements, a scaffold protein such as PSD-95 can in principle connect NMDA receptors to the cytoskeleton, as well as to cytoplasmic signaling proteins. Consistent with this idea, PSD-95 and its postsynaptic relatives are indeed highly insoluble proteins of the PSD. Several sets of protein-protein interactions have been identified that might anchor PSD-95 to the postsynaptic cytoskeleton.

SAP97 (a member of the PSD-95 family, also known as hDlg) has been shown to bind in vitro to band 4.1, an actin/spectrin-binding protein (22, 66). This interaction involves a stretch of basic amino acids in an alternatively spliced exon between the SH3 and GK domains of SAP97 and possibly an additional site within the N-terminal region (67). Whether PSD-95 and its postsynaptic relatives interact with band 4.1 (or other members of the ezrin-radixin-moesin family of actin-binding proteins) is unclear, but an analogous interaction between the MAGUK family member CASK and protein 4.1 has been reported (68). Such an interaction has the potential to link NMDA receptors indirectly to F-actin, which is the predominant cytoskeleton in dendritic spines.

Although tubulin is present in PSD preparations and microtubule-associated proteins such as MAP2 have been immunocytochemically localized at synapses (69–71), microtubules are generally thought to be sparse or absent from dendritic spines. Somewhat surprisingly, therefore, it has been found that PSD-95 interacts with microtubule-associated proteins. The third PDZ domain of PSD-95 binds to CRIPT, a small polypeptide that associates with microtubules (72; M Passafaro & M Sheng, unpublished observations). PSD-95 family proteins can also bind directly to MAP1A; intriguingly, this MAP1A binding occurs via the GK domain of PSD-95 and seems to be stimulated by occupancy of the neighboring PDZ domains (61). The interaction of PSD-95 family proteins with microtubule-binding proteins such as CRIPT or MAP1A may link NMDA receptors indirectly to a postsynaptic tubulin-based cytoskeleton. Interestingly, another report suggests that the C termini of NR1 and NR2B subunits bind directly to soluble tubulin (73). It is controversial whether tubulin contributes to the cytoskeletal organization of the PSD in dendritic spines (74, 75). However, microtubule anchoring may be relevant for the minor fraction of excitatory synapses that are made onto microtubule-rich dendritic shafts (such as the aspiny excitatory synapses of inhibitory interneurons). Anchoring of ionotropic receptors via microtubule-binding proteins seems to apply particularly to the inhibitory receptors, such as GABA receptors and glycine receptors, which typically are found postsynaptically on dendritic shafts rather than on dendritic spines (see below).

Clustering/Aggregation   We use the word clustering here to mean aggregation or packing at high density in the membrane; thus clustering is conceptually distinct from localization in a defined microdomain. By analogy to the nicotinic ACh receptors of the NMJ, it is believed that glutamate receptors are present at high density in the postsynaptic membrane (although this has not been directly measured like the nicotinic receptor at the NMJ). Aggregation of nicotinic ACh receptors is probably dependent on interaction of receptor subunits with rapsyn (reviewed in 1). Heterologous expression experiments suggest that NMDA receptors can be aggregated by their binding to PSD-95. A striking feature is the mutual coclustering of PSD-95 with NR2 (or NR1/NR2 heteromers) when these interacting proteins are coexpressed in heterologous cells—when separately expressed, PSD-95 and NMDA receptors are diffusely distributed (21). These findings led to the idea that PSD-95 may aggregate its binding partners at high density in the postsynaptic membrane, analogously to rapsyn. The clustering activity of PSD-95 is dependent on its N-terminal region (upstream of PDZ1), which contains a pair of cysteines, and on PDZ1 or PDZ2, which bind to NR2 (76, 77). The N-terminal region and its pair of cysteines are also essential for multimerization (76, 77), palmitoylation, and synaptic targeting of PSD-95 (78, 79). How these properties relate mechanistically to each other remains to be determined. Similarly, the connection between PSD-95–dependent clustering of NMDA receptors in heterologous cells and the high concentration of NMDA receptors in the PSD is unclear. Thus the in vivo significance of PSD-95–mediated aggregation remains unresolved.

Interactions of the NR1 Subunit

NMDA receptors contain the essential NR1 subunit in addition to the NR2 subunits that bind to PSD-95 family proteins. NR1 undergoes alternative splicing of its C-terminal cytoplasmic tail, which is considerably shorter than that of the NR2 subunits. In general, NR1 does not bind to PSD-95, although there is some uncertainty about the minor C-terminal splice variants of NR1 (8). Despite its short length ($\sim$100 aa), the cytoplasmic tail of NR1 has been shown to interact with several different cytoplasmic proteins (Figure 2).

α-Actinin, an actin-binding protein, interacts with the membrane-proximal segment (termed C0) of NR1's cytoplasmic tail (80, 81). Because α-actinin is enriched in the PSD, its interaction with NR1 may contribute to NMDA receptor-cytoskeletal anchoring at postsynaptic sites. Ca^{2+}/calmodulin binds to two distinct sites in the NR1 tail—with moderate affinity to the C0 segment ($K_d \sim 80$ nM) and with higher affinity (K_d 3.7 nM) to the C1 segment, which is encoded by the differentially spliced exon 22 of the gene (82). The binding of Ca^{2+}/calmodulin inhibits NMDA receptor opening and reduces mean channel open time (82). The calmodulin- and α-actinin–binding sites overlap in C0, and these proteins compete in vitro for binding to NR1 (80). Interplay between calmodulin and α-actinin appears to be important in vivo for calcium-dependent inactivation of NMDA receptors, which is modulated by the actin cytoskeleton (4). Recent studies suggest that calcium-dependent inactivation occurs by the competitive displacement of α-actinin from NR1 by Ca^{2+}/calmodulin (83, 84). The C0 segment of the NR1 cytoplasmic tail is required for calcium-dependent inactivation of NMDA receptors, and it may be directly involved in channel gating. Direct

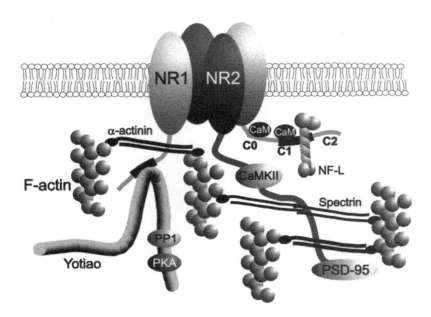

Figure 2 *N*-methyl-D-aspartate receptor interactions mediated independently of postsynaptic density (PSD)-95. C1 and C2 are alternatively spliced segments of the NR1 cytoplasmic tail. Black filled circles represent actin-binding domains of α-actinin and spectrin. CaM, Ca^{2+}/calmodulin; CaMKII, calmodulin-dependent kinase type II; PP1, protein phosphatase 1; PKA, protein kinase A; NF-L, neurofilament-L.

binding and regulation of ion channels by calmodulin is emerging as a common theme (reviewed in 85). By analogy with L-type calcium channels and calcium-dependent K^+ channels (85), it will be interesting to determine whether calmodulin is constitutively bound to NMDA receptors in a calcium-independent manner, poised to respond to calcium influx through the NMDA receptor channel.

The C1 exon segment of the NR1 tail is not required for calcium-dependent inactivation of NMDA receptors despite binding calmodulin, but it does contain several protein kinase C (PKC) phosphorylation sites that play a role in the clustering of NR1, at least when overexpressed in heterologous cells (86). Two proteins, yotiao (87) and neurofilament L (88), have been found to interact specifically with splice variants of NR1 containing the C1 exon. The functions of yotiao and neurofilament L in the context of NMDA receptors are unclear. Yotiao binds to both protein kinase A (PKA) and protein phosphatase 1; its function in synapses may be to target PKA and protein phosphatase 1 to NMDA receptors, thus facilitating bidirectional NMDA receptor modulation by these enzymes (89).

Other Interactions of *N*-Methyl-D-Aspartate Receptors

S-SCAM, a protein with an N-terminal GK domain followed by two WW motifs and five PDZ domains, has been shown to bind to NR2 subunits with its fifth PDZ domain (90). S-SCAM belongs to a family of proteins that includes AIP1 and MAGI; it is present in the PSD, but not as enriched as is PSD-95 or SAPAP. The in vivo significance of S-SCAM in NMDA receptor function remains to be determined.

Spectrin, a well-known actin-binding protein, is reported to bind to the cytoplasmic domains of NR1, NR2A, and NR2B, but not to the AMPA (α-amino-3-hydroxy-5-methylisoxazole-4-propionic acid) receptor subunit GluR1 (91). The spectrin-binding site in NR2B is distinct from the α-actinin– and PSD-95–binding regions. A specific form of brain spectrin is abundant in the PSD and may thus offer another mode for attaching NMDA receptors to the postsynaptic actin cytoskeleton. Spectrin interaction with NR2B is sensitive to tyrosine phosphorylation and calcium, whereas the binding of spectrin to NR1 is inhibited by PKC/PKA phosphorylation and calmodulin (91). These findings suggest possible mechanisms for activity-dependent regulation of the NMDA receptor anchoring to the cytoskeleton.

AMPA RECEPTORS

AMPA receptors are typically composed of heteromeric combinations of GluR1–4 subunits (6, 7). The membrane topology of GluR subunits is analogous to that of NMDA receptor subunits, with a C-terminal tail that is cytoplasmically disposed. Several groups have used the yeast two-hybrid system to isolate AMPA receptor-binding proteins in the same way as was done for NMDA receptors. Most identified proteins have been found via interaction with the GluR2/3 subunits (Figure 3). Interestingly, the GluR2 subunit confers calcium impermeability on AMPA receptors and is found in the majority of AMPA receptors in principal neurons of the forebrain (92). Despite coexisting at the same excitatory synapses, AMPA receptors bind to a set of cytoplasmic proteins distinct from those for NMDA receptors. Nevertheless, continuing the theme established by NMDA receptors, a major set of AMPA receptor interactions is mediated by C-terminal binding to specific PDZ-containing scaffold proteins.

Interactions with PDZ Proteins

GluR2 and GluR3 subunits share a common C-terminal sequence (–SVKI) that interacts with the 5th PDZ domain of GRIP (now termed GRIP1), a protein containing seven PDZs and no other recognizable domains (93, 94). A protein with 6 PDZ domains [AMPA receptor-binding protein (ABP)] was also isolated by its binding to GluR2/3 (95). ABP appears to be a splice variant of a GRIP-

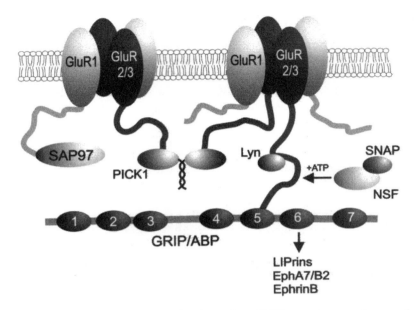

Figure 3   The AMPA receptor-associated complex. AMPA receptors are shown as heteromers of GluR1 and GluR2/3. PICK-1 is depicted hypothetically as a dimer cross-linking two AMPA receptors. *N*-ethylmaleimide-sensitive factor (NSF) binds to the GluR2/3 cytoplasmic tail in an ATP-dependent manner. Binding partners for most of the PDZ domains of GRIP/AMPA receptor-binding protein (ABP) remain to be identified. SAP97, synapse-associated protein; SNAP, soluble NSF attachment protein.

related protein (also called GRIP2) that contains seven PDZs (ABP lacking the N terminus and PDZ7 of GRIP2) (96; 96a,b). Although a large fraction of GluR2/3 appears to be biochemically associated with GRIP in vivo (96a), the function of the GluR2/3-GRIP interaction is still unclear. At the subcellular level, GRIP is not as specifically associated with synapses as is PSD-95, and its expression predates AMPA receptors during development (94; 96a,b). Thus GRIP almost certainly is involved in functions other than AMPA receptor anchoring in synapses. GRIP also differs from PSD-95 in being relatively abundant in intracellular compartments in dendrites and cell bodies of neurons, suggesting that GRIP may be more important for trafficking than for synaptic anchoring of AMPA receptors (94; 96a,b). The fact that overexpression of the C-terminal tail of GluR2 in neurons inhibits synaptic clustering of AMPA receptors (93) is consistent with either an anchoring or trafficking role for GRIP. Trafficking of AMPA receptors to the synapse is of interest because of the emerging concept of silent synapses being activated by postsynaptic insertion of AMPA receptors (97).

Containing seven and six PDZ domains, respectively, GRIP and ABP have the capacity to assemble a complex protein architecture around AMPA receptors.

GRIP has been shown to bind to EphB2 and EphA7, members of the large family of Eph receptor tyrosine kinases, and to the ephrin B ligands for Eph receptors (96, 98). Eph receptor–ephrin interactions are involved in axon guidance, cell migration, and establishment of tissue boundaries (99). LIPrins, proteins that bind to the LAR family of receptor tyrosine phosphatases (100), also bind to GRIP, utilizing PDZ6 (M Wyszynski, M Sheng, unpublished observations). LAR tyrosine phosphatases are also involved in axon guidance (101). The relevance of these GRIP-mediated interactions to AMPA receptors is unclear at present.

In addition to GRIP/ABP, the C-terminal sequence of GluR2/3 mediates binding to PICK-1 (102), another PDZ-containing protein previously shown to bind PKC (103). PICK1 colocalizes with GluR2 in synapses and is capable of clustering GluR2 in heterologous cells, probably via coiled-coil dimerization (102). Because PKCα is enriched in synapses, the possibility exists that PICK1 may recruit PKC to AMPA receptors, although this has yet to be demonstrated. The relative importance of PICK-1 and GRIP/ABP in AMPA receptor anchoring/trafficking in vivo remains to be worked out, but the situation illustrates the point that there can be several PDZ partners for a given C-terminal sequence.

The GluR1 subunit of AMPA receptors does not bind to GRIP, ABP, or PICK-1, but its C terminus has been recently shown to associate with SAP97, a member of the PSD-95 family of MAGUKs (104). Because SAP97 is thought to be predominantly presynaptic (23), however, the physiological significance of this interaction is uncertain.

Interactions with NSF and Signaling Proteins

As with NMDA receptors, C-terminal PDZ interactions are not the only means of linking the AMPA receptor to its molecular entourage. Via a membrane proximal segment of its cytoplasmic tail (distinct from the C terminus that binds to GRIP or PICK-1), GluR2 binds to NSF, an ATPase required for the vesicle fusion cycle (105–107). The functional significance of this surprising interaction is not yet understood, but it may relate to the vesicle trafficking or molecular chaperoning of AMPA receptors (reviewed in 108).

Additionally, AMPA receptors have been shown to interact with the Src-related nonreceptor tyrosine kinase Lyn, which coimmunoprecipitates with GluR2/3 from cerebellar extracts (109). This interaction requires the SH3 domain of Lyn and a membrane-proximal 20-aa region of the GluR2 C-terminal tail (just upstream of the NSF-binding site). Lyn is activated by AMPA and is required for AMPA receptor-mediated stimulation of MAP kinase and *BDNF* gene expression, but this interaction is unusual in that it appears not to require ion flux by the glutamate receptor. Instead, the authors propose that the signal is transduced by conformational changes in the receptor upon binding of AMPA (109). This mechanism is reminiscent of the activation of a heterotrimeric G protein (G_i) by AMPA receptors in cortical neurons (110), which also appears to be independent of GluR channel function. Stimulation by AMPA dissociates the $G_{\alpha i1}$ subunit from $G_{\beta\gamma i}$, an event correlated with a rapid association of $G_{\alpha i1}$ with GluR1. However, it is not known whether $G_{\alpha i1}$ binds to GluR1 directly or via an adapter protein.

KAINATE RECEPTORS AND δ RECEPTORS

Kainate receptors represent a third class of glutamate-gated ion channel and are made up of subunits (GluR5–7, KA1, and KA2) that are homologous to AMPA receptor subunits. The cytoplasmic domains of GluR6 and KA2 have been shown to bind to the PDZ1 domain and to the SH3 and GK domains of PSD-95, respectively (65), but the in vivo significance of these interactions for kainate receptors is unclear.

Another member of the ionotropic glutamate receptor superfamily is GluRδ, distantly related (~25% identity) to NMDA and AMPA/kainate receptors. GluRδ2, which is the best studied member of this family, is expressed specifically in cerebellar Purkinje cells. Although not functional in heterologous expression systems, GluRδ2 plays a physiological role as evidenced by gain-of-function mutations in this gene underlying the phenotype of Lurcher mice (111) and by gene-targeting experiments demonstrating a requirement for GluRδ2 in synapse function and development in cerebellum (112). Roche et al have shown that GluRδ2 binds to PSD-93/chapsyn in vitro and colocalizes with PSD-93 in parallel fiber synapses in vivo (113).

GABA RECEPTORS

Fast inhibitory transmission in the brain is mediated mainly by ionotropic GABA (principally $GABA_A$) receptors with diverse subunit composition drawn from ≥6 different gene families. These ligand-gated chloride channels are segregated from NMDA and AMPA receptors and concentrated specifically in the postsynaptic membrane of GABA-ergic synapses (114). Could the differential subcellular localization of ionotropic GABA receptors be mediated by their interaction with distinct intracellular proteins? Although GABA receptors have a membrane topology that is quite different from excitatory amino acid receptors, recent evidence indicates that they do indeed interact with cytoplasmic proteins, just like glutamate-gated channels.

As members of the pentameric ligand-gated ion channel superfamily exemplified by the nicotinic ACh receptor, GABA receptor subunits expose their C termini on the extracellular side of the membrane. The major cytoplasmic portion of GABA receptors is the loop between the third and fourth TM segments (TM3 and TM4; Figure 4). Recently, two groups have used this loop from different GABA receptor subunits to identify interacting proteins by the yeast two-hybrid system. One group (115) used the intracellular loop of γ2 (the most abundant $GABA_A$ subunit in the central nervous system) to clone a novel $GABA_A$ receptor-

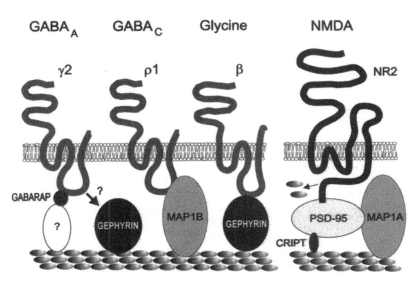

Figure 4 Interactions of inhibitory ionotropic receptors and N-methyl-D-aspartate (NMDA) receptors with microtubules and tubulin. GABA receptor-associated protein (GABARAP) is depicted as binding to a hypothetical microtubule-associated protein (MAP). The mechanism of GABA$_A$ receptor interaction with gephyrin is unknown. PSD-95, postsynaptic density 95.

associated protein (GABARAP). GABARAP binds specifically to an 18-aa of the γ2 intracellular loop; it does not interact with β1 or several α subunits of GABA$_A$ receptors. GABARAP and GABA$_A$ receptors appear to be associated in vivo, based on coimmunoprecipitation from brain extracts and immunocytochemical colocalization in cultured cortical neurons. GABARAP is a small 117-aa polypeptide with ~30% identity to light chain-3 of microtubule-associated proteins MAP1A and MAP1B. This similarity in primary structure suggests that GABARAP may also be a component of some MAP complex, and indeed GABARAP fractionates with microtubules (115). Remarkably, MAP1B itself was isolated as a specific binding protein for the ρ1 subunit of ionotropic GABA$_C$ receptors (116), a GABA receptor subtype expressed almost exclusively in the retina. The intracellular loop of ρ1 binds to a region adjacent to the microtubule binding domain of MAP1B. Because MAP1B binds in vitro to actin as well as microtubules (117), the interaction of ρ1 and MAP1B could potentially link GABA$_C$ receptors to both actin- and tubulin-based cytoskeletons. The subunit specificity of MAP1B and GABARAP interactions raises the possibility that differential localization of GABA$_A$ and GABA$_C$ receptors within the retina may be caused by their specific association with GABARAP and MAP1B, respectively. Genetic experiments are required to test the functional significance of MAP1B and GABARAP in synaptic localization of ionotropic GABA receptors.

GLYCINE RECEPTORS

The interaction of ionotropic GABA receptors with MAP1B and GABARAP is reminiscent of the interaction between inhibitory glycine receptors (composed of heteromers of a β subunit and various α subunits) and gephyrin, another microtubule-binding protein (reviewed in 118). The gephyrin interaction is analogously mediated by the intracellular loop between TM3 and TM4 of the glycine receptor β subunit (119) (Figure 4). Recently, the importance of gephyrin in synaptic localization of glycine receptors was confirmed by gene targeting in mice (120). Gephyrin is also found in GABA-ergic synapses, and genetic evidence indicates that gephyrin and GABA$_A$ receptors are dependent on each other for proper postsynaptic localization (121); however, no direct biochemical interaction has been shown between gephyrin and GABA$_A$ receptor subunits.

Binding to specific microtubule-associated proteins appears to be the primary mode of cytoskeletal attachment for inhibitory ionotropic receptors. The specific interaction of GABA$_A$, GABA$_C$, and glycine receptors with different microtubule-binding proteins is consistent with the idea that GABARAP, MAP1B, and gephyrin mediate the segregation of these receptors among different subsets of inhibitory synapses. However, such an idea may be too simplistic, given the complex subcellular distribution of GABA$_A$ receptor subtypes in particular (see for example 122). It remains to be seen whether these microtubule-associated proteins also function as adaptors for binding to signal transduction proteins, in addition to their roles as cytoskeletal anchors. Presumably, inhibitory ionotropic receptors are also associated with a specific modulatory enzyme and signaling proteins at postsynaptic sites, but these interactions have yet to be uncovered.

COMPARISON OF ANCHORING MECHANISMS

To simplify the evidence at hand, it appears that inhibitory ionotropic receptors, NMDA receptors and AMPA receptors interact with cytoskeleton in different ways. GABA and glycine receptors bind directly to microtubule-associated proteins, which can anchor them to microtubules. Thus the anchoring of inhibitory receptors to the cytoskeleton seems to be relatively simple, at least at the present time. NMDA receptors may also interact with microtubules, albeit more indirectly via PSD-95 and CRIPT and MAP1A. However, their main connections are with the actin cytoskeleton; this can be through direct interactions with actin-binding proteins such as α-actinin and spectrin or indirectly through scaffold proteins (e.g. via PSD-95–mediated interactions). NMDA receptor subunits may also interact directly with tubulin and neurofilaments via less-well-defined mechanisms. In sum, NMDA receptors associate with cytoskeleton by several independent pathways. On the other hand, the characterized protein interactions mediated by AMPA receptor subunits have so far not revealed any obvious means of anchorage to the cytoskeleton (except possibly via a SAP97-mediated linkage of GluR1 to protein 4.1). These different modes or levels of cytoskeletal interaction can be usefully rationalized based on known properties of the specific receptors. For instance, involvement of microtubule-binding proteins in the cytoskeletal anchoring of ionotropic GABA and glycine receptors correlates with the fact that inhibitory synapses form primarily on the shafts of proximal dendrites (in which microtubules are abundant) rather than on dendritic spines (in which microtubules are sparse or absent). The multiple modes of NMDA receptor association with cytoskeleton are likely to explain the high degree of detergent insolubility of NMDA receptors and their abundance as core components of the PSD. By comparison with NMDA receptors, AMPA receptors are much more easily extractable by detergents from brain tissue, perhaps reflecting the paucity of their known interactions with cytoskeleton. Thus NMDA receptors can be considered more stably anchored to the PSD, whereas the biochemical properties of AMPA receptors correlate with the more dynamic character of AMPA receptor trafficking that occurs in neurons.

CONCLUDING REMARKS

From the many recent studies reviewed above, a daunting picture has emerged of the complexity of ionotropic-receptor interactions with cytoplasmic proteins. This is particularly true of the NMDA receptors, which play prominent roles in intracellular signaling by virtue of their calcium permeability. Both the NR1 and NR2 subunits of NMDA receptors participate in specific sets of interactions with a variety of intracellular proteins. These NMDA receptor–interacting proteins may have direct effects on receptor-channel activity (such as α-actinin and calmodulin), or they may function as adaptor/scaffold proteins (like PSD-95) to connect the receptor to the cytoskeleton and to intracellular-signaling pathways. The overall impression is of a branching network of specific protein-protein interactions that extend like roots of a tree from the NMDA receptor cytoplasmic tails into the cell interior. These analogies extend to AMPA receptors, whose different subunits appear to mediate interactions with distinct sets of cytoplasmic proteins, including the multi-PDZ scaffolds GRIP and ABP. In many cases, the identity of the interacting protein was unexpected (such as NSF binding to AMPA receptor GluR2 subunits), leading to novel insights about receptor function and regulation. Inhibitory ionotropic receptors so far appear to interact only with cytoskeletal elements; this may reflect their relatively passive activity as ligand-gated chloride channels or the fact that research into their cytoplasmic binding partners is at an earlier stage.

In any case, identification of the cytoskeletal and signaling proteins that interact with ligand-gated ion channels is only a first step in a long endeavor. The major challenges of the future are to quantify the stoichiometry of these protein interactions; to picture their geometry by microscopic and structural biological approaches; to reveal the dynamic regulation of receptor-associated protein complexes during development and in response to activity; and, perhaps most importantly, to understand the functional significance of these protein interactions in channel regulation, synapse development, and synaptic plasticity.

Visit the Annual Reviews home page at www.AnnualReviews.org.

LITERATURE CITED

1. Colledge M, Froehner SC. 1998. Signals mediating ion channel clustering at the neuromuscular junction. *Curr. Opin. Neurobiol.* 8:357–63

2. Kennedy MB. 1997. The postsynaptic density at glutamatergic synapses. *Trends Neurosci.* 20:264–68

3. Ziff EB. 1997. Enlightening the postsynaptic density. *Neuron* 19:1163–74

4. Rosenmund C, Westbrook GL. 1993. Calcium-induced actin depolymerization reduces NMDA channel activity. *Neuron* 10:805–14

5. Paoletti P, Ascher P. 1994. Mechanosensitivity of NMDA receptors in cultured mouse central neurons. *Neuron* 13:645–55

6. Dingledine R, Borges K, Bowie D, Traynelis SF. 1999. The glutamate receptor ion channels. *Pharmacol. Rev.* 51:7–61

7. Hollmann M, Heinemann S. 1994. Cloned glutamate receptors. *Annu. Rev. Neurosci.* 17:31–108

8. Kornau H-C, Schenker LT, Kennedy MB, Seeburg PH. 1995. Domain interaction between NMDA receptor subunits and the postsynaptic density protein PSD-95. *Science* 269:1737–40

9. Niethammer M, Kim E, Sheng M. 1996. Interaction between the C terminus of NMDA receptor subunits and multiple members of the PSD-95 family of membrane-associated guanylate kinases. *J. Neurosci.* 16:2157–63

10. Sheng M. 1996. PDZs and receptor/channel clustering: rounding up the latest suspects. *Neuron* 17:575–78

11. Kornau HC, Seeburg PH, Kennedy MB.

1997. Interaction of ion channels and receptors with PDZ domain proteins. *Curr. Opin. Neurobiol.* 7:368–73

12. O'Brien R, Lau L, Huganir R. 1998. Molecular mechanisms of glutamate receptor clustering at excitatory synapses. *Curr. Opin. Neurobiol.* 8:364–69

13. Ponting CP, Phillips C, Davies KE, Blake DJ. 1997. PDZ domains: targeting signalling molecules to sub-membranous sites. *BioEssays* 19:469–79

14. Doyle DA, Lee A, Lewis J, Kim E, Sheng M, et al. 1996. Crystal structures of a complexed and peptide-free membrane protein-binding domain: molecular basis of peptide recognition by PDZ. *Cell* 85:1067–76

15. Songyang Z, Fanning AS, Fu C, Xu J, Marfatia SM, et al. 1997. Recognition of unique carboxyl-terminal motifs by distinct PDZ domains. *Science* 275:73–77

16. Cowburn D. 1997. Peptide recognition by PTB and PDZ domains. *Curr. Opin. Struct. Biol.* 7:835–38

17. Kim E, Niethammer M, Rothschild A, Jan YN, Sheng M. 1995. Clustering of Shaker-type K$^+$ channels by interaction with a family of membrane-associated guanylate kinases. *Nature* 378:85–88

18. Cho K-O, Hunt CA, Kennedy MB. 1992. The rat brain postsynaptic density fraction contains a homolog of the Drosophila discs-large tumor suppressor protein. *Neuron* 9:929–42

19. Kistner U, Wenzel BM, Veh RW, Cases-Langhoff C, Garner AM, et al. 1993. SAP90, a rat presynaptic protein related to the product of the *Drosophila* tumor

suppressor gene *dlg*-A. *J. Biol. Chem.* 268:4580–83

20. Brenman JE, Christopherson KS, Craven SE, McGee AW, Bredt DS. 1996. Cloning and characterization of postsynaptic density 93, a nitric oxide synthase interacting protein. *J. Neurosci.* 16:7407–15

21. Kim E, Cho K-O, Rothschild A, Sheng M. 1996. Heteromultimerization and NMDA receptor-clustering activity of chapsyn-110, a member of the PSD-95 family of proteins. *Neuron* 17:103–13

22. Lue RA, Marfatia SM, Branton D, Chishti AH. 1994. Cloning and characterization of hdlg: the human homologue of the Drosophila discs large tumor suppressor binds to protein 4.1. *Proc. Natl. Acad. Sci. USA* 91:9818–22

23. Müller BM, Kistner U, Veh RW, Cases-Langhoff C, Becker B, et al. 1995. Molecular characterization and spatial distribution of SAP97, a novel presynaptic protein homologous to SAP90 and the *Drosophila* discs-large tumor suppressor protein. *J. Neurosci.* 15:2354–66

24. Müller BM, Kistner U, Kindler S, Chung WJ, Kuhlendahl S, et al. 1996. SAP102, a novel postsynaptic protein that interacts with the cytoplasmic tail of the NMDA receptor subunit NR2B. *Neuron* 17:255–65

25. Woods DF, Bryant PJ. 1991. The discs-large tumor suppressor gene of Drosophila encodes a guanylate kinase homolog localized at septate junctions. *Cell* 66:451–64

26. Guan B, Hartmann B, Kho Y-H, Gorczyca M, Budnik V. 1996. The *Drosophila* tumor suppressor gene, *dlg,* is involved in structural plasticity at a glutamatergic synapse. *Curr. Biol.* 6:695–706

27. Tejedor FJ, Bokhari A, Rogero O, Gorczyca M, Zhang J, et al. 1997. Essential role for *dlg* in synaptic clustering of Shaker K$^+$ channels in vivo. *J. Neurosci.* 17:152–59

28. Thomas U, Kim E, Kuhlendahl S, Ho Koh Y, Gundelfinger ED, et al. 1997. Synaptic clustering of the cell adhesion molecule fasciclin II by discs-large and its role in the regulation of presynaptic structure. *Neuron* 19:787–99

29. Zito K, Fetter RD, Goodman CS, Isacoff EY. 1997. Synaptic clustering of fasciclin II and shaker: essential targeting sequences and role of dlg. *Neuron* 19:1007–16

30. Tsunoda S, Sierralta J, Sun Y, Bodner R, Suzuki E, et al. 1997. A multivalent PDZ-domain protein assembles signalling complexes in a G-protein-coupled cascade. *Nature* 388:243–49

31. Montell C. 1998. TRP trapped in fly signaling web. *Curr. Opin. Neurobiol.* 8:389–97

32. Bredt DS. 1998. Sorting out genes that regulate epithelial and neuronal polarity. *Cell* 94:691–94

33. Migaud M, Charlesworth P, Dempster M, Webster LC, Watabe AM, et al. 1998. Enhanced long-term potentiation and impaired learning in mice with mutant postsynaptic density-95 protein. *Nature* 396:433–39

34. Mori H, Manabe T, Watanabe M, Sath Y, Suzuki N, et al. 1998. Role of the carboxy-terminal region of the GluR epsilon2 subunit in synaptic localization of the NMDA receptor channel. *Neuron* 21:571–80

35. Sprengel R, Suchanek B, Amico C, Brusa R, Burnasheve N, et al. 1998. Importance of the intracellular domain of NR2 subunits for NMDA receptor function in vivo. *Cell* 92:279–89

36. Leonard AS, Lim IA, Hemsworth DE, Horne MC, Hell JW. 1999. Calcium/calmodulin-dependent protein kinase II is associated with the *N*-methyl-D-aspartate receptor. *Proc. Natl. Acad. Sci. USA* 96:3239–44

37. Strack S, Colbran RJ. 1998. Autophosphorylation-dependent targeting of calcium/calmodulin-dependent protein kinase II by the NR2B subunit of the *N*-

methyl-D-aspartate receptor. *J. Biol. Chem.* 273:20689–92

38. Shen K, Meyer T. 1999. Dynamic control of CaMKII translocation and localization in hippocampal neurons by NMDA receptor stimulation. *Science* 284:162–66

39. Craven S, Bredt D. 1998. PDZ proteins organize synaptic signaling pathways. *Cell* 93:495–98

40. Brenman JE, Chao DS, Gee SH, McGee AW, Craven SE, et al. 1996. Interaction of nitric oxide synthase with the postsynaptic density protein PSD-95 and α1-syntrophin mediated by PDZ domains. *Cell* 84:757–67

41. Dawson VL, Dawson TM, London ED, Bredt DS, Snyder SH. 1991. Nitric oxide mediates glutamate neurotoxicity in primary cortical cultures. *Proc. Natl. Acad. Sci. USA* 88:6368–71

42. Holscher C. 1997. Nitric oxide, the enigmatic neuronal messenger: its role in synaptic plasticity. *Trends Neurosci.* 20:298–303

43. Kim JH, Liao D, Lau LF, Huganir RL. 1998. SynGAP: a synaptic RasGAP that associates with the PSD-95/SAP90 protein family. *Neuron* 20:683–91

44. Chen HJ, Rojas-Soto M, Oguni A, Kennedy MB. 1998. A synaptic Ras-GTPase activating protein (p135 SynGAP) inhibited by CaM kinase II. *Neuron* 20:895–904

45. Yun H, Gonzalez-Zulueta M, Dawson V, Dawson T. 1998. Nitric oxide mediates *N*-methyl-D-aspartate receptor-induced activation of p21ras. *Proc. Natl. Acad. Sci.* 95:5773–78

46. Zhang W, Vazquez L, Apperson M, Kennedy MB. 1999. Citron binds to PSD-95 at glutamatergic synapses on inhibitory neurons in the hippocampus. *J. Neurosci.* 19:96–108

47. Furuyashiki T, Fujisawa K, Fujita A, Madaule P, Uchino S, et al. 1999. Citron, a Rho-target, interacts with PSD-95/

SAP-90 at glutamatergic synapses in the thalamus. *J. Neurosci.* 19:109–18

48. Wang YT, Salter MW. 1994. Regulation of NMDA receptors by tyrosine kinases and phosphatases. *Nature* 369:233–35

49. Köhr G, Seeburg PH. 1996. Subtype-specific regulation of recombinant rat and mouse NMDA receptor-channels by protein tyrosine kinase of the *src* family. *J. Physiol.* 492:445–52

50. Lu YM, Roder JC, Davidow J, Salter MW. 1998. Src activation in the induction of long-term potentiation in CA1 hippocampal neurons. *Science* 279:1363–67

51. Rostas JA, Brent VA, Voss K, Errington ML, Bliss TV, et al. 1996. Enhanced tyrosine phosphorylation of the 2B subunit of the *N*-methyl-D-aspartate receptor in long-term potentiation. *Proc. Natl. Acad. Sci. USA* 93:10452–56

52. Rosenblum K, Dudai Y, Richter-Levin G. 1996. Long-term potentiation increases tyrosine phosphorylation of the *N*-methyl-D-aspartate receptor subunit 2B in rat dentate gyrus in vivo. *Proc. Natl. Acad. Sci. USA* 93:10457–60

53. Tezuka T, Umemori H, Akiyama T, Nakanishi S, Yamamoto T. 1999. PSD-95 promotes fyn-mediated tyrosine phosphorylation of the *N*-methyl-D-aspartate receptor subunit NR2A. *Proc. Natl. Acad. Sci. USA* 96:435–40

54. Yu X, Askalan R, Keil G, Salter M. 1997. NMDA channel regulation by channel-associated protein tyrosine kinase Src. *Science* 275:674–78

55. Kuhlendahl S, Spangenberg O, Konrad M, Kim E, Garner C. 1998. Functional analysis of the guanylate kinase-like domain in the synapse-associated protein SAP97. *Eur. J. Biochem.* 252:305–13

56. Kim E, Naisbitt S, Hsueh Y-P, Rao A, Rothschild A, et al. 1997. GKAP, a novel synaptic protein that interacts with the guanylate kinase-like domain of the PSD-95/SAP90 family of channel clus-

tering molecules. *J. Cell Biol.* 136:669–78

57. Naisbitt S, Kim E, Weinberg RJ, Rao A, Yang F-C, et al. 1997. Characterization of guanylate kinase-associated protein, a postsynaptic density protein at excitatory synapses that interacts directly with post-synaptic density-95/synapse-associated protein 90. *J. Neurosci.* 17:5687–96

58. Takeuchi M, Hata Y, Hirao K, Toyoda A, Irie M, et al. 1997. SAPAPs, a family of PSD-95/SAP90-associated proteins localized at postsynaptic density. *J. Biol. Chem.* 272:11943–51

59. Satoh K, Yanai H, Senda T, Kohu K, Nakamura T, et al. 1997. DAP-1, a novel protein that interacts with the guanylate kinase-like domains of hDLG and PSD-95. *Genes Cells* 2:415–24

60. Deguchi M, Hata Y, Takeuchi M, Ide N, Hirao K, et al. 1998. BEGAIN (brain-enriched guanylate kinase-associated protein), a novel neuronal PSD-95/SAP90-binding protein. *J. Biol. Chem.* 273:26269–72

61. Brenman JE, Topinka RJ, Cooper EC, McGee AW, Rosen J, et al. 1998. Localization of postsynaptic density-93 to dendritic microtubules and interaction with microtubule-associated protein 1A. *J. Neurosci.* 18:8805–13

62. Xu X-ZS, Choudhury A, Li X, Montell C. 1998. Coordination of an array of signaling proteins through homo- and het-eromeric interactions between PDZ domains and target proteins. *J. Cell Biol.* 142:545–55

63. Matsumine A, Ogai A, Senda T, Oku-mura N, Satoh K, et al. 1996. Binding of APC to the human homolog of the *Drosophila* discs large tumor suppressor protein. *Science* 272:1020–23

64. Pawson T. 1995. Protein modules and signalling networks. *Nature* 373:573–80

65. Garcia EP, Mehta S, Blair LA, Wells DG, Shang J, et al. 1998. SAP90 binds and

clusters kainate receptors causing incom-plete desensitization. *Neuron* 21:727–39

66. Marfatia SM, Cabral JH, Lin L, Hough C, Bryant PJ, et al. 1996. Modular organization of the PDZ domains in the human discs-large protein suggests a mechanism for coupling PDZ domain-binding proteins to ATP and the membrane cytoskeleton. *J. Cell Biol.* 135:753–66

67. Lue RA, Brandin E, Chan EP, Branton D. 1996. Two independent domains of hDlg are sufficient for subcellular targeting: the PDZ1–2 conformational unit and an alternatively spliced domain. *J. Cell Biol.* 135:1125–37

68. Cohen AR, Woods DF, Marfatia SM, Walther Z, Chishti AH, et al. 1998. Human Cask/Lin-2 binds syndecan-2 and protein 4.1 and localizes to the baso-lateral membrane of epithelial cells. *J. Cell Biol.* 142:129–38

69. Kelly PT, Cotman CW. 1978. Synaptic proteins. Characterization of tubulin and actin and identification of a distinct post-synaptic density polypeptide. *J. Cell Biol.* 79:173–83

70. Caceres A, Binder LI, Payne MR, Bender P, Rebhun L, et al. 1984. Differential sub-cellular localization of tubulin and the microtubule-associated protein MAP2 in brain tissue as revealed by immunocy-tochemistry with monoclonal hybridoma antibodies. *J. Neurosci.* 4:394–410

71. Walsh MJ, Kuruc N. 1992. The postsyn-aptic density: constituent and associated proteins characterized by electrophore-sis, immunoblotting, and peptide sequencing. *J. Neurochem.* 59:667–78

72. Niethammer M, Valtschanoff JG, Kapoor TM, Allison DW, Weinberg RJ, et al. 1998. CRIPT, a novel postsynaptic pro-tein that binds to the third PDZ domain of PSD-95/SAP90. *Neuron* 20:693–707

73. van Rossum D, Kuhse J, Betz H. 1999. Dynamic interaction between soluble tubulin and C-terminal domains of *N-*

methyl-*N*-methyl-D-aspartate receptor subunits. *J. Neurochem.* 72:962–73

74. Lai SL, Ling SC, Kuo LH, Shu YC, Chow WY, et al. 1998. Characterization of granular particles isolated from postsynaptic densities. *J. Neurochem.* 71:1694–701

75. Harris KM, Kater SB. 1994. Dendritic spines: cellular specializations imparting both stability and flexibility to synaptic function. *Annu. Rev. Neurosci.* 17:341–71

76. Hsueh Y-P, Kim E, Sheng M. 1997. Disulfide-linked head-to-head multimerization in the mechanism of ion channel clustering by PSD-95. *Neuron* 18:803–14

77. Hsueh Y-P, Sheng M. 1999. Requirement of N-terminal cysteines of PSD-95 for PSD-95 multimerization and ternary complex formation, but not for binding to potassium channel Kv1.4. *J. Biol. Chem.* 174:532–36

78. Topinka JR, Bredt DS. 1998. N-terminal palmitoylation of PSD-95 regulates association with cell membranes and interaction with K⁺ channel Kv1.4. *Neuron* 20:125–34

79. Craven SE, El-Husseini AE, Bredt DS. 1999. Synaptic targeting of the postsynaptic density protein PSD-95 mediated by lipid and protein motifs. *Neuron* 22:497–509

80. Wyszynski M, Lin J, Rao A, Nigh E, Beggs AH, et al. 1997. Competitive binding of alpha-actinin and calmodulin to the NMDA receptor. *Nature* 385:439–42

81. Wyszynski M, Kharazia V, Shanghvi R, Rao A, Beggs AH, et al. 1998. Differential regional expression and ultrastructural localization of α-actinin-2, a putative NMDA receptor-anchoring protein, in rat brain. *J. Neurosci.* 18:1383–92

82. Ehlers MD, Zhang S, Bernhardt JP, Huganir RL. 1996. Inactivation of NMDA receptors by direct interaction of calmodulin with the NR1 subunit. *Cell* 84:745–55

83. Zhang S, Ehlers MD, Bernhardt JP, Su CT, Huganir RL. 1998. Calmodulin mediates calcium-dependent inactivation of *N*-methyl-D-aspartate receptors. *Neuron* 21:443–53

84. Krupp JJ, Vissel B, Thomas CG, Heinemann SF, Westbrook GL. 1999. Interactions of calmodulin and alpha-actinin with the NR1 subunit modulate Ca^{2+} dependent inactivation of NMDA receptors. *J. Neurosci.* 19:1165–78

85. Levitan I. 1999. It is calmodulin after all! Mediator of the calcium modulation of multiple ion channels. *Neuron* 22:645–48

86. Ehlers MD, Tingley WG, Huganir RL. 1995. Regulated subcellular distribution of the NR1 subunit of the NMDA receptor. *Science* 269:1734–37

87. Lin JW, Wyszynski M, Madhavan R, Sealock R, Kim JU, et al. 1998. Yotiao, a novel protein of neuromuscular junction and brain that interacts with specific splice variants of NMDA receptor subunit NR1. *J. Neurosci.* 18:2017–27

88. Ehlers MD, Fung ET, O'Brien RJ, Huganir RL. 1998. Splice variant-specific interaction of the NMDA receptor subunit NR1 with neuronal intermediate filaments. *J. Neurosci.* 18:720–30

89. Westphal RS, Tavalin SJ, Lin JW, Alto NM, Iain DC, et al. 1999. Regulation of NMDA receptors by an associated phosphatase kinase signaling complex. *Science* 285(5424):93–95

90. Hirao K, Hata Y, Ide N, Takeuchi M, Irie M, et al. 1998. A novel multiple PDZ domain-containing molecule interacting with *N*-methyl-D-aspartate receptors and neuronal cell adhesion proteins. *J. Biol. Chem.* 273:21105–10

91. Wechsler A, Teichberg V. 1998. Brain spectrin binding to the NMDA receptor is regulated by phosphorylation, calcium

and calmodulin. *EMBO J.* 17(14):3931–39

92. Wenthold RJ, Petralia RS, Blahos JI, Niedzielski AS. 1996. Evidence for multiple AMPA receptor complexes in hippocampal CA1/CA2 neurons. *J. Neurosci.* 16:1982–89

93. Dong H, O'Brien RJ, Fung ET, Lanahan AA, Worley PF, et al. 1997. GRIP: a synaptic PDZ domain-containing protein that interacts with AMPA receptors. *Nature* 386:279–84

94. Wyszynski M, Kim E, Yang F-C, Sheng M. 1998. Biochemical and immunocytochemical characterization of GRIP, a putative AMPA receptor anchoring protein, in rat brain. *Neuropharm.* 37:1335–44

95. Srivastava S, Osten P, Vilim F, Khatri L, Inman G, et al. 1998. Novel anchorage of GluR2/3 to the postsynaptic density by the AMPA receptor-binding protein ABP. *Neuron* 21:581–91

96. Bruckner K, Pablo Labrador J, Scheiffele P, Herb A, Seeburg PH, et al. 1999. EphrinB ligands recruit GRIP family PDZ adaptor proteins into raft membrane microdomains. *Neuron* 22:511–24

96a. Wyszynski M, Valtschanoff JG, Naisbitt S, Dunah AW, Kim E, et al. 1999. Association of AMPA receptors with a subset of glutmate receptor-interacting protein in vivo. *J. Neurosci.* 19:6528–37

96b. Dong H, Zhang P, Song I, Petralia RS, Liao D, et al. 1999. Characterization of the glutamate receptor-interacting proteins GRIP1 and GRIP2. *J. Neurosci.* 19:6930–41

97. Malenka RC, Nicoll RA. 1997. Silent synapses speak up. *Neuron* 19:473–76

98. Torres R, Firestein BL, Dong H, Staudinger J, Olson EN, et al. 1998. PDZ proteins bind, cluster, and synaptically colocalize with Eph receptors and their ephrin ligands. *Neuron* 21:1453–63

99. Flanagan JG, Vanderhaeghen P. 1998. The ephrins and Eph receptors in neural development. *Annu. Rev. Neurosci.* 21:309–45

100. Serra-Pages C, Medley QG, Tang M, Hart A, Streuli M. 1998. Liprins, a family of LAR transmembrane protein-tyrosine phosphatase-interacting proteins. *J. Biol. Chem.* 273:15611–20

101. Van Vactor D. 1998. Protein tyrosine phosphatases in the developing nervous system. *Curr. Opin. Cell Biol.* 10:174–81

102. Xia J, Zhang X, Staudinger J, Huganir RL. 1999. Clustering of AMPA receptors by the synaptic PDZ domain-containing protein PICK1. *Neuron* 22:179–87

103. Staudinger J, Zhou J, Burgess R, Elledge SJ, Olson EN. 1995. PICK1: a perinuclear binding protein and substrate for protein kinase C isolated by the yeast two-hybrid system. *J. Cell Biol.* 128:263–71

104. Leonard AS, Davare MA, Horne MC, Garner CC, Hell JW. 1998. SAP97 is associated with the alpha-amino-3-hydroxy-5-methylisoxazole-4-propionic acid receptor GluR1 subunit. *J. Biol. Chem.* 273:19518–24

105. Nishimune A, Isaac JT, Molnar E, Noel J, Nash SR, et al. 1998. NSF binding to GluR2 regulates synaptic transmission. *Neuron* 21:87–97

106. Osten P, Srivastava S, Inman GJ, Vilim FS, Khatri L, et al. 1998. The AMPA receptor GluR2 C terminus can mediate a reversible, ATP- dependent interaction with NSF and alpha- and beta-SNAPs. *Neuron* 21:99–110

107. Song I, Kamboj S, Xia J, Dong H, Liao D, et al. 1998. Interaction of the *N*-ethylmaleimide-sensitive factor with AMPA receptors. *Neuron* 21:393–400

108. Lin JW, Sheng M. 1998. NSF and AMPA receptors get physical. *Neuron* 21:267–70

109. Hayashi T, Umemori H, Mishina M, Yamamoto T. 1999. The AMPA receptor interacts with and signals through the

protein tyrosine kinase Lyn. *Nature* 397:72–76

110. Wang Y, Small DL, Stanimirovic DB, Morley P, Durkin JP. 1997. AMPA receptor-mediated regulation of a Gi-protein in cortical neurons. *Nature* 389:502–4

111. Zuo J, De Jager PL, Takahashi KA, Jiang W, Linden DJ, et al. 1997. Neurodegeneration in Lurcher mice caused by mutation in δ2 glutamate receptor gene. *Nature* 388:769–73

112. Kashiwabuchi N, Ikeda K, Araki K, Hirano T, Shibuki K, et al. 1995. Impairment of motor coordination, Purkinje cell synapse formation, and cerebellar long-term depression in GluRδ2 mutant mice. *Cell* 81:245–52

113. Roche KW, Ly CD, Petralia RS, Wang Y-X, McGee AW, et al. 1999. Postsynaptic density-93 interacts with the δ2 glutamate receptor subunit at parallel fiber synapses. *J. Neurosci.* In press

114. Craig AM, Blackstone CD, Huganir RL, Banker G. 1994. Selective clustering of glutamate and γ-aminobutyric acid receptors opposite terminals releasing the corresponding neurotransmitters. *Proc. Natl. Acad. Sci. USA* 91:12373–77

115. Wang H, Bedford FK, Brandon NJ, Moss SJ, Olsen RW. 1999. GABA$_A$-receptor-associated protein links GABA$_A$ receptors and the cytoskeleton. *Nature* 397:69–72

116. Hanley JG, Koulen P, Bedford F, Gordon-Weeks PR, Moss SJ. 1999. The protein MAP-1B links GABA$_C$ receptors to the cytoskeleton at retinal synapses. *Nature* 397:66–69

117. Fujii T, Watanabe M, Ogoma Y, Kondo Y, Arai T. 1993. Microtubule-associated proteins, MAP1A and MAP1B, interact with F-actin in vitro. *J. Biochem. (Tokyo)* 114:827–29

118. Kuhse J, Betz H, Kirsch J. 1995. The inhibitory glycine receptor: architecture, synaptic localization and molecular pathology of a postsynaptic ion-channel complex. *Curr. Opin. Neurobiol.* 5:318–23

119. Meyer G, Kirsch J, Betz H, Langosch D. 1995. Identification of a gephyrin binding motif on the glycine receptor β subunit. *Neuron* 15:563–72

120. Feng G, Tintrup H, Kirsch J, Nichol M, Kuhse J, et al. 1998. Dual requirement for gephyrin in glycine receptor clustering and molybdoenzyme activity. *Science* 282:1321–24

121. Essrich C, Lopez M, Benson JA, Fritschy J-M, Luscher B. 1998. Postsynaptic clustering of major GABA$_A$ receptor subtypes requires the γ$_2$ subunit and gephyrin. *Nat. Neurosci.* 1:563–71

122. Nusser Z, Sieghart W, Somogyi P. 1998. Segregation of different GABA$_A$ receptors to synaptic and extrasynaptic membranes of cerebellar granule cells. *J. Neurosci.* 18:1693–703

Annu. Rev. Physiol. 2000. 62:779–802

INSIGHTS FROM MOUSE MODELS INTO THE MOLECULAR BASIS OF NEURODEGENERATION

N. Heintz[1] and H. Y. Zoghbi[2]

[1]Howard Hughes Medical Institute, The Rockefeller University, New York, New York, 10021; e-mail: heintz@rockvax.rockefeller.edu; [2]Howard Hughes Medical Institute, Baylor College of Medicine, Houston, Texas, 77030; e-mail: hzoghbi@bcm.tmc.edu

Key Words   polyglutamine diseases, neurotransmitter receptor, ion channel, ischemic cell death

■ **Abstract**   Thanks largely to cloning the genes for several neurodegenerative diseases over the past decade and the existence of mouse mutants, the molecular basis of neurodegeneration is finally beginning to yield some of its secrets. We discuss what has been learned about the pathogenesis of "triplet repeat" diseases through mouse models for spinocerebellar ataxia types 1 and 3 and Huntington disease, including the roles of nuclear aggregates and protein cleavage. We also discuss the neurologic phenotypes that arise from mutations in neurotransmitter receptors (*lurcher* mice) and ion channels (*weaver, leaner,* and *tottering* mice), drawing parallels between ischemic cell death and the neurodegeneration that occurs in the *lurcher* mouse. Finally, we discuss common mechanisms of cell death and lessons learned from these mouse models that might have broader relevance to other neurologic disorders.

INTRODUCTION

The inexorable neurodegenerative processes of Alzheimer and Parkinson disease, amyotrophic lateral sclerosis, Huntington disease, and the spinocerebellar ataxias (SCAs) are as difficult to elucidate as they are devastating. For decades the molecular basis of neuronal degeneration was a matter of guesswork, but the identification of the genes mutated in these disorders made it possible to examine pathogenesis at a basic level. Capitalizing on this knowledge, recent studies in human patients and mouse models have yielded insights into the molecular changes leading to neuronal dysfunction and death in the polyglutamine diseases. Contemporaneous studies of existing mouse mutants known to display neurological phenotypes led to the discovery of another class of neurodegenerative disorders, those secondary to an alteration in ion channel or neurotransmitter receptor function. While a complete understanding of the mechanism of neuronal loss has yet to materialize in either case, certain themes beginning to emerge from these studies may have broader relevance.

0066–4278/00/0315–0779$12.00

THE POLYGLUTAMINE DISEASES

A new class of neurodegenerative diseases was born in 1991 with the discovery of unstable trinucleotide repeats (1, 2). The family of triplet repeat diseases has itself expanded since then to encompass 15 neurological disorders, 8 of which—spinobulbar muscular atrophy (SBMA), Huntington disease (HD), and the spinocerebellar ataxias (including dentatorubropallidoluysian atrophy, or DRPLA)—are neurodegenerative diseases that result from expansion of CAG repeats coding for polyglutamine tracts in the respective proteins. With the exception of SBMA, these disorders are dominantly inherited. All 8 appear most commonly in midlife and lead to progressive neuronal dysfunction and neuronal loss within 10 to 20 years of symptom onset. The repeats are intergenerationally unstable to varying degrees, but it is axiomatic that for each disease, the greater the number of CAG repeats on expanded alleles, the earlier the age of onset and more severe the symptoms and progression. Curiously, only a certain subset of neurons is affected in each of these diseases, despite the ubiquitous expression of the relevant disease proteins throughout the brain and other tissues. The normal functions of these proteins remain a mystery, except for the androgen receptor (SBMA) and the α_{1A}-voltage-dependent calcium channel (SCA6). We do know, however, that the polyglutamine tracts confer a novel toxic function onto the respective proteins rather than the proteins losing normal function: Neither human patients with deletions of the androgen receptor, HD, or SCA1 genes, nor knockout mice (for HD or SCA1) develop the triplet repeat disease phenotype. Transgenic mice do develop this phenotype, however, and we now discuss mouse models for three of the polyglutamine disorders, SCA1, SCA3, and HD, that have shed light on different aspects of polyglutamine toxicity.

Spinocerebellar Ataxia Type 1

Neuronal Dysfunction or Loss?   The cerebellar atrophy with severe Purkinje cell degeneration (3) that is a hallmark of SCA1 is caused by the expansion of a polyglutamine tract in the SCA1 protein, ataxin-1, which is predominantly nuclear in neurons but cytoplasmic in non-neuronal peripheral tissue. To examine SCA1 Purkinje cell pathology, Burright et al (4) expressed full-length human SCA1 cDNAs with different numbers of CAG repeats in Purkinje cells using a Purkinje cell-specific promoter from the Pcp2/L7 gene. The resulting mice highly express either a wild-type (wt) SCA1 allele with 30 repeats (30Q) or an expanded allele with 82 repeats (82Q). 30Q mice are indistinguishable from their wt littermates, but adult 82Q mice (the B05 line) develop severe ataxia and progressive Purkinje cell pathology that closely parallels that seen in human SCA1 patients (5). The only notable pathologic difference between murine and human SCA1 Purkinje cells is that the former lack axonal dilatations; the B05 line thus provides a reliable animal model for SCA1.

The first histologic abnormalities, detectable at postnatal day 25 (P25) in mice, are cytoplasmic vacuoles. Loss of proximal dendritic arborization and dendritic spines becomes apparent at 5 weeks, when the mice begin to show mild difficulty on the rotating rod. By 12 to 15 weeks, B05 mice are overtly ataxic, Purkinje cell dendritic arborization is mostly lost, the molecular layer is atrophied, and some heterotopic Purkinje cells have moved to the molecular layer. Mutant ataxin-1 localizes to ubiquitin-positive aggregates or nuclear inclusions (NIs), as it does in affected neurons in SCA1 patients (6). NIs in mice appear as early as 3.5 weeks and are detectable in 90% of the Purkinje cells by 12 weeks. Cell death becomes significant only after 6 months of age, long after the phenotype has appeared, demonstrating that it is not cell death but rather progressive neuronal dysfunction that produces the SCA1 phenotype.

Must Ataxin-1 Localize to the Nucleus or Aggregate to Cause Disease? Klement et al (7) generated transgenic mice that express an expanded (82Q) version of ataxin-1 with a mutated nuclear localization sequence. Although these mice, like the original SCA1 (82Q) transgenic mice, expressed high levels of ataxin-1 in Purkinje cells, they never developed Purkinje cell pathology or motor dysfunction. Ataxin-1 was diffusely distributed throughout the cytoplasm and formed no aggregates, even when the mice were a year old.

Could the lack of phenotype be attributed to the absence of aggregates? Klement et al also generated transgenic mice using ataxin-1[77]Δ, which contains 77Q but lacks amino acids in the self-association region found to be essential for ataxin-1 dimerization. These mice developed ataxia and Purkinje cell pathology similar to the original SCA1(82Q) mice, but without NIs. Thus although nuclear localization of ataxin-1 is necessary to produce disease, nuclear aggregation of ataxin-1 is not. One might object that deletion of 122 amino acids could compromise the protein in various ways (folding, turn-over rate, interactions), but this truncated ataxin-1 retained its ability to interact with its known partner, leucine-rich acidic nuclear protein, and replicated all the neurobehavioral and pathologic features of the 82Q mice. It seems safe to say, then, that ataxin-1[77]Δ exerts the same pathogenicity as full-length expanded ataxin-1 but without accumulating in visible aggregates.

In sum, sequences within ataxin-1 in addition to the polyglutamine tract specify the site and course of disease. The neuronal dysfunction that causes SCA1 symptoms begins with the localization of ataxin-1 to the nucleus; once there, because of misfolding or abnormal conformation, mutant ataxin-1 interacts with other nuclear proteins and/or causes changes in nuclear architecture that alter gene expression, all of which may contribute to neuronal dysfunction, symptomatology, and eventual cell loss.

Machado-Joseph Disease/Spinocerebellar Ataxia Type 3: Polyglutamine-Induced Neuronal Death

A somewhat different picture emerges from studies of Machado-Joseph Disease (MJD)/SCA3 mice. SCA3 is clinically similar to SCA1, but it is the dentate neurons rather than Purkinje cells that are the primary targets of dysfunction in the cerebellum. Ikeda and colleagues (8) generated transgenic mice expressing full-length and truncated versions of the MJD/SCA3 protein, ataxin-3, using the Pcp2/L7 promoter region. Interestingly, neither mice expressing full-length protein (MJD79) nor those bearing a truncated ataxin-3 with 35 repeats (Q35C) developed ataxia. Q79C mice, however, which expressed a truncated form of the protein that included an expanded 79-repeat glutamine tract and 42 amino acids C terminal to the repeat, developed ataxia by 4 weeks of age, as did mice expressing only a 79 glutamine residue tract (Q79).

Cerebellar degeneration in 8-week-old Q79C transgenic mice is so severe that the region occupies only one eighth its normal volume. All three layers of the cerebellum are involved, with thinning of the molecular layer, altered morphology of Purkinje cells with attenuation of their dendrites and reduced calbindin immunoreactivity, and loss of granule neurons. This study indicated that the expanded polyglutamine tract in a truncated protein can induce neuronal cell death, in contrast to the toxicity induced by full-length ataxin-1, which causes slow and progressive neuronal dysfunction. Ikeda and colleagues proposed that ataxin-3 undergoes proteolytic cleavage, which frees the toxic polyglutamine tract to induce cell death. This may be the case, but there is no direct evidence yet that ataxin-3 cleavage occurs in affected brain regions of MJD/SCA3 patients. We also cannot be certain that full-length ataxin-3 is not toxic, because data on expression levels from the various transgenes were not provided.

Huntington Disease

Repeat Tract Toxicity and the Influence of Protein Context There is much evidence indicating that polyglutamine tracts are themselves toxic, however. Mangiarini and colleagues (9) generated mice using a 1.9 Kb human genomic fragment containing HD 5′ flanking sequences and exon 1, with an unstable expanded CAG tract of ~130 repeats. R6/2 mice (with 144 repeats) ubiquitously express the first 69 amino acids of huntingtin, with the elongated CAG tract at lower than endogenous levels. Surprisingly, this small fragment—only 3% of huntingtin—was enough to create a progressive neurological phenotype with some HD-like features. At 9–11 weeks, R6/2 mice show handling-induced seizures, limb dyskinesia, tremor, and stereotypic involuntary movements. As the disease worsens, the mice lose weight, develop urinary incontinence and unusual vocalizations, and die suddenly of unknown causes between 10 and 13 weeks. Despite the neurologic signs, neuropathology revealed only that R6/2 brains are smaller than normal and develop nuclear inclusions throughout the CNS, prior to any neurobehavioral changes. These amembranous NIs show a filamentous morphology and stain positively for ubiquitin (10). None of the neurodegeneration typical of HD is apparent, but Cha et al (11) found that R6/2 mice have altered expression of several neurotransmitter receptors: metabotropic glutamate receptors (mGluR) type 1, 2, and 3; dopamine receptors; and muscarinic cholinergic receptors. Similar alterations have been observed in post-mortem HD tissue. The loss of striatal mGluR2 in R6/2 mice might lead to abnormal release of synaptic glutamate and contribute to the pathogenic effects of the transgene.

The finding that mice bearing only 3% of huntingtin manifest the receptor alterations found in human HD tissue raises an interesting question: Does the truncated peptide used by Mangiarini et al retain the full-length protein's ability to interact with certain cell-specific factors, or does the expanded polyglutamine tract produce a generalized toxicity that overlaps with some features of HD? To assess polyglutamine toxicity, Ordway and colleagues (12) introduced a 146-unit repeat into the mouse hypoxanthine phosphoribosyltransferase (Hprt) gene. These mutant mice, like the R6/2, acquire seizures, tremors, and die prematurely; they also develop nuclear inclusions, without neurodegeneration. In contrast to the R6/2 line, however, they gain weight. The expanded polyglutamine tract is thus toxic independent of protein context, but context mediates the phenotypic differences and selective neuronal vulnerability of the polyglutamine diseases.

Further support for the protein context hypothesis comes from mice generated by Reddy and colleagues (13), who expressed full-length HD cDNA with 16, 48, or 89 CAG repeats at high levels (two to five times endogenous) under the control of a cytomegalovirus promoter. Mice with 48 or 89 repeats develop progressive neurobehavioral abnormalities: clasping at 8 weeks; hyperactivity at 20 weeks; urinary incontinence and decreased locomotor activity by 24 weeks, which progresses to akinesia and death by 28 to 30 weeks. During the hypokinetic phase, striatal degeneration with human HD-like apoptosis and gliosis occurs. Apoptosis also occurs in other areas typically affected in HD, supporting the notion that selective neuronal vulnerability requires the context of full-length huntingtin. Moreover, transgenic mice expressing full-length HD develop most of the phenotypic features at a much later time (20 weeks) than R6/2 mice (9 weeks), even though the former have much higher levels of huntingtin expression. Interestingly, NIs appear in brain regions typically spared in HD (e.g. Purkinje cells) and are rare (<1%) in the striatum, where apoptosis is most conspicuous. This is further indication that NIs do not initiate pathogenesis.

Effect of Protein Levels on Pathogenicity To produce HD transgenic mice with the disease-causing mutation in the same developmental and tissue-specific pattern seen in human HD patients, Hodgson and colleagues (14) used yeast artificial chromosomes (YACs) with the complete human *HD* locus carrying repeat lengths corresponding to normal, adult-onset-, and juvenile-onset-causing tracts in humans. Only the YAC72 mice, which bear the largest expansion (72 glutamines) and express the protein at twice endogenous levels, display any behavioral changes (hyperactivity). Both YAC46 (with 46 repeats) and YAC72 mice develop progressive electrophysiological dysfunction.

At 6 months, slices from YAC72 mice showed somatic spiking and very broad excitatory post-synaptic potentials (EPSPs), which were blocked by the NMDA receptor blocker D-AP5, providing in vivo evidence of excitotoxicity in early HD pathogenesis. At 10 months neither YAC46 nor YAC72 showed long-term potentiation (LTP) after high-frequency stimulation at Schaeffer collaterals, perhaps because of the high resting levels of calcium. The electrophysiological abnormalities precede any neurobehavioral or neuropathologic changes, suggesting that cytoplasmic functions (e.g. neurotransmitter behavior and calcium regulation) are affected early in HD pathogenesis. In a YAC72 mouse, translocation of huntingtin to the nucleus is evident at 12 months only in the medium spiny neurons, which are susceptible to neurodegeneration; hyperchromasia and striatal atrophy in this mouse suggest that selective neuronal vulnerability in HD may correlate with the translocation of the protein to the nucleus.

Knock-in mice, carrying CAG expansions within the endogenous genetic locus, should in principle provide the most accurate mouse models for HD and other polyglutamine diseases. Two such HD knockins have been made. Mice bearing 50 CAG repeats have developed no neurological, pathological or physiological changes, although the mutant protein is expressed at wt levels and rescues the embryonic lethality of the *Hd* null mutation (15). Mice with 72–80 repeats in the *Hd* locus (16, 17) show few abnormalities besides aggressive behavior at 3 months and impaired LTP at Schaeffer collateral-CA1 synapses. Reduced posttetanic potentiation and paired-pulse facilitation suggest the mice may be unable to sustain neurotransmission during repetitive stimulation. Although these phenotypic changes do not directly correlate with an HD phenotype, alterations in synaptic plasticity and subtle emotional disturbances could precede the motor and cognitive abnormalities typical of HD.

In these knockin mice, appropriate spatial and temporal expression of a full-length protein with an expanded glutamine tract is insufficient to produce overt phenotypes. Overexpression of the mutant protein seems necessary for mice to manifest symptoms paralleling human disease, probably because the life-span of the mouse (hence the time during which mouse neurons are exposed to a mutant protein) is so short.

In sum, several proteins with expanded polyglutamine tracts are neurotoxic; perhaps they misfold or otherwise disrupt nuclear functions. Misfolding is implicated in the formation of NIs; the findings of Cummings et al (18) that NIs stain positively for the proteasome, ubiquitin, and molecular chaperones suggest that they contain misfolded proteins targeted for proteolysis, which is obviously not occurring successfully. Aggregation does not initiate pathogenesis, but the fact that NIs occur in HD, SBMA, SCA1, 3, 7, and DRPLA patients seems significant (19). The finding of ubiquitin-positive aggregates not only in this group but in other neurodegenerative diseases as well—Alzheimer disease, amyotrophic lateral sclerosis, and Parkinson disease—suggests that misfolding and protein turnover alteration may be a common molecular mechanism in neurodegeneration. Altered protein conformation could lead to abnormal or enhanced protein-protein interactions which in turn affect neuronal function. Specific interactions determined by the unique peptide sequence in the respective proteins may account for the cell specificity of the respective phenotypes. It is conceivable that the proteins, aggregating over time, eventually interfere with the normal function of the proteolytic machinery or physically alter some cellular activities in later stages of disease progression.

The potent toxicity of the protein fragments—truncated ataxin-3, the 3% fragment of huntingtin, and the HPRT protein with 146Q—could be explained by their small size, less than 50 kDa, which likely facilitates their transport into the nucleus. Truncation of the parent protein seems an important step in the pathogenesis of several of these diseases; Wellington et al (20) found that the proteins affected in DRPLA, SBMA, and SCA3 are cleaved in apoptotic extracts by caspases. More convincing still, Ona et al (21) recently showed not only that caspase-1 is activated in the R6/2 mice, but that inhibiting caspase activity reduces endogenous huntingtin cleavage and delays NI formation and death. The full protein context may delay symptom onset by hindering cleavage or nuclear translocation; it may also lead to gains of function through new protein-protein interactions, thereby mediating selective toxicity.

NEUROTRANSMITTER RECEPTOR ACTIVATION

Olney and Sharpe's 1969 discovery (21a) that exposure of infant rhesus monkeys to excess glutamate could cause toxicity and neuronal cell death led to a number of studies investigating brain lesions caused by the application of glutamate or glutamate receptor agonists. Subsequent studies established the importance of both NMDA and AMPA type glutamate receptors for excitotoxic cell death in vitro and uncovered a central role of Ca^{2+} influx in this process (22). Taken together, these studies intimated that glutamate toxicity is an important factor in a variety of neurologic disorders, and led to the hypothesis that elevated intracellular Ca^{2+} could play a central role in the pathogenic mechanisms of disease. Evidence supporting this hypothesis has come from clinical studies of a variety of human diseases, including reports of aberrant processing of the EAAT2 glutamate transporter mRNA in a subset of patients suffering from amyotrophic lateral sclerosis (23). Recent studies of *lurcher* mutant mice and mouse models of neuronal death during ischemia/reperfusion have contributed genetically tractable models for the investigation of detailed mechanisms of the toxicity associated with glutamate receptor activation in vivo.

Lurcher (Lc)

The* Lurcher *Phenotype *Lc* is a semidominant mouse mutation first described in 1960 in an ataxic mouse strain with gross cerebellar abnormalities. Heterozygous *lurcher* (*Lc/+*) mice develop ataxia during the second postnatal week due to loss of cerebellar Purkinje cells (24). Homozygous *lurcher* animals are much more severely affected, dying at birth because of massive loss of neurons in the hindbrain and brainstem (25, 26). Analysis of mouse chimeras created by fusion of wt and *Lc/+* embryos established that the *lurcher* gene acts cell-autonomously in cerebellar Purkinje cells and that the death of cerebellar granule cells and inferior olivary neurons in *Lc/+* animals is a consequence of Purkinje cell loss and not a direct effect of the mutation (27, 28).

Lc/+ mouse pup Purkinje cells die during the period of intensive growth of their dendritic arbor, formation of parallel fiber synapses onto Purkinje cells, and pruning of climbing fiber afferents (24). Several molecules that participate in the regulation of the apoptotic death pathway are induced in *Lc/+* Purkinje cells prior to their death. Wullner et al (29) reported the induction of *Bax* and *Bcl-X* in *Lc/+* Purkinje cells at the time of cell death; Selimi et al (30) also found an increase in procaspase 3 expression in all *Lc/+* Purkinje cells postnatally, and the presence of mature, active caspase 3 in individual *Lc/+* Purkinje cells during the period of degeneration. These studies provide strong support for the idea that the *lurcher* gene may activate intracellular pathways that induce programmed cell death (31).

The* Lurcher *Gene   Positional cloning of the *lurcher* gene (32) revealed that both of the known alleles arose from identical point mutations in the orphan glutamate receptor GluRδ2 (*Grid2*). The delta family (*Grid1, Grid2*) of ionotropic glutamate receptors share approximately 20–30% identity with both NMDA and AMPA/kainate receptors and have similar predicted membrane topology (33, 34).

Ionotropic glutamate receptors are ligand-gated ion channels that can function either as homodimers or heteromers. In contrast to other members of this gene family, neither *Grid1* or *Grid2* have been shown to bind glutamate or to display ion channel activity alone or in combination with other members of the family (34, 35). Furthermore, immunoprecipitation studies of Grid2 from cerebellar extracts failed to find interacting proteins with the stoichiometry necessary to be considered candidates for required subunits for this receptor (36). The delta receptors are thus designated orphan receptors because there are no data that identify them as responsive to glutamate or demonstrate ion channel activity for the wild-type receptors.

Grid2 is expressed at high levels in cerebellar Purkinje cells, and at lower levels in some brainstem neurons (34, 35). In general, the cells most affected by the *lurcher* mutation are those known to express the receptor, as expected from the cell-autonomous action of the mutation (27). *Grid2* is expressed as early as embryonic day 15 in cerebellar Purkinje cells, and the level of expression in this cell type increases significantly after birth (37). One of the most interesting properties of *Grid2* is its specific localization to the postsynaptic density of only those Purkinje cell dendritic spines that make contact with granule cell parallel fibers (37–39). This is unlike other ionotropic glutamate receptors in Purkinje cells, which can be found both at the parallel fiber synapse and the climbing fiber synapse.

The identification of the *lurcher* mutation as a missense mutation in *Grid2,* along with the semidominant nature of the *lurcher* phenotype, suggested that this might be a gain-of-function mutation. Definitive proof comes from phenotypic comparison of *Grid2^{Lc}* and the null mutation *Grid2^{−/−}* (40). While both mutations cause ataxia and impair motor learning, the *Grid2* null allele is recessive and does not cause Purkinje cell degeneration or perinatal death. These phenotypic differences are important for two reasons. First, when considering the mechanisms leading to Purkinje cell death in *lurcher,* it is important to realize that the properties of the *Grid2^{Lc}* receptor may not accurately reflect the role of the wt *Grid2* molecule in vivo. Second, the dose-dependent effect of the *Grid2^{Lc}* allele is readily explained because functional ionotropic glutamate receptors are thought to be tetramers. Thus if the presence of wt subunits in mixed channels in *Lc/+* animals can mitigate the effects of the mutant subunits, then the phenotypic severity of this gain-of-function allele will be lessened in *Lc/+* animals.

Constitutive Activation of the GRID2^{LC} Receptor To investigate the physiological effects of the *Lc* mutation, Purkinje cells in thin slices of cerebellar vermis from P10 and P11 mutant and wt (32) animals were analyzed electrophysiologically. In comparison with wt Purkinje cells, *Lc/+* Purkinje cells require a greater magnitude of holding current to clamp the neuron at −70 mV; measurements of the initial currents and membrane conductance in the affected cells are much greater, and their resting potential is depolarized. These effects can be reversed by substituting *N*-methyl-D-glucamine (NMDG), a relatively large organic cation, for most Na^+ in the external saline, demonstrating that the *Lc*-specific conductance is selective and not the result of poor *Lc/+* membrane integrity or leakage at the pipette/membrane interface. Furthermore, the large reduction in holding current magnitude and decrease in membrane conductance caused by reducing the external Na^+ concentration strongly suggest that Na^+ is a major current carrier of the *Lc*-specific, constitutive inward current.

The constitutive inward current in *Lc/+* Purkinje cells results from direct activation of the *Grid2^{Lc}* receptor. *Xenopus* oocytes expressing cRNAs from the wt and mutant alleles were assayed for electrophysiological activity; wt *Grid2* expressing oocytes were not significantly different from their uninjected counterparts in resting potential either in the absence or presence of NMDG. In contrast, injection of *Grid2^{Lc}* produced a dramatic depolarization in the resting potential that could be completely reversed by replacing external Na^+ with NMDG. Since these changes in resting potential and whole-cell conductance were observed in the absence of any ligand, these measurements demonstrate that cells injected with the mutant *Grid2^{Lc}* express a large, constitutive conductance under physiological conditions.

Mechanisms of Cell Death in **Lurcher** *Animals* The observation that features characteristic of neuronal apoptosis occur in *Lc/+* Purkinje cells is intriguing given the constitutive activation of the *Grid2^{Lc}* receptor and the demonstration that excitotoxic cell death in cultured neurons occurs through necrosis (41). Two attempts to rescue cell death in *lurcher* mice using transgenic mice overexpressing Bcl-2 in all neurons have been reported (42, 43). In neither case was rescue successful, although Purkinje cell death was delayed in one of these studies. Interestingly, the death of inferior olivary neurons was rescued by Bcl-2 in these studies. A direct test of the requirement for *Bax* in *lurcher*-mediated cell death has also been completed recently (44). The development of the *lurcher* phenotype on a *Bax*$^{-/-}$ background is dramatically altered: secondary death of cerebellar granule cells is almost completely rescued, and Purkinje cell death is delayed. Both primary and secondary cell death in *lurcher* animals may involve components of the apoptotic pathway and require caspase activation. However, the mechanisms mediating apoptosis through the constitutive activation of *Grid2^{Lc}* and granule cell death as a consequence of target cell deprivation in *lurcher* mice are distinct. A brief discussion of ischemic cell death (below) highlights interesting similarities to the *lurcher* phenotype.

ISCHEMIC CELL DEATH

Transient Focal Ischemia

Studies of excitotoxic cell death after administration of glutamate or glutamate receptor agonists in vivo and studies of glutamate toxicity in cultured neurons have provided the foundation for models of ischemic cell death following stroke, cardiac arrest, or head trauma in humans. The excitotoxic hypothesis for ischemic injury has been supported by a variety of experiments demonstrating glutamate release during ischemia, a preferential loss of glutaminergic neurons at the site of lesion, and the ability of glutamate receptor antagonists to protect against ischemic cell death (45). Although these studies have been conducted in several species, we include a brief discussion of this process here because an understanding of the complexity of ischemic cell death is beginning to emerge from genetic experiments on mouse models of acute brain injury.

Transient focal ischemia such as that seen in stroke patients is a complex phenomenon that involves extensive, acute cell death at the site of the lesion and delayed cell death in the penumbra surrounding this core. The sensitivity of specific neuronal types in the lesion and the penumbra is not uniform and may depend upon the class of glutamate receptor expressed in those cells. Both NMDA and AMPA receptor antagonists have been shown to exert strong neuroprotective effects in animal models of transient focal ischemia (46, 47). Furthermore, pharmacologic studies using Na^{+} and Ca^{2+} blockers to dampen glutamate release both lower the concentration of glutamate at the site of the lesion and reduce lesion volume in experimental models of ischemia (48). Finally, mice carrying a null mutation in the gene encoding the NMDA receptor NR2A subunit show a reduction in injury following ischemia (49). Based on these results, and the central role for Ca^{2+} flux in excitotoxic cell death in vitro, it is probable that Ca^{2+} flux plays an important role in ischemic cell death in vivo.

Mechanisms of Ischemic Cell Death

The first step in ischemic cell death involves very rapid death of large numbers of neurons at the focus of the lesion. At this core, the mechanism of cell death is thought to be closely related to excitotoxic cell death in cultured neurons. In particular, the increased vulnerability of glutaminergic cells at the site of the lesion may be due to a calcium-dependent activation of a necrotic cell death pathway (50). The second phase of cell death develops from the core of the lesion, spreading into the adjacent tissue and significantly increasing the volume of the lesion. Cell death in this penumbra appears to include cells directly responding to increased glutamate levels (albeit at concentrations lower than those seen at the core) and to target deprivation resulting from the acute, initial necrotic neuronal death at the site of the lesion. Accumulated evidence demonstrates an important role for apoptosis in neuronal death during this phase of the response. All the events typically associated with apoptotic death are observed: induction of *Bax* (51), caspase activation (52–56), in situ DNA fragmentation (57–59), and release of cytochrome *c* from mitochondria (60, 61). MK-801 (an NMDA receptor antagonist) and peptide inhibitors of caspase activation act synergistically to reduce injury after transient focal ischemia in mice (62). In vivo, overexpression of Bcl-2 (63–65) and Bcl-X$_L$ (66) using pan-neuronal promoters in transgenic mice results in ischemic lesions of less volume than those in non-transgenic littermates. In many respects, the progression of events that occurs during delayed cell death in transient focal ischemia in the cortex is quite similar to that occurring in the *lurcher* cerebellum.

ION CHANNEL MUTATIONS

Weaver (wv)

The* Weaver *Phenotype The *weaver* phenotype was first described as a recessive mouse mutation that causes ataxia (67). Rakic & Sidman (68) reported gross cerebellar abnormalities due to a deficit of granule cells in the cerebellar cortex (69). This defect is most pronounced at the midline; granule cells in the lateral hemispheres behave relatively normally and are able to generate a nearly normal internal granule layer (IGL). Granule cells in *wv* mice fail to migrate from the external granular layer (EGL) and die in the postmitotic zone of the EGL (70). As in other agranular cerebella, Purkinje cell abnormalities are evident in *wv* mice. Studies of embryonal chimeras composed of *wv/wv* and wt cells (71) have shown that wt cells in these animals exit the EGL and execute their normal differentiation program, whereas the *wv/wv* mutant granule cells die in the EGL. These results prove that the *weaver* gene acts intrinsically within cerebellar granule cells and that abnormalities of other cerebellar cell types are secondary. Cultured *wv/wv* granule cells also exhibit an intrinsic defect (72), although interactions with wt granule cells can rescue the mutant cells, indicating that interactions among neighboring granule cells can have an impact on expression of the *weaver* phenotype (73). Subsequent studies of *wv* mice document a substantial decrease in the numbers of dopamine-containing cells in the midbrain, most notably the substantia nigra and retrorubral nucleus (74–76). Although the phenotype of *wv/wv* mice is considerably more severe than that seen in *wv/+* mice, abnormalities are evident even in the heterozygous animals, documenting clear dosage dependence for *weaver* gene action (77).

The* Weaver *Gene   The *weaver* mutation is a missense mutation in the G protein–gated inward rectifier channel *GIRK2* (78). That the *weaver* mutation results in a gain-of-function for *GIRK2* is demonstrated by the absence of morphological abnormalities in *GIRK2* null mice in contrast to the extensive loss of cerebellar and midbrain neurons in *wv/wv* (79). The *wv* mutation (Gly156Ser) occurs in the highly conserved H5 domain of the *GIRK2* channel, suggesting a direct involvement in its permeation pore (78). In general, the cells that die as a consequence of the *wv* mutation express *GIRK2* (80), consistent with the cell-intrinsic action of the mutation revealed in embryonic chimeras (81).

Several studies addressing the effects of the *wv* mutation on *GIRK2* channel function in *Xenopus* oocytes showed that *GIRK2^wv^* homomeric channels display a loss of selectivity for monovalent cations, abnormal permeability for Ca^{2+} ions, and constitutive activation of the channel (82–86). While the mutation seems to directly affect the permeation and selectivity properties of the channel, the constitutive activation due to *GIRK2^wv^* homomeric channels appears to be a secondary effect of increased intracellular Na^+ concentrations (86). The *GIRK2^wv^* channel's high permeability to Na^+ ions can result in a regenerative link that produces the constitutive activation of the channel. This would lead to rapid, dramatic increases in intracellular Na^+ concentrations, with possibly severe pathologic consequences.

In contrast to the behavior of homomeric *GIRK2^wv^* channels, heteromeric channels formed by interaction with *GIRK1* show less current through the channel than wt heteromers, and little or no *GIRK* currents in cultured granule cells (85–88). The differential effect on homomeric versus heteromeric channels in these experiments is an important issue because *GIRK1* and *GIRK2* are both expressed in cerebellar granule cells. Several studies have directly measured G protein–coupled inwardly rectifying currents in cerebellar granule cells, primary culture, and in slice preparation (89). The data show that, unlike wt cells, *wv/wv* granule cells fail to express a G protein–activated inwardly rectifying current. This current is present in wt granule cells at the premigratory phase of differentiation, the point in development when most granule cells die as a consequence of the mutation, which led the authors to conclude that the loss of the inwardly rectifying current may play a major role in the pathogenesis of the *weaver* mutation.

Given the presence of the regenerative loop demonstrated by Silverman et al (86), it is tempting to postulate that the increased ion flux into granule cells is the initial pathogenic event leading to death of cells expressing the *GIRK2^wv* subunit. The presence of the *GIRK1* subunit in these same cells, the inhibitory effects of the *GIRK2^wv* subunit on heteromeric channels, and the loss of *GIRK* currents in slice preparations of *weaver* cerebellum (89), however, suggest that the stimulus for cell death is the loss of *GIRK* activity. In this case, the difference in the phenotypes of *weaver* and *GIRK2* null mice would be due to the dominant-negative effect of *GIRK2^wv* on other *GIRK* channel subunits present in granule cells. Further examination of *GIRK2^wv* action in situ will be necessary to reveal the relative contributions of these two possible mechanisms.

Cell Death in* Weaver *Neurons   Detailed analysis of cerebellar development in *wv/+* and *wv/wv* animals provided the first indication that cell death was an important initial feature of the *weaver* phenotype (70). An increase in cell death was observed in the EGL as early as at birth and continued during the first postnatal week. These cells were pycnotic and contained clumped heterochromatic nuclei, suggestive of an apoptotic death. Morphological analysis of dying *wv/wv* granule cells at the light and electron microscopic levels revealed a typical apoptotic morphology. DNA fragmentation assays and in situ end-labeling have both revealed nuclear DNA degradation in *wv/wv* granule cells lost postnatally in the EGL. Finally, increased *Bax* expression has been reported in dying *wv/wv* granule cells. These data provide strong evidence for activation of an apoptotic cell death pathway in *wv/wv* granule cells, although no direct genetic test of the activity of *Bax*, other Bcl-2 family members, or caspase in these cells has been reported.

The mechanism of cell death in the midbrain of *weaver* mice is much less clear. While the degeneration of tyrosine hydroxylase (TH)-positive neurons in the substantia nigra and retrorubral nucleus has been carefully documented, the morphology of these dying cells is not typical of apoptosis, and no DNA fragmentation was detected in TH-positive cells using in situ end-labeling (90). Nonetheless, extensive vacuolar and autophagic morphological changes were observed in these TH-positive cells in *wv/wv* substantia nigra. The loss of membrane and organelle integrity, a common feature of necrotic cell death, was not found.

Tottering (tg)

The *tottering* mouse is a spontaneous neurologic mutant with normal viability and intermittent seizures that begin in the second postnatal week (91). All alleles (*tg, tg^la, tg^rol*) exhibit the gait abnormalities and the absence of seizures typical of the original strain, and all three display histologic abnormalities in the cerebellum (92). Hyperinnervation from the locus ceruleus and persistent expression of TH are also apparent (93, 94). The original *tg* strain suffers from intermittent motor seizures that progress over a 20 to 30-min period to all limbs (95), but are not accompanied by any characteristic abnormality of the electroencephalogram. These motor seizures are not present in either the *leaner* (*tg^la*) or *rolling mouse Nagoya* (*tg^rol*) strains, but both these strains suffer degeneration and death of

Purkinje cells and other cerebellar neurons. Our discussion focuses primarily on *leaner* mice because they display the most severe phenotype.

Cerebellar Degeneration in the **Leaner** *Mouse*   The *leaner* phenotype develops over an extended period and involves progressive loss of neurons from the cerebellar cortex (96). Death of cerebellar granule cells is first evident in these animals beginning at postnatal day 10 (P10), and continues throughout the first postnatal year. There is also extensive loss of both Purkinje and Golgi neurons from the cerebellar cortex, although this occurs later in development (the Purkinje cell population is most affected). Neuronal loss is most severe in the anterior cerebellar folia, with an apparent boundary at the superior surface of the lobulus simplex. The loss of Purkinje cells from the cerebellar cortex occurs in alternating longitudinal zones that are reminiscent of the parasaggital domains of zebrin expression (97). Comparison of the profile of cell death in *leaner* mutant mice with the expression of the zebrin epitope shows that the surviving Purkinje cells are positive for the zebrin marker and that they retain the ectopic pattern of TH expression characteristic of all alleles (98).

$\alpha 1_A$ *Calcium Channel Subunit Mutations in the* **TG** *and* **TG**^{LA} *Strains*   The mutations responsible for both the *tottering* and *leaner* phenotypes have been identified as missense mutations in the $\alpha 1_A$ calcium channel subunit gene (98). Mutations in the $\alpha 1_A$ gene are also associated with the human diseases familial hemiplegic migraine, episodic ataxia type 1 (99), and spinocerebellar ataxia type 6 (SCA6) (100).

The large number of mutations in the $\alpha 1_A$ calcium channel gene and their very different consequences for CNS function raise a variety of interesting questions. In the context of this review, one would like to understand why the SCA6 and tg^{la} mutations cause the death of Purkinje, granule, and Golgi neurons, while other mutations in this gene cause episodic functional disturbances whose major effects on the nervous system do not include neurodegeneration. Comparative analysis of the functional consequences of the *tg* and tg^{la} mutations and their phenotypic consequences can contribute to our understanding of this issue.

The *tg* allele causes a proline-to-leucine amino acid substitution close to the P domain of $\alpha 1_A$, whereas the tg^{la} mutation results in replacement of the C-terminal cytoplasmic domain of the channel due to aberrant splicing (98). Two different products (termed the short and long forms) can be produced from the *leaner* allele due to exon skipping or the inclusion of intronic sequences in the aberrantly spliced mRNAs. Measurements of Ca^{2+} channel activities in Purkinje cells from *tottering* and *leaner* mice showed that P-type calcium currents were strongly reduced in both cases (101–103). In *leaner* Purkinje cells, a distinctive change in the voltage dependence of activation and inactivation of P-type currents was also noted. Characterization of the *tg* and tg^{la} alleles after expression in BHK cells confirmed these results, revealing a strong reduction in current density for both the *tg* and tg^{la} (*short*) alleles. In these experiments, a change in the voltage-dependent activation and inactivation of the Ca^{2+} currents was observed for only the tg^{la} (*long*) allele. These results suggest that both the *tottering* and *leaner* mutations may decrease intracellular Ca^{2+} levels and that at least one of the aberrant splice products of the *leaner* allele can cause a significant change in the voltage-dependent gating of this channel. The effects of the CAG expansion on the function of the channel in Purkinje cells will have to await the generation of SCA6 mouse models.

Cell Death in* Leaner *Mice   Neuronal death in *leaner* mice is restricted to a very specific subset of cerebellar neurons despite the high levels of expression of the $\alpha 1_A$ calcium channel subunit throughout the cerebellum and in many other CNS neurons (98). The specificity of this aspect of the *leaner* phenotype is not yet understood, although the pattern of cell death in Purkinje cells correlates with the expression of zebrin and the retention of TH expression in adult *tottering* and *leaner* animals. Although the significance of these observations for the mechanism(s) of cell death in *leaner* neurons is not clear, there is evidence that these cells die by an apoptotic mechanism (98). The *leaner* mouse, therefore, provides an interesting model for investigation of altered Ca^{2+} flux and apoptotic neuronal death in vivo.

COMMON THEMES AND MECHANISMS

Mouse models of neurodegeneration due to CAG repeat expansion or alterations in ion channels or neurotransmitter receptors allow investigation of details of pathogenesis that could not be assessed in other systems. Several themes have emerged from these studies that may help explain why certain mutations can lead to widespread neuronal loss, whereas others may result in severe functional disturbances without cell death.

Neuronal Dysfunction Versus Primary and Secondary Cell Death

Motor dysfunction precedes neuronal death by months in SCA1 transgenic mice, demonstrating that mutant ataxin-1 produces the SCA1 phenotype not by killing cells but by affecting Purkinje cell function. Similarly, HD mice that express the full-length proteins experience neurobehavioral and electrophysiologic changes before losing cells. Neuronal degeneration does occur in some of these mouse models late in the course of the disease, and in the MJD/SCA3 mouse, which expresses a truncated protein with a long polyglutamine tract in Purkinje cells, massive cerebellar loss occurs by a mere eight weeks. As noted above, protein fragments seem to be particularly toxic, and it may be the gradual accumulation of such truncated peptides due to protein cleavage that contributes to eventual neuronal loss in the more gradual phenotypes.

Comparison of the patterns of cell death in each model system reveals that in addition to those neurons that die as a direct consequence of the mutation, a number of neurons are susceptible to secondary cell death. Two features of cells vulnerable to secondary damage are notable. First, the susceptibility of cells to loss of their afferent partners varies both with cell type and the time of development. For example, the *lurcher* gene acts during the second two postnatal weeks to kill cerebellar Purkinje cells, leading to secondary, near-total loss of cerebellar granule cells and inferior olivary neurons. Vestibular ganglion neurons, on the other hand, which project the earliest mossy fiber afferents to the cerebellar cortex, survive loss of their granule cell targets as a result of the *lurcher, weaver,* or *Purkinje cell degeneration (pcd)* mutations (104). Furthermore, the *pcd* mutation, which causes virtually complete loss of Purkinje cells beginning at approximately P20, results in little granule cell or inferior olivary neuron death (105–107). For granule cells and inferior olivary neurons, therefore, the critical period of susceptibility to target cell deprivation appears to occur during early postnatal life. Second, the molecules that participate in the execution of the cell death pathway as a direct consequence of the mutation can be distinct from those mediating secondary cell loss. *Bax* is required for secondary granule cell death in *lurcher* mice, but it plays a minor role in cell death that results from *lurcher* gene action. These observations echo those from previous studies of neuronal death as a consequence of target deprivation and support the hypothesis that secondary cell death occurs by reactivation of the normal developmental cell death pathways.

Activation of Apoptosis

Evidence demonstrating the involvement of the effector components of the apoptotic machinery has begun to accumulate from neurologic mutant mouse strains and mouse models of ischemic cell death; induction of Bcl-2 family proteins, caspase activation, and DNA degradation have been observed in several of these models. Interestingly, several of the proteins mutated in polyglutamine disorders have also been found to be substrates for caspases and/or induce apoptosis in cell culture (20). Given the large variety of stimuli that can activate the effector phase of apoptosis, the central issue for this discussion is whether a common pathway is triggering neurodegeneration in response to altered neurotransmitter receptor or ion channel function or expanded polyglutamine proteins. Recent studies of the mechanisms of apoptotic cell death provide interesting indications that a common cell death mechanism might be operating.

At least two mechanisms have been identified that participate in caspase activation in dying cells (108–110). The first involves the ligation of death receptors by their appropriate ligands and recruitment of their cognate adaptor (e.g. FADD). These adaptors directly interact with caspase precursors. Formation of the receptor/adaptor/procaspase complex leads to activation of the bound caspase by proteolytic cleavage, resulting in stimulation of the caspase cascade and initiating the effector phase of apoptotic cell death. Although neurotransmitter receptors and ion channels clearly bind scaffolding molecules that are important for regulation of their activity and signaling, there is as yet no evidence that these complexes can directly activate the caspase cascade. Mitochondria play a central role in a second pathway that activates the effector phase of apoptosis. In this case, dynamic regulation of Bcl family proteins and their insertion into the mitochondrial membrane regulates the release of cytochrome c from the mitochondrion. Cytochrome c then binds to and activates a complex containing Apaf-1 and caspase-9, leading to cleavage of caspase-3 and activation of the effector phase of apoptotic cell death. Although the particular molecules participating in cytochrome c release from the mitochondrion and activation of the caspase cascade may vary in different cell types, the critical role of Bcl-2 family members in this pathway and the role of mitochondria as the focus for activation of the caspase cascade are fundamental.

The identification of the mitochondrion as a central component of a commonly occurring pathway for activation of the effector phase of apoptosis has implications for a wide variety of neurodegenerative diseases. Abnormal mitochondrial morphology and function has been recognized as a factor in neurodegenerative disease for many years (111–113). The discovery that proteins from the apoptotic pathway are directly associated with mitochondria provides a mechanistic link between the large literature documenting mitochondrial abnormalities in neurologic disease and a concrete mechanism of neuronal cell death. Evidence indicating the involvement of this pathway has been obtained in each of the mouse models of neurodegeneration resulting from altered ion channel or neurotransmitter receptor function and also in some of the polyglutamine mouse models. Morphologic abnormalities in mitochondria have been reported from the very earliest studies of the spontaneous mouse neurologic mutants (24, 114), and the activation of Bcl-2 family members and caspases in these mice is well documented. The mitochondrial pathway for activation of the effector phase of apoptosis is operative in many cases in which cellular stress is the stimulus, and it plays a critical role in developmental cell death in the nervous system. Knockout mice for caspase 3 (115), caspase 9 (116), and Apaf1 (117) all display massive malformations of the CNS resulting from overproduction of CNS cell types. Overexpression of a dominant-negative mutant for caspase-1 slows the progression of the amyotrophic lateral sclerosis phenotype in mice expressing a mutant form of Cu/Zn superoxide dismutase and prolongs survival of the R6/2 HD mice (21). The idea that secondary cell death in neurodegenerative disease involves the reactivation of developmental cell death pathways in afferent cell types is very attractive.

The available mice and future mouse models for neurodegeneration provide an excellent opportunity to study pathophysiology in unprecedented detail. They will form the foundation for future in vivo studies aimed at finding therapeutic approaches that might slow disease progression or completely block some of the earlier events in the pathogenic cascade.

ACKNOWLEDGMENTS

The authors thank V Brandt for critical input on the manuscript and gratefully acknowledge the support of the NIH/NINDS and the Howard Hughes Medical Institute. Due to space constraints, we were unable to cite all the papers that merit note; we apologize for these sometimes arbitrary omissions.

Visit the Annual Reviews home page at www.AnnualReviews.org.

LITERATURE CITED

1. Fu Y-H, Kuhl DPA, Pizutti A, Pieretti M, Sutcliffe JS, et al. 1991. Variation of the CGG repeat at the fragile X site results in genetic instability: resolution of the Sherman paradox. *Cell* 67:1047–58

2. La Spada AR, Wilson EM, Lubahn DB, Harding AE, Fischbeck H. 1991. Androgen receptor gene mutations in X-linked spinal and bulbar muscular atrophy. *Nature* 352:77–79

3. Zoghbi HY, Ballabio A. 1995. Spinocerebellar ataxia Type 1. In *The Metabolic and Molecular Bases of Inherited Disease,* ed. CR Scriver, AL Beaudet, WS Sly, R Valle, pp. 4559–67. New York: McGraw-Hill. 7th ed.

4. Burright EN, Clark HB, Servadio A, Matilla T, Feddersen RM, et al. 1995. SCA1 transgenic mice: a model for neurodegeneration caused by an expanded CAG trinucleotide repeat. *Cell* 82:937–48

5. Clark HB, Burright EN, Yunis WS, Larson S, Wilcox C, et al. 1997. Purkinje cell expression of a mutant allele of SCA1 in transgenic mice leads to disparate effects on motor behaviors, followed by a progressive cerebellar dysfunction and histological alterations. *J. Neurosci.* 17(19):7385–95

6. Skinner PJ, Koshy B, Cummings C, Klement IA, Helin K, et al. 1997. Ataxin-1 with extra glutamines induces alterations in nuclear matrix-associated structures. *Nature* 389:971–74

7. Klement IA, Skinner PJ, Kaytor MD, Yi H, Hersch SM, et al. 1998. Ataxin-1 nuclear localization and aggregation: role in polyglutamine-induced disease in SCA1 transgenic mice. *Cell* 95(1):41–53

8. Ikeda H, Yamaguchi M, Sugai S, Aze Y, Narumiya S, et al. 1996. Expanded polyglutamine in the Machado-Joseph disease protein induces cell death in vitro and in vivo. *Nat. Genet.* 13:196–202

9. Mangiarini L, Sathasivam K, Seller M, Cozens B, Harper A, et al. 1996. Exon 1 of the HD gene with an expanded CAG repeat is sufficient to cause a progressive neurological phenotype in transgenic mice. *Cell* 87:493–506

10. Davies SW, Turmaine M, Cozens BA, DiFiglia M, Sharp AH, et al. 1997. Formation of neuronal intranuclear inclusions underlies the neurological dysfunction in mice transgenic for the HD mutation. *Cell* 90(3):537–48

11. Cha J-HJ, Kosinski CM, Kerner JA, Alsdorf SA, Mangiarini M, et al. 1998. Altered brain neurotransmitter receptors in transgenic mice expressing a portion of an abnormal human Huntington disease gene. *Proc. Natl. Acad. Sci. USA* 95:6480–85

12. Ordway JM, Tallaksen-Greene S, Gutekunst CA, Bernstein EM, Cearley JA, et al. 1997. Ectopically expressed CAG repeats cause intranuclear inclusions and a progressive late onset neurological phenotype in the mouse. *Cell* 91(6):753–63

13. Reddy PH, Williams M, Charles V, Garrett L, Pike-Buchanan L, et al. 1998.

Behavioural abnormalities and selective neuronal loss in HD transgenic mice expressing mutated full-length HD cDNA. *Nat. Genet.* 20(2):198–202

14. Hodgson JG, Agopyan N, Gutekunst C-A, Leavitt BR, LePiane F, et al. 1999. A YAC mouse model for Huntington's disease with full-length mutant huntingtin, cytoplasmic toxicity, and selective striatal neurodegeneration. *Neuron* 23:181–92

15. White JK, Auerbach W, Duyao MP, Vonsattel JP, Gusella JF, et al. 1997. Huntingtin is required for neurogenesis and is not impaired by the Huntington's disease CAG expansion. *Nat. Genet.* 17(4):404–10

16. Shelbourne PF, Killeen N, Hevner RF, Johnston HM, Tecott L, et al. 1999. A Huntington's disease CAG expansion at the murine Hdh locus is unstable and associated with behavioural abnormalities in mice. *Hum. Mol. Genet.* 8(5):763–74

17. Usdin MT, Shelbourne PF, Myers RM, Madison DV. 1999. Impaired synaptic plasticity in mice carrying the Huntington's disease mutation. *Hum. Mol. Genet.* 8(5): 839–46

18. Cummings CJ, Mancini MA, Antalffy B, DeFranco DB, Orr HT, et al. 1998. Chaperone suppression of aggregation and altered subcellular proteasome localization imply protein misfolding in SCA1. *Nat. Genet.* 19:148–54

19. Paulson HL. 1999. Protein fate in neurodegenerative proteinopathies: polyglutamine diseases join the (mis) fold. *Am. J. Hum. Genet.* 64:339–45

20. Wellington CL, Ellerby LM, Hackam AS, Margolis RL, Trifiro MA, et al. 1998. Caspase cleavage of gene products associated with triplet expansion disorders generates truncated fragments containing the polyglutamine tract. *J. Biol. Chem.* 273(15):9158–67

21. Ona VO, Li M, Vonsattel JP, Andrews LJ, Khan SQ, et al. 1999. Inhibition of

caspase-1 slows disease progression in a mouse model of Huntington's disease. *Nature* 399(6733):263–67

21a. Olney JW, Sharpe LG. 1969. Brain lesions in an infant rhesus monkey treated with monosodium glutamate. *Science* (166)903:386–88

22. Choi DW. 1994. Calcium and excitotoxic neuronal injury. *Ann. NY Acad. Sci.* 747:162–71

23. Lin CL, Bristol LA, Jin L, Dykes-Hoberg M, Crawford T, et al. 1998. Aberrant RNA processing in a neurodegenerative disease: the cause for absent EAAT2, a glutamate transporter, in amyotrophic lateral sclerosis. *Neuron* 20(3):589–602

24. Caddy KW, Biscoe TJ. 1979. Structural and quantitative studies on the normal C3H and Lurcher mutant mouse. *Philos. Trans. R. Soc. London Ser. B* 287:167–201

25. Cheng SS, Heintz N. 1997. Massive loss of mid- and hindbrain neurons during embryonic development of homozygous lurcher mice. *J. Neurosci.* 17:2400–7

26. Resibois A, Cuvelier L, Goffinet AM. 1997. Abnormalities in the cerebellum and brainstem in homozygous lurcher mice. *Neuroscience* 80:175–90

27. Wetts R, Herrup K. 1982. Interaction of granule, Purkinje and inferior olivary neurons in lurcher chimeric mice. II. Granule cell death. *Brain Res.* 250:358–62

28. Wetts R, Herrup K. 1982. Interaction of granule, Purkinje and inferior olivary neurons in lurcher chimaeric mice. I. Qualitative studies. *J. Embryol. Exp. Morphol.* 68:87–98

29. Wullner U, Weller M, Schulz JB, Krajewski S, Reed JC, Klockgether T. 1998. Bcl-2, Bax and Bcl-x expression in neuronal apoptosis: a study of mutant weaver and lurcher mice. *Acta Neuropathol. (Berl.)* 96:233–38

30. Selimi F, Doughty ML, Delhaye-Bouchaud N, Mariani J. 1999. Target-related and intrinsic neuronal death in Lurcher

mutant mice involve different apoptotic pathways, but are both mediated by caspase-3 activation. *Mol. Cell. Neurosci.* In press

31. Heintz N. 1993. Cell death and the cell cycle: a relationship between transformation and neurodegeneration? *Trends Biochem. Sci.* 18:157–59

32. Zuo J, De Jager PL, Takahashi KA, Jiang W, Linden DJ, Heintz N. 1997. Neurodegeneration in Lurcher mice caused by mutation in delta2 glutamate receptor gene. *Nature* 388:769–73

33. Yamazaki M, Araki K, Shibata A, Mishina M. 1992. Molecular cloning of a cDNA encoding a novel member of the mouse glutamate receptor channel family. *Biochem. Biophys. Res. Commun.* 183:886–92

34. Lomeli H, Sprengel R, Laurie DJ, Kohr G, Herb A, et al. 1993. The rat delta-1 and delta-2 subunits extend the excitatory amino acid receptor family. *FEBS Lett.* 315:318–22

35. Araki K, Meguro H, Kushiya E, Takayama C, Inoue Y, Mishina M. 1993. Selective expression of the glutamate receptor channel delta 2 subunit in cerebellar Purkinje cells. *Biochem. Biophys. Res. Commun.* 197:1267–76

36. Mayat E, Petralia RS, Wang YX, Wenthold RJ. 1995. Immunoprecipitation, immunoblotting, and immunocytochemistry studies suggest that glutamate receptor delta subunits form novel postsynaptic receptor complexes. *J. Neurosci.* 15:2533–46

37. Takayama C, Nakagawa S, Watanabe M, Mishina M, Inoue Y. 1995. Light- and electron-microscopic localization of the glutamate receptor channel delta 2 subunit in the mouse Purkinje cell. *Neurosci. Lett.* 188:89–92

38. Landsend AS, Amiry-Moghaddam M, Matsubara A, Bergersen L, Usami S, et al. 1997. Differential localization of delta glutamate receptors in the rat cerebellum: coexpression with AMPA receptors in

parallel fiber-spine synapses and absence from climbing fiber-spine synapses. *J. Neurosci.* 17:834–42

39. Zhao HM, Wenthold RJ, Wang YX, Petralia RS. 1997. Delta-glutamate receptors are differentially distributed at parallel and climbing fiber synapses on Purkinje cells. *J. Neurochem.* 68:1041–52

40. Kashiwabuchi N, Ikeda K, Araki K, Hirano T, Shibuki K, et al. Y. 1995. Impairment of motor coordination, Purkinje cell synapse formation, and cerebellar long-term depression in GluR delta 2 mutant mice. *Cell* 81:245–52

41. Gwag BJ, Koh JY, DeMaro JA, Ying HS, Jacquin M, Choi DW. 1997. Slowly triggered excitotoxicity occurs by necrosis in cortical cultures. *Neuroscience* 77:393–401

42. Zanjani H, Rondi-Reig L, Vogel M, Martinou JC, Delhaye-Bouchaud N, Mariani J. 1998. Overexpression of a Hu-bcl-2 transgene in Lurcher mutant mice delays Purkinje cell death. *C.R. Acad. Sci. III* 321:633–40

43. Zanjani HS, Vogel MW, Martinou JC, Delhaye-Bouchaud N, Mariani J. 1998. Postnatal expression of Hu-bcl-2 gene in Lurcher mutant mice fails to rescue Purkinje cells but protects inferior olivary neurons from target-related cell death. *J. Neurosci.* 18:319–27

44. Doughty ML, Lohof A, Selimi F, Delhaye-Bouchaud N, Mariani J. 1999. Afferent-target cell interactions in the cerebellum: negative effect of granule cells on Purkinje cell development in lurcher mice. *J. Neurosci.* 19:3448–56

45. Lee JM, Zipfel GJ, Choi DW. 1999. The changing landscape of ischaemic brain injury mechanisms. *Nature* 399:A7–14

46. Simon RP, Swan JH, Griffiths T, Meldrum BS. 1984. Blockade of *N*-methyl-D-aspartate receptors may protect against ischemic damage in the brain. *Science* 226:850–52

47. Wieloch T. 1985. Hypoglycemia-induced

neuronal damage prevented by an *N*-methyl-D-aspartate antagonist. *Science* 230:681–83

48. Goldin SM, Subbarao K, Sharma R, Knapp AG, Fischer JB, et al. 1995. Neuroprotective use-dependent blockers of Na^+ and Ca^{2+} channels controlling presynaptic release of glutamate. *Ann. NY Acad. Sci.* 765:210–29

49. Morikawa E, Mori H, Kiyama Y, Mishina M, Asano T, Kirino T. 1998. Attenuation of focal ischemic brain injury in mice deficient in the epsilon1 (NR2A) subunit of NMDA receptor. *J. Neurosci.* 18:9727–32

50. Martin LJ, Al Abdulla NA, Brambrink AM, Kirsch JR, Sieber FE, Portera-Cailliau C. 1998. Neurodegeneration in excitotoxicity, global cerebral ischemia, and target deprivation: a perspective on the contributions of apoptosis and necrosis. *Brain Res. Bull.* 46:281–309

51. Isenmann S, Stoll G, Schroeter M, Krajewski S, Reed JC, Bahr M. 1998. Differential regulation of Bax, Bcl-2, and Bcl-X proteins in focal cortical ischemia in the rat. *Brain Pathol.* 8:49–62

52. Loddick SA, MacKenzie A, Rothwell NJ. 1996. An ICE inhibitor, z-VAD-DCB attenuates ischaemic brain damage in the rat. *NeuroReport* 7:1465–68

53. Asahi M, Hoshimaru M, Uemura Y, Tokime T, Kojima M, et al. 1997. Expression of interleukin-1 beta converting enzyme gene family and bcl- 2 gene family in the rat brain following permanent occlusion of the middle cerebral artery. *J. Cereb. Blood Flow Metab.* 17:11–18

54. Chen J, Nagayama T, Jin K, Stetler RA, Zhu RL, et al. 1998. Induction of caspase-3-like protease may mediate delayed neuronal death in the hippocampus after transient cerebral ischemia. *J. Neurosci.* 18:4914–28

55. Namura S, Zhu J, Fink K, Endres M, Srinivasan A, et al. 1998. Activation and cleavage of caspase-3 in apoptosis induced by experimental cerebral ischemia. *J. Neurosci.* 18:3659–68

56. Velier JJ, Ellison JA, Kikly KK, Spera PA, Barone FC, Feuerstein GZ. 1999. Caspase-8 and caspase-3 are expressed by different populations of cortical neurons undergoing delayed cell death after focal stroke in the rat. *J. Neurosci.* 19:5932–41

57. Heron A, Pollard H, Dessi F, Moreau J, Lasbennes F, et al. 1993. Regional variability in DNA fragmentation after global ischemia evidenced by combined histological and gel electrophoresis observations in the rat brain. *J. Neurochem.* 61:1973–76

58. MacManus JP, Buchan AM, Hill IE, Rasquinha I, Preston E. 1993. Global ischemia can cause DNA fragmentation indicative of apoptosis in rat brain. *Neurosci. Lett.* 164:89–92

59. Li Y, Chopp M , Jiang N, Zhang ZG, Zaloga C. 1995. Induction of DNA fragmentation after 10 to 120 minutes of focal cerebral ischemia in rats. *Stroke* 26:1252–57

60. Fujimura M, Morita-Fujimura Y, Murakami K, Kawase M, Chan PH. 1998. Cytosolic redistribution of cytochrome c after transient focal cerebral ischemia in rats. *J. Cereb. Blood Flow Metab.* 18:1239–47

61. Perez-Pinzon MA, Xu GP, Born J, Lorenzo J, Busto R, et al. 1999. Cytochrome c is released from mitochondria into the cytosol after cerebral anoxia or ischemia. *J. Cereb. Blood Flow Metab.* 19:39–43

62. Ma J, Endres M, Moskowitz MA. 1998. Synergistic effects of caspase inhibitors and MK-801 in brain injury after transient focal cerebral ischaemia in mice. *Br. J. Pharmacol.* 124:756–62

63. Martinou JC, Dubois-Dauphin M, Staple JK, Rodriguez I, Frankowski H, et al. 1994. Overexpression of BCL-2 in transgenic mice protects neurons from naturally occurring cell death and experimental ischemia. *Neuron* 13:1017–30

64. Kitagawa K, Matsumoto M, Tsujimoto Y, Ohtsuki T, Kuwabara K, et al. 1998. Amelioration of hippocampal neuronal damage after global ischemia by neuronal overexpression of BCL-2 in transgenic mice. *Stroke* 29:2616–21

65. Wang HD, Fukuda T, Suzuki T, Hashimoto K, Liou SY, et al. 1999. Differential effects of Bcl-2 overexpression on hippocampal CA1 neurons and dentate granule cells following hypoxic ischemia in adult mice. *J. Neurosci. Res.* 57:1–12

66. Parsadanian AS, Cheng Y, Keller-Peck CR, Holtzman DM, Snider WD. 1998. Bcl-xL is an antiapoptotic regulator for postnatal CNS neurons. *J. Neurosci.* 18:1009–19

67. Rezai Z, Yoon CH. 1972. Abnormal rate of granule cell migration in the cerebellum of "Weaver" mutant mice. *Dev. Biol.* 29:17–26

68. Rakic P, Sidman RL. 1973. Sequence of developmental abnormalities leading to granule cell deficit in cerebellar cortex of weaver mutant mice. *J. Comp. Neurol.* 152:103–32

69. Sotelo C. 1975. Anatomical, physiological and biochemical studies of the cerebellum from mutant mice. II. Morphological study of cerebellar cortical neurons and circuits in the weaver mouse. *Brain Res.* 94:19–44

70. Smeyne RJ, Goldowitz D. 1989. Development and death of external granular layer cells in the weaver mouse cerebellum: a quantitative study. *J. Neurosci.* 9:1608–20

71. Goldowitz D. 1989. The weaver granuloprival phenotype is due to intrinsic action of the mutant locus in granule cells: evidence from homozygous weaver chimeras. *Neuron* 2:1565–75

72. Hatten ME, Liem RK, Mason CA. 1986. Weaver mouse cerebellar granule neurons fail to migrate on wild-type astroglial processes in vitro. *J. Neurosci.* 6:2676–83

73. Gao WQ, Liu XL, Hatten ME. 1992. The weaver gene encodes a nonautonomous signal for CNS neuronal differentiation. *Cell* 68:841–54

74. Schmidt MJ, Sawyer BD, Perry KW, Fuller RW, Foreman MM, Ghetti B. 1982. Dopamine deficiency in the weaver mutant mouse. *J. Neurosci.* 2:376–80

75. Graybiel AM, Ohta K, Roffler-Tarlov S. 1990. Patterns of cell and fiber vulnerability in the mesostriatal system of the mutant mouse weaver. I. Gradients and compartments. *J. Neurosci.* 10:720–33

76. Roffler-Tarlov S, Pugatch D, Graybiel AM. 1990. Patterns of cell and fiber vulnerability in the mesostriatal system of the mutant mouse weaver. II. High affinity uptake sites for dopamine. *J. Neurosci.* 10:734–40

77. Goldowitz D, Mullen RJ. 1982. Granule cell as a site of gene action in the weaver mouse cerebellum: evidence from heterozygous mutant chimeras. *J. Neurosci.* 2:1474–85

78. Patil N, Cox DR, Bhat D, Faham M, Myers RM, Peterson AS. 1995. A potassium channel mutation in weaver mice implicates membrane excitability in granule cell differentiation. *Nat. Genet.* 11:126–29

79. Signorini S, Liao YJ, Duncan SA, Jan LY, Stoffel M. 1997. Normal cerebellar development but susceptibility to seizures in mice lacking G protein-coupled, inwardly rectifying K^+ channel GIRK2. *Proc. Natl. Acad. Sci. USA* 94:923–27

80. Schein JC, Hunter DD, Roffler-Tarlov S. 1998. Girk2 expression in the ventral midbrain, cerebellum, and olfactory bulb and its relationship to the murine mutation weaver. *Dev. Biol.* 204:432–50

81. Goldowitz D. 1989. The weaver granuloprival phenotype is due to intrinsic action of the mutant locus in granule cells: evidence from homozygous weaver chimeras. *Neuron* 6:1565–75

82. Slesinger PA, Patil N, Liao YJ, Jan YN, Jan LY, Cox DR. 1996. Functional effects

of the mouse weaver mutation on G protein-gated inwardly rectifying K^+ channels. *Neuron* 16:321–31

83. Kofuji P, Hofer M, Millen KJ, Millonig JH, Davidson N, et al. 1996. Functional analysis of the weaver mutant GIRK2 K^+ channel and rescue of weaver granule cells. *Neuron* 16:941–52

84. Tong Y, Wei J, Zhang S, Strong JA, Dlouhy SR, et al. 1996. The weaver mutation changes the ion selectivity of the affected inwardly rectifying potassium channel GIRK2. *FEBS Lett.* 390:63–68

85. Surmeier DJ, Mermelstein PG, Goldowitz D. 1996. The weaver mutation of GIRK2 results in a loss of inwardly rectifying K^+ current in cerebellar granule cells. *Proc. Natl. Acad. Sci. USA* 93:11191–95

86. Silverman SK, Kofuji P, Dougherty DA, Davidson N, Lester HA. 1996. A regenerative link in the ionic fluxes through the weaver potassium channel underlies the pathophysiology of the mutation. *Proc. Natl. Acad. Sci. USA* 93:15429–34

87. Mjaatvedt AE, Cabin DE, Cole SE, Long LJ, Breitwieser GE, Reeves RH. 1995. Assessment of a mutation in the H5 domain of Girk2 as a candidate for the weaver mutation. *Genome Res.* 5:453–63

88. Lauritzen I, De Weille J, Adelbrecht C, Lesage F, Murer G, et al. 1997. Comparative expression of the inward rectifier K^+ channel GIRK2 in the cerebellum of normal and weaver mutant mice. *Brain Res.* 753:8–17

89. Rossi P, De Filippi G, Armano S, Taglietti V, D'Angelo E. 1998. The weaver mutation causes a loss of inward rectifier current regulation in premigratory granule cells of the mouse cerebellum. *J. Neurosci.* 18:3537–47

90. Oo TF, Blazeski R, Harrison SM, Henchcliffe C, Mason CA, et al. 1996. Neuron death in the substantia nigra of weaver mouse occurs late in development and is not apoptotic. *J. Neurosci.* 16:6134–45

91. Green MC, Sidman RL, Pivetta OH. 1972. Cribriform degeneration (cri): a new recessive neurological mutation in the mouse. *Science* 176:800–3

92. Tsuji S, Meier H. 1971. Evidence for allelism of leaner and tottering in the mouse. *Genet. Res.* 17:83–88

93. Levitt P. 1988. Normal pharmacological and morphometric parameters in the noradrenergic hyperinnervated mutant mouse, "tottering." *Cell Tissue Res.* 252:175–80

94. Hess EJ, Wilson MC. 1991. Tottering and leaner mutations perturb transient developmental expression of tyrosine hydroxylase in embryologically distinct Purkinje cells. *Neuron* 6:123–32

95. Noebels JL, Sidman RL. 1979. Inherited epilepsy: spike-wave and focal motor seizures in the mutant mouse tottering. *Science* 204:1334–36

96. Herrup K, Wilczynski SL. 1982. Cerebellar cell degeneration in the leaner mutant mouse. *Neuroscience* 7:2185–96

97. Heckroth JA, Abbott LC. 1994. Purkinje cell loss from alternating sagittal zones in the cerebellum of leaner mutant mice. *Brain Res.* 658:93–104

98. Fletcher CF, Lutz CM, O'Sullivan TN, Shaughnessy JD, Hawkes R, et al. 1996. Absence epilepsy in tottering mutant mice is associated with calcium channel defects. *Cell* 87:607–27

99. Ophoff RA, Terwindt GM, Vergouwe MN, van Eijk R, Oefner PJ, et al. 1996. Familial hemiplegic migraine and episodic ataxia type-2 are caused by mutations in the Ca^{2+} channel gene CACNL1A4. *Cell* 87:543–52

100. Zhuchenko O, Bailey J, Bonnen P, Ashizawa T, Stockton DW, et al. 1997. Autosomal dominant cerebellar ataxia (SCA6) associated with small polyglutamine expansions in the alpha 1A-voltage-dependent calcium channel. *Nat. Genet.* 15:62–69

101. Dove LS, Abbott LC, Griffith WH. 1998. Whole-cell and single-channel analysis

of P-type calcium currents in cerebellar Purkinje cells of leaner mutant mice 17. *J. Neurosci.* 18:7687–99

102. Wakamori M, Yamazaki K, Matsunodaira H, Teramoto T, Tanaka I, et al. 1998. Single tottering mutations responsible for the neuropathic phenotype of the P-type calcium channel. *J. Biol. Chem.* 273:34857–67

103. Lorenzon NM, Lutz CM, Frankel WN, Beam KG. 1998. Altered calcium channel currents in Purkinje cells of the neurological mutant mouse leaner. *J. Neurosci.* 18:4482–89

104. Baurle J, Guldin W. 1998. Vestibular ganglion neurons survive the loss of their cerebellar targets. *NeuroReport* 9:4119–22

105. Mullen RJ, Eicher EM, Sidman RL. 1976. Purkinje cell degeneration, a new neurological mutation in the mouse. *Proc. Natl. Acad. Sci. USA* 73:208–12

106. Landis SC, Mullen RJ. 1978. The development and degeneration of Purkinje cells in pcd mutant mice. *J. Comp. Neurol.* 177:125–43

107. Shojaeian H, Delhaye-Bouchaud N, Mariani J. 1988. Stability of inferior olivary neurons in rodents. I. Moderate cell loss in adult Purkinje cell degeneration mutant mouse. *Brain Res.* 466:211–18

108. Green DR. 1998. Apoptotic pathways: the roads to ruin. *Cell* 94:695–98

109. Los M, Wesselborg S, Schulze-Osthoff K. 1999. The role of caspases in development, immunity, and apoptotic signal transduction: lessons from knockout mice. *Immunity* 10:629–39

110. Vaux DL, Korsmeyer SJ. 1999. Cell death in development. *Cell* 96:245–54

111. Montal M. 1998. Mitochondria, glutamate neurotoxicity and the death cascade. *Biochim. Biophys. Acta* 1366:113–26

112. Murphy AN, Fiskum G, Beal MF. 1999. Mitochondria in neurodegeneration: bioenergetic function in cell life and death. *J. Cereb. Blood Flow Metab.* 19:231–45

113. Fiskum G, Murphy AN, Beal MF. 1999. Mitochondria in neurodegeneration: acute ischemia and chronic neurodegenerative diseases. *J. Cereb. Blood Flow Metab.* 19:351–69

114. Landis SC. 1973. Ultrastructural changes in the mitochondria of cerebellar Purkinje cells of nervous mutant mice. *J. Cell Biol.* 57:782–97

115. Hakem R, Hakem A, Duncan GS, Henderson JT, Woo M, et al. 1998. Differential requirement for caspase 9 in apoptotic pathways in vivo. *Cell* 94:339–52

116. Kuida K, Haydar TF, Kuan CY, Gu Y, Taya C, et al. 1998. Reduced apoptosis and cytochrome c-mediated caspase activation in mice lacking caspase 9. *Cell* 94:325–37

117. Yoshida H, Kong YY, Yoshida R, Elia AJ, Hakem A, et al. 1998. Apaf1 is required for mitochondrial pathways of apoptosis and brain development. *Cell* 94:739–50

Annu. Rev. Physiol. 2000. 62:803–23

SPATIAL CONSIDERATIONS FOR STIMULUS-DEPENDENT TRANSCRIPTION IN NEURONS

Sohyun Ahn, Antonella Riccio, and David D. Ginty

Department of Neuroscience, The Johns Hopkins University School of Medicine, Baltimore, Maryland 21205–2185; e-mail: dginty@jhmi.edu

Key Words   signal transduction, transcription, glutamate, NGF, CREB

■ **Abstract**   Most neurons have elaborate dendrites as well as an axon emanating from the cell body that form synaptic connections with one or many target cells, which may be located a considerable distance from the cell body. Such complex and impressive morphologies allow some types of neurons to integrate inputs from one to many thousands of pre-synaptic partners and to rapidly propagate electrical signals, often over long distances, to post-synaptic target cells. Much slower, non-electrical signals also propagate from dendrites and distal axons to neuronal nuclei that influence survival, growth, and plasticity. The distances between distal dendrites and/or distal axons and cell bodies of neurons can be hundreds of microns to more than one meter. This long-range biochemical signal propagation from distal dendrites and distal axons to neuronal nuclei is entirely unique to neurons. This review is focused on excitatory neurotransmitter signaling from dendritic synapses to neuronal nuclei as well as on retrograde growth factor signaling from distal axons to neuronal nuclei.

INTRODUCTION

Signaling from Dendrites to Neuronal Nuclei

In the nervous system, rapid transfer of information occurs through the propagation of electrical signals and release of neurotransmitters from pre-synaptic terminals, which influences spiking or activity of the post-synaptic cell. In addition to rapid transfer of electrical signals between pre- and post-synaptic neurons, bursts of synaptic activity can result in long-lasting neuronal adaptive responses. Some long-lasting, activity-dependent changes in neuron function are dependent on alterations in gene transcription, which occurs within the nucleus of the neuron. Neuronal activity-regulated genes include those encoding transcription factors, which may govern the expression of other late-response genes, and a variety of additional functionally important genes such as those encoding ion channels, structural proteins, neurotransmitter synthesizing enzymes, proteins involved in neurotransmitter receptor clustering, and growth factors (1, 2). In this manner,

0066–4278/00/0315–0803$12.00

synaptic activity regulates the expression of genes that influence the overall physiological and morphological state of the neuron.

Retrograde Signaling from Distal Axons to Neuronal Nuclei

In addition to neurotransmitter signals that propagate from ionotropic and metabotropic receptors found on dendrites to neuronal nuclei, distal axons of neurons also receive input derived from synaptic release and/or factors released from their target fields that is retrogradely communicated to neuronal nuclei. Among the neuronal inputs that act upon distal axons are retrogradely acting neurotransmitters and target-derived growth factors that can control certain forms of synaptic plasticity, as well as growth and survival of neurons, through their influence on gene expression.

Neurotransmitters and target-derived factors acting on either distal dendrites or distal axons have the capacity to modulate or even direct the nature of the overall genetic program of a neuron. In this way, a neuron has the capacity to sense and respond, indeed adapt, to particular changes in patterns of pre-synaptic activity and to its target environment by employing the power and complexity of its entire arsenal of genes. Although many of the molecular participants in neurotransmitter and growth factor signaling mechanisms as well as transcription factors and other nuclear effectors have been identified over the past two decades, understanding how biochemical signals flow from dendrites and distal axons to nuclei remains a major current challenge. Here, we review recent work that has addressed mechanisms of stimulus-dependent transcription in neurons with particular emphasis on spatial considerations that are unique to neurons.

Stimulus-Dependent Transcription and the CRE-Binding Protein, CREB

Among the most critical targets of signaling pathways that convert extracellular stimuli to nuclear responses are transcription factors that control the expression of immediate early genes (IEGs) and late response genes. Perhaps the best characterized of all extracellular stimulus-regulated transcription factors is CREB (cyclic AMP response element binding protein) (reviewed in 3). CREB and its closely related family members, ATF-1 and CREM,[1] are widely expressed tran-

---

[1]Abbreviations used in this review: CRE, cyclic AMP response element; CREB, CRE binding protein; ATF-1, activating transcription factor-1; CREM, CRE modulator; CBP, CREB binding protein; HAT, histone acetyltransferase; PKA, protein kinase A; CaMK, Ca^{2+}/calmodulin-dependent kinase; ERK, extracellular signal-regulated kinase; MAPK, mitogen-activated protein kinase; MEK, MAPK/ERK kinase; MAPKAP kinase 2, MAPK-activated protein kinase 2; PKB, protein kinase B; p70 S6K, 70 kDa ribosomal S6 kinase; MSK1, mitogen and stress-activated protein kinase 1; PP-1, protein phosphatase-1; PP-2A, protein phosphatase-2A; NGF, nerve growth factor; VSCC, voltage-sensitive calcium channel; LTP, long-term potentiation; LTD, long-term depression; NMDA, N-methyl-D-

scription factors that bind constitutively to *cis*-acting elements (CREs) found in genomic regulatory regions of many neurotransmitter– and growth factor–sensitive genes (4). CREB activity is regulated by phosphorylation on a serine residue, Ser133. Upon exposure of cells to many different extracellular stimuli, including excitatory neurotransmitters and growth factors, CREB Ser133 becomes newly phosphorylated, and this phosphorylation event is necessary for its ability to promote initiation of gene transcription. Interestingly, phosphorylation of CREB Ser133 may not always be sufficient for activation of transcription (4, 5), and the duration of phosphorylation of CREB following cell stimulation is one key determinant of whether a stimulus can activate CREB-mediated gene transcription. Once phosphorylated on Ser133, CREB recruits co-activators CBP (CREB binding protein) and p300 (6), which have intrinsic histone acetyltransferase (HAT) activity (7, 8). Upon their recruitment to the promoter, CBP and p300 promote transcription initiation through direct interactions with components of the basal transcription factor machinery as well as through acetylation of histones. Histone acetylation is believed to decondense chromatin and facilitate access of basal transcription factors to the core promoter region. Because phosphorylation of CREB Ser133 is a key regulatory event governing stimulus-dependent gene expression, much research has focused on identification of kinases and phosphatases that control this phosphorylation event. This, it turns out, has not been a simple task.

CREB Kinases and Phosphatases

As with all phosphoproteins, the level of phosphorylation of CREB Ser133 reflects of the activities of kinases and phosphatases working in opposition. Several candidate stimulus-dependent CREB kinases have been identified to date. These include PKA (9); CaMKI, II, and IV (10–12); Rsk1, 2, and 3 (13, 14); MAPKAP kinase 2 (15); Akt/PKB (16); p70 S6K (17); p38/RK/HOG-1-dependent p108 CREB kinase (18); and MSK1 (19) (Figure 1). Each of these kinases becomes activated upon exposure of cells to one or more extracellular stimuli, and each can phosphorylate CREB Ser133 in vitro. In most cases, the active kinase is localized, at least in part, to the nucleus. It is likely that multiple CREB kinases are activated following cell stimulation and that the nature of the stimulus, the magnitude and duration of the stimulation, and the proximity of the cell surface receptor and its signaling effectors to the nucleus and the transcrip-

---

nasparate; BDNF, brain-derived neurotrophic factor; NT3, neurotrophin 3; NT4/5 neurotrophin 4/5; SRE, serum response element; DRE, downstream regulatory element; DREAM, DRE-antagonist modulator; CDF, cholinergic differentiation factor; p75[LNGRF], 75-kDa low-affinity NGF receptor; SH2, Src homology region 2; PTB, phosphotyrosine binding domain; PLC-γ, phospholipase C-γ; IEG, immediate early gene; LRG, late response gene; LIF, leukemia inhibitory factor; CNTF, ciliary neurotrophic factor, TGF-β, transforming growth factor-β.

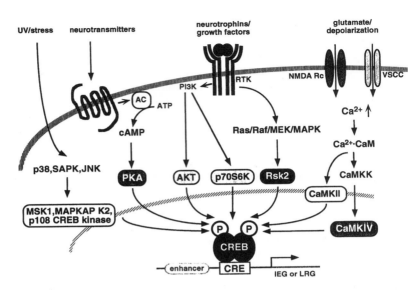

Figure 1 Multiple signaling pathways lead to phosphorylation of CREB Ser133. Abbreviations: SAPK (stress-activated protein kinase); JNK (c-Jun N-terminal kinase); MSK1 (mitogen- and stress-activated protein kinase-1); MAPKAP K2 (MAPK-activated protein kinase 2); AC (adenylate cyclase); RTK (receptor tyrosine kinase); PI3K (phosphatidylinositol 3-kinase); AKT (also called protein kinase B); p70S 6K (70-kDa ribosomal S6 kinase); MEK (MAPK/ERK kinase); MAPK (mitogen-activated protein kinase); NMDA Rc (N-methyl-D-aspartate subtype of glutamate receptor); VSCC (voltage-sensitive calcium channel); CaM (calmodulin); CaMKK (Ca^{2+}/calmodulin-dependent protein kinase kinase); CaMKII/IV (Ca^{2+}/calmodulin-dependent protein kinase II/IV); CRE (cAMP response element); CREB (CRE-binding protein); IEG (immediate early gene); LRG (late response gene); PKA (protein kinase A).

tional machinery coordinately determine which of the CREB kinase(s) is responsible for catalysis of CREB phosphorylation.

In contrast to the large body of work describing stimulus-dependent CREB kinases, CREB phosphatases have received relatively little attention. The best candidate CREB phosphatases are PP-1 and PP-2A (20, 21). PP-1 is likely to catalyze dephosphorylation of CREB Ser133 in hippocampal neurons (22). Because PP-1 can be regulated by neuronal activity (23), this enzyme could be an important mediator of activity-dependent CREB phosphorylation. Therefore, CREB is regulated by stimulus-dependent kinases and phosphatases.

In the next section, we discuss the mechanisms by which release of the neurotransmitter glutamate at excitatory synapses leads to phosphorylation of CREB in post-synaptic neurons as an example of dendrite-to-nucleus signaling. Subsequently, we discuss how nerve-growth factor (NGF), a target-derived neurotrophic growth factor that can act on its receptors on distal axonal terminals, propagates a biochemical signal from distal axons to CREB as an example of long-range retrograde signaling to the nucleus.

CREB AND SIGNALING FROM THE SYNAPSE TO THE NUCLEUS

Glutamate Regulation of Gene Expression

Bursts of activity at many excitatory synapses result in activation of ligand-gated ionotropic neurotransmitter receptors and voltage-sensitive calcium channels (VSCC) located in post-synaptic membranes and subsequent Ca^{2+} influx into the post-synaptic neuron. Glutamate, the major excitatory neurotransmitter in the CNS, activates ionotropic as well as metabotropic receptors on post-synaptic cells. Activation of ionotropic glutamate receptors and subsequent influx of Ca^{2+} into post-synaptic neurons are required for glutamate-mediated changes in synaptic efficacy, including long-term potentiation (LTP) and long-term depression (LTD) (24, 25), which are cellular phenomena that may underlie aspects of learning and memory. The maintenance phase of these forms of long-term changes in synaptic efficacy requires new gene transcription (26, 27), indicating that signaling pathways propagated from ionotropic glutamate receptors located on the dendrites of a post-synaptic neuron to the nucleus are essential for activity-dependent plasticity.

Activation of glutamatergic synapses in vivo can trigger changes in gene expression within post-synaptic neurons within minutes (28, 29). Thus signals that couple NMDA receptor activation and engagement of the transcription initiation machinery are very rapid. This is noteworthy because excitatory synapses can be quite far from the nucleus. For example, typical Schaffer collateral–CA1 synapses within the hippocampus are 400 microns from cell bodies of the post-synaptic CA1 neuron. Thus the excitatory neurotransmitter signal is carried from the membrane of the post-synaptic cell to the nucleus by rapidly propagated signaling cascades. This is in contrast to the considerably slower form of retrograde signaling described below.

CREB is a Mediator of Activity-Dependent Gene Expression

Several lines of evidence indicate that CREB is a key nuclear target for activity-dependent signaling at excitatory glutamatergic synapses. First, synaptic stimulation as well as bath application of excitatory neurotransmitters, including glutamate, trigger robust phosphorylation of CREB Ser133 (30, 31). Second, many genes that become newly transcribed following bursts of neuronal activity, including c-fos (32), zif/268 (33), somatostatin (34), and BDNF (35, 36), contain CREB binding sites in their upstream regulatory regions. Third, activation of glutamatergic synapses can enhance transcription of a CRE-lacZ transgene in vivo

(37, 38). Lastly, CREB activity appears to be critical for the formation of certain forms of long-term memory. Injection of either CRE oligonucleotides or CREB antibodies into pre-synaptic nuclei of Aplysia sensory neurons blocks long-term facilitation (39–41). Likewise, induction of repressor or activator forms of dCREB modulates long-term memory in Drosophila (42, 43). Moreover, the late phase of hippocampal LTP and long-term spatial memory are impaired in mice lacking the α/δ isoforms of CREB (44). Finally, inhibition of CREB's DNA-binding activity blocks the maintenance phase of LTD in cerebellar Purkinje cells (45). Thus neurotransmitters activate CREB-dependent transcription, and CREB activity is critical for long-lasting activity-dependent increases and decreases in synaptic strength as well as certain forms of learning.

An Increase in Post-Synaptic Ca^{2+} is the Initial Trigger Leading to Phosphorylation of CREB at Glutamatergic Synapses

Activation of glutamatergic synapses leads to phosphorylation of CREB Ser133 in vitro and in vivo within seconds to minutes (22, 31). This phosphorylation event is dependent upon influx of extracellular Ca^{2+} because it is prevented by chelation of extracellular Ca^{2+} with EGTA. Under these excitatory synaptic stimulation conditions, extracellular Ca^{2+} can enter neurons through NMDA receptors as well as through VSCCs. In addition, Ca^{2+} is released from intracellular pools including the endoplasmic reticulum (reviewed in 46). Interestingly, activation of both NMDA receptors and VSCCs is necessary for CREB phosphorylation and c-fos induction following bath application of glutamate to cultures of dissociated striatal neurons (47). In contrast, Ca^{2+} flux through NMDA receptors, but not through L-type VSCC, is necessary for Ca^{2+} induction of expression of the IEG c-fos in hippocampal neurons following bath application of glutamate (48). The differences in the contribution of the L-channel during glutamate induction of IEG expression between hippocampal and striatal neurons may be a reflection of the greater density of NMDA receptors found on hippocampal neurons than on striatal neurons. Recent experiments, using synaptic stimuli, indicate that Ca^{2+} flux through both NMDA receptors and L-type VSCCs is required for CREB phosphorylation in hippocampal neurons (49). It is likely that synaptic activation of NMDA receptors, which have long opening times (50), facilitates opening of L-type VSCCs. The L-type VSCCs are found at high density in proximal dendrites and cell bodies (51), and their opening leads to an increase in levels of cytosolic and nuclear Ca^{2+}. Thus following activation of hippocampal synapses, levels of intracellular Ca^{2+} rise throughout the neuron including within the cell body and nucleus (52). But where within a neuron is an increase in levels of Ca^{2+} needed for triggering phosphorylation of CREB Ser133? The answer to this question should provide important insight into the nature of the signal that is carried from the synapse to the nucleus.

It had been assumed that a rise in levels of nuclear Ca^{2+} is necessary for triggering phosphorylation of CREB Ser133 in neurons since candidate activity-dependent CREB kinases, such as CaMKIV, are found in the nucleus. Also, an increase in Ca^{2+} within nuclei of AtT20 cells, a pituitary cell line, is necessary to trigger CREB-dependent gene expression (53). Nuclear Ca^{2+} chelators that buffer changes in the levels of Ca^{2+} within the nucleus, but not within the cytoplasm, block Ser133-phosphoCREB-mediated transcription in AtT20 cells. Therefore, it was somewhat surprising when Deisseroth et al reported that a rise in the level of Ca^{2+} within nuclei of hippocampal neurons is neither necessary nor sufficient for synaptic activity-dependent CREB phosphorylation (54). Rather, an increase in levels of calcium within the immediate vicinity of the plasma membrane of post-synaptic hippocampal neurons appears to be both necessary and sufficient for phosphorylation of CREB (54). These conclusions are based on experiments that examined synaptically evoked CREB phosphorylation in primary hippocampal neurons in which intracellular levels of Ca^{2+} were buffered with Ca^{2+} chelators (54). The differences between the nuclear site of action of Ca^{2+} found in the AtT20 cell experiments and the submembranous site of action in the hippocampal neuron experiments may be a reflection of inherent differences between primary hippocampal neurons and a pituitary cell line. Although additional experiments are clearly needed to fully establish the roles of submembranous, cytoplasmic, and nuclear Ca^{2+} during activity-dependent gene activation, it does appear that synaptically evoked Ca^{2+} influx functions within close proximity of the membrane to trigger CREB phosphorylation in hippocampal neurons.

Ca^{2+}-Calmodulin and CaMKIV as Mediators of Synaptic Signals to CREB.

If an increase in submembranous Ca^{2+} is sufficient to trigger phosphorylation of CREB Ser133, then which of the kinases shown in Figure 1 is responsible for activity-dependent phosphorylation of CREB, and how does the submembranous Ca^{2+} signal lead to activation of this kinase? Of the potential CREB kinases, CaMKIV has received much attention as a Ca^{2+}-sensitive CREB kinase. Ca-MKIV is widely expressed in the nervous system (55), and CREB Ser133 is an excellent substrate for this enzyme in vitro (12). Furthermore, CaMKIV, like CREB, resides mainly in the nucleus (56), so it is in the appropriate cellular compartment to catalyze activity-dependent phosphorylation of CREB. Importantly, treatment of cultured hippocampal neurons with antisense oligonucleotides directed against CaMKIV blocks CREB phosphorylation following brief membrane depolarization and Ca^{2+} influx (22). But how can a local increase in submembranous Ca^{2+} trigger activation of CaMKIV within the nucleus? One possibility is that an increase in submembranous Ca^{2+} activates a CaMKIV activator, which may translocate from a latent pool located near the plasma membrane to the nucleus. Other activator molecules may also translocate to the nucleus. Indeed, Deisseroth et al (49) have found that either electrical stimulation or a brief 3-min depolarization with 90 mM KCl triggers translocation of calmodulin from the cytosol to the nucleus. Moreover, like synaptically evoked phosphorylation of CREB Ser133, translocation of calmodulin is dependent upon activation of both the NMDA receptor and L-type Ca^{2+} channels; Ca^{2+} flux through N and P/Q type VSCCs cannot support calmodulin translocation or CREB phosphorylation. While nuclear calmodulin appears necessary for activity-dependent CREB phosphorylation (49), it remains to be determined whether translocation of calmodulin is necessary for this phosphorylation event. Thus Ca^{2+} that fluxes through NMDA receptors and L-type VSCCs appears to serve a privileged role in regulating signaling to CREB in hippocampal neurons, perhaps through its unique ability to trigger calmodulin translocation.

The Ras/ERK Pathway and Rsk2 as Mediators of Ca^{2+} Signaling to CREB

In addition to activation of CaMKs, Ca^{2+} influx through NMDA receptors initiates a series of events leading to activation of the Ras-ERK pathway (57–60) and, like the CaMKIV pathway, this pathway has also been strongly implicated in coupling Ca^{2+} influx and CREB phosphorylation in hippocampal neurons. Using dominant-negative forms of Ras and MEK and pharmacological inhibitors of MEK, Impey et al (14) showed that the Ras-ERK pathway is necessary for Ca^{2+} regulation of CREB phosphorylation and CREB-dependent gene expression in primary hippocampal neurons following membrane depolarization with KCl. Additional experiments showed that membrane depolarization and Ca^{2+} influx promote translocation of the CREB kinase Rsk2 into the nucleus, and chromatography and immunodepletion experiments indicate that Rsk2, not CaMKIV, is the major Ca^{2+}-regulated CREB kinase in hippocampal neurons. Interestingly, PKA appears to modulate the activity of the Ras-ERK pathway (14, 61), either by promoting nuclear entry of ERKs or Rsk2 (14), or by enhancing ERK activation through B-Raf (62). Several differences between these studies by Impey et al and those by Deisseroth et al described above may account for the different conclusions regarding the identity of the glutamate-sensitive CREB kinase in hippocampal neurons. Importantly, Bito et al (22) examined CREB phosphorylation following brief depolarization (90 mM KCl, 1 min), while Impey et al (14) used a more prolonged depolarization stimulation protocol and focused on CREB phosphorylation at later times.

While these studies strongly support a role for both CaMKIV and Rsk2 as activity-dependent CREB kinases, both employed membrane depolarization as the mode of stimulation, so one cannot conclude that these protein kinases catalyze synaptically evoked phosphorylation of CREB. Recently, Sgambato et al (63) performed in vivo electrical stimulation of the glutamatergic cortical afferents of the corticostriatal pathway and pharmacological inhibition experiments to demonstrate that synaptically evoked phosphorylation of CREB Ser133 is dependent upon the Ras-ERK pathway. This stimulation paradigm may be the closest to a true physiological mode of stimulation used thus far to characterize signaling pathways coupling synaptically evoked NMDA receptor activation to CREB phosphorylation. As for calmodulin translocation, ERKs and Rsk kinase translocation to the nucleus may be a critical step coupling an increase in submembranous Ca^{2+} to phosphorylation of CREB. Consistent with this idea, Bading and colleagues (64) have recently shown that both CaMK and Ras-MEK-ERK pathways contribute to membrane depolarization induction of CREB phosphorylation in hippocampal neurons. Thus one testable model consistent with most observations predicts that translocation of calmodulin and activation of CaMKIV within the nucleus are necessary for CREB phosphorylation within seconds to minutes of Ca^{2+} influx, while translocation of the ERK/Rsk complex could mediate CREB phosphorylation at later times, i.e. after five minutes following Ca^{2+} influx (Figure 2).

Other Modes of Ca^{2+}-Dependent Transcription

Although we have focused on CREB as a critical target of *trans*-synaptic signaling to nuclei of neurons, the importance of other nuclear targets controlled by synaptic, submembranous, cytosolic, and/or nuclear pools of Ca^{2+} as mediators of synapse-to-nucleus signaling should be emphasized. Recent experiments underscore this point. For example, in AtT-20 cells, cytosolic Ca^{2+}, not nuclear Ca^{2+}, appears necessary for Ca^{2+}-dependent, SRE-mediated transcription (53). Additional recent experiments point toward a potentially important contribution of nuclear Ca^{2+} as a direct mediator of transcription factor activity. The transcriptional repressor DREAM, an EF hand–containing transcription factor, represses transcription of the prodynorphin gene through binding to the DRE sequence found in the upstream regulatory region of prodynorphin. Upon binding Ca^{2+}, DREAM dissociates from the DRE, thereby relieving inhibition of transcription (65). Thus an increase in levels of nuclear Ca^{2+} can influence transcription factor activities indirectly through activation of enzymes that catalyze post-translational modifications of transcription factors, as seen with CREB, and directly through binding to nuclear transcription factors, as in the case of DREAM. Taken together with the observation that levels of Ca^{2+} within dendrites, cell bodies, and nuclei all increase following bursts of synaptic activity, it is likely that several different intracellular pools of Ca^{2+} mediate transcription factor activity by multiple distinct mechanisms.

Unresolved Spatial Considerations for Synapse-to-Nucleus Signaling

It is possible, perhaps likely, that glutamate triggers activation of spatially and temporally distinct intracellular signals depending upon the mode of receptor activation, the density of ionotropic receptors and VSCCs, and the distance between the glutamate receptor and the nucleus. Because a large number of dis-

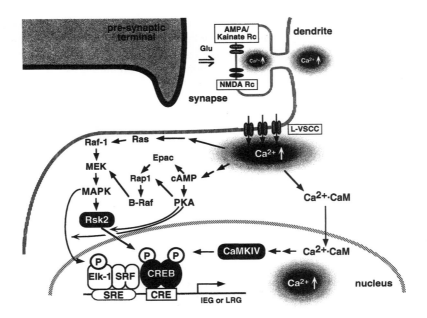

Figure 2 Signaling from excitatory glutamatergic synapses to CREB within neuronal nuclei. Upon its release from pre-synaptic terminals, glutamate binds to and activates non-NMDA receptors. Subsequent membrane depolarization results in release of a magnesium block and activation of NMDA receptors located on dendritic spines. Activation of NMDA receptors leads to prolonged membrane depolarization and activation of L-type VSCCs, which are predominantly located on proximal dendrites and cell bodies of post-synaptic neurons. As a result, levels of Ca^{2+} rise within spines, cell bodies, and probably nuclei of post-synaptic neurons. The Ca^{2+} signal is relayed to CREB within the nucleus through translocation of calmodulin and members of the ERK-Rsk pathways from the cytoplasm into the nucleus. In addition, nuclear Ca^{2+} may regulate CREB phosphorylation more directly, perhaps through the activation of nuclear calmodulin and CaMKs, such as CaMKIV. Abbreviation: Epac (exchange protein directly activated by cAMP).

tinct signaling pathways culminate in the phosphorylation and activation of CREB (Figure 1), then how and where NMDA receptors and L-type Ca^{2+} channels become activated and targeted are paramount considerations when addressing how signals flow from the synapse to the nucleus. Thus a major challenge for cellular physiologists is to establish roles for specific signaling pathways that have already been identified in simpler model systems, in the context of normal synaptic signaling to neuronal nuclei, rather than in model systems that employ stimulation by bath application. Importantly, synaptic inputs that differ in their capacity to influence cytoplasmic and nuclear levels of calcium in post-synaptic neurons may regulate different nuclear responses and, therefore, different complex programs of gene expression. Thus one experimentally testable hypothesis predicts that two excitatory synapses that differ only in their proximity to the cell body of the post-synaptic neuron may have different degrees of influence over the nature of the nuclear response manifested in the post-synaptic cell. Additional current challenges include understanding the privileged role of Ca^{2+} flux through NMDA receptors and L-type VSCCs, as opposed to other routes of Ca^{2+} entry, during synapse to CREB signaling, and the identification and characterization of Ca^{2+} targets, in addition to CREB, that are nuclear mediators of synaptic activity-dependent gene activation.

RETROGRADE GROWTH FACTOR SIGNALING TO CREB IN NEURONS

Neurotrophin Signals Propagate from the Axon Terminal to the Nucleus

Many peptide growth factors function by binding to cell surface receptors located on cell bodies, and this mode of growth factor signaling to nuclear proteins, such as CREB, can be studied using cell culture paradigms in which bath application of the growth factor is employed. In contrast to this general mode of growth factor function, target-derived neuronal growth factors are synthesized and secreted by neuronal target tissues, and they activate receptors located on distal axons of developing and adult neurons (66, 67). Compartmentalized cultures of neurons provide a valuable model system for studying the role of target-derived factors on peripheral neurons in vitro (68).

The prototypic target-derived growth factor is NGF, which supports survival and growth of sympathetic and cutaneous small-diameter sensory neurons (69). Another example of a target-derived growth factor is cholinergic differentiation factor, CDF, an instructive cue that promotes a switch in neurotransmitter phenotype of subpopulations of postganglionic sympathetic neurons from adrenergic to cholinergic (70, 71). One truly remarkable feature of target-derived growth factors is their capacity to initiate a signal within axon terminals that propagates in a retrograde fashion to cell bodies, which can be located centimeters or more from the axon terminals. Indeed, both NGF and CDF can act on distal axons to control key regulatory events far away within the cell body, including gene transcription within the nucleus. Therefore, to understand target-derived growth factor signaling to the nucleus, one must answer this question: How does a biochemical signal generated at the tips of distal axons travel all the way to the cell body and, ultimately, to the nucleus of a neuron? This section focuses on the mechanisms by which target-derived NGF signals are retrogradely propagated to CREB within nuclei of developing peripheral neurons.

An Overview of TrkA Signaling

NGF is the prototypic member of a family of neurotrophic growth factors, the neurotrophins, that also includes BDNF, NT3, and NT4/5. Neurotrophins exert their effects on developing neurons through interactions with members of the Trk family of receptor tyrosine kinases and a structurally unrelated receptor, p75[LNGFR] (72, 73). It is now well established that TrkA is a critical signaling receptor of NGF.

Upon binding to NGF, TrkA receptors homodimerize and autophosphorylate on multiple tyrosine residues. Autophosphorylation serves two functions: (*a*) Autophosphorylation of tyrosine residues within the catalytic loop enhances overall kinase activity of the receptor, and (*b*) TrkA phosphotyrosine residues provide docking sites for TrkA effectors that are recruited to the inner surface of the membrane. Upon binding tyrosine-phosphorylased TrkA receptors through their SH2 or PTB domains, intracellular signaling proteins such as PLC-γ, Shc, SH2-B, and rAPS mediate NGF signaling within neurons (74–76). Some of the Trk effectors possess enzymatic activity while others, such as Shc, are adaptors that bring additional effectors, including Grb2, to the plasma membrane (77). Thus a number of distinct Trk effector molecules propagate intracellular signals that support neuronal growth and survival.

Nuclear Responses to NGF-Dependent Retrograde Signaling

Neurotrophins regulate expression of a variety of genes in developing neurons and in the pheochromocytoma-derived cell line, PC12, and the mechanisms coupling TrkA activation and NGF-dependent gene expression have been investigated in considerable detail. Perhaps somewhat surprising was the finding that CREB is a critical target of neurotrophin signaling, as had been previously described for neurotransmitter signaling (see above). Upon exposure of PC12 cells to NGF or cortical neurons to BDNF, CREB becomes newly phosphorylated on Ser133, and this phosphorylation event is required for NGF activation of transcription of the immediate early gene (IEG) c-*fos* (4, 78). Because many neurotrophin-regulated genes contain CREB binding sites within their upstream regulatory regions (4), CREB is likely to be a mediator of the general nuclear response to neurotrophins. Indeed, our recent work has indicated that NGF activation of CREB-dependent gene transcription is necessary for survival of sympathetic neurons, at least in part, through regulation of expression of pro-survival genes such as *bcl-2* (79). Moreover, NGF acting on its receptors located on distal axons initiates a signal that is retrogradely propagated to the nucleus, where it triggers robust phosphorylation of CREB Ser133 (80) and CREB-mediated gene expression (79). Thus an interesting and important question is how is the target-derived NGF signal retrogradely propagated all the way to CREB and other transcription factors within nuclei of sympathetic neurons?

Some Models for Retrograde NGF Signaling in Developing Neurons

Several potential models could explain long-range retrograde NGF signaling to CREB. In one model, NGF binds to its receptors on axon terminals and triggers signal transduction events locally, within the distal axon, that are retrogradely propagated to the nucleus. In another model, NGF is internalized within the distal axon, retrogradely transported to the cell body where it activates its receptors, thereby influencing signaling pathways that promote growth and survival. A third model, the signaling endosome model (81, 82), states that an NGF-TrkA receptor complex forms at distal axons, internalizes and undergoes retrograde transport to cell bodies where it propagates its growth-promoting signal. Yet other models exist. The preponderance of evidence to date supports the signaling endosome model to explain how the NGF signal is carried from distal axon terminals to CREB within the nuclei of sympathetic neurons.

Evidence in Support of a NGF-Dependent Retrograde Signaling Endosome

It is widely accepted that NGF itself is internalized and retrogradely transported, via a microtubule-based vesicular transport mechanism, from distal axon terminals to cell bodies of sympathetic neurons. This is based largely on experiments that have used [^{125}I]NGF, which can be injected into targets of sympathetic neurons such as the eye, and its appearance monitored within neuronal cell bodies (83, 84). Most reports indicate that NGF is retrogradely transported in neurons at a rate of ~2.5 mm/h (83–85); however, faster retrograde transport rates of up to 20 mm/h have been reported in vitro (86). Because it is retrogradely transported, NGF itself has been long-considered a component of the retrograde signal. Yet microinjection of NGF alone into the cell soma does not support differentiation, and microinjection of antibodies directed against NGF into the cell body does not block NGF signaling (87). Thus if retrogradely transported NGF is a component of the signal, it alone cannot account for retrograde signaling.

Recent evidence supports the idea that TrkA, like NGF, is retrogradely transported in NGF-dependent neurons and that this NGF receptor is likely to be a component of the retrograde signal. Phosphorylated Trk receptors accumulate distal to a ligation or crush in rat sciatic nerve (88, 89). Likewise, in vitro, P-TrkA accumulates in cell bodies and proximal processes of compartmentalized sympathetic neurons following exposure of distal axons to NGF (80, 90). However, rapid retrograde appearance of phosphorylated Trk receptors has been described (90, 91), raising the possibility that phosphorylated Trks may travel in a rapidly transported vesicle or by a vesicle-independent mechanism. Therefore, these results are consistent with the idea that P-TrkA is retrogradely transported, but they do not rule out the alternate possibility that retrogradely transported NGF activates TrkA found distal to a ligation or crush, or within cell bodies of compartmentalized sympathetic neurons.

Evidence from at least four types of experiment supports the idea that retrograde transport of an NGF-TrkA complex is responsible for retrograde signaling to CREB. First, NGF covalently bound to large diameter beads, which cannot be internalized or retrogradely transported, cannot promote retrograde signaling to CREB when applied to distal axons. Yet, NGF-coated beads do activate TrkA receptors, and they effectively induce phosphorylation of CREB Ser133 when applied directly to cell bodies of sympathetic neurons (80). Thus activation of TrkA in distal axons, under conditions that prevent retrograde transport, is not sufficient to promote signaling to CREB. Second, recent cell surface biotinylation experiments indicate that phosphorylated Trk receptor itself is internalized within distal axons and retrogradely transported to cell bodies of sympathetic neurons (92, 92a). These studies also revealed that retrogradely transported TrkA is physically associated with retrogradely transported NGF. Third, internalized P-TrkA co-localizes with vesicular proteins, such as clathrin, in sciatic nerve and in PC12 cells (93, 94), which is consistent with the idea that TrkA is retrogradely transported through a vesicular transport mechanism. Lastly, pharmacological inhibition of TrkA catalytic activity within cell bodies, under conditions in which TrkA activity in distal axons remains normal, completely blocks NGF-dependent retrograde signaling to CREB (80). These experiments indicate that TrkA autophosphorylation and signaling within distal axons alone is not sufficient to support phosphorylation of CREB within the nucleus. Rather, collectively, these support a model in which a P-TrkA–NGF complex that forms in distal axons is retrogradely transported to the cell body where it propagates a signal to CREB in the nucleus (Figure 3).

Mechanisms of Retrograde Vesicular Transport in Neurons

The mechanisms by which an NGF–TrkA complex is internalized into clathrin-coated vesicles and the molecular composition of the retrograde signaling endosome remain unknown. PI3K may contribute to ligand-dependent TrkA internalization, since this signaling intermediate mediates ligand-dependent receptor internalization of other growth factor receptors, including the PDGF receptor (95). In addition, the low affinity receptor p75 might play a role in the formation and internalization of an NGF–TrkA complex (96). Mobley and colleagues have begun to characterize a TrkA-containing endosome isolated from PC12 cells that may be similar or identical in composition to the retrograde signaling vesicle found in neurons (93, 94). Also, it will be of interest to determine whether other target-derived factors, such as CNTF or LIF or TGF-β family ligands, which employ distinct receptor systems (97, 98), propagate retrograde signals in a manner similar to that of NGF and the neurotrophins. While LIF can be retrogradely transported in neurons (99), and while it can promote the adrenergic-to-cholinergic switch when applied to distal axons of sympathetic neu-

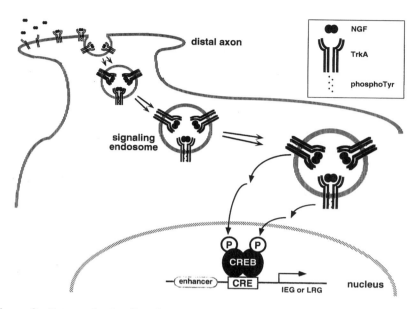

Figure 3 Retrograde signaling from neurotrophin receptors on distal axons to CREB within neuronal nuclei. Target-derived growth factors, such as NGF, bind to their receptors located on the surface of distal axons. The signaling endosome model states that target-derived growth factor – receptor complexes are internalized and retrogradely transported to cell bodies. Upon arrival in the cell bodies, ligand-receptor complexes can propagate signals to CREB and other nuclear targets. Evidence described in the text supports the signaling endosome model to explain retrograde NGF signaling to CREB in sympathetic neurons.

rons (100), it remains to be determined whether LIF or CNTF is retrogradely co-transported with its receptor complex through a vesicular transport mechanism. Finally, the TrkA substrates and downstream effectors that mediate retrograde signaling to CREB are unknown. PC12 cell and cortical neuron experiments indicate that the Ras-ERK-Rsk pathway is a mediator of neurotrophin induction of CREB phosphorylation following bath application of the factors. But whether Rsk2 or some other NGF-activated CREB kinase mediates retrograde signaling to CREB in developing neurons remains an open question. Also, the identity of Trk signals acting on axons versus cell bodies remains unknown.

SUMMARY

Much research over the past several years has led to the identification and characterization of many molecular participants that mediate signaling from the plasma membrane to the nucleus. Yet, the complexity of signal transduction is made greater because of a high degree of cross-talk between signaling pathways and because many key regulatory events within the cell are wrought with redundancy. This is exemplified by the nuclear transcription factor CREB, which can be phosphorylated by a large number of stimulus-dependent protein kinases. Thus to understand stimulus-dependent signaling from neurotransmitter and growth factor receptors to nuclei of neurons, greater emphasis is currently being placed on the mode of neuronal stimulation and spatial considerations that are unique to neurons. A picture is beginning to emerge that suggests that neurons make use of unique features of the electrical properties of their membranes, as well as long-range, microtubule-based vesicular transport mechanisms, to relay information from dendrites and distal axons to neuronal nuclei. In this way, a morphologically complex neuron can support a flow of communication from neurotransmitter and growth factor receptors, which are located on the cell surfaces of distal processes, to its nucleus, thereby allowing the nucleus to contribute to, perhaps even direct, events underlying plasticity, growth, and survival.

ACKNOWLEDGMENTS

The authors thank Hilmar Bading, Jay Baraban, Jocelyn Caboche, Jean-Francois Cloutier, Rejji Kuruvilla, Ravi Misra, and Xiaozhong Qian for their many thoughtful comments on this manuscript. The authors' research and the preparation of this article were supported by National Institutes of Health grants NS34814 and MH57825. David D Ginty is a Pew Scholar in the Biomedical Sciences.

Visit the Annual Reviews home page at www.AnnualReviews.org.

LITERATURE CITED

1. Morgan JI, Curran T. 1991. Stimulus-transcription coupling in the nervous system: involvement of the inducible proto-oncogenes fos and jun. *Annu. Rev. Neurosci.* 14:421–51
2. Lanahan A, Worley P. 1998. Immediate-early genes and synaptic function. *Neurobiol. Learn. Mem.* 70:37–43
3. Meyer TE, Habener JF. 1993. Cyclic adenosine 3',5'-monophosphate response element binding protein (CREB) and related transcription-activating deoxyribonucleic acid-binding proteins. *Endocr. Rev.* 14:269–90
4. Bonni A, Ginty DD, Dudek H, Greenberg ME. 1995. Serine 133-phosphory-lated CREB induces transcription via a cooperative mechanism that may confer specificity to neurotrophin signals. *Mol. Cell. Neurosci.* 6:168–83
5. Liu FC, Graybiel AM. 1996. Spatiotemporal dynamics of CREB phosphorylation: transient versus sustained phosphorylation in the developing striatum. *Neuron* 17:1133–44
6. Chrivia JC, Kwok RPS, Lamb N, Hagiwara M, Montminy MR, et al. 1993. Phosphorylated CREB binds specifically to the nuclear protein CBP. *Nature* 365:855–59
7. Ogryzko VV, Schiltz RL, Russanova V, Howard BH, Nakatani Y. 1996. The tran-

scriptional coactivators p300 and CBP are histone acetyltransferases. *Cell* 87:953–59

8. Bannister AJ, Koukarides T. 1996. The CBP co-activator is a histone acetyltransferase. *Nature* 384:641–43

9. Gonzalez GA, Montminy MR. 1989. Cyclic AMP stimulates somatostatin gene transcription by phosphorylation of CREB at serine 133. *Cell* 59:675–80

10. Sheng ME, Thompson MA, Greenberg ME. 1991. CREB: a Ca^{2+}-regulated transcription factor phosphorylated by CaM kinases. *Science* 252:1427–30

11. Dash PK, Karl KA, Colicos MA, Prywes R, Kandel ER. 1991. cAMP response element-binding protein is activated by Ca^{2+}/calmodulin- as well as cAMP-dependent protein kinase. *Proc. Natl. Acad. Sci. USA* 88:5061–65

12. Sun P, Enslen H, Myung PS, Maurer RA. 1994. Differential activation of CREB by Ca^{2+}/calmodulin-dependent protein kinases type II and type IV involves phosphorylation of a site that negatively regulates activity. *Genes Dev.* 8:2527–39

13. Xing J, Ginty DD, Greenberg ME. 1996. Coupling of the RAS-MAPK pathway to gene activation by RSK2, a growth factor-regulated CREB kinase. *Science* 273:959–63

14. Impey S, Obrietan K, Wong ST, Poser S, Yano S, et al. 1998. Cross talk between ERK and PKA is required for Ca^{2+} stimulation of CREB-dependent transcription and ERK nuclear translocation. *Neuron* 21:869–83

15. Tan Y, Rouse J, Zhang A, Caraiti S, Cohen P, et al. 1996. FGF and stress regulate CREB and ATF-1 via a pathway involving p38 MAP kinase and MAP-KAP kinase-2. *EMBO J.* 15:4629–42

16. Du K, Montminy M. 1998. CREB is a regulatory target for the protein kinase Akt/PKB. *J. Biol. Chem.* 273:32377–79

17. de Groot RP, Ballou LM, Sassone-Corsi P. 1994. Positive regulation of the cAMP-responsive activator CREM by

the p70 S6 kinase: an alternate route to mitogen-induced gene expression. *Cell* 79:81–91

18. Iordanov M, Bender K, Ade T, Schmid W, Sachsenmaier C, et al. 1997. CREB is activated by UVC through a p38/HOG-1-dependent protein kinase. *EMBO J.* 16:1009–22

19. Deak M, Clifton AD, Lucocq LM, Alessi DR. 1998. Mitogen- and stress-activated protein kinase-1 (MSK1) is directly activated by MAPK and SAPK2/p38, and may mediate activation of CREB. *EMBO J.* 17:4426–41

20. Hagiwara M, Alberts A, Brindle O, Meinkoth J, Ferimisco J, et al. 1992. Transcriptional attenuation following cAMP induction requires PP-1-mediated dephosphorylation of CREB. *Cell* 70:105–13

21. Wadzinski BE, Wheat WH, Jaspers S, Peruski LF Jr, Lickteig RL, et al. 1993. Nuclear protein phosphatase 2A dephosphorylates protein kinase A-phosphorylated CREB and regulates CREB transcriptional stimulation. *Mol. Cell. Biol.* 13:2822–34

22. Bito H, Deisseroth K, Tsien RW. 1996. CREB phosphorylation and dephosphorylation: a calcium- and stimulus duration-dependent switch for hippocampal gene expression. *Cell* 87:1203–14

23. Mulkey RM, Endo S, Shenolikar S, Malenka RC. 1994. Involvement of a calcineurin/inhibitor-1 phosphatase cascade in hippocampal long-term depression. *Nature* 369:486–88

24. Collingridge GL, Bliss TV. 1995. Memories of NMDA receptors and LTP. *Trends Neurosci.* 18:54–56

25. Bear MF, Abraham WC. 1996. Long-term depression in hippocampus. *Annu. Rev. Neurosci.* 19:437–62

26. Nguyen PT, Abel T, Kandel ER. 1994. Requirement of a critical period of transcription for induction of a late phase of LTP. *Science* 265:1104–7

27. Linden DJ. 1996. A protein synthesis-

dependent late phase of cerebellar long-term depression. *Neuron* 17:483–90

28. Cole AJ, Saffen DW, Baraban JM, Worley PF. 1989. Rapid increase of an immediate early gene messenger RNA in hippocampal neurons by synaptic NMDA receptor activation. *Nature* 340:474–76

29. Wisden W, Errington ML, Williams S, Dunnett SB, Waters C, et al. 1990. Differential expression of immediate early genes in the hippocampus and spinal cord. *Neuron* 4:603–14

30. Vanhoutte P, Barnier JV, Guibert B, Pages C, Besson MJ, et al. 1999. Glutamate induces phosphorylation of Elk-1 and CREB, along with c-fos activation, via an extracellular signal-regulated kinase-dependent pathway in brain slices. *Mol. Cell. Biol.* 19:136–46

31. Ginty DD, Kornhauser JM, Thompson MA, Bading H, Mayo KE, et al. 1993. Regulation of CREB phosphorylation in the suprachiasmatic nucleus by light and a circadian clock. *Science* 260:238–41

32. Berkowitz LA, Riabowal KT, Gilman MZ. 1989. Multiple sequence elements of a single functional class are required for cyclic AMP responsiveness of the mouse c-fos promoter. *Mol. Cell. Biol.* 9:4272–81

33. Alexandre C, Charnay P, Verrier B. 1991. Transactivation of Krox-20 and Krox-24 promoters by the HTLV-1 Tax protein through common regulatory elements. *Oncogene* 6:1851–57

34. Montminy MR, Sevarino KA, Wagner JA, Mandel G, Goodman RH. 1986. Identification of a cyclic-AMP responsive element within the rat somatostatin gene. *Proc. Natl. Acad. Sci. USA* 83:6682–86

35. Shieh PB, Hu SC, Bobb K, Timmusk T, Ghosh A. 1998. Identification of a signaling pathway involved in calcium regulation of BDNF expression. *Neuron* 20:727–40

36. Tao X, Finkbeiner S, Arnold DB, Shay-

witz AJ, Greenberg ME. 1998. Ca^{2+} influx regulates BDNF transcription by a CREB family transcription factor-dependent mechanism. *Neuron* 20:709–26

37. Impey S, Mark M, Villacres EC, Poser S, Chavkin C, et al. 1996. Induction of CRE-mediated gene expression by stimuli that generate long-lasting LTP in area CA1 of the hippocampus. *Neuron* 16:973–82

38. Pham TA, Impey S, Storm DR, Stryker MP. 1999. CRE-mediated gene transcription in neocortical neuronal plasticity during the developmental critical period. *Neuron* 22:63–72

39. Dash PK, Hochner B, Kandel ER. 1990. Injection of the cAMP-responsive element into the nucleus of Aplysia sensory neurons blocks long-term facilitation. *Nature* 345:718–21

40. Bartsch D, Ghirardi M, Skehel PA, Karl KA, Herder SP, et al. 1995. Aplysia CREB2 represses long-term facilitation: relief of repression converts transient facilitation into long-term functional and structural change. *Cell* 83:979–92

41. Bartsch D, Casadio A, Karl KA, Serodio P, Kandel ER. 1998. CREB1 encodes a nuclear activator, a repressor, and a cytoplasmic modulator that form a regulatory unit critical for long-term facilitation. *Cell* 95:211–23

42. Tully T, Preat T, Boynton SC, Del Vecchio M. 1994. Genetic dissection of consolidated memory in Drosophila. *Cell* 79:35–47

43. Yin JCP, Wallach JS, Del Vecchio M, Wilder EL, Zhou H, et al. 1994. Induction of a dominant negative CREB transgene specifically blocks long-term memory in Drosophila. *Cell* 79:49–58

44. Bourtchuladze R, Frenguelli B, Blendy J, Cioffi D, Schutz G, et al. 1994. Deficient long-term memory in mice with a targeted mutation of the cAMP-responsive element-binding protein. *Cell* 79:59–68

45. Ahn S, Ginty DD, Linden DJ. 1999. A late phase of cerebellar long-term depres-

sion requires activation of CaMKIV and CREB. *Neuron* 23:559–68

46. Berridge MJ. 1998. Neuronal calcium signaling. *Neuron* 21:13–26

47. Rajadhyaksha A, Barczak A, Macias W, Leveque JC, Lewis S, et al. 1999. L-type Ca^{2+} channels are essential for gluta-mate-mediated CREB phosphorylation and c-fos gene expression in the striatum. *J. Neurosci.* 19:6348–59

48. Bading H, Ginty DD, Greenberg ME. 1993. Regulation of gene expression in hippocampal neurons by distinct calcium signaling pathway. *Science* 260:181–86

49. Deisseroth K, Heist EK, Tsien RW. 1998. Translocation of calmodulin to the nucleus supports CREB phosphorylation in hippocampal neurons. *Nature* 392: 198–202

50. Ascher P, Nowak L. 1987. Electrophys-iological studies of NMDA receptors. *Trends Neurosci.* 10:284–88

51. Westenbroek RE, Ahlijanian MK, Cat-terall WA. 1990. Clustering of L-type Ca^{2+} channels at the base of major den-drites in hippocampal pyramidal neu-rons. *Nature* 347:281–84

52. Regehr WG, Connor JA, Tank DW. 1989. Optical imaging of calcium accu-mulation in hippocampal pyramidal cells during synaptic activation. *Nature* 341:533–36

53. Hardingham GE, Chawla S, Johnson CM, Bading H. 1997. Distinct functions of nuclear and cytoplasmic calcium in the control of gene expression. *Nature* 385:260–65

54. Deisseroth K, Bito H, Tsien RW. 1996. Signaling from synapse to nucleus: post-synaptic CREB phosphorylation during multiple forms of hippocampal synaptic plasticity. *Neuron* 16:89–101

55. Heist EK, Schulman H. 1998. The role of Ca^{2+}/calmodulin-dependent protein kinases within the nucleus. *Cell Calcium* 23:103–14

56. Jensen KF, Ohmstede CA, Fisher RS, Sahyoun, N. 1997. Nuclear and axonal

localization of Ca^{2+}/calmodulin-depen-dent protein kinase type Gr in rat cere-bellar cortex. *Proc. Natl. Acad. Sci. USA* 88:2850–53

57. Rosen LB, Ginty DD, Weber MJ, Green-berg ME. 1994. Membrane depolariza-tion and calcium influx stimulate MEK and MAP kinase via activation of ras. *Neuron* 12:1207–21

58. Bading H, Greenberg ME. 1991. Stimu-lation of protein tyrosine phosphoryla-tion by NMDA receptor activation. *Science* 253:912–14

59. Xia Z, Dudek H, Miranti CK, Greenberg ME. 1996. Calcium influx via the NMDA receptor induces immediate early gene transcription by a MAP kinase/ ERK-dependent mechanism. *J. Neurosci.* 16:5425–36

60. Murphy TH, Blatter LA, Bhat RV, Fiore RS, Wier WG, et al. 1994. Differential regulation of calcium/calmodulin-dependent protein kinase II and p42 MAP kinase activity by synaptic trans-mission. *J. Neurosci.* 14:1320–31

61. Roberson ED, English JD, Adams JP, Selcher JC, Kondratick C, et al. 1999. The mitogen-activated protein kinase cascade couples PKA and PKC to cAMP response element binding protein phos-phorylation in area CA1 of hippocampus. *J. Neurosci.* 19:4337–48

62. Vossler MR, Yao H, York RD, Pan MG, Rim CS, et al. 1997. cAMP activates MAP kinase and Elk-1 through a B-Raf-and Rap1-dependent pathway. *Cell* 89: 73–82

63. Sgambato V, Pages C, Rogard M, Besson MJ, Caboche J. 1998. Extracellular sig-nal-regulated kinase (ERK) controls immediate early gene induction on cor-ticostriatal stimulation. *J. Neurosci.* 18:8814–25

64. Hardingham GE, Chawla S, Cruzalegui FH, Bading H. 1999. Control of recruit-ment and transcription-activating func-tion of CBP determines gene regulation

by NMDA receptors and L-type calcium channels. *Neuron* 22:789–98

65. Carrion AM, Link WA, Ledo F, Mellstrom B, Naranjo JR. 1999. DREAM is a Ca^{2+}-regulated transcriptional repressor. *Nature* 398:80–84

66. Barde Y-A. 1989. Trophic factors and neuronal survival. *Neuron* 2:1525–34

67. Oppenheim RW. 1991. Cell death during development of the nervous system. *Annu. Rev. Neurosci.* 14:453–501

68. Campenot RB. 1977. Local control of neurite development by nerve growth factor. *Proc. Natl. Acad. Sci. USA* 74:4516–19

69. Levi-Montalcini R, Hamburger V. 1953. A diffusible agent of mouse sarcoma, producing hyperplasia of sympathetic ganglia and hyperneurotization of viscera in the chick embryo. *J. Exp. Zool.* 1123:233–87

70. Landis SC. 1990. Target regulation of neurotransmitter phenotype. *Trends Neurosci.* 13:344–50

71. Schotzinger R, Yin X, Landis SC. 1994. Target determination of neurotransmitter phenotype in sympathetic neurons. *J. Neurobiol.* 25:620–39

72. Bothwell M. 1995. Functional interactions of neurotrophins and neurotrophin receptors. *Annu. Rev. Neurosci.* 18:223–53

73. Chao MV. 1994. The p75 neurotrophin receptor. *J. Neurobiol.* 25:1373–85

74. Segal RA, Greenberg ME. 1996. Intracellular signaling pathways activated by neurotrophic factors. *Annu. Rev. Neurosci.* 19:463–89

75. Kaplan DR, Stephens RM. 1994. Neurotrophin signal transduction by the trk receptor. *J. Neurobiol.* 25:1404–17

76. Qian X, Zhang Y, Riccio A, Ginty DD. 1998. Identification and characterization of novel substrates of Trk receptors in developing neurons. *Neuron* 21:1017–29

77. Rozakis-Adcock M, McGlade J, Mbamulu G, Pelicci G, Daly R, et al. 1992. Association of the Shc and Grb2/Sem5 SH2-containing proteins is implicated in activation of the Ras pathway by tyrosine kinases. *Nature* 360:689–92

78. Ginty DD, Bonni A, Greenberg ME. 1994. Nerve growth factor activates a Ras-dependent protein kinase that stimulates c-fos transcription via phosphorylation of CREB. *Cell* 77:713–25

79. Riccio A, Ahn S, Davenport CM, Blendy JA, Ginty DD. 1999. Mediation by a CREB family transcription factor of NGF-dependent survival of sympathetic neurons. *Science.* In press

80. Riccio A, Pierchala BA, Ciarallo C, Ginty DD. 1997. An NGF-TrkA-mediated retrograde signal to transcription factor CREB in sympathetic neurons. *Science* 227:1097–100

81. Misko TP, Radeke MJ, Shooter EM. 1987. Nerve growth factor in neuronal development and maintenance. *J. Exp. Biol.* 132:177–90

82. Halegoua S, Armstrong RC, Kremer NE. 1990. Dissecting the mode of action of a neuronal growth factor. *Curr. Top. Microbiol. Immunol.* 165:119–70

83. Hendry IA, Stockel K, Thoenen H, Iversen LL. 1974. The retrograde axonal transport of nerve growth factor. *Brain Res.* 68:103–21

84. Korsching S, Thoenen H. 1983. Quantitative demonstration of the retrograde axonal transport of endogenous nerve growth factor. *Neurosci. Lett.* 39:1–4

85. Claude P, Hawrot E, Dunis DA, Campenot RB. 1982. Binding, internalization, and retrograde transport of 125I-nerve growth factor in cultured rat sympathetic neurons. *J. Neurosci.* 2:431–42

86. Ure DR, Campenot RB. 1997. Retrograde transport and steady state distribution of 125-NGF in rat sympathetic neurons in compartmentalized cultures. *J. Neurosci.* 17:1282–90

87. Seeley PJ, Keith CH, Shelanski ML, Greene LA. 1983. Pressure microinjection of nerve growth factor and anti-nerve growth factor into the nucleus and

cytoplasm: lack of effects on neurite outgrowth from pheochromocytoma cells. *J. Neurosci.* 3:1488–94

88. Ehlers MD, Kaplan DR, Price DL, Koliatsos VE. 1995. NGF-stimulated retrograde transport of TrkA in the mammalian nervous system. *J. Cell Biol.* 130:149–56

89. Johanson SO, Crouch MF, Hendry IA. 1995. Retrograde axonal transport of signal transduction proteins in rat sciatic nerve. *Brain Res.* 690:55–63

90. Senger DL, Campenot RB. 1997. Rapid retrograde tyrosine phosphorylation of TrkA and other proteins in rat sympathetic neurons in compartmented cultures. *J. Cell Biol.* 138:411–21

91. Bhattacharyya A, Watson F, Bradlee T, Pomeroy S, Stiles C, et al. 1997. Trk receptors function as rapid retrograde signal carriers in the adult nervous system. *J. Neurosci.* 17:7007–16

92. Tsui-Pierchala, BA, Ginty, DD. 1999. Characterization of an NGF – P-TrkA retrograde signaling complex and age-dependent regulation of TrkA phosphorylation in sympathetic neurons. *J. Neurosci.* 19:8207–18

92a. Watson Fl, Heerssen MM, Moheban DB, Lin MZ, Sauvageot CM, et al. 1999. Rapid nuclear responses to target-derived neurotrophins require retrograde transport of ligand-receptor complex. *J. Neurosci.* 19:7889–90

93. Grimes ML, Zhou J, Beattle EC, Yuen EC, Hall DE, et al. 1996. Endocytosis of activated TrkA: evidence that nerve growth factor induces formation of signaling endosomes. *J. Neurosci.* 16:7950–64

94. Grimes ML, Beattie E, Mobley WC. 1997. A signaling organelle containing the nerve growth factor-activated receptor tyrosine kinase, TrkA. *Proc. Natl. Acad. Sci. USA* 94:9909–14

95. Joly M, Kazlauskas A, Fay FS, Corvera S. 1994. Disruption of PDGF receptor trafficking by mutation of its PI-3 kinase binding sites. *Science* 263:684–87

96. Johnson EM, Taniuchi M, Clark HB, Springer JE, Koh S, et al. 1987. Demonstration of the retrograde transport of nerve growth factor receptor in the peripheral and central nervous system. *J. Neurosci.* 7:923–29

97. Stahl N, Yancopoulos GD. 1994. The tripartite CNTF receptor complex: activation and signaling involves components shared with other cytokines. *J. Neurobiol.* 25:1454–66

98. Massagué J. 1998. TGF-beta signal transduction. *Annu. Rev. Biochem.* 67:753–91

99. Thompson SW, Vernallis AB, Heath JK, Priestley JV. 1997. Leukemia inhibitory factor is retrogradely transported by a distinct population of adult rat sensory neurons: co-localization with trkA and other neurochemical markers. *Eur. J. Neurosci.* 9:1244–51

100. Ure DR, Campenot RB, Acheson A. 1992. Cholinergic differentiation of rat sympathetic neurons in culture: effects of factors applied to distal neurites. *Dev. Biol.* 154:388–95

Annu. Rev. Physiol. 2000. 62:825–46

Lung Development and Function in Preterm Infants in the Surfactant Treatment Era

Alan H. Jobe and Machiko Ikegami

Pulmonary Biology/Neonatology, Children's Hospital Medical Center, Cincinnati, Ohio 45229; e-mail: JOBEAØ@CHMCC.ORG

Key Words   lung maturation, respiratory distress syndrome, bronchopulmonary dysplasia, chronic lung disease, alveolarization

■ **Abstract**   Mortality of infants of <1-kg birth weight has decreased because of surfactant treatments, antenatal glucocorticoid treatments, and new ventilation strategies. However, many of these infants develop a chronic lung disease characterized by an arrest of lung development and interference with alveolarization. Antenatal glucocorticoids can induce early lung maturation clinically, but new information from transgenic and other experimental models indicates that traditional explanations for glucocorticoid effects on the developing lung are inadequate. These very preterm infants have lungs with small lung gas volumes and delicate lung tissue that are susceptible to injury with the initiation of ventilation and subsequent ventilation. Antenatal proinflammatory exposures are frequent in very preterm infants, and postnatal injury is associated with elevations of proinflammatory cytokines in the lungs. One hypothesis is that proinflammatory cytokines can promote or interfere with lung development as well as promote lung injury. Mechanisms of lung injury being characterized in the adult lung may have unique characteristics in the developing lung.

INTRODUCTION

The widespread introduction of surfactant treatment for respiratory distress syndrome (RDS) after 1990, together with increased use of antenatal glucocorticoids and newer approaches to ventilation of preterm infants, has changed the characteristics of preterm infants that are at risk for lung injury (1). Preterm infants developing lung injury now are generally very small and have antenatal and postnatal histories that differ from those of preterm infants in previous eras. Therefore, issues of lung development and lung function that relate to clinical medicine also differ and can be usefully evaluated to identify factors that are important to the pulmonary outcomes of such infants. The extremely low-birth-weight (ELBW) infants likely to have lung injury are generally born at between 24 and 28 weeks gestation with birth weights between 0.5 and 1 kg (1). Lung development and function compose a very broad and large subject; this review discusses only issues that have bearing on the clinical outcome for the preterm lung. This review does not answer many questions, because clear answers are not available. However, new ideas based on epidemiologic observations suggest new avenues for research that offer insights into maturation and treatment strategies for the preterm lung.

The article emphasizes the continuum between antenatal and postnatal lung development, which are the determinants of postnatal lung function and subsequent lung injury (Figure 1). The theme of this review is that normal lung development is disrupted by antenatal events and the need for the immature lung to provide gas exchange after preterm birth. The question is how to allow lung development to proceed as normally as possible in an abnormal environment (air breathing with high pulmonary blood flow). The problem is that the regulators of normal lung development during late gestation are not known, nor are the mediators that interfere with lung development well understood.

ANTENATAL LUNG DEVELOPMENT—NORMAL PROCESSES

Preterm infants born at 24 weeks gestation presently survive ~30% of the time, but most of these infants develop chronic lung disease, defined for epidemiologic purposes as the need for supplemental oxygen at 36 weeks gestation (1). The lung of a 20-week human fetus has branched completely to have all airways, but the potential gas exchange region of the lung is composed of simple saccular

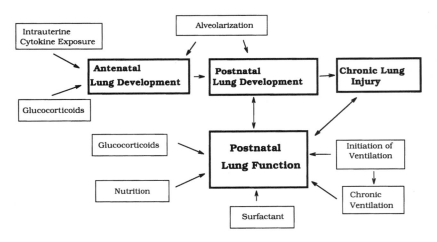

Figure 1 Diagram emphasizing the continuum from antenatal to postnatal lung development and subsequent lung injury. Some of the variables that influence development are shown.

structures lined by cuboidal epithelium (2). No alveoli are present, the capillary bed is poorly developed and not closely opposed to the epithelium, and the epithelial cells have not begun to produce surfactant. By 24 weeks, sufficient maturation has occurred to permit gas exchange at least transiently in most infants if they receive surfactant soon after birth. Occasionally these infants have mature lungs, as defined empirically by normal partial O_2 pressure (Po_2) and partial CO_2 pressure (Pco_2) values, while receiving minimal supplemental O_2 and assisted ventilation. Normal alveolarization, as identified by septation originating along elastin fibers, begins after ~28 weeks gestation in the few human specimens that have been evaluated (3, 4). Alveolarization then proceeds rapidly to achieve alveolar numbers that are perhaps 20% to 50% of the adult number of 300×10^6 by term (40 weeks gestation). Concurrently, pulmonary capillaries elaborate, type II cells differentiate, and surfactant accumulates to high levels by term. These developmental events, which are tightly linked and regulated during normal lung development, clearly can be disturbed by preterm birth (5). The concept that gas exchange can occur without alveoli in ELBW infants seems untenable to the physiologist who has worked only with the mature lung. However, rodents are normally born with a saccular lung that is comparable to the human lung at 24–26 weeks gestation (6).

Surfactant treatments have made the acute deficiency of surfactant less of a problem clinically. However, normal surfactant development and metabolism are important for the maintenance of lung function. Mature lamellar bodies do not normally appear until after ~24 weeks gestation in the human. The messenger RNA (mRNA) for the surfactant protein (SP)-C appears very early in gestation and is concentrated where airways branch (7). Despite lung tissue levels of SP-C mRNA at 19 days gestation in rabbits that are similar to levels at term, mature SP-C does not appear in the airspaces until ~29 days gestation (term is 31 days) (8, 9). Mature SP-B increases in amniotic fluid of humans during late gestation, and SP-A is the last protein to appear in amniotic fluid (10). Surfactant from the preterm lung has less saturated phosphatidylcholine, less phosphatidylglycerol, and more phosphatidylinositol. The surfactant proteins are decreased relative to the lipids, and the surfactant from the preterm lung has decreased function when tested in vivo for its effects on the preterm lung (11). The surfactant from the preterm lung also is more sensitive to inhibition of function by protein, probably because of decreased amounts of the surfactant proteins (12). Surfactant metabolism in the preterm newborn is characterized by slow secretion, minimal catabolism, and efficient reuse of phospholipid and protein components (13). A major benefit of surfactant treatment seems to be the provision of surfactant components as substrate for the preterm lung.

REGULATORS OF LUNG DEVELOPMENT

Although surfactant appearance and rapid expansion of saccules do not occur until after ~24 weeks, explants of human lungs in organ culture from 15- to 20-week fetuses rapidly develop mature type II cells that synthesize surfactant proteins and develop expanding airspaces within several days in culture (14, 15). Extremely early maturation can be further stimulated by glucocorticoids. The accelerated development of lung tissue many weeks before it would normally occur in the fetus and in the absence of exogenous hormones suggests that the fetal lung is repressed by unknown factors to favor growth over differentiation. Multiple hormones and growth factors can modulate lung maturation in in vitro systems (16). However, except for glucocorticoids, consistent and large effects have not been reported for in vivo evaluations of these growth factors and hormones by treatment strategies that are clinically relevant.

Glucocorticoids are used routinely to induce lung maturation and to decrease RDS in infants at risk for preterm delivery (17). Liggins (18) originally proposed that fetal exposure to glucocorticoids induced surfactant synthesis as their primary effect on the fetal lung. After 30 years of intense research with often conflicting results, a number of clinical and experimental observations are warranted.

Clinical Observations with Fetal Exposure to Glucocorticoids

1. Antenatal glucocorticoids decrease the incidence of RDS by ~50% (17). Even with optimal antenatal treatments, many fetuses do not respond to antenatal glucocorticoids.
2. Repetitive courses of antenatal glucocorticoids do not consistently further decrease the risk of RDS (this point is untested in randomized controlled trials) (19).
3. Antenatal glucocorticoids seem to be less effective at preventing RDS in preterms resulting from multiple births (20).
4. Infants that have been "stressed" by events such as fetal growth retardation, preeclampsia, and preterm prolonged rupture of membranes do not have a consistently lower incidence of RDS (21–23).
5. Although the incidence of RDS increases as gestational age decreases, infants born at very early gestation ages can have "mature" lungs (early spontaneous maturation) (24).

Experimental Observations with Fetal Exposure to Glucocorticoids

1. Antenatal glucocorticoids improve lung mechanics of the fetal lung after treatment-to-delivery intervals as short as 15 h (25, 26).
2. The improved lung mechanics soon after glucocorticoid treatments result from thinning of the alveolar wall and increased potential lung gas volume and not an increase in surfactant (25, 27).
3. High-dose and prolonged fetal exposure to glucocorticoids results in smaller lungs with fewer alveoli (28, 29).
4. Changes in the surfactant system in fetal sheep require >4 days or multiple repetitive weekly courses of glucocorticoids (30, 31).

5. Rapid increases in surfactant components can occur if the fetus is stressed before glucocorticoid exposure (32).
6. Maternal treatments with glucocorticoids cause fetal growth retardation in rodents, sheep, and primates, often at doses similar to those used clinically (29, 33, 34).
7. Fetal glucocorticoid treatments do not cause fetal growth retardation but are also less potent as lung-maturational agents in sheep (31).

Experimental Observations from Transgenic Mice

1. Animals that are deficient in corticotropin-releasing hormone [CRH($-/-$)] have normal lungs if born to dams that are CRH($+/-$) (35).
2. CRH($-/-$) fetuses born to CRH($-/-$) dams die of respiratory failure at birth with inadequate airspace development but with only modest delays in surfactant (36).
3. Most mice that are glucocorticoid receptor (GR) deficient (GR $-/-$) die soon after birth with lungs that have inadequate airspace development but normal amounts of surfactant proteins. Occasional newborn GR($-/-$) mice survive (37).
4. Newborn mice that have the glucocorticoid receptor mutated to prevent dimerization and DNA binding have normal lungs (38).

These multiple observations of glucocorticoid effects on the fetal lungs indicate that glucocorticoids function primarily as modulators of development. The traditional concepts that fetal glucocorticoids bind to GREs, increase before lung maturation, and are essential for lung development are not tenable (39). Type II cells can differentiate, and airspaces can develop in explants of fetal human lung without glucocorticoids (14). The results with CRH($-/-$) transgenic mice tell us that very low fetal corticosterone levels that result from a leak of maternal corticosterone across the placenta from the dam are sufficient to support normal lung maturation (35). GRE binding by the GR is not required for lung maturation, suggesting that glucocorticoid function may be mediated by GR monomer interactions with transcription factors (38). The effects of glucocorticoids to induce early lung maturation are primarily to mature lung structure by thinning of the alveolar walls and increasing lung gas volume (25). This effect can result in an interruption in alveolar septation, as best illustrated by glucocorticoid treatment of the postnatal rat and the prenatal primate (28, 40). Glucocorticoid-induced increases in steady-state mRNA levels for the surfactant proteins SP-A, SP-B, and SP-C can occur within 15 h of fetal glucocorticoid exposure, but the induction is transient, and the mRNA levels return to baseline values within several days (Figure 2) (41, 42). Increases in alveolar surfactant lipid and protein pools require treatment to evaluation intervals of ~7 days in previously unstressed fetuses. On the other hand, fetal animals can be stressed (by surgery for example), and fetal humans can be stressed such that there is early lung maturation (24). Stressed fetuses probably respond to antenatal glucocorticoids with more rapid increases

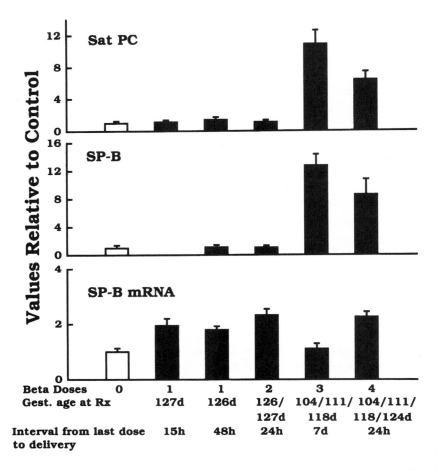

Figure 2 Changes in saturated phosphatidylcholine (Sat PC), surfactant protein (SP)-B (SP-B), and SP-B mRNA after beta methasone treatments (beta doses) of fetal sheep. The number of beta doses, the gestational ages at treatment, and intervals from last dose to delivery are given on the horizontal axis. All values are expressed relative to values for saline-injected controls. Alveolar Sat PC and SP-B did not increase for the short-term treatment-to-delivery intervals. Large increases in alveolar Sat PC and SP-B occurred after repetitive beta methasone treatments. The mRNA for SP-B increased within 48 h of treatment but decreased to control levels even after multiple retreatments, unless the last treatment was close to the time of delivery (the 4-dose beta group). Data are from Ballard et al (42) and Tan et al (41).

in surfactant components. The 50% of human fetuses that respond to antenatal glucocorticoids with a decreased incidence and severity of RDS may be the fetuses that are stressed and therefore are more rapidly responsive to glucocorticoids. A major gap in knowledge is an understanding of what constitutes fetal stress and what makes the fetal lung responsive to glucocorticoids. Human fetuses can have a global insult that results in growth retardation without having induced lung maturation (21).

Recent results with the fetal sheep model further complicate the interpretations of how antenatal glucocorticoids may be working. When beta methasone is given to a pregnant ewe, there is potent lung maturation but also fetal growth retardation (33). Treatment of the fetus with beta methasone to yield a plasma glucocorticoid level approximately threefold higher than after maternal dosing results in no fetal growth retardation and a less potent effect on the fetal lung (31). This result suggests that glucocorticoids may be acting primarily on the placenta to signal the diverse fetal responses. It is safe to state that, although antenatal glucocorticoids are effective, their mechanisms of action are pleiotropic and not well understood.

INFLAMMATORY INFLUENCES ON LUNG DEVELOPMENT

The epidemiologic associations of indicators of infection/inflammation with early preterm birth are well established (43). Amniotic-fluid samples that contain elevated interleukin (IL)-6 levels predict preterm delivery (44), and the presence of positive cultures from amniotic fluid and IL-6 levels can be used to predict time of preterm delivery (45). The percent of women with bacterial vaginosis and/or elevated proinflammatory cytokine levels in amniotic fluid is much higher for very early preterm deliveries than for later preterm deliveries (43). Indicators of fetal inflammatory responses also are highly associated with early preterm delivery (46). The stimuli result from low-grade chronic colonization of fetal membranes and/or amniotic fluid with multiple different low-pathogenic organisms (47). The most frequently isolated organism, *Ureaplasma urealyticum,* is associated with robust proinflammatory responses in amniotic fluid [a 15-fold median increase for IL-6, an 81-fold increase for IL-1β, a 36-fold increase for tumor necrosis factor (TNF)-α, and an increase in leukocytes from 3 to 306 cells/ml] (48). Therefore, many ELBW infants are born after exposure to proinflammatory stimuli, presumably by activation of the prostanoid cascade that causes preterm labor.

The new information is the striking correlation between antenatal cytokine exposure and major undesirable neonatal outcomes. Yoon et al (49, 50) reported that IL-6, TNF-α, IL-1β, and IL-8 elevations in amniotic fluid sampled within 5 days of delivery of preterm infants at <33 weeks gestation correlated with the subsequent development of chronic lung injury, periventricular leukomalacia, and cerebral palsy. The median proinflammatory cytokine levels were increased by 20- to 40-fold in the amniotic fluid of the infants with chronic lung disease compared with levels in infants without chronic lung injury. A fetal inflammatory response as assessed by increased fetal plasma IL-6 also was a strong risk factor for severe neonatal morbidity (51). These associations of elevated amniotic-fluid cytokines are consistent with the correlations of increased incidences of chronic lung injury with clinical or histologic chorioamnionitis (52, 53).

The association between antenatal inflammation and chronic lung injury is not simple. Hitti et al (54) reported that elevated TNF-α in amniotic fluid was associated with an increased incidence of RDS and with the subsequent development of bronchopulmonary dysplasia. In contrast Watterberg et al (53) found that, although only 33% of preterm infants from pregnancies with histologic chorioamnionitis developed RDS, 67% of these infants with chorioamnionitis developed bronchopulmonary dysplasia. This counterintuitive outcome is consistent with recent epidemiologic information indicating that ELBW infants without RDS have a risk of developing bronchopulmonary dysplasia that is similar to that in infants with RDS (24). Necrotizing funisitis and increased leukocyte elastase in tracheal aspirates at birth also are highly associated with the development of lung injury (55, 56). Therefore, in ELBW infants, ventilation and oxygen exposure from birth are not necessary factors for the development of chronic lung injury. Because chronic lung injury in ELBW infants means abnormal development and repair, it is important to understand how proinflammatory agents interact with the developing lung.

Experimentally the proinflammatory cytokine IL-1α can act as a maturational agent, another counterintuitive result. Bry et al (57) reported that intra-amniotic injection of high doses of human recombinant IL-1α induced the mRNAs for SP-A and SP-B in preterm rabbit fetuses and improved the compliance of the preterm lungs (Figure 3). Intra-amniotic IL-1α given 48 h before preterm delivery also increased surfactant lipid pools and improved the lung function of lambs (58). The maturational effect of IL-1α occurred without elevations of blood leukocytes, cortisol, or catecholamines. The IL-1α could induce a generalized proinflammatory response in amniotic fluid that is transmitted to the fetus via the membranes, the gastrointestinal tract by swallowing the amniotic fluid, or the lungs directly from aspirated fluid. The pathways and agents that result in the maturational effects on the fetal lung are not known.

To test the effects of a general proinflammatory stimulus, 20 mg of *Escherichia coli* 055:B5 endotoxin was given by intra-amniotic injection to fetal sheep, and the lungs of lambs were evaluated after premature delivery and compared with those of fetuses given beta methasone (59). Lung gas volumes and compliance were increased more by endotoxin than by the beta methasone treatment, at 6 days after endotoxin exposure. Alveolar surfactant lipid and SP-A and SP-B pools were increased 7- to 10-fold for endotoxin-exposed fetuses, and there were only modest increases for the beta methasone–treated animals. In contrast, 0.05 mg of endotoxin given by fetal intramuscular injection caused fetal death. Therefore proinflammatory stimuli given into amniotic fluid can cause lung maturation. The characteristics of the inflammatory response in the amniotic fluid and the subse-

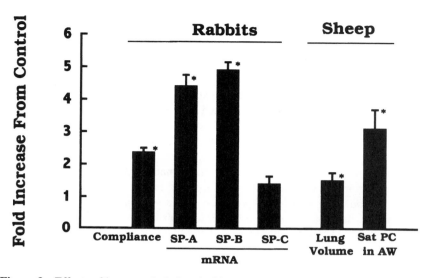

Figure 3   Effects of intra-amniotic interleukin-1α (IL-1α) on indicators of lung maturation in rabbits and sheep after preterm delivery. Intra-amniotic IL-1α increased compliance and surfactant protein (SP)-A and SP-B mRNA levels in preterm rabbits compared with control values normalized to 1.0 (data are abstracted from 57). Intra-amniotic IL-1α also increased lung gas volumes measured at 40-cmH$_2$0 pressure and the amount of saturated phosphatidylcholine (Sat PC) in alveolar washes of preterm sheep 48 h after fetal exposure (data are abstracted from 58). (*$p < 0.05$ vs. the control value for each measurement.)

quent fetal responses remain to be defined. However, these experiments suggest that cytokines and growth factors may be potent regulators of lung development.

POSTNATAL LUNG DEVELOPMENT AND ALVEOLARIZATION

The infants at risk for chronic lung disease in the era of surfactant treatment are just beginning to septate their distal gas exchange saccules (4). Therefore, from the developmental perspective, they are quite different from more mature infants in whom alveolarization is well established. The pathologic observations are that the few infants who have died incidentally after surviving chronic lung disease have lungs with fewer and larger alveoli (60). Hislop et al (5) noted, in 1987, that preterm infants who died after mechanical ventilation had fewer alveoli than unventilated preterm infants dying of nonrespiratory causes. Husain et al (61) found that those infants who died after 40 weeks gestation had a decrease in radial alveolar counts and an increase in mean linear intercept compared with infants without chronic lung disease. The infants who died of chronic lung disease did not have striking inflammation or very much fibrosis. Stahlman has provided sections from two infants that died with a clinical diagnosis of chronic lung disease 4–6 weeks after very preterm birth (Figure 4). The lungs appear not to have developed, based on the appearance anticipated for the gestational age at preterm birth. This maturational arrest is associated with minimal capillary development, and inflammation and fibrosis are not prominent.

This pathology has been replicated in 140-day preterm baboons ventilated with 100% oxygen for 7 days, and 125-day preterm baboons ventilated for 14 days with oxygen concentrations of generally <50% (62). At 33 weeks after birth, the 140-day preterm baboons exposed to oxygen had a 50% decrease in alveoli and epithelial surface area compared with animals ventilated with less oxygen (63). Ventilation of preterm lambs over a period of 2 to 3 weeks also stopped alveolarization and resulted in fewer alveoli that were larger (64). In rodents that do not alveolarize their lungs until after term birth, alveolarization can be interrupted by oxygen exposure, glucocorticoid treatment, and nutritional deprivation (6). An interesting observation is that mice that overexpress TNF-α only in the lungs under control of the SP-C promoter have fewer distal saccules at birth, and the lungs are inflamed and do not alveolarize (65). TNF-α is elevated in amniotic fluid and tracheal aspirates of very preterm infants destined to develop chronic lung disease (66). In similar experiments, overexpression of TGF-α in the fetal lung under control of the SP-C promoter results in less alveolarization and fibrosis (67). It is a reasonable hypothesis that cytokines interfere with postnatal alveolarization in very preterm infants. How antenatal or postnatal glucocorticoid treatments interact with normal alveolarization or cytokine-altered alveolarization remains to be evaluated. Of interest, retinoic acid blocks the postnatal inhibition of alveolarization caused by glucocorticoids in rats (68).

Physiological Constraints of the Preterm Lung for Ventilation

Spontaneous ventilation for the average 0.8-kg infant born at 26 weeks gestational age often is not adequate because of inadequate respiratory drive and insufficient muscle mass to sustain ventilation with a chest wall that is poorly ossified and very compliant. However, above and beyond respiratory control and chest mechanics deficits, the preterm lung has intrinsic developmental limitations that both compromise ventilation and make the lung uniquely susceptible to injury. Lung gas volume is small because the lung is just beginning to alveolarize (4). Maximal lung gas volumes can be estimated from gas volumes at peak pressure measured using pressure-volume curves, volumes measured by gas washout techniques and plethysmography, and volumes and alveolarization measured morphometrically. Gribetz et al (69) used pressure-volume curves in 1959 to measure total lung gas volumes of 7 ml/kg for infants who died of RDS and volumes of 27 ml/kg for preterm infants dying of other causes. Preterm monkeys that died of RDS had total lung gas volumes measured at 35 cmH$_2$O static pressure of 19

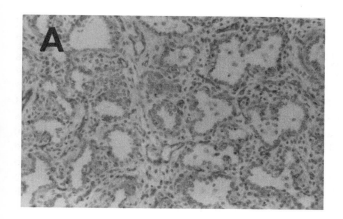

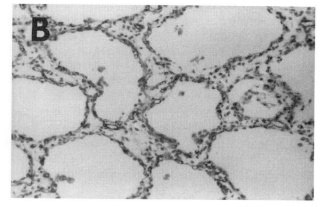

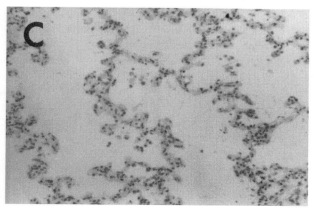

Figure 4   Lung histology of infants who died of chronic lung disease. (*A*) Lung tissue of a 24-week gestation infant who died after 39 days of ventilation. (*B*) Lung tissue of a 28-week gestation infant who survived for 6 weeks. (*C*) Lung of a term infant for comparison. The lungs of the preterm infants appear not to have developed beyond the level anticipated for the gestations at delivery. Inflammation and fibrosis are not prominent. The micrographs were kindly provided by MT Stahlman, Vanderbilt University (×155).

ml/kg, and values for monkeys recovering from RDS and preterm monkeys without RDS were 33 ml/kg and 55 ml/kg, respectively (70). Preterm 1.2-kg humans with severe RDS had a functional residual capacity of about 11 ml/kg and a total lung capacity of only 19 ml/kg (71). In contrast, 1.95-kg preterm infants without RDS had an average functional residual capacity of 22 ml/kg and a total lung capacity of 48 ml/kg. For comparison, the total lung capacity of the term infant is ~50 ml/kg and is ~80 ml/kg for the adult human. Lung weight or volume per kilogram of body weight does not change very much during the last third of human fetal development, but the potential gas volume of inflation-fixed lungs increases from 21% at 20 weeks to 36% at 30 weeks and to 50% of total tissue volume at term (4). The potential gas volume of the term infant lung estimated from inflation-fixed specimens was ~55 ml/kg. Lung volumes measured in vivo for preterm infants with severe RDS are smaller than their potential anatomic volume because of atelectasis and the inability to completely open the lungs with static pressures of 35 or 40 cmH$_2$O (72). The collagen and elastin matrix is underdeveloped, and the pressure-volume curve for the preterm lung will not achieve a plateau or maximal volume. Increasing pressures will yield linearly increasing volumes until the lung ruptures.

Surfactant deficiency significantly complicated ventilation of the preterm infant before the era of surfactant treatment because lungs of preterm infants had low functional residual capacities, low maximal lung volumes, and nonuniform ventilation with overdistention of the aerated lung and atelectasis or edema filling of the nonaerated lung (73). Surfactant treatments have profound effects on static lung volumes that translate into better lung mechanics, improved gas exchange, and a 30% to 40% decrease in mortality for preterm infants with RDS. Maximal lung volumes defined at a pressure of 35 cmH$_2$O (Figure 5) doubled after natural surfactant treatment, and a similar effect occurred after treatment with a synthetic surfactant containing recombinant human SP-C (74). The increases in lung gas volumes with surfactant treatment result in a lung with new pressure-volume relationships. The dead space contributed by the airways should not change. Therefore, the increase in maximal lung volumes represents the recruitment of new gas exchange surface (reversal of atelectasis), an effect that improves oxygenation. The other major lung volume effect is the increase in functional residual capacity resulting from the increased stability of the lungs on deflation. An increase in functional residual capacity of 150% was measured after surfactant treatment in infants with RDS (75). This increased functional residual capacity also will improve oxygenation in a manner analogous to the use of positive end expiratory pressure to improve oxygenation (76).

Mechanisms of Lung Injury with Ventilation

Because outcomes of ventilated adults with acute RDS have been so poor, major research efforts have been directed at better understanding ventilator-associated lung injury. Dreyfuss & Saumon (77) recently reviewed the compelling infor-

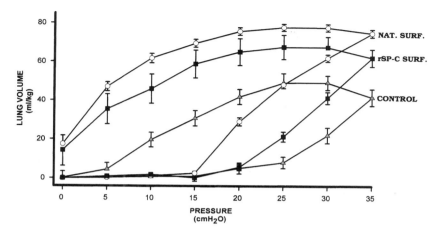

Figure 5   Pressure-volume curves for lungs of preterm rabbits measured after 15 min of ventilation after treatment with a lipid-extracted natural sheep surfactant (Nat-Surf) or a synthetic surfactant containing 2% recombinant human surfactant protein (SP)-C (rSP-C Surf). The control rabbits were not treated with surfactant. Data are from Davis et al (74).

mation demonstrating that lungs are injured if they are inflated to volumes that exceed total lung capacity. Regional or uniform overinflation results in leukocyte migration into lungs, increased permeability, and interstitial and alveolar edema. Different combinations of functional residual capacities and tidal volumes are injurious if the sum of functional residual capacity and tidal volume exceeds total lung capacity. If chest expansion is limited by binding or casting, then very high pressures do not result in lung injury (78). Overinflation of a lung (or a region of lung if lung injury is nonuniform) defines the high-volume injury zone on the pressure-volume curve for that lung (76). Overdistension of the lung can disrupt structural elements and can stimulate the lung to release multiple products that promote an inflammatory cascade. These factors do not come initially from peripheral leukocytes because isolated and perfused lungs release TNF-α, IL-1, and IL-6, and mRNA levels for TNF-α increase within 2 h (79). The overinflated lung also begins to synthesize extracellular-matrix components and growth factors (80). The cytokines and chemokines generated by the lung then amplify the injury response by attracting peripheral leukocytes into the lungs. Exposure of the adult rat lung to endotoxin before overdistension results in an increased release of proinflammatory mediators, indicating that the lung can be primed for promotion of proinflammatory injury (79).

The other lesson from experiments with mature lungs is that ventilation of lungs below a normal functional residual capacity results in cyclic opening and closing of lung units and injury (76). In lungs made surfactant deficient by lavage, ventilation at low lung volumes causes release of cytokines in vivo and in isolated and perfused lungs (79, 81). As with overdistension, ventilation at low lung volumes promotes accumulation and activation of peripheral leukocytes in the lungs. Injury to surfactant-deficient lungs can be minimized by recruiting lung volumes and then maintaining a higher-than-normal functional residual capacity by high-frequency oscillatory ventilation (82). Therefore the lung also has a low-volume injury zone. Ventilation of the preterm lung results in accumulation of granulocytes in the lungs with associated edema, and surfactant treatment can decrease the granulocyte accumulation and the edema (83).

Lung Injury with the Initiation of Ventilation

The preterm lung is uniquely susceptible to injury with the initiation of ventilation (84). There is no gas in the lung because the functional residual capacity is occupied by fluid, surfactant concentrations may be low, and gas volumes need to increase rapidly. Vyas et al (85) measured lung expansion after term birth and observed high negative esophageal pressures with inspiration and high positive esophageal pressures with expiration. Adequate tidal volumes and functional residual capacities were achieved most effectively in asphyxiated term infants when 5-s inspiratory times were used to initiate ventilation (86). The long inspiratory times and relatively high pressures overcome the resistance of fluid movement down the airways, a process facilitated by high surfactant concentrations in fetal lung fluid at term. There have been no systematic studies of the initiation of ventilation in ELBW infants. In animal models, air opening pressures for fluid-filled fetal lungs decrease as fetal lung fluid volumes decrease and as surfactant concentrations increase (87, 88). Initiation of ventilation in preterm infants often requires pressures of >30 cmH$_2$O, probably because surfactant concentrations are low and fetal lung fluid volumes are high as a result of immature fluid clearance pathways. The generally accepted goal for ventilation of the preterm infant after delivery is to achieve a pink infant with a Pco$_2$ of $\sim$40 mmHg as soon as possible, and this may not be easily achievable without risking lung injury (84). The preterm infant destined to have RDS may have a total lung capacity of only 20 ml/kg. The lungs will inflate poorly and nonuniformly because of surfactant deficiency despite the use of high pressures, and ventilation in the midst of a resuscitation may not effectively limit tidal volumes to volumes that will not overdistend the lung.

Recent studies of the initiation of ventilation by using preterm lambs demonstrate the risks of using high tidal volumes. Bjorklund et al (89) found that six manual inflations of 35–40 ml/kg in 128-day gestation lambs with potential lung gas volumes of $\sim$50 ml/kg resulted in persistent respiratory failure and pneumothorax despite surfactant treatment at 30 min of age. After 4 h of ventilation, inspiratory capacities (lung gas volume above functional residual capacities) were only $\sim$10 ml/kg after the six large initial inflations, in comparison with inspiratory capacities of $\sim$30 ml/kg for animals that were not "bagged." Wada et al (90) found that ventilation of preterm lambs for 30 min after birth with tidal volumes of 20 ml/kg resulted in Pco_2 values of 24 mmHg at 20 min of age and initially high compliance. However, surfactant treatment at 30 min of age and subsequent ventilation resulted in lungs that were less compliant, less able to exchange gas, and more greatly injured (as indicated by increased alveolar wash proteins) than were lungs initially ventilated with 5- or 10-ml/kg tidal volumes. The higher tidal volumes compromised the response to surfactant treatment. However, the lower tidal volumes that minimized injury resulted in hypercarbia and increased blood flow to the brain. These studies point out the dilemma that it may not be possible to initiate ventilation for some ELBW infants to quickly achieve normal Pco_2 values because their small, fluid-filled, and surfactant-deficient lungs cannot exchange sufficient Pco_2 without causing lung injury from overinflation.

Surfactant treatment before the initiation of ventilation can increase lung volumes, increase uniformity of inflation, and decrease injury, but high-volume ventilation remains a risk because the lungs are developmentally small. The presumed mechanism for injury with the use of high tidal volumes for the initiation of ventilation is by lung overinflation, which activates the same injury mechanisms described above for the adult lung (79). We recently found that 1 h of modest hyperventilation of preterm lambs to Pco_2 values of 25–30 cmH_2O resulted in an increase in TNF-α mRNA, which did not occur in animals that were not hyperventilated.

Lung Injury from Continued Mechanical Ventilation

Ventilation of preterm infants with RDS results in an increase in macrophages and an influx of granulocytes into the airspaces (91). Infants that progress to chronic lung disease have a persistence of leukocytes in alveolar lavages. Airway samples contain high levels of the same cytokines/chemokines identified in amniotic fluid for infants at risk for bronchopulmonary dysplasia (92). Airway samples also contain elevations of other factors that can promote leukocyte migration to the lungs and other indicators of lung injury (e.g. laminin, fibronectin, complement, and elastase) (66). Anti-inflammatory cytokines such as IL-10 are low when proinflammatory cytokines are high (93). The relative importance of the different components of this mixture of effector molecules is not known. There are no techniques available to routinely measure functional residual capacities or total lung capacities in ventilated preterm infants. Routine ventilation probably further promotes the proinflammation in many infants, because only 10–20 ml/kg of lung gas volume is available between functional residual capacity and total lung capacity for safe ventilation of the preterm infant without hyperinflation.

Ventilation of the ELBW infant seems to interfere not only with alveolarization but also with the surfactant system. Preterm infants destined to develop chronic lung disease have low levels of SP-A, as do preterm ventilated monkeys (94, 95). Chronic ventilation of 125-day gestation baboons that were surfactant treated

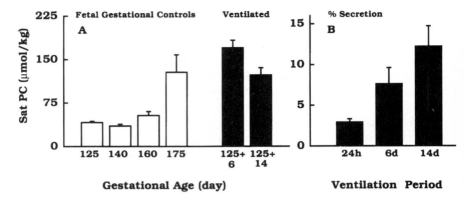

Figure 6 Amount of saturated phosphatidylcholine (Sat PC) and percent secretion in preterm baboons delivered at 125 days gestation and ventilated for periods of 24 h or 6 or 14 days. The amount of Sat PC in the lungs of the ventilated animals is increased relative to the gestation controls that were not ventilated (*A*). The percent of ^{3}H-Sat PC that was recovered by alveolar wash relative to ^{3}H-Sat PC in the total lung 24 h after an intravascular injection of ^{3}H-palmitic acid is an estimate of secretion of Sat PC. The percent secretion increased with age after preterm delivery at 125 days gestation. The percent secretion is low relative to adult animals with values of 20–40% of total lung Sat PC. Data are from Seidner et al (96).

resulted in very abnormal surfactant metabolism (Figure 6) (96). The lung saturated phosphatidylcholine pools increased from fetal values of ~40 μmol/kg to 170 μmol/kg within 6 days. These values exceeded fetal saturated phosphatidylcholine pool sizes in 175-day fetuses. Therefore the ventilated preterm animals accumulated very large surfactant lipid pools in tissue, but alveolar pools stayed relatively low at ~20 μmol/kg of saturated phosphatidylcholine. The type II cells that line the distal saccules were dysmature in that some were full of glycogen and others had little glycogen but the lamellar bodies were not uniform or as osmophilic as anticipated. Kinetic measurements indicated decreased secretion of de novo–synthesized saturated phosphatidylcholine and increased catabolism. The surfactant recovered by alveolar wash also had decreased function. The mechanistic explanations for these aberrations of surfactant metabolism are not known. However, cytokine and growth factor abnormalities can cause large surfactant lipid accumulations in the lungs of transgenic mice. Granulocyte-macrophage colony stimulating factor deficiency causes alveolar proteinoses with lung tissue accumulation of surfactant lipids as a result of decreased catabolism (97). Overexpression of IL-4 in Clara cells in mice causes an alveolar proteinosis characterized by increased synthetic and catabolic rates with increased macrophages and granulocytes in alveoli (98). Infants developing chronic lung disease have elevations of IL-4 in tracheal aspirates (66).

A UNIFIED HYPOTHESIS OF ABNORMAL DEVELOPMENT AND LUNG INJURY IN THE PRETERM INFANT

Lung injury in the previously uninjured adult is initiated by physical factors such as stretching and oxygen and is propagated by proinflammatory mechanisms (77). In contrast, the reciprocal situation applies to the lung inflamed with pneumonia or by a systemic inflammatory response in which ventilation and oxygen intensify the injury (79). The same situations probably apply to the developing lung, the profound difference being that the mediators of injury are also modulators of development. Intrauterine cytokine exposure can induce lung maturation, but very preterm infants without RDS develop chronic lung disease, often without much ventilation or oxygen exposure. We interpret this sequence to indicate that the proinflammatory stimuli promote and perpetuate inflammatory responses that lead to lung injury and inhibition of alveolarization. Initiation of ventilation can either initiate or further promote injury of the preterm lung that has been primed by an antenatal proinflammatory exposure. Subsequent ventilation and oxygen exposure further perpetuate the injury sequence by maintaining elevated levels of the signaling molecules. Although glucocorticoids may suppress components of the inflammatory response, they also can suppress alveolarization and interfere with lung development. Surfactant treatments permit many more very preterm infants to be ventilated sufficiently to survive and thus result in more preterm infants having aberrations in lung development. The challenges for the future are to learn what factors normally regulate lung development and which factors of the fetal response to inflammation interfere with lung development.

Visit the Annual Reviews home page at www.AnnualReviews.org.

LITERATURE CITED

1. Stevenson DK, Wright LL, Lemons JA, Oh W, Korones SB, et al. 1998. Very low birth weight outcomes of the National Institute of Child Health and Human Development Neonatal Research Network, January 1993 through December 1994. *Am. J. Obstet. Gynecol.* 179: 1632–39
2. Burri PW. 1985. Developmental and growth of the human lung. In *Handbook of Physiology: the Respiratory System*, ed. AP Fishman, AB Fisher, pp. 1–46. Bethesda, MD: *Am. Physiol. Soc.*
3. Hislop AA, Wigglesworth JS, Desai R. 1986. Alveolar development in the human fetus and infant. *Early Hum. Dev.* 13:1–11
4. Langston C, Kida D, Reed M, Thurlbeck W. 1984. Human lung growth in late gestation and in the neonate. *Am. Rev. Respir. Dis.* 129:607–13
5. Hislop AA, Wigglesworth JS, Desai R, Aber V. 1987. The effects of preterm delivery and mechanical ventilation on human lung growth. *Early Hum. Dev.* 15:147–64
6. Massaro GD, Massaro D. 1996. Formation of pulmonary alveoli and gas-exchange surface area: quantitation and regulation. *Annu. Rev. Physiol.* 58:73–92

7. Khoor A, Stahlman MT, Gray ME, Whitsett JA. 1994. Temporal-spatial distribution of SP-B and SP-C proteins and mRNAs in developing respiratory epithelium of human lung. *J. Histochem. Cytochem.* 42:1187–99

8. Ohashi T, Polk D, Ikegami M, Ueda T, Jobe A. 1994. Ontogeny and effects of exogenous surfactant treatment on SP-A, SP-B, and SP-C mRNA expression in rabbit lungs. *Am. J. Physiol.* 267:L46–51

9. Ross GF, Ikegami M, Steinhilber W, Jobe AH. 1999. Surfactant protein C (SP-C) levels in fetal and ventilated preterm rabbit lungs. *Pediatr. Res.* 45:222A

10. Pryhuber GS, Hull WM, Fink I, McMahan MJ, Whitsett JA. 1991. Ontogeny of surfactant protein-A and protein-B in human amniotic fluid as indices of fetal lung maturity. *Pediatr. Res.* 30:597–605

11. Ueda T, Ikegami M, Jobe AH. 1994. Developmental changes of sheep surfactant: in vivo function and in vitro subtype conversion. *J. Appl. Physiol.* 76:2701–6

12. Ikegami M, Rebello CM, Jobe AH. 1996. Surfactant inhibition by plasma: gestational age and surfactant treatment effects in preterm lambs. *J. Appl. Physiol.* 81:2517–22

13. Ikegami M, Jobe AH. 1993. Surfactant metabolism. *Sem. Perinatol.* 17:223–40

14. Gonzales LW, Ballard PL, Ertsey R, Williams MC. 1986. Glucocorticoids and thyroid hormones stimulate biochemical and morphological differentiation of human fetal lung in organ culture. *J. Clin. Endocrinol. Metab.* 62:678–91

15. Snyder JM, Johnston JM, Mendelson CR. 1981. Differentiation of type II cells of human fetal lung in vitro. *Cell Tissue Res.* 220:17–25

16. Mendelson CR, Boggaram V. 1991. Hormonal control of the surfactant system in fetal lung. *Annu. Rev. Physiol.* 53:415–40

17. Crowley P. 1995. Antenatal corticosteroid therapy: a meta-analysis of the randomized trials—1972–1994. *Am. J. Obstet. Gynecol.* 173:322–35

18. Liggins GC. 1969. Premature delivery of fetal lambs infused with glucocorticoids. *J. Endocrinol.* 45:515–23

19. French NP, Hagan R, Evans SF, Godfrey M, Newnham JP. 1999. Repeated antenatal corticosteroids: size at birth and subsequent development. *Am. J. Obstet. Gynecol.* 180:114–21

20. Turrentine MA, Wilson PD, Wilkins IA. 1996. A retrospective analysis of the effect of antenatal steroid administration on the incidence of respiratory distress syndrome in preterm twin pregnancies. *Am. J. Perinatol.* 13:351–54

21. Tyson JE, Kennedy K, Broyles S, Rosenfeld CR. 1995. The small for gestational age infant: accelerated or delayed pulmonary maturation? Increased or decreased survival? *Pediatrics* 95:534–38

22. Friedman SA, Schiff E, Kao L, Sibai BM. 1995. Neonatal outcome after preterm delivery for preeclampsia. *Am. J. Obstet. Gynecol.* 172:1785–92

23. Hallak M, Bottoms SF. 1993. Accelerated pulmonary maturation from preterm premature rupture of membranes: a myth. *Am. J. Obstet. Gynecol.* 169:1045–49

24. Rojas MA, Gonzalez A, Bancalari E, Claure N, Poole C, Silva-Neto G. 1995. Changing trends in the epidemiology and pathogenesis of neonatal chronic lung disease. *J. Pediatr.* 126:605–10

25. Kauffman SL. 1977. Acceleration of canalicular development in lungs of fetal mice exposed transplacentally to dexamethasone. *Lab. Invest.* 36:395–401

26. Ikegami M, Polk D, Jobe A. 1996. Minimum interval from fetal betamethasone treatment to postnatal lung responses in preterm lambs. *Am. J. Obstet. Gynecol.* 174:1408–13

27. Pinkerton KE, Willet KE, Peake J, Sly PD, Jobe AH, Ikegami M. 1997. Prenatal glucocorticoid and T4 effects on lung

morphology in preterm lambs. *Am. J. Respir. Crit. Care Med.* 156:624–30

28. Bunton TE, Plopper CG. 1984. Triamcinolone-induced structural alterations in the development of the lung of the fetal rhesus macaque. *Am. J. Obstet. Gynecol.* 148:203–15

29. Johnson JWC, Mitzner W, Beck JC, London WT, Sly DL, et al. 1981. Long-term effects of betamethasone on fetal development. *Am. J. Obstet. Gynecol.* 141:1053–61

30. Ikegami M, Jobe AH, Newnham J, Polk DH, Willet KE, Sly P. 1997. Repetitive prenatal glucocorticoids improve lung function and decrease growth in preterm lambs. *Am. J. Respir. Crit. Care Med.* 156:178–84

31. Jobe AH, Newnham J, Willet K, Sly P, Ikegami M. 1998. Fetal versus maternal and gestational age effects of repetitive antenatal glucocorticoids. *Pediatrics* 102:1116–25

32. Tabor BL, Lewis JF, Ikegami M, Polk D, Jobe AH. 1994. Corticosteroids and fetal intervention interact to alter lung maturation in preterm lambs. *Pediatr. Res.* 35:479–83

33. Jobe AH, Wada N, Berry LM, Ikegami M, Ervin MG. 1998. Single and repetitive maternal glucocorticoid exposures reduce fetal growth in sheep. *Am. J. Obstet. Gynecol.* 178:880–85

34. Frank L, Roberts RJ. 1979. Effects of low-dose prenatal corticosteroid administration on the premature rat. *Biol. Neonate* 36:1–9

35. Muglia L, Jacobson L, Dikkes P, Majzoub JA. 1995. Corticotropin-releasing hormone deficiency reveals major fetal but not adult glucocorticoid need. *Nature* 373:427–32

36. Muglia LJ, Bae DS, Brown TT, Vogt SK, Alvarez JG, et al. 1999. Proliferation and differentiation defects during lung development in corticotropin-releasing

hormone-deficient mice. *Am. J. Respir. Cell Mol. Biol.* 20:181–88

37. Cole TJ, Blendy JA, Monaghan AP, Krieglstein K, Schmid W, et al. 1995. Targeted disruption of the glucocorticoid receptor gene blocks adrenergic chromaffin cell development and severely retards lung maturation. *Gene Dev.* 9:1608–21

38. Reichardt HM, Kaestner KH, Tuckermann J, Kretz O, Wessely O, et al. 1998. DNA binding of the glucocorticoid receptor is not essential for survival. *Cell* 93:531–41

39. Ballard PL. 1989. Hormonal regulation of pulmonary surfactant. *Endocr. Rev.* 10:165–81

40. Massaro D, Massaro GD. 1986. Dexamethasone accelerates postnatal alveolar wall thinning and alters wall composition. *Am. J. Physiol.* 251:R218–24

41. Tan RC, Gonzales J, Strayer MS, Ballard PL, Ikegami M, et al. 1998. Developmental and glucocorticoid regulation of surfactant protein mRNAs in fetal sheep. *Pediatr. Res.* 43:55A

42. Ballard PL, Ning Y, Polk D, Ikegami M, Jobe A. 1997. Glucocorticoid regulation of surfactant components in immature lambs. *Am. J. Physiol.* 273:L1048–57

43. Watts DH, Krohn KA, Hillier SL, Eschenbach DA. 1992. The association of occult amniotic fluid infection with gestational age and neonatal outcome among women in preterm labor. *Obstet. Gynecol.* 79:351–57

44. Wenstrom KD, Andrews WW, Hauth JC, Goldenberg RL, DuBard MB, Cliver SP. 1998. Elevated second-trimester amniotic fluid interleukin-6 levels predict preterm delivery. *Am. J. Obstet. Gynecol.* 178:546–50

45. Greci LS, Gilson GJ, Nevils B, Izquierdo LA, Qualls CR, Curet LB. 1998. Is amniotic fluid analysis the key to preterm labor? A model using interleukin-6 for

predicting rapid delivery. *Am. J. Obstet. Gynecol.* 179:172–78

46. Romero R, Gomez R, Ghezzi F, Yoon BH, Mazor M, et al. 1998. A fetal systemic inflammatory response is followed by the spontaneous onset of preterm parturition. *Am. J. Obstet. Gynecol.* 179: 186–93

47. Oyarzún E, Yamamoto M, Kato S, Gómez R, Lizama L, Moenne A. 1998. Specific detection of 16 micro-organisms in amniotic fluid by polymerase chain reaction and its correlation with preterm delivery occurrence. *Am. J. Obstet. Gynecol.* 179:1115–19

48. Yoon BH, Romero R, Park JS, Chang JW, Kim YA, et al. 1998. Microbial invasion of the amniotic cavity with *Ureaplasma urealyticum* is associated with a robust host in fetal, amniotic, and maternal compartments. *Am. J. Obstet. Gynecol.* 179:1254–60

49. Yoon BH, Romero R, Kim CJ, Koo JN, Choe G, et al. 1997. High expression of tumor necrosis factor-alpha and interleukin-6 in periventricular leukomalacia. *Am. J. Obstet. Gynecol.* 177:406–11

50. Yoon BH, Romero R, Jun JK, Park KH, Park JD, et al. 1997. Amniotic fluid cytokines (interleukin-6, tumor necrosis factor-α interleukin-1β, and interleukin-8) and the risk for the development of bronchopulmonary dysplasia. *Am. J. Obstet. Gynecol.* 177:825–30

51. Gomez R, Romero R, Ghezzi F, Yoon BH, Mazor M, Berry SM. 1998. The fetal inflammatory response syndrome. *Am. J. Obstet. Gynecol.* 179:194–202

52. Alexander JM, Gilstrap LC, Cox SM, McIntire DM, Leveno KJ. 1998. Clinical chorioamnionitis and the prognosis for very low birth weight infants. *Obstet. Gynecol.* 91:725–29

53. Watterberg KL, Demers LM, Scott SM, Murphy S. 1996. Chorioamnionitis and early lung inflammation in infants in whom bronchopulmonary dysplasia develops. *Pediatrics* 97:210–15

54. Hitti J, Krohn MA, Patton DL, Tarczy-Hornoch P, Hillier SL, et al. 1997. Amniotic fluid tumor necrosis factor-alpha and the risk of respiratory distress syndrome among preterm infants. *Am. J. Obstet. Gynecol.* 177:50–56

55. Matsuda T, Nakajima T, Hattori S, Hanatani K, Fukazawa Y, et al. 1997. Necrotizing funisitis: clinical significance and association with chronic lung disease in premature infants. *Am. J. Obstet. Gynecol.* 177:1402–7

56. Fujimura M, Kitajima H, Nakayama M. 1993. Increased leukocyte elastase of the tracheal aspirate at birth and neonatal pulmonary emphysema. *Pediatrics* 92: 564–69

57. Bry K, Lappalainen U, Hallman M. 1997. Intraamniotic interleukin-1 accelerates surfactant protein synthesis in fetal rabbits and improves lung stability after premature birth. *J. Clin. Invest.* 99:2992–99

58. Emerson GA, Bry K, Hallman M, Jobe AH, Wada N, et al. 1997. Intra-amniotic interleukin-1 alpha treatment alters postnatal adaptation in premature lambs. *Biol. Neonate* 72:370–79

59. Jobe AH, Newnham JP, Willet KE, Sky PD, Ervin MG, Ikegami M. 1999. Antenatal intraamniotic endotoxin stimulates lung maturation in preterm sheep. *Pediatr. Res.* 45:202A

60. Sobonya RE, Logvinoff MM, Taussig LM, Theriault A. 1982. Morphometric analysis of the lung in prolonged bronchopulmonary dysplasia. *Pediatr. Res.* 16:969–72

61. Husain NA, Siddiqui NH, Stocker JR. 1998. Pathology of arrested acinar development in postsurfactant bronchopulmonary dysplasia. *Hum. Pathol.* 29:710–17

62. Coalson JJ, Winter VT, Gerstmann DR, Idell S, King RJ, deLemos RA. 1992. Pathophysiologic, morphometric, and

biochemical studies of the premature baboon with bronchopulmonary dysplasia. *Am. Rev. Respir. Dis.* 145:872–81

63. Coalson JJ, Winter V, deLemos RA. 1995. Decreased alveolarization in baboon survivors with bronchopulmonary dysplasia. *Am. J. Respir. Crit. Care Med.* 152:640–46

64. Albertine KH, Jones GP, Starcher BC, Bohnsack JF, Davis PL, et al. 1999. Chronic lung injury in preterm lambs. *Am. J. Respir. Crit. Care Med.* 159:945–58

65. Miyazaki Y, Araki K, Vesin C, Garcia I, Kapanci Y, et al. 1995. Expression of a tumor necrosis factor-alpha transgene in murine lung causes lymphocytic and fibrosing alveolitis. *J. Clin. Invest.* 96:250–59

66. Groneck P, Speer CP. 1995. Inflammatory mediators and bronchopulmonary dysplasia. *Arch. Dis. Child.* 73:F1–3

67. Hardie WD, Bruno MD, Huelsman KM, Iwamoto HS, Carrigan PE, et al. 1997. Postnatal lung function and morphology in transgenic mice expressing transforming growth factor-alpha. *Am. J. Pathol.* 151:1075–83

68. Massaro GD, Massaro D. 1996. Postnatal treatment with retinoic acid increases the number of pulmonary alveoli in rats. *Am. J. Physiol.* 270:L305–10

69. Gribetz I, Frank NR, Avery ME. 1959. Static volume-pressure relations of excised lungs of infants with hyaline membrane disease, newborn and still-born infants. *J. Clin. Invest.* 38:2168–75

70. Jackson JC, Standaert TA, Truog WE, Murphy JH, Palmer S, et al. 1985. Changes in lung volume and deflation stability in hyaline membrane disease. *J. Appl. Physiol.* 59:1783–89

71. Vilstrup CT, Björklund LJ, Werner O, Larsson A. 1996. Lung volumes and pressure-volume relations of the respiratory system in small ventilated neonates with severe respiratory distress syndrome. *Pediatr. Res.* 39:127–33

72. Elkady T, Jobe AH. 1987. Corticosteroids and surfactant increase lung volumes and decrease rupture pressures of preterm rabbit lungs. *J. Appl. Physiol.* 63:1616–21

73. Jobe AH. 1993. Pulmonary surfactant therapy. *N. Engl. J. Med.* 328:861–68

74. Davis AJ, Jobe AH, Häfner D, Ikegami M. 1998. Lung function in premature lambs and rabbits treated with a recombinant SP-C surfactant. *Am. J. Respir. Crit. Care Med.* 157:553–59

75. Goldsmith LS, Greenspan JS, Rubinstein SD, Wolfson MR, Shaffer TH. 1991. Immediate improvement in lung volume after exogenous surfactant: alveolar recruitment versus increased distention. *J. Pediatr.* 119:424–28

76. Jobe AH. 1998. Surfactant and mechanical ventilation. In *Physiological Basis of Ventilatory Support,* ed. JJ Marini, AS Slutsky, pp. 209–30. New York: Marcel Dekker

77. Dreyfuss D, Saumon G. 1998. Ventilator-induced lung injury. *Am. J. Respir. Crit. Care Med.* 157:294–323

78. Hernandez LA, Peevy KJ, Moise AA, Parker JC. 1989. Chest wall restriction limits high airway pressure-induced lung injury in young rabbits. *J. Appl. Physiol.* 66:2364–68

79. Tremblay L, Valenza F, Ribeiro SP, Li J, Slutsky AS. 1997. Injurious ventilatory strategies increase cytokines and c-fos m-RNA expression in an isolated rat lung mode. *J. Clin. Invest.* 99:944–52

80. Berg JT, Fu Z, Breen EC, Tran H, Mathieu-Costello O, West JB. 1997. High lung inflation increases mRNA levels of ECM components and growth factors in lung parenchyma. *J. Appl. Physiol.* 83:120–28

81. Muscedere JG, Mullen JBM, Gan K, Slutsky AS. 1994. Tidal ventilation at low airway pressures can augment lung

injury. *Am. J. Respir. Crit. Care Med.* 149:1327–34

82. Froese AB, McCullouch PR, Sugiura M, Vaclavik S, Possmayer F, Moller F. 1993. Optimizing alveolar expansion prolongs the effectiveness of exogenous surfactant therapy in the adult rabbit. *Am. Rev. Respir. Dis.* 148:569–77

83. Carlton DP, Albertine KH, Cho SC, Lont M, Bland RD. 1997. Role of neutrophils in lung vascular injury and edema after premature birth in lambs. *J. Appl. Physiol.* 83:1307–17

84. Jobe AH, Ikegami M. 1998. Mechanisms initiating lung injury in the preterm. *Early Hum. Dev.* 53:81–94

85. Vyas H, Field D, Milner AD, Hopkin IE. 1986. Determinants of the first inspiratory volume and functional residual capacity at birth. *Pediatr. Pulmonol.* 2:189–93

86. Vyas H, Milner AD, Hopkin IE, Boon AW. 1981. Physiologic responses to prolonged and slow-rise inflation in the resuscitation of the asphyxiated newborn infant. *J. Pediatr.* 99:635–39

87. Kobayashi T, Shido A, Nitta K, Inui S, Ganzuka M, Robertson B. 1990. The critical concentration of surfactant in fetal lung liquid at birth. *Respir. Physiol.* 80:181–92

88. Faridy EE. 1987. Air opening pressure in fetal lungs. *Respir. Physiol.* 68:293–300

89. Bjorklund LL, Ingimarsson J, Curstedt T, John J, Robertson B, et al. 1997. Manual ventilation with a few large breaths at birth compromises the therapeutic effect of subsequent surfactant replacement in immature lambs. *Pediatr. Res.* 42:348–55

90. Wada K, Jobe AH, Ikegami M. 1997. Tidal volume effects on surfactant treatment responses with the initiation of ventilation in preterm lambs. *J. Appl. Physiol.* 83:1054–61

91. Ogden BE, Murphy S, Saunders GC, Johnson JD. 1983. Lung lavage of newborns with respiratory distress syndrome. *Chest* 83S:31–33

92. Bancalari E. 1997. Neonatal chronic lung disease. In *Neonatal-Perinatal Medicine,* ed. AA Fanaroff, RJ Martin, pp. 1074–89. St. Louis: Mosby

93. Jones CA, Cayabyab RG, Kwong KYC, Stotts C, Wong B, et al. 1996. Undetectable interleukin (IL)-10 and persistent IL-8 expression early in hyaline membrane disease: a possible development basis for the predisposition to chronic lung inflammation in preterm newborns. *Pediatr. Res.* 39:966–75

94. Hallman M, Merritt TA, Akino T, Bry K. 1991. Surfactant protein-A, phosphatidylcholine, and surfactant inhibitors in epithelial lining fluid—correlation with surface activity, severity of respiratory distress syndrome, and outcome in small premature infants. *Am. Rev. Respir. Dis.* 144:1376–84

95. King RJ, Coalson JJ, Delemos RA, Gerstmann DR, Seidner SR. 1995. Surfactant protein-A deficiency in a primate model of bronchopulmonary dysplasia. *Am. J. Respir. Crit. Care Med.* 151:1989–97

96. Seidner SR, Jobe AH, Coalson JJ, Ikegami M. 1998. Abnormal surfactant metabolism and function in preterm ventilated baboons. *Am. J. Respir. Crit. Care Med.* 158:1982–89

97. Ikegami M, Ueda T, Hull W, Whitsett JA, Mulligan RC, et al. 1996. Surfactant metabolism in transgenic mice after granulocyte macrophage-colony stimulating factor ablation. *Am. J. Physiol.* 270:L650–58

98. Ikegami M, Chroneos Z, Whitsett JA, Jobe AH. 1999. Interleukin-4 alters surfactant saturated phosphatidylcholine metabolism. *Am. J. Respir. Crit. Care Med.* 159:A895

Annu. Rev. Physiol. 2000. 62:847–74

VENTILATORY RESPONSES TO CHANGES IN TEMPERATURE IN MAMMALS AND OTHER VERTEBRATES

Jacopo P. Mortola[1] and Peter B. Frappell[2]

[1]*Department of Physiology, McGill University, Montreal, Quebec H3G 1Y6, Canada, e-mail: jacopo@med.mcgill.ca;* [2]*Department of Zoology, La Trobe University, Bundoora, Victoria 3083, Australia, e-mail: p.frappell@zoo.latrobe.edu.au*

Key Words body temperature, control of breathing, hyperthermia, hypothermia, respiration

■ **Abstract** This article reviews the relationship between pulmonary ventilation ($\dot{V}E$) and metabolic rate (oxygen consumption) during changes in ambient temperature. The main focus is on mammals, although for comparative purposes the $\dot{V}E$ responses of ectothermic vertebrates are also discussed. First, the effects of temperature on pulmonary mechanics, chemoreceptors, and airway receptors are summarized. Then we review the main $\dot{V}E$ responses to cold and warm stimuli and their interaction with exercise, hypoxia, or hypercapnia. In these cases, mammals attempt to maintain both oxygenation and body temperature, although conflicts can arise because of the respiratory heat loss associated with the increase in ventilation. Finally, we consider the $\dot{V}E$ responses of mammals when body temperature changes, as during torpor, fever, sleep, and hypothermia. In ectotherms, during changes in temperature, $\dot{V}E$ control becomes part of a general strategy to maintain constant relative alkalinity and ensure a constancy of pH-dependent protein functions (alphastat regulation). In mammals on the other hand, $\dot{V}E$ control is aimed to balance metabolic needs with homeothermy. Therefore, alphastat regulation in mammals seems to have a low priority, and it may be adopted only in exceptional cases.

INTRODUCTION

The maintenance of adequate tissue oxygenation and body temperature (Tb) is among the highest priorities for survival. The corresponding regulatory systems occasionally operate synergistically, but in other cases their priorities conflict. In fact, breathing and thermal regulation are linked in a complex and dynamically operating matrix, in which needs for gas transport and protection of Tb continuously balance against the needs for water conservation and acid-base control. In this article we focus on the relationship between pulmonary ventilation ($\dot{V}e$) and

0066–4278/00/0315–0847$12.00

metabolic rate in endotherms, specifically mammals, although for comparative purposes the ventilatory responses of ectothermic vertebrates are also considered.

TERMINOLOGY AND DEFINITIONS

Heat is a manifestation of the energy resulting from molecular agitation, and temperature (T) is a measure of this energy. Because the sun is the primary source of heat, ambient temperatures (Ta) vary greatly with altitude and latitude. At the same geographical location, seasonal and daily changes in T can be very large and different between water and air, owing to the difference in heat capacitance between these two media. Chemical reactions depend on kinetic energy, which determines the frequency of collision of the particles, and these reactions increase 2 to 3% for every 1°C increase in T. Enzymatic reactions follow a similar pattern, often quantified by the Q_{10} (Arrhenius) factor, which expresses the rise in reaction velocity for a 10°C increase in T,

$$Q_{10} = (A'/A'')^{[10/(T' - T'')]} \qquad 1.$$

where A' and A'' are the enzymatic activities or reaction velocities at the corresponding temperatures T' and T''. Hence, on first approximation, the higher the T, the greater the enzymatic functions of the cell, including its oxygen consumption ($\dot{V}o_2$). However, the T range compatible with animal life is only a tiny fraction of Ta. Protein and nucleic acid denaturation and lipid melting or solidification are the ultimate irreversible effects of, respectively, low and high Ta, although protein homologs exhibit important variations in thermal sensitivities (1). Even before these molecular alterations occur, modifications in membrane permeability and enzyme inactivation can be incompatible with cellular survival. At the organ and systemic level, T tolerance is further reduced because the most sensitive cells, for example neuronal cells, dictate the survival of the whole organism; hence, failure of the systems requiring neural control can cause death of the whole organism at T values that would be tolerable at the cellular or molecular level. Animal life in its more evolved forms is therefore restricted to a narrow fraction of Ta, usually between 5 and 43°C, optimally between 30 and 41°C.

The fact that Ta spans a range several orders of magnitude larger than that compatible with most forms of life poses a fundamental problem for survival. Its solution is offered by thermoregulation, a cohort of mechanisms oriented to limit the oscillations in Tb against changes in Ta. Absence of thermoregulation can occur in only a few conditions of steady Ta. Embryos and fetuses in utero and marsupials within the pouch can count on maternal thermoregulation for the protection of their own Tb. A similar, albeit not as stable, situation occurs before hatching during embryonic development in incubated eggs.

Thermal control by behavioral means (behavioral thermoregulation) is the most common mechanism of Tb control, and all forms of animal life adopt it to various degrees and in very disparate versions, whether to accumulate heat (sun basking of lizards) or disperse it (ear flapping of elephants). In endotherms, heat is endogenously produced, with shivering—the activation of skeletal muscles for the purpose of producing heat—and nonshivering thermogenesis by activation mostly of the brown adipose tissue. As Ta increases and approaches thermoneutrality,[1] heat production decreases, and heat dissipation mechanisms (e.g. peripheral vasodilatation and sweating) become operational; $\dot{V}E$ can then become an important contributor to heat loss by evaporation. Most mammals and birds are homeotherms that thermoregulate at Tb values of 36–38°C and 39–41°C, respectively. Some mammals (monotremes and marsupials) thermoregulate at lower Tb values, commonly between 31 and 34°C. In conformity with previous usage, the term hyperpnea refers to an absolute increase in $\dot{V}E$, whereas the term hyperventilation indicates an increase in alveolar ventilation $\dot{V}A$ relative to metabolic rate; that is, a drop in the alveolar partial pressure of CO_2 (PCO_2)[2] regardless of the absolute $\dot{V}E$ level.

TEMPERATURE AND THE RESPIRATORY SYSTEM

Respiratory Mechanics

The effects of T on the mechanical properties of the respiratory system are important for the interpretation of $\dot{V}E$ responses, because, for any given neural output, tidal volume depends on respiratory system compliance and resistance.

Over the T range of 15 to 45°C (2–4), at low T the pressure [P (x-axis)]-volume [V (y-axis)] curve of the lung is displaced to the right, although the changes are not large. At lower T (4°C), the P-V curve is clearly displaced to the right, with a substantial decrease in lung compliance (5). The alterations in the P-V curve are caused more by modifications in the properties of the surfactant than alterations in the properties of the lung tissue, with possible effects on the process of recruitment and derecruitment of the alveoli during inflation and deflation (6).

In the adult sheep, measurements in situ have indicated a drop in pulmonary compliance at T = 15 and 25°C, which is more evident than in isolated lungs (7). In squirrels during hibernation at Tb = 8°C, in comparison with their active periods, the lung P-V was displaced to the right, with lower compliance. Milsom & Reid (8) also made measurements of respiratory work during artificial ventilation and found that, in hibernating squirrels, it was ~50% higher than during the off-hibernation period. They pointed out that the difference in respiratory work

---

[1]Thermoneurality = Ta range over which Tb is constant with minimal $\dot{V}O_2$ in normoxia.
[2]Alveolar PCO_2 = $(\dot{V}CO_2/\dot{V}A) \cdot Pb$, where Pb = dry barometric P; $\dot{V}CO_2$ = CO_2 production.

corresponded to a fourfold change if considered in relation to the $\dot{V}O_2$ of the animal.

Because of the importance of airway cooling in bronchoconstriction and the pathophysiology of asthma, many studies have considered the effects of changes in Ta on airway resistance. When Ta is very low, some increase in airway resistance can occur even in normal subjects when breathing at high $\dot{V}E$ levels (9). In most circumstances, however, in healthy individuals breathing air even at subfreezing temperatures, airway resistance does not appreciably increase (10), owing to the warming of the inspired air in its passage through the upper airways. Cooling of the skin could also increase bronchomotor tone (10). The effects on airway resistance could therefore be more dramatic when the whole body, rather than just the airways, is challenged by cold. No information is available on the effects of changes in Tb on the resistive properties of the lung tissue and chest wall.

Chemoreceptors

As for other neural endings and sensors, carotid afferent activity increases with T, whereas cooling reduces the membrane potential and the firing rate (11–14). Although less studied, the activity of the aortic chemoreceptors is also T dependent, with a Q_{10} of ~2.5 (15), and similar to that of the carotid afferents (16).

The T sensitivity of the carotid body is consistent with that of the chemoreceptors of the avian lungs (17) and of the CO_2-sensitive intrapulmonary receptors of ectothermic vertebrates (18–20). The important difference, however, is that CO_2 stimulates the activity of the mammalian peripheral chemoreceptors, whereas it depresses that of the intrapulmonary chemoreceptors of birds (21) or other vertebrates. This implies that, during hyperthermic hyperventilation, the hypocapnia in mammals blunts the T effects on the peripheral activation (22), whereas in other vertebrates it can act synergistically, further increasing the $\dot{V}E$ responses to chemical stimuli (23–25).

Hyperoxia decreases the activity of the carotid bodies; hence the magnitude of the $\dot{V}E$ drop with a few breaths of O_2 is often taken as a functional index of the activity of these receptors (26, 27). Consistently with the electrophysiological data, hyperoxia has been found to decrease inspiratory activity more at 40°C than at 35 to 37°C (28, 29).

Airway Receptors and Reflexes

Lowering Tb decreases the vagal afferent activity from the lungs. The pulmonary stretch receptors (PSR) and rapidly adapting receptors are more T sensitive than the nonmyelinated pulmonary C fibers (30). Changes in PSR activity with T have been observed with both in vivo and in vitro preparations (31, 32). At ~7°C, that is the Tb of some hibernating mammals, the activity of PSRs and rapidly adapting receptors is almost entirely abolished, whereas ~40% of C fibers are still active (30).

T-related changes in PSR activity have also been observed in ectotherms. Raising Tb from 20°C to 30°C increased PSR activity in garter snakes and alligators (19, 20). Because the Q_{10} of PSR ($Q_{10} \sim 2$) is less than that of the intrapulmonary CO_2-sensitive receptors ($Q_{10} \sim 3$), as Tb increases the CO_2 receptors assume progressively more importance in the control of breathing. The T sensitivity of the rapidly adapting receptors was difficult to quantify because of their erratic and unpredictable firing behavior (20).

In adult anesthetized animals, a rise in Tb increased the reflex expiratory prolongation during lung inflation and decreased the volume required to terminate inspiration (33). Similarly, in conscious newborn rats, an increase in Tb increased the inhibition of $\dot{V}E$ promoted by lung inflation (Hering-Breuer inspiration-inhibitory and expiration-promoting reflex), and the opposite occurred when Tb was lowered by cold (34). Although all of these results are consistent with the response pattern of PSRs to changes in T, other mechanisms could also play a role. For example, hyperthermia is thought to increase the central effectiveness of vagal inhibitory inputs (35–37), and Tb-induced changes in metabolic rate could also play an important role in the strength of the Hering-Breuer reflex (34, 38).

Many receptors of the upper airways, specifically of the laryngeal region, are T sensitive (39, 40) and could be involved in the regulation of breathing. Often, their reflex effects inhibit breathing, especially in newborns (41, 42). However, most studies of upper-airway reflexes are performed on anesthetized subjects, and it is difficult to apply the results to conscious animals. If these receptors and their reflex responses were as important as some experiments on subjects under anesthesia suggest, one would expect removal of the superior laryngeal nerves to have major consequences on breathing. However, the breathing pattern of conscious adult rats or newborn kittens with chronic section of the superior laryngeal nerves differed minimally from that of intact animals (43, 44).

THERMOREGULATORY ROLE OF THE RESPIRATORY SYSTEM

Upper Airways

The involvement of breathing in thermoregulation occurs at multiple sites. The upper-airway passages have long been recognized for their important role both in heating and humidifying the inspired air and in recovering heat and water during expiration (45). These functions occur not only in mammals but also in birds, lizards, and probably other vertebrates. In mammals the nasal turbinates are the main upper-airway structures participating in the control of heat and water balance (46). Earlier it was thought that, in large species, nasal heat exchange and water recovery are of minor importance because of the relatively small heat exchange area compared with the sizes of the passages. This may be so in humans

(47); in other large mammals, nasal exchange does provide an important contribution to heat and water balance (48).

In some species, the nasal passages are used to control brain T independently of Tb, because of a special circulatory counter-current arrangement, the "carotid arterial rete mirable." Experiments in the natural environment on the wildebeest and the springbok have questioned the real function of the selective control of brain T. In fact it was noticed that, contrary to routine daily life, during very severe heat stress, brain T measurements were almost 42°C and not lower than Tb. Hence, it has been argued (49) that the uncoupling of brain T from Tb may not be desirable during extreme heat because the lower brain T would impede full manifestation of panting and respiratory evaporation. Therefore, in severe heat, brain T would be allowed to rise with Tb to use heat dissipation mechanisms to their fullest capabilities. Some control of brain T may apply to a larger number of mammalian species than previously thought (50), and indirect evidence has also been provided for humans (51).

Pulmonary Ventilation

Because the lungs are the only route for gas exchange, one may expect that the changes in $\dot{V}E$ with Ta may be close to those of $\dot{V}O_2$. The lungs, however, are also a large wet surface prone to heat loss by evaporation. Hence, values of $\dot{V}E$ larger or smaller than those strictly required by metabolic demands may be desirable, respectively, in hot or cold conditions. The conflict between gas exchange and heat and water control increases during exercise or hypoxia. Some of these factors are considered in more detail below.

CHANGES IN AMBIENT TEMPERATURE

Cold Exposure

In the cold, despite peripheral vasoconstriction, heat loss increases because of the larger thermal gradient between skin and environment. Small animals have larger heat losses than larger species because of their greater surface-to-volume ratio, and they require greater metabolic responses to cold (52). Behavioral thermogenesis and nonshivering thermogenesis are immediate responses to a drop in Ta, whereas shivering is initiated by stronger stimuli. Anesthesia severely impairs all forms of thermoregulation (53), and, in anesthetized animals, shivering often begins only when Tb is already falling (54).

The increase in $\dot{V}O_2$ in the cold could be met by an increase in $\dot{V}E$, pulmonary extraction, or both, as is apparent from an application of the Fick equation,

$$\dot{V}O_2 = (\dot{V}E \cdot O_2I) \cdot [(O_2I - O_2E)/O_2I] \qquad 2.$$

where O_2I and O_2E are, respectively, the inspired and expired O_2 concentrations. Many species including humans accommodate the cold-induced increase in $\dot{V}O_2$ with a proportional increase in $\dot{V}E$ (53, 55, 56). Among marsupials, the kowaris and, possibly, the Tasmanian devil are other examples (57, 58). Also some avian species increase $\dot{V}E$ in proportion to $\dot{V}O_2$ (59). In all of these cases, $\dot{V}E/\dot{V}O_2$ and the O_2 extraction coefficient remain as in normothermia. In other species, however, like the pig and a neotropical bat (60, 61), $\dot{V}E$ increases less than $\dot{V}O_2$, and the limitations in pulmonary convection are compensated for by an increase in pulmonary extraction. At the opposite end are some small arctic mammals, like the tundra vole and the lemming, in which the efficiency of O_2 extraction is drastically reduced in the cold to the point that their $\dot{V}E$ increases twice as much as their $\dot{V}O_2$ (52, 62) (Figure 1). Usually in the cold, both tidal volume and breathing rate contribute to the increases in $\dot{V}E$.

Why some species respond to the cold-induced metabolic demands by increasing pulmonary convection and others respond by increasing pulmonary extraction is not clear, because there are advantages in either strategy. An increase in $\dot{V}E$ proportional to $\dot{V}O_2$, especially if contributed by increases in tidal volume, is likely to maintain the proportionality between metabolic rate and alveolar ventilation and therefore the constancy of alveolar blood gases. On the other hand, the hyperpnea favors heat loss, because the T of the expired air is invariably higher than Ta, and this loss can become a substantial fraction of the total heat production (52, 60).

Interaction with Exercise   In the cold, exercise can be considered a form of behavioral thermogenic response. Indeed, during vigorous muscle contraction, the level of metabolic rate does not vary with Ta, indicating that the heat generated by the exercising muscles is sufficient to compensate for the heat loss to the cold. In humans, for example, the level of $\dot{V}E$ was found to be proportional to that of $\dot{V}O_2$, whether the increase in $\dot{V}O_2$ was determined by cold, muscle exercise, or any combination of the two (63). This emphasizes the importance of the $\dot{V}O_2$ level per se, regardless of the causes, in determining the magnitude of the hyperpnea.

Interaction with Hypercapnia or Hypoxia   In conscious dogs during hypercapnia, cold exposure increased $\dot{V}O_2$ more than it increased $\dot{V}E$. Hence, in the cold the hypercapnic dogs were hypoventilating in comparison with their response in the warm state, a result interpreted as an attempt to conserve heat (64). Similar results were obtained in hypercapnic rats (65, 66), which were more acidotic and had higher arterial P_{CO_2} in cold than in warm conditions (67). On the other hand, studies in rabbits and humans gave different results, with larger $\dot{V}E$ responses to CO_2 in the cold (68, 69).

In adults of many species hypercapnia tends to lower Tb, especially in the cold, and humans are no exception (68, 70). This is attributable to the greater heat dissipation that accompanies the hyperpnea and the CO_2-mediated peripheral vasodilatation.

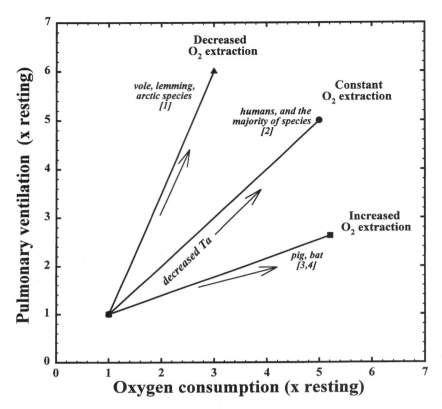

Figure 1 Semi-schematic representation of the changes in oxygen consumption and pulmonary ventilation in response to a cold stimulus. Both variables are represented as multiples of the resting values. With the increase in thermogenesis, in the majority of species including humans, pulmonary ventilation increases approximately in proportion to oxygen consumption. In some species, exemplified by some arctic mammals, O_2 extraction decreases and pulmonary ventilation increases out of proportion with oxygen consumption (cf Equation 2). At the opposite end are species that increase O_2 extraction in the cold, exemplified by pigs and bats, and therefore do not need to increase pulmonary ventilation as much as do other species. *[1]* = reference 62; *[2]*, 63; *[3]*, 61; *[4]*, 60.

During hypoxia, $\dot{V}E$ increases substantially less in cold than in warm conditions (71, 72). In fact, in some cases in the cold, $\dot{V}E$ during hypoxia may be similar to or even below the normoxic value (73, 74). The interpretation of these responses must take into account that hypoxia lowers metabolic rate and particularly that component of $\dot{V}O_2$ related to thermogenesis (53). When the response to hypoxia is evaluated from the change in $\dot{V}E/\dot{V}O_2$ or decrease in arterial P_{CO_2}, instead of simply from the degree of hyperpnea, the response to cold is closer to that observed in warm conditions (71, 73). The remaining small, yet consistent difference could be attributed to many causes. The decrease in Tb, a common occurrence during the association of cold and hypoxia especially in small species, could decrease the hyperventilation. Indeed, in rats breathing hypoxic-hypercapnic gases, $\dot{V}E/\dot{V}O_2$ was less in cold than in warm conditions, but the values became similar when Tb was controlled by an abdominal heat exchanger (66). It is also likely that, in the cold during hypoxia, as mentioned earlier for hypercapnia, the importance of protecting tissue oxygenation is balanced against the necessity of minimizing heat loss, which in turn limits the increase in $\dot{V}E$.

Heat Exposure

As Ta increases above thermoneutrality and the Tb-Ta difference decreases, the effectiveness of radiation, convection, and conduction for thermolysis is reduced. Water evaporation is therefore the primary means of heat loss. In fact, in birds and many mammals, which unlike humans have no sweat glands, evaporation via the respiratory tract is the only mechanism of heat dissipation. $\dot{V}E$ favors evaporation from the respiratory surfaces just like a breeze favors evaporation from the skin, with the advantage that $\dot{V}E$ can be controlled by the animal itself.

The breathing pattern is usually rapid and shallow (thermal polypnea or panting), with the obvious goal of favoring heat loss without major disturbances to alveolar ventilation ($\dot{V}A$). In birds, this is accompanied by gular flutter—rapid vibration of the throat region (75). As mentioned earlier for the shivering response to cold, panting also occurs before any change in Tb unless the animal is anesthetized (75). Changes in breathing pattern offer enormous capabilities for increases in $\dot{V}E$ without altering $\dot{V}A$ (Figure 2). In addition, the physiological dead space can increase (76), further enhancing the possibility of using $\dot{V}E$ for heat dissipation without disturbing $\dot{V}A$ (Figure 2). Nevertheless, some hypocapnia can develop during heat exposure, both in mammals and in birds [e.g. dogs (77) and pigeons (78)], indicating some degree of true hyperventilation. This is the case even in the ox, which is one of the species most capable of increasing dead-space ventilation without affecting $\dot{V}A$ (79). With very severe heat stress, the breathing pattern may reverse from rapid and shallow to deep and slow (75), and at this point the hyperventilation is very marked with severe respiratory alkalosis (79–81). Even at these high levels of $\dot{V}E$, the cost of breathing is small and smaller than the cost required by hypercapnic hyperventilation (82). In fact, for the same $\dot{V}E$ with a shallow and fast pattern, the elastic (volume-related) work is reduced more than the airflow-resistive (frequency-dependent) work is increased. Furthermore, during panting, breathing rate can be close to the resonant frequency of the respiratory system (83) as the inertial (acceleration-dependent) and elastic (volume-dependent) pressures cancel out because they are equal in magnitude and opposite in phase. Therefore, only the airflow-dependent resistive pressure determines the work of breathing.

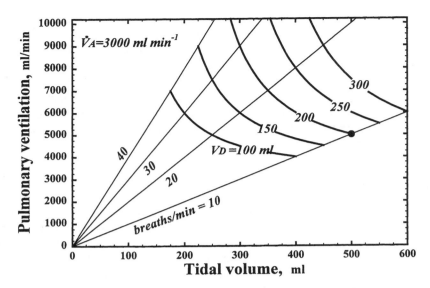

Figure 2 Effects of changes in breathing pattern or dead space (V_D) on pulmonary ventilation, with an alveolar ventilation ($\dot{V}A$) constant at 3000 ml/min. Lines radiating from the origin are isofrequency lines. Isopleths indicate constant V_D. Filled circle, Tidal volume (V_T), 500 ml; breathing rate (breaths/min), 10 ; V_D, 200 ml; pulmonary ventilation ($\dot{V}E$), 5000 ml/min. For any given V_D, as the pattern becomes shallower and faster, pulmonary ventilation can increase greatly while maintaining alveolar ventilation constant, and the $\dot{V}E$-$\dot{V}A$ difference increases with the V_D. Hence, a very rapid and shallow breathing pattern with a large physiological V_D has the highest potential for heat dissipation with minimal disturbance to the alveolar gases.

Interaction with Exercise   Exercise, especially if prolonged, can increase Tb even if performed at a comfortable Ta. The increase in Tb could stimulate $\dot{V}E$ (84, 85), but it is probably of minor importance in determining the hyperpnea during exercise (86). During exercise in the heat, $\dot{V}E$ increases out of proportion to $\dot{V}o_2$. However, the breathing pattern tends to become rapid and shallow as it does in the heat at rest (87), which implies that the hyperventilation is not as marked as measurements of $\dot{V}E$ would suggest. Indeed, this is another example of the role of the breathing pattern in maximizing respiratory heat dissipation without major disturbances in alveolar gas homeostasis.

Interaction with Hypercapnia or Hypoxia   Some degree of hyperventilation, and therefore of hypocapnia, during heat stress could favor thermal polypnea. In fact, CO_2 has an inhibitory effect on panting, promoting a deeper and slower breathing pattern (69, 88–90). The mechanisms for the action of CO_2 on thermal polypnea are not clear. One possibility is that the vasodilating action of CO_2 on the cerebral vasculature increases brain blood flow, therefore reducing brain T and the stimulus for the central thermoreceptors.

Hypoxia, on the other hand, in conscious animals facilitates thermal polypnea, contrary to what was previously believed from studies on anesthetized subjects. The synergistic action of hypoxia and heat on breathing patterns occurs centrally, and it is not mediated by peripheral chemoreceptors (81, 91). In fact, stimulation of the peripheral chemoreceptors appears to inhibit, rather than enhance, thermal polypnea (92) and could be another possible mechanism for the inhibitory action of CO_2 on panting.

CHANGES IN BODY TEMPERATURE IN ECTOTHERMS

Ectothermic vertebrates comprise many species of different classes (fish, amphibian, and reptile) characterized by a labile Tb closely influenced by Ta and by the possibility of using both air and water as media for the exchange of respiratory gases. Differences in the respiratory media have implications for breathing and its response to changes in T (93, 94).

In ectotherms, as in endotherms, $\dot{V}E$ is regulated mainly to balance the O_2 demands with the needs for CO_2 elimination, the latter within the general context of acid-base regulation. In both air and water breathers, with rising T, $\dot{V}O_2$ increases [Q_{10} (Equation 1)] and the O_2 affinity of hemoglobin (Hb) decreases. Most water breathers, despite the scarcity of O_2 and the energetic cost of $\dot{V}E$ in aquatic environments, maintain a similar $\dot{V}E$-metabolic rate ratio at various T values. In contrast, with rising T, air-breathing ectotherms are characterized by nonproportional increases in $\dot{V}E$ and metabolic rate; that is, the Q_{10} for $\dot{V}E$ is lower than that for metabolic rate, such that $\dot{V}E/\dot{V}O_2$ declines (25). With a few exceptions, most measurements indicate that, in ectotherms, blood pH changes inversely with T; however, in air breathers the arterial partial pressure of O_2 (PO_2) and the PCO_2 vary in proportion with T, whereas, in water breathers, blood gases remain stable (95, 96). The decline in $\dot{V}E$ versus metabolic rate with increasing T in air breathers is one aspect of control mechanisms oriented toward the protection of protein function, as further discussed below.

Acid-Base Regulation in Air and Water Breathers

The pH of the blood is related to the transport of CO_2 as indicated by the Henderson-Hasselbalch equation:

$$pH = pK' + \log \{[HCO_3^-]/(\beta CO_2 \cdot PaCO_2)\} \qquad 3.$$

where pK' is the dissociation constant of the bicarbonate system, $PaCO_2$ is the arterial PCO_2, βCO_2 is the capacitance coefficient for CO_2, and [HCO_3^-] represents the bicarbonate ion concentration within the plasma. At constant CO_2 content, T-

induced changes in blood pH of ectotherms are parallel to the changes in pH of neutral water ($\cong 0.016$ U/°C); that is, a constant ratio between $[OH^-]$ and $[H^+]$ (or constant relative alkalinity) is maintained with changes in T (97). To ensure a constancy of pH-dependent properties of proteins, in particular enzyme function, ectotherms also maintain a constant pH-pK difference with imidazole (IM) derivatives of the amino acid histidine (95, 98); that is, they maintain a constant fractional dissociation ratio (alpha) for IM (alphastat regulation). IM, the most concentrated blood buffer, possesses a pK (pK_{IM}) within the range of intra- and extracellular pH values and varies with T with a coefficient similar to the pH of the blood ($dpK_{IM}/dT \cong 0.017$ U/°C). The regulatory mechanisms and specifically the sensors at the basis of alphastat regulation have yet to be identified. One view is that changes in intra- or extracellular pH could be sensed by histidines within the membrane of a chemoreceptor protein involved in pH regulation (99). It has further been suggested that changes in pK_{IM}, in the absence of changes in $[H^+]$, could also be the mechanism activating a chemoreceptor (100).

The $[HCO_3^-]/(\beta CO_2 \cdot Paco_2)$ of Equation 3 characterizes the bicarbonate buffer system, which represents the blood CO_2 stores of the animal. Because the pK$'$ of the bicarbonate system (more precisely carbonic acid) is almost T independent ($dpK'/dT \cong 0.005$ U/°C) (101), as T changes, constancy in pH-pK_{IM} can be achieved by control of either the denominator ($\beta CO_2 \cdot Paco_2$) or the numerator ($[HCO_3^-]$). In reptiles, alterations in $\dot{V}E$ compared with metabolic rate, along with changes in T, allow rapid changes in $Paco_2$. Numerous examples can be found to support the concept that reptiles (turtles, snakes, lizards, and crocodilians) adjust $\dot{V}E$ to achieve alphastat regulation (25, 102–107). Some exceptions, however, do occur. Wood et al (108) found that in the African savanna monitor lizard, the ratio between $\dot{V}E$ and carbon dioxide productin ($\dot{V}CO_2$) and arterial pH remained independent of T within the normally encountered physiological range. Although a rise in $Paco_2$ with T was still observed, attributable to an enlargement of dead space, this was compensated for by alterations in $[HCO_3^-]$. Indeed, there is increasing evidence that acid-base adjustments with changes in T are achieved not solely by respiratory mechanisms in reptiles. Several reptiles, including the black racer snake, yellow-eared slider, and sea turtles, also use relatively slow ion exchange (metabolic) mechanisms to adjust the acid-base status (106, 109–111). For black racer snakes, a fall in Tb initially resulted in an increase in $\dot{V}E/\dot{V}CO_2$, a lowering of $Paco_2$, and an elevation in plasma pH. With time, plasma $[HCO_3^-]$ rose, $\dot{V}E/\dot{V}CO_2$ declined, and $Paco_2$ increased with only a small decrease in pH. This suggests that the drop in Tb resulted in a metabolic acidosis initially compensated for by the respiratory system because of the time required for the slow adjustment of $[HCO_3^-]$ (106).

Whereas most reptiles rely almost exclusively on the lungs for elimination of CO_2, amphibians eliminate substantial amounts of CO_2 via the skin (112). In the predominantly skin-breathing salamander, the acid-base response to increasing T is in perfect agreement with alphastat regulation ($dpH/dT \cong 0.016$ U/°C), and this agreement is caused exclusively by the passive elevation in $Paco_2$ with the increase in metabolic rate (113). In fact, the amount eliminated across the skin alters little with T. The minimal effect of T on skin exchange implies that, with increasing T, cutaneous CO_2 loss becomes a lower fraction of the total CO_2 exchange, as in bullfrogs and toads (114–116). Therefore, with the increase in T as the metabolic rate rises, alveolar P_{CO_2} increases (116). In addition, $\dot{V}_E$ becomes more effective in controlling Pa_{CO_2}, and lower changes in $\dot{V}_E$ are required for acid-base regulation. In amphibians with lungs, as T increases, the gradual shift in emphasis from cutaneous to pulmonary CO_2 exchange and rise in Pa_{CO_2} are reflected by an increase in the respiratory exchange ratio (RER $= \dot{V}_{CO_2}/\dot{V}_{O_2}$) (116, 117). Increases in RER with warming have also been observed in turtles, lizards, snakes, and crocodilians (106). During warming or cooling, the time course of the changes in CO_2 content parallels the changes in RER and takes considerably longer than the time required for Tb to adjust. This suggests that physiological adjustments related to acid-base regulation continue after the change in Tb (106, 109, 117). A large number of air-breathing ectotherms vary RER with T, and these changes probably reflect a combination of rapid (respiratory) and slow (metabolic) mechanisms to maintain acid-base regulation.

In water breathers, because of the low O_2 content of water, $\dot{V}_E/\dot{V}_{O_2}$ is high. Further, because the β_{CO_2} in water is 30-fold higher than the O_2 coefficient (β_{O_2})[3], the expired-inspired difference in P_{CO_2} is 1/30th of the inspired-expired P_{O_2} difference, that is only 1–2 mm Hg. Hence, the P_{CO_2} is extremely low in the water surrounding the gills, blood, and tissues (93, 118). This implies that, in water breathers, changes in $\dot{V}_E$ have minimal impact on P_{CO_2}, effectively uncoupling $\dot{V}_E$ from acid-base control. Hence, one would expect that, in water breathers with changes in T, adjustments of pH are achieved mostly by changes in $[HCO_3^-]$ rather than changes in $\dot{V}_E$. Indeed, in teleost fish, pH commonly falls with rising T, the average dpH/dT being 0.013 U/°C (119) and within the range of values reported for air-breathing ectotherms. In the carp and pacu, on the other hand, acute T increases were accompanied by significant increases in Pa_{CO_2}, whereas $[HCO_3^-]$ remained constant (120, 121), a pattern of alphastat regulation more reminiscent of air-breathing than water-breathing ectotherms.

The adjustment of $[HCO_3^-]$ is a slow process, given the volume and buffer capacity of the intracellular compartment compared with that of the extracellular systems, and probably involves manipulation of active ion exchange across com0partment boundaries (96, 122, 123). Several species of fish appear not to maintain a constant CO_2 content, and some alter both Pa_{CO_2} and CO_2 content (96, 101, 122–124). In the skipjack tuna the effect of T change on in vitro pH when blood P_{CO_2} was held constant (-0.013 U/°C) was only slightly different from that found under conditions of constant CO_2 content (-0.016 U/°C) (101). The decrease in pH under constant P_{CO_2} conditions was accompanied by a large loss

---

[3]Note that the ratio between β_{CO_2} and β_{CO_2} decreases with increasing T, as an increase in T lowers the capacitance for CO_2 more than for O_2.

of CO_2 from the system. Perry et al (101) suggested that the CO_2 loss is determined by a dissociation of Hb, which allows H^+ ions to combine with HCO_3^-, permitting HCO_3^- to be removed from the system as gaseous CO_2. Such a passive mechanism offers the advantage of rapid changes in pH compared with a system that relies solely on active adjustment of HCO_3^-.

In conclusion, to what extent acid-base regulation of ectotherms fully complies with the alphastat hypothesis is still debated. Collation of reported values for a number of fish, amphibians, and reptiles yielded an average dpH/dT of 0.011 U/°C (119), close but not quite identical to the expected -0.017 U/°C. Further, as evidenced above, it is known that a number of species, in particular fish, do not maintain constant CO_2 content with alterations in T.Many measurements of acid-base parameters were limited to the plasma compartment. It is known that intracellular acid-base regulation, at least in amphibians and turtles, is relatively independent of extracellular acid-base regulation (125, 126), that different tissues have unique intracellular T-CO_2 content relationships (117), and that transfer of strong ions is likely to occur between the intra- and extracellular compartments (96, 117). However, recent direct analysis of the alpha-IM by nuclear magnetic resonance in the white skeletal muscle of the newt is in support of the alphastat regulation of pH at the intracellular level (127).

Effects on Oxygenation

With the increase in T,the combination of the low $\dot{V}E/\dot{V}O_2$ and the decreased Hb affinity for O_2 should decrease arterial oxygenation. This has been shown to occur in the racer snake for $T > 30°C$ (128), but it is not the common finding among ectotherms. In fact, in many reptiles and amphibians, PaO_2 not only does not decrease, but actually increases with T (107, 116, 129–132). This effect is a consequence of the incomplete anatomical separation of the systemic and pulmonary circulation. Because of a right-to-left shunt, the systemic arterial blood is mixed blood with incomplete Hb saturation. In such a situation, with the increase in T the rightward shift of the Hb-O_2 curve results in an increase in PaO_2 even if the Hb-O_2 saturation remains constant (129, 133). Furthermore, with increased T, an increased O_2 saturation has been noticed in some reptiles (107, 134, 135) and can be attributed to a reduction in the magnitude of the right-to-left cardiac shunt (136, 137).

Few studies have examined the effects of T on PaO_2 in fish. The T independency of PaO_2 observed in the trout and the carp agrees with the constancy of $\dot{V}E/\dot{V}O_2$ in water breathers at different T values, as previously mentioned (120, 138). Further, the gill of the teleost fish is an efficient gas exchange organ and appears to lack significant shunts within the branchial circulation (121, 139). Some decrease in PaO_2 as T increased was observed in the pacu, but with no consequences on arterial O_2 saturation because the PaO_2 values reported (94 mm Hg) were on the flattened upper portion of the Hb-O_2 dissociation curve (121).

Ventilation and Thermoregulation

As T increases, in many air-breathing ectotherms $\dot{V}E/\dot{V}O_2$ decreases, in agreement with alphastat regulation. However, as T continues to rise, $\dot{V}E$ is progressively more involved in the task of evaporative heat dissipation rather than acid-base regulation. For example, in the lizard and freshwater turtle, $\dot{V}E/\dot{V}O_2$ decreased as T increased, but at $Tb >40°C$ a marked rise in $\dot{V}E/\dot{V}O_2$ occurred, with a reduction in tidal volume and an increase in frequency (140–142). Further, this hyperventilation was accompanied by an increase in dead space. This pattern is very reminiscent of the mammalian response to heat stress discussed previously. The increase in dead space enhances the possibility of using $\dot{V}E$ as a heat-dissipating mechanism with less impact on $\dot{V}A$ and blood gas homeostasis (Figure 2).

Breathing Pattern and Chemosensitivity

In ectotherms a rise in T increases $\dot{V}E$, even if, as discussed earlier, in many air-breathers the hyperpnea is not in proportion to $\dot{V}O_2$, and $\dot{V}E/\dot{V}O_2$ decreases. The increase in $\dot{V}E$ is usually achieved by an increase in breathing rate, whereas changes in tidal volume are more variable (25). In reptiles and amphibians, increasing T also shortens the breath-hold period and increases the number of breaths per burst (103, 141, 143–146).

In general, moderate to severe hypoxia increases $\dot{V}E$. In addition, the response to hypoxia appears to be greater at higher T in fish (147), air-breathing fish (148), amphibians (145), and reptiles (149, 150).

In air-breathing fish, CO_2 elicits minor changes in $\dot{V}E$, whereas a clear $\dot{V}E$ response occurs in amphibians based on the degree of the respiratory acidosis (151). In reptiles, CO_2 inhalation regularly results in increases in both tidal volume and breathing rate and a shortening of the breath-hold period (25). An increase in Tb has been shown to increase the $\dot{V}E$ sensitivity to CO_2 in crocodilians, turtles, and lizards (25, 104, 144, 146, 152), although little is known about the mechanisms. The current view is that central chemoreceptors are essential for the $\dot{V}E$ response to hypercapnia, with peripheral receptors playing a crucial role in alligators (19, 24, 104), less of a role in turtles (153), and little role in amphibians (154, 155). In reptiles it has been hypothesized (104) that the apparent insensitivity [$Q_{10} \sim 1$, e.g. in the turtle (156)] of the central chemoreceptors and of the structures integrating their signals could act as a modulator for the large T-dependency of vagal CO_2-sensitive peripheral receptors.

CHANGES IN BODY TEMPERATURE IN MAMMALS

Circadian Rhythms

Even in homeotherms, Tb varies daily. Such circadian rhythms, like those in $\dot{V}O_2$, persist in constant light or darkness and in the absence of any external cue, with the period being slightly different from 24 h. They are not explained by, nor temporally linked to, daily changes in activity (157, 158). The amplitude of the Tb oscillations is often ~1°C–1.5°C, and it is magnified by cold exposure (159). In the giraffe, the daily Tb swing of 3°C reduces evaporative heat loss by decreasing the nocturnal Tb-Ta difference (160). Much larger circadian Tb swings, like the 10–15°C daily oscillation of the tenrec (161), can occur in mammals with periods of daily torpor.

Whether the circadian Tb oscillations and corresponding metabolic changes are accompanied by changes in $\dot{V}E$ has received limited attention. In one study on adult rats, which are nocturnal animals, the morning and evening values of $\dot{V}E$, tidal volume, and breathing rate did not differ significantly (162). In 1-week-old rats, Tb and $\dot{V}O_2$ were slightly higher at 7:30 PM than at 7:30 AM, and the higher Tb values were accompanied by higher $\dot{V}E$, in proportion to metabolic rate (163). In the giraffe the highest Tb values corresponded to the highest levels of $\dot{V}O_2$ and breathing rate (160). These observations need to be greatly expanded before definitive conclusions about circadian oscillations in $\dot{V}E$ can be made. If $\dot{V}E$ had a circadian rhythm, it would be of interest to know not only its magnitude but also the temporal relation with the oscillations in Tb, $\dot{V}O_2$, and activity. In fact, the oscillations of these variables are not perfectly synchronous, yet each of them has the possibility of affecting $\dot{V}E$.

Sleep

During sleep, Tb decreases below the value obtained during wakefulness. Peripheral vasodilatation and increased sweating at the onset of sleep are consistent with the idea of a resetting of thermoregulation to a lower Tb (164). Thermoregulatory mechanisms remain operative during slow-wave sleep (SS) but not in rapid-eye-movement (REM or desynchronized) sleep, during which a drop in Ta results in a drop in Tb, both in adults and newborns (165, 166). For example, in cats in the transition from SS to REM sleep, common responses to cold (shivering) and to heat (tachypnea) disappear. This is part of a general inactivation of the autonomic thermoregulatory mechanisms and leads to the conclusion that REM sleep is a "poikilothermic" state (165).

In humans and several animal species, during SS $\dot{V}E$ decreases more than does metabolic rate. This results in a small yet consistent increase in alveolar PCO_2 and $PaCO_2$ and a decrease in the corresponding PO_2s (166–168). The pattern of breathing tends to be deeper and slower than during wakefulness. The bulk of the evidence suggests that the hypoventilation results from removal of the cortical "wakefulness" stimulus and consequent depression of the medullary or spinal respiratory neurons (167). Responses to chemical stimuli (hypoxia and hypercapnia) are maintained during SS, in support of the idea that the hypoventilation represents a resetting of the regulatory point around a higher $PaCO_2$ value, just as the reduction in Tb is interpreted as a readjustment of the thermoregulatory set point.

During REM sleep in humans, both $\dot{V}CO_2$ and $\dot{V}E$ increase slightly and in proportion, whereas in other species metabolic rate decreases below the value of the SS (53). Breathing is irregular during REM, with asynchronous motions of the rib cage and abdomen (169). The ventilatory responses to hypoxia and hypercapnia are reduced and characteristically very variable; in fact, it looks as if, during REM sleep, the metabolic control of breathing is of minor importance compared with the behavioral regulation (167). Hence, during sleep both the thermoregulatory and respiratory systems are part of a generalized phenomenon involving changes in the set points with maintenance of control during the SS phase and loss of homeostasis during the REM phase.

Torpor

Many mammals periodically enter a period of inactivity, lasting only a few hours or many weeks and accompanied by a reduction in energy requirements, Tb, and a variety of functions. In some cases, $\dot{V}O_2$ is only 1–5% of the awake normothermic value, and Tb is only a few degrees above freezing T.

During torpor, values of pH and Pa_{CO_2} are close to the awake normothermic values, meaning that, at the low Tb, the animal has a profound acidosis and hypercapnia (170, 171). Therefore, a mammal during torpor does not regulate acid-base balance as an ectotherm (alphastat); rather, it maintains pH around the same normothermic value (pH-stat). It has been argued that the profound acidosis contributes to the hypometabolic state (172), although some data indicated that, during forced hypothermia, $\dot{V}O_2$ was lower when pH increased above the normothermic value (173). Also, it has been pointed out that the pocket mouse hyperventilates during both the arousal phase and the onset of hibernation, which is inconsistent with the idea of respiratory acidosis being an important factor for the induction of the metabolic depression (174). The desert ground squirrel is an example of the combination of the two strategies; during periods of torpor (Tb = 11°C–28°C), arterial pH and Pa_{CO_2} were similar to the normothermic (37°C) values, indicating that, as in other mammals, this species had a profound acidosis. During wakefulness, the large Tb changes that are characteristic of this species (between 30 and 42°C) were met by changes in blood acid-base similar to those of ectotherms, that is, alphastat regulation (175). The bat, during torpor, lowers Tb from 37 to 5°C and breathes intermittently. During the breathing phases, $\dot{V}E/\dot{V}O_2$ and pH varied inversely with Tb, with a pattern close to that of ectothermic regulation (176, 177). These observations indicate that alphastat regulation is not confined to ectotherms and can be adopted by mammals in special circumstances.

During torpor, the $\dot{V}E$ responses to chemical stimuli are present. Therefore, torpor does not represent a functional depression of respiratory regulation; rather, functions remain operative around new values of Tb, pH, and Pa_{CO_2} (174). This ability to regulate is astonishing considering that, at such low Tb values, airway receptors and chemoreceptors of nonhibernating animals are almost silenced, and respiratory system compliance is greatly decreased (see above).

Hypoxia and Hypercapnia

Hypoxia in mammals depresses all forms of thermogenesis (53). Hence, Tb decreases especially when hypoxia occurs in cold conditions. Hypercapnia favors peripheral vasodilation, and Tb drops because of the increased heat loss.

Although no study has specifically addressed the issue of acid-base control during mammalian hypometabolism induced by hypoxia, the available data indicate that hypoxic $\dot{V}E/\dot{V}O_2$ and blood gases are similar between warm and cold conditions despite differences in Tb. For example, adult rats presented the same degree of respiratory alkalosis during hypoxia, with Tb $= 38.1°C$ and Tb $= 34.5°C$ (73). In newborn dogs, $PaCO_2$ decreased by the same amount during progressive hypoxia in warm and cold conditions, although in the latter case Tb was 5°C lower (74). Artificial warming of hypoxic kittens increased their Tb with no effect on blood gases (178). In adult rats during hypercapnia or asphyxia, $\dot{V}E/\dot{V}O_2$ was lower and the respiratory acidosis more marked in cold than in warm conditions, even if Tb was lower in the cold (66, 67). In summary, the few measurements available indicate no signs of alphastat regulation in mammals with changes in Tb that accompany hypoxia or hypercapnia.

Fever

In rabbits, at the onset of fever, respiratory rate greatly decreased, whereas artificial lowering of Tb in febrile rabbits increased breathing rate (179, 180). In cats, on the other hand, the breathing pattern hardly changed, despite the increase in $\dot{V}O_2$, implying some degree of hypoventilation (90). Administration of CO_2 in febrile cats increased $\dot{V}E$ but also decreased the rate of rise in Tb (90). Hence, it seems that the respiratory system in these species contributes to the rising phase of Tb at the onset of fever by reducing respiratory heat loss, even if this results in hypoventilation. Data in humans are surprisingly sparse. It is nevertheless accepted that breathing rate increases in fever, and in children respiratory rate is proportional to the rise in Tb (181).

Hypothermia

In contrast to the drop in Tb during sleep, hypoxia, and torpor or the increase in Tb during fever, hypothermia is not accompanied by a change of the thermoregulatory set point. Hypothermia results when, during cold exposure, thermolysis exceeds thermogenesis (accidental hypothermia). Eventually metabolic rate falls owing to the Q_{10} effect prevailing over thermogenesis. Metabolic acidosis, which can occur because of the strenuous shivering or a drop in $[HCO_3^-]$ (182), further lowers metabolic rate. A partial respiratory compensation, indicated by a drop in $PaCO_2$, occurs, but eventually it is not enough to prevent the increase in CO_2.

Ventilation is probably impeded by the depressant effect of Tb, the possible increase in dead space, and increased ventilation-perfusion mismatch owing to a reduced cardiac output (183–185). High values of Pa_{CO_2} have a narcotic effect on $\dot{V}_E$, leading to a vicious cycle of respiratory insufficiency. Hence, opposite to what would be desirable for alphastat regulation, in hypothermia a severe acidosis of metabolic and respiratory origin can occur.

SUMMARY AND CONCLUSIONS

In mammals, when Ta changes, $\dot{V}_E$ often deviates from its primary commitment for gas exchange to accommodate thermoregulatory needs. An adequate breathing pattern and adjustments in dead space favor a satisfactory compromise between these two functions. When Tb changes, $\dot{V}_E$ often retains its proportionality to $\dot{V}_{O_2}$, and pH varies little. Hence, in mammals during changes in Tb, pH regulation takes priority over alphastat regulation. This is quite different from the acid-base control of ectotherms. Perhaps this difference has to do with the fact that changes in Tb in homeotherms are small. In fact, when Tb changes are large, some data (see above) suggest that mammals also may opt for alphastat regulation. Furthermore, in severe hypothermia, functions may be better with alphastat than pH-stat management of acid-base balance (186), although it is highly probable that the optimal strategy of acid-base regulation may vary among tissues, organs, and species.

As Tb drops, alphastat regulation would require progressively higher $\dot{V}_E/\dot{V}_{O_2}$. If this were achieved by an increase in $\dot{V}_E$, it would conflict with the needs to minimize heat loss, whereas a drop in $\dot{V}_{O_2}$ would conflict with the attempt of all mammals to protect Tb by thermogenesis. On the other hand, a drop in $\dot{V}_E/\dot{V}_{O_2}$ is required for alphastat regulation as Tb increases. In homeotherms, this can be achieved only by decreasing $\dot{V}_E$, which, apart from the potential risks for oxygenation, would hinder the mechanisms of evaporative heat loss. Hence, in endotherms the control of Tb is in conflict with alphastat regulation, and it seems likely that the latter may be adopted only in exceptional circumstances in which Tb is no longer regulated or, perhaps, in small species and neonatal mammals with limited abilities for homeothermy.

ACKNOWLEDGMENTS

We are grateful to Erin Seifert for her critical reading of the manuscript.

Visit the Annual Reviews home page at www.AnnualReviews.org.

LITERATURE CITED

1. Somero GN. 1996. Temperature and proteins: little things can mean a lot. *News Physiol. Sci.* 11:72–77
2. Lempert J, Macklem PT. 1971. Effect of temperature on rabbit lung surfactant and pressure-volume hysteresis. *J. Appl. Physiol.* 31:380–85
3. Horie T, Ardila R, Hildebrandt J. 1974. Static and dynamic properties of excised cat lung in relation to temperature. *J. Appl. Physiol.* 36:317–22
4. Mautone AJ, Antonio-Santiago MT, Clutario BC, Scarpelli EM. 1992. Temperature affects mechanics and stability during initial inflation-deflation of mature fetal lung. *Pediatr. Pulmonol.* 13:203–8
5. Inoue H, Inoue C, Hildebrandt J. 1982. Temperature effects on lung mechanics in air- and liquid-filled rabbit lungs. *J. Appl. Physiol.* 53:567–75
6. Jones TA, Petsonk EL, Frazer DG. 1996. Effect of temperature on pressure-volume hysteresis of excised lungs. *Respir. Physiol.* 106:47–55
7. Deal CW, Warden JC, Monk I. 1970. Effect of hypothermia on lung compliance. *Thorax* 25:105–9
8. Milsom WK, Reid WD. 1995. Pulmonary mechanics of hibernating squirrels (*Spermophilus lateralis*). *Respir. Physiol.* 101:311–20
9. O'Cain CF, Dowling NB, Slutsky AS, Hensley MJ, Strohl KP, et al. 1980. Airway effects of respiratory heat loss in normal subjects. *J. Appl. Physiol.* 49:875–80
10. McFadden ER Jr, Ingram RH Jr. 1986. Thermal factors in respiratory mechanics. In *Handbook of Physiology, Section 3: the Respiratory System,* Vol. III, part 2, ed. PT Macklem, J Mead, 39:703–9. Bethesda, MD: Am. Physiol. Soc.
11. Alcayaga J, Sanhueza Y, Zapata P. 1993. Thermal dependence of chemosensory activity in the carotid body superfused in vitro. *Brain Res.* 600:103–11
12. Eyzaguirre C, Baron M, Gallego R. 1977. Effects of temperature and stimulating agents on carotid body cells. In *Chemoreception in the Carotid Body,* ed. H Acker et al, pp. 71–78. Berlin: Springer-Verlag
13. Baron M, Eyzaguirre C. 1975. Thermal responses of carotid body cells. *J. Neurobiol.* 6:521–27
14. Baron M, Eyzaguirre C. 1977. Effects of temperature on some membrane characteristics of carotid body cells. *Am. J. Physiol.* 233:C35–46
15. Paintal AS. 1971. The responses of chemoreceptors at reduced temperatures. *J. Physiol.* 217:1–18
16. McQueen DS, Eyzaguirre C. 1974. Effects of temperature on carotid chemoreceptor and baroreceptor activity. *J. Neurophysiol.* 37:1287–96
17. Barnas GM, Hempleman SC, Burger RE. 1983. Effect of temperature on the CO_2 sensitivity of avian intrapulmonary chemoreceptors. *Respir. Physiol.* 54:233–40
18. Douse MA, Mitchell GS. 1988. Temperature effects on CO2-sensitive intrapulmonary chemoreceptors in the lizard, *Tupinambis nigropunctatus. Respir. Physiol.* 72:327–42
19. Douse MA, Powell FL, Milsom WK, Mitchell GS. 1989. Temperature effects on pulmonary receptor responses to airways pressure and CO_2 in *Alligator mississippiensis. Respir. Physiol.* 78:331–44
20. Furilla RA, Bartlett D Jr. 1988. Intrapulmonary receptors in the garter snake (*Thamnophis sirtalis*). *Respir. Physiol.* 74:311–22
21. Fedde MR, Peterson DF. 1970. Intrapulmonary receptor response to changes in airway-gas composition in *Gallus domesticus. J. Physiol.* 209:609–25
22. Loyola H, Fadic R, Cardenas H, Larrain

C, Zapata P. 1991. Effects of body temperature on chemosensory activity of the cat carotid body in situ. *Neurosci. Lett.* 132:251–54

23. Barnas GM, Burger RE. 1983. Interaction of temperature with extra- and intrapulmonary chemoreceptor control of ventilatory movements in the awake chicken. *Respir. Phsyiol.* 54:223–32

24. Branco LGS, Wood SC. 1993. Effect of temperature on central chemical control of ventilation in the alligator *Alligator mississippiensis. J. Exp. Biol.* 179:261–72

25. Shelton G, Jones DR, Milsom WK. 1986. Control of breathing in ectothermic vertebrates. In *Handbook of Physiology, Section 3: The Respiratory System,* Vol II, part 2, ed. NS Cherniack, JG Widdicombe, 28:857–909. Bethesda, MD: Am. Physiol. Soc.

26. May P. 1957. L'action immédiate de l'oxygène sur la ventilation chez l'homme normal. *Helv. Physiol. Acta* 15:230–40

27. Dejours P. 1957. Intérêt méthodologique de l'étude d'un organisme vivant à la phase initiale de rupture d'un équilibre physiologique. *C. R. Acad. Sci. (Paris)* 245:1946–48

28. Fadic R, Larrain C, Zapata P. 1991. Thermal effects on ventilation in cats: participation of carotid body chemoreceptors. *Respir. Physiol.* 86:51–63

29. Itturiaga R, Larrain C, Zapata P. 1994. Phrenic nerve activity during artificial ventilation at different body temperatures and its relationships with carotid chemosensory activity. *Biol. Res.* 27:145–57

30. Jonzon A, Pisarri TE, Roberts AM, Coleridge JCG, Coleridge HM. 1988. Attenuation of pulmonary afferent input by vagal cooling in dogs. *Respir. Physiol.* 72:19–34

31. Schoener EP, Frankel HM. 1972. Effect of hyperthermia and Pa_{CO_2} on the slowly adapting pulmonary stretch receptors. *Am. J. Physiol.* 222:68–72

32. Bradley GW, Scheurmier N. 1977. The transduction properties of tracheal stretch receptors *in vitro. Respir. Physiol.* 31:365–75

33. von Euler C, Trippenbach T. 1976. Temperature effects on the inflation reflex during expiratory time in the cat. *Acta Physiol. Scand.* 96:338–50

34. Merazzi D, Mortola JP. 1999. Effects of changes in ambient temperature on the Hering-Breuer reflex of the conscious newborn rat. *Pediatr. Res.* 45:370–76

35. Grunstein MM, Younes M, Milic-Emili J. 1973. Control of tidal volume and respiratory frequency in anesthetized cats. *J. Appl. Physiol.* 35:463–76

36. Bradley GW, von Euler C, Martilla I, Roos B. 1974. Steady state effects of CO_2 and temperature on the relationship between lung volume and inspiratory duration (Hering-Breuer threshold curve). *Acta Physiol. Scand.* 92:351–63

37. Widdicombe JG, Winning A. 1974. Effects of hypoxia, hypercapnia and changes in body temperature on the pattern of breathing in cats. *Respir. Physiol.* 21:203–21

38. Matsuoka T, Mortola JP. 1995. Effects of hypoxia and hypercapnia on the Hering-Breuer reflex of the conscious newborn rat. *J. Appl. Physiol.* 78:5–11

39. Sant'Ambrogio G, Mathew OP, Sant'Ambrogio FB, Fisher JT. 1985. Laryngeal cold receptors. *Respir. Physiol.* 59:35–44

40. Sant'Ambrogio G, Sant'Ambrogio FB, Mathew OP. 1986. Effect of cold air on laryngeal mechanoreceptors in the dog. *Respir. Physiol.* 64:45–56

41. Al-Shway SF, Mortola JP. 1982. Respiratory effects of airflow through the upper airways in newborn kittens and puppies. *J. Appl. Physiol.* 53:805–14

42. Mathew OP, Anderson JW, Oriani GP, Sant'Ambrogio FB, Sant'Ambrogio G. 1990. Cooling mediates the ventilatory

depression associated with airflow through the larynx. *Respir. Physiol.* 82:359–68

43. Mortola JP, Piazza T. 1987. Breathing pattern in rats with chronic section of the superior laryngeal nerves. *Respir. Physiol.* 70:51–62

44. Mortola JP, Rezzonico R. 1989. Ventilation in kittens with chronic section of the superior laryngeal nerves. *Respir. Physiol.* 76:369–82

45. Jackson DC, Schmidt-Nielsen K. 1964. Countercurrent heat exchange in the respiratory passages. *Proc. Natl. Acad. Sci. USA* 51:1192–97

46. Schroter RC, Watkins NV. 1989. Respiratory heat exchange in mammals. *Respir. Physiol.* 78:357–68

47. Proctor DF, Andersen IB, Lundqvist GR. 1977. Human nasal mucosal function at controlled temperatures. *Respir. Physiol.* 30:109–24

48. Langman VA, Maloiy GMO, Schmidt-Nielsen K, Schroter RC. 1979. Nasal heat exchange in the giraffe and other large mammals. *Respir. Physiol.* 37:325–33

49. Jessen C. 1998. Brain cooling: an economy mode of temperature regulation in artiodactyls. *News Physiol. Sci.* 13:281–86

50. Parmeggiani PL, Azzaroni A, Calasso M. 1998. A pontine-hypothalamic temperature difference correlated with cutaneous and respiratory heat loss. *Respir. Physiol.* 114:49–56

51. White MD, Cabanac M. 1995. Respiratory heat loss and core temperatures during submaximal exercise. *J. Therm. Biol.* 20:489–96

52. Withers PC, Casey TM, Casey KK. 1979. Allometry of respiratory and haematological parameters of arctic mammals. *Comp. Biochem. Physiol.* 64A:343–50

53. Mortola JP, Gautier H. 1995. Interaction between metabolism and ventilation: effects of respiratory gases and temperature. In *Regulation of Breathing*, ed. JA Dempsey, AI Pack, 23:1011–64. New York: Dekker

54. Gautier H, Bonora M, Lahiri S. 1992. Control of metabolic and ventilatory responses to cold in anesthetized cats. *Respir. Physiol.* 87:309–24

55. Chappell MA. 1985. Effects of ambient temperature and altitude on ventilation and gas exchange in deer mice (*Peromyscus maniculatus*). *J. Comp. Physiol. B* 155:751–58

56. Chappell MA. 1992. Ventilatory accommodation of changing oxygen demand in sciurid rodents. *J. Comp. Physiol. B* 162:722–30

57. Nicol SC, Maskrey M. 1980. Thermoregulation, respiration and sleep in the Tasmanian devil, *Sarcophilus harrisii* (Marsupialia: Dasyuridae). *J. Comp. Physiol. B* 140:241–48

58. Hallam JF, Dawson TJ. 1993. The pattern of respiration with increasing metabolism in a small dasyurid marsupial. *Respir. Physiol.* 93:305–14

59. Chappell MA, Souza SL. 1988. Thermoregulation, gas exchange, and ventilation in Adelie penguins (*Pygoscelis adeliae*). *J. Comp. Physiol. B* 157:783–90

60. Ingram DL, Legge KF. 1969–1970. The effect of environmental temperature on respiratory ventilation in the pig. *Respir. Physiol.* 8:1–12

61. Chappell MA, Roverud RC. 1990. Temperature effects on metabolism, ventilation, and oxygen extraction in a neotropical bat. *Respir. Physiol.* 81:401–12

62. Casey TM, Withers PC, Casey KK. 1979. Metabolic and respiratory responses of arctic mammals to ambient temperature during the summer. *Comp. Biochem. Physiol.* 64A:331–41

63. Newstead CG. 1987. The relationship between ventilation and oxygen consumption in man is the same during both moderate exercise and shivering. *J. Physiol.* 383:455–59

64. Cain SM. 1971. Ventilatory and metabolic responses of unanesthetized dogs to

CO_2 at 2 and 18C. *J. Appl. Physiol.* 31:647–50

65. Gautier H, Bonora M, Trinh HC. 1993. Ventilatory and metabolic responses to cold and CO_2 in intact and carotid body-denervated awake rats. *J. Appl. Physiol.* 75:2570–79

66. Mortola JP, Maskrey M. 1998. Ventilatory response to asphyxia in conscious rats: effect of ambient and body temperatures. *Respir. Physiol.* 111:233–46

67. Saiki C, Mortola JP. 1996. Effect of CO_2 on the metabolic and ventilatory responses to ambient temperature in conscious adult and newborn rats. *J. Physiol.* 491:261–69

68. Bullard RW, Crise JR. 1961. Effects of carbon dioxide on cold exposed human subjects. *J. Appl. Physiol.* 16:663–38

69. Maskrey M, Nicol SC. 1979. Responses of conscious rabbits to CO_2 at ambient temperatures of 5, 20, and 35°C. *J. Appl. Physiol.* 47:522–26

70. Wagner JA, Matsushita K, Horvath SM. 1983. Effects of carbon dioxide inhalation on physiological responses to cold. *Aviat. Space Environ. Med.* 54:1074–79

71. Gautier H. 1996. Interactions among metabolic rate, hypoxia, and control of breathing. *J. Appl. Physiol.* 81:521–27

72. Mortola JP. 1996. Ventilatory responses to hypoxia in mammals. In *Tissue Oxygen Deprivation: from Molecular to Integrated Function,* ed. GG Haddad, G Lister, 15:433–77. New York: Dekker

73. Saiki C, Matsuoka T, Mortola JP. 1994. Metabolic-ventilatory interaction in conscious rats: effect of hypoxia and ambient temperature. *J. Appl. Physiol.* 76:1594–99

74. Rohlicek CV, Saiki C, Matsuoka T, Mortola JP. 1998. Oxygen transport in conscious newborn dogs during hypoxic hypometabolism. *J. Appl. Physiol.* 84:763–68

75. Richards SA. 1970. The biology and comparative physiology of thermal panting. *Biol. Rev.* 45:223–64

76. Jennings DB, Chen CC, Phillips HH, Sparling J. 1973. Respiration and metabolism in panting and nonpanting resting conscious dogs. *J. Appl. Physiol.* 35:490–96

77. Jennings DB. 1984. Breathing patterns and drives during thermal and nonthermal panting. In *Thermal Physiology,* ed. JRS Hales, pp. 335–40. New York: Raven

78. Calder WA Jr, Schmidt-Nielsen K. 1966. Evaporative cooling and respiratory alkalosis in the pigeon. *Proc. Natl. Acad. Sci. USA* 55:750–56

79. Hales JRS. 1966. The partition of respiratory ventilation of the panting ox. *J. Physiol.* 188:45P–46P

80. Hales JRS, Webster MED. 1967. Respiratory function during thermal tachypnoea in sheep. *J. Physiol.* 190:241–60

81. Hales JRS, Dampney RAL, Bennett JW. 1975. Influences of chronic denervation of the carotid bifurcation regions on panting in the sheep. *Pflügers Arch.* 360:243–53

82. Hales JRS, Findlay JD. 1968. The oxygen cost of thermally-induced and CO_2-induced hyperventilation in the ox. *Respir. Physiol.* 4:353–62

83. Crawford EC Jr. 1962. Mechanical aspects of panting in dogs. *J. Appl. Physiol.* 17:249–51

84. Henry JG, Baiton CR. 1974. Human core temperature increase as a stimulus to breathing during moderate exercise. *Respir. Physiol.* 21:183–91

85. White MD, Cabanac M. 1996. Exercise hyperpnea and hyperthermia in humans. *J. Appl. Physiol.* 81:1249–54

86. Forster HV, Pan LG. 1997. Control of breathing during exercise. In *The Lung: Scientific Foundations,* ed. RG Crystal, JB West, PJ Barnes, ER Weibel, 150:2001–10. Philadelphia: Lippincott-Raven. 2nd ed.

87. Martin BJ, Morgan EJ, Zwillich CW,

Weil JV. 1979. Influence of exercise hyperthermia on exercise breathing pattern. *J. Appl. Physiol.* 47:1039–42

88. Maskrey M, Nicol SC. 1976. Respiratory and thermoregulatory responses of rabbits breathing carbon dioxide during heat exposure. *J. Physiol.* 261:375–86

89. Maskrey M, Hales JRS, Fawcett AA. 1981. Effect of a constant arterial CO_2 tension on respiratory pattern in heat-stressed sheep. *J. Appl. Physiol.* 50:315–19

90. Sachdeva U, Jennings DB. 1994. Effects of hypercapnia on metabolism, temperature, and ventilation during heat and fever. *J. Appl. Physiol.* 76:1285–92

91. Bonora M, Gautier H. 1989. Effects of hypoxia on thermal polypnea in intact and carotid body-denervated conscious cats. *J. Appl. Physiol.* 67:578–83

92. Bonora M, Gautier H. 1990. Role of dopamine and arterial chemoreceptors in thermal tachypnea in conscious cats. *J. Appl. Physiol.* 69:1429–34

93. Piiper J, Scheid P. 1992. Gas exchange in vertebrates through lungs, gills, and skin. *News Physiol. Sci.* 7:199–203

94. Dejours P. 1988. Respiration in water and air. In *Adaptation-Regulation-Evolution,* pp. 19–30. Amsterdam: Elsevier. 176 pp.

95. Reeves RB. 1977. The interaction of body temperature and acid-base balance in ectothermic vertebrates. *Annu. Rev. Physiol.* 39:559–86

96. Cameron JN. 1984. Acid-base status of fish at different temperatures. *Am. J. Physiol.* 246: R452–59

97. Rahn H. 1967. Gas transport from the external environment to the cell. In *Development of the Lung,* ed. R Porter, AVS de Reuck, pp. 3–23. London: Churchill Livingstone

98. Reeves RB. 1972. An imidazole alphastat hypothesis for vertebrate acid-base regulation: tissue carbon dioxide content and body temperature in bullfrogs. *Respir. Physiol.* 14:219–36

99. Nattie EE. 1990. The alphastat hypothe-

sis in respiratory control and acid-base balance. *J. Appl. Physiol.* 69:1201–7

100. Jennings DB. 1993. Breathing for protein function and $[H^+]$ homeostasis. *Respir. Physiol.* 93:1–12

101. Perry SF, Daxboeck C, Emmett B, Hochachka PW, Brill RW. 1985. Effects of temperature change on acid-base regulation in skipjack tuna (*Katsuwonus pelamis*) blood. *Comp. Biochem. Physiol.* 81A:49–53

102. Milsom WK. 1990. Control and co-ordination of gas exchange in air breathers. In *Advances in Comparative and Environmental Physiology,* Vol 6. *Vertebrate Gas Exchange: from Environment to Cell,* ed. RG Boutilier, pp. 347–400. Berlin: Springer-Verlag

103. Frappell PB, Daniels CB. 1991. Ventilation and oxygen consumption in agamid lizards. *Physiol. Zool.* 64:985–1001

104. Douse MA, Mitchell GS. 1992. Effects of vagotomy on ventilatory responses to CO_2 in alligators. *Respir. Physiol.* 87:63–76

105. Branco LG, Glass ML, Wang T, Hoffmann A. 1993. Temperature and central chemoreceptor drive to ventilation in toad (*Bufo paracnemis*). *Respir. Physiol.* 93:337–46

106. Stinner JN, Grguric MR, Beaty SL. 1996. Ventilatory and blood acid-base adjustments to a decrease in body temperature from 30 to 10°C in black racer snakes *Coluber constrictor. J. Exp. Biol.* 199:815–23

107. Wang T, Abe AS, Glass ML. 1998. Temperature effects on lung and blood gases in *Bufo paracnemis:* consequences of bimodal gas exchange. *Respir. Physiol.* 113:231–38

108. Wood SC, Glass ML, Johansen K. 1977. Effects of temperature on respiration and acid-base balance in a monitor lizard. *J. Comp. Physiol.* 116:287–96

109. Nolan W, Frankel HM. 1982. Effects of temperature on ventilation and acid-base status in the black racer snake, *Coluber*

constrictor. *Comp. Biochem. Physiol.* 73A:57–61

110. Stinner JN, Wardle RL. 1988. Effect of temperature upon carbon dioxide stores in the snake *Coluber constrictor* and the turtle *Chrysemys scripta. J. Exp. Biol.* 137:529–48

111. Lutz PL, Bergey A, Bergey M. 1989. Effects of temperature on gas exchange and acid-base balance in the sea turtle *Caretta caretta* at rest and during routine activity. *J. Exp. Biol.* 144:155–69

112. Feder ME, Burggren WW. 1985. Cutaneous gas exchange in vertebrates: designs, patterns, control and implications. *Biol. Rev.* 60:1–45

113. Moalli R, Meyers RS, Ultsch GR, Jackson DC. 1981. Acid-base balance and temperature in a predominantly skin-breathing salamander, *Cryptobranchus alleganiensis. Respir. Physiol.* 43:1–11

114. Jackson DC. 1978. Respiratory control and CO_2 conductance: temperature effects in a turtle and a frog. *Respir. Physiol.* 33:103–14

115. McKenzie JA, Jackson DC. 1978. The effect of temperature on cutaneous CO_2 loss and conductance in the bullfrog. *Respir. Physiol.* 32:313–23

116. Wang T, Abe AS, Glass ML. 1998. Effects of temperature on lung and blood gases in the South American rattlesnake *Crotalus durissus terrificus. Comp. Biochem. Physiol. A* 121:7–11

117. Stinner JN, Newlon DL, Heisler N. 1994. Extracellular and intracellular carbon dioxide concentration as a function of temperature in the toad *Bufo marinus. J. Exp. Biol.* 195:345–60

118. Rahn R, Baumgardner FW. 1972. Temperature and acid-base regulation in fish. *Respir. Physiol.* 14:171–82

119. Heisler N. 1986. Comparative aspects of acid-base regulation. In *Acid-Base Regulation in Animals,* ed. N Heisler, pp. 397–450. Amsterdam: Elsevier

120. Glass ML, Andersen NA, Kruhoffer M, Williams EM, Heisler N. 1990. Combined effects of environmental PO_2 and temperature on ventilation and blood gases in the carp *Cyprinus carpio* l. *J. Exp. Biol.* 148:1–17

121. Soncini R, Glass ML. 1997. The effects of temperature and hyperoxia on arterial PO_2 and acid-base status in *Piaractus mesopotamicus. J. Fish Biol.* 51:225–33

122. Heisler N. 1980. Regulation of the acid-base status in fishes. In *Environmental Physiology of Fishes,* ed. A Ali, pp. 123–32. New York: Plenum

123. Cameron JN. 1980. Body fluid pools, kidney function, and acid-base regulation in the freshwater catfish *Ictalurus punctatus. J. Exp. Biol.* 86:171–85

124. Cameron JN, Kormanik GA. 1982. Intracellular and extracellular acid-base status as a function of temperature in the freshwater channel catfish, *Ictalurus punctatus. J. Exp. Biol.* 99:127–42

125. Boutilier RG, Glass ML, Heisler N. 1987. Blood gases, and extracellular/intracellular acid-base status as a function of temperature in the anuran amphibian *Xenopus laevis* and *Bufo marinus. J. Exp. Biol.* 130:13–25

126. Wasser JS, Warburton SJ, Jackson DC. 1991. Extracellular and intracellular acid-base effects of submergence anoxia and nitrogen breathing in turtles. *Respir. Physiol.* 83:239–52

127. Hitzig BM, Perng WC, Burt T, Okunieff P, Johnson DC. 1994. 1H-NMR measurement of fractional dissociation of imidazole in intact animals. *Am. J. Physiol.* 266:R1008–15

128. Stinner JN. 1987. Thermal dependence of air convection requirement and blood gases in the snake *Coluber constrictor. Am. Zool.* 27:41–47

129. Wood SC. 1982. Effect of O_2 affinity on arterial PO_2 in animals with central vascular shunts. *J. Appl. Physiol.* 53:1360–64

130. Wood SC, Hicks JW. 1985. Oxygen homeostasis in vertebrates with cardiovascular shunts. In *Cardiovascular*

Shunts; Phylogenetic, Ontogenetic and Clinical Aspects, ed. J Johansen, WW Burggren, pp. 354–66. Copenhagen: Munksgaard

131. Glass ML, Boutilier RG, Heisler N. 1985. Effects of body temperature on respiration, blood gases and acid-base status in the turtle *Chrysemys picta bellii. J. Exp. Biol.* 114:37–51

132. Glass ML, Soncini R. 1995. Regulation of acid-base status in ectothermic vertebrates: the consequences for oxygen pressures in lung gas and arterial blood. *Braz. J. Med. Biol. Res.* 28:1161–66

133. Wood SC. 1984. Cardiovascular shunts and oxygen transport in lower vertebrates. *Am. J. Physiol.* 247:R3–14

134. Tucker VA. 1966. Oxygen transport by the circulatory system of the green iguana (*Iguana iguana*) at different body temperatures. *J. Exp. Biol.* 44:77–92

135. Stinner JN. 1982. Ventilation, gas exchange and blood gases in the snake, *Pituophis melanoleucus. Respir. Physiol.* 47:279–98

136. Wang T, Hicks JW. 1996. The interaction of pulmonary ventilation and the right-left shunt on arterial oxygen levels. *J. Exp. Biol.* 199:2121–29

137. Hicks JW, Wang T. 1996. Functional role of cardiac shunts in reptiles. *J. Exp. Zool.* 275:204–16

138. Randall DJ, Cameron JN. 1973. Respiratory control of arterial pH as temperature changes in rainbow trout, *Salmo gairdneri. Am. J. Physiol.* 225:997–1002

139. Gilmour KM, Perry SF. 1994. The effects of hypoxia, hyperoxia or hypercapnia on the acid-base disequilibrium in arterial blood of rainbow trout. *J. Exp. Biol.* 192:269–84

140. Crawford EC Jr, Kampe G. 1971. Physiological responses of the lizard *Sauromalus obesus* to changes in ambient temperature. *Am. J. Physiol.* 220:1256–60

141. Crafter S, Soldini MI, Daniels CB, Smits AW. 1995. The effect of temperature and

hypoxia-hypercapnia on the respiratory pattern of the unrestrained lizard, *Pogona vitticeps. Aust. J. Zool.* 43:165–72

142. Pagés T, Fuster JF, Palacios L.1994. Ventilatory responses to temperature variation in the fresh water turtle, *Mauremys caspica leprosa. J. Comp. Physiol. B* 164:390–95

143. Davies DG, Thomas JL, Smith EN. 1982. Effect of body temperature on ventilatory control in the alligator. *J. Appl. Physiol.* 52:114–18

144. Funk GD, Milsom WK. 1987. Changes in ventilation and breathing pattern produced by changing body temperature and inspired CO_2 concentration in turtles. *Respir. Physiol.* 67:37–51

145. Kruhøffer M, Glass ML, Abe AS, Johansen K. 1987. Control of breathing in an amphibian *Bufo paracnemis:* effects of temperature and hypoxia. *Respir. Physiol.* 69:267–75

146. Munns SL, Frappell PB, Evans BK. 1998. The effects of environmental temperature, hypoxia and hypercapnia on the breathing pattern of saltwater crocodiles (*Crocodylus porosus*). *Physiol. Zool.* 71:267–73

147. Fernandes MN, Barrionuevo WR, Rantin FT. 1995. Effects of thermal stress on respiratory responses to hypoxia of a South American Prochilodontid fish, *Prochilodus scrofa. J. Fish Biol.* 46:123–33

148. Glass ML, Ishimatsu A, Johansen K. 1986. Responses of aerial ventilation to hypoxia and hypercapnia in *Channa argus,* an air-breathing fish. *J. Comp. Physiol. B* 156:425–30

149. Jackson DC. 1973. Ventilatory response to hypoxia in turtles at various temperatures. *Respir. Physiol.* 18:178–87

150. Glass ML, Boutilier RG, Heisler N. 1983. Ventilatory control of arterial PO_2 in the turtle *Chrysemys picta bellii:* effects of temperature and hypoxia. *J. Comp. Physiol.* 151:145–53

151. Boutilier RG. 1990. Control and co-ordi-

nation of gas exchange in bimodal breathers. In *Advances in Comparative and Environmental Physiology,* Vol. 6. *Vertebrate Gas Exchange: from Environment to Cell,* ed. RG Boutilier, pp. 279–345. Berlin: Springer-Verlag

152. Milsom W, Chan P. 1986. The relationship between lung volume, respiratory drive and breathing pattern in the turtle, *Chrysemys picta. J. Exp. Biol.* 120:233–47

153. Hitzig BM. 1982. Temperature-induced changes in turtle CSF pH and central control of ventilation. *Respir. Physiol.* 49:205–22

154. Smatresk NJ, Smits AW. 1991. Effects of central and peripheral chemoreceptor stimulation on ventilation in the marine toad, *Bufo marinus. Respir. Physiol.* 83:223–38

155. Branco LGS, Glass ML, Hoffmann A. 1992. Central chemoreceptor drive to breathing in unanesthetised toads, *Bufo paracnemis. Respir. Physiol.* 87:195–204

156. Johnson SM, Johnson RA, Mitchell GS. 1998. Hypoxia, temperature, and pH/CO_2 effects on respiratory discharge from a turtle brain stem preparation. *J. Appl. Physiol.* 84:649–60

157. Refinetti R. 1994. Contribution of locomotor activity to the generation of the daily rhythm of body temperature in golden hamsters. *Physiol. Behav.* 56:829–31

158. Decoursey PJ, Pius S, Sandlin C, Wethey D, Schull J. 1998. Relationship of circadian temperature and activity rhythms in two rodent species. *Physiol. Behav.* 65:457–63

159. Refinetti R, Menaker M. 1992. The circadian rhythm of body temperature. *Physiol. Behav.* 51:613–37

160. Langman VA, Bamford OS, Maloiy GMO. 1982. Respiration and metabolism in the giraffe. *Respir. Physiol.* 50:141–52

161. Hildwein G, Kayser C. 1970. Relation entre la température colonique et la consommation d'oxygène d'un Insectivore,

le Tenrec, au cours du nyctémère (Valeur numérique du Q_{10}). *Can. R. Soc. Biol.* 164:429–32

162. Peever JH, Stephenson R. 1997. Day-night differences in the respiratory response to hypercapnia in awake adult rats. *Respir. Physiol.* 109:241–48

163. Saiki C, Mortola JP. 1995. Hypoxia abolishes the morning-night differences of metabolism and ventilation in 6-day-old rats. *Can. J. Physiol. Pharmacol.* 73:159–64

164. Parmeggiani PL. 1990. Thermoregulation during sleep in mammals. *News Physiol. Sci.* 5:208–12

165. Berger PJ, Horne RSC, Walker AM. 1989. Cardio-respiratory responses to cool ambient temperature differ with sleep state in neonatal lambs. *J. Physiol.* 412:351–63

166. Reinberg A, Gervais P. 1972. Circadian rhythms in respiratory functions, with special reference to human chronophysiology and chronopharmacology. *Bull. Physiol.-Pathol. Resp.* 8:663–75

167. Phillipson EA, Bowes G. 1986. Control of breathing during sleep. In *Handbook of Physiology,* Section 3: *the Respiratory System,* Vol. II, part 2, ed. NS Cherniack, JG Widdicombe, 19:649–89. Bethesda, MD: Am. Physiol. Soc.

168. Douglas NJ. 1997. Gas exchange during sleep. In *The Lung: Scientific Foundation,* ed. RG Crystal, JB West, ER Weibel, PJ Barnes, 158:2085–92. Philadelphia: Lippincott-Raven. 2nd ed.

169. Pack AI. 1995. Changes in respiratory motor activity during rapid eye movement sleep. In *Regulation of Breathing,* ed. JA Dempsey, AI Pack, 22:983–1010. New York: Marcel Dekker

170. Kent KM, Peirce EC II. 1967. Acid-base characteristics of hibernating animals. *J. Appl. Physiol.* 23:336–40

171. Malan A. 1982. Respiration and acid-base state in hibernation. In *Hibernation and Torpor in Mammals and Birds,* ed.

CP Lyman, JS Willis, A Malan, LCH Wang, pp. 237–82. New York: Academic

172. Malan A. 1986. pH as a control factor in hibernation. In *Living in the Cold: Physiological and Biochemical Adaptations,* ed. HC Heller, XJ Musacchia, LCH Wang, pp. 61–70. New York: Elsevier

173. Willford DC, Hill EP, White FC. 1986. Oxygen consumption rates, cardiac output, and ventricular dP/dt during hypothermia with different pH strategies. *Physiologist* 29:178

174. Tenney SM, Boggs DF. 1986. Comparative mammalian respiratory control. In *Handbook of Physiology,* Section 3: *the Respiratory System,* Vol. II, part 2, ed. NS Cherniack, JG Widdicombe, 27:833–55. Bethesda, MD: Am. Physiol. Soc.

175. Bickler PE. 1984. Blood acid-base status of an awake heterothermic rodent, *Spermophilus tereticaudus. Respir. Physiol.* 57:307–16

176. Szewczak JM, Jackson DC. 1992. Acid-base state and intermittent breathing in the torpid bat, *Eptesicus fuscus. Respir. Physiol.* 88:205–15

177. Szewczak JM, Jackson DC. 1992. Ventilatory response to hypoxia and hypercapnia in the torpid bat, *Eptesicus fuscus. Respir. Physiol.* 88:217–32

178. Rohlicek CV, Saiki C, Matsuoka T, Mortola JP. 1996. Cardiovascular and respiratory consequences of body warming during hypoxia in conscious newborn cats. *Pediatr. Res.* 40:1–5

179. Szelényi Z, Székeli M. 1979. Comparison of the effector mechanisms during endotoxin fever in the adult rabbit. *Acta Physiol. Acad. Sci. Hung.* 54:33–41

180. Cooper KE, Preston E, Veale WL. 1976. Effects of atropine, injected into a lateral cerebral ventricle of the rabbit, on fevers due to intravenous leucocyte pyrogen and hypothalamic and intraventricular injections of prostaglandin E1. *J. Physiol.* 254:729–41

181. O'Dempsey TJD, Laurence BE, McArdle TF, Todd JE, Lamont AC, Greenwood BM. 1993. The effect of temperature reduction on respiratory rate in febrile illnesses. *Arch. Dis. Child.* 68:492–95

182. Alfaro V, Peinado V, Palacios L. 1995. Factors influencing acid-base status during acute severe hypothermia in unanaesthetised rats. *Respir. Physiol.* 100:139–49

183. Maclean D, Emslie-Smith D. 1977. *Accidental Hypothermia,* pp. 97–100, 116–22. Oxford, UK: Blackwell. 476 pp.

184. Cooper KE, Veale WL. 1986. Effects of temperature on breathing. In *Handbook of Physiology,* Section 3: *the Respiratory System,* Vol. II, part 2, ed. NS Cherniack, JG Widdicombe, 20:691–702. Bethesda, MD: Am. Physiol. Soc.

185. Frappell P. 1998. Hypothermia and physiological control: the respiratory system. *Clin. Exper. Pharmacol. Physiol.* 25:159–64

186. McConnell DH, White F, Nelson RL, Goldstein SM, Maloney JV Jr, et al. 1975. Importance of alkalosis in maintenance of "ideal" blood pH during hypothermia. *Surg. Forum* 26:263–65

Annu. Rev. Physiol. 2000. 62:875–915

ROLE OF TRANSCRIPTION FACTORS IN FETAL LUNG DEVELOPMENT AND SURFACTANT PROTEIN GENE EXPRESSION

Carole R. Mendelson

Departments of Biochemistry and Obstetrics-Gynecology, The University of Texas Southwestern Medical Center at Dallas, Dallas, Texas 75235–9038; e-mail: cmende@biochem.swmed.edu

Key Words pulmonary, morphogenesis, genes, growth factors, SP-A

■ **Abstract** Branching morphogenesis of the lung and differentiation of specialized cell populations is dependent upon reciprocal interactions between epithelial cells derived from endoderm of embryonic foregut and surrounding mesenchymal cells. These interactions are mediated by elaboration and concerted actions of a variety of growth and differentiation factors binding to specific receptors. Such factors include members of the fibroblast growth factor family, sonic hedgehog, members of the transforming growth factor-β family, epidermal growth factor, and members of the platelet-derived growth factor family. Hormones that increase cyclic AMP formation, glucocorticoids, and retinoids also play important roles in branching morphogenesis, alveolar development, and cellular differentiation. Expression of the genes encoding these morphogens and their receptors is controlled by a variety of transcription factors that also are highly regulated. Several of these transcription factors serve dual roles as regulators of genes involved in early lung development and in specialized functions of differentiated cells. Targeted null mutations of genes encoding many of these morphogens and transcription factors have provided important insight into their function during lung development. In this chapter, the cellular and molecular mechanisms that control lung development are considered, as well as those that regulate expression of the genes encoding the surfactant proteins.

INTRODUCTION

Branching morphogenesis, growth, and differentiation of the fetal lung and development of its capacity to synthesize the lipoprotein surfactant are extraordinarily complex and highly orchestrated processes that are essential for transition of the fetus from an aqueous to an air-breathing environment. It is clear that reciprocal interactions between epithelial cells derived from foregut endoderm and surrounding splanchnic mesoderm are essential for the elaboration of a variety of growth and differentiation factors, which play critical roles in morphologic development,

0066–4278/00/0315–0875$12.00

875

cellular differentiation, vasculogenesis, and synthesis of surfactant lipids and proteins. Systemically derived hormones and factors also serve important regulatory roles, particularly during the latter third of gestation after establishment of capillary networks within the fetal lung has taken place. In recent years, there have been major advances in our knowledge concerning the transcription factors that regulate formation and differentiation of the developing lung and expression of the genes encoding the lung surfactant proteins. Interestingly, a number of these transcription factors appear to serve dual roles in the control of morphologic development and expression of the surfactant protein genes. It is the objective of this review to provide a current perspective of these transcription factors, the roles that they play, and our present understanding of the mechanisms involved in their activation. The first half of this chapter concerns the morphologic phases of fetal lung development, the growth factors that appear to regulate this process, and the transcription factors that control their expression and mediate their actions. The second half considers the properties of surfactant lipids and proteins, their regulation by hormones and factors, the transcription factors that appear to mediate developmental and hormonal regulation of surfactant protein gene expression in fetal lung, and the mechanisms involved in transcription factor regulation.

LUNG DEVELOPMENT AND ITS REGULATION

Lung Morphogenesis

Lung development is initiated in the embryo as a ventral outpouching of endodermal cells from the anterior foregut into the surrounding mesenchyme at 9.5 days postconception (E9.5) in the mouse and ~3 weeks gestation in the human (for review see Reference 1). This ventral diverticulum grows caudally to form the primitive trachea and subsequently divides to form the two lung buds. Division of the foregut by a longitudinal septum separates the ventral trachea from the dorsal esophagus. Between the 7th and 16th weeks of human gestation (pseudoglandular phase; E9.5–E16 in the mouse), the lung buds undergo repeated dichotomous branching to form the bronchioles, respiratory bronchioles, and the alveolar ducts. During the early pseudoglandular phase when branching morphogenesis is actively taking place, the ductular epithelial cells remain relatively undifferentiated. It is apparent that paracrine factors produced by the surrounding splanchnic mesenchyme are essential for the dichotomous branching of the bronchiolar epithelium during this phase of development. The 16th through 24th weeks of human gestation (E16–E17 in the mouse) make up the canalicular phase of lung development. During this period, the rapid growth rate diminishes, dichotomous branching has been completed, and differentiation of the epithelial cells lining the ducts begins to take place. This phase is characterized by the initiation of capillary growth within the developing lung and the first appearance of type II cells containing lamellar bodies, the cellular organelles that contain lung surfactant. During the terminal saccular phase of lung development (weeks 25 to term in the human fetus; E17 to term in the mouse), there is continued growth of capillaries and remodeling of the distal lung to resemble adult lung parenchyma. This remodeling involves continued development of capillary networks, cellular differentiation, thinning of mesenchyme-derived stroma, and expansion of presumptive alveoli (1). Augmented surfactant synthesis and secretion occur after ~30 weeks gestation in preparation for the transition to air breathing (see below).

Regulatory Factors in Lung Development

Members of the fibroblast growth factor (FGF), transforming growth factor-β (TGF-β), and epidermal growth factor (EGF) families, as well as the secreted morphogen, sonic hedgehog (Shh), appear to play important regulatory roles in lung branching morphogenesis and epithelial cell differentiation.

FGF Family   There is accumulating evidence to suggest that FGF family members serve an important role as mediators of the mesenchymal-epithelial interactions essential for lung bud formation, branching morphogenesis, and cellular differentiation (2, 3). FGF-10, which is produced by the splanchnic mesenchyme surrounding the lung buds as early as E9.5 in the mouse (4), appears to play a critical role in lung bud outgrowth formation through binding to the FGF type 2 receptor (FGFR2), which is uniformly expressed in endoderm (4, 5). Mice homozygous for a targeted deletion in the FGF-10 gene *(fgf10$^{-/-}$)* have a trachea, but no bronchi or lungs (6), implicating the importance of FGF-10 in the formation of bronchi and in branching morphogenesis of peripheral lung tissues. The phenotype of these mice is nearly identical to that of transgenic mice expressing a dominant-negative form of FGFR2 under control of the human surfactant protein (SP)-C promoter (7).

FGF-7 (keratinocyte growth factor, KGF), another member of the mesenchyme-derived FGF family, also appears to be important in lung development. FGF-7, which also binds to the FGFR2 receptor, is expressed early in lung development and appears to play a role as a proliferation factor for lung epithelium (8–10).

Sonic Hedgehog   The secreted morphogen sonic hedgehog (Shh), which is widely produced by the foregut endoderm, is upregulated specifically in distal regions where branching occurs (11–13). Shh, which binds to the patched-smoothened receptor complex in mesenchyme (14), plays a critical role in epithelial patterning by stimulating mesenchyme proliferation and regulating its capacity to produce FGF-10. In transgenic mice carrying an *SP-C:Shh* fusion gene, which promotes inappropriate expression of *Shh* throughout the distal lung epithelium, there is increased epithelial and mesenchymal proliferation and a lack of functional alveoli (15). On the other hand, in *Shh$^{-/-}$* mutant mouse embryos, the lungs form a rudimentary sac due to an absence of branching morphogenesis of the primary lung buds, with greatly reduced mesenchymal proliferation and increased expression of *fgf-10* (16, 17). The mutant mice also lack the dorsal-ventral separation of the esophagus and trachea. Surprisingly, the lungs of the *Shh* null mice exhibit normal proximo-distal differentiation of epithelial cells. Proximally, the lung epithelium expresses the gene-encoding Clara cell secretory protein (CCSP or CC-10), whereas more distally, alveolar sacs express the type II cell-specific protein, SP-C (17). These findings indicate that whereas Shh is essential for formation of the tracheo-esophageal septum, for branching morphogenesis and lobation, it is not critical for differentiation of pulmonary epithelium.

TGF-β Family   TGF-β family members bind to receptor serine/threonine kinases. Mice homozygous for a targeted deletion of the gene encoding TGF-β3 manifest delayed pulmonary development and decreased *SP-C* expression (18), suggesting an essential role of TGF-β3 in lung morphogenesis. By contrast, TGF-β1 decreases branching morphogenesis and formation of saccular buds in cultured embryonic lung buds (19) and in transgenic mice overexpressing a constitutively active form in lung epithelium (20), while abrogation of TGF-β type II receptor signaling results in increased embryonic lung branching morphogenesis in culture (21).

Bone morphogenetic protein-4 (BMP-4), another member of the TGF-β super-family, is expressed at high levels in epithelium at the distal ends of lung buds and at lower levels in mesenchyme (22). Overexpression of *bmp-4* throughout developing lung epithelium in transgenic mice carrying *SP-C:bmp-4* fusion genes results in aberrant lung morphogenesis, reduced numbers of type II cells, and decreased epithelial cell proliferation (23). It has been suggested that BMP-4 specifically inhibits proliferation of epithelial cells at the tips of the end buds to facilitate branching (23).

EGF and PDGF Families   EGF is produced by epithelial and mesenchymal cells in developing lung. Targeted deletion of the gene encoding the EGF receptor (EGFR) in mice was found to have variable effects on lung morphogenesis and function depending upon the genetic background. Whereas EGFR$^{-/-}$ mice in a CF-1 background died by E7.5 to E8.5, a small percentage of EGFR$^{-/-}$ CD-1 outbred mice survived to term. Although the survivors had numerous defects that prevented them from living beyond 3 weeks of age, lung morphologic and bio-chemical development were apparently unaffected (24).

PDGFs are encoded by the *PDGF-A* and *-B* genes and bind as homo- or heterodimers to the PDGFα or PDGFβ tyrosine kinase receptors. Whereas, tar-geted deletion of the *PDGF-B* gene in mice had no apparent effects on lung development (25), mice homozygous for targeted deletion of the *PDGF-A* gene manifested hyperinflated alveoli with emphysema that resulted from defects in septation. The findings indicate that PDGF-A, which is produced by developing lung epithelium and binds to the PDGFαR in mesenchyme, plays a critical role in alveologenesis by regulating proliferation and migration of smooth muscle cells surrounding developing alveoli.

Cyclic AMP   The majority of studies of the effects of cyclic AMP (cAMP) on morphologic development of the fetal lung have been carried out using fetal lung explants maintained in organ culture. Lung explants from midgestation human abortuses (26, 27) and 19- or 21-day gestational age fetal rabbits (28) differentiate spontaneously when placed in organ culture in serum-free, defined medium. Before culture, the tissue is composed of small ducts surrounded by abundant connective tissue; the ductular epithelial cells are columnar and contain no lamellar bodies. Within 2 to 4 days of organ culture, the ducts enlarge, the amount of connective tissue is decreased, and the epithelium differentiates into recognizable type II cells containing lamellar bodies (26). These changes in morphology are associated with an induction of the levels of SP-A mRNA and protein and increased synthesis of surfactant glycerophospholipids (26–30).

Treatment of lung explants with dibutyryl cAMP (Bt$_2$cAMP) causes an enlargement of the prealveolar ducts and accelerates the rate of type II cell differentiation compared with tissues cultured in control medium (31). These effects of cAMP on morphologic development are apparent only at early time points of culture. After longer periods of incubation, volume densities of type II cells and of the lumens of prealveolar ducts of control explants are increased to levels comparable to those of cAMP-treated tissues (31). The spontaneous differentiation of midgestation fetal lung cultured in control medium may be caused by endogenously produced prostaglandins (32) and other factors that increase cAMP formation. In other studies, we also observed that spontaneous differentiation and cAMP induction of *SP-A* gene expression in the cultured lung tissue is dependent upon the oxygen tension of the environment; at environmental oxygen tensions of $\leq 5\%$ the effects of Bt$_2$cAMP on morphology and on *SP-A* gene expression were abolished (33).

Glucocorticoids   A role for glucocorticoids in lung development was originally suggested by the findings that cortisol treatment of fetal lambs accelerated lung maturation (34). Since that initial report, numerous studies have suggested that glucocorticoids enhance lung development and type II cell differentiation. Treatment of pregnant rabbits with the synthetic glucocorticoid betamethasone on days 25 and 26 of gestation (term = day 31) was found to increase the volume density of presumptive airspaces and the proportion of type II cells in the prealveolar epithelium of the fetal lungs (35). Glucocorticoid receptor (*GR*) mRNA is primarily localized to lung mesenchyme, although bronchial epithelium manifests low levels of *GR* transcripts (36). Interestingly, it has been suggested that glucocorticoids act on the fetal lung fibroblast to promote synthesis of a differentiation factor termed fibroblast pneumonocyte factor (FPF), which acts on lung epithelium to enhance alveolar type II cell differentiation and surfactant synthesis (37). To date, FPF has not been isolated and characterized.

Transcription Factors Involved in Lung Morphogenesis

Gli *Gene Family*   The *Gli* family comprises three genes encoding transcription factors, Gli1, Gli2, and Gli3, each containing five zinc fingers. The *Gli* genes are expressed in splanchnic and lung mesenchyme in different spatiotemporal patterns during embryonic lung development. It was found that all three *Gli* genes are expressed during early lung development, and expression declines toward birth (38); however, the temporal patterns of expression of *Gli1* and *Gli3* are more similar to that of *Shh* and the gene encoding its receptor Patched than is that of *Gli2* (38). Transgenic mouse studies suggest that the *Gli1* gene is a target of *Shh* and that Gli1 may mediate Shh regulation of *patched* expression (38). In mice homozygous for a targeted deletion of the *Gli3* gene, the lungs are reduced in size and there is a disproportional decrease in length of the left lobe (38). By contrast, in $Gli2^{-/-}$ mice, both lungs are markedly reduced in size because of defects in lung proliferation (39). Furthermore, the right lung has only one lobe, instead of the normal four lobes. Despite these defects in lung morphogenesis, expression of *SP-C* and *CCSP* as markers of lung epithelial cell differentiation are similar to that of wild-type embryos (39). Whereas, *Shh* expression in the *Gli2* null embryos are unaffected, expression levels of *patched* and *Gli1* are reduced, suggesting a decreased response to the Shh signal (39). In $Gli2^{-/-}/Gli3^{+/-}$ mice, there is failure of separation of the trachea and esophagus; the lung is more hypoplastic and does not separate into right and left lobes. On the other hand, mice homozygous for deletion of both *Gli2* and *Gli3* genes ($Gli2^{-/-}/Gli3^{-/-}$) mostly die at E10.5; however, those surviving until E13.5–E14.5 lack lungs, trachea, and esophagus (39). These findings indicate the essential role of mesenchymally expressed *Gli2* and *Gli3* in development of the foregut endoderm into trachea, esophagus, and lungs and highlight the importance of interactions between the splanchnic mesenchyme and foregut endoderm in development of the lung and trachea. The finding that the lung and tracheal/esophageal phenotype of the $Gli2^{-/-}$ and $Gli2^{-/-}/Gli3^{+/-}$ embryos is similar to that of $Shh^{-/-}$ mice suggests that transcription factors Gli2 and Gli3 mediate the effects of Shh on foregut development into these structures.

Retinoid Receptors   Retinoids appear to have a role in maintaining the differentiated state of the respiratory epithelium. These effects presumably are mediated by retinoid receptors, which are members of the nuclear receptor superfamily that regulate expression of target genes. There are three related retinoic acid receptors (RARs), RAR-α, -β, and -γ, that exist in several isoforms. RARs regulate expression of retinoid responsive genes by binding to retinoic acid responsive elements (RAREs) as heterodimers with the related retinoid-X receptors (RXR-α, -β, and -γ). RAR-α is expressed ubiquitously throughout the developing mouse lung (40). RAR-β2 is expressed in foregut endoderm and bronchial epithelium, as well as in tracheal epithelium and mesenchyme. Whereas, RAR-β2 is not detectable in epithelium of the distal lung, it has been found in distal lung mesenchyme (40).

In a detailed analysis of the effects of targeted deletions of various members of the RAR and RXR subfamilies, it was found that, whereas RXR-$\alpha^{-/-}$ mouse embryos have defects in heart and liver development, there is no obvious lung phenotype (41). Similarly, mice carrying double knockouts of *RXR*-α and *RAR*-α or *RAR*-γ genes were not reported to manifest a lung phenotype (42). However, mice carrying targeted deletions of both the *RAR-α1* and *RAR-β2* genes manifest failure of separation of the esophagus and trachea, agenesis and hypoplasia of the left lung, hypoplasia of the right lung, and defects in lobation. There also are abnormalities in cartilage formation in the larynx and trachea (43). Interestingly, the defects in lung morphogenesis and tracheal/esophageal separation in the *RAR*-α1/*RAR*-β2 double-knockout mice are highly similar to those observed in *Shh*$^{-/-}$ and in *Gli2*$^{-/-}$/*Gli3*$^{+/-}$ embryos, suggesting an interrelationship of Shh/Gli and retinoid signaling pathways in lung development.

SMAD Transcription Factors   As discussed above, TGF-β ligands exert an inhibitory effect on lung branching morphogenesis. These actions of TGF-β are mediated by binding to the TGF-βIIR, a serine/threonine kinase. In response to TGF-β binding, the type II receptor heterodimerizes with the type I receptor, which in turn is phosphorylated. The activated type I receptor subsequently recruits and phosphorylates receptor-regulated SMAD proteins (SMAD2 or SMAD3), which in turn associate with another SMAD protein (SMAD4) and move into the nucleus. Within the nucleus, the SMAD heterodimeric complex associates with a DNA-binding protein (e.g. the forkhead transcription factor, FAST-1) that mediates binding of the SMAD complex to TGF-β responsive genes (44). In studies using antisense oligonucleotides to attenuate the actions of SMAD2, -3, and -4 in E11 embryonic mouse lung cultures, a concentration-dependent increase in branching morphogenesis was observed (45). Addition of exogenous TGF-β1 did not overcome the stimulatory effect of the antisense SMAD oligonucleotides on lung branching. Because SMAD2 and -3 are 97% identical, the antisense oligonucleotides to SMAD2 and -3 also inhibit one another's expression. It was, therefore, concluded that SMAD2 and/or SMAD3, as well as SMAD4, mediate the inhibitory actions of TGF-β on branching morphogenesis in developing lung (45).

N-myc   N-*myc* is a member of a family of proto-oncogenes (including c-*myc* and L-*myc),* encoding basic helix-loop-helix-leucine zipper (bHLH-LZ) transcription factors that bind as heterodimers with the bHLH-LZ protein Max (46) to regulatory elements of genes involved in cellular proliferation and differentiation. N-*myc* expression is confined to certain epithelial cell lineages of the embryo and is not detected in mesenchyme (47). N-*myc* expression is elevated in these epithelial cells at early stages of differentiation and is later downregulated. In developing lung, N-*myc* expression is particularly high in bronchiolar epithelium at the distal tips of developing airways (48). N-*myc*$^{-/-}$ embryos die at E11.5 and have major defects in heart, central nervous system, mesonephros, lung, and gut development (47). A more revealing view of the role of N-*myc* in embryonic development was achieved in another study in which a leaky mutation of the N-*myc* gene was created that reduced expression of the normal N-myc transcripts by 25 to 50% (48). Mice homozygous for this hypomorphic mutation die at birth from respiratory distress caused by severe defects in lung branching morphogenesis. The lungs are ~50% of the size of those of wild-type mice and have reduced numbers of airspaces, suggesting a role of N-myc in mediating proliferation of lung epithelium in response to growth factor signals derived from lung mesenchyme. The homozygous mutant mice also manifest a marked reduction in spleen size; however, none of the other organs that normally express N-*myc* appear to be affected (48). In another series of experiments, mice carrying the leaky N-*myc* mutation were crossed with the N-*myc* null mutants to create compound heterozygotes (49). The compound heterozygotes, which expressed N-*myc* at ~15% of wild-type levels, have more severe defects in lung branching morphogenesis and heart development than the homozygous leaky mutants and die at ~E12 to E15 (49). Although lung buds form in these mutants, there is only a rudimentary branching pattern evident at E12.5, similar to the lung phenotype in homozygous N-*myc* null embryos (48). These findings suggest that although N-myc does not appear to be involved in formation of the lung buds, it does play an important role in branching morphogenesis.

Thyroid Transcription Factor-1 (TTF-1/Nkx2.1)   Nkx2.1/TTF-1/T/ebp is a homeodomain transcription factor selectively expressed in thyroid and lung epithelium and in specific regions within the diencephalon of the brain (50). TTF-1 serves a regulatory role in expression of thyroid-specific genes, including thyroid peroxidase (51); thyroglobulin (52) and the thyrotropin receptor (53); and the lung-specific genes *SP-A* (54–56), *SP-B* (57), *SP-C* (58), and *CCSP* (59, 60). *TTF-1* expression is first detected in the rat embryo at ~E10.5 in the thyroid anlagen, the primitive bronchial epithelium and in the floor of the diencephalon and infundibulum (equivalent to E9–9.5 in the mouse) (50, 61). Mice homozygous for a targeted deletion of the *TTF-1* gene develop to term but are stillborn. The mutant mice lack thyroid, ventral forebrain, and pituitary gland (61). Although lung lobar bronchi are present, there is an absence of lung parenchyma, suggesting a role of *TTF-1* in branching morphogenesis of the lobar bronchi (61). In the *TTF-1* null mice, the lobar bronchi are connected to dilated sacs. Furthermore, there is a failure of septation of the anterior foregut along the dorsoventral axis to form distinct tracheal and esophageal structures (62), similar to that observed in mice lacking genes encoding RAR-α1/-β2, Gli2, or Shh. Expression of *bmp-4* in lung epithelium of the *TTF-1* null mice was found to be markedly reduced compared with that in wild-type mice, although *Shh* expression appeared normal (62). These findings suggest a possible role of TTF-1 in the regulation of *bmp-4* expression. The 5'-flanking region of the *TTF-1* gene contains binding sites for the transcription factor HNF-3 family members. In a transfected mouse lung epithelial (MLE) cell line, HNF-3β was found to increase expression of a cotrans-

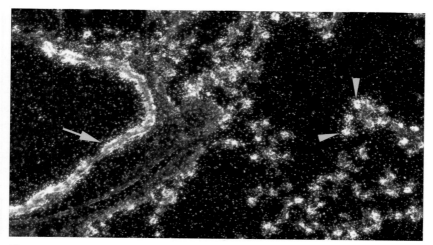

Figure 2 *SP-A:hGH* fusion genes containing 378-bp of *SP-A 5'*-flanking DNA are expressed in type II cells and in bronchioalveolar epithelial cells in lung tissues of transgenic mice. Lung tissue sections from an adult transgenic mouse carrying an *SP-A_378:hGH* fusion gene were subjected to in situ hybridization analysis using an 35S-labeled anti-sense hGH cRNA probe and examined by dark-field microscopy. *hGH* mRNA transcripts are detectable in type II cells (arrowheads) and in bronchiolar epithelium (arrow) (x 330) *hGH* mRNA transcripts were not detected in lung sections from non-transgenic littermates hybridized with the 35S-labeled *hGH* cRNA probe (not shown). Reprinted in a modified form from Alcorn et al (177), with permission.

fected *TTF-1:luciferase* fusion gene (63). *TTF-1* promoter activity also is increased by cotransfection of the zinc finger transcription factor GATA-6, which is co-expressed with *TTF-1* in developing lung epithelium (64) and in type II cells isolated from adult lung tissue (65).

Hepatocyte Nuclear Factor 3β (HNF-3β)   HNF-3β, a member of the winged helix family of transcription factors related to the Drosophila forkhead DNA-binding protein, is expressed in gut endoderm from the earliest stages of its development. During mouse embryogenesis, HNF-3β transcripts are detected in the anterior portion of the primitive streak, which gives rise to endoderm, and subsequently in epithelial cells of endodermally derived organs, including the intestine, lung, liver, and pancreas (66, 67). In developing lung, HNF-3β is expressed at higher levels in epithelial cells lining the proximal airways than in cells of the distal airways, suggesting an anterior-posterior gradient (68).

Targeted mutagenesis of the HNF-3β gene in mice results in embryonic lethality between E9.5 and E11.5. In HNF-3β null embryos, there is an absence of node and its derived notochord, as well as a lack of gut development (66). By contrast, in transgenic mice overexpressing HNF-3β in distal lung epithelium under control of the human *SP-C* promoter, there is a disruption of branching morphogenesis and arrest of differentiation of distal lung epithelial cells at the late pseudoglandular stage of development, which results in perinatal death (68). Vasculogenesis is also adversely affected, as is expression of the cell adhesion protein E-cadherin. Interestingly, differentiating lung epithelial cells in the *SP-C/ HNF-3β* transgenic mice lack lamellar bodies and glycogen, which serves as a reservoir of precursors for surfactant glycerophospholipid synthesis. Although mRNAs encoding SP-A, SP-B, and SP-C are detected in lung epithelial cells, neither SP-A protein nor the proproteins for SP-B and SP-C are detectable, which suggests a defect in posttranscriptional processing (68). The finding that expression of *TTF-1* appears to be normal in the lungs of the transgenic mice is surprising in light of the observation that HNF-3β activates *TTF-1* expression in transfected MLE cells (63). It was suggested that reversal of the normal proximal-to-distal gradient of endogenous HNF-3β by overexpression of exogenous HNF-3β in the distal respiratory epithelium of the transgenic mice may have interfered with the actions of other members of the winged helix transcription factor family by competing for binding to *cis*-acting elements and/or altering their ability to transactivate key regulatory genes (68).

Hepatocyte Nuclear Factor/Forkhead Homologue 4 (HFH-4)   HFH-4, another member of the winged helix family of transcription factors, is expressed in lung, spermatids, oviduct, choroid plexus, and fetal kidney (69). In lung, *hfh-4* expression is restricted to bronchial and bronchiolar epithelium; expression is detected from the mid-pseudoglandular phase, continues postnatally (70, 71), and is evident in ciliated cells of the respiratory tract (69). In *hfh-4*$^{-/-}$ mice, there is an absence of ciliated cells in all tissues, including the respiratory tract, suggesting a role for *hfh-4* in differentiation and/or maintenance of ciliated cells (69). The finding that *hfh-4* expression is evident in subsets of lung epithelial cells in $TTF-1^{-/-}$ mice suggests that differentiation of the ciliated lung epithelium is independent of TTF-1 (72).

Glucocorticoid Receptor   The glucocorticoid receptor (GR) is a member of the nuclear receptor superfamily of transcription factors. Upon binding hormone, GR dissociates from a complex with heat shock proteins, enters the nucleus, and binds as an activated homodimer to specific glucocorticoid response elements (GREs) in the regulatory regions of target genes. The GR dimer bound to the GRE recruits coactivator proteins, which facilitate formation of a stable preinitiation complex resulting in binding of RNA polymerase II and transcription initiation (73). GR mRNA expression, which is detectable in embryonic lung during the pseudo-glandular phase, appears to be localized mainly to mesenchyme, although lower levels of GR can be detected in bronchial epithelium (36). As mentioned above, the effects of GR on lung may be mediated by GR induction of a mesenchymal factor(s) that acts upon the epithelium to regulate morphogenesis and function (37).

The finding that mice homozygous for targeted deletion of the *GR* gene ($GR^{-/-}$) die within several hours of birth as a result of respiratory failure caused by atelectatic underdeveloped lungs (74) emphasizes the importance of GR in lung development. It was suggested that the lack of GR impaired development of the terminal bronchioles and alveoli beyond E15.5. Of note, however, was the finding of comparable numbers of alveolar type II cells and apparently normal levels of mRNA encoding SP-A, SP-B, and SP-C in lung tissues of newborn $GR^{-/-}$ mice, compared with those in heterozygous or wild-type animals (74). The recent report that mice homozygous for a point mutation in the GR that prevents its dimerization and DNA-binding are viable, despite lack of inducibility of a number of GR-regulated genes, suggests that the actions of glucocorticoids to enhance lung development occur through DNA-binding–independent mechanisms (75). The importance of glucocorticoids in lung development is further indicated by findings that *corticotropin-releasing hormone* (*crh*) gene-targeted mice develop cyanosis and die within 24 h of birth (76). These mice manifest adrenal atrophy and impaired production of glucocorticoids (77). The lungs of the $crh^{-/-}$ mice exhibit an increase in mesenchymal and epithelial cellularity primarily from increased cell proliferation (76).

We have observed that glucocorticoids have profound effects on morphologic development of midgestation human fetal lung in organ culture. Dexamethasone (Dex) has dose-dependent biphasic effects on volume density of alveolar lumen and of type II cells (78). At a concentration of 10^{-10}M, Dex increases both alveolar lumen size and type II cell volume density. Surprisingly, incubation with Dex at 10^{-7}M causes a significant decrease in both type II cell and alveolar lumen volume densities compared with explants incubated in control medium. These biphasic effects of Dex on morphology of the human fetal lung tissue mirror glucocorticoid effects on the levels of SP-A mRNA and protein (see below).

Cyclic AMP Response Element-Binding Protein (CREB)   cAMP regulates transcription of a wide variety of eukaryotic genes. Stimulatory effects of cAMP on gene expression can be mediated by cAMP-dependent protein kinase (PKA) phosphorylation of the transcription factor CREB, a member of the basic leucine zipper (bZIP) superfamily of transcription factors (79). A role of CREB in fetal lung development is suggested by recent findings that mice homozygous for a targeted deletion of the *creb* gene die within 15 min of birth from severe atelectasis (80). Interestingly, the lungs of these animals contain normal levels of the surfactant proteins SP-A, SP-B, and SP-C; however, *SP-D* levels in the lungs of $creb^{-/-}$ mice are only 20% of those of the wild-type mice. Because mice homozygous for targeted deletion of the *SP-D* gene are viable (81, 82), it is unlikely that this decrease in *SP-D* expression in the $creb^{-/-}$ mice contributes to their perinatal mortality.

CCAAT-Enhancer-Binding Proteins (C/EBPs)   C/EBPα, β, and δ are closely related members of a family of bZIP transcription factors postulated to serve important roles in adipocyte differentiation (83, 84). Furthermore, C/EBPs are expressed at relatively high levels in tissues that have the capacity to synthesize, store, and metabolize lipids at exceptionally high rates, including adipose tissue, liver, placenta, small intestine, and lung (85). Whereas *c/ebpα* is expressed at highest levels in liver and adipose tissues, *c/ebpβ* expression is more widespread, although it is detected at the highest levels in intestine, liver, lung, and adipose tissues (86). On the other hand, *c/ebpδ* is expressed at highest levels in lung, with lower levels in intestine and adipose tissues (85, 86). All three family members are expressed in lung epithelium (87, 88, L Wang & CR Mendelson, unpublished observations). *c/ebpα* expression is detectable in fetal rat lung just prior to birth; expression is restricted to type II cells and is extinguished when the type II cells de-differentiate in culture on plastic dishes (87). On the other hand, *c/ebpδ* expression is developmentally regulated in fetal rabbit lung, reaching peak levels in association with the temporal induction of type II cell differentiation and surfactant synthesis (88). A role of C/EBPα in lung development is suggested by the finding that mice homozygous for a targeted mutation of the *c/ebpα* gene have lungs described as "morphologically immature" due to the presence of multicellular layers of epithelial cells lining the alveolar ducts (89). Based on this finding, it is likely that C/EBPα maintains a quiescent state and restricts type II cell proliferation. The $c/ebp\alpha^{-/-}$ mice die within 10 h after birth from severe hypoglycemia caused by defective neonatal induction of liver enzymes required for glucose metabolism (90); however, ~20% of the $c/ebp\alpha^{-/-}$ mice die immediately after birth from apparent respiratory distress (89). The cause of the respiratory distress is unclear because expression of *TTF-1, SP-C,* and *CCSP* appear to be normal in lungs of the $c/ebp\alpha^{-/-}$ mice (89). Mice lacking both *c/ebpβ* and *c/ebpδ* die during early postnatal development; however, in contrast to the *c/ebpα* $-/-$ mice, the *c/ebpβ* $^{-/-}$/*c/ebpδ* $^{-/-}$ mice manifest no histological abnormalities of the lung and are not hypoglycemic (91).

SURFACTANT PROTEIN GENE EXPRESSION AND ITS REGULATION

Lung Surfactant Composition and Function

Pulmonary surfactant is a developmentally and hormonally regulated phospholipid-rich lipoprotein synthesized exclusively by type II cells of the lung alveoli where surfactant is stored as lamellated inclusions termed lamellar bodies. The lamellar bodies are secreted into the lumens of the lung alveoli where they unwind and are transformed into the quadratic lattice structure of tubular myelin. This, in turn, gives rise to a monolayer surface film of surfactant lipids and proteins, which act to reduce surface tension, increase compliance, and prevent alveolar collapse. Prematurely born infants that manifest inadequate surfactant synthesis are at risk of developing respiratory distress syndrome (RDS), the leading cause of neonatal morbidity and mortality in developed countries. Surfactant is composed primarily of phosphatidylcholine (PC). The principal glycerophospholipid is a disaturated form of PC, dipalmitoylphosphatidylcholine (DPPC), which has remarkable surface-active properties (for review, see 92).

Lung surfactant contains four associated proteins, surfactant protein (SP)-A, SP-B, SP-C, and SP-D. SP-B and SP-C, extremely hydrophobic proteins of 79 and 35 amino acids, respectively, are derived from higher molecular weight precursors by proteolytic processing (93, 94). These hydrophobic proteins serve a critical role in adsorption and spreading of the surfactant surface film at the alveolar air-liquid interface (92). Infants born with congenital SP-B deficiency (95) and mice with a targeted deletion of the *SP-B* gene (96) succumb to respiratory distress syndrome because of inadequate surfactant function. Interestingly, in both SP-B–deficient humans and mice, there is incomplete processing of SP-C (97), suggesting a possible role of SP-B in SP-C transport and processing. SP-A and SP-D are members of the collectin sub-group of the C-type lectin family of proteins (98) and contain N-terminal collagen-like and C-terminal lectin-like domains. In gene targeting studies in mice, $SP\text{-}D^{-/-}$ mice developed marked accumulation of surfactant lipids and proteins within the lung alveoli and in alveolar macrophages, suggesting a major role of SP-D in re-uptake and metabolism of secreted surfactant (81, 82). The lungs of $SP\text{-}A^{-/-}$ mice lack tubular myelin and clear *Pseudomonas aeruginosa* and group B streptococci less efficiently than wild-type mice, suggesting a role of SP-A in immune defense within the alveolus (99, 100).

The Surfactant Protein Genes and Their Regulation

In consideration of the substantial literature that has accumulated since we last reviewed this subject in the *Annual Review of Physiology* (101), we place major emphasis in the present review on regulation of *SP-A* gene expression as a prototype to be compared with findings of regulatory mechanisms for *SP-B, SP-C* and *SP-D* gene expression. Pertinent reviews on regulation of the other surfactant protein genes are cited whenever possible.

Cell-Specific and Developmental Regulation of Expression   SP-A is encoded by two highly similar genes (*SP-A1* and *SP-A2*) in humans (102, 103) and baboons (104) and by a single-copy gene in mice (105), rats (106), and rabbits (107, 108). *SP-A* gene expression is essentially lung specific (107), occurs primarily in alveolar type II cells, and to a lesser extent in bronchioalveolar epithelial (Clara) cells of the proximal and distal airways (109–111). In second trimester human fetal lung, SP-A mRNA and protein have also been detected in nonmucous tracheal and bronchial glands, and in isolated cells of conducting airway epithelium (112). *SP-A* expression in fetal lung is developmentally regulated; *SP-A* gene transcription is initiated in fetal lung after ~75% of gestation is completed and reaches maximal levels just prior to birth (101). The developmental induction of *SP-A* gene expression in fetal lung is more closely associated with the increase in surfactant glycerophospholipid synthesis and appearance of identifiable type II cells than is the temporal regulation of the genes encoding *SP-B, SP-C,* and *SP-D* (see below). For example, *SP-A* gene transcription is first discernible in fetal rabbit lung tissue on day 24 of gestation and reaches maximum levels by day 28 (113). The developmental induction of *SP-A* gene transcription is associated with the appearance of SP-A mRNA and protein on day 26 (29, 30, 107, 111), in concert with the appearance of differentiated type II cells (114), and just prior to induction of augmented surfactant glycerophospholipid synthesis. In human fetal lung tissue, SP-A mRNA and protein are undetectable at 16 to 20 weeks of gestation (115, 116). Immunoreactive SP-A protein is detectable in amniotic fluid at 30 weeks of gestation and is increased further during development in association with the increase in the lecithin:sphingomyelin (L/S) ratio in amniotic fluid (117).

SP-B and SP-C proproteins are encoded by single-copy genes that are expressed in an essentially lung-specific manner. Whereas SP-B mRNA transcripts are present both in type II and in bronchiolar epithelial cells (118), *SP-C* gene expression is restricted to type II cells (119–122). *SP-B* and *SP-C* gene expression is initiated at an earlier stage in fetal development than is *SP-A*. In fetal rabbit lung tissue, SP-C mRNA transcripts are detectable as early as day 19 of gestation, ~1 week prior to the appearance of differentiated type II cells (122, 123). SP-B mRNA transcripts were first detected in cuboidal prealveolar epithelial cells of fetal rabbit lung tissue on day 24 of gestation (111). In human fetal lung, mRNAs for SP-B and SP-C are detectable as early as 13 weeks of gestation (124,

125) and continue to increase during development so that by 24 weeks the levels of SP-B and SP-C mRNA are 50 and 15%, respectively, of adult levels (124).These findings are indicative that the genes encoding *SP-A, SP-B,* and *SP-C* are independently regulated during fetal and postnatal development.

SP-D is encoded by a single-copy gene that is expressed in nonciliated bronchioalveolar epithelial and type II cells and tracheobronchial glands of lung, as well as in salivary and lacrimal glands, gastric mucosa, and in mammary and sweat glands (126). SP-D protein and mRNA levels are detectable in fetal rat lung tissue late in gestation, just prior to birth, and continue to increase during the early postnatal period, reaching their highest levels in adults (126). In human fetal lung, SP-D mRNA is first detected at low levels in the second trimester; expression continues to increase throughout fetal development and postnatally (127).

Multifactorial Regulation Surfactant protein gene expression in fetal lung appears to be regulated by a number of hormones and factors: retinoids, insulin, growth factors, cytokines, glucocorticoids, and agents that increase formation of cAMP (for review, see 128). In studies using midgestation human fetal lung in culture, we have found that cAMP and glucocorticoids have the most pronounced regulatory effects on *SP-A* expression. Effects of cAMP on expression of *SP-B* and *SP-C* genes are more modest; glucocorticoid effects are more pronounced. Whereas cAMP effects on SP-A, SP-B, and SP-C are primarily exerted at the level of gene transcription, glucocorticoid actions are far more complex, may be indirect, and appear to involve transcriptional and posttranscriptional mechanisms.

Cyclic AMP cAMP increases expression of the *SP-A* gene in rabbit, baboon, and human fetal lung tissue in culture. The stimulatory effects of cAMP on SP-A mRNA levels are associated with comparable stimulatory effects on *SP-A* gene transcription (113, 129, 130). By contrast, the rat (131, 132) and mouse (JL Alcorn & CR Mendelson, unpublished data) *SP-A* genes are unresponsive to cAMP. Since we have found that cAMP greatly stimulates promoter activity of the human, rabbit, and baboon *SP-A* genes in transfected rat type II cells in primary culture, (132–134), it is likely that differences in cAMP responsiveness are due to species-specific differences in *cis*-acting regulatory elements, rather than in *trans*-acting factors. In studies using midgestation human fetal lung explants, it was found that the *hSP-A2* gene is far more responsive to the inductive effects of cAMP analogues than is the gene encoding *hSP-A1* (135, 136), whereas both *bSP-A1* and *bSP-A2* genes appear to be equivalently induced by cAMP treatment (56). Because the sequences of the *bSP-A1* and *bSP-A2* genes are more similar to each other than those of *hSP-A1* and *hSP-A2* (104), it is likely that during evolution, divergence of the *hSP-A1* gene resulted in a decrease in its responsiveness to cAMP. Although the hormones and factors that increase cAMP formation by type II cells in fetal lung during development have not been defined, our findings suggest that catecholamines acting through β-adrenergic receptors (31), vasoactive intestinal peptide (VIP) produced by nerve endings in the lung (137; K Ozsvath, V Boggaram CR Mendelson, unpublished observations), and locally produced prostaglandin E_2 (PGE_2) and prostacyclin (32), may act by cAMP-mediated mechanisms to increase *SP-A* expression.

cAMP analogues appear to have only modest stimulatory effects on SP-B and SP-C mRNA levels in human fetal lung in culture (124, 125) compared with their marked stimulatory effects on *SP-A* gene expression. Furthermore, the effects of cAMP analogues on the levels of SP-B and SP-C mRNA in human fetal lung in culture were not found to be associated with any changes in the levels of the corresponding immunoreactive polypeptides (124). In studies using lung explants from 18-day fetal rats, cAMP analogues were found to have a modest effect on the levels of mRNA for SP-B (138), whereas a more pronounounced stimulatory effect on *SP-C* gene expression was observed (139). Treatment of fetal rabbit lung explants with cAMP analogues results in an increase in SP-B (140) and SP-C (141) mRNA levels. The stimulatory effects of cAMP are the result of increased gene transcription (140, 141).

Glucocorticoids   Consistent with their effects on morphologic development of human fetal lung in culture, glucocorticoids have dose-dependent, biphasic effects on *SP-A* gene expression that are due to differential effects on *SP-A* gene transcription and on SP-A mRNA stability. In studies using midgestation human fetal lung explants, we observed that Dex causes a dose-dependent induction of *SP-A* gene transcription and acts synergistically with Bt_2cAMP (129, 130); however, Dex causes a dose-dependent decrease in the levels of SP-A mRNA and protein and antagonizes the stimulatory effects of Bt_2cAMP (78). This apparent inhibitory effect of glucocorticoids, which is due to a dominant action to decrease SP-A mRNA stability (129, 130), is reversible and blocked by the glucocorticoid receptor antagonist RU486 (130).

Similar to findings using midgestation human fetal lung, in lung explants from 90-, 125-, and 140-day gestational age fetal baboons (term = 184 days), Dex also causes a dose-dependent inhibition of SP-A mRNA levels and antagonizes the stimulatory effect of Bt_2cAMP (142). By contrast, SP-A mRNA, which is present at relatively high levels in lung tissues of 160- and 174-day fetal baboons prior to culture, is essentially unaffected by incubation with Bt_2cAMP or Dex (142). These findings suggest that with increased lung maturation and the developmental induction of *SP-A* gene expression, there is a decrease in responsiveness of the fetal lung to the stimulatory effects of cAMP and the inhibitory effects of glucocorticoids on *SP-A* gene expression.

In fetal rabbit lung, glucocorticoids have both acute inhibitory and subsequent stimulatory effects on *SP-A* gene transcription that appear to be related to the state of differentiation of the fetal lung tissue (113). We suggest that these differentiation-related changes in glucocorticoid responsiveness may be related to changes in chromatin structure accompanying cellular differentiation that could render glucocorticoid-responsive enhancer (GRE) elements accessible to *trans*-acting factors (e.g. the glucocorticoid receptor). In rats, Dex appears to have the greatest effect to stimulate *SP-A* gene expression during the glandular phase of lung development (143).

Glucocorticoids have marked dose-dependent stimulatory effects on the levels of SP-B and SP-C mRNA in human fetal lung in vitro (124, 125). At concentrations of Dex (10^{-7} M) that cause a pronounced inhibition of the levels of SP-A mRNA in human fetal lung explants, the levels of SP-B and SP-C mRNA are markedly stimulated. In studies using the NCI-H441 human lung adenocarcinoma cell line (144), as well as lung explants from fetal rabbits (140) and midgestation human abortuses (145, 146), it was found that glucocorticoid induction of SP-B mRNA levels results from combined effects to increase both *SP-B* gene transcription and SP-B mRNA stability. By contrast, the effect of Dex to increase SP-C mRNA levels in human fetal lung in vitro appears to be mediated entirely at the level of *SP-C* gene transcription (145, 146). On the other hand, in studies using fetal rabbit lung in culture, it was observed that Dex induction of SP-C mRNA was due to effects on SP-C mRNA stability (141).

Despite these well-documented actions of glucocorticoids on surfactant protein gene expression in cultured lung tissues and in animals, the physiological role of endogenous glucocorticoids in the regulation of *SP-A* gene expression in fetal lung is unclear in regard to findings in mice homozygous for targeted disruption of the *GR* gene (74). As discussed above, $GR^{-/-}$ mice die shortly after birth as a result of respiratory distress (74). However, the lungs of newborn $GR^{-/-}$ mice contain comparable numbers of alveolar type II cells and apparently normal levels of mRNA encoding SP-A, SP-B, and SP-C, compared with heterozygous or wild-type animals (74). It was suggested that the respiratory failure of the $GR^{-/-}$ neonates was due not to inadequate development of the surfactant system, but rather to decreased expression of the glucocorticoid-responsive amiloride-sensitive epithelial Na^+ channel (ENaC), which normally is induced in alveolar epithelium after E17 in mouse and is essential for lung liquid clearance (147). Since study of the lungs of the $GR^{-/-}$ mice did not include analysis of surfactant synthesis or composition, it remains possible that perinatal mortality of these animals is due, in part, to inadequate surfactant glycerophospholipid synthesis and/or secretion.

In studies using human fetal lung explants, glucocorticoids were found to increase *SP-D* expression (127). By contrast, neither interferon-γ (IFNγ), phorbol esters, nor tumor necrosis factor-α (TNF-α) had an effect to alter *SP-D* expression.

Retinoids   Retinoids have well-recognized effects as embryonic morphogens and as regulators of epithelial cell differentiation (see above). In studies of human fetal lung in culture, it was found that retinoic acid causes a dose-dependent inhibition of SP-A mRNA levels, as well as a decrease in epithelium volume density and corresponding increase in connective tissue volume density. By contrast, retinoic acid causes a dose-dependent increase in SP-B mRNA levels;

whereas *SP-C* gene expression is inhibited, but only at the highest levels of reti-noic acid tested. (148). In studies using cultured lung buds from 13.5-day ges-tational age rat embryos, retinoic acid causes a dose-dependent inhibition of mRNAs encoding SP-A, SP-B, and SP-C (149). Interestingly, retinoic acid recep-tor-β expression is reported to be restricted to the trachea and larger proximal airways in the early mouse embryo (40). This likely contributes to the effects of retinoids on the embryonic mouse lung to promote development of the proximal airways at the expense of branching and differentiation of distal epithelial buds and may explain its effect to inhibit expression of all three surfactant protein genes.

Insulin   It has been suggested that the fetal hyperinsulinemia associated with maternal diabetes (150) exerts a deleterious effect on lung development, resulting in an increased incidence of RDS in term infants of mothers with certain forms of diabetes (151). The observation that the incidence of RDS is increased in newborn infants of diabetic mothers, despite amniotic fluid L/S ratios indicative of fetal lung maturity, suggests that a surfactant component other than phospha-tidylcholine (PC) is affected. In two independent studies, it was found that SP-A levels in amniotic fluid samples from diabetic women were significantly reduced compared with gestational age-matched nondiabetic subjects (117, 152). In a third study, no differences in amniotic fluid SP-A levels were found between diabetic and nondiabetic subjects (153). It was suggested that lung maturation and SP-A production in the infants of diabetic mothers in this study may be due to improved metabolic control.

In studies using midgestation human fetal lung in organ culture, it was observed that insulin caused a dose-dependent inhibition of accumulation of SP-A (116) and its mRNA (154, 155). On the other hand, only the highest concen-tration of insulin tested (2.5µg/ml) had an inhibitory effect on SP-B mRNA, and no effect on mRNA encoding SP-C was apparent (154). Inhibitory effects of insulin on SP-A and SP-B mRNA levels in NCI-H441 cells also have been reported (156).

Growth Factors and Cytokines   A number of growth factors and cytokines have been reported to regulate surfactant protein gene expression in fetal lung. Whereas EGF exerts stimulatory effects, TGF-β and TNF-α have been found to be inhib-itory. EGF causes a dose-dependent induction of SP-A synthesis and mRNA levels in midgestation human fetal lung in culture (157) and increases *SP-C* gene expression in cultured embryonic mouse lung buds (158). Furthermore, in mice homozygous for a targeted deletion of the EGFR, there are apparent defects in surfactant function and in *SP-A* and *SP-C* expression (159, 160).

On the other hand, TGF-β antagonizes the stimulatory effects of EGF in mid-gestation human fetal lung explants (157). TGF-β_1, -β_2, and -β_3 were found to be equally effective in inhibiting *SP-A* expression in NCI-H441 lung adenocarci-noma cells (161). In transgenic mice expressing TGF-β1 under control of the human *SP-C* promoter, there is evidence of decreased epithelial cell differentiation, manifested by decreased levels of *proSP-C* and *CCSP* gene expression (20). The inhibitory effects of TGF-β1 on *SP-A, SP-B,* and *SP-C* expression in human fetal lung appear to be mediated at the transcriptional level (162).

TNF-α and phorbol esters inhibit *SP-A* transcription in pulmonary adenocarcinoma cell lines (163–165) and in human fetal lung explants (166). It should be noted that, whereas phorbol esters cause activation of protein kinase C (PK-C), TNF-α effects are mediated by several signal transduction pathways, including activation of protein kinase C, sphingomyelinase, and protease cascades (167). It is not known whether one or more of these mechanisms mediate the pronounced inhibitory effects of TNF-α on *SP-A* expression; however in studies with NCI-H441 lung adenocarcinoma cells, the actions of TNF-α to inhibit *SP-A* expression occur in the absence of effects on cell growth or viability (165). TNF-α also inhibits *SP-B* and *SP-C* gene expression (168, 169). Inhibitory effects appear to be independent of the transcription factor NF-κB (168) and to be exerted at the transcriptional level (169).

IFNγ causes dose-dependent induction of the levels of SP-A and its mRNA in midgestation human fetal lung in culture; IFNγ and Dex had a synergistic effect to increase SP-A content. By contrast, no effects of IFNγ on *SP-B* or *SP-C* expression were observed (170). Interleukin-1 (IL-1) is an example of another inflammatory cytokine produced by activated macrophages that has been found to induce *SP-A* expression in fetal lung. IL-1α when injected into the amniotic sacs of fetal rabbits causes a dose-dependent increase in SP-A mRNA levels in fetal lung tissue, and an increase in compliance of lungs of prematurely delivered pups (171). Treatment of fetal lung explants with IL-1α also increases *SP-A* expression (172).

In studies using type II cells in primary culture, maintenance of cellular differentiation, surfactant glycerophospholipid biosynthesis, and *SP-A, SP-B,* and *SP-C* gene expression are dependent upon type II cell-extracellular matrix (ECM) interactions (173, 174), cell shape (173), and type II cell-fibroblast interactions (175). When adult rat type II cells are cultured on ECM in the absence of added fibroblasts, keratinocyte growth factor/FGF-7 (KGF/FGF-7), which is produced by lung fibroblasts, markedly induces SP-A and SP-B mRNA levels, as well as surfactant glycerophospholipid synthesis (176). In studies using mesenchyme-free embryonic lung epithelial cell cultures, it was found that FGF-7 stimulates epithelial proliferation and enhances expression of SP-A and SP-B mRNAs throughout the explant (10).

Mechanisms in the Regulation of Surfactant Protein Gene Transcription

In order to define the regulatory elements required for lung-cell specific, developmental, and multifactorial regulation of surfactant protein gene expression, studies utilizing transgenic mice and transfected type II cells have been done.

Transgenic mice comprise the most relevant system for analysis of genomic regions required for tissue/cell-specific and developmental regulation of expression, whereas transfected cells provide an appropriate means for identification of response elements required for multifactorial regulation of expression. In this section, we emphasize our own studies on characterization of the *cis*-acting elements and transcription factors that regulate expression of the *SP-A* gene. Relevant studies of others in characterization of regulatory mechanisms of *SP-A* and the other surfactant protein genes are referenced where appropriate.

Analysis of Gene Regulatory Regions Using Transgenic Mice   In recent studies to define regions surrounding the *SP-A* gene that mediate lung cell-specific and developmental regulation of expression, we created lines of transgenic mice carrying various amounts ($-4,000$ to -47bp) of 5'-flanking DNA from the rabbit *SP-A* gene fused to the *human growth hormone* (*hGH*) structural gene, as reporter (*SP-A:hGH*). Expression of fusion genes containing -47bp of *SP-A* 5'-flanking DNA was undetectable in lung and other tissues of transgenic mice. By contrast, we found that *SP-A:hGH* fusion genes containing $-4,000$bp of *SP-A* 5'-flanking DNA were expressed in a lung-specific manner and were developmentally regulated in concert with the endogenous mouse *SP-A* gene (Figure 1) (177). By deletion mapping, we observed that in two of five lines of transgenic mice carrying *SP-A$_{-378}$:hGH* fusion genes, transgene expression was essentially lung specific. In three other lines carrying this transgene, expression also was detected in heart, thymus, and spleen; however, expression levels were always highest in lung (177). Similar findings were obtained in transgenic mice carrying *SP-A$_{-991}$:hGH* fusion genes. We suggest that the increased ectopic expression of *SP-A:hGH* fusion genes containing <991bp of *SP-A* 5'-flanking DNA, compared with *SP-A$_{-4000}$:hGH* transgenes, may be due to the presence of binding sites for ubiquitously expressed transcription factors, as well as the absence of putative silencer elements that block expression in other tissues. *SP-A:hGH* fusion genes containing 378 and 991bp of *SP-A* 5'-flanking DNA also were developmentally regulated in association with expression of the endogenous mouse *SP-A* gene (177).

By in situ hybridization analysis of hGH mRNA in lungs of transgenic mice carrying *SP-A$_{-378}$:hGH* fusion genes, we found that transgene expression was localized to type II cells and bronchioalveolar epithelial cells (Figure 2, see color insert) (177), cell types that express the endogenous *SP-A* gene. These findings suggest that as little as 378bp of 5'-flanking sequence from the rabbit *SP-A* gene contain all the necessary elements for lung-selective, cell type-specific, and developmental regulation of expression of *SP-A* promoter activity. In transgenic mouse studies to define regions of the human *SP-C* gene required for lung cell-specific and developmental regulation of expression, it was found that 3.7kb of DNA flanking the 5'-end of the human *SP-C* gene fused to the bacterial *chloramphenicol acetyltransferase* (*CAT*) gene mediated high levels of lung-specific CAT expression (120, 178). Transgene expression in lung is observed in type II and

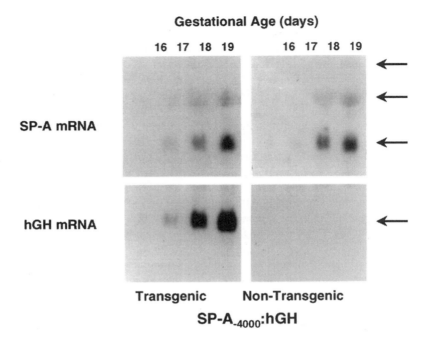

Figure 1 A fusion gene composed of 4000bp of 5'-flanking sequence from the rabbit *SP-A* gene linked to the *human growth hormone* structural gene (*SP-A−4000:hGH*), as reporter, is developmentally regulated in concert with endogenous *SP-A* gene in transgenic mice. Total RNA (30 μg) isolated from lung tissues of 16–19 day fetal transgenic mice carrying the *SP-A−4000:hGH* transgene and their nontransgenic littermates was analyzed for *SP-A* (*upper panel*) and *hGH* (*lower panel*) mRNA transcripts by northern blotting. Shown are the autoradiograms of the northern blots from these experiments. Reprinted from Alcorn et al (177), with permission.

bronchioalveolar epithelial cells, whereas expression of the endogenous mouse *SP-C* gene is type II cell specific. High levels of expression of the *SP-C:CAT* transgene are detected in epithelium of primordial lung buds of transgenic fetal mice as early E10. By contrast, low levels of expression of the endogenous *SP-C* gene are detected one day later, and expression is restricted to the more distal epithelial cells of the primitive lobar bronchi (178). These findings suggest that the 3.7kb *SP-C* 5'-flanking region mediates similar, but not identical cell-specific and developmental patterns of expression as the endogenous mouse *SP-C* gene.

Analysis of Response Elements Required for Multifactorial Regulation of Surfactant Protein Gene Expression Using Transfected Cells While transgenic mice provide the most appropriate model system for defining genomic elements that mediate tissue- and cell-specific and developmental regulation of gene expression, transfection of cultured cells with chimeric promoter/reporter gene constructs provides the most convenient system for identifying response elements required for multifactorial regulation of expression.

SP-A   In consideration of the fact that the *SP-A* gene is expressed in a lung-specific manner in type II cells, we reasoned that transfection studies characterizing response elements involved in the regulation of *SP-A* gene expression should be carried out using type II cells that have maintained phenotypic properties, particularly with regard to *SP-A* gene expression. Because no established lung cell lines exist that have retained the majority of type II cell characteristics, we devised a method for primary monolayer culture of type II cells isolated from rat, rabbit, mouse, and human fetal lung (174). The cultured lung epithelial cells contain osmiophilic lamellated inclusions with the ultrastructural characteristics of lamellar bodies and continue to express the *SP-A* gene at elevated levels for up to three weeks of culture (174). To functionally define the *cis*-acting elements required for cAMP and glucocorticoid regulation of *SP-A* promoter activity, fusion genes were constructed containing various amounts of 5'-flanking DNA from the rabbit, human, and baboon *SP-A* genes linked to the *hGH* structural gene as the reporter. Because the type II cells are resistant to conventional methods of DNA transfection, the fusion gene constructs were incorporated into a replication-defective human adenovirus vector (Ad5) and introduced into the type II cells by infection (132). This results in highly efficient and reproducible transfection of fusion gene constructs. *SP-A* promoter activity is analyzed by radioimmunoassay of hGH protein secreted into the culture medium over each 24-h period for 5 days.

In deletion mapping studies of 5'-flanking sequences from rabbit *SP-A* (132), human (134), and baboon (56) *SP-A2* genes, we observed that *SP-A:hGH* fusion genes containing ~300bp of *SP-A* 5'-flanking DNA mediate high levels of basal and cAMP-induced expression in the primary cultures of type II cells (for review, see 128). When these fusion genes were transfected into two lung adenocarcinoma cell lines of presumed type II cell origin, NCI-H358 and A549, which do not express *SP-A,* there were relatively high levels of basal expression; however, little or no stimulatory effect of cAMP was apparent (132, 134). By contrast, in primary cultures of cAMP-responsive ovarian granulosa and thecal cells, and in the cAMP-responsive adrenal Y1 and hepatoma 4IIE cell lines, *SP-A:hGH* fusion gene expression was barely detectable and no stimulatory effect of cAMP was apparent (132, 134). These findings suggest that cAMP induction of *SP-A* gene expression requires the interaction of type II cell-specific transcription factors with tissue-specific enhancers. These cell-specific transcription factors may be reduced in the lung adenocarcinoma cell lines and absent in the ovarian and adrenal Y1 cells. Alternatively, the H358 and A549 cells may be deficient in some component of the cAMP response pathway.

In type II cell transfection studies to define response elements of the rabbit *SP-A* gene that mediate glucocorticoid regulation of *SP-A* gene transcription, primary cultures of type II cells transfected with *SP-A:hGH* fusion genes containing various amounts of *SP-A* 5'-flanking DNA (47, 378, 991, and 1766bp) were incubated in the absence or presence of Dex and Bt$_2$cAMP, singly or in combination. We observed that Dex (10^{-7}M), which had little effect when added alone, caused a pronounced inhibition of cAMP-induced expression of *SP-A$_{-1766}$:hGH, SP-A$_{-991}$:hGH,* and *SP-A$_{-378}$:hGH* fusion genes (132). This inhibitory effect of Dex was unanticipated because, as discussed above, we found that Dex increases transcription of the endogenous *SP-A* gene in rabbit lung explants and has an additive stimulatory effect with Bt$_2$cAMP (113). In the cell transfection studies, we observed that the inhibitory effect of Dex on cAMP induction of *SP-A:hGH* expression was dose dependent; half-maximal inhibition was observed at a Dex concentration of 8 x 10^{-10}M, similar to the K_d for binding of Dex to the GR (132). The finding that this inhibitory action of Dex was blocked by the GR antagonist RU486 (132) suggests an action of the GR to antagonize the cAMP induction of *SP-A:hGH* expression in transfected type II cells.

The mechanism(s) whereby glucocorticoids exert this inhibitory effect on cAMP induction of *SP-A* promoter activity has not been determined. Based on sequence analysis of the rabbit *SP-A* gene and surrounding genomic regions, we have been unable to find a palindromic glucocorticoid response element (GRE; AGAACAnnnTGTTCT) (179) within 3.0kb of 5'-flanking DNA or within the structural gene; however, two GRE half-sites were noted within the first intron. It is apparent that these are not functional GREs because the inhibitory effect of Dex is still apparent in type II cells transfected with *SP-A:hGH* fusion genes that contained 991bp of 5'-flanking DNA and sequences contained within the first intron (132). Furthermore, when lung explants from fetal mice carrying *SP-A$_{-4000}$:hGH* transgenes are incubated with Dex and Bt$_2$cAMP alone and in combination, Dex treatment inhibits fusion gene expression and antagonizes the stimulatory effect of Bt$_2$cAMP (177). These findings suggest that the stimulatory effect of glucocorticoids on expression of the endogenous *SP-A* gene are mediated by sequences that lie far upstream, within the *SP-A* structural gene downstream of the second exon, or within the 3'-flanking sequence. In the absence of a functional GRE within the fusion gene constructs, we postulate that the GR may either interact with a transcription factor(s) that mediates cAMP stimulation and inhibit its function, or else compete for coactivators essential for cAMP induction of *SP-A* promoter activity. As a consequence of the perceived complexity of glucocorticoid regulation of *SP-A* gene expression, we subsequently have focused our studies on defining the mechanisms whereby cAMP regulates *SP-A* gene expression in type II cells.

The findings of deletion mapping and mutagenesis studies of the human, rabbit, and baboon *SP-A* gene 5'-flanking sequences indicate that basal and cAMP-induced expression of *SP-A* promoter activity in lung type II cells are critically dependent upon the cooperative interactions of transcription factors bound to at least four regulatory elements that lie within ~400bp upstream of the *SP-A* gene transcription initiation site (Figure 3). These include an E-box-like motif (proximal-binding element; PBE) (180, 181), a cAMP-response element-like sequence

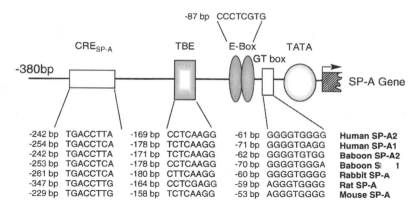

Figure 3 The *SP-A* gene 5'-flanking region contains response elements conserved among various species. Sequences and positions of the CRE_{SP-A}, TTF-1-binding element (TBE), E-box and GT-box elements relative to the start sites of transcription of the SP-A genes of various species are shown. The position of the TATA box and the start of transcription (arrow) are indicated. Reprinted in a modified form from Young & Mendelson (182), with permission.

(CRE_{SP-A}) (132–134), a GT-box (GT_{SP-A}) (182), and several thyroid transcription factor-1 (TTF-1/Nkx2.1) binding elements (TBE) (55) (Figure 3). Mutagenesis of any one of these elements markedly reduces basal and cAMP induction of *SP-A* promoter activity (for review, see 128). CRE_{SP-A}, TBE and GT_{SP-A} are highly conserved with regard to sequence and position in the 5'-flanking regions of all the *SP-A* genes thus far characterized (only exception is the position of CRE_{SP-A} in the 5'-flanking sequence of the rat *SP-A* gene (183) (Figure 3). Although the PBE at -87bp appears unique to the rabbit *SP-A* gene 5'-flanking region, we found that proximal 5'-flanking sequences of the human and baboon *SP-A2* genes compete with rabbit type II cell nuclear proteins for binding to the PBE (E Gao & CR Mendelson, unpublished data), suggesting the presence of related element(s) within *SP-A* 5'-flanking regions of other species.

SP-B and SP-C A ~218-bp sequence upstream of the human *SP-B* gene was found to mediate relatively high levels of reporter gene expression in transfected NCI-H441 cells but not in heterologous cell lines (57). The human SP-B 5'-flanking region contains closely spaced binding sites for TTF-1 and HNF-3 critical for activity of the SP-B promoter in transfected NCI-H441 cells (57). In other studies using H441 cells transfected with rabbit *SP-B:CAT* fusion genes, the *SP-B* sequences from –236 to +39bp were shown to mediate high levels of fusion gene expression. By mutagenesis, DNA-binding elements for TTF-1, HNF-3α, and Sp1/Sp3 transcription factors proved necessary for maintenance of *SP-B* promoter activity. Mutagenesis of any one of these elements caused a pronounced reduction of *SP-B* promoter activity (184). In studies to characterize regulatory regions upstream of the mouse *SP-C* gene, 5'-flanking sequences between −197 and −158bp were deemed critical for TTF-1-induction of *SP-C* promoter activity in transfected mouse lung epithelial (MLE) and HeLa cells. This region contains two binding sites for TTF-1 that are essential for TTF-1 induction of the *SP-C* promoter (58). Thus far, response elements for glucocorticoid regulation of *SP-B* and *SP-C* gene expression have not been identified.

Transcription Factors That Mediate Basal and Cyclic AMP Induction of SP-A Promoter Activity in Type II Cells   As mentioned above, it is evident from our studies that transcription factors bound to CRE_{SP-A}, TBEs, PBE, and GT-box cooperatively interact to promote basal and cAMP induction of *SP-A* promoter activity in type II cells. In the following sections, we review studies that characterize the transcription factors binding to these response elements, and provide some insight into the mechanisms whereby these factors mediate developmental, type II cell-specific and cAMP regulation of *SP-A* gene expression.

CRESP-A May Bind a Member of the Nuclear Receptor Superfamily CRE_{SP-A} ($TGACCT^{C}/_{T}A$) has sequence similarity to the palindromic consensus cAMP-response element (CRE_{pal}, TGACGTCA), which is known to bind the basic leucine zipper (bZIP) transcription factor, CREB, as a homodimer (79). However, in studies to define the role of CRE_{SP-A} in cAMP induction of *SP-A* gene expression in transfected cells, we observed that mutagenesis of CRE_{SP-A} to CRE_{pal} markedly reduced basal and cAMP-induced expression of rabbit *SP-A:hGH* fusion genes (133). Furthermore, the findings of electrophoretic mobility shift assays (EMSA), *UV* crosslinking, and southwestern blotting analysis indicated that neither CREB nor other related bZIP transcription factors (CREM, ATF-1) bind to CRE_{SP-A} (133). By competition EMSA using mutagenized CRE_{SP-A} oligonucleotides, the critical protein-binding nucleotides in CRE_{SP-A} were found to constitute a hexameric element, TGACCT, which corresponds to a half site for binding members of the nuclear receptor superfamily (133). Because the TGACCT motif is highly conserved and present as a single site in the *SP-A* genes of a variety of species, we propose that a member of the nuclear receptor superfamily may bind to this element as a monomer.

The GT-Box Binds Sp1 and Other Related Factors   As mentioned above, the results of mutagenesis studies in transfected type II cells indicate that a highly conserved GT-box at −60bp also is critical for basal and cAMP induction of *SP-A* promoter activity (182). By EMSA, it was observed that nuclear proteins isolated from primary cultures of type II cells bound the GT-box as five specific complexes. Nuclear proteins isolated from lung fibroblasts display markedly reduced binding activity. Competition and supershift EMSA indicate that the ubiquitously expressed transcription factor Sp1, a GC-box-binding protein of

~100 kDa, is a component of the complex of proteins that bind the GT-box of *hSP-A2* (182). The finding that only two of the five GT-box-binding complexes are supershifted by incubation with Sp1 antibody suggests that a factor(s) in type II cell nuclear extracts distinct from Sp1 also interacts with GT_{SP-A}. By *UV* cross-linking and SDS/PAGE/EMSA analysis, we have identified a ~55 kDa GT-box-binding factor in type II cell nuclear proteins that preferentially binds the GT-box of *SP-A2* over the consensus Sp1 GC-box sequence. This 55-kDa factor is able to bind the GT-box independently of Sp1 (182). Sp1 is a ubiquitously expressed member of the Krüppel family of zinc finger–containing transcription factors. Several recently identified novel proteins belonging to the Krüppel family manifest significantly higher binding activity toward the GT/CA box than does Sp1 (185). We suggest that the 55-kDa factor that interacts with the GT-box of *SP-A2* is a new member of this protein family.

In studies to characterize the rabbit *SP-B* promoter, two response elements required for high levels of basal expression of *SP-B* promoter activity in transfected NCI-H441 cells were found to bind Sp1 and the structurally related zinc finger transcription factor Sp3 (184). It was postulated that Sp1 and Sp3 bind to these sites cooperatively with TTF-1 and HNF-3α proteins bound to nearby response elements within the *SP-B* 5'-flanking region (184).

The PBE Binds USF1, Which Is Selectively Expressed in Lung Epithelial Cells and Is Developmentally Regulated in Fetal Lung The PBE also is critical for basal and cAMP-induced expression of the SP-A promoter in transfected type II cells (180). Interestingly, the position of the PBE coincides approximately with the location of a DNase I hypersensitive site at ~ − 100bp, which is present in nuclei from fetal rabbit lung several days prior to the time of initiation of SP-A gene transcription on day 24, but not in nuclei from liver or kidney tissues (108). To characterize transcription factors that bind to these E-box motifs, radiolabeled PBE was used to screen a rabbit fetal lung cDNA expression library; cDNA inserts were isolated encoding two alternatively spliced forms of the basic-helix-loop-helix-zipper transcription factor upstream stimulatory factor 1 (rUSF1a and b) (181). By use of reverse transcriptase PCR, rUSF1a and rUSF1b mRNAs were identified in fetal rabbit lung and other tissues. USF1 gene expression is developmentally regulated in fetal rabbit lung. Interestingly, the levels of rUSF1 mRNAs reach a peak in fetal rabbit lung at 23 days gestation, in concert with the time of initiation of SP-A gene transcription (181). The finding that binding complexes of nuclear proteins from fetal rabbit lung tissue or type II cells with radiolabeled PBE were supershifted by addition of anti-rUSF1 IgG indicates that USF1 binds to the PBE. USF1-binding activity was found to be highly enriched in type II cells compared with lung fibroblasts. The finding that overexpression of rUSF1s in A549 adenocarcinoma cells positively regulates SP-A promoter activity of co-transfected reporter gene constructs suggests that rUSF1 may serve a key role in the regulation of SP-A gene expression in pulmonary type II cells (181).

TTF-1 Binding Elements (TBEs) Are Required for cAMP Induction of SP-A Promoter Activity in Type II Cells; Binding and Transcriptional Activation of TTF-1 Is Increased by cAMP-Dependent Protein Kinase or PKA   As discussed above, the homeodomain transcription factor TTF-1/Nkx2.1 serves a critical role during embryogenesis in branching morphogenesis of the developing lung. TTF-1 also is expressed in lung tissues of postnatal and adult animals, where expression is restricted to type II cells and Clara cells. It is apparent from studies of a number of laboratories, including our own, that TTF-1 also plays a critical role in basal expression of genes encoding SP-A (54, 55), SP-B (57, 184), SP-C (58), and CCSP (59, 186).

We have identified three TTF-1-binding elements (TBE) within 255bp of 5'-flanking region of the baboon *SP-A2* gene (56). One of these elements (TBE1) is highly conserved with regard to position and sequence among all of the *SP-A* genes thus far characterized (Figure 3). In type II cell transfection experiments, we observed that mutagenesis of TBE1 has a more pronounced effect to reduce basal and cAMP-induced expression of *bSP-A2* promoter activity than mutagenesis of either TBE2 or TBE3 (56).

In studies to define the mechanism(s) whereby TTF-1 mediates cAMP induction of *SP-A* gene expression in type II cells, we observed that binding of type II cell nuclear proteins to the TBE was increased by cAMP treatment (Figure 4) (55). These findings indicate for the first time that cAMP specifically increases TTF-1 binding activity in type II cells. Our findings that cAMP does not alter the levels of immunoreactive TTF-1 in nuclear extracts of type II cells (Figure 4), or the rate of incorporation of [^{35}S]methionine into immunoisolated TTF-1 (55), suggest that cAMP induction of TTF-1 binding activity is not mediated by changes in its nuclear localization or expression. In association with its effect to stimulate TTF-1 DNA binding activity, we observed that cAMP treatment markedly increases the rate of ^{32}P-phosphate incorporation into immunoisolated TTF-1 (55). The finding that phosphatase treatment effectively abolishes the cAMP induction of TTF-1 DNA binding activity indicates that cAMP-induced TTF-1 phosphorylation mediates the increase in binding activity for TBEs within the *bSP-A2* 5'-flanking sequence (55). A PKA phosphorylation site near the N terminus (Thr^9) of TTF-1 was identified and found to be essential for PKA activation of *SP-B* promoter activity in transfected NCI-H441 cells (187).

To analyze effects of PKA on TTF-1 transcriptional activity, A549 cells, a lung adenocarcinoma cell line that lacks TTF-1, were co-transfected with a *bSP-A2*$_{-255}$:*hGH* fusion gene (which contains three TBEs), and with expression vectors for TTF-1 and for PKA catalytic (PKA-cat) subunits α and β (Figure 5A). Co-transfection of TTF-1 caused an induction of *bSP-A2* promoter activity (Figure 5A). The response to TTF-1 was increased further by co-transfection of PKA catalytic subunits. The finding that PKA-cat had no effect to increase *bSP-A2* promoter activity in the absence of co-transfected TTF-1 and that mutation of the major TTF-1 binding site abolished PKA induction of TTF-1 transcriptional activity (55) suggests that the effect of PKA to induce *bSP-A2* gene expression is

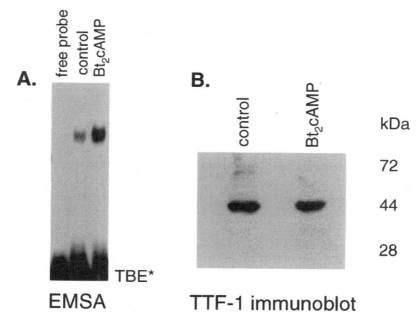

Figure 4 cAMP treatment of human fetal type II cells increases nuclear protein binding activity for the TTF-1-binding element (TBE) without altering nuclear levels of immunoreactive TTF-1. (*A*) Electrophoretic mobility shift assay (EMSA). Nuclear proteins (10 µg) isolated from human fetal type II cells previously cultured for 5 days in the absence or presence of Bt_2cAMP (1mM) were incubated with ^{32}P-labeled TBE as radiolabeled probe. DNA-protein complexes were separated from free probe by 5% nondenaturing polyacrylamide gel and visualized by autoradiography. (*B*) Immunoblot of TTF-1 protein in nuclear extracts of type II cells cultured in the absence or presence of Bt_2cAMP. Nuclear proteins (25 µg) isolated from human fetal type II cells cultured in control or Bt_2cAMP (1 mM)-containing medium were analyzed for TTF-1 protein by immunoblotting. Shown is an autoradiogram of the immunoblot. From Li et al (55), with permission.

mediated, in part, through TTF-1. We also have observed that the TTF-1 induction of *bSP-A2*$_{-255}$*:hGH* fusion gene expression in the absence of co-transfected PKA-cat was prevented by co-transfection of a dominant-negative form of PKA RIα (55). This suggests that the inductive effect of TTF-1 on *bSP-A2* promoter activity in A549 cells is dependent upon phosphorylation by endogenous PKA. To further substantiate the role of TTF-1 in PKA induction of *SP-A* promoter activity, A549 cells transfected with a reporter gene containing three tandem TBEs fused upstream of the *bSP-A2* gene TATA box and transcription initiation site (*TBE₃SP-A2:hGH*) were co-transfected with PKA-cat and TTF-1 expression vectors (Figure 5*B*). The finding that PKA-cat enhanced transactivation of *TBE₃SP-A:hGH* by co-transfected TTF-1 indicates that the effect of PKA to increase *SP-A*

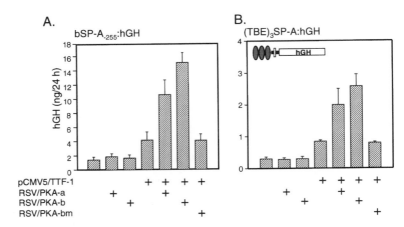

Figure 5 PKA increases TTF-1 transcriptional activity in A549 cells that were transfected with either *bSP-A2₋₂₅₅:hGH* (A) or a *(TBE)₃SP-A2:hGH* fusion gene composed of three tandem copies of TBE fused to a basal *bSP-A2* promoter linked to *hGH*, as reporter (*B*). The reporter gene constructs were transfected in the absence or presence of a TTF-1 expression vector (*pCMV5/TTF-1*) or *pCMV5* empty vector, and with expression vectors for PKA catalytic subunit-α (*RSV/PKA-cat-α*), PKA catalytic subunit β (*RSV/PKA-cat-β*), a mutated form of PKA catalytic subunit β (*RSV/PKA-cat-βm*), or the corresponding empty vector *pRSV*, plus internal control, *RSV-βgal*. Shown are the levels of hGH secreted into the medium over a 24-h period, 48 h after transfection. Data are the means + SEM from two independent experiments, each conducted in triplicate, normalized to β-galactosidase activity. Reprinted from Li et al (55), with permission.

promoter activity is mediated specifically by TTF-1 binding to TBEs. These findings, together with those that indicate that cAMP specifically increases TTF-1 binding activity in type II cells, suggest that TTF-1 is the cAMP-responsive transcription factor in lung type II cells.

As discussed above, phorbol esters and TNF-α inhibit surfactant protein gene expression in lung adenocarcinoma cell lines and in human fetal lung explants (163–166, 168, 169). We have observed that treatment of human fetal type II cells with phorbol esters causes a decrease in *SP-A* gene expression. This is associated with increased phosphorylation and decreased DNA binding of TTF-1; however, the levels of nuclear immunoreactive TTF-1 are unaffected by phorbol ester treatment (55). By contrast, in studies using NCI-H441 cells, it was observed that phorbol esters cause a dose-dependent decrease in the levels of TTF-1 and HNF-3 in nuclear extracts, with accumulation of the transcription factors in the cytoplasm. Ballard and colleagues (188) conclude that downregulation of *SP-B* promoter activity by phorbol esters is mediated by cytoplasmic trapping of TTF-1 and HNF-3 and loss of these factors from the nucleus.

Transcription Factors Involved in SP-B and SP-C Gene Expression   A number of transcription factors have been implicated in regulation of expression of the genes encoding SP-B and SP-C. Whereas, TTF-1 appears to serve an important role in regulation of expression of all the surfactant protein genes (54, 57, 58, 184), as well as CCSP (59), a regulatory role for HNF-3 has been reported only for SP-B (57, 184) and CCSP (189). In studies to define mechanisms regulating *SP-B* gene expression, TTF-1 and HNF-3 were shown to functionally interact to regulate SP-B promoter activity (57, 184). As discussed above, whereas retinoic acid increases *SP-B* gene expression in human fetal lung explants, it inhibits expression of *SP-A* and *SP-C* (48). A retinoic acid response element (RARE) was identified within the 5'-flanking region of the human *SP-B* gene at -415 to -440bp that is required for retinoic acid induction of SP-B promoter activity in transfected NCI-H441 cells (190). Furthermore, a dominant-negative retinoic acid receptor (RAR) mutant inhibited basal and retinoic acid–induced expression of a human SP-B reporter construct in transfected H441 cells (191). It also has been found that the ubiquitously expressed transcription factor nuclear factor 1 (NF1) binds to sites within the proximal promoter and distal enhancer region of the mouse *SP-C* gene and is required for *SP-C* promoter activity in MLE cells (192).

CONCLUSIONS

It is apparent that the highly complex events accompanying morphologic and biochemical development of the lung are controlled by an array of transcription factors, some of which play dual roles in lung morphogenesis and in regulation of cell differentiation and surfactant protein gene expression. Findings from our studies using transgenic mice and transfected type II cells indicate that conserved response elements within a 400-bp region upstream of the rabbit, human, and baboon *SP-A* genes mediate lung cell-specific, developmental, and cAMP-induced expression of *SP-A* promoter activity. These response elements include a CRE-like sequence (CRE_{SP-A}), which may bind a member of the nuclear receptor superfamily, several TTF-1 binding sites, an E-box that binds the transcription factor USF1, and a GT-box that binds Sp1, together with other factors that may be tissue-selective members of the Krüppel family of proteins (Figure 6). Each one of these elements appears to be essential for cAMP induction of the *SP-A* promoter, suggesting a cooperative interaction of the proteins that bind to these sites. cAMP-induced expression of the *SP-A* gene is associated with a PKA-catalyzed increase in TTF-1 phosphorylation, resulting in increased TTF-1 DNA binding and transcriptional activity. Thus it appears that the PKA-mediated increase in TTF-1 phosphorylation and DNA-binding activity may constitute the primary mechanism for cAMP induction of *SP-A* gene expression. We suggest that the increase in TTF-1 phosphorylation and DNA-binding activity may facilitate its interactions with transcription factors bound to the other *cis*-acting elements that are essential for cAMP stimulation of *SP-A* promoter activity, as well

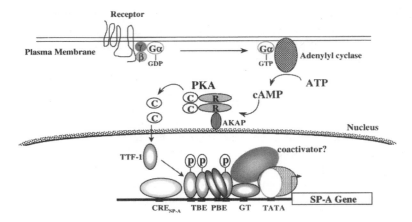

Figure 6   Proposed mechanism for cAMP induction of *SP-A* gene expression in type II cells. Binding of regulatory hormone to its receptor results in activation of adenylyl cyclase, increased cAMP formation and activation of PKA tethered to the nuclear membrane by a specific A-kinase anchor protein (AKAP). Entry of activated PKA catalytic subunit (C) into the nucleus results in increased phosphorylation of TTF-1 and its enhanced binding to TBEs. This, in turn, results in the interaction of TTF-1 with transcription factors bound to CRE$_{SP-A}$, E-box, and GT-box sequences. Certain of these factors are found to be developmentally regulated in fetal lung (e.g. USF1 bound to PBE) and selectively expressed in type II cells (e.g. USF1 and GT-box-binding proteins that include Sp1). Cooperative interaction of these transcription factors with each other and putative co-activators leads to induction of SP-A promoter activity and increased *SP-A* gene transcription.

as with coactivators and components of the basal transcription machinery (Figure 6). The unique combinatorial interactions of these transcription factors within the *SP-A* gene 5'-flanking region may contribute to its singular temporal and spatial patterns of expression. It is likely that the different properties of SP-A, SP-B, and SP-C with regard to cell-specific, developmental, and multifactorial regulation of expression are controlled by enhancer elements that bind both shared and gene-specific transcription factors, which interact to regulate promoter activity of each gene in a distinct manner.

ACKNOWLEDGMENTS

This research has been supported by National Institutes of Health grants R37 HL50022 and U01 HL52647.

Visit the Annual Reviews home page at www.AnnualReviews.org.

LITERATURE CITED

1. Snyder JM, Mendelson CR, Johnston JM. 1985. The morphology of lung development in the human fetus. In *Pulmonary Development: Transition from Intrauterine to Extrauterine Life,* ed. GH Nelson, pp. 19–46. New York: Dekker

2. Shannon JM. 1994. Induction of alveolar type II cell differentiation in fetal tracheal epithelium by grafting distal lung mesenchyme. *Dev. Biol.* 166:600–14

3. Shannon JM, Nielson LD, Gebb SA, Randell SH. 1998. Mesenchyme specifies epithelial differentiation in reciprocal recombination of embryonic lung and trachea. *Dev. Dyn.* 212:482–94

4. Bellusci S, Grindley J, Emoto H, Itoh N, Hogan BLM. 1997. Fibroblast growth factor 10 (FGF10) and branching morphogenesis in the embryonic mouse lung. *Development* 124:4867–78

5. Park WY, Miranda B, Lebeche D, Hashimoto G, Cardoso WV. 1998. FGF-10 is a chemotactic factor for distal epithelial buds during lung development. *Dev. Biol.* 201:125–34

6. Min H, Danilenko DM, Scully SA, Bolon B, Ring BD, Tarpley JE, DeRosa M, Simonet WS. 1998. Fgf-10 is required for both limb and lung development and exhibits striking functional similarity to *Drosophila* branchless. *Genes Dev.* 12:3156–61

7. Peters K, Werner S, Liao X, Wert S, Whitsett J, Williams L. 1994. FGF-10 is a chemotactic factor for distal epithelial buds during lung development. *Dev. Biol.* 201:125–34

8. Post M, Souza P, Liu J, Tseu I, Wang J, et al. 1996. Keratinocyte growth factor and its receptor are involved in regulating early lung branching. *Development* 122:3107–15

9. Simonet WS, DeRose M, Bucay N, Nguyen HQ, Wert S, et al. 1995. Pulmonary malformation in transgenic mice expressing human keratinocyte growth factor in the lung. *Proc. Natl. Acad. Sci. USA* 29:12461–65

10. Cardoso WV, Ito A, Nogawa H, Mason I, Brody JS. 1997. FGF-1 and FGF-7 induce distinct patterns of growth and differentiation in embryonic lung epithelium. *Dev. Dyn.* 208:398–405

11. Bitgood MJ, McMahon AP. 1995. *Hedgehog* and *Bmp* genes are coexpressed at many diverse sites of cell-cell interaction in the mouse embryo. *Dev. Biol.* 172:126–38

12. Urase K, Mukasa T, Igurashi H, Ishii Y, Yasagi S, et al. 1996. Spatial expression of Sonic hedgehog in the lung epithelium during branching morphogenesis. *Biochem. Biophys. Res. Commun.* 225: 161–66

13. Hogan BLM. 1999. Morphogenesis. *Cell* 96:225–33

14. Murone M, Rosenthal A, de Sauvage FJ. 1999. Sonic hedgehog signaling by the patched-smoothened receptor complex. *Curr. Biol.* 9:76–84

15. Bellusci S, Furuta Y, Rusg MG, Henderson R, Winnier G, Hogan BLM. 1997. Involvement of Sonic hedgehog (*Shh*) in mouse embryonic lung growth and morphogenesis. *Development* 124:53–63

16. Litingtung Y, Lei L, Westphal H, Chiang C. 1998. Sonic hedgehog is essential to foregut development. *Nat. Genet.* 20: 58–61

17. Pepicelli CV, Lewis PM, McMahon AP. 1998. Sonic hedgehog regulates branching morphogenesis in the mammalian lung. *Curr. Biol.* 8:1083–86

18. Kaartinen V, Voncken JW, Shuler C, Warburton D, Bu D, et al. 1995. Abnormal lung development and cleft palate in mice lacking TGF-β3 indicates defects of epithelial-mesenchymal interaction. *Nat. Genet.* 11:415–21

19. Serra R, Pelton RW, Moses HL. 1994.

TGF-β1 inhibits branching morphogenesis and *N-myc* expression in lung bud organ cultures. *Development* 20:2153–61

20. Zhou L, Dey CR, Wert SE, Whitsett JA. 1996. Arrested lung morphogenesis in transgenic mice bearing an *SP-C-TGF-β1* chimeric gene. *Dev. Biol.* 175:227–38

21. Zhao J, Bu D, Lee M, Slavkin HC, Hall FL, Warburton D. 1996. Abrogation of transforming growth factor-beta type II receptor stimulates embryonic mouse lung branching morphogenesis in culture. *Dev. Biol.* 180:242–57

22. Bitgood MJ, McMahon AP. 1995. *Hedgehog* and *Bmp* genes are coexpressed at many diverse sites of cell-cell interaction in the mouse embryo. *Dev. Biol.* 172:126–38

23. Bellusci S, Henderson R, Winnier G, Oikawa T, Hogan BL. 1996. Evidence from normal expression and targeted misexpression that bone morphogenetic protein (Bmp-4) plays a role in mouse embryonic lung morphogenesis. *Development* 122:1693–702

24. Threadgill DW, Dlugosz AA, Hansen LA, Tennenbaum T, Lichti U, et al. 1995. Targeted disruption of mouse EGF receptor: effect of genetic background on mutant phenotype. *Science* 269:230–34

25. Leveen P, Pekny M, Gebre-Medhin S, Swolin B, Larsson E, Betsholtz C. 1994. Mice deficient for PDGF B show renal, cardiovascular, and hematological abnormalities. *Genes Dev.* 8:1875–87

26. Snyder JM, Johnston JM, Mendelson CR. 1981. Differentiation of type II cells of human fetal lung in vitro. *Cell Tissue Res.* 220:17–25

27. Mendelson CR, Johnston JM, MacDonald PC, Snyder JM. 1981. Multihormonal regulation of surfactant synthesis by human fetal lung in vitro. *J. Clin. Endocrinol. Metab.* 53:307–17

28. Snyder JM, Mendelson CR, Johnston JM. 1981. The effect of cortisol on rabbit fetal lung maturation in vitro. *Dev. Biol.* 85:129–40

29. Mendelson CR, Chen C, Boggaram V, Zacharias C, Snyder JM 1986. Regulation of the synthesis of the major surfactant apoprotein in fetal rabbit lung tissue. *J. Biol. Chem.* 261:9938–43

30. Snyder JM, Mendelson CR. 1987. Induction and characterization of the major surfactant apoprotein during rabbit fetal lung development. *Biochim. Biophys. Acta* 920:226–36

31. Odom MJ, Snyder JM, Mendelson CR. 1987. Adenosine 3',5'-monophosphate analogs and beta-adrenergic agonists induce the synthesis of the major surfactant apoprotein in human fetal lung in vitro. *Endocrinology* 121:1155–63

32. Acarregui MJ, Snyder JM, Mitchell MD, Mendelson CR. 1990. Prostaglandins regulate *surfactant protein A (SP-A)* gene expression in human fetal lung in vitro. *Endocrinology* 127:1105–13

33. Acarregui MJ, Snyder JM, Mendelson CR. 1993. Oxygen modulates the differentiation of human fetal lung in vitro and its responsiveness to cAMP. *Am. J. Physiol.* 264:L465–74

34. Liggins GC. 1969. Premature delivery of foetal lambs infused with glucocorticoids. *J. Endocrinol.* 45: 515–523

35. Snyder JM, Rodgers HF, O'Brien JA, Mahli N, Magliato SA, Durham PL. 1992. Glucocorticoid effects on rabbit fetal lung maturation in vivo: an ultrastructural morphometric study. *Anat. Rec.* 232:133–40

36. Kitraki E, Kittas C, Stylianopoulou F. 1997. *Glucocorticoid receptor* gene expression during rat embryogenesis. An in situ hybridization study. *Differentiation* 62:21–31

37. Smith BT, Post M. 1989. Fibroblast-pneumocyte factor. *Am. J. Physiol.* 257:L174–78

38. Grindley JC, Bellusci S, Perkins D, Hogan BL. 1997. Evidence for the involvement of the *Gli* gene family in embryonic mouse lung development. *Dev. Biol.* 188:337–48

39. Motoyama J, Liu J, Mo R, Ding Q, Post M, Hui CC. 1998. Essential function of Gli2 and Gli3 in the formation of lung, trachea and oesophagus. *Nat. Genet.* 20:54–57

40. Dolle P, Ruberte E, Leroy P, Morriss-Kay G, Chambon P. 1990. Retinoic acid receptors and cellular retinoid binding proteins. I. A systematic study of their differential pattern of transcription during mouse organogenesis. *Development* 110:1133–51

41. Sucov HM, Izpisua-Belmonte JC, Ganan Y, Evans RM. 1995. Mouse embryos lacking RXR alpha are resistant to retinoic-acid-induced limb defects. *Development* 121:3997–4003

42. Kastner P, Grondona JM, Mark M, Gansmuller A, LeMeur M, et al. 1994. Genetic analysis of RXR alpha developmental function: convergence of RXR and RAR signaling pathways in heart and eye morphogenesis. *Cell* 78:987–1003

43. Mendelsohn C, Lohnes D, Decimo D, Lufkin T, LeMeur M, et al. 1994. Function of the retinoic acid receptors (RARs) during development (II). Multiple abnormalities at various stages of organogenesis in RAR double mutants. *Development* 120:2749–71

44. Massague J. 1998. TGF-beta signal transduction. *Annu. Rev. Biochem.* 67: 753–91

45. Zhao J, Lee M, Smith S, Warburton D. 1998. Abrogation of *Smad3* and *Smad2* or of *Smad4* gene expression positively regulates murine embryonic lung branching morphogenesis in culture. *Dev. Biol.* 194:182–95

46. Blackwood EM, Eisenman RN. 1991. Max: a helix-loop-helix zipper protein that forms a sequence-specific DNA-binding complex with Myc. *Science* 251:1211–17

47. Stanton BR, Perkins AS, Tessarollo L, Sassoon DA, Parada LF.1992. Loss of N-myc function results in embryonic lethality and failure of the epithelial com-

ponent of the embryo to develop. *Genes Dev.* 6:2235–47

48. Moens CB, Auerbach AB, Conlon RA, Joyner AL, Rossant J. 1992. A targeted mutation reveals a role for N-myc in branching morphogenesis in the embryonic mouse lung. *Genes Dev.* 6:691–704

49. Moens CB, Stanton BR, Parada LF, Rossant J. 1993. Defects in heart and lung development in compound heterozygotes for two different targeted mutations at the *N-myc* locus. *Development* 119:485–99

50. Lazzaro D, Price M, De Felice M, Di Lauro R. 1991. The transcription factor TTF-1 is expressed at the onset of thyroid and lung morphogenesis and in restricted regions of foetal brain. *Development* 113:1093–104

51. Kikkawa F, Gonzalez FJ, Kimura S. 1990. Characterization of a thyroid-specific enhancer located 5.5 kilobase pairs upstream of the human thyroid peroxidase gene. *Mol. Cell. Biol.* 10:6216–24

52. Civitareale D, Lonigro R, Sinclair AJ, Di Lauro R. 1989. A thyroid-specific nuclear protein essential for tissue-specific expression of the thyroglobulin promoter. *EMBO J.* 8:2537–42

53. Shimura H, Okajima F, Ikuyama S, Shimura Y, Kimura S, et al. 1994. Thyroid-specific expression and cyclic adenosine 3′,5′-monophosphate autoregulation of the *thyrotropin receptor* gene involves thyroid transcription factor-1. *Mol. Endocrinol.* 8:1049–69

54. Bruno MD, Bohinski RJ, Huelsman KM, Whitsett JA, Korfhagen TR. 1995. Lung cell-specific expression of the *murine surfactant protein A (SP-A)* gene is mediated by interactions between the SP-A promoter and thyroid transcription factor-1. *J. Biol. Chem.* 270:6531–36

55. Li J, Gao E, Mendelson CR. 1998. Cyclic AMP-responsive expression of the *surfactant protein-A* gene is mediated by increased DNA-binding and transcriptional activity of thyroid transcription factor-1. *J. Biol. Chem.* 273:4592–600

56. Li J, Gao E, Seidner SR, Mendelson CR. 1998. Differential regulation of the *baboon SP-A1* and *SP-A2* genes and structural and functional analysis of their 5'-flanking regions. *Am. J. Physiol.* 275:L1078–88

57. Bohinski RJ, Di Lauro R, Whitsett JA. 1994. The lung-specific *surfactant protein B* gene promoter is a target for thyroid transcription factor 1 and hepatocyte nuclear factor 3, indicating common factors for organ-specific gene expression along the foregut axis. *Mol. Cell. Biol.* 14:5671–81

58. Kelly SE, Bachurski CJ, Burhans MS, Glasser SW. 1996. Transcription of the lung-specific *surfactant protein C* gene is mediated by thyroid transcription factor 1. *J. Biol. Chem.* 271:6881–88

59. Ray MK, Chen CY, Schwartz RJ, DeMayo FJ. 1996. Transcriptional regulation of a mouse *Clara cell-specific protein (mCC10)* gene by the NKx transcription factor family members thyroid transcription factor 1 and cardiac muscle-specific homeobox protein (CSX). *Mol. Cell. Biol.* 16:2056–64

60. Sawaya PL, Luse DS. 1994. Two members of the HNF-3 family have opposite effects on a lung transcriptional element; HNF-3 alpha stimulates and HNF-3 beta inhibits activity of region I from the *Clara cell secretory protein (CCSP)* promoter. *J. Biol. Chem.* 269:22211–16

61. Kimura S, Hara Y, Pineau T, Fernandez-Salguero P, Fox CH, et al. 1996. The *T/ebp* null mouse: thyroid-specific, enhancer-binding protein is essential for organogenesis of the thyroid, lung, ventral forebrain, and pituitary. *Genes Dev.* 10:60–69

62. Minoo P, Su G, Drum H, Bringas P, Kimura S. 1999. Defects in tracheoesophageal and lung morphogenesis in *Nkx2.1(−/−)* mouse embryos. *Dev. Biol.* 209:60–71

63. Ikeda K, Shaw-White JR, Wert SE, Whitsett JA. 1996. Hepatocyte nuclear factor 3 activates transcription of thyroid transcription factor 1 in respiratory epithelial cells. *Mol. Cell. Biol.* 16:3626–36

64. Morrisey EE, Ip HS, Lu MM, Parmacek MS. 1996. GATA-6: a zinc finger transcription factor that is expressed in multiple cell lineages derived from lateral mesoderm. *Dev. Biol.* 177:309–22

65. Shaw-White JR, Bruno MD, Whitsett JA. 1999. GATA-6 activates transcription of thyroid transcription factor-1. *J. Biol. Chem.* 274:2658–64

66. Ang SL, Rossant J. 1994. HNF-3 beta is essential for node and notochord formation in mouse development. *Cell* 78:561–74

67. Sasaki H, Hogan BL. 1993. Differential expression of multiple *fork head* related genes during gastrulation and axial pattern formation in the mouse embryo. *Development* 118:47–59

68. Zhou L, Dey CR, Wert SE, Yan C, Costa RH, Whitsett JA. 1997. Hepatocyte nuclear factor-3beta limits cellular diversity in the developing respiratory epithelium and alters lung morphogenesis in vivo. *Dev. Dyn.* 210:305–14

69. Chen J, Knowles HJ, Hebert JL, Hackett BP. 1998. Mutation of the *mouse hepatocyte nuclear factor/forkhead homologue 4* gene results in an absence of cilia and random left-right asymmetry. *J. Clin. Invest.* 102:1077–82

70. Clevidence DE, Overdier DG, Peterson RS, Porcella A, Ye H, et al. 1994. Members of the HNF-3/forkhead family of transcription factors exhibit distinct cellular expression patterns in lung and regulate the surfactant protein B promoter. *Dev. Biol.* 166:195–209

71. Hackett BP, Brody SL, Liang M, Zeitz ID, Bruns LA, Gitlin JD. 1995. Primary structure of *hepatocyte nuclear factor/forkhead homologue 4* and characterization of gene expression in the developing respiratory and reproductive epithelium. *Proc. Natl. Acad. Sci. USA* .92:4249–53

72. Tichelaar JW, Lim L, Costa RH, Whitsett

JA. 1999. HNF-3/forkhead homologue-4 influences lung morphogenesis and respiratory epithelial cell differentiation in vivo. *Dev. Biol.* 213:405–17

73. McKenna NJ, Lanz RB, O'Malley BW. 1999. Nuclear receptor coregulators: cellular and molecular biology. *Endo. Rev.* 20:321–44

74. Cole TJ, Blendy JA, Monaghan P, Kriegelstein K, Schmid W, et al. 1995. Targeted disruption of the *glucocorticoid receptor* gene blocks adrenergic chromaffin cell development and severely retards lung maturation, *Genes Dev.* 9:1608–21

75. Reichardt HM, Kaestner KH, Tuchermann J, Kretz O, Wessely O, Bock R, Gass P, Schmid W, Herrlich P, Angel P, Schütz G. 1998. DNA binding of the glucocorticoid receptor is not essential for survival. *Cell* 93:531–41

76. Muglia LJ, Bae DS, Brown TT, Vogt SK, Alvarez JG, et al. 1999. Proliferation and differentiation defects during lung development in corticotropin-releasing hormone-deficient mice. *Am. J. Respir. Cell Mol. Biol.* 20:181–88

77. Muglia L, Jacobson L, Dikkes P, Majzoub JA. 1995. Corticotropin-releasing hormone deficiency reveals major fetal but not adult glucocorticoid need. *Nature* 373(6513):427–32

78. Odom MJ, Snyder JM, Boggaram V, Mendelson CR. 1988. Glucocorticoid regulation of the major surfactant-associated protein (SP-A) and its mRNA and of morphologic development of human fetal lung in vitro. *Endocrinology* 123:1712–20

79. Brindle PK, Montminy MR. 1992. The CREB family of transcription activators. *Curr. Opin. Genet. Dev.* 2:199–204

80. Rudolph D, Tafuri A, Gass P, Hämmerling GJ, Arnold, B, Schütz, G. 1998. Impaired fetal T cell development and perinatal lethality in mice lacking the cAMP response element binding protein. *Proc. Natl. Acad. Sci. USA* 95:4481–86

81. Botas C, Poulain F, Akiyama J, Brown C, Allen L, et al. 1998. Altered surfactant homeostasis and alveolar type II cell morphology in mice lacking surfactant protein D. *Proc. Natl. Acad. Sci. USA* 95:11869–74

82. Korfhagen TR, Sheftelyevich V, Burhans MS, Bruno MD, Ross GF, et al. 1998. Surfactant protein-D regulates surfactant phospholipid homeostasis in vivo. *J. Biol. Chem.* 273:28438–43

83. Friedman AD, Landschulz WH, McKnight SL. 1989. CCAAT/enhancer binding protein activates the promoter of the *serum albumin* gene in cultured hepatoma cells. *Genes Dev.* 3:1314–22

84. Christy RJ, Yang VW, Ntambi JM, Geiman DE, Landschulz WH, et al. 1989. Differentiation-induced gene expression in 3T3–L1 preadipocytes: CCAAT/enhancer binding protein interacts with and activates the promoters of two adipocyte-specific genes. *Genes Dev.* 3:1323–35

85. Birkenmeier EH, Gwynn B, Howard S, Jerry J, Gordon JI, et al. 1989. Tissue-specific expression, developmental regulation, and genetic mapping of the gene encoding CCAAT/enhancer binding protein. *Genes Dev.* 3:1146–56

86. Cao Z, Umek RM, McKnight SL. 1991. Regulated expression of three C/EBP isoforms during adipose conversion of 3T3–L1 cells. *Genes Dev.* 5:1538–52

87. Li F, Rosenberg E, Smith CI, Notarfrancesco K, Reisher SR, et al. 1995. Correlation of expression of transcription factor C/EBP alpha and surfactant protein genes in lung cells. *Am. J. Physiol.* 269:L241–47

88. Breed DR, Margraf LR, Alcorn JL, Mendelson CR. 1997. Transcription factor C/EBPdelta in fetal lung: developmental regulation and effects of cyclic adenosine 3',5'-monophosphate and glucocorticoids. *Endocrinology* 138:5527–34

89. Flodby P, Barlow C, Kylefjord H, Ahrlund-Richter L, Xanthopoulos KG. 1996.

Increased hepatic cell proliferation and lung abnormalities in mice deficient in CCAAT/enhancer binding protein alpha. *J. Biol. Chem.* 271:24753–60

90. Wang ND, Finegold MJ, Bradley A, Ou CN, Abdelsayed SV, et al. 1995. Impaired energy homeostasis in *C/EBP alpha* knockout mice. *Science* 269:1108–12

91. Tanaka T, Yoshida N, Kishimoto T, Akira S. 1997. Defective adipocyte differentiation in mice lacking the *C/EBPbeta* and/or *C/EBPdelta* gene. *EMBO J.* 16:7432–43

92. Veldhuizen R, Nag K, Orgeig S, Possmayer F. 1998. The role of lipids in pulmonary surfactant. *Biochim. Biophys. Acta* 1408:90–108

93. Hawgood S, Derrick M, Poulain F. 1998. Structure and properties of surfactant protein B. *Biochim. Biophys. Acta* 1408:150–60

94. Weaver TE. 1998. Synthesis, processing and secretion of surfactant proteins B and C. *Biochim. Biophys. Acta* 1408:173–79

95. Nogee LM, deMello DM, Dehner LP, Colten HR. 1993. Deficiency of surfactant protein B in congential alveolar proteinosis. *N. Engl. J. Med.* 328:406–10

96. Clark JC, Wert SE, Bachurski CJ, Stahlman MT, Stripp BR, et al. 1995. Targeted disruption of the *surfactant protein B* gene disrupts surfactant homeostasis causing respiratory failure in newborn mice. *Proc. Natl. Acad. Sci. USA* 92:7794–98

97. Vorbroker DK, Profitt SA, Nogee LM, Whitsett JA. 1995. Aberrant processing of surfactant protein C (SP-C) in hereditary SP-B deficiency. *Am. J. Physiol.* 268:L647–56

98. McCormack FX. 1998. Structure, processing and properties of surfactant protein A. *Biochim. Biophys. Acta* 1408:109–31

99. Korfhagen TR, Bruno MD, Ross GF, Huelsman KM, Ikegami M, et al. 1996. Altered surfactant function and structure in *SP-A* gene targeted mice. *Proc. Natl. Acad. Sci. USA* 93:9594–99

100. Ikegami M, Korfhagen TR, Whitsett JA, Bruno MD, Wert SE, et al. 1998. Characteristics of surfactant from SP-A-deficient mice. *Am. J. Physiol.* 275:L247–54

101. Mendelson CR, Boggaram V. 1991. Hormonal control of the surfactant system in fetal lung. *Annu. Rev. Physiol.* 53:415–40

102. Katyal SL, Singh G, Locker J. 1992. Characterization of a second human pulmonary surfactant associated protein *SP-A* gene. *Am. J. Respir. Cell Mol. Biol.* 6:446–52

103. McCormick SM, Boggaram V, Mendelson CR. 1994. Characterization of mRNA transcripts and exon-intron organization of the *human surfactant protein (SP)-A1* and *SP-A2* genes. *Am. J. Physiol.* 266:L354–66

104. Gao E, Wang Y, McCormick SM, Li J, Seidner SR, Mendelson CR. 1996. Characterization of two *baboon surfactant protein A* genes. *Am. J. Physiol.* 271:L617–30

105. Korfhagen TR, Bruno MD, Glasser SW, Ciraolo PJ, Whitsett, JA, et al. 1992. *Murine pulmonary surfactant SP-A* gene: cloning, sequence, and transcriptional activity. *Am. J. Physiol.* 263:L546–L554

106. Fisher JH, Emrie PA, Shannon J, Sano K, Hattler B, Mason RJ. 1988. Rat pulmonary surfactant protein A is expressed as two differently sized mRNA species which arise from differential polyadenylation of one transcript. *Biochim. Biophys. Acta* 950:338–45

107. Boggaram V, Qing K, Mendelson CR. 1988. Rabbit pulmonary surfactant apoprotein: elucidation of primary sequence and hormonal and developmental regulation. *J. Biol. Chem.* 263:2939–47

108. Chen Q, Boggaram V, Mendelson CR. 1992. *Rabbit surfactant protein A (SP-A)* gene: identification of a lung-specific DNaseI hypersensitive site in the 5'-

flanking region. *Am. J. Physiol.* 262: L662–71

109. Phelps DS, Floros J. 1988. Localization of surfactant protein synthesis in human lung by in situ hybridization. *Am. Rev. Respir. Dis.* 137:939–42

110. Auten RL, Watkins RH, Shapiro DL, Horowitz S. 1990. Surfactant apoprotein A (SP-A) is synthesized in airway cells. *Am. J. Respir. Cell Mol. Biol.* 3:491–96

111. Wohlford-Lenane CL, Snyder JM. 1992. Localization of the surfactant-associated proteins SP-A and SP-B mRNA in fetal rabbit lung by in situ hybridization. *Am. J. Respir. Cell Mol. Biol.* 7:335–43

112. Khoor A, Gray ME, Hull WM, Whitsett JA, Stallman MT. 1993. Developmental expression of SP-A and SP-A mRNA in the proximal and distal respiratory epithelium in the human fetus and newborn. *J. Histochem. Cytochem.* 41:1311–19

113. Boggaram V, Mendelson CR. 1988. Transcriptional regulation of the gene encoding the major surfactant-associated protein (SP-A) in rabbit fetal lung. *J. Biol. Chem.* 263:19060–65

114. Snyder JM, Magliato SA. 1991. An ultrastructural, morphometric analysis of rabbit fetal lung type II cell differentiation in vivo. *Anat. Rec.* 229:73–85

115. Ballard PL, Hawgood S, Liley H, Wellenstein G, Gonzales LW, et al. 1986. Regulation of pulmonary surfactant apoprotein SP 28–36 gene in fetal human lung. *Proc. Natl. Acad. Sci USA* 83: 9527–31

116. Snyder JM, Mendelson CR. 1987. Insulin inhibits the accumulation of the major lung surfactant apoprotein in human fetal lung explants maintained *in vitro*. *Endocrinology* 120:1250–57

117. Snyder JM, Kwun JE, O'Brien JA, Rosenfeld CR, Odom MJ. 1988. The concentration of the 35–kDa surfactant apoprotein in amniotic fluid from normal and diabetic pregnancies. *Pediatr. Res.* 24:728–34

118. Phelps DS, Floros J. 1988. Localization of surfactant protein synthesis in human lung by in situ hybridization. *Am. Rev. Respir. Dis.* 137:939–42

119. Phelps DS, Floros J. 1991. Localization of pulmonary surfactant proteins using immunohistochemistry and tissue in situ hybridization. *Exp. Lung Res.* 17:985–95

120. Glasser SW, Korfhagen TR, Wert SE, Bruno MD, McWilliams KM, Vorbroker DK, Whitsett JA. 1991. Genetic element from *human surfactant protein SP-C* gene confers bronchiolar-alveolar cell specificity in transgenic mice. *Am. J. Physiol.* 261:L349–56

121. Horowitz S, Watkins RH, Auten RL Jr, Mercier CE, Cheng ER. 1991. Differential accumulation of surfactant protein A, B, and C mRNAs in two epithelial cell types of hyperoxic lung. *Am. J. Respir. Cell Mol. Biol.* 5:511–15

122. Wohlford-Lenane CL, Durham PL, Snyder JM. 1992. Localization of surfactant-associated protein C (SP-C) mRNA in fetal rabbit lung tissue by in situ hybridization. *Am J. Respir. Cell Mol. Biol.* 6:225–34

123. Boggaram V, Margana RK. 1992. Rabbit surfactant protein C: cDNA cloning and regulation of alternatively spliced surfactant protein C mRNAs. *Am. J. Physiol.* 263:L634–44

124. Liley HG, White RT, Warr RG, Benson BJ, Hawgood S, Ballard PL. 1989. Regulation of mRNAs for the hydrophobic surfactant proteins in human lung. *J. Clin. Invest.* 83:1191–97

125. Whitsett JA, Weaver TE, Clark JC, Sawtell N, Glasser SW, et al. 1987. Glucocorticoid enhances surfactant proteolipid Phe and pVal synthesis and RNA in fetal lung. *J. Biol. Chem.* 262:15618–23

126. Crouch EC. 1998. Structure, biologic properties, and expression of surfactant protein D (SP-D). *Biochim. Biophys. Acta* 1408:278–89

127. Dulkerian SJ, Gonzales LW, Ning Y, Ballard PL. 1996. Regulation of surfactant

protein D in human fetal lung. *Am. J. Respir. Cell Mol. Biol.* 15:781–86

128. Mendelson CR, Gao E, Li J, Young PP, Michael LF, Alcorn JL. 1998. Regulation of expression of surfactant protein-A. *Biochim. Biophys. Acta* 1408:132–49

129. Boggaram V, Smith ME, Mendelson CR. 1989. Regulation of expression of the gene encoding the major surfactant protein (SP-A) in human fetal lung in vitro. *J. Biol. Chem.* 264:11421–27

130. Boggaram V, Smith ME, Mendelson CR 1991. Posttranscriptional regulation of surfactant protein A (SP-A) mRNA in human fetal lung in vitro by glucocorticoids. *Mol. Endocrinol.* 5:414–23

131. Nichols KV, Floros J, Dynia DW. 1990. Regulation of surfactant protein A mRNA by hormones and butyrate in cultured fetal rat lung. *Am. J. Physiol.* 259:L488–95

132. Alcorn JL Gao E, Chen Q, Smith ME, Gerard RD, Mendelson CR. 1993. Genomic elements involved in transcriptional regulation of the *rabbit surfactant protein-A (SP-A)* gene. *Mol. Endocrinol.* 7:1072–85

133. Michael LF, Alcorn JL, Gao E, Mendelson CR. 1996. Characterization of the cyclic AMP response element of the *rabbit surfactant protein-A* gene: evidence for transactivators distinct from CREB/ATF family members. *Mol. Endocrinol.* 10:159–70

134. Young PP, Mendelson CR. 1996. A CRE-like element plays an essential role in cyclic AMP regulation of the *human surfactant protein-A2 (SP-A2)* gene. *Am. J. Physiol.* 271:L287–99

135. McCormick SM, Mendelson CR. 1994. The human *SP-A1* and *SP-A2* genes are differentially regulated during development and by cyclic AMP and glucocorticoids. *Am. J. Physiol.* 266:L367–74

136. Kumar AR, Snyder JM. 1998. Differential regulation of *SP-A1* and *SP-A2* genes by cAMP, glucocorticoids and insulin. *Am. J. Physiol.* 274:L177–85

137. Said SI, Mutt V. 1970. Polypeptide with broad biological activity: isolation from small intestine. *Science* 169:1217–18

138. Floros J, Gross I, Nichols KV, Veletza SV, Dynia D, et al. 1991. Hormonal effects on the surfactant protein B (SP-B) mRNA in cultured fetal rat lung. *Am. J. Respir. Cell Mol. Biol.* 4:449–54

139. Veletza SV, Nichols KV, Gross I, Lu H, Dynia DW, Floros J. 1992. Surfactant protein C: hormonal control of SP-C mRNA levels in vitro. *Am. J. Physiol.* 262:L684–87

140. Margana RK, Boggaram V. 1995. Transcription and mRNA stability regulate developmental and hormonal expression of *rabbit surfactant protein B* gene. *Am. J. Physiol.* 268:L481–90

141. Boggaram V, Margana RK. 1994. Developmental and hormonal regulation of *surfactant protein C (SP-C)* gene expression in fetal lung. Role of transcription and mRNA stability. *J. Biol. Chem.* 269:27767–72

142. Seidner SR, Smith ME, Mendelson CR. 1996. Developmental and hormonal regulation of *SP-A* gene expression in baboon fetal lung. *Am. J. Physiol.* 271:L609–16

143. Schellhase DE, Shannon JM. 1991. Effects of maternal dexamethasone on expression of SP-A, SP-B, and SP-C in the fetal rat. *Am. J. Respir. Cell Mol. Biol.* 4:304–12

144. O'Reilly MA, Clark JC, Whitsett JA. 1991. Glucocorticoid enhances pulmonary *surfactant protein B* gene transcription. *Am. J. Physiol.* 260:L37–43

145. Venkatesh VC, Iannuzzi DM, Ertsey R, Ballard PL. 1993. Differential glucocorticoid regulation of the pulmonary hydrophobic surfactant proteins SP-B and SP-C. *Am. J. Respir. Cell Mol. Biol.* 8:222–28

146. Ballard PL, Ertsey R, Gonzales LW, Gonzales J. 1996. Transcriptional regulation of human pulmonary surfactant proteins SP-B and SP-C by glucocorti

coids. *Am. J. Respir. Cell Mol. Biol.* 14:599–607

147. Hummler E, Barker P, Gatzy J. 1996. Early death due to defective neonatal lung liquid clearance in αENaC-deficient mice. *Nat. Genet.* 12:325–28

148. Metzler MD, Snyder JM. 1993. Retinoic acid differentially regulates expression of surfactant-associated proteins in human fetal lung. *Endocrinology* 133:1990–98

149. Cardoso WV, Williams MC, Mitsialis SA, Joyce-Brady M, Rishi AK, Brody JS. 1995. Retinoic acid induces changes in the pattern of airway branching and alters epithelial cell differentiation in the developing lung in vitro. *Am. J. Respir. Cell Mol. Biol.* 12:464–76

150. Obenshain SS, Adam PA, King KC, Teramo K, Raivio KO, et al. 1970. Human fetal insulin response to sustained maternal hyperglycemia. *N. Engl. J. Med.* 283:566–70

151. Robert MF, Neff RK, Hubbell JP, Taeusch HW, Avery ME. 1976. Association between maternal diabetes and the respiratory-distress syndrome in the newborn. *N. Engl. J. Med.* 294:357–60

152. Katyal SL, Amenta JS, Singh G, Silverman JA. 1984. Deficient lung surfactant apoproteins in amniotic fluid with mature phospholipid profile from diabetic pregnancies. *Am. J. Obstet. Gynecol.* 148:48–53

153. McMahan MJ, Mimouni F, Miodovnik M, Hull WM, Whitsett JA. 1987. Surfactant associated protein (SAP-35) in amniotic fluid from diabetic and nondiabetic pregnancies. *Obstet. Gynecol.* 70:94–98

154. Dekowski SA, Snyder JM. 1992. Insulin regulation of messenger ribonucleic acid for the surfactant-associated proteins in human fetal lung in vitro. *Endocrinology* 131:669–76

155. Mendelson CR, Boggaram V. 1992. Hormonal and developmental regulation of the surfactant-associated proteins in fetal lung. In *Hormones and Fetal Pathophysiology,* ed. JR Pasqualini, R Scholler, pp. 87–118. New York: Dekker

156. Miakotina OL, Dekowski SA, Snyder JM. 1998. Insulin inhibits *surfactant protein A* and *B* gene expression in the H441 cell line. *Biochim. Biophys. Acta.* 1442:60–70

157. Whitsett JA, Weaver TE, Lieberman MA, Clark JC, Daugherty C. 1987. Differential effects of epidermal growth factor and transforming growth factor-beta on synthesis of $M_r = 35,000$ surfactant-associated protein in fetal lung. *J. Biol. Chem.* 262:7908–13

158. Nielsen HC, Martin A, Volpe MV, Hatzis D, Vosatka RJ. 1997. Growth factor control of growth and epithelial differentiation in embryonic lungs. *Biochem. Mol. Med.* 60:38–48

159. Miettinen PJ, Berger JE, Meneses J, Phung Y, Pedersen RA, et al. 1995. Epithelial immaturity and multiorgan failure in mice lacking epidermal growth factor receptor. *Nature* 376:337–41

160. Sibilia M, Wagner EF. 1995. Strain-dependent epithelial effects in mice lacking the EGF receptor. *Science* 269:234–38

161. Whitsett JA, Budden A, Hull WM, Clark JC, O'Reilly MA. 1992. Transforming growth factor-beta inhibits surfactant protein A expression in vitro. *Biochim. Biophys. Acta* 1123:257–62

162. Beers MF, Solarin KO, Guttentag SH, Rosenbloom J, Kormilli A, et al. 1998. TGF-beta1 inhibits surfactant component expression and epithelial cell maturation in cultured human fetal lung. *Am. J. Physiol.* 275:L950–60

163. Pryhuber GS, O'Reilly MA, Clark JC, Hull WM, Fink I, Whitsett JA. 1990. Phorbol ester inhibits surfactant protein SP-A and SP-B expression. *J. Biol. Chem.* 265:20822–28

164. Whitsett JA, Clark JC, Wispe JR, Pryhuber GS. 1992. Effects of TNF-alpha and phorbol ester on human surfactant

protein and MnSOD gene transcription in vitro. *Am. J. Physiol.* 262:L688–93

165. Wispe JR, Clark JC, Warner BB, Fajardo D, Hull WE, et al. 1990. Tumor necrosis factor-alpha inhibits expression of pulmonary surfactant protein. *J. Clin. Invest.* 86:1954–60

166. Planer BC, Ning Y, Kumar SA, Ballard PL. 1997. Transcriptional regulation of surfactant proteins SP-A and SP-B by phorbol ester. *Biochim. Biophys. Acta* 1353:171–79

167. Fraser A, Evan G. 1996. A license to kill. *Cell* 85:781–84

168. Pryhuber GS, Khalak R, Zhao Q. 1998. Regulation of surfactant proteins A and B by TNF-alpha and phorbol ester independent of NF-kappa B. *Am. J. Physiol.* 274:L289–95

169. Bachurski CJ, Pryhuber GS, Glasser SW, Kelly SE, Whitsett JA. 1995. Tumor necrosis factor-alpha inhibits *surfactant protein C* gene transcription. *J. Biol. Chem.* 270:19402–7

170. Ballard PL, Liley HG, Gonzales LW, Odom MW, Ammann AJ, et al. 1990. Interferon-gamma and synthesis of surfactant components by cultured human fetal lung. *Am. J. Respir. Cell Mol. Biol.* 2:137–43

171. Bry K, Lappalainen U, Hallman M. 1997. Intraamniotic interleukin-1 accelerates surfactant protein synthesis in fetal rabbits and improves lung stability after premature birth. *J. Clin. Invest.* 99:2992–99

172. Dhar V, Hallman M, Lappalainen U, Bry K. 1997. Interleukin-1α upregulates the expression of surfactant protein-A in rabbit lung explants. *Biol. Neonate* 71:46–52

173. Shannon JM, Emrie PA, Fisher JH, Kuroki Y, Jennings SD, Mason RJ. 1990. Effect of a reconstituted basement membrane on expression of surfactant apoproteins in cultured adult rat alveolar type II cells. *Am. J. Respir. Cell Mol. Biol.* 1:183–92

174. Alcorn JL, Smith ME, Smith J, Margraf L, Mendelson CR. 1997. Primary cell culture of human type II pneumonocytes: maintenance of a differentiated phenotype and transfection with recombinant adenoviruses, *Am. J. Respir. Cell Mol. Biol.* 17: 672–82

175. Deterding RR, Jacoby CR, Shannon JM. 1996. Acidic fibroblast growth factor and keratinocyte growth factor stimulate fetal rat pulmonary epithelial growth. *Am. J. Physiol.* 271:L495–505

176. Sugahara K, Rubin JS, Mason RJ, Aronsen EL, Shannon JM. 1995. Keratinocyte growth factor stimulates mRNAs for SP-A and SP-B in adult rat alveolar type II cells in culture. *Am. J. Physiol.* 269:L344–50

177. Alcorn JL, Hammer RE, Graves KR, Smith ME, Maika SD, et al. 1999. Analysis of genomic regions involved in regulation of the *rabbit surfactant protein A* gene in transgenic mice. *Am. J. Physiol.* 277:L349–61

178. Wert SE, Glasser SW, Korfhagen TR, Whitsett JA. 1993. Transcriptional elements from the *human SP-C* gene direct expression in the primordial respiratory epithelium of transgenic mice. *Dev. Biol.* 156:426–43

179. Glass CK. 1994. Differential regulation of target genes by nuclear receptor monomers, dimers and heterodimers. *Endocr. Rev.* 15:391–407

180. Gao E, Alcorn JL, Mendelson CR. 1993. Identification of enhancers in the 5'-flanking region of the *rabbit surfactant protein-A* gene and characterization of their binding proteins. *J. Biol. Chem.* 268:19697–709

181. Gao E, Wang Y, Alcorn JL, Mendelson CR. 1997. The basic helix-loop-helix-zipper transcription factor USF1 regulates expression of the *surfactant protein-A* gene. *J. Biol. Chem.* 272: 23398–406

182. Young PP, Mendelson CR. 1997. A GT box element is essential for basal and

cyclic adenosine 3',5'-monophosphate regulation of the *human surfactant protein A2* gene in alveolar type II cells: evidence for the binding of lung nuclear proteins distinct from Sp1. *Mol. Endocrinol.* 11:1082–93

183. Lacaze-Masmonteil T, Fraslon C, Bourbon J, Raymondjean M, Kahn A. 1992. Characterization of the *rat pulmonary surfactant protein A* promoter. *Eur. J. Biochem.* 206: 613–23

184. Margana RK, Boggaram V. 1997. Functional analysis of *surfactant protein B (SP-B)* promoter. Sp1, Sp3, TTF-1, and HNF-3alpha transcription factors are necessary for lung cell-specific activation of *SP-B* gene transcription. *J. Biol. Chem.* 272:3083–90

185. Miller I, Bieker JJ. 1993. A novel, erythroid cell-specific murine transcription factor that binds to the CACCC element and is related to the Krüppel family of nuclear proteins. *Mol. Cell. Biol.* 13: 2776–786

186. Zhang L, Whitsett JA, Stripp BR. 1997. Regulation of *Clara cell secretory protein* gene transcription by thyroid transcription factor-1. *Biochim. Biophys. Acta* 1350:359–67

187. Yan C, Whitsett JA. 1997. Protein kinase A activation of the *surfactant protein B* gene is mediated by phosphorylation of thyroid transcription factor 1. *J. Biol. Chem.* 272:17327–32

188. Kumar AS, Venkatesh VC, Planer BC, Feinstein SI, Ballard PL. 1997. Phorbol ester down-regulation of lung *surfactant protein B* gene expression by cytoplasmic trapping of thyroid transcription factor-1 and hepatocyte nuclear factor 3. *J. Biol. Chem.* 272:20764–73

189. Bingle CD, Hackett BP, Moxley M, Longmore W, Gitlin JD. 1995. Role of hepatocyte nuclear factor-3 alpha and hepatocyte nuclear factor-3 beta in *Clara cell secretory protein* gene expression in the bronchiolar epithelium. *Biochem. J.* 308:197–202

190. Yan C, Ghaffari M, Whitsett JA, Zeng X, Sever Z, Lin S. 1998. Retinoic acid-receptor activation of *SP-B* gene transcription in respiratory epithelial cells. *Am. J. Physiol.* 275:L239–46

191. Ghaffari M, Whitsett JA, Yan C. 1999. Inhibition of *hSP-B* promoter in respiratory epithelial cells by a dominant negative retinoic acid receptor. *Am. J. Physiol.* 276:L398–404

192. Bachurski CJ, Kelly SE, Glasser SW, Currier TA. 1997. Nuclear factor I family members regulate the transcription of *surfactant protein-C. J. Biol. Chem.* 272:32759–66

Views and Overviews of the 20th Century

Annu. Rev. Physiol. 2000. 62:919–26

A CENTURY OF THINKING ABOUT CELL MEMBRANES

Paul De Weer

Department of Physiology, University of Pennsylvania, Philadelphia, Pennsylvania
19104–6085; e-mail: deweer@mail.med.upenn.edu

If a centenary be marked in general cell physiology, it probably should be that of the concept of a lipoid membrane enclosing plant and animal cells, clearly enunciated in three papers read by Ernest Overton, then Dozent at the University of Zürich (where Adolph Fick taught a half century earlier), before the Natural History Society of that city, and later published in the society's quarterly (48–50). A promised magnum opus detailing experimental protocols and tabulated results was, unfortunately, never completed (10). Overton made other seminal contributions (see 39): He formulated (independently from and simultaneously with Meyer, 43) the lipid-water partition theory for the mode of action of general anesthetics (48, 51); he proposed an exchange of external Na^+ for internal K^+ during the excitation/contraction process in muscle (52); and he stated that, besides (lipid-phase) diffusional processes, other transmembrane (including uphill) movements must exist that require expenditure of metabolic energy by the cell (50). Thus Overton's legacy affords a pertinent departure point for a brief overview of a century of progress in our understanding of cell membranes and movements across them.

The notion of a cell "membrane," a barrier between cytoplasm and the cell's environment (the milieu intérieur for animal cells), was already old at the turn of the century. Earliest formulation is usually attributed to Nägeli & Cramer (44) in their report on osmosis in plant cells. However, Kleinzeller (38) has shown that now-forgotten studies by William Hewson in 1773 (27) on red blood cells, including hypotonicity-induced lysis, proved that these "corpuscles" were in fact fluid-containing, envelope-bounded vesicles that would shrink or swell (and sometimes burst) depending on the nature of the bathing fluid. This was two generations before the concept of a living cell was defined by François-Vincent Raspail in 1825 (57). At any rate, from the earliest studies forward the cell membrane has been assumed, explicitly or implicitly, to be permeable to water but not to solutes. Cells (plant cells earlier than animal cells) were thought of as osmometers—before the term was used or its laws defined by Jakob van 't Hoff (72)—whose changes in volume and/or pressure (for plant cells surrounded by a stiff wall) resulted from transmembrane water movements somehow governed by the composition of the bathing fluid. In a paper on the osmotic properties of red beet cells

Hugo de Vries (14) noted that the only solute he found to readily penetrate into the cells was ammonia; later he also found glycerol to penetrate slowly (15). By the time Overton lectured before the Zürich naturalist society he had classified hundreds of organic solutes as to their permeability across cell membranes and concluded that permeation rates were determined not by a compound's size but by its oil-water partition coefficient. The osmotic barrier, he stated, must be a lipid-impregnated boundary layer with properties similar to those of cholesterol esters and lecithin. Its thickness remained a matter of conjecture until the 1920s when Fricke (18) first measured the electrical capacitance of the red cell membrane and—assuming it to be oil-like—derived a thickness of about 33 Å. Many cells were found to have a similar capacitance of about $1 \mu F \, cm^{-2}$ (9). Gorter & Grendel (21) calculated that red blood cells, which lack membrane-bounded organelles, contain sufficient lipid to yield a monolayer of area twice that of the cell surface and thus proposed the now familiar bimolecular leaflet model for the cell membrane. A decade later Danielli & Davson (12) introduced what they later called the pauci-molecular model characterized by a lipoid center (of varying, sometimes virtual, dimension reflecting uncertainty about the membrane's actual thickness) sandwiched between monolayers of lipid and of protein. Some of Danielli's sketches featured peptide-lined pores across the membrane (e.g. 69). Advances in electron microscopy allowed Robertson (59, 60) to formulate the concept of the "unit membrane" according to which all cell membranes are indeed composed of a bimolecular (polar) lipid leaflet covered with nonlipid monolayers, mainly carbohydrates, on the external face. The current paradigm, the "fluid mosaic" membrane (66), finally assigns an appealing locus to the membrane proteins: they are embedded in the lipid layer, some on one or the other side, some spanning the bilayer. The initial property of extreme lateral mobility (two-dimensional solutions) of these lipids and proteins was later tempered somewhat by the addition of a cytoplasmic proteinaceous mesh that restricts the motion of integral proteins (65) and provides strength and mechanical continuity with extra-cellular structures.

Whereas Overton's view of the cell membrane as a lipid-impregnated boundary underwent considerable refinement over the past century, his notion that many substances cross the cell membrane in proportion to their lipid solubility was mature enough to stand the test of time. Had Overton published the detailed experimental evidence on which his conclusion was based, others might not have felt the need to supply it (10). If Overton and his predecessors or successors were curious about the mechanism of the high water permeability of cell membranes, they did not dwell much on the question in print. Only about the 1950s did a debate arise, with some believing the pure lipid bilayer to be sufficiently water-permeable to explain the facts (17), and others not (55, 69). The cloning and functional expression (56) of the first of a large and evolutionarily ancient family of transmembrane proteins termed aquaporins resolved the issue and explained the observed variability and physiological regulation of water permeability. Cryo-electron microscopy of two-dimensional crystals has yielded a three-dimensional structure at 6–7 Å resolution (8, 73) clearly outlining six (predicted) transmembrane helices in each subunit of a tetramer. A surprising recent development (11) is that aquaporins may subserve (at least part of) the membrane's permeability to CO_2 which, since Overton's days, had universally been assumed to be lipid mediated.

By the time Overton (52) observed that immersion of muscle (but not of nerve, a difference he ascribed to the perineural sheath) in isotonic sucrose solutions caused loss of excitability, the electrical nature of excitability was well established through the work of Emil Du Bois-Reymond, Hermann Helmholtz, and Julius Bernstein. The latter had established that the interior of nerve and muscle cells at rest is permanently and everywhere at a negative potential with respect to the outside. Bernstein (4) had also formulated the so-called membrane theory of resting (injury) and action potentials according to which the former results from a preexisting transmembrane K^+ concentration difference and selective potassium permeability, and the latter from a transient loss of selectivity–the membrane becoming permeable to all ion species, which causes the transmembrane voltage to collapse. Remarkably (see 22) in his earliest publications, Bernstein (3) had produced evidence for what is now called the sign reversal or overshoot of the nerve action potential—a phenomenon firmly established only much later by Hodgkin & Huxley (31)—but he did not return to the issue in his later work. From his experiments Overton concluded that extracellular Na^+ is essential for excitability (only Li^+ could replace it, and the nature of the anion was irrelevant) and surmised that there must be an exchange of sodium for potassium during nerve excitation and muscle contraction. It did not escape his attention that a secretory mechanism might be required to prevent intracellular Na^+ accumulation following repeated contractions. Overton's conjectured exchange of Na^+ for K^+ was only proven a half-century later by Hodgkin & Katz (33). Then came the brilliant analysis by Hodgkin & Huxley (32) of the voltage- and time-dependent Na^+ and K^+ conductance changes underlying excitability, culminating in their theoretical reconstruction of a propagated action potential. The physical nature of the conductance elements (as well as the answer to the question whether a single element subserved both conductances) remained unknown at first. Pores, for example, seemed unlikely to confer the requisite Na^+ selectivity, but unmistakable K^+ channels were invoked by Hodgkin & Keynes (35) to explain the single-filing character of K^+ movements across the cuttlefish axon membrane. However, over the next two decades the notion of discrete and distinct proteinaceous channels for Na^+, K^+, and other ions received cumulative experimental support, thanks in part to the discovery of specific blockers such as tetrodotoxin for Na^+ channels (45) and tetraethylammonium for K^+ channels (1, 71) and to increasingly refined and consistent estimates of their pore dimensions (28). The development of the gigaohm-seal patch-clamp technique by Neher & Sakmann (46) clinched the evidence for discrete and selective ion channels as molecular conductance elements. Shortly after his group determined the cDNA sequences of the subunits of the electric-eel nicotinic acetylcholine channel, Numa published the sequence of the

Na^+ channel from the same source (47), the first of an ever-accelerating stream of published channel sequences whose taxonomic relationships prove their great evolutionary antiquity. Putative topologies deduced from hydropathy plots, chemical labeling, and other techniques, together with recombinant DNA and directed mutagenesis techniques in the hands of researchers too numerous to quote (see 29) have yielded plausible molecular channel models with specific domains that sense transmembrane voltage, bind blockers or toxins, line the pore, cause inactivation, or confer ion selectivity. MacKinnon's group (16) has published the first X-ray analysis, to 3.2 Å, of a (bacterial, non-voltage-sensing) K^+ channel, with a clearly identified short K-selective filter lined by peptide backbone carbonyl oxygen atoms. The study of transmembrane ion-specific channels is entering an era of greatly enhanced understanding of their structure and function.

A final motif from Overton's legacy whose evolution through the past century can be traced is the idea that "uphill" transport of certain compounds across the cell membrane must exist, requiring expenditure of metabolic energy. The idea was not Overton's alone: Pfeffer (53) had invoked it to explain the uptake of dyes by plant cells, and Reid (58) unambiguously demonstrated transepithelial, metabolism-dependent fluid movements in the absence of an osmotic gradient. Overton, as already stated, was first to surmise the need for active extrusion of Na^+ if muscle excitation/contraction involves an exchange of Na^+ for K^+.

What follows is a brief sketch of the course of research and thinking, over the past century, on the need for and molecular mechanism of sodium extrusion from (most) animal cells. For a perceptive account of the history of active membrane transport and bioenergetics, see Robinson (61).

If Pfeffer, Reid, and Overton unambiguously enunciated the notion of what is now called active transport, none of these authors pointed to the cell membrane as the agent of such transport. As well, the possibility that Na^+ might be permeant, let alone actively transported, disappeared from the literature of the first third of the 20th century and was vigorously denied by some into the 1940s (5). However, the observation of transmembrane movements of Na^+ in muscle, both radioisotopic (26) and net (70), led Dean (13) to propose a pump located in the membrane. Erythrocytes also proved capable of gaining (36) and losing (25) sodium. By mid-century, active transport of Na^+ was an established fact for both muscle (23, 40) and erythrocytes (41). Harris & Maizels (24) suggested that "inward transport of K is 'geared' to outward Na transport by the use of a common carrier." The work of the Cambridge group on giant axons had left no doubt (32) that nerves must also possess a mechanism for maintaining their ionic gradients. Hodgkin & Keynes (34) showed on cuttlefish and squid axons that metabolic poisons inhibit sodium extrusion and potassium uptake with little effect on sodium movements associated with impulses and that external K^+ removal inhibits Na^+ extrusion. They, too, concluded that Na^+ and K^+ transport are coupled. Schatzmann's discovery (62) of the highly specific inhibitory action of cardiotonic steroids on the sodium pump had a major impact on the field since a defining tool was now available. This tool was used to help establish the erythrocyte pump's stoichiometry as $3Na^+/2K^+$ by Post & Jolly (54) and as $3Na^+/2K^+/1ATP$ by

Sen & Post (63). The large size of squid axons, which allows mechanical injection of test compounds, indeed allowed Caldwell et al (7) to find very strong support for the notion (19, 20) that the Na/K pump is fueled by ATP. More definitive proof was harder to come by (6, 30).

Skou's discovery of a Na,K-ATPase in crab nerve (67) that is inhibited by ouabain (68) opened an era of feverish research. The enzyme was shown to be "all of and nothing but" the pump with the requisite sidedness (R Post, I Glynn, J Hoffman) and to undergo Na-dependent phosphorylation and K-dependent dephosphorylation during its cycle (R Post, W Albers). A new generation of researchers too numerous to quote (see 61) now joined the pioneers to purify and characterize the enzyme (it contains two, sometimes three subunits) and unravel its kinetics (conformational changes; phosphorylation/dephosphorylation; ion occlusion) and modes of operation (unconventional ion transport modes in addition to 3Na/2K exchange). The cDNA sequences for the sodium pump α subunit from sheep kidney (64) and electric ray (37) were published simultaneously. It was soon evident that the sodium pump is a member of a large family of so-called P-type (undergoing phosphorylation) transport ATPases of great evolutionary antiquity. Current consensus recognizes ten transmembrane helices. Directed mutagenesis, chemical labeling, and other techniques are slowly identifying domains involved in ATP and Mg^{2+} binding, Na and K binding and occlusion, α-β subunit interaction, and cardiotonic steroid binding. Three-dimensional structures have been obtained from two-dimensional crystals of Na/K-ATPase at 20–25 Å (42) and of *Neurospora* H-ATPase at 8 Å resolution (2), and from tubular crystals of sarcoplasmic Ca-ATPase at 8 Å resolution (74). A complete atomic-resolution map of a P-type pump is imminent.

Charles Ernest Overton would be pleased. The lipoid nature of the cell membrane, now refined to the fluid-mosaic lipid bilayer model, is universally accepted, as is its role in the permeation of lipid-soluble molecules. All other transmembrane movements including those of ions, water, and small hydrophilic molecules (and perhaps some gases) are mediated by highly specific integral proteins. Some of these movements are thermodynamically uphill, driven by ATP hydrolysis or dissipation of concentration gradients. Many of these membrane proteins–pores, channels, carriers, and pumps–have been identified and sequenced, and structural maps at atomic resolution, if not already here, are just around the corner.

Visit the Annual Reviews home page at www.AnnualReviews.org.

LITERATURE CITED

1. Armstrong CM. 1971. Interaction of tetraethylammonium ion derivatives with the potassium channels of giant axons. *J. Gen. Physiol.* 58:413–37

2. Auer M, Scarborough GA, Kühlbrandt W. 1998. Three-dimensional map of the plasma membrane H^+-ATPase in the open conformation. *Nature* 392:840–43

3. Bernstein J. 1868. Über den zeitlichen Verlauf der negativen Schwankung des Nervenstroms. *Pflügers Arch.* 1:173–07

4. Bernstein J. 1902. Untersuchungen zur

Thermodynamik der bioelektrischen Ströme. *Pflügers Arch.* 92:521–62

5. Boyle PJ, Conway EJ. 1941. Potassium accumulation in muscle and associated changes. *J. Physiol.* 100:1–63

6. Brinley FJ Jr, Mullins LJ. 1968. Sodium fluxes in internally dialyzed axons. *J. Gen. Physiol.* 52:181–211

7. Caldwell P, Hodgkin AL, Keynes RD, Shaw TI. 1960. The effects of injecting "energy-rich" phosphate compounds on the active transport of ions in the giant axons of *Loligo*. *J. Physiol.* 152:561–90

8. Cheng A, van Hoek AN, Yeager M, Verkman AS, Mitra AK. 1997. Three-dimensional organization of a human water channel. *Nature* 387:627–30

9. Cole KS. 1968. *Membranes, Ions, and Impulses.* Berkeley: Univ. California Press

10. Collander R. 1937. The permeability of plant protoplasts to non-electrolytes. *Trans. Faraday Soc.* 33:985–90

11. Cooper GJ, Boron WF. 1998. Effects of PCMBS on CO_2 permeability of *Xenopus* oocytes expressing aquaporin 1 or its C189S mutant. *Am. J. Physiol.* 275: C1481–86

12. Danielli JF, Davson H. 1935. A contribution to the theory of permeability of thin films. *J. Cell. Comp. Physiol.* 5:495–508

13. Dean RB. 1941. Theories of electrolyte equilibrium in muscle. *Biol. Symp.* 3:331–48

14. de Vries H. 1871. Sur la perméabilité du protoplasma des betteraves rouges. *Arch. Néerl. Sci. Exactes Nat.* 6:117–26

15. de Vries H. 1888. Über den isotonischen Coefficient des Glycerins. *Bot. Z.* 46:230–35, 245–53

16. Doyle DA, Cabral JM, Pfuetzner RA, Kuo A, Gulbis JM, et al. 1998. The structure of the potassium channel: molecular basis of K^+ conduction and selectivity. *Science* 280:69–77

17. Finkelstein A. 1976. Water and nonelec-

trolyte permeability of lipid bilayer membranes. *J. Gen. Physiol.* 68:127–35

18. Fricke H. 1925. The electrical capacity of suspensions with special reference to blood. *J. Gen. Physiol.* 9:137–52

19. Gárdos G. 1954. Akkumulation der Kaliumionen durch menschliche Blutkörperchen. *Acta Physiol. Hung.* 6:191–99

20. Glynn IM. 1957. The ionic permeability of the red cell membrane. *Progr. Biophys.* 8:242–305

21. Gorter E, Grendel F. 1925. On bimolecular layers of lipoids on chromatocytes of blood. *J. Exp. Med.* 41:439–43

22. Grundfest H. 1965. Julius Bernstein, Ludimar Hermann and the discovery of the overshoot of the axon spike. *Arch. Ital. Biol.* 103:483–90

23. Harris EJ, Burn GP. 1949. The transfer of sodium and potassium ions between muscle and the surrounding medium. *Trans. Faraday Soc.* 45:508–28

24. Harris EJ, Maizels M. 1852. Distribution of ions in suspensions of human erythrocytes. *J. Physiol.* 118:40–53

25. Harris JE. 1941. The influence of the metabolism of human erythrocytes on their potassium content. *J. Biol. Chem.* 141:579–95

26. Heppel LA. 1940. The diffusion of radioactive sodium into the muscles of potassium-deprived rats. *Am. J. Physiol.* 128:449–54

27. Hewson W. 1773. On the figure and composition of the red particles of the blood, commonly called the red globules. *Philos. Trans. R. Soc. London* 63:306–24

28. Hille B. 1975. Ionic selectivity of Na and K channels of nerve membranes. In *Membranes – A Series of Advances,* ed. G Eisenman, 3:255–323. New York: Dekker

29. Hille B. 1992. *Ionic Channels of Excitable Membranes.* Sunderland, MA: Sinauer

30. Hoffman JF. 1980. The link between metabolism and active transport of

sodium in human red cell ghosts. *J. Membr. Biol.* 57:143–61

31. Hodgkin AL, Huxley AF. 1939. Action potentials recorded from inside a nerve fibre. *Nature* 144:710–11

32. Hodgkin AL, Huxley AF. 1952. A quantitative description of membrane current and its application to conduction and excitation in nerve. *J. Physiol.* 117:500–44

33. Hodgkin AL, Katz B. 1949. The effect of sodium ions on the electrical activity of the giant axon of the squid. *J. Physiol.* 108:37–77

34. Hodgkin AL, Keynes RD. 1955. Active transport of cations in giant axons from *Sepia* and *Loligo*. *J. Physiol.* 128:28–60

35. Hodgkin AL, Keynes RD. 1995. The potassium permeability of a giant nerve fibre. *J. Physiol.* 128:61–88

36. Jeanneney G, Servantie L, Ringenbach G. 1938. Les modifications du rapport potassium/sodium du plasma dans le sang citraté conservé à la glacière. *Compt. Rend. Soc. Biol.* 130:472–73

37. Kawakami K, Noguchi S, Noda M, Takahashi H, Ohta T, et al. 1985. Primary structure of the α-subunit of *Torpedo californica* ($Na^+ + K^+$)ATPase deduced from cDNA sequence. *Nature* 316:733–36

38. Kleinzeller A. 1996. William Hewson's studies of red blood corpuscles and the concept of a cell membrane. *Am. J. Physiol.* 271:C1–8

39. Kleinzeller A. 1999. Charles Ernest Overton's concept of a cell membrane. *Curr. Top. Membr.* 48:1–22

40. Levi H, Ussing HH. 1948. The exchange of sodium and chloride ions across the fibre membrane of the isolated frog sartorius. *Acta Physiol. Scand.* 16:232–49

41. Maizels M. 1949. Cation control in human erythrocytes. *J. Physiol.* 108:247–63

42. Maunsbach AB, Skriver E, Hebert H. 1991. Two-dimensional crystals and three-dimensional structure of Na,K-ATPase analyzed by electron microscopy. In *The Sodium Pump: Structure, Mechanism, and Regulation*, ed. JH Kaplan, P De Weer, pp. 159–72. New York: Rockefeller Univ. Press

43. Meyer HH. 1899. Zur Theorie der Alkoholnarkose. I. Mitteilung. *Arch. Exp. Pathol. Pharmakol.* 42:109–18

44. Nägeli C, Cramer C. 1855. *Pflanzenphysiologische Untersuchungen*. Zürich: Schulthess

45. Narahashi T, Moore JW, Scott WR. 1964. Tetrodotoxin blockage of sodium conductance increase in lobster giant axons. *J. Gen. Physiol.* 47:965–74

46. Neher E, Sakmann B. 1976. Single-channel currents recorded from membrane of denervated frog muscle fibres. *Nature* 260:779–802

47. Noda M, Shimizu S, Tanabe T, Takai T, Kayano T, et al. 1984. Primary structure of *Electrophorus electricus* sodium channel deduced from cDNA sequence. *Nature* 312:121–27

48. Overton E. 1895. Über die osmotischen Eigenschaften der lebenden Pflanzen und Thierzelle. *Vierteljahrsschr. Naturforsch. Ges. Zürich* 40:159–201

49. Overton E. 1896. Über die osmotischen Eigenschaften der Zelle und ihre Bedeutung für die Toxikologie und Pharmakologie. *Vierteljahrsschr. Naturforsch. Ges. Zürich* 41:383–406

50. Overton E. 1899. Über die allgemeinen osmotischen Eigenschaften der Zelle, ihre vermutliche Ursachen und ihre Bedeutung für die Physiologie. *Vierteljahrsschr. Naturforsch. Ges. Zürich* 44:88–114

51. Overton E. 1901. *Studien über die Narkose, zugleich ein Beitrag zur allgemeinen Pharmakologie*. Jena, Germany: Fischer Verlag

52. Overton E. 1902. Beiträge zur allgemeinen Muskel- und Nervenphysiologie. II. Mitteilung. Über die Unentbehrlichkeit von Natrium- (oder Lithium-) Ionen für

den Contractionsact des Muskels. *Pflüg-ers Arch.* 92:346–86

53. Pfeffer WFP. 1886. Über Aufnahme von Anilinfarben in lebende Zellen. *Unter-such. Botan. Inst. Tübingen* 2:179–331

54. Post RL, Jolly PC. 1957. The linkage of sodium, potassium, and ammonium active transport across the human eryth-rocyte membrane. *Biochim. Biophys. Acta* 25:118–28

55. Prescott DM, Zeuthen E. 1953. Compar-ison of water diffusion and water filtra-tion across cell surfaces. *Acta Physiol. Scand.* 28:77–94

56. Preston GM, Carroll TP, Guggino WB, Agre P. 1992. Appearance of water chan-nels in *Xenopus* oocytes expressing red cell CHIP28 protein. *Science* 256:385–87

57. Raspail F-V. 1825. Développement de la fécule dans les organes de la fructifica-tion des céréales. *Ann. Sci. Nat.* 6:224–39

58. Reid EW. 1882. Report on experiments upon absorption without osmosis. *Brit. Med. J.* 323–26

59. Robertson JD. 1957. The cell membrane concept. *J. Physiol.* 140:58P-59

60. Robertson JD. 1960. The molecular structure and contact relationships of cell membranes. *Prog. Biophys. Biophys. Chem.* 10:344–418

61. Robinson JD. 1997. *Moving Questions. A History of Membrane Transport and Bioenergetics.* Oxford, UK: Oxford Univ. Press

62. Schatzmann HJ. 1953. Herzglykoside als Hemmstoffe für den aktiven Kalium- und Natriumtransport durch die Erythrocy-tenmembran. *Helv. Physiol. Acta* 11:346–54

63. Sen AK, Post RL. 1964. Stoichiometry and localization of adenosine triphos-phate-dependent sodium and potassium

transport in the erythrocyte. *J. Biol. Chem.* 239:345–52

64. Shull GE, Schwartz A, Lingrel JB. 1985. Amino-acid sequence of the catalytic subunit of the $(Na^+ + K^+)$ATPase de-duced from a complementary DNA. *Nature* 316:691–95

65. Singer SJ. 1974. The molecular organi-zation of membranes. *Annu. Rev. Biochem.* 43:805–33

66. Singer SJ, Nicholson GL. 1972. The fluid mosaic model of the structure of cell membranes. *Science* 175:720–31

67. Skou JC. 1975. The influence of some cations on an adenosine triphosphatase from peripheral nerves. *Biochim. Bio-phys. Acta* 23:394–401

68. Skou JC. 1960. Further investigations on a $Mg^{++} + Na^+$-activated adenosine-triphosphatase, possibly related to the active, linked transport of Na^+ and K^+ across the nerve membrane. *Biochim. Biophys. Acta* 42:6–23

69. Stein WD, Danielli JF. 1956. Structure and function in red cell permeability. *Discuss. Faraday Soc.* 21:238–51

70. Steinbach HB. 1940. Electrolyte balance of animal cells. *Cold Spring Harbor Symp. Quant. Biol.* 8:242–52

71. Tasaki I, Hagiwara S. 1957. Demonstra-tion of two stable potential states in the squid giant axon under tetraethylammon-ium chloride. *J. Gen. Physiol.* 40:859–85

72. van 't Hoff JH. 1887. Die Rolle des osmotischen Druckes in der Analogie zwischen Lösungen und Gasen. *Z. Phy-sikal. Chem.* 1:481–93

73. Walz T, Hirai T, Murata K, Heymann JB, Mitsuoka K, et al. 1997. The 6 Å three-dimensional structure of aquaporin-1. *Nature* 387:624–27

74. Zhang P, Toyoshima C, Yonekura K, Green NM, Stokes DL. 1998. Structure of the calcium pump from sarcoplasmic reticulum at 8-Å resolution. *Nature* 392:835–39

Annu. Rev. Physiol. 2000. 62:927–37

UNITY IN DIVERSITY: A Perspective on the Methods, Contributions, and Future of Comparative Physiology

George N. Somero

Hopkins Marine Station, Stanford University, Pacific Grove, California 93950; e-mail: somero@leland.stanford.edu

This brief essay on the methods, objectives, achievements, and future promise of the discipline known as comparative physiology focuses on three principle issues. First, how is this discipline defined in terms of its approaches and goals? What does the adjective comparative denote, and what makes the comparative approach unique? Second, what are illustrative examples of the successes of the comparative method in the study of physiology? Why has the comparative approach so often been critical in the development of basic understanding of physiological systems? Third, how is comparative physiology likely to contribute in the near future to the biological sciences, here broadly defined to include research ranging from study of the consequences of global change to the development of biomedical technology? And, conversely, how are advances in other disciplines in biology likely to enhance comparative physiology?

I hope to demonstrate that comparative physiology is an essential complement to other disciplines within physiology that commonly exploit a relatively small number of so-called model organisms in attempts to elucidate basic mechanisms of physiological function. I argue that there exists a creative interplay between physiologists doing comparative work and others who carry out primarily reductionist studies with model species. Whereas the latter types of studies offer the comparative physiologist many useful new techniques and insights into basic mechanisms, it is the comparative physiologist who often uncovers important new phenomena for investigation and who, through the logic of comparative analysis, elucidates key principles that might not emerge from the study of conventional model organisms.

THE COMPARATIVE APPROACH: UNIQUE ATTRIBUTES

What, then, is comparative physiology, and—importantly in this age of biomedically oriented work with model systems—why should one do it? To use Knut Schmidt-Nielsen's apt phrase, comparative physiologists are fundamentally curious about "how animals work." To approach this central issue, comparative physiologists typically study variation among organisms in commons types of

0066-4278/00/0315-0927$12.00

physiological systems in an effort to determine how this natural variation allows organisms to function in the diverse habitat conditions they face. This physiological variation may be interspecific and acquired over many generations, or it may be variation that occurs during the life span of the individual. The latter might occur through field acclimatization to new conditions, as might be linked to seasonal changes in the environment, or in controlled studies of laboratory acclimation, in which only a single factor is manipulated.

The success of the comparative approach is marked by the emergence of a unity of principle from the study of diverse solutions to a common problem, hence the theme of "unity in diversity" that characterizes the basic approach of comparative physiology. This underlying logic of the method of comparative analysis often reveals those aspects of the process in question that are invariably conserved, either through evolutionary change or through regulatory processes occurring in the individual in response to a physiological challenge. These conserved characteristics of the organisms' physiology tell us what is most important about the process in question and provide lessons for how organisms are modified during evolution, acclimatization, and acclimation to allow sustained activity in the face of changes in the environment.

The history of comparative physiology reveals that natural variation in physiological systems has, in fact, played two important and somewhat distinct roles in the development of the discipline. Natural variation has not only been at the intellectual core of the field, but has also been the focus of an exploratory spirit in comparative physiologists, the best of whom seem to be natural historians at heart. As is evidenced in the writings of many of the century's pre-eminent comparative physiologists, for instance, George Bartholomew, Peter Hochachka, August Krogh, C Ladd Prosser, Knut Schmidt-Nielsen, Per Scholander, and C Richard Taylor, fascination with natural variation has sparked a tremendous amount of exploratory effort—with the word exploratory denoting not only intellectual exploration in the laboratory but also adventurous field exploration in out-of-the-way corners of the planet [read Scholander et al's classic paper (1) on freezing resistance in Labrador fishes for a taste of adventurous physiology and a sense of the colorful nature of writing formerly allowed in the now rather staid scientific literature!]. (Parenthetically, I've long been curious as to what early influences lead one to pursue this type of comparative-exploratory work. Perhaps it is close childhood contact with pristine environments replete with diverse assemblages of species that draws comparative physiologists toward their particular calling. Conversely, it may be that growing up within the confines of a large city draws one to work with models such as rodents, flies, and *Escherichia coli*.)

The charting of natural variation by comparative physiologists has uncovered a wealth of novel phenomena begging deeper, mechanistic analysis. Analyses of these natural curiosities—for instance, Why don't polar fishes freeze? How can cells withstand desiccation? Why can desert rodents survive without drinking water? Why do sharks accumulate urea? What allows prolonged breath-hold diving in seals? What keeps tuna fishes warm?—by means of the comparative method have often led to major new concepts about the most basic aspects of physiology.

SUCCESS OF THE COMPARATIVE APPROACH: ILLUSTRATIVE EXAMPLES

There are many examples of the successes of the comparative approach in deducing unifying principles through study of physiological diversity. Below, I focus on two illustrative cases that I think are especially relevant for an essay designed to convey an historical perspective on the field of comparative physiology. Both examples concern extensions of a core concept in physiology credited to the great 19th century physiologist Claude Bernard, the conservation of the *milieu intérieur.*

The first case involves what can be regarded as the smallest constituent of the *milieu intérieur,* the proton, and focuses on the development of our understanding of the ultimate cause of the variation in pH observed among organisms with different body temperatures [see the excellent reviews by Reeves (2) and Cameron (3) for details]. During the early decades of study of physiological pH values, emphasis was strongly focused on the pH of blood of mammals with core temperatures near 37°C. Thus arose the concept that the "normal" pH of organisms was near 7.4 (2). This paradigmatic view of the normal pH of cells was strongly held for decades, despite the gradual accumulation of data, beginning as early as the late 1920s (4), showing that the pH values of blood of ectothermic organisms whose body temperatures were lower than 37°C were typically a few tenths of a pH unit above 7.4. It was not until the early 1960s that physiologists, spurred by work of Eugene Robin (5) and others, took a renewed interest in temperature-pH issues. As new information was gathered on the pH values of diverse ectothermic species, it became increasingly clear that the mammalian paradigm was correct only in a limited sense, that is, only for organisms with body temperatures near 37°C. Thus arose the need for a new unifying principle that could explain the ultimate cause of temperature-dependent variation in pH. The alphastat hypothesis (2), which was based largely on theoretical and experimental efforts of Herman Rahn, Robert Blake Reeves, and their colleagues, provided the needed synthesis. The alphastat hypothesis provided a precise mechanistic account of why it is important to conserve pH, not at a constant value at all temperatures, but at a value that favors a stable fractional dissociation state of histidine imidazole side-chains. As Cameron (3) points out in his review, there were important historical precedents for the alphastat hypothesis, yet it took the clear statements of Rahn, Reeves, and colleagues and the large comparative data base accumulated on pH values of organisms with widely different body temperatures to establish the new paradigm. The alphastat hypothesis provided biochemists with a clearer sense of why changes in pH affect so many aspects of protein function, and why the preservation of protein structure and function at different temperatures demands a temperature-dependent solution pH. The comparative approach thus was corrective of an erroneous view held by the majority of physiologists for decades and proved to be critical in identifying a new unifying principle of physiology. With a deeper understanding of temperature-pH relationships both biomedical practice and in vitro biochemistry could be conducted in a more rational and realistic fashion.

A second illustration of how the comparative approach enabled a unifying theory of physiology to be developed from a broad examination of physiological diversity concerns another key aspect of the composition of the *milieu intérieur,* the low-molecular-weight organic molecules (organic osmolytes) that constitute the bulk of osmotically active materials in cells of osmotically concentrated species. Comparative physiologists surveying the composition of the cytosol of widely different taxa—including animals, plants, protists, fungi, and bacteria—discovered that four distinct groups of low-molecular-weight organic molecules were exploited in osmotically concentrated organisms: free amino acids (e.g. glutamate, alanine, and proline) and their derivatives (e.g. taurine), methylammonium and methylsulfonium solutes (e.g. trimethylamine-*N*-oxide and glycine betaine), polyhydric alcohols (e.g. glycerol and trehalose), and urea (6). Was there something special about these particular types of organic solutes that made them fit for use at high concentrations in osmotically concentrated organisms? What unifying principle could explain the recurrent exploitation of these particular types of solutes by phylogenetically diverse organisms? The unity underlying this diversity in organic osmolyte composition was first explained by Mary Clark (7), who drew attention to the findings that Hofmeister made in the 1880s regarding the differential effects of various ions on protein solubility. His experiments led to the development of an empirical ranking of ions (the Hofmeister series) in terms of their influences on protein stability and solubility. Clark pointed out that the chemical groups found on organic osmolytes typically resemble stabilizing organic ions (e.g. methylammonium ions) of the Hofmeister series. She hypothesized that natural selection favors the accumulation of organic molecules whose fitness results from their favorable effects on protein structure and function, with urea being a curious exception to this rule, as discussed below. This hypothesis was a major extension of Bernard's concept concerning the importance of regulating the *milieu intérieur.* Regulation of the organic osmolyte composition of the cytosol is recognized to be important not only in the short-term responses of euryhaline osmoconformers but, even more fundamentally, in the initial development at the dawn of cellular evolution of an intracellular solution that was compatible with macromolecular function.

The principles underlying osmolyte fitness for macromolecular function and structure have received detailed analysis from physical chemists, biomedical researchers, and, most recently, biotechnologists. The physical chemical studies of Serge Timasheff (8), Wayne Bolen (9), and their colleagues have provided an elegant mechanistic explanation of how organic osmolytes affect protein structure. Timasheff, who had made seminal discoveries about the effects of inorganic ions on proteins, became fascinated with the physicochemical basis for evolutionary selection of particular classes of organic osmolytes. His studies of organic osmolytes showed that, with the exception of urea, they are excluded from the water immediately adjacent to the protein surface. This preferential exclusion of stabilizing osmolytes favors a compact folding of the protein, whereas the preferential interaction with the protein of destabilizing solutes like urea favors unfolding (denaturation). Bolen and colleagues (9) recently demonstrated that these solute effects are dominated by the influences that stabilizing and destabilizing osmolytes have on the solubility of peptide backbone linkages; side-chain effects are of much less importance. Thus, in common with the comparative analysis of pH-temperature relationships discussed above, the comparative study of organic osmolytes has led to a deeper understanding of how proteins are stabilized within the cell and, thereby, to an appreciation of a fundamental principle underlying the evolution and regulation of the *milieu intérieur.*

Comparative studies of organic osmolyte systems have also had important impacts in biomedicine and biotechnology. The discovery by Paul Yancey (6) that methylammonium compounds present in urea-rich fishes counteract the effects of urea on proteins led to a re-examination of the intracellular milieu of mammalian kidney cells, most notably, by Maurice Burg and colleagues (10). The heretofore unexplained occurrence of methylammonium solutes like glycerophosphorylcholine in cells of the inner medulla of the kidney could now be interpreted as an example of urea-counteraction. Homer Smith, whose classic book *From Fish to Philosopher* (11) discussed the anomaly of high urea levels in cartilaginous fishes, would no doubt be pleased to learn that sharks and philosophers (at least in the latter's inner medullas) opt for a common osmotic strategy.

In biotechnological research designed to develop solution conditions favoring stability of macromolecules, stabilizing osmolytes are playing an increasingly important role. What is termed "formulation" science is focusing strongly on the lessons provided by comparative physiologists, whose studies of natural variation in osmolyte systems point the way toward engineering media for preservation of biological materials in both the frozen and the dried states.

In summary, the two lines of research discussed above, each of which focuses on a different aspect of the evolution and regulation of the *milieu intérieur,* illustrate how comparative study of physiological diversity can lead to discovery of unifying principles of biological design. In many such cases, it is difficult to imagine how substantial progress in developing these key principles could have been made without the comparative approach.

HOW PHYSIOLOGICAL SYSTEMS GET TO BE THE WAY THEY ARE: EVOLUTIONARY PHYSIOLOGY

Much as physiologists are interested in how organisms work, they are increasingly interested in how physiological systems arose initially and how they achieved their particular states in organisms living under different environmental conditions. Origin and adaptation are central themes throughout comparative physiology. This being said, providing definitive evidence for the adaptive significance of trait, much less explaining how the trait came into being (or, for that matter, even defining what a trait is), is often a difficult and controversial matter. There has been much uncritical writing about the putative adaptive significance of traits, and the tradition here is a long one. Thus, prior to the 1859 publication of Charles Darwin's *The Origin of Species by Means of Natural Selection,* many leading scholars in the natural sciences viewed the traits of plants and animals as illustrations of God's ability to create perfectly adapted organisms [see the fascinating account of the adaptationist thinking of Linnaeus, Buffon, Cuvier, Lamarck, and other predecessors of Charles Darwin in historian John Greene's book *The Death of Adam* (12)]. The so-called Panglossian Paradigm (13) did not originate with 20th century biologists. The last two decades have been marked by a serious re-examination of the more secular concept of adaptation, with the seminal paper by Steven J Gould and Richard Lewontin (13) providing much of the stimulation for this analysis. Although this brief essay does not permit an extended discourse on the shortcomings of the adaptationist paradigm (for a lengthy analysis see Reference 14), two clear lessons have emerged from the critique of studies of physiological adaptation. One, as outlined clearly by Gould and Lewontin (13) and others (14) is that caution must be used in employing terminology pertaining to adaptation. A trait serving some function in a contemporary species should be viewed as an aptation, rather than as an adaptation, unless one can demonstrate that the trait currently fulfills the function for which it was originally selected. This logical vocabulary for discussing the function of traits has not been widely adopted by physiologists, for reasons that are not entirely clear. Perhaps in the new millennium, things will be different.

Adaptationist thinking is currently undergoing analysis that leads to a second and related lesson concerning the difficulties of discerning unambiguously if a particular characteristic of an organism represents an adaptation (or aptation) to an environmental condition or, instead, is merely a reflection of phylogeny (phylogenetic inertia or historical contingency) (15). Study of putative adaptive variation should be conducted in the appropriate phylogenetic context, in order to be what is commonly termed a phylogenetically correct analysis. Thus, the study of physiological evolution and adaptation is now increasingly being conducted jointly with phylogenetic analysis, the latter often employing molecular techniques. This type of dual analysis is proving to be an effective means for discerning the adaptive importance of physiological variation.

COMPARATIVE PHYSIOLOGY IN THE SERVICE OF ECOLOGY

The study of adaptive variation among species not only can provide insights into basic physiological principles—the unity that emerges from the study of diversity—but can also yield rewards for investigations at higher levels of biological organization. The discipline of ecological physiology, which builds on the efforts of comparative physiology, is concerned with how changes in the environment are apt to modify ecosystems through direct and indirect effects of the environment on the functions of organisms. As comparative physiologists clarify more definitively what the environmental optima and tolerance limits are for diverse physiological processes, the ability of ecologically oriented physiologists to make predictions about the effects of habitat change will be enhanced. For instance, characterizing the differences between eurythermal and stenothermal species and discovering the physiological differences that explain their varied thermal tolerance limits may assist ecologists in developing predictions about the effects of global warming.

GENETIC BASES OF PHYSIOLOGICAL VARIATION

The genetic bases of physiological variation are becoming an increasingly important focal point in comparative physiology. This focus is certain to strengthen the discipline for several reasons. As the genetic underpinnings of physiological variation are discovered, ambiguities about the adaptive significance of traits and the origins of these traits during evolution will be reduced or eliminated. An illustration of progress along these lines is provided by recent studies of the genes encoding antifreeze glycoproteins (AFGPs) in polar fishes (16, 17). The presence of AFGPs with the same primary structures in both Antarctic notothenioid fishes and Arctic fishes of the cod family might conceivably be a consequence of the occurrence of a single progenitor AFGP-encoding gene in a common ancestor of these two lines of fishes. Such an ancestral AFPG gene might have persisted in the two lineages during their diversification and have taken on a key role in cold adaptation when the two groups independently encountered the threat of ice formation in their body fluids. However, as Chen et al (16, 17) have shown, the genes encoding the AFGPs of Antarctic and Arctic freeze-resistant fishes arose independently in response to cooling of their habitats approximately 14 and 2.5 million years ago, respectively. Moreover, Chen et al showed that the AFGP-encoding gene of notothenioid fishes arose from portions of a gene, including fragments of an intron region, that encoded the proteolytic enzyme trypsinogen (16). The progenitor of the AFGP-encoding gene of Arctic cods is unknown (17). Studies of AFGPs and antifreeze peptides demonstrate that adaptation to the threat of freezing has led to the independent origin of macromolecular antifreezes in numerous taxa and that the genetic raw material used to effect these adaptations has been highly varied.

Analysis of how these diverse macromolecular antifreezes work has revealed a unity of mechanism among structurally diverse antifreeze molecules. Despite wide variations in primary, secondary, and tertiary structure, all antifreezes studied to date appear to have surfaces that interact strongly with ice, leading to inhibition of ice crystal expansion (18). Here again, the comparative approach has elucidated a fascinating example of convergent evolution toward a unified mechanism of function in disparate lineages.

I find it satisfying that the initial curiosity that drove Scholander and his colleagues to perform adventurous field studies in the Arctic has led, some four decades later, to the discovery of how the genes enabling fishes to resist freezing originated, to elucidation of how the AFGPs and peptides work at the molecular level, and, recently, to investigations of how these novel molecules might be exploited through biotechnology to preserve cells at low temperatures. Here is a clear illustration of how the comparative approach has contributed broadly to the biological sciences.

FUTURE PROSPECTS FOR COMPARATIVE PHYSIOLOGY

It is a cliché, although nonetheless usually a partial truth, to say that the future of a field of research will be technology-driven. The validity of this statement in the context of comparative physiology is seen in on-going exploitation of a variety of new methodologies that are allowing novel experimentation across a wide range of spatial and temporal scales and with organisms whose study has been difficult or impossible to carry out in the past. Field work using remote sensing technology based on miniaturized, microprocessor-based systems and satellite-based communication links is allowing heretofore difficult-to-monitor organisms to be tracked over long distances and periods of time in their natural environments. For instance, current work on large pelagic fishes like bluefin tuna, which move through thousands of kilometers of the ocean and change depth frequently, exemplifies the potential of these new technologies to advance field-oriented physiological studies (19). Through learning how difficult-to-monitor organisms behave in the field, the physiological characteristics of these organisms will be placed in a more meaningful context and, as is almost certain to be the case in such natural history explorations, new phenomena will be discovered that will lead to novel lines of study.

Molecular approaches are already playing major roles in comparative physiology in a wide variety of contexts, and the power of this new technology will continue to contribute to the development of the field in many ways. Studies in which specific proteins of animals are modified using site-directed mutagenesis and then expressed in vivo, where the physiological impacts of the mutation can be studied, are beginning to shed new light on such processes as muscle function. Recent work on molecular engineering of regulatory subunits of myosin in *Drosophila* is illustrative of the power of this approach (20, 21). Genes removed from or introduced into organisms, followed by physiological experimentation designed to test the effects of these manipulations of the genome, will help to more fully define the roles of genes whose products are of putative importance in adaptation. An interesting illustration of the genetic knockout approach is given by a recent study in which the myoglobin gene was knocked out of the mouse (22). As more and more species become amenable to these types of molecular genetic manipulations, comparative physiologists will be increasingly able to test novel predictions about adaptive significance of traits. Comparative analysis of protein sequences is revealing the regions within proteins where adaptive change appears to be focused, and how amino acid substitutions at these adaptational hot spots bring about changes in function (23). Rapidly developing techniques for screening patterns of gene expression, for instance, the DNA microarray methodologies that involve robotics and permit huge data sets to be gathered, are likely to contribute to our understanding of environmental and developmental regulation of gene expression (24). In one sense, the survey studies made possible by DNA microarray technology are logically equivalent to a natural history survey, albeit at the fine-scale of molecular diversity. As Brown & Botstein (24) state in a recent review, the vast numbers of new genes being discovered in genome sequencing efforts are "an exhilarating reminder that much of the natural world remains to be explored at the molecular level." Once physiologists determine what genes are turned on, in different tissues, under different types of environmental stresses, then the functions of these genes may become clearer (or, in many cases described for the first time) (24), and unifying new concepts about gene expression in response to environmental change may emerge.

To imply that the future success of comparative physiology will depend entirely on the exploitation of molecular methods and other new types of technology is not my intent, for such a prediction would ignore an essential point: the strength of the discipline of comparative physiology lies not with any particular method—these evolve rapidly and no one can predict what, ten or twenty years down the road, will be the leading-edge method of the day—but rather with a unique logic for resolving biological questions. The logic of comparative physiology permits analysis of a wide range of questions, ranging from the determination of basic mechanisms of physiological function to the elucidation of evolutionary pathways to the prediction of effects resulting from environmental change. Common to these diverse goals is what is probably the most famous principle of comparative physiology, the August Krogh principle (25). As commonly phrased, this principle states that, for any particular question in biology, nature holds an ideal study system. It is up to the creativity of the biologist to identify this system to advance the study in question. Although comparative physiologists may tend to view the August Krogh principle as their own, this principle has been applied throughout biology, for instance, in the choice of tractable organisms for studying genetics and heredity (first *Drosophila,* then simpler systems like yeasts and bacteria). By judicious application of the August Krogh principle, comparative physiologists have been able to select appropriate sets of organisms with which to conduct their analyses. Much of the discussion of phylogenetic correctness in experimental design can be viewed as an attempt to develop more logical means for exploiting the wisdom found in the August Krogh principle!

With the appropriate choice of study organisms and the use of appropriate methodologies—leading-edge or otherwise—comparative physiologists will continue to make vital contributions to mechanistic and evolutionary physiology. The esthetic lure of diverse biological systems will continue to attract to the field individuals who possess a desire to explore nature's variation. Through exploitation of the logic of comparative analysis, study of this natural variation will continue to yield insights about the most basic workings of organisms and the pathways by which their component systems have arisen and have been modified to permit life in the incredible diversity of environments in which it is found.

Visit the Annual Reviews home page at www.AnnualReviews.org.

LITERATURE CITED

1. Scholander PF, van Dam L, Kanwisher JW, Hammel HT, Gordon MS. 1957. Supercooling and osmoregulation in Arctic fish. *J. Comp. Cell. Physiol.* 49:5–24

2. Reeves RB. 1977. The interaction of body temperature and acid-base balance in ectothermic vertebrates. *Annu. Rev. Physiol.* 39:559–86

3. Cameron JN. 1989. Acid-base homeostasis: past and present perspectives. *Physiol. Zool.* 62:845–65

4. Austin JH, Sunderman FW, Camack JG. 1927. The electrolyte composition and the pH of serum of a poikilothermous animal at different temperatures. *J. Biol. Chem.* 72:677–85

5. Robin ED. 1962. Relationship between temperature and plasma pH and carbon dioxide tension in the turtle. *Nature* 195:249–51

6. Yancey PH, Clark ME, Hand SC, Bowlus RD, Somero GN. 1982. Living with water stress: evolution of osmolyte systems. *Science* 217:1214–22

7. Clark ME. 1985. The osmotic role of amino acids: discovery and function. In *Transport Processes, Iono- and Osmoregulation,* ed. R Gilles, M Gilles-Baillien, pp. 412–23. Berlin: Springer-Verlag

8. Timasheff SN. 1992. A physicochemical basis for the selection of osmolytes by nature. In *Water and Life.* ed. GN Somero, CB Osmond, CL Bolis, pp. 70–84, Berlin: Springer-Verlag

9. Qu Y, Bolen CL, Bolen DW. 1998. Osmolyte-driven contraction of a random coil protein. *Proc. Natl. Acad. Sci. USA* 95:9268–73

10. Burg M, Kwon ED, Kultz D. 1997. Regulation of gene expression by hypertonicity. *Annu. Rev. Physiol.* 59:437–55

11. Smith HW 1953. *From Fish to Philosopher,* Boston: Little Brown.

12. Greene J. 1959. *The Death of Adam.* Ames: Iowa State Univ. Press

13. Gould SJ, Lewontin RC. 1979. The spandrels of San Marco and the Panglossian paradigm. A critique of the adaptationist program. *Proc. R. Soc. London Ser. B* 205:581–98

14. Rose MR, Lauder GV. 1996. *Adaptation.* San Diego: Academic.

15. Garland T, Carter P. 1994. Evolutionary physiology. *Annu. Rev. Physiol.* 56:579–621

16. Chen L, DeVries AL, Cheng C-H C 1997. Evolution of antifreeze glycoprotein gene from a trypsinogen gene in Antarctic notothenioid fish. *Proc. Natl Acad. Sci. USA* 94:3811–16

17. Chen L, DeVries AL, Cheng C-H C 1997. Convergent evolution of antifreeze glycoproteins in Antarctic notothenioid

fish and Arctic cod. *Proc. Natl. Acad. Sci. USA* 94:3817–22

18. Jia Z, DeLuca CI, Chao H, Davies PL. 1996. Structural basis for the binding of a globular antifreeze protein to ice. *Nature* 384:285–88

19. Block BA, Dewar H, Williams T, Prince ED, Farwell C, Fudge D. 1998. A new satellite technology for tracking the movements of Atlantic bluefin tuna. *Proc. Natl. Acad. Sci. USA* 95:9384–89

20. Dickinson MH, Hyatt CJ, Lehmann F, Moore JR, Reedy MC, et al. 1997. Phosphorylation-dependent power output of transgenic flies: an integrated study. *Biophys. J.* 73:3122–34

21. Maughan DW, Vigoreaux JO. 1999. An integrated view of insect flight muscle: genes, motor molecules, and motion. *News Physiol. Sci.* 14:87–92

22. Garry DJ, Ordway GA, Lorenz, JN, Radford ND, Chin ER, et al. 1998. Mice without myoglobin. *Nature* 395:905–8

23. Fields PA, Somero GN. 1998. Hot spots in cold adaptation: localized increases in conformational flexibility in lactate dehydrogenase A_4 orthologs of Antarctic notothenioid fishes. *Proc. Natl. Acad. Sci. USA* 95:11476–81

24. Brown PO, Botstein D. 1999. Exploring the new world of the genome with DNA microarrays. *Nat. Genet. Suppl.* 21:33–37

25. Krogh A. 1929. Progress in physiology. *Am. J. Physiol.* 90:243–51

Annu. Rev. Physiol. 2000. 62:939–46

ONE-HUNDRED YEARS OF INQUIRY: The Mechanism of Glucose Absorption in the Intestine

Luis Reuss

Department of Physiology and Biophysics, University of Texas Medical Branch, Galveston, Texas 77555–0641; e-mail: lreuss@utmb.edu

Instead of attempting to review the many breakthroughs in our understanding of the physiology of the digestive system during this century, I have decided to focus on one story, that pertaining to the mechanism of glucose absorption in the small intestine. The story begins near the turn of the century and continues today, after the critical molecule involved in this process was identified. I think that it illustrates very well some patterns of change of physiologists' thinking during the twentieth century.

FROM THE TURN OF THE CENTURY TO THE 1950s: PRE-CRANE PERIOD

The notion that the mucosa of the small intestine has a "selective permeability" was proposed around the turn of the century by several investigators (1–3). This thesis was based on the fact that the rates of sugar absorption, as well as the effects of iodoacetate and phlorizin on absorption, differed widely among sugar molecular species. Cori (e.g. 4) carried out a series of studies that characterized in detail the phenomenon of intestinal sugar absorption. These studies suggested the existence of two distinct mechanisms, which eventually were identified as active and passive transport, respectively. The first serious explanation attempting to account for the dependence of glucose absorption on metabolism was the phosphorylation-dephosphorylation hypothesis (reviewed by Crane, 5), which proposed that the osmotic work in concentrative (uphill) transport of a substance is accomplished by a change in substrate structure, i.e. metabolic energy is used in the chemical transformation of the substrate. Glucose would permeate the apical membrane by diffusion, be phosphorylated inside the cell, becoming impermeant and thus trapped. It would be then be dephosphorylated near the basolateral membrane and leave the cell by diffusion.

In 1939, Bárány & Sperber (6) found that glucose can disappear from a rabbit intestine loop even when the concentration in the loop is lower than in blood. These experiments followed micropuncture studies in the kidney of the salamander *Necturus maculosus* (7, 8). The studies of Bárány & Sperber were consistent with the notion of active transport of glucose but did not rule out the possibility that the glucose was metabolized by the enterocytes. The definitive demonstration of transepithelial active glucose transport was provided by experiments that ruled out this objection. Campbell & Davson (9) showed uphill absorption of 3-O-methyl-D-glucose, a non-metabolized hexose. Atkinson et al (10) demonstrated that during in vivo absorption of radioactive glucose in dogs, the glucose concentration in the blood could be higher than that in the intestine lumen. These results indisputably demonstrate that glucose transport can occur actively, i.e. against an unfavorable glucose chemical gradient.

By the 1950s it was known that certain sugars, including D-glucose, undergo uphill transport in the small intestine and can be concentrated approximately 12-fold in the epithelial cells (11). Uphill transport occurs only with sugar molecules having specific structural features, shows saturation kinetics, and can be inhibited by other transported sugars. Uphill sugar transport is also inhibited by hypoxia and metabolic inhibitors. In contrast, sugars that do not fit the structural requirements for uphill transport undergo only downhill transport, without apparent saturation at relatively low concentrations, and without metabolic dependence. The mechanism of active sugar transport was not understood.

FIRST MILESTONE: CRANE'S SODIUM-GRADIENT HYPOTHESIS

The Role of Na^+ in Intestinal Glucose Absorption

The widely recognized sodium-gradient hypothesis, now a central concept in cell physiology, was first presented by Crane in 1960, at a meeting held in Prague (12). The critical experimental observations were that active glucose absorption by the hamster small intestine requires Na^+ in the bathing medium and is blocked by the cardioactive steroid ouabain. Crane concluded that the energy stored in the sodium gradient across the cell membrane was the source for active (concentrative) glucose transport. He hypothesized that the sodium entering the cell with glucose would recycle across the apical membrane and be extruded into the lumen by the Na^+,K^+-ATPase. The contribution of ATP hydrolysis to the transport of glucose would be indirect, i.e. ATP hydrolysis would energize the maintenance of the Na^+ electrochemical gradient. In Crane's original formulation, transepithelial glucose absorption would not be coupled to Na^+ absorption, but to a futile Na^+ recycling across the apical membrane (12–15). In 1963, Schultz & Zalusky (16, 17) corrected the initial formulation by demonstrating that during glucose absorption there is simultaneous Na^+ transport in the same direction and that Na^+ extrusion from the cell occurs across the basolateral, not across the apical membrane (16, 17). The mechanism of intestinal glucose transport at the cell membrane level had thus been established by 1964.

The General Sodium-Gradient Hypothesis. A New Paradigm in Cell Physiology

These studies of intestinal glucose absorption prompted Crane to formulate a hypothesis that with some generalizations and modifications explains numerous other transport processes in animal cells. The central tenet of the general sodium-gradient hypothesis is that the energy contained in the transmembrane Na^+ electrochemical gradient can be partly utilized for coupled transport processes, allowing for the uphill transport of other substrates. This phenomenon is now known as secondary-active transport and differs from primary-active transport in that the energy driving the active process does not come directly from a metabolic process (e.g. ATP hydrolysis), but indirectly from the electrochemical gradient generated by primary-active transport. In some biological membranes (bacteria, mitochondria) the driving force is the proton-motive force, i.e. the H^+ electrochemical gradient, and H^+ is the ionic substrate instead of Na^+. The fluxes of cation and cotransported solute can be in the same direction (symport, cotransport) or in opposite directions (antiport, exchange).

SECOND MILESTONE: OPENING THE BLACK BOX, DIRECT TESTING OF THE PREDICTIONS OF SODIUM-GLUCOSE COTRANSPORT

In the 1970s, the use of conventional and ion-sensitive microelectrodes allowed for measurements of transmembrane voltages and intracellular ion activities, confirming electrophysiological predictions of the above hypothesis (18, reviewed in 19). The co-exposure of the apical membrane to Na^+ and glucose (or Na^+ and a cotransported amino acid) produces apical membrane depolarization and an apparent increase in its conductance, both indicative of an inward membrane current, i.e. an electrogenic transport process. The simplest explanation for these observations is that there is cotransport of Na^+ and glucose. These experiments demonstrated that the membrane voltage is part of the driving force for Na^+-glucose cotransport, in addition to the Na^+ chemical gradient.

Cotransport of Na^+ and organic solute depolarizes the apical membrane, thus reducing the driving force for continued cotransport. An interesting adaptive phenomenon occurs, namely an increase in the K^+ electrodiffusive permeability (P_K) of the basolateral membrane. Inasmuch as the two cell membrane domains are electrically connected by the paracellular pathway (reviewed in 20), the increase in basolateral membrane P_K hyperpolarizes both membranes, thus helping to maintain the driving force for entry of Na^+ and organic solute across the apical membrane (21, 22; reviewed in 19). The phenomenon described is one of several examples of physiological coordination of the two-membrane domains, a field pioneered by Schultz (23) and commonly referred to as cell membrane cross-talk in epithelia.

The two-membrane hypothesis of Ussing and coworkers (24), formulated in 1958 (i.e. two decades earlier) to account for transepithelial Na^+ transport, is a simple and elegant construction that remains essentially valid today. One of the tenets of this hypothesis was that Na^+ entry across the apical membrane occurs by electrodiffusion. The discovery of the mechanism of Na^+-organic substrate cotransport in small intestine and renal proximal tubule and the generalized Na^+-gradient hypothesis expanded our understanding of the Na^+ entry step in epithelial cells. In all Na^+ absorptive epithelia, extrusion of Na^+ from the cell to the interstitial fluid is by primary-active transport via the Na^+, K^+-ATPase. In contrast, the mechanism of Na^+ entry differs among epithelia. Electrodiffusion, which occurs via the epithelial Na^+ channel (ENaC), is one such mechanism present in a subset of epithelia. In other epithelia, Na^+ entry involves cotransport (Na^+ coupled to glucose, amino acids, anions, and other substrates) or exchange (e.g. with H^+). For a classification of Na^+ absorptive epithelia, see Reference 20. This notion of multiple Na^+ entry pathways merges Ussing's two-membrane hypothesis and the Na^+-gradient hypothesis.

THIRD MILESTONE: MOLECULAR IDENTIFICATION OF THE SODIUM-GLUCOSE COTRANSPORTER

In the mid-1980s, Wright's group developed the strategy of "expression cloning" and succeeded in cloning the Na^+-glucose cotransporter from rabbit intestine (25). This protein (SGLT1) was the first eukaryote Na^+ cotransporter cloned. SGLT1 has a high affinity for glucose ($K_m = 0.35$ mM), low transport capacity and a Na^+:glucose stoichiometry of 2:1. It is the only SGLT isoform found in enterocytes and one of the two expressed in the renal proximal tubule (SGLT1 is found in the late proximal tubule, S2, and S3 segments). The intestinal and renal Na^+/glucose cotransporters account for all of glucose and galactose transport and contribute to salt and water absorption.

Glucose absorption in the small intestine consists of two steps. Influx across the apical membrane occurs via the Na^+-glucose cotransporter SGLT1 (26), and efflux across the basolateral membrane occurs via the glucose uniporter GLUT2 (27). SGLT1 is a 664-residue protein with significant N-linked glycosylation. The most likely membrane topology indicates extracellular N and C termini and 14 transmembrane domains (28). The domain that binds and translocates Na^+, identified from studies on deletion mutants and chimeras, consists of the N-terminal region until the extracellular loop connecting TM domains 4 and 5; the glucose binding and translocation region includes TM helices 10–13. Although the region spanned by TM 5–8 is not needed for cotransport, it may have a regulatory role.

(the neutralization of helix-8 K321 has effects on Na$^+$ and sugar transport). This information is reviewed in Reference 29.

SGLT1, unlike other carrier proteins, lacks a large cytosolic domain, which suggests the existence of additional regulatory subunit(s). Although SGLT1 alone cotransports glucose and Na$^+$, the protein RS1, anchored in apical membranes, has been reported to increase significantly the V_{max} of the uptake expressed by SGLT1 (30). RS1 was suggested to be a regulatory subunit of SGLT1 (30), but later studies showed that it modulates other transporters as well (31). The cloning of rabbit SGLT1 was rapidly followed by the cloning of orthologs in other mammals, all exhibiting highly conserved sequences. Further studies during the last decade indicate the existence of a gene family with over 30 identified members. These proteins share structural and functional features. They have 13 or more transmembrane helices and utilize the electrochemical gradient for either Na$^+$ or H$^+$ to perform secondary active transport of a variety of substrates including sugars, amino acids, organic anions, urea, vitamins, and others. It is likely that they share a common transport mechanism although the cotransported substrate varies considerably (29).

Functional studies of SGLT1 expressed in heterologous systems (e.g. 32–34) revealed substrate specificity and kinetic features similar to those observed in native cells. Transport by SGLT1 expressed in *Xenopus* oocytes is best explained by a kinetic model rate-limited (at 0 mV) by the return of the empty carrier to the extracellular surface. At physiological range membrane potential, the rate-limiting step is Na$^+$ dissociation at the cytosolic surface (33, 34). Membrane depolarization with no sugar present causes transient currents attributable to voltage-dependent conformational changes. These and other functional aspects of SGLT1, recently reviewed by Wright et al (29), include the intriguing proposal that water is cotransported with Na$^+$ and glucose. This notion is currently under study and remains controversial.

A highly significant consequence of the molecular studies of SGLT1 has been the identification of mutations in individuals affected by the genetic disease glucose and galactose malabsorption (GGM). This is an infrequent autosomal-recessive disorder, whose clinical manifestations are dramatic: newborn profuse diarrhea that can be fatal unless glucose, galactose (and lactose) are eliminated from the diet. The existence of this disease indicates that SGLT1 is the only pathway for glucose uptake at the apical membrane of enterocytes. It is possible that heterozygotes have reduced absorption of these sugars. In studies of over 30 cases, missense mutations were found in about 65%. The mutations can occur at numerous regions of the protein, in all but one instance resulting in protein misfolding and lack of delivery to the plasma membrane (35). Interestingly, the same protein traffic defect was found in intestine biopsies and when the mutants were expressed in Xenopus oocytes. Studies with the SGLT1 mutant Q457R revealed that it is inserted in the membrane but does not transport. Site-directed mutagenesis studies strongly suggest that Q457 is part of the glucose-binding site (35).

EPILOGUE: WHAT WILL BE THE NEXT PHASE?

The essential parts of the clockwork have been identified, and we are beginning to understand their functions at the molecular level. However, classic molecular biology techniques are unlikely to provide unambiguous answers. For instance, unique interpretations of site-directed mutagenesis results are always questionable because the possibility of distant conformational changes cannot be ruled out a priori. Hence, I think that the next breakthrough in understanding the function of membrane carriers will derive from obtaining their atomic structure, both for the wild-type under basal conditions and exposed to substrate(s), inhibitors, or activators, and for mutants. Molecular biology studies after the structure is known will be powerful to ascertain the transport mechanism at the atomic level, including an understanding of the basal structure of the molecule, its conformational changes, and the energetics of each step in the transport process. The recently obtained crystal structure of a bacterial K^+ channel elegantly illustrates the power of the structural biology approach (36).

However, the remaining tasks do not end with the structure and structure-function correlation of the transport proteins. After they are established, it is essential to approach the process from a cell physiology perspective, to understand the ways in which these components interact with each other, how they are regulated, and what ways exist for rational pharmacological intervention. These endeavors will involve integrative approaches at the levels of the cell, the tissue, and the system. Given the complexity of genomic and nongenomic control mechanisms, this is a daunting task for physiologists at the threshold of the new century.

ACKNOWLEDGMENTS

Thanks to E Bello-Reuss, M Brodwick, and A Pajor for comments on a preliminary version of this article.

Visit the Annual Reviews home page at www.AnnualReviews.org.

REFERENCES

1. Höber R. 1899. Uber resorption im Dünndarm. *Arch. Ges. Physiol. Pflüger's* 74:246–71
2. Hédon ME. 1900. Sur la resorption intestinale des sucres en solutions isotoniques. *Compt. Rend. Soc. Biol.* 52:87–89
3. Nagano J. 1902. Zur Kenntnis der resorption einfacher, im besonderen stereoiso-
merer Zucker im Dünndarm. *Arch.Ges. Physiol. Pflüger's* 90:389–404
4. Cori CF. 1925. Fate of sugar in the animal body. I. Rate of absorption of hexoses and pentoses from the intestinal tract. *J. Biol. Chem.* 66:691–715
5. Crane RK. 1960. Intestinal absorption of sugars. *Physiol. Rev.* 60:789–825
6. Bárány E, Sperber E. 1939. Absorption

of glucose against a concentration gradient by the small intestine of the rabbit. *Skand. Arch. Physiol.* 81:290–99

7. Walker AM, Reisinger JA. 1933. Quantitative studies of the composition of glomerular urine. IX. Concentration of reducing substances in glomerular urine from frogs and necturi determined by an ultramicroadaptation of the method of Sumner. Observations on the action of phlorhizin. *J. Biol. Chem.* 101:223–37

8. Walker AM, Hudson C. 1937. Reabsorption of glucose from the renal tubule in amphibia and the action of phlorhizin upon it. *Am. J. Physiol.* 118:130–43

9. Cambell PN, Davson H. 1948. Absorption of 3-methyglucose from the small intestine of the rat and the cat. *Biochem. J.* 43:426–29

10. Atkinson PM, Parsons BJ, Smyth DH. 1957. Intestinal absorption of glucose. *J. Physiol.* 135:581–89

11. McDougal DB Jr, Little KD, Crane RK. 1960. Studies on the mechanism of the intestinal absorption of sugars. IV. Microenzymatic localization of galactose concentrations within the intestinal wall during active transport, in vitro. *Biochim. Biophys. Acta* 45:483–89

12. Crane RK, Miller D, Bihler I. 1961. The restrictions on possible mechanisms of intestinal active transport of sugars. In *Membrane Transport and Metabolism.* ed. A Kleinzeller, A Kotyk, pp. 439–49. London: Academic

13. Bihler I, Crane RK. 1962. Studies on the mechanisms of the intestinal absorption of sugars. V. The influence of several cations and anions on the active transport of sugars, in vitro, by various preparations of hamster small intestine. *Biochim. Biophys. Acta* 59:78–93

14. Bihler I, Hawkins KA, Crane RK. 1962. Studies on the mechanism of intestinal absorption of sugars. VI. The specificity and other properties of Na$^+$-dependent entrance of sugars into intestinal tissue

under anaerobic conditions in vitro. *Biochim. Biophys. Acta* 59:94–102

15. Crane RK. 1962. Hypothesis for mechanisms of intestinal active transport of sugars. *Fed. Proc.* 21:891–95

16. Schultz SG, Zalusky R. 1963. The interaction between active sodium transport and active sugar transport in the isolated rabbit ileum. *Biochim. Biophys. Acta* 71:503–5

17. Schultz SG, Zalusky R. 1964. Ion transport in isolated rabbit ileum. II. The interaction between active sodium and active sugar transport. *J. Gen. Physiol.* 47:1043–59

18. Rose RC, Schultz SG. 1971. Studies on the electrical potential profile across rabbit ileum. Effects of sugars and amino acids on transmural and transmucosal electrical potential differences. *J. Gen. Physiol.* 57:639–63

19. Schultz SG, Hudson RL. 1991. Biology of sodium-absorbing epithelial cells: dawning of a new era. In *Handbook of Physiology, Sect. 6. The Gastrointestinal System, Vol. IV. Intestinal Absorption and Secretion,* ed. SG Schultz, M Field, RA Frizzell, pp. 45–81. New York: Oxford Univ. Press

20. Reuss L. 1997. Epithelial transport. In *Handbook of Physiology, Sect. 14: Cell Physiology,* ed. JE Hoffman, J Jamieson, pp. 309–88. New York: Oxford Univ. Press

21. Costantin J, Alcalen S, Otero AS, Dubinsky WP, Schultz SG. 1989. Reconstitution of an inwardly rectifying potassium channel from the basolateral membranes of *Necturus* enterocytes into planar lipid bilayers. *Proc. Natl. Acad. Sci. USA* 86:5212–16

22. Gunter-Smith PJ, Grasset E, Schultz SG. 1982. Sodium-coupled amino acid and sugar transport by *Necturus* small intestine. *J. Membr. Biol.* 66:25–39

23. Schultz SG. 1981. Homocellular regulatory mechanisms in sodium-transporting epithelia: avoidance of extinction by

"flush-through." *Am. J. Physiol.* 241: F579–90

24. Koefoed-Johnsen V, Ussing HH. 1958. The nature of the frog skin potential. *Acta Physiol. Scand.* 42:298–308

25. Hediger MA, Coady MJ, Ikeda TS, Wright EM. 1987. Expression cloning and cDNA sequencing of the Na^+/glucose cotransporter. *Nature* 330:379–81

26. Wright EM. 1993. The intestinal Na^+/glucose cotransporter. *Annu. Rev. Physiol.* 55:575–89

27. Thorens B. 1993. Facilitated glucose transporters in epithelial cells. *Annu. Rev. Physiol.* 55:591–608

28. Turk E, Wright EM. 1997. Membrane topological motifs in the SGLT cotransporter family. *J. Membr. Biol.* 159:1–20

29. Wright EM, Loo D, Panayotova-Heiermann M, Hirayama B, Turk E, et al. 1998. Structure and function of the Na^+/glucose cotransporter. *Acta Physiol. Scand.* 163:257–64

30. Koepsell H, Veyh M. 1994. Structure of Na^+-D-glucose cotransport system. *Cell Physiol. Biochem.* 4:206–16

31. Reihardt J, Veyhl M, Wagner K, Gambarayan S, Dekel C, et al. 1999. Cloning and characterization of the transport modifier RS1 from rabbit which was previously assumed to be specific for Na^+-D-glucose cotransport. *Biochim. Biophys. Acta* 1417:131–43

32. Birner B, Loo D, Wright EM. 1991. Voltage-clamp studies of the intestinal Na^+/glucose cotransporter cloned from rabbit small intestine. *Pflügers Arch.* 418:79–85

33. Parent L, Supplisson S, Loo D, Wright EM. 1992. Electrogenic properties of the cloned Na^+/glucose cotransporter. I. Voltage-clamp studies. *J. Membr. Biol.* 125:49–62

34. Parent L, Supplisson S, Loo D, Wright EM. 1992. Electrogenic properties of the cloned Na^+/glucose cotransporter. II. A transport model under nonrapid equilibrium conditions. *J. Membr. Biol.* 125: 63–79

35. Wright EM. 1998. Genetic disorders of membrane transport. I. Glucose galactose malabsorption. *Am. J. Physiol.* 275: G879–82

36. Doyle DA, Cabral JM, Pfuetzner RA, Kuo A, Gulbis JM, et al. 1998. The structure of the potassium channel: molecular basis of K^+ conduction and selectivity. *Science* 280:69–77

Annu. Rev. Physiol. 2000. 62:947–50

ENDOCRINOLOGY: Survival as a Discipline in the 21st Century?

Jean D. Wilson

University of Texas Southwestern Medical Center, Dallas, Texas 75235–8857; e-mail: jwils1@mednet.swmed.edu

Endocrinology, the branch of physiology that deals with the communication between cells and/or organs via chemical messengers, (as distinct from neurogenic and immune communication), is for all practical purposes a discipline of the 20th century. Most physiological disciplines evolved slowly as the result of the accumulation of knowledge, but historians are in agreement that endocrinology began on June 1, 1889. On that date the neurophysiologist Charles-Edouard Brown-Sequard (then 72 years of age) reported at a meeting in Paris of the Societe de Biology that following the self-injection of aqueous extracts of guinea pig and dog testes he had experienced enhancement of physical strength, improvement in mental capacity, and increased sexual potency (1). In the words of Herbert Evans, endocrinology had "suffered obstetric deformation in its very birth" (2). Brown-Sequard's sensational presentation was reported widely in the press both within and beyond France. At the clinical level, this fiasco gave impetus to a bevy of rejuvenation quacks who continue to the present day to prey on the incredulous and the desperate (3), and it required many years and many appropriately controlled studies to prove the rejuvenation concept wrong. According to Dale, clinical endocrinology achieved respectability only with the discovery of insulin (4). On the other hand, in disproving the Brown-Sequard claims, the fundamental principles of endocrine physiology were established, and evidence was accumulated for many types of chemical messengers.

Some of the early milestones of endocrinology are listed in Table 1. From its inception endocrine science was a mixture of clinical and basic endeavors, and by 1922 the discipline was in the forefront of biomedical science since it was possible to treat three human endocrine disorders successfully–hypothyroidism, diabetes insipidus, and diabetes mellitus (3). The initial focus in the field was on the identification and purification of hormones, characterization of the regulatory processes that control their secretion, and definition of the effects of hormone deficits and excess. The fact that the synthesis and/or secretion of all hormones is controlled by complex regulatory feedback control processes was recognized to be a distinguishing feature of endocrine physiology. The chemical isolation and characterization of hormones, including epinephrine and norepinephrine, the thyroid hormones, testosterone, aldosterone, ecdysone, estradiol, glucagon, and cortisol, and the pituitary hormones, represent some of the most dramatic accom-

TABLE 1   Some early endocrine milestones

1889	Brown-Sequard injects himself with testicular extracts
1891	Murray treats myxedema with thyroid extracts
1894	Oliver and Schaefer demonstrate a pressor substance in the adrenal
1897	Abel crystallizes epinephrine
1903	Bayliss and Starling discover secretin
1904	Starling delivers Croonian Lectures and coins the word hormone
1909	MacCallum and Voegtlin establish role of parathyroids in calcium metabolism
1912	Antidiuretic hormone characterized in posterior pituitary extracts
1914	Kendall crystallizes thyroxine
1916	Endocrine society founded as the Society for the Study of Internal Secretions
1917	Volume 1 of *Endocrinology* published
1921	Evans and Long describe growth hormone
	Posterior pituitary extract made available for treating patients with diabetes insipidus
1922	Banting and Best provide insulin for treatment of diabetes mellitus

plishments of organic chemistry in this century. By the 1950s the major hormones had been identified, and the pathophysiology of most hormone deficiency states had been characterized. (Elucidation of the pathophysiology of hormone excess states has lagged somewhat behind because of the paucity of appropriate animal models for such studies prior to the development of transgenic technology.)

Since 1950 the field has been altered profoundly by advances of several types. First, development of the radioimmunoassay and of other immunometric techniques made it possible to quantify rapidly and accurately even small changes in hormone levels. As a consequence the discipline has become one of the most quantitative not only in medicine but in all of biology, making it possible to recognize minor perturbations in the physiology of the standard hormones and to identify an additional class of chemical messengers that operate at very low plasma concentrations (dihydrotestosterone, catechol estrogens, enteroglucagon, activin and inhibin, follistatin, somatostatin, pituitary releasing hormones, etc). An unanticipated consequence of these advances in quantification is that cellular regulation by chemical messengers is now recognized to be more complicated than originally formulated. Indeed, hormones that circulate in the plasma are only one class of chemical mediators, some of which work in limited circulatory compartments such as the hypothalamic-pituitary portal circulation, others exert effects on cells adjacent to the sites of synthesis (paracrine or juxtacrine actions), and still others work on the same cells in which they are synthesized. The net consequence is that the borders between endocrinology and cellular biology are no longer distinct.

Second, separation of the endocrine system (chemical control) from the neurogenic and immune control systems has also become blurred with the recognition that many hormones (norepinephrine, epinephrine, vasoactive intestinal peptide, etc) act under some circumstances as neuromediators. Likewise, hormones interdigitate with immune mediators in many circumstances so that all homeostatic control mechanisms must now be viewed as a complex interacting system.

Third, beginning with the recognition by Fuller Albright and his colleagues that pseudohypoparathyroidism is a disorder not of hormones per se but of hormone action (5), the focus in the field has shifted from hormones themselves to the receptors, second messengers, and enzymatic processes that mediate hormone effects in cells. Resistance states to the action of almost every hormone are now recognized to cause human disease, and if diabetes mellitus type II proves to be a primary disorder of insulin resistance, disorders of hormone action will be more common causes of endocrinopathy than states of hormone deficiency and excess combined. At the basic level, the focus on hormone action has served to blur even further the distinction between endocrinology and cellular physiology and biochemistry. By way of example, investigation of the mechanism of action of insulin has provided major insight into intracellular control processes.

These various developments have so eroded the concept of endocrinology as a distinct field as to make it uncertain whether the discipline will survive in its present form during the next decades, much less the next century. This uncertainty is not unique to endocrinology and may be an inevitable and desirable consequence of the many advances in molecular genetics and cellular biology that have served to breach the disciplinary barriers that have separated the branches of biology and physiology. Such branches were erected when the methodologies of science were so limited that the divisions were useful formulations. If endocrinology does survive as a distinct field, it may do so only because of recognition of the fact that many of the unresolved issues in the field involve whole animal physiology. Such issues include the interactions of multiple hormones in the control of complex physiological processes (growth, temperature regulation, metabolic rates, etc), the interaction of biological rhythms with the endocrine system, the integration at the level of the central nervous system of chemical and neurogenic control mechanisms, and the complex behavioral and physiological processes involved in sexual differentiation, gender role behavior, and reproduction. Indeed, endocrinology is poised to lead the renaissance in the physiology of organ systems and whole animals, an arena that is now eclipsed by the revolutionary developments in genetics and molecular biology.

Visit the Annual Reviews home page at www.AnnualReviews.org.

LITERATURE CITED

1. Brown-Sequard CE. 1889. Des effets produits chez l'homme par des injections sous-sutanees d'un liquide retire des testicles frais cobaye et de chien. *C.R. Soc. Biol.* (Ser. 9) 1:415–19

2. Evans HM. 1933. Present position of our knowledge of anterior pituitary function. *JAMA* 101:425–32

3. Dale H. 1935. The Harveian oration on "Some epochs in medical research." London: Lewis

4. Wilson JD. 1990. Charles-Edouard Brown-Sequard and the centennial of endocrinology. *J. Clin. Endocrinol. Metab.* 71:1403–9

5. Albright F, Burnett CH, Smith PH, Parson W. 1942. Pseudo-hypoparathyroidism: an example of Seabright-Bantam syndrome. *Endocrinology* 30:363–76

Annu. Rev. Physiol. 2000. 62:951–60

THE 20TH CENTURY IN RESPIRATORY PHYSIOLOGY: One View

Donald Massaro

Department of Medicine, Georgetown University School Of Medicine, Washington, DC 20007–2197; e-mail: massarod@gusun.georgetown.edu

The reviews in Volume 62 of the *Annual Review of Physiology* were chosen two years ago. The chance occurrence of my being Editor of the Respiratory Section at that time, and the publication of these reviews at onset of a new millenium, have thrust upon me the task of trying to record, in one place, the highlights of respiratory physiology of the 20th century. I am not adequate to the task, but I can't duck the assignment. I apologize to all offended by what I have included or excluded from this list.

1903. C Bohr. The hemoglobin-oxygen disassociation curve of whole blood is S-shaped (1).

1904. C Bohr, KA Hesselbalch, A Krough. Discovered that adding CO_2 to blood releases O_2, which has since been referred to as the Bohr effect (2).

1905. JS Haldane and JG Priestly. Showed that under resting conditions ventilation is regulated by CO_2 not O_2 (3).

1909. C Bohr. Described the Bohr Integration to estimate the average PO_2 in the blood of pulmonary capillaries and calculated the diffusion capacity of the lung for oxygen (4).

1910. A Krough and M Krough. Put to rest the notion that oxygen entry into the blood is by secretion from lung cells. Using an improved aerotonometer, which they developed, they demonstrated a pressure difference for O_2 between alveolar gas and the blood indicating the "absorption of oxygen and the elimination of carbon dioxide in the lungs takes place by diffusion and by diffusion alone" (5).

1913. WHF Addison and HW How. Discovered that the lungs of fetal mammals are filled with fluid (5a).

1915. M Krogh. Measured DLco by breath-holding and steady-state methods and showed DLco increased with an exercise-caused increased need for O_2 (6).

1923. T Lumsden. Identified areas of the pons and medulla involved in respiratory rhythmicity (7, 8).

1925. F. Rohrer. Measured dimensions of conducting airways, characterized the relationship between static pressure and volume of the respiratory system, estimated the resistance to airflow in the airways, and demonstrated there is a specific rate of breathing at which the work of breathing is lowest. His great contribution, in a career cut short by death at age 38, was a conceptual, compre-

0066-4278/00/0315-0951$12.00

hensive, quantitative analysis of respiratory mechanics including simplification of breathing to two variables, pressure and volume (for summary see 9).

1926, 1928. F De Castro. Anatomist who, on the basis of his microscopic examination proposed the carotid body was a sensory organ that responded to modifications of the composition of blood (10, 11).

1929. W Forssmann. Introduced a ureteral catheter into the right atrium of his own heart (12).

1929. K von Neergaard. Demonstrated the critical role of surface tension in lung recoil (13), an observation not pursued until mid-century.

1930. C Heymans et al. Using cross circulation involving multiple dogs demonstrated that hypercapnia, increased acidity, and hypoxia acted through the carotid sinuses and carotid body to reflexly stimulate ventilation (14).

1930. CM Van Allen, GE Lindskog, and HG Richter. Demonstrated the presence of collateral ventilation between adjacent lung lobules (14a, 14b).

1933. ED Adrian. Pioneered the use of single nerve fiber recordings (15).

1934. RV Christie. Demonstrated the elastic recoil of emphysematous lungs is diminished and that this contributed to premature closure of conducting airways (16).

1939. CL Bayliss and GW Robertson. Described the viscoelastic properties of normal lungs (17).

1941. AF Cournand and HA Ranges. Catheterized the right auricle and opened the modern era of cardiopulmonary hemodynamics (18).

1942. MF Warren and CF Drinker. Began quantitative studies of lung lymph flow and the composition of lung lymph by developing methods to cannulate lymphatic vessels that drained both heart and lung (18a). These studies, however, required the use of anesthetized artificially ventilated animals. Staub markedly advanced the field by developing a method to measure lymph flow in awake chronically instrumented sheep.

1946. H Rahn, AB Otis, LE Chadwick, and WO Fenn. Described the pressure-volume diagram of the thorax and lung from which one can estimate the elastic, resistive, and viscous forces needed to move air in and out of the lung (19).

1947. P Gruenwald. This work (20) like that of Neergaard (13), was remarkably ahead of its time. He noted that "a given amount of air enters the smallest possible number of alveoli and fills these completely . . . no additional alveoli are aerated until sufficient air is aspirated to distend the open air spaces to the limit of their normal expansion"—an early recognition of "opening pressure" (20). He went on to state "Surface active substances reduce pressure necessary for aeration. This suggests the administration of surface active substances to the air or oxygen which is being spontaneously breathed in or introduced by a respirator might aid in relieving the initial atelectasis of newborn infants" (20)—almost exogenous surfactant about 40 years early! However, in spite of his keen insights, Gruenwald did not in his article comment on the insufficient surface activity of lungs of prematurely born infants. That awaited the profound discovery of Avery and Mead (21).

1948. A Jost and A Policard. Reported that ligation of the trachea of fetal rabbits caused their lungs to become distended with fluid thereby indicating the pulmonary source of the fluid (22). See Adamson et al below.

1948. AB Otis and DF Proctor. Measured alveolar pressure in humans using the interrupter method allowing the calculation of airway resistance (23).

1949. H Rahn. Developed the concept of mean alveolar air and the notion, previously put forth by Bohr (4), that uneven ventilation/perfusion can significantly lower the arterial PO_2 (24).

1950. AB Otis, WO Fenn, and H Rahn. Initiated what was to be an intense surge of interest in respiratory mechanics; provided a subdivision of the total work of breathing into its elastic, viscous, and flow-resistive components (25).

1951. RL Riley, A Cournand, and KW Donald. Theoretical and clinical analysis (26, 27) of factors affecting partial pressure of O_2 and CO_2 in the blood; confirmation of the work by Bohr (4) that a venous-arterial shunt in the lung and uneven ventilation/perfusion can significantly lower the arterial PO_2.

1951. R Austrian et al. Described the physiologic features of the syndrome of "alveolar-capillary block" (27a).

1952. C von Euler and U Söderberg. The effect of CO_2 and pH on breathing included a central (medullary) effect (28).

1952. N Low. Used the recently available electron microscope to settled a long-time argument as to the presence of a continuous epithelial layer in alveoli by clearly demonstrating its presence (29).

1954. CC Macklin. A long-time proponent of the presence of a continuous cellular lining in alveoli, he summarized his work and thinking including evidence for the presence of an extracellular fluid film that lined alveoli, correctly surmised it maintained a "favorable alveolar surface tension," but incorrectly assumed the tension was constant (30). Macklin correctly ascribed "exocrinosity" to the granular pneumocyte (now called the alveolar type 2 cell), suggesting that it secretes components of the extracellular lining film (30).

1955. RE Pattle. Observed the great stability of bubbles present in lung edema fluid. Because of this stability he concluded that the surface tension of the material forming the wall of the bubble must be zero. He could not form the bubbles by agitation of edema fluid with air and concluded the lining layer of the stable bubbles present in edema fluid "must therefore have formed the original lining layer of the fine air spaces" (31). Keen observation and brilliant reasoning.

1955. H Rahn and WO Fenn. Publication of the classical, extremely useful, graphical analysis of respiratory gas exchange—the O_2-CO_2 diagram (32).

1956. AB Otis et al. Described mechanical factors affecting the distribution of pulmonary ventilation (33).

1956. AB DuBois, SY Botelho, and JH Comroe. Developed a rapid way, using a body plethysmograph, to measure thoracic gas volume (34).

1956. LC Clark, Jr. Described an electrode (Clark electrode) to measure PO_2 that is now widely used throughout the world (35).

1956. ES Brown. Reported that alveolar surface tension, calculated from pressure-volume relations, fell to low values during lung deflation (36).

1956. JA Clements. Demonstrated the dependence of the lung's pressure-volume characteristics on intrinsic surface-active material (37).

1958. RE Hyatt, DP Schilder, and DL Fry. Constructed isovolume pressure flow curves and found discrete maximum flow rates that diminished as volume fell (38). These studies advanced and made well known the concept of expiratory flow limitation.

1957. JA Clements. Showed lung extracts lower surface tension to less than 10 dynes/cm and that surface active material prevents alveolar collapse; the first direct evidence to show that the lung contained surface-active material (39). Clement's work, based on theory and proven at the bench, opened the modern era of lung biology and led to a major clinical advance—the use of exogenous surface-active material in the treatment of prematurely born infants.

1959. AC Guyton and AW Lindsey. Demonstrated the effect of plasma protein osmotic pressure on the development of pulmonary edema (40).

1959. ES Brown, RP Johnson, and JA Clements. Found the surface tension of lung extracts was area dependent, reaching very low values as area was diminished, and that the surface tension of the extracts exhibited marked hysteresis as occurs between inflation and deflation in the intact lung (41).

1959. ME Avery and J Mead. Reported lung extracts from infants over 1100–1200 grams and in children and adults substantially lowered surface tension; lung extracts of smaller premature infants and of infants dying with hyaline membrane disease lowered surface tension to a much smaller extent (21). These observations demonstrated the clinical importance of pulmonary surfactant, which resulted in a marked influx of workers into the field; together with the work of Clements and colleagues (36, 37, 39) this resulted in the treatment of prematurely born infants with exogenous surfactant, a treatment that markedly decreased, the mortality of premature birth.

1961. JBL Howell, S Permutt, DF Proctor, and RL Riley. Demonstrated the effect of positive pressure inflation on pulmonary blood vessels is dependent on the location of the vessels. As alveolar pressure rises and lung volume increases alveolar vessels are compressed but large extra-alveolar vessels "dilate" (42).

1961. J Piiper, P Haab, and H Rahn. Demonstrated the unequal distribution of diffusion capacity (43).

1963. ER Weibel. Published his classical book that developed and applied morphometric methods to lung anatomy and pathology (43a). This work initiated the modern era of morphometry and stereology, which has not by any means been confined to respiratory research.

1963. FH Adams, T Fujiwara, G Rowshan. Analyzed the electrolyte composition of fetal lung fluid and found it was different from that of fetal plasma (44).

1963. SM Tenney, JE Remmers. Documented the relationship between oxygen uptake and alveolar size and surface area (45). The magnitude of alveolar surface area scaled directly with O_2 consumption to the power one. Lung volume scaled directly to body weight to the power one. To meet the higher body mass-specific O_2 consumption of small compared with large species, small mammals subdivide their gas-exchange surface (more alveoli/kg) more than large mammals. By contrast lung volume is a constant percent of body mass across species.

1966. J Milic-Emili, JAM Henderson, MB Dolovich, D Trop, and K Kaneko. Described the regional distribution of expired gas in the lung (46).

1967. PT Macklem and J Mead. Developed a method to separately measure resistance in central and peripheral airways (47) that led to the concept of diseases of the small airways and that chronic disease of these airways can go undetected by most clinical pulmonary function tests until it involves a great percentage of these airways; hence that region has been called the "silent zone" of the lung.

1967. NC Staub, RD Bland, KL Brigham, RH Demling, and AJ Erdmann, III. Demonstrated the intrapulmonary sequence of the occurrence of pulmonary edema (48).

1968. TC Lloyd. Discovered the need for perivascular tissue in hypoxic pulmonary vasoconstriction; this suggests nonvascular cells release chemicals that cause vasoconstriction (49).

1968. PD Wagner, NF Naumann, and RB Laravuso. Simultaneous measurement of eight foreign gases in blood by gas chromatography (50).

1968. ER Weibel and J Gil. Demonstrated conclusively there is an extracellular alveolar lining layer; it is a duplex layer, and it contains tubular myelin, which was later postulated to be the immediate precursor of the monomolecular film of the duplex layer (51).

1968. TM Adamson, RDH Boyd, HS Platt, and LB Strang. Based on a comparison of the electrolyte compoition of alveolar fluid, lymph, and blood concluded that alveolar fluid was a "special material elaborated by the fetal lung" (52).

1969. GC Liggins. Infusion of corticosteroid hormones into fetal lambs accelerates maturation of the lung's surfactant system (53). This work led to the treatment with corticosteroids of mothers with threatened premature delivery and resulted in improved survival of infants, a major clinical advance.

1970. J Mead, T Takishima, and D Leith. Put forth the interdependence theory of the lung parenchyma (54).

1973. RJ King, DJ Klass, EG Gikas, and JA Clements. Identification of lung-specific proteins as part of pulmonary surfactant (55).

1973. FM La Force, WJ Kelly, and GL Huber. Demonstration of a role for pulmonary surfactant in bacteriostasis in the alveolus, an action beyond maintaining alveoli patent (55a). The modest beginning of the now burgeoning interest in the immunomodulary function of pulmonary surfactant (see 55b for review).

1974. PD Wagner, HA Salzman, and JB West. The theory behind the measurement of continuous distributions of ventilation-perfusion ratios (56).

1975. NC Staub, RD Bland, KL Brigham, RH Demling. and AJ. Erdmann, III. Developed a method to collect lung lymph that is widely used and paved the way for a major increase in knowledge of physiologic and clinical aspects of lung edema (57).

1976. S Schürch, J Goerke, and JA Clements. Direct determination of surface tension in the alveolus that showed it drops to the very low values predicted by theory and surface balance studies (58).

1980. T Fujiwara, H Maeta, S Chida, T Morita, Y Watabe, and T Abe. The instillation of surfactant prepared from cow lung into the airway of prematurely born infants with respiratory distress (58a). The number of cases treated was small but the improved survival was dramatic. This study generated tremendous interest and resulted in large clinical trials of exogenous surfactant in the treatment of prematurely born infants.

1981. H Sahebjami and JA Wirman. Discovered that caloric-restriction, which alters oxygen consumption, resulted in alveolar remodeling. Refeeding, which returns oxygen consumption to normal, resulted in evidence of the induction of alveolus formation (58b). This study, not widely recognized, demonstrates plasticity of alveolar size and alveolus formation in adult rats in response to changes in oxygen need.

1989. RC Levitt and W Mitzner. Demonstrated autosomal-recessive inheritance of airway hyperactivity (59).

1991. RH Phibbs et al. The intratracheal administration of defined exogenous surfactant improves survival of prematurely born infants (60). Part of the payoff for 40 years of fundamental research.

1993. C Youngson, C Nurse, H Yeger, and E Cutz. Identified an O_2-sensing mechanism, i.e. the presence of an O_2-sensitive potassium channel coupled to an O_2 sensor protein, in cells of pulmonary neuroepithelial bodies (61).

1999. KT Takeyama, et al. Found that the epidermal growth factor system regulates mucin production in conducting airways by increasing expression of MUC5AC and that this induction is blocked by selective EGF-R tyrosine kinase inhibitors (62).

ACKNOWLEDGMENTS

Supported by HLBI grants HL20366, HL59432, HL60115 and bequest from the Wiggins Family. D Massaro is Cohen Professor of Pulmonary Research at Georgetown University and Senior Fellow of the Lovelace Respiratory Research Institute, Alburquerque, NM.

Visit the Annual Reviews home page at www.AnnualReviews.org.

LITERATURE CITED

1. Bohr C. 1905. Blutgase and respiratoresche Gaswechsel. In *Handbueke der physiologie des menschen.* ed. W Nagel. 1:54

2. Bohr C, Hasselbalch KA, Krough A. 1904. Ueber-einen in biologischer Beziehung wichtigen Einfluss, den die Kohlenäurespannung des Blutes auf dessen

Sauerstoffbindung übt. *Skand. Arch. Physiol.* 16:402–12

3. Haldane JS, Priestley JG. 1905. The regulation of lung ventilation. *J. Physiol.* 32:225–66

4. Bohr C. 1909. Ueber die spezifische Tätigkeit der Lungen bei der respiratorischen Gasaufnalme und ihr Verhalten Zu der durch die Alveolarwand stattfindenden Gasdiffusion. *Skand. Arch. Physiol.* 22:221–80

5. Krough A, Krough M. 1910. On the tensions of gases in the arterial blood. *Skand. Arch. Physiol.* 23:248–78

5a. Addison WHF, How HF. 1913. On the prenatal and neonatal lung. *Am. J. Anat.* 15:199–214

6. Krough M. 1915. Diffusion of gases through the lungs of Man. *J. Physiol.* 49:271–300

7. Lumsden T. 1923. Observations on the respiratory centres in the cat. *J. Physiol.* 57:153–60

8. Lumsden T. 1923. Observations on the respiratory centres. *J. Physiol.* 57:354–67

9. Rohrer F. 1925. Physiologie der atembervegung. In *Handbuch der normalen und pathologischen Physiologie,* ed. A Bethe, G von Bergmann, G Embden, A Ellinger, 2:70–127. Berlin: Springer.

10. De Castro F. 1926. Sur la structure et l'innervation de la glande intercarotidienne (glomus caroticum) de l'homme et des mammifères, et sur un nouveau systime d'innervation autonome du nerf glossopharyngien. *Trav. Lab. Rech. Biol. Univ. Madrid* 24:365–432

11. De Castro F. 1928. Sur la structure et l'innervation du sinus carotidien de l'homme et de mammifères. Nouveaux faits sur l'innervation et la fonction du glomus caroticum. *Trav. Lab. Rech. Biol. Univ. Madrid* 25:331–80

12. Forssman W. 1929. Die Sondierung des rechten. *Herzens. Klin. Wschr.* 8:2085

13. von Neergaard K. 1929. Neue auffassungen ilber einen grundbegriff der atemmechanik. Die retraktionkraft der lunge,

abhängig von der oberflächenspannung in den alveolen. *Z. Gesamte Exp. Med.* 66:1–22

14. Heymans C, Bouckaert JJ, Dautrebande L. 1930. Sinus carotidien et réflexes respiratoires. Pt. II. Influences respiratoires réflexes de l'acidose, de l'alcalose, de l'anhydride carbonique, de l'ion hydrogéne, et de l'anoxémie. Échanges respiratories dans les poumans et au delà des poumons. *Arch. Intern. Pharmacodyn.* 39:400–45

14a. Van Allen, CM, Lindskog GE, Richter HG. 1930. Gaseous interchange between adjacent lung lobules. *Yale J. Biol. Med.* 2:297–300

14b. Van Allen CM, Lindskog GE, Richter HG. 1931 Collateral respiration: transfer of air collaterally between pulmonary lobules. *J. Clin. Invest.* 10:559–90

15. Adrian ED. 1933. Afferent impulses in the vagus and their effect on respiration. *J. Physiol.* 79:332–58

16. Christie RV. 1934. The elastic properties of the emphysematous lung and their significance. *J. Clin. Invest.* 94:1711

17. Bayliss LE, Robertson GW. 1934. The viscoelastic properties of the lungs. *Am. J. Exp. Physiol.* 29:27–47

18. Cournand AF, Ranges HA. 1941. Catheterization of the right auricle in man. *Proc. Soc. Exp. Biol. Med.* 46:462

18a. Warren MF, Drinker CK. 1941. The flow of lymph from the lungs of dogs. *Am. J. Physiol.* 136:207–21

19. Rahn H, Otis AB, Chadwick LE, Fenn W. 1946. The pressure-volume diagram of the thorax and lung. *Am. J. Physiol.* 146:161–78

20. Gruenwald P. 1947. Surface tension as a factor in the resistance of neonatal lungs to aeration. *Am. J. Obst. Gyn.* 53:996–1007

21. Avery ME, Mead J. 1959. Surface properties in relation to atelectasis and hyaline membrane disease. *Am. J. Dis. Child.* 97:517–23

22. Jost A, Policard A. 1948. Contribution experimental a l'etude du development

prenatal du poumon chez le lapin. *Arch. Anat. Microsc. Morphol. Exp.* 37:323–32

23. Otis AB, Proctor DF. 1948. Measurement of alveolar pressure in human subjects. *Am. J. Physiol.* 152:106–12

24. Rahn HA. 1949. A concept of mean alveolar air and the ventilation-bloodflow relationships during pulmonary gas exchange. *Am. J. Physiol.* 158:21–30

25. Otis AB, Fenn WO, Rahn W. 1950. Mechanisms of breathing in man. *J. Appl. Physiol.* 2:592–607

26. Riley RL, Cournand A. 1951. Analysis of factors affecting partial pressures of oxygen and carbon dioxide in gas and blood of lungs: theory. *J. Appl. Physiol.* 4:77–100

27. Riley RL, Cournand A, Donald KW. 1951. Analysis of factors affecting partial pressures of oxygen and carbon dioxide in gas and blood of lungs: methods. *J. Appl. Physiol.* 4:102–20

27a. Austrian R, McClement JH, Renzetti AD Jr, Donald KW, Riley R, Cournand A. 1951. Clinical and physiologic features of some types of pulmonary diseases with impairment of alveolar-capillary diffusion. The syndrome of "alveolar-capillary block". *Am. J. Med.* 11:667–85

28. von Euler C, Trippenbach A. 1952. Medullary chemo-sensitive receptors. *J. Physiol.* 118:545–54

29. Low FN. 1952. Electron microscopy of the rat lung. *Anat. Rec.* 113:437–43

30. Macklin CC. 1954. The pulmonary alveolar mucoid film and the pneumocytes. *Lancet* 266:1099–104

31. Pattle RE. 1955. Properties, function and origin of the alveolar lining layer. *Nature* 175:1125–26

32. Rahn H, Fenn O. 1955. *A Graphical Analysis of the Respiratory Gas Exchange; the O_2-CO_2 Diagram.* Washington, DC: Am. Physiol. Soc.

33. Otis AB, McKerrow CB, Bartlett RA, Mead J, McIlroy MB, et al. 1956. Mechanical factors in the distribution of pulmonary ventilation. *J. Appl. Physiol.* 8:427–43

34. DuBois AB, Botello SY, Bedell GN, Marshall R, Conroe JH Jr. 1956. A rapid plethysmographic method for measuring thoracic gas volume: a comparison with a nitrogen washout for measuring functional residual capacity in normal subjects. *J. Clin. Invest.* 35:322–26

35. Clark LC Jr. 1956. Monitoring and control of blood and tissue O_2 tensions. *Trans. Am. Soc. Artif. Intern. Organs* 2:41

36. Brown ES. 1956. Lung area from surface tension effects. *Fed. Proc.* 15:26

37. Clements JA. 1956. Dependence of pressure-volume characteristics of lungs on intrinsic surface-active material. *Am. J Physiol.* 187:592

38. Hyatt RE, Schilder DP, Fry DL. 1958. Relationship between maximum expiratory flow and degree of lung inflation. *J. Appl. Physiol.* 13:331–36

39. Clements JA. 1957. Surface tension of lung extracts. *Proc. Soc. Exp. Biol. Med.* 95:170–72

40. Guyton AC, Lindsey AW. 1959. Effect of elevated left atrial pressure and decreased plasma protein concentration on the development of pulmonary edema. *Circ. Res.* 7:649–57

41. Brown ES, Johnson RP, Clements JA. 1959. Pulmonary surface tension. *J. Appl. Physiol.* 14:717–20

42. Howell JBL, Permutt S, Proctor DF, Riley RL. 1961. Effect of inflation of the lungs on different parts of pulmonary vascular bed. *J. Appl. Physiol.* 16:71–76

43. Piiper J, Haab P, Rahn H. 1961. Unequal distribution of pulmonary diffusing capacity in the anesthetized dog. *J. Appl. Physiol.* 16:499–506

43a. Weibel ER. 1963. *Morphometry of the Human Lung.* Berlin: Springer-Verlag

44. Adams FH, Fujiwara T, Rowshan G. 1963. The native and origin of the fluid in the fetal lamb lung. *J. Pediatr.* 63:881–88

45. Tenney SM, Remmers JE. 1963. Comparative quantitative morphology of the mammalian lung: diffusing area. *Nature* 197:54–56

46. Milic-Emili J, Henderson JAM, Dolovich MB, Trop D, Kaneko K. 1966. Regional distribution of inspired gas in the lung. *J. Appl. Physiol.* 21:749–59

47. Macklem PT, Mead J. 1967. Resistance of central and peripheral airways measured by a retrograde catheter. *J. Appl. Physiol.* 22:395–401

48. Staub NC, Nagano H, Pearce ML. 1967. Pulmonary edema in dogs, especially the sequence of fluid accumulation in the lungs. *J. Appl. Physiol.* 22:227–40

49. Lloyd TC. 1968. Hypoxic pulmonary vasoconstriction: role of perivascular tissue. *J. Appl. Physiol.* 25:560–65

50. Wagner PD, Naumann PF, Laravuso RB. 1974. Simultaneous measurement of eight foreign gases in blood gas chromatography. *J. Appl. Physiol.* 36:600–5

51. Weibel ER, Gil J. 1968. Electron microscopic demonstration of an extracellular duplex lining layer of alveoli. *Respir. Physiol.* 4:42–57

52. Adamson TM, Boyd RDH, Platt HS, Strang B. 1969. Composition of the alveolar liquid in the fetal lamb. *J. Physiol.* 204:159–68

53. Liggins GC. 1969. Premature delivery of fetal lambs infused with glucocorticoids. *J. Endocrinol.* 45:515–23

54. Mead J, Takishima T, Leath D. 1970. Stress distribution in lungs: a model of pulmonary elasticity. *J. Appl. Physiol.* 28:596–608

55. King RS, Klass DJ, Gikas EG, Clements JA. 1973. Isolation of apoproteins from canine surface active material. *Am. J. Physiol.* 224:788–95

55a. La Force FM, Kelly WJ, Huber GL. 1973. Inactivation of staphlycocci by alveolar macrophages with preliminary observations on the importance of alveolar lining material. *Am. Rev. Respir. Dis.* 108:784–90

55b. Wright JR. 1997. Immunomodulary functions of surfactant. *Physiol. Rev.* 77:931–62

56. Wagner PD, Saltzman HA, West, JB. 1974. Measurement of continuous distributions of ventilation-perfusion ratios: theory. *J. Appl. Physiol.* 36:533–37

57. Staub NC, Bland RD, Brigham KL, Demling RH, Erdmann AJ III. 1975. Preparation of chronic lung lymph fistulas in sheep. *J. Surg. Res.* 19:315–20

58. Schürch, S, Goerke J, Clements JA. 1976. Direct determination of surface tension in the lung. *Proc. Natl. Acad. Sci. USA* 73:4698–702

58a. Fujiwara T, Maeta H, Chida S, Morita T, Watabe Y, Abe T. 1980. Artificial surfactant therapy in hyaline membrane disease. *Lancet* 1:55–59

58b. Sahebjami H, Wirman JA. 1981. Emphysema-like changes in the lungs of starved rats. *Am. Rev. Respir. Dis.* 124:619–24

59. Levitt RC, Mitzner W. 1989. Autosomal recessive inheritance of airway hyperreactivity to 5-hydroxytrystamine. *J. Appl. Physiol.* 67:1125–32

60. Phibbs RH, Ballard RA, Clements JA, Heilbron DC, Phibbs CS, et al. 1991. Initial clinical trial of EXOSURF, a protein-free synthetic surfactant, for the prophylaxis and early treatment of hyaline membrane disease. *Pediatrics* 88:1–9

61. Youngson C, Nurse C, Yeger H, Cutz E. 1993. Oxygen sensing in airway chemoreceptors. *Nature* 365:153–55

62. Takeyama D, Dabbagh K, Lee HM, Agusti C, Lausier JA, et al. 1999. Epidermal growth factor system regulates mucin production in airways. *Proc. Natl. Acad. Sci. USA* 96:3081–86

Annu. Rev. Physiol. 2000. 62:961–63

TOWARD THE NEW MILLENNIUM

Jeffrey Robbins

Children's Hospital Research Foundation, Cincinnati, Ohio 45229–3039; e-mail: jeff.robbins@chmcc.org.

As the millennium passes, we are witnessing the end of a first wave in the revolution that cardiovascular physiology has undergone as the discipline fully embraces the tools of molecular genetics. This is amply illustrated in the chapters in the Cardiovascular section (pp. 25–109): what were previously descriptive phenomena are described in terms of their molecular components. The ability of molecular genetics to dissect, purify, isolate, and define the structure-function relationships that underlie normal and abnormal cardiovascular function is unparalleled. Similar approaches will continue define the field for the next decade.

Philosophically, the reductionist approach would appear to be antithetical to the mission of physiology, an integrative science. However, biological reductionism, coupled with the powerful tools of molecular genetic manipulation, allows both gain-of-function and loss-of-function studies to be carried out in the whole animal (see the Special Topic: Transgenic Approaches to Cardiovascular Function, this volume). One can now test a specific protein's structure-function relationships in whole organ and whole animal contexts via the transgenic and gene targeting methodologies. This gives the cardiovascular physiologist an unprecedented set of tools for understanding both the fundamental players' roles in cardiovascular function and how they are integrated into whole organ and whole animal physiology.

The articles in the Cardiovascular section illustrate the experimental approaches currently in use and accurately reflect the state of the field at the millennium's edge. They describe important normal and abnormal organ function, invoke sophisticated modeling, contain descriptive analyses at the whole organ level, and uncover the basis of some of these phenomena at the single channel and receptor levels. Certainly, they take advantage of the tools that molecular genetics provides. However, they also reflect a discipline that is firmly grounded in integrating the systems that are so necessary for normal (and abnormal) whole organ and animal function.

It is humbling to realize that we are attempting to describe complex physiological systems without a complete understanding or appreciation of the players' identities. Estimates for the number of genes in the mammalian genome range from 60,000 to 140,000, but currently only about 10% of these genes have been described in any useful way. Thus we may be missing most of the basic information needed for understanding genetic output. This should change, likely in the next two to three years, with the completion of the human genome project.

0066-4278/00/0315-0961$12.00

Comparative information on other useful mammalian systems such as the rat and mouse will follow rapidly. Although these data provide the structural basis for a complete understanding of mammalian physiology, in their raw state they do little to help the physiologist. Their value rests largely on how efficiently the data bases are mined for informational content. This can range from simple sequence extraction to complex modeling of potential interactions based on topological and transcriptional considerations, both within a single-cell type and between cells/organs/systems that potentially interact with one another. In the near-term, bioinformatics networks will be able to talk to one another in real time and be able to adjust the methods used in a particular analysis based upon continuous updates of the relevant databases. Undoubtedly, the algorithms used for establishing such relationships will continue to improve, providing the first clues as to the sequences' biological function(s). An immediate challenge for cardiovascular physiology will be to embrace the tools of bioinformatics and genomics. Only then can we participate in developing those tools that will be relevant to the discipline. Thus our field could play a prominent role in analyzing the data so that useful information is gleaned and applied in an integrated fashion to cardiovascular function.

Even if the data are mined to their full potential in terms of sequences, shared domains, modeled functional homologies, and potential interactions, understanding the structural basis of the entire genome is only a first step. Physiology's ultimate goal is to see past the individual components and understand the integrative whole at the cell, organ system, and animal levels. This necessarily requires a complete understanding of what part of the genome is actually transcribed into useful information in a particular cell type at a specific time and in response to discrete stimuli. The total messenger RNA complement or transcriptome of a cell or organ needs to mapped. The individual transcripts present in the cell will need to be identified and their steady-state levels determined. The control points responsible for their activation and inactivation will need to be analyzed as well. Transcriptome analyses using high density arrays of defined sequences, in parallel with proteonomic analyses, which involve defining the protein complement of a cell population, will be key to carrying out the kinds of syntheses that underlie physiological analyses in the future. Eventually these technologies will become fast enough and so cost effective that they will be carried out on an individual basis. One can envision baseline data being stored for each person in their normal state or for a high-risk population so that when cardiovascular disease occurs, custom-made pharmaceutical cocktails can be quickly developed to treat the nascent disease.

One has only to look at the literature to see the limitations of current paradigms in dealing with these issues. We can now easily manipulate single genes, resulting in the creation of unique animal models. However, genetic technology has far outstripped our capability and capacity to analyze the resultant phenotype(s). Indeed, as the rate at which these animals are created accelerates (there are now approximately 100 cardiovascular models described in the literature), our ability to analyze a particular model in terms of an integrative whole, falls farther and farther behind. In attempting to determine the physiological consequences of these single mutations, the cardiovascular scientific community reminds one of the group of blind men touching an elephant—each describing the animal in terms of a narrow interest and particular focus, but missing the integrated whole that truly defines the beast.

Understanding cell and organ system function in terms of the ultimate genetic output is a formidable task, even when one takes into account the rapidly evolving technologies of functional genomics and proteomics. Classic methodologies for measuring informational content in a single differentiated cell, using hybridization kinetics as a measure of sequence complexity, held open the promise of relative simplicity. Transcript complexity estimates ranged from 1800 to 6000 transcripts except for some specialized organs such as brain (50,000 transcripts). Unfortunately however, using more modern tools, initial data indicate the scope of the task is much more complex, with investigators finding that a typical single-cell type can contain some 30,000 to 40,000 unique transcripts. Adding to the potential difficulties involved, most of these transcripts (60–85%) appear to be present in low numbers at 0.5–5 copies/cell. What does this mean? Is it a reflection of the inherent leakiness of an imperfect biological system, where some genes are always transcribed at very low efficiencies and can effectively be thought of as turned off? This would mean that the transcripts/proteins being detected at such low levels reflect biological noise and are physiologically irrelevant. An alternative explanation is that these low-abundance species are powerful biological effectors, whose physiological consequences, even at barely detectable levels, can be profound and are critical for normal function.

Existing paradigms are unable to resolve these critical issues, and new approaches and technologies will be needed in order to make integrative sense of the comprehensive maps that bioinformatics, transcriptional microarrays, and proteomics will give us in the next 3 to 15 years. Physiology is uniquely positioned as a discipline to take advantage of these rapidly evolving technologies. It is the biological integration of the individual players that will eventually result in a coherent description of larger biological systems. If the networks can be fully described, we should be able to understand cell, organ, and organism function from their most basic to integrated levels. Understanding how the serial and parallel pathways intersect and under what circumstances will eventually lead to a comprehensive grasp of how normal and disease pathways in the cardiovascular system interact to drive whole organ function and dysfunction.

Cardiovascular physiology faces a number of challenges as we approach the millennium but central to the discipline's future will be how to best utilize the vast databases that will be collected through genomics, transcriptome analyses, and proteomics. A complete description of the players involved will provide the raw information needed to unravel their mechanistic relationships at all levels. Physiology's challenge is to undertake the laborious task of integrating the players up through the complex intra- and intercellular networks so that their roles in whole organ and whole animal physiology can be appreciated and understood as an integrated whole.

Visit the Annual Reviews home page at www.AnnualReviews.org

Annu. Rev. Physiol. 2000. 62:965–69

Commentary on the Special Topic Section on the Use of Transgenic Models

Evangelia G. Kranias

Department of Pharmacology and Cell Biophysics, University of Cincinnati, College of Medicine, Cincinnati, Ohio 45267–0575; e-mail: kraniaeg@email.uc.edu

A number of genetically engineered mouse models with altered cardiac function have been generated over the past decades, and analysis of their phenotypes has provided valuable insights into the molecular mechanisms underlying Ca^{2+} homeostasis, contractility, growth hormone pathways, and adrenergic receptor signaling in the heart. The mouse provides a powerful and excellent experimental system for genetic manipulation because its genetics and development have been well characterized, germline transmission of exogenous genes and gene deletions in the species (for both gain- and loss-of-function) is possible, and the gestation period (21 days), as well as the time (4–6 weeks) to sexual maturity, is relatively short. Two techniques are currently available for stable modification of the mouse genome: transgenesis and gene targeting. Transgenesis is mainly mediated by pronuclear injection, which is based on the ability to microinject the transgenic construct into the pronucleus of one-celled embryos that are then implanted into pseudopregnant females. Transgene expression results in either an increase (over-expression) or a decrease (antisense) in the levels of the gene of interest. Transgenes expressing dominant-inhibitory proteins can also be used to block endogenous protein function rather than expression. On the other hand, gene targeting allows for precise genetic manipulation of the mouse genome. This technique is based on the ability of DNA to undergo homologous recombination in embryonic stem cells–totipotent cells derived from the inner cell mass of a mouse blastocyst. The targeting construct is electroporated into embryonic stem cells; the cells, which have undergone homologous recombination, are selected and microinjected into blastocysts, which are then implanted into pseudopregnant females for the generation of heterozygous and homozygous mice for the targeted allele.

Analysis of the cardiac phenotypes of genetically engineered mice entails morphological, molecular, biochemical, and physiological measurements. Morphological studies are usually obtained at the gross or histological level, but depending on the obtained phenotype, detailed examination at the ultrastructural level is often necessary. Molecular studies coupled with biochemical and functional assays of subcellular preparations provide evidence for altered protein

0066-4278/00/0315-0965$12.00

function in the genetically engineered mouse heart. Furthermore, these studies are designed to assess whether any compensatory mechanisms accompany the genetic manipulation of a specific gene product, possibly contributing to the obtained phenotype. It is increasingly apparent that fine-tuning cross-talk between the gene of interest and other genes results in interactive changes in the expression levels of multiple gene products, which collectively contribute to observed phenotypic alterations. Therefore, such compensatory responses must be identified before assigning a specific functional phenotype to a specific genetic manipulation in vivo. The functional phenotype is mainly determined by physiological analysis performed at various levels to provide an integrative approach to our understanding of the in vivo function of single gene products. At the cellular level, cardiomyocytes allow assessment of contractility or relaxation, which are intrinsic parameters to the cardiomyocyte and independent of geometric constraints, extracellular matrix, loading conditions, and neurohumoral factors. In addition, contractile parameters may be correlated with intracellular Ca^{2+} alterations, yielding important insights into the subcellular mechanisms underlying alterations in excitation-contraction coupling of genetically engineered mice. At the tissue level, the papillary muscle represents a multicellular preparation with uniform fiber orientation that allows measurements of isotonic or isometric muscle performance independent of geometric constraints, fiber orientation, or loading. The isolated perfused heart represents an intact organ tissue preparation in which assessment of contractile parameters can be performed using either a Langendorff or a work-performing mode. The Langendorff preparation involves retrograde coronary perfusion with oxygenated buffer in an unloaded state or under isovolumic conditions, which allows determination of function independent of coronary perfusion pressure (1). The work-performing heart represents a system in which the cardiac muscle performs work at defined loading conditions (preload and afterload), allowing assessment of Starling length-tension relations (2). At the intact animal level, cardiac function of the genetically manipulated myocardium is examined in the presence of neurohumoral effectors and any compensatory physiological responses that may develop in vivo. High-fidelity measurements of left ventricular function have been developed using both invasive (closed and open chest) and non-invasive methods (3). More recently, magnetic resonance imaging, which allows simultaneous assessment of both morphological and functional data (4), and methodology to perform whole animal electrophysiologic studies (allowing detection and quantitation of abnormalities of SA nodal, intra-atrial, AV nodal and ventricular conduction) (5) have been developed. Finally, microchip technology and advanced microcomputing capabilities have made it possible to measure heart rate, QT interval (6), blood pressure (7, 8), respiratory rate, cardiac output, and oxygen consumption (9) in the fully conscious mouse.

Thus our ability to manipulate the mouse genome, coupled with the development of miniaturized technology to study the obtained cardiac phenotypes at multiple levels, has exponentially expanded our understanding of the molecular mechanisms underlying Ca^{2+} homeostasis and contractility in cardiac muscle. The elementary events involved in Ca^{2+} homeostasis are (*a*) the rapid influx of trigger Ca^{2+} following sarcolemma membrane depolarization via the L-type voltage-gated Ca^{2+}-channels, which causes the release of activator Ca^{2+} from the sarcoplasmic reticulum via the Ca^{2+} release channels or ryanodine receptors; (*b*) the binding of this activator Ca^{2+} to troponin C, which in turn inhibits the binding of troponin I to actin; (*c*) the ensuing conformational change in tropomyosin, which allows the myosin head to interact with actin, resulting in force generation; and (*d*) the resequestration of cytosolic Ca^{2+} into the sarcoplasmic reticulum lumen by the Ca^{2+}-ATPase, and extrusion of Ca^{2+} through the sarcolemma, resulting in muscle relaxation. Thus there are three major Ca^{2+}-handling pools in the cell: the sarcolemma, sarcoplasmic reticulum, and myofilaments. The sarcolemma or outer cell membrane maintains a Ca^{2+} gradient between the myocyte interior and the blood through the extrusion of cell Ca^{2+} by a Ca^{2+}-ATPase and/or by a Na^+/Ca^{2+} exchanger. L-type Ca^{2+} channels and receptor proteins, which are important in translating neurohumoral signals into intracellular events, are also present in the sarcolemmal membrane. This outer cell membrane comes in contact with the sarcoplasmic reticulum and such contact areas are important in translating the Ca^{2+} trigger through the sarcolemma to Ca^{2+} release through the sarcoplasmic reticulum. The sarcoplasmic reticulum is the intracellular membrane system surrounding the myofibrils, and it is the principal Ca^{2+} storage system during relaxation and the major Ca^{2+} source during contraction. Ca^{2+} is stored by binding to calsequestrin, a low-affinity and high-capacity Ca^{2+}-binding protein in the sarcoplasmic reticulum lumen. Ca^{2+} released from the sarcoplasmic reticulum binds to the myofilaments for the initiation of contraction. The myofilaments are composed of thick (myosin heavy and light chains and the myosin binding-protein C) and thin (actin, tropomyosin, and troponins) filaments. The troponin-tropomyosin complex prevents the reaction of myosin with actin. When Ca^{2+} binds to troponin C, the inhibitory effects of the troponin-tropomyosin complex are removed and the interaction of actin and myosin occurs. Myosin hydrolyzes ATP and the liberated energy moves the myofilaments toward the center of the sarcomere, thus generating force.

The special topic section in this volume (pp. 236–351) devoted to genetic models with altered adult cardiovascular function includes four major classes, based on the subcellular compartment or signal transduction pathway harboring the modified gene product: (*a*) cell surface receptors and their signal transduction pathways, which mediate alterations in cardiac function through second messenger molecules; (*b*) contractile proteins, which consist of the thick and thin filaments, and are the molecular motors for muscle contraction; (*c*) sarcoplasmic reticulum and sarcolemmal Ca^{2+}-handling proteins, which are responsible for the sequestration or extrusion of Ca^{2+} during diastole, its storage into the sarcoplasmic reticulum lumen, and the release of Ca^{2+} from the sarcoplasmic reticulum for the initiation of contraction; and (*d*) growth and control proteins, including regulators of proliferation during embryogenesis, inhibitors of proliferation in the post-mitotic heart, and mediators of hypertrophic growth in response to mechanical load or various cardiac agonists.

In combination, these chapters indicate that over the past two decades, the advances in genetic manipulation of the mouse genome, resulting in gene addition, gene deletion, or gene modification, coupled with the development of miniaturized technology to assess cardiac function in this species, have added a wealth of new information to our understanding of the molecular mechanisms underlying cardiac function and dysfunction. The progress in this area has been rapid and the generation of genetically engineered mouse models has united molecular biologists, biochemists, cell biologists, pathologists, and structural biologists in providing integrative approaches toward the analysis of the obtained cardiac phenotypes. It is likely that information will exponentially expand over the next few years in the new millennium. New advances in mouse genetic engineering and in miniaturized technology, for assessment of cardiac function in the conscious mouse, will deepen our understanding of cardiovascular mechanisms in health and disease. Techniques are rapidly developing that will allow the generation of sophisticated models with cardiac-specific inactivation of the target gene to control the temporal and spatial regulation of gene expression; inducible gene expression to control the timing and level of gene expression in a cardiac-specific compartment; and introduction of specific mutations in the target gene to assess cardiac-specific structural and functional relations. Furthermore, the application of genetic engineering to mammalian species that are closer to humans, which thus could provide relevant insights to human cardiac function, is being developed in several laboratories. These genetic and physiological advances will be complemented with new high through-put technology, which will allow screening for differential expression of genes (genomics) and proteins (proteomics) in a variety of developmental, physiological, and disease conditions. Temporal changes in the expression of a large number of gene products in a quantitative and qualitative fashion will be obtained and analysis of this information (bioinformatics) will reveal new horizons for cardiovascular research. Thus, although studies in the beginning and middle of the past century concentrated on the function of the heart as a pump, the era of molecular genetics in the last few decades has provided important insights into the mechanisms controlling the pump's function and dysfunction. The new millennium holds great promise for an exciting and productive period in cardiovascular research as the rapid and exponential development of new technologies will enable us to address an unlimited number of questions and refine our knowledge in this field.

Visit the Annual Reviews home page at www.AnnualReviews.org.

LITERATURE CITED

1. Kameyama T, Chen Z, Bell SP, Fabian J, LeWinter MM. 1998. Mechanoenergetic studies in isolated mouse heart. *Am. J. Physiol.* 274:H366–74
2. Grupp IL, Subramaniam A, Hewett TE, Robbins J, Grupp G. 1993. Comparison of normal, hypodynamic, and hyperdynamic mouse hearts using isolated work-performing heart preparations. *Am. J. Physiol.* 265:H1401–10
3. Hoit BD, Khoury SF, Kranias EG, Ball N, Walsh RA. 1995. In vivo echocardiographic detection of enhanced left ventricular function in gene-targeted mice with phospholamban deficiency. *Circ. Res.* 77:632–37
4. Siri FM, Jelicks LA, Leinwand LA, Gardin JM. 1997. Gated magnetic resonance imaging of normal and hypertrophied murine hearts. *Am. J. Physiol.* 272:H2394–402
5. Berul CI, Christe ME, Aronovitz MJ, Seidman CE, Seidman JG, Mendelsohn ME. 1997. Electrophysiological abnormalities and arrhythmias in αMHC mutant familial hypertrophic cardiomyopathy mice. *J. Clin. Invest.* 99:570–76
6. Mitchell GF, Jeron A, Koren G. 1998. Measurement of heart rate and Q-T interval in the conscious mouse. *Am. J. Physiol.* 274:H747–51
7. Krege JH, Hodgin JB, Hagaman JR, Smithies O. 1995. A noninvasive computerized tail-cuff system for measuring blood pressure in mice. *Hypertension* 25:1111–15
8. Ito M, Oliverio MI, Mannon PJ, Best CF, Maeda N, et al. 1995. Regulation of blood pressure by the type 1A angiotensin II receptor gene. *Proc. Natl. Acad. Sci. USA* 92:3521–25
9. Desai KH, Sato R, Schauble E, Barsh GS, Kobilka BK, Bernstein D. 1997. Cardiovascular indexes in the mouse at rest and with exercise: new tools to study models of cardiac disease. *Am. J. Physiol.* 272:H1053–61

Subject Index

A

α1$_N$ calcium channel subunit mutations
mouse models of neurodegeneration and, 792–93

Acetylcholine
atrial fibrillation and, 56
CFTR and colon, 470, 473

Acid-base regulation
ventilatory responses to changes in temperature in mammals and other vertebrates, 857–60

Acinar cells
Cl$_{(Ca)}$ channel activation in secretory cells and, 493–507

Acquisition problem
human language faculty and, 709–10, 713–15

Acrobates pygmaeus
diapause and, 357, 359

Actin
filament polymerization ischemic preconditioning and, 79, 95
remodeling cardiac sarcomere using transgenesis, 269, 272, 274–75
transgenic models and, 967

Action potentials
atrial fibrillation and, 51, 62–66

Activation
CFTR and colon, 467
Cl$^-$ secretion and, 558–59
Cl$_{(Ca)}$ channel activation in secretory cells and, 493–507

ENaC-Deg family of ion channels and, 578–80
endothelial signal integration in vascular assembly, 649, 652, 656, 661
guanylin and cGMP in kidney, 673
ischemic preconditioning and, 79
mouse models of neurodegeneration and, 785
multiple endocrine neoplasias and, 392–94
thyroid hormones and, 444–48
ventricular fibrillation and, 25, 28, 30, 38

Active transport
mechanisms underlying cost of living in animals, 207

Activin
endocrinology views and overviews, 948

Activity-dependent gene expression
stimulus-dependent transcription in neurons and, 807–8

Activity modulators
ligand-gated ion channel interactions with cytoskeletal and signaling proteins, 755

Acyl composition
membrane
mechanisms underlying cost of living in animals, 207, 215–17

Adaptation
comparative physiology and, 932

neural adaptation of rhythmic behavior and, 723–43

Adenosine
ischemic preconditioning and, 79, 82–90, 100
myocardial adrenergic receptor signaling and, 249

Adenosine triphosphate (ATP)
cell membrane and, 922–23
CFTR and colon, 469
diapause and, 366
flight respiration and energetics, 180, 185, 188
ischemic preconditioning and, 79, 82, 91–92, 97–100
probing function in conscious brain and, 18–19
remodeling cardiac sarcomere using transgenesis, 268
sodium-calcium exchange and, 124–25
transgenic models and, 967

Adenylate cyclase
intrarenal dopamine and, 636

Adipose tissue
leptin and, 413–28

Adrenergic receptor signaling
intrarenal dopamine and, 621, 631–32
myocardial
βARK1, 246–48, 250–51

971

CUMULATIVE INDEXES

CONTRIBUTING AUTHORS, VOLUMES 58–62

1013

CHAPTER TITLES, VOLUMES 58–62

SPECIAL TOPICS